CULTURE AREAS:

I. Chibcha
II. Andean
III. Antillean
IVA. Amazon
IVB. Eastern Brazilian Highlands
V. Chaco
VI. Patagonian
VII. Araucanian
VIII. Fuegian

TRIBAL GROUPS:

1. Carib
2. Arawak
3. Jivaro
4. Mundurucú
5. Apinayé
6. Inca
7. Aymara
8. Sirionó
9. Botocudo
10. Tupinamba
11. Araucanians
12. Ona
13. Yahgan

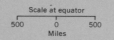
Scale at equator

500   0   500
Miles

SOUTH AMERICA

Anthropology

Anthropology: *The Study of Man*

E. Adamson Hoebel
University of Minnesota

Third edition

McGraw-Hill Book Company

New York   St. Louis   San Francisco
Toronto   London   Sydney

Anthropology

Library of Congress Catalog Card Number 65-28817
29136
891011CRVH7543210

This book is set in fototronic News Gothic.
The chapter titles are Bulmer italic.
Line illustrations by Russell Peterson.
Research on illustrations and photographic editing
by Sam Holmes.
Color photograph for cover by Elizabeth Little.
The cover photograph shows a Pre-Columbian (Remojadas)
figure from Veracruz, Mexico. The figure belongs to the collection
of The Museum of Primitive Art, New York City, New York.

To
Irene, and Fran,
Bart, Cindy, and Sue.

In the years that have passed since the previous edition of this book in 1958, anthropology has seen many new advances in fact and theory. The world about has plunged more deeply into the "new revolution of the atomic age" and the ensuing cultural era of *sururbanization*, the successor to civilization. An anxious humanity that looks to the moon and planets as its next sphere of conquest also steals fearful glances over its shoulder at the prospect of possible total extinction. A growing concern with man's past is evidenced by the renaissance of interest in evolution—not only biological but cultural as well. This interest, combined with the sequence of fossil precursors of modern man which have been discovered in rapid sequence in Africa, has led to a thorough rethinking and reordering of the data of prehistoric anthropology. Genetic breakthroughs have shed new light on the mechanics of race formation and organic evolution as they affect man. In the light of this, all of the chapters in this text which deal with physical anthropology and prehistoric archaeology have been entirely rewritten.

In order that the nature of culture in human affairs may illuminate the prehistoric processes of development more effectively, Part I has been greatly expanded; it now provides a more adequate conceptual explanation of the nature of culture, society, and human behavior. In response to many requests, the treatment of culture and language has been given greater depth and breadth. In this area, I am indebted to my colleague, Dr. Robert F. Spencer, whose assistance with that chapter went beyond coun-

sel and advice and into the realm of coauthorship.

New thinking on the theory of race has led to the formulations of racial categories based upon the concept of Mendelian populations and adaptive radiation, and this has been incorporated into the new treatment of race in Chapter 13.

Approaches to the study of primitive social organization have remained more stable during the post-World War II years, and it has not been necessary to effect such drastic changes in rewriting this section. One new feature is the utilization of the computer data from *Cross Tabulations of Murdock's World Ethnographic Sample*, released in the spring of 1965. Where these valuable tables of correlations show significant validation or disvalidation of important anthropological generalizations, we have attempted to bring them to bear on the discussions in the text.

The section on Marriage and Kinship has been reformulated in an effort to achieve greater clarity and systematization in terms of present anthropological interests. And finally, new chapters on religion and world view, the history and uses of anthropology, and the disappearance of the primitive world have been added in the hope that they may assist the reader to achieve a fuller understanding of the changes that are taking place in the present era.

Thus, this third edition of the text that was once called *Man in the Primitive World* has involved more than a change in title and format. The title change reflects the fact that the primitive world is close to extinction, and, although anthropology will continue to rely on the data from primitive societies as the major grist for its mills, anthropology, too, is changing as its proper sphere of attention increases to include all of mankind. The many new features of format and design, including the functional use of color, have improved the attractiveness and readability of the new edition.

In the years since 1948 when the original edition appeared, the literature and the coverage of anthropology have seen a phenomenal increase. It seems safe to say that almost every subfield and specialization has developed a body of experts and findings as large as that of the total discipline twenty years ago. I have found it immensely exciting—if indeed trying at times—to attempt to master and digest this wealth of new material in my efforts to update this book. The work and writing of hundreds of scientists and scholars have added to my ever-increasing respect and unceasing satisfaction with the field of anthropology. It is, of course, their work and their thoughts that have made the improvement of this book possible. To all—students and professionals, known and unknown—who have directly or indirectly contributed to the improvement and production of this work, my heartfelt thanks.

E. Adamson Hoebel

Contents

Preface   *vii*
Credits   *xi*

Part 1   The concept of culture

1   Anthropology: The Study of Man   *3*

2   Man, Culture, and Society   *16*

3   Culture and Language   *33*

4   Culture and Personality   *52*

5   The Growth of Culture: Invention and Diffusion   *71*

6   The Evolution of Culture   *85*

Part 2   The evolution of man and culture

7   Man's Place among the Primates   *97*

8   Evolution and the Primates   *114*

9   The Transition to Man   *133*

10   *Homo erectus* and the Lower Paleolithic Age   *147*

11   Prehistoric *Homo sapiens* and the Upper Paleolithic Age   *160*

12   The Dawn of Civilization   *183*

Part 3   Race & culture

13   Races of Mankind   *207*

14   Race and Cultural Capacity   *224*

Part 4 Primitive culture and society

15 Food Getting *235*

16 Housing *251*

17 Handicrafts *263*

18 Clothing and Ornament *277*

19 Art *287*

20 Status and Role *308*

21 The Life Cycle *319*

22 Mating and Marriage *331*

23 The Family *356*

24 The Extension of Kinship: Kindred, Lineage, Clan, Moiety, and Phratry *369*

25 Kinship Systems and Terminology *382*

26 Clubs and Age Groups *392*

27 Social Classes *401*

28 The Ownership of Goods and Ideas *413*

29 Gifts, Trade, and Inheritance *426*

30 Law and the Social Order *437*

31 Political Organization *452*

32 Animism, Mana, and the Supernatural *464*

33 Shamans, Priests, and Cults *478*

34 Culture and World View *490*

Part 5 Anthropology today and tomorrow

35 Anthropology: Its Growth, Methods, and Purposes *505*

36 Beyond Civilization *526*

Appendix I & Appendnx II *533*
Bibliography *539*
Glossary *559*
Index *575*

Credits for chapter opening photographs

Page 3 Dr. Karl Heider, ethnologist, working with the Dani people of New Guinea. (Film Study Center, Harvard University.)

Page 16 Vietnam villagers cooperate in the moving of a house roof. (Peter Schmid.)

Page 33 An Amarakaeri tribesman watches a linguist taperecord his speech. (Cornell Capa, Magnum, from Matthew Huxley and Cornell Capa's *Farewell to Eden;* Harper & Row, New York.)

Page 52 Dani father and child. (Film Study Center, Harvard University.)

Page 71 Japanese family watches TV. (Marc Riboud, Magnum.)

Page 85 Cultural manifestations juxtaposed. (René Burri, Magnum.)

Page 97 Gorilla mother dandles her baby. (Copyright by Elsbeth Siegrist.)

Page 114 Frontal view of *Paranthropus robustus* skull. (Courtesy of J. T. Robinson.)

Page 133 Skull of Taung baby held in a man's hand. (Jerry Cooke.)

Page 147 Second interglacial hand ax. (Reuben Goldberg. Courtesy of The University Museum, Philadelphia.)

Page 160 Lascaux Cave painting. (Photograph by Hans Hinz, with permission of Caisse Nationale des Monuments Historiques.)

Page 183 Stonehenge. (George Rodger, Magnum.)

Page 207 United Nations leaders at the UN General Assembly. (United Nations.)

Page 224 Youths of three races at an American school. (Constantine Manos, Magnum.)

Page 235 Lagoon fishing in Dahomey. (FAO.)

Page 251 An Amahuaca Indian builds a house. (Robert Russell, Wycliffe Bible Translators, Inc.)

Page 263 Amahuaca pottery making. (Robert Russell, Wycliffe Bible Translators, Inc.)

Page 277   Ornate tattoos of a Bororo girl, Niger. (Marc Riboud, Magnum.)

Page 287   Pre-Columbian (Remojadas) figure from Veracruz, Mexico. (Photograph by Charles Uht. Courtesy of The Museum of Primitive Art.)

Page 308   Ghana tribal chief and his retinue of attendants. (Marc and Evelyne Bernheim. From Rapho Guillumette Pictures.)

Page 319   Marogo woman with her child. (Belgian Government Information Center.)

Page 331   Kanana courtship ceremony, Waghi Valley, New Guinea. (Laurence LeGuay.)

Page 356   Family in Nsawam, Ghana. (Photograph by Ken Hyman from Margaret Mead and Ken Hyman's *Family*, The Macmillan Company, New York.)

Page 369   Chief of the Zongos, West Africa, with wives and child. (United Nations.)

Page 382   Tlingit totem poles in Alaska. (Charles May, Black Star.)

Page 392   Zululand, South Africa, maturity dance. (United Nations International.)

Page 401   A portrait of the sister of the Mwami (sultan) of the Batutsi in Burundi. (United Nations.)

Page 413   Branding by Karamojong tribesmen. (Rada and Neville Dyson-Hudson, *Natural History.*)

Page 426   Kirdis marketplace in the Sudan. (Peter W. Haeberlin.)

Page 437   Ibo statuette.

Page 452   Village meeting in Ethiopia. (FAO photo by G. Gregoire.)

Page 464   Dancing to restore an eclipsed moon, Kwakiutl, British Columbia. (Courtesy of the American Museum of Natural History.)

Page 478   Sun dance priests of the Cheyenne Indians. (Courtesy of the American Museum of Natural History.)

Page 490   Earth and Sky. Reproduction of a sand painting made on cotton cloth by the Navaho medicine man, Klah-Tso, *c.* 1905. (Smithsonian Office of Anthropology, Bureau of American Ethnology Collection.)

Page 505   Illustration from the Florentine Codex. (From Bernardo de Sahagun, *General History of the Things of New Spain: The Florentine Codex.* Translated by Arthur J. O. Anderson and Charles E. Dibble. Published by The School of American Research and The University of Utah. Illustration from Book IV. Copyright 1957 by the University of Utah.)

Page 526   New Guinea motorcyclist. (Bill Brindle, Optik Photo, Ltd.)

Anthropology

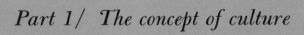

Part 1/ The concept of culture

Anthropology: the study of man

As Augustine observed: "Man wonders over the restless sea, the flowing waters, the sight of the sky, and forgets that of all wonders man himself is the most wonderful." The ultimate wonder of man is his ability to create: to think and bring forth new ways of living. Man deserves study for his own sake, even if it were to bring no more reward than satisfaction to the probing curiosity of mind. Out of such study grows knowledge, and out of such knowledge grows the power to modify nature and to influence man's destiny. Thus anthropology, like any disciplined study of natural phenomena, not only leads to the satisfaction of intellectual curiosity; it also inevitably becomes a tool through which to learn more of the nature of man, to the end that we may more effectively understand man's problems and how to solve them.

The distinctive qualities of anthropology

Man is a part of nature—the universe with all its phenomena. The study of man called *anthropology* (Gr. *anthropos,* man + *logia,* study), when followed in accordance with the principles and methods of science, is consequently a natural science. One of its branches is concerned with the physical structure and nature of man, and with his physiological processes. This branch is traditionally known as *physical anthropology* or, sometimes as *human biology.* But anthropology involves a good deal more than just the study of the natural history of man's physical nature. It is concerned with all the works and activities of man—social, artistic, and technological. Anthropology is therefore also the *science of man and culture.* As such it is a major social science, and more, for in its concern with the arts and in the anthropologist's efforts to sense and communicate the total life-ways of specific peoples, it is also a *humanistic discipline.*

Many sciences and disciplines are concerned with one aspect or another of man or his works. What, then, is so special about anthropology that it should be named "*the* science of man"?

The study of mankind as a whole First of all, anthropology sets as its goal the study of mankind as a whole. Political science studies man's government; economics, his production and distribution of goods; neurophysiology, his nervous system; architecture, his housing and building; musicology, his music; and sociology, his society. But none of these, or any of the other specialized disciplines one might name, professes systematically to research all the manifestations of the human being and of human activity in a unified way.

A fundamental proposition of anthropology is that no part can be fully, or even accurately, understood apart from the whole. And conversely, the whole—man and his manifestations—cannot be accurately perceived without acute and specialized knowledge of the parts. Anthropology touches upon, draws from, and feeds into virtually any field of knowledge one might care to name. The skills of the anthropologist must be highly diversified, but the unity of his discipline is maintained by concentration on the holistic character of man and culture.

The use of the comparative method A second hallmark of anthropology is its deep-rooted and long-standing commitment to the use of the *comparative method.*[1] An anthropologist refuses to accept any generalization about human nature that emerges from his experience with his own society alone, or even with two or three other societies, especially if these are a part of the same cultural tradition in which he has been brought up. If one is going to talk about man and human nature, one needs to know what the whole range of human biology, human behavior, and human social forms actually is. To acquire this knowledge, the physical anthropologist studies and compares the widest possible range of human populations, ancient and modern, to determine what are the common and what are the unique biological qualities of man. The cultural anthropologist studies and compares the widest possible range of human societies, primitive and civilized, in all parts of the world, to determine what are the common and what are the unique social and cultural features of man's behavior. The general anthropologist undertakes to relate the physical and cultural manifestations in all their variety.

Fieldwork as a substitute for the experimental laboratory When an experimental scientist, such as a chemist, is confronted with a problem, he works out an experiment designed to test the validity of the hypothesis about which

[1]One of the very earliest anthropological studies, written by the French missionary Joseph François Lafitau, compared Iroquois and Huron Indian cultures with those of Greece and Rome. It was based upon Lafitau's fieldwork as a Jesuit missionary in western New York between 1712 and 1717 and was called *Moeurs des sauvages Américains, comparées aux moeurs des premiers temps* (*Customs of American Savages, compared with Customs of Early Times*). See Chap. 35.

he is concerned. The method of laboratory experimentation is to manipulate and thereby control the quantity and action of certain known factors in order to determine how they influence one another. This fundamental tool of the physical sciences is ordinarily not available to the social sciences, which must to a great extent limit themselves to observation of existing situations rather than those which may be experimentally designed to suit their needs. Anthropologists, however, have found a highly useful substitute in the combination of field studies with the comparative method. Faced with a problem to be solved, the modern anthropologist seeks a society or a series of societies that already contain the combination of factors necessary for a testing of the theory or hypothesis in question. He may search for the data in preexisting field reports in anthropological libraries, or he may plan a fieldwork expedition to study an appropriate tribe or society.[2]

Margaret Mead's famous study of adolescence in Samoa is a classic example of this procedure. What adults consider teen-agers' turbulent emotional state and propensity to rebellion have long concerned psychologists and educators. In the United States during the 1920s, the storm and stress of adolescence was generally accepted as a natural part of the process of growing up. This view had the scientific imprint of the authoritative work of the psychologist G. Stanley Hall.[3] Dr. Mead had her doubts, entertaining an alternative hypothesis that the emotional disturbance suffered by adolescents in American and Western European society is a psychological reaction to specific stresses built into American and European cultures. If a society could be found in which these stress conditions were absent (and in which no hidden variables were present that could also produce the emotional upset), that society should reveal an absence of adolescent disturbance and the presence of an easy tran-

siton from childhood to adult life. Such a conclusion, then, would point to the cultural determination of adolescent behavior. Familiar with the ethnographies of the South Seas (Polynesia), Dr. Mead believed that the culture and social organization of Samoa, which was also reasonably accessible, probably would provide the requisite "controlled" conditions. She therefore chose Samoa as her first laboratory. Her field observations, as reported in *Coming of Age in Samoa,* fulfilled the expectancy, or prediction, and demonstrated the invalidity of Hall's theory.

The importance of comparative cross-cultural testing for another behavioral science[4] has recently been stated by an eminent psychologist: "Anthropological evidence has been, and can continue to be, of invaluable service as a crucible in which to put to more rigorous test psychology's tentative theories, enabling one to edit them and select among alternatives in ways which laboratory experiments and correlational studies within our own culture might never make possible."[5]

The concept of culture A third distinguishing feature of anthropology is its development of the concept of culture and the importance of this concept in anthropological thought. *Culture is the integrated system of learned behavior patterns which are characteristic of the members of a society and which are not the result of biological inheritance.* Culture is not genetically predetermined; it is noninstinctive. It is wholly the result of social invention and is transmitted and maintained solely through communication and learning.

These are the essential components of the concept of culture as the term is currently used by most anthropologists. Other phrasings

---

[2]Compare F. Eggan, "Social Anthropology and the Method of Controlled Comparison" (*American Anthropologist,* Vol. 56, 1954), pp. 743–763; also O. Lewis, "Comparisons in Cultural Anthropology," in W. L. Thomas, Jr. (ed.), *Yearbook of Anthropology: 1955,* pp. 259–292.

[3]G. S. Hall, *Adolescence.*

[4]Since World War II, the more experimental and empirically oriented social scientists in the United States have preferred to identify their fields as *behavioral* rather than *social* sciences. The behavioral sciences include experimental psychology (excluding clinical), sociology (excluding social philosophy and social work), economics, government (excluding political philosophy and public administration), and anthropology.

[5]D. T. Campbell, "The Mutual Methodological Relevance of Anthropology and Psychology," in F. L. K. Hsu (ed.), *Psychological Anthropology,* p. 334.

are, of course, possible. Thus, Kroeber and Kluckhohn, after review and evaluation of some five hundred phrasings and uses of the concept, gave the following definition:

Culture consists of patterns, explicit and implicit, of and for behavior acquired and transmitted by symbols, constituting the distinctive achievements of human groups, including their embodiments in artifacts; the essential core of culture consists of tradi-

tional (i.e., historically derived and selected) ideas and especially their attached values; culture systems may, on the one hand, be considered as products of action, and on the other as conditioning elements of further action.[6]

Every separate society has its distinctive culture. The consequent effect is that the characteristic behaviors of the members of one society are in some respects significantly different from the characteristic behaviors of the members of all other societies. Anthropology has demonstrated that the distinctive behavior of different human populations, race differences, for example, is overwhelmingly the product of cultural experience rather than the consequence of genetic inheritance. The importance of the cultural concept in anthropology is so great that most of the rest of this book is devoted to a consideration of its nature and its manifestations in human behavior.

[6]A. L. Kroeber and C. Kluckhohn, "Culture: A Critical Review of Concepts and Definitions" (*Papers of the Peabody Museum of American Archaeology and Ethnology, Harvard University,* Vol. 47, 1952), p. 181.

Fig. 1-1 Anthropology and the interrelation of its parts. The subdivisions of anthropology represent successive levels of generalization or abstraction. On the first level, anthropometry, archaeology, and ethnography are the empirical, or fact-finding, specializations. The second-level specializations are concerned with studies in depth of limited aspects of man or his works. On the third level, physical anthropology and cultural anthropology collate the findings concerning the human organism and human culture, respectively. Anthropology combines them all in a single discipline.

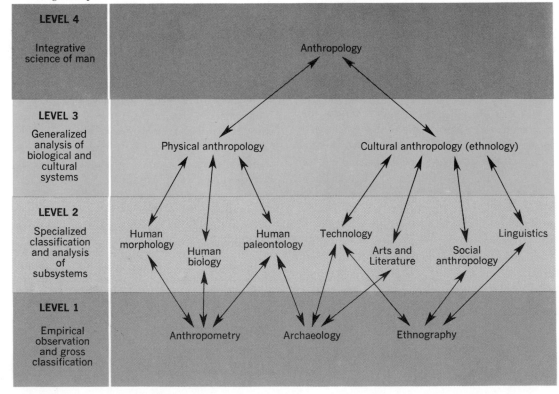

LEVEL 4 Integrative science of man	Anthropology
LEVEL 3 Generalized analysis of biological and cultural systems	Physical anthropology — Cultural anthropology (ethnology)
LEVEL 2 Specialized classification and analysis of subsystems	Human morphology — Human biology — Human paleontology — Technology — Arts and Literature — Social anthropology — Linguistics
LEVEL 1 Empirical observation and gross classification	Anthropometry — Archaeology — Ethnography

The subdivisions of anthropology

Anthropology is so diversified that in order to achieve precision, its practitioners must of necessity specialize. The two major aspects of the subject are the biological and the cultural; the two main subdivisions are therefore (1) physical anthropology and (2) cultural anthropology. Each, in turn, has a number of specialized subdivisions of its own. Archaeology occupies an important place in anthropology and is usually thought of as a main subdivision in its own right. Archaeology, however, is best viewed as a special technique for providing data for physical anthropology and cultural anthropology rather than as constituting a unique subject-matter in and of itself (see Fig. 1-1).

Physical anthropology Man is first of all a biological organism and only secondarily a social animal. The study of the nature of the human organism through physical anthropology is therefore basic to understanding the nature of man. The aim of physical anthropology is to develop an exact body of knowledge concerning the biological characteristics of human populations, ancient and modern. It is, of course, only through the study of living or recently deceased people that physical anthropologists can learn about the structure, growth, and physiology of the human body in any very detailed way. They have developed ingenious instruments and special techniques for precisely measuring innumerable ratios of size, composition of the body, dental patterns, hair form and color, skin color, blood pressure, blood groups, basal metabolism, and so forth. Because physical anthropologists are interested in the characteristics of populations, they customarily deal with large masses of measurements which are statistically processed. Physical anthropologists are commonly the most practiced statisticians among anthropologists. Their field is also closest to physiology, anatomy, and zoology among the collateral sciences.

The evolution of man is also the special concern of physical anthropology. Evolution raises two questions: "What happened?" and "How did it happen?" The first question is answered largely through the comparative study of fossils, including the monkeys, apes, and man, known as *paleontology* (Gr. *palaios*, old + *onta*, living things + *logia*, study). The answer to the query "How?" is derived largely from human genetics and the study of biological adaptation to environment—both the province of the physical anthropologist.

A "new" physical anthropology has developed since World War II. Its major quality is a shift of emphasis from measurement and classification of human types toward a much greater concern with the influence of genetics on stability and variation in human populations, plus the behavior of apes and monkeys, and with experimental work on the effects of differing muscle stress on bone shape as fac-

Fig. 1-2 In his search for man's origins, the physical anthropologist meticulously compares and analyzes prehistoric fossil remains, particularly skulls, teeth, femurs, and pelvic bones. (Ted Koryn, Black Star.)

tors in evolutionary change; on dietary influences on body composition, nutrition, and health; on genetic processes as they determine morphology; on blood typing; on the effects of culture as it influences human breeding patterns; and on many other problems. Physical anthropology has thus become highly dynamic and has assumed a new importance in human affairs.

Cultural anthropology   That branch of anthropology which deals with learned behavior characteristics in human societies is known as *cultural anthropology*. It, in turn, has many subdivisions, of which *ethnography, ethnology, social anthropology,* and *linguistics* are the most prominent.

Ethnography   The foundation of cultural anthropology is ethnography (Gr. *ethnos,* race, peoples + *graphein,* to write). Literally, the word "ethnography" means to write about peoples. As we use the term, it refers to the descriptive study of human societies. Early ethnographies were almost wholly derived from the reports of explorers, missionaries, traders, and soldiers. It was only toward the end of the nineteenth century that trained observers such as Franz Boas entered the field to study human societies directly. Now, most ethnographic work is done by trained anthropologists who carefully learn participant-observer techniques calling for objective and penetrating observation and interviewing, empathic rapport with a people, and accurate reporting. Modern cultural anthropologists are expected to earn their spurs in ethnographic fieldwork before they are fully qualified as anthropologists.

All ethnographic monographs have some theoretical framework implicit in their organization, but they do not deal explicitly with theoretical problems. They are, we may repeat, descriptive reports of data and are little concerned with comparison per se, hypothesis, or theory. Ethnography provides the building blocks for cultural anthropology, but it is necessary to look elsewhere for the grand design.

Ethnology   Ethnology is the "science of peoples, their cultures, and life histories as groups."[7] It differs from ethnography in that as a science it seeks interrelationships between peoples and their environments, between human beings as organisms and their cultures, between different cultures, and between the differing aspects of cultures. As a science, ethnology strives to derive explanations that go beyond description, emphasizing analysis and comparison. Since each culture is clearly a changing continuum through time, ethnology is much concerned with the historical background of cultures. This aspect of ethnology is sometimes called *cultural history.* When its concern is with general principles of cultural development, it expresses itself as *cultural evolutionism.* Ethnology and ethnography, taken together, may best be thought of as the two main branches of cultural anthropology.

Ethnology, in turn, breaks down into a number of subdivisions in accordance with degree of specialization. Thus there are specialists in, and specialized studies on primitive kinship and family life, economic activities, law and government, religion; material culture and technology; language; the arts of painting, sculpture, music, and dance; folklore and mythology—almost any major aspect of human cultural manifestations that one might think of.

Social anthropology   Ethnologists who concentrate on social relations, such as family and kinship, age groups, political organization, law and economic activities—in short, what is called *social structure*—prefer to be called *social anthropologists.* English anthropologists who accepted the position of A. R. Radcliffe-Brown deny the usefulness of historical studies in anthropology and wish to divorce cultural anthropology from history. They have established a separate subdivision of cultural anthropology under the rubric *social anthropology,* which they also at times call *comparative sociology.*[8] Social anthropology is nonhistorical in their view, while ethnology is historical.

[7]A. L. Kroeber, *Anthropology* (2d ed.), p. 5.
[8]See Chap. 35 for a more detailed discussion.

Linguistics Linguistics is the science of language. Many linguists look upon their discipline as a completely autonomous science in its own right, and there is a growing trend in American universities to establish independent departments of linguistics. However, languages are aspects of cultures, intimately interacting with all the other manifestations of culture, and are therefore best understood in the cultural context. Consequently, among the social sciences, the scientific study of languages is widely held to be a branch of cultural anthropology. In the United States, at least, all the larger departments of anthropology include linguistic analysis as a part of their programs. However, traditional language studies in archaic (Sanskrit, Greek, and Latin, for example) and modern Indo-European languages have been part of university activities in areas outside anthropology for centuries. Anthropologists, once they had begun to base their studies on objective fieldwork, were forced to learn many primitive languages from scratch, with never a book of grammar to guide them. This proved to be a good thing. A universal system of phonetic writing had to be developed so that records could be kept of what native informants were saying in tongues for which no systems of writing existed. This soon led to a realization that different cultures organize speech in accordance with principles very different from those which govern the old, familiar Indo-European languages. Some anthropologists, fascinated by their new discoveries, began to concentrate their efforts on recording and analyzing primitive languages, and linguistics as a specialized branch of anthropology developed in a way that is currently revolutionizing all language study (see Chapter 3).

Archaeology Archaeology (Gr. *archaios,* ancient + *logia,* study) is commonly confused with anthropology by the uninitiated. People who have never heard of ethnology know about "those scientists who dig up skeletons and arrowheads." They think this is anthropology. True, it is an important and fascinating segment of anthropology, but it is no more than

Fig. 1-3 Archaeology recovers the material evidence of early man and past cultures and the people who produced them. Excavations at Choukoutien, in China, produced fossil and cultural evidence of Peking man. Note division of the site into square zones for careful digging and search. (Courtesy of the American Museum of Natural History.)

a part and should not be confused with the whole. Archaeology is concerned with the recovery of the remains of ancient man himself and with stripping the mantle of earth from the material remains of his ancient cultures to recover what may still exist.

Aside from its obvious effect of filling museum cases and storerooms, the real significance of archaeology is its function of providing evidence from the past for scientific analysis by physical anthropologists and students of cultural history. Because prehistoric men left no written records, the fruits of the archaeologist's painstaking work are often all we have to go on. In archaeological fieldwork, the task is largely a matter of using rigorous excavation techniques to achieve the fullest possible reconstruction of the time, the life conditions, and the interrelations of the recovered remains in their original setting. But in the interpretation of archaeological findings, the intellectual task is no different from that faced by other anthropologists who are concerned with cultural history and developmental processes. It is one of relating the facts to general principles that adequately explain what was taking place. A student of prehistory must understand cultures and cultural processes to breathe life and meaning into the dead bones and silent stones of the long-lost past.

Not only must a modern prehistoric archaeologist[9] have full command of general anthropology, but he must also be well-versed in geology and paleontology, in addition to possessing the special skills of archaeological techniques. Archaeology must be an exacting specialization to meet the canons of modern science.

The branches of anthropology in relation to levels of scientific research

Science as the systematic, objective study of empirical phenomena and the resultant bodies of knowledge may be said to utilize techniques, methods, and theories. By techniques we mean

[9]Most professional prehistoric archaeologists are anthropologists. Practitioners of classical archaeology are usually specialists in ancient history.

the devices and procedures for objective observation of facts, as in the laboratory or in fieldwork. What one sees and hears depends on what one has to see and hear with, and on how skillfully he uses his instruments. By method we mean the logical and experimental procedures by means of which theory and fact are made to interact upon each other as theory guides research and as new facts confirm or disconfirm hypothesis and theory. By theory we mean the systematic scheme of assumptions, propositions, or postulates about the nature of things upon which is built a body of explanatory principles or generalizations: hypotheses and laws. By levels of generalization we mean the degrees through which the scientific thinker moves from narrow, specific observation, to broader and more abstract formulations which relate phenomena in ever more general terms.

Figure 1-1 shows a schematic representation of anthropology and its main subdivisions according to four levels of generalization, or degrees of abstraction. On the first level, anthropometry, archaeology, and ethnography observe and record the primary facts of the human populations and prehistoric and recent cultures. On the second level, limited generalizations are formulated and tested by specialists in the designated areas of interest. On the third level, generalizations concerning human evolution, growth and development, and racial characteristics are formulated by the physical anthropologist, while generalizations concerning cultures are worked out and tested by the cultural anthropologist on the basis of the findings of the specializations on the second level. Finally, on the fourth level, the general anthropologist undertakes to synthesize the results of physical and cultural anthropology into a universal scientific interpretation of man and his works.

The overall view of man which is presented in this text consists largely of the broadest general rules that scientific discovery has been able to formulate for man and culture, supported by reference to more special tests of theories and hypotheses on the third and

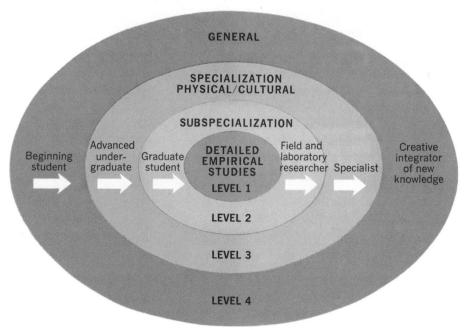

General

SPECIALIZATION
PHYSICAL/CULTURAL

SUBSPECIALIZATION

Beginning student → Advanced under-graduate → Graduate student → DETAILED EMPIRICAL STUDIES → Field and laboratory researcher → Specialist → Creative integrator of new knowledge

LEVEL 1

LEVEL 2

LEVEL 3

LEVEL 4

second levels. These illustrative generalizations are based upon first-level observations, that is, numerous references to the biological traits of specific fossil men and modern populations or to the customs and institutions of real tribes.

The relation of anthropology to the social sciences

Anthropology is usually organized as a social science in American universities, although it is clear from all that has been said thus far that anthropology is a good deal more than that. Nonetheless, its dominant identity among the social sciences is due to the fact that the bulk of anthropological work is focused upon culture and, within culture, upon social organization. We have discussed the features of anthropology that distinguish it as a discipline. Each of these bears on the question of the relation of anthropology to the sister sciences, and yet the often-asked question: "How does anthropology tie in to history, sociology, and psychology?" deserves a more specific answer.

History Early in this century, the English anthropologist R. R. Marett declared that anthro-

Fig. 1-4 The student beginning to study anthropology as a science first approaches the subject through the mastery of general principles. As he moves on to more specialized courses, he enters an area in which generalizations become narrower and the empirical data loom larger. As a graduate student, he masters the technique of empirical observation and research in the field and laboratory. As a professional anthropologist, he moves on to the formulation of specialized hypothesis and theory. Finally, he may formulate new and encompassing generalizations that are aimed at synthesizing all the empirical findings of the subspecializations of physical and cultural anthropology.

pology is history, or it is nothing. He did not mean that it is history in the formal sense; he was emphasizing that time is a basic dimension in which all human experience occurs. The stream of life is a continuous flow. All anthropologists grant this fact, but they differ over how much value there is to anthropology in history and historical research. Archaeologists are of course staunchly committed to the value of the historical component. Many social anthropologists, on the other hand, are apt to hold that it is sufficient to concentrate on the search for understanding of societies that currently exist. Prehistoric and historic data, they aver, can never be obtained in sufficient detail or with sufficient validity to serve adequately the demands of science.

A balanced view of the relation of anthropology to history would hold that a comparison of directly observable societies does indeed put the study of man on a firmer scientific footing in terms of verifiable and validated results. Yet it would also agree that it is scientifically important to study the processes of the growth and change of cultures. Culture and society are not momentary things. They come out of the past, exist in the present, and continue into the future. What they *are* is the product of what they *have been,* worked upon by presently impinging conditions and influences. What they *will be* is the product of what they *have been,* and *are,* worked upon by the conditions and influences that engage them today and will engage them in the future. Neither the present nor the future can be wholly understood without a knowledge of the past, however faulty.

There are, of course, historians and historians, histories and histories. The historian is a social scientist when he undertakes to derive general laws of social change or to explain specific events by noting repeated regularities observed through time. Or he may be a philosopher of history if he strives to explain what took place at particular times in history in terms of an a priori scheme of interpretation. Or, if the historian's interest is no more than the "scholarly pursuit of special knowledge of particular fact," he is neither social scientist nor philosopher; he is simply an historian *sui generis.* His emphasis is then on the uniqueness of the situation. "History never repeats itself," he says. The time and the place and what happened then and there—stated exactly, accurately, and specifically—are what is important to the historian as a chronicler.

In science, as opposed to history, a fact is not itself of central interest. The object of science is to relate a multitude of facts to one another so as to make valid, general propositions about the nature of things. The anthropologist's ways of organizing his knowledge are different from those of the historian, and his methods of operation are basically different also. The "field" for the historian is the library. His working unit is a document. His joy is the discovery of a long-lost packet of letters or reports. For the anthropologist, the "field" is a remote tribal group or an archaeological site. His working unit is the person and a people. His joy is the discovery of a new type of social relation, fossil, or set of artifacts. A student of contemporary Africa puts it succinctly: "Africa has two kinds of history: the conventional kind to be studied through European accounts of exploration, settlement, and colonial rule, and an unconventional kind to be studied through anthropological accounts of indigenous economic and social organization."[10]

Sociology Sociology and anthropology are the closest kin among the social sciences. It is for this reason that they are frequently to be found in the same department in American universities. Their similarity is in their interest in social organization and behavior. In these fields, the basic theoretical approaches have much in common; indeed, in many respects they are indistinguishable. But their specific interests and ways of going about their work may be very different. Sociologists do not usually receive the biological, archaeological, and linguistic training that is so important to anthropologists. Anthropologists work as participant-observers in small societies, supplemented by intensive, day-after-day, person-to-person discourse on cultural practices. Their emphasis is on people-in-culture. Sociologists usually work with larger samples of more limited aspects of society; hence their heavy emphasis on statistical data and procedures. The questionnaire and the census reports are likely to be the sociologist's major factual resource. Also, sociology devotes a great deal of attention to problems of social

[10]G. Dalton, "Traditional Production in Primitive African Economies" (*The Quarterly Journal of Economics,* August, 1962), p. 378.

pathology and social work: delinquency, crime, poverty, mental illness, and broken homes, as they occur in *American* society. This has been a commitment of sociology in the United States from the very beginning. Anthropology has only lately, and somewhat reluctantly, turned its conscious attention to social problems and administration.

Psychology Anthropology and psychology are both concerned with behavior and hence have much in common. But whereas anthropology is interested primarily in group organization of behavior and the cultural patterning of behavior, psychology is more concerned with the behavior of the individual organism and how it responds to specific stimuli. Psychologists are much more oriented to the use of laboratory experiments, tests, and measurements and to statistical expression of their findings in an effort to achieve scientific precision in their field. The behavioral situations studied by experimental psychologists tend to be simplified and neat, that is, controlled experiments that eliminate extraneous variables. Anthropologists

Fig. 1-5 Anthropology: its subdivisions and related sciences in terms of its historical-scientific and biological-cultural orientations.

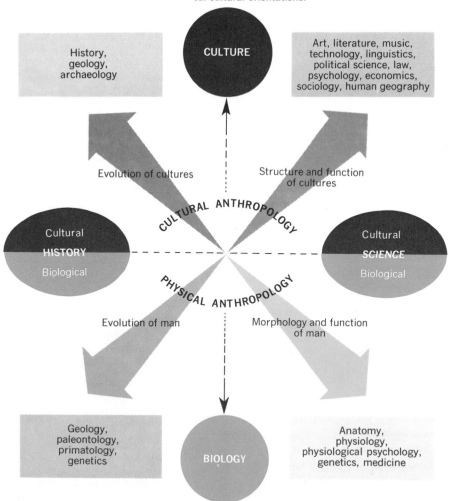

undertake to relate the simple but verified findings of psychology to the complexities of the real-life situations which they confront in going societies, where their findings are indeed less rigorously verified. Anthropologists as anthropologists study man. Experimental psychologists, although not all of them share this penchant, are more than likely to forsake man, with all his complexities, to study the more manageable mouse, rat, guinea pig, monkey, or pigeon.

While contemporary social psychologists also incline strongly toward laboratory experimentation, clinical psychologists and psychoanalysts are forced by the nature of their tasks to treat whole persons in the context of their total social settings. The deep probing of psychoanalysis into the hidden psychic processes has engendered a number of insightful concepts that have proved very useful to anthropologists in the interpretation of cultural systems and their relations to tribal personality types. The field of culture and personality (see Chapter 4) has been one of the most active and productive areas of anthropology in the past three decades.

Learning theory as developed in psychology is of course of great importance to anthropology; culture is acquired only through learning. Psychology teaches us how the human animal learns and how he learns to learn. Anthropology, in turn, teaches us what is learned in various societies, how it is taught, and what the rewards and punishments provided by each society for proper learning or failure to learn are. "Culture," note Miller and Dollard, ". . . is a statement of the design of the human maze, of the type of reward involved, and of what responses are to be rewarded. In this sense it is a recipe for learning."[11] Because cultures vary so widely, the conditions of human learning and human behavior vary widely. Anthropology offers psychology a wider factual base against which to test its theories and assumptions. This is recognized by the psy-

[11] N. Miller and J. Dollard, *Social Learning and Imitation*, p. 5.

chologist Donald Campbell in these terms:

Implicitly, the laboratory psychologist still assumes that his college sophomores provide an adequate base for a general psychology of man. . . . For social psychology these tendencies have been very substantively curbed through confrontation with the anthropological literature. Continued confrontation, however, will be required to prevent relapse. For the general psychologist, most of the lesson is yet to be learned.[12]

Law, political science, economics, and public health Law is an aspect of any society's culture, and it is exceedingly important as a shaper of cultures, since it is explicitly devoted to discouraging certain forms of behavior while supporting others. Because legal anthropology places so much emphasis on the functions of law in total social systems, it has proved particularly fruitful in illuminating by comparison the foundations of our own law system. "Law," according to Bohannan, "is one of the best-studied sub-disciplines of anthropology; the literature is small but of high quality."[13]

Only since World War II and the consequent emergence of independent, developing countries from the erstwhile empire holdings in Asia and Africa, have economics and political science in the United States become actively interested in the indigenous cultures of these parts of the world. But now the economics and government of these areas have taken on extreme importance. Technical-assistance programs and schemes for economic development, military missions, and Peace Corps activities can be wholly successful only if they relate meaningfully to the basic cultures of the peoples they would influence.

The expansion of public health programs to all parts of the world has had a like effect in stimulating close cooperation between anthropology and the practice of medicine. Cultural anthropology is now widely accepted as indispensable to the training of public health pro-

[12] D. T. Campbell, ."The Mutual Methodological Relevance of Anthropology and Psychology," in F. L. K. Hsu (ed.), *Psychological Anthropology*, p. 334.

[13] P. Bohannan, *Social Anthropology*, p. 284.

fessionals and has recently been recognized by the United States National Institutes of Health as a basic medically related science.[14]

It should be clear by now that anthropology in many of its aspects participates vitally in the dynamic complex of the social sciences. If we can refer to anthropology as the study of dead bones and live issues, we can also say that this live subject gets livelier by the year.

SUMMARY

Anthropology is a natural and a social science, and it is also one of the humanities in its concern with the study of man and his cultures. Its subdivisions include anthropometry, archaeology, and ethnography on the first level of observation and gross classification of facts. On the level of specialized study, human morphology, biology, and paleontology occupy the natural science side; technology, the study of arts and literature, social anthropology, and linguistics occupy the cultural side. These two types of specialized study, which involve generalized analysis of biological and cultural systems, respectively, are called *physical* and *cultural* anthropology.

Anthropology is distinguished by three factors: (1) its emphasis on the study of mankind as a whole, (2) its use of the comparative method, and (3) its development and use of the concept of culture. It overlaps all the social sciences and many of the biological sciences and thus is intimately related to each of them. Yet it retains its own unique identity by virtue of its holistic orientation and its special theories and methods. The study of anthropology is essential to a knowledge of man and to a liberal education.

[14]B. D. Paul, "Teaching Anthropology in Schools of Public Health," in D. G. Mandelbaum, G. W. Lasker, and E. M. Albert (eds.), *The Teaching of Anthropology,* p. 503.

SELECTED READINGS

Evans-Pritchard, E. E.: *Social Anthropology* (1953). A series of six lectures on the nature and uses of social anthropology delivered in 1950 to the radio audience of England.

Gillin, J. P.: *For a Science of Social Man: Convergences in Anthropology, Psychology and Sociology* (1954). Seven leading American social scientists examine the interrelations of their various fields.

Henry, J.: *Culture against Man* (1964). A hypercritical look at American culture and society which should be read for an appreciation of the way in which the author combines the technique of the participant-observer with the use of anthropological theory to shed a flood of new light on aspects of American family life, schooling, mental illness, and treatment of the aged.

Hole, F., and R. F. Heizer: *An Introduction to Prehistoric Archaeology* (1965). The essentials of archaeological technique and method are set forth in a readily understandable manner.

Kluckhohn, C.: *Mirror for Man: The Relation of Anthropology to Modern Life* (1949). Selected by Whittlesey House in 1949 as the winner of a contest for the best book explaining a science to the layman. *Mirror for Man* is readable, and it speaks with authority on what modern anthropolgy is, what it does, and what the findings of anthropology mean for mankind today.

Lewis, O.: *The Children of Sanchez* (1962). A fascinating example of modern ethnographic techniques applied to the study of human living in a great urban center— Mexico City. It has little to say explicitly about anthropological theory and method, but the meaning of "anthropological insight" comes clear on every page.

Mandelbaum, D. G., G. W. Lasker, and E. M. Albert (eds.): *The Teaching of Anthropology* (1963). Written by a number of anthropologists, primarily for teachers of anthropology, it covers all the subdivisions of anthropology and all the relations of anthropology to other subjects. Inquisitive students should find it interesting to see how their teachers go about deciding what to teach them.

Man, culture, and society

chapter 2

Once there was neither man nor culture. Today man threatens to crowd all other animals from the face of the earth, save only those which serve his purposes. Man has invented culture, and by means of culture he has domesticated himself and numerous plants, animals, and natural forces. Before long he promises to "domesticate" the entire world. By means of his cultural achievements, he has begun to probe outer space, and in the future he may be capable of interplanetary travel.

The culture-creating capacity

How did man, the animal, become man, the human being, *Homo sapiens?* The process has been a prolonged and unceasing response to environmental situations in which the biological processes of natural selection, working upon genetic variations in living organisms, have produced biological, or organic, evolution. One million or more years ago, man had become sufficiently differentiated from the other animals so that we can now look back on him as representing a new form of life. A feature of this differentiation was the elaboration of his nervous system, the brain in particular, to the point where he could not only see, smell, and act but also symbolically represent a wide range of experience. He acquired the capacity to think and to speak. He could experience things and situations vicariously, not in the instant act but "dramatized" within the nervous system. He learned how to communicate experience to himself and to others through those symbolic representations we call "concepts," "thoughts," and "words." The "animal" became contemplative. And thinking, he began a process of self-organization. He began to "see" the universe about him not only in terms of the immediately confronted stimulus but also in terms of what he "remembered," not just through conditioned habit but also through word representations of past experience. He acquired the capacity to project past experience into the future by thinking of what might be. He learned to create experience which had not yet happened and which might never take place at all. He became imaginative.[1]

Along with the development of his thinking brain, this creature, man, also was broadening the range of his physiological processes and physical activity. But the great innovation lay in the degree to which he could organize a relatively small number of movements into large and various combinations. He acquired the capacity to invent new behavior.

As a result of biological evolution, man acquired the capacity to produce culture on the grand scale and in turn to become the product of his cultures. Culture, like life, began

very simply and humbly. Like life, it has gradually grown and assumed a greater and greater variety of forms in an unbroken continuity from preexistent forms.

Levels of natural phenomena The first level of natural phenomena to take evolutionary form consisted of inorganic matter—earth materials and cosmic stuff. With the birth of life, something new was added. The inorganic became organic, and a new level of phenomena was reached. No one mistakes the fact that between living organisms and inorganic matter there is a *difference in kind,* even though all organisms are composed of inorganic elements.

Quite late in organic evolution, certain forms of life developed nervous systems. For the third time in emergent evolution, a new order was established—the psycho-organic. Just as we recognize a basic difference between nonliving and living things, so we recognize that sentient animals are different in kind from nonsentient viruses, metazoa, protozoa, and plants.

Thus we come to cultural phenomena, the latest and most complex product of the evolutionary process. As happened twice before, something new was added to what had previously existed. Man crossed the culture-producing threshold; a yet higher level of phenomena came into being. While it rests on the organic and the psychic, it is more than either—the more than organic, the psychocultural-organic.[2]

An interesting and incidental bypath of the sequence of levels of phenomena is the historical order of the development of the sciences. Astronomy, physics, chemistry, and geology—which deal primarily with the lowest order of phenomena, the inorganic—are the oldest and most highly developed of the sciences. Zoology, biology, physiology, and those sci-

[1]William Golding treats this process in a simple and empathic way in his novel *The Inheritors,* a fictionalized account of the last of the Neandertals.

[2]In earlier editions of this book, the nineteenth-century English sociologist Herbert Spencer and the American anthropologist Alfred L. Kroeber were followed in characterizing culture as *superorganic.* H. Spencer, *The Principles of Sociology,* Vol. 1, pp. 2–16; A. L. Kroeber, "The Superorganic" (*American Anthropologist,* Vol. 19, 1917), pp. 163–213; E. A. Hoebel, *Man in the Primitive World,* 2d ed., pp. 168–172. The term *"psychocultural-organic"* is now proposed as more explicit and encompassing.

Table 2-1   Levels of Natural Phenomena and the Hierarchy of Sciences

level of phenomena	type of material phenomena	hierarchy of sciences
IV. Psychocultural-organic	Man	Anthropology, sociology, social psychology, political science, economics, jurisprudence, linguistics, musicology, etc.
III. Psycho-organic	Sentient animals	Psychology, physiological psychology, neurology
II. Organic	Nonsentient animals, plants, metazoa, protozoa	Physiology, zoology, botany, organic chemistry
I. Inorganic	Earth and cosmic matter	Chemistry, physics, geology, astronomy

ences predominantly concerned with the vital organic were next to emerge and approach maturity. Psychology and the social sciences were last upon the scene. Among these infant sciences, anthropology was the very last to emerge as a full-fledged discipline. Mastery or near mastery of the lower levels of phenomena seems to have been a necessary prerequisite to scientific awareness of the existence of the higher levels.[3] There is hope that, given another century of development, psychology, sociology, and anthropology may approximate the exactitude of their older predecessors.

The non-instinctive nature of culture

In the first chapter, culture was defined as the integrated system of learned behavior that is characteristic of the members of a society. It is the essence of the concept of culture that instincts, innate reflexes, and any other biologically predetermined forms of behavior are ruled out. Culture is therefore acquired behavior. But it is as much a part of the natural universe as the stars in the heavens, for it is a natural product of man's activities, and man is part of nature.

[3]Leslie White has discussed this fact in some detail. See his article, "The Expansion of the Scope of Science" (*Journal of the Washington Academy of Science,* Vol. 37, 1947), pp. 191–210.

Learned behavior   That cultural behavior is learned behavior may be demonstrated by answering the question: "What would happen if a group of babies were cut off from all adult care, training, and supervision?" The answer is, of course: "They would die." Therefore, we must modify our question and put it in this form: "What would happen if a group of babies could be fed and protected without adult supervision or training and without any form of contact with adults? Would they manifest any of the special traits of behavior that were characteristic of their parents?"

Our answer cannot be based upon direct empirical observation; legend, mythology, and the testimony of honorable men notwithstanding, wolves, jailers, or scientific experimenters have never set up such a situation under conditions of control or observation that meet the elementary canons of scientific acceptability.[4] But enough is known of infant physiology, learning, and psychology to justify an answer in unequivocal terms. Assuming the survival of the infants, they would eat, drink, defecate, urinate, and gurgle and cry. These would be direct responses to basic biological drives. But what they would eat, when they

[4]For a sarcastic debunking of the wolf-child stories, B. Evans, *The Natural History of Nonsense,* is good reading.

would eat, and how they would eat would not be according to the tastes and palates of any group of men we now know. It is quite unlikely that they would cook their food. Presumably they would sooner or later get up on their hind legs, and even before adolescence they would experiment in mating without benefit of incest tabus or any preferred approaches of courtship. They would communicate emotional states through gesture and sounds. But they would be devoid of language, utensils, fire, arts, religion, government, and all the other features of life that distinguish man among the animals. They would develop few of the traits which we characterize as "human."

In spite of their shortcomings, however, these hapless children would enjoy a kind of social life. They would constitute not only an animal aggregation but also an animal society. It is quite probable, however, because they are human beings, that they would very quickly begin the accumulation of incipient culture.

Instinctive behavior Many animals in addition to man have a social life and even social organization. Ant society has long been recognized for its well-delineated division of labor among drones, workers, fighters, males, females, and queen. The organization of the colony, with its living quarters and storage rooms for eggs, presents the picture of a well-ordered society. The ants interact with one another in an integrated, sustained set of relationships. These relationships are preset in the genetic organization of the ants. So far as is known, little if any of their behavior is learned from adult ants. If eggs are hatched without any adult ants being present, a host of new ants is produced, which, when they attain maturity, apparently reenact every single aspect of all the forms of social life that have characterized their species for untold generations.

The dance of the bees The behavior of certain other insects is also highly social and involves the communication of information within the society. Honeybees have been studied with great care and with fascinating results in a series of experimental observations by Karl von Frisch, of Munich. Female "scout" bees search out the location of sweet, pollen-bearing plants. When she has found a good source, the scout determines the location, takes a fix on the sun, and returns immediately to the hive. She then executes a dance in which she moves along a straight line pointing toward the source. She circles back to the starting point, alternately to the left and right. The speed at which she makes her straight runs indicates approximately how far away the source of supply is. The smell of the pollen indicates the sweetness, or potential honey content. The workers fall in behind her in the dance, and when they have received the message, they take off unerringly to the right spot. Different species do different dances, but the basic pattern is the same.

This fascinating dance of the bees emphasizes the importance of communication in group living, but it does not represent cultural behavior. As von Frisch himself has written:

> The brain of the bee is the size of a grass seed and is not made for thinking. The actions of a bee are mainly governed by instinct. Therefore, the student of even so complicated and purposeful activity as the communication dance must remember that he is dealing with innate patterns, impressed on the nervous system of the insects over the immense reaches of time of their phylogenetic development.[5]

Protoculture among apes and monkeys On the other hand, we would be taking undue credit unto ourselves if we denied *all* culture-creating capacity to all subhuman creatures.

Monkeys and apes have been shown to be quite capable of solving a number of problems posed for them by experimenters. Chimpanzees show considerable intelligence and inventiveness. What is more, they are quite definitely capable of learning from each other through direct imitation. Apes ape each other.

Thus when one of a group of experimental apes accidentally jabbed the end of a pole into

[5] K. von Frisch, "Dialects in the Language of the Bees" (*Scientific American*, August, 1962; SA reprint series No. 130), p. 3.

Fig. 2-1 A classic experiment in learning and insight among chimpanzees. By piling up boxes, the chimpanzee, Grande, is able to solve the problem of how to reach a banana. Note the sympathetic gesture of the seated chimpanzee, Sultan. (From Wolfgang Köhler, The Mentality of Apes, *1921; courtesy of Springer-Verlag.)*

the ground and found to his immense delight that he could hoist himself skyward, all the other members of the colony were soon searching for sticks; pole vaulting was the rage. Another discovered that by scattering bread outside the bars of his cage, he could lure unwary yard chickens in close, while he lurked with a stick in his hand with which to jab them. An-noying the chickens then became the current sport of the group. The alarmed squawks of the hens provided rich simian diversion. These and other tricks were discovered by the apes without help from psychologists. When they had spread among the group, they had for the time being all the qualities of customs. But, alas, when interest wore off and enthusiasm waned, as it always did after a few days or weeks, each practice was forgotten, never to be performed again. Their destiny was that of fads; they did not endure to become customs.

However, the semiwild Japanese monkeys that are being carefully studied in their natural habitats by Japanese scientists clearly show that elemental discoveries are communicated within the group and do become established as cultural features. Direct observation of colonies of Japanese monkeys (*Macaca fuscata*) reveals, for example, that each troop has its own characteristic food prejudices. This, surely, is the most elemental of cultural universals.

According to Syuno Kawamura: "The monkeys of the Minno Ravine know how to remove the earth of the slope by scratching with their hands to get the roots of Boehmeria nivea, and also probably of Lilium spp. and Dioscorea spp., while those of Takasakiyama entirely lack such knowledge."[6]

Food habits are established among un-weaned infant monkeys, who, sitting by their mothers, pick up the food she drops from her mouth. Without their mother's example, experimental infants of the same species find it hard to learn to take any food but milk. "Even when they have advanced in learning, they will never acknowledge many of the common foods of Japanese macaques as their own food. So we presume that for Japanese macaques, the only food which is recognized as such through instinct is milk."[7]

New foods have been experimentally introduced to troops of wild monkeys by the Japanese scientists with very illuminating results. When candy is introduced, the two-or three-

[6]S. Kawamura, "The Process of Sub-culture Propagation among Japanese Macaques," in C. H. Southwick (ed.), *Primate Social Behavior*, pp. 83–84.
[7]*Ibid.*

year-olds are the first to take it up as a food. Later the mothers learn from their children to eat it. And once a mother has acquired a taste for candy, that taste is "handed down to her baby without exception." The adult males who supervise the young monkeys also soon learn to eat candy, but the young males who have little to do with juveniles take it up last of all. New culture traits spread differentially within the troop.

In another troop, the new habit of eating wheat was introduced by an adult male. His example was followed by the "chief" of the troop and from him was passed on to the "chief female," who in turn transmitted it to her offspring. Within four hours, wheat had been tried and accepted by the entire troop. Only half of another troop ever accepted the candy eating that had been introduced by a child, however.[8]

Incipient culture building is clearly within the province of primates other than man. Yet they evidently lack the capacity to express experience symbolically. This is the great human achievement. (See Chapter 7, pages 111–112, for a further discussion of primate behavior.)

Symbolism and culture Many of the elemental behavior patterns that make up a culture may be learned directly without reliance on symbolic content. This may be seen in the behavior of the deaf child who learns to master simple manual skills without the use of language and without the usual means of assimilating many of the more complex ideas which other children get at an early age. It is equally obvious just how much of his society's culture is shut off from such a child. Without skillful remedial education, available only in the most advanced cultures and societies, the congenitally deaf child can rarely share the thoughts, beliefs, or attitudes or acquire the reasoning skills of his people except on the crudest level. He will know little of his people's gods, music, folktales and legends, star lore, or magic. He will be barred from comprehension of his people's kinship system, law, poli-

tics, and rules of inheritance and trade. He may learn to paint through imitation, but he will know little of the meanings of the designs he copies or the significance of the colors he uses. All these manifestations of culture, and more, will be beyond him, for his infirmity denies him the one truly distinctive attribute of man—language, the "purely human and non-instinctive method of communicating ideas, emotions, and desires by means of a system of voluntarily produced symbols."[9]

The clue to understanding the nature of language, that cultural product without which culture is limited, is to realize that language is the major device for *symbolizing*. A sound may be no more than a noise, a disturbance of the air that stimulates no discernible response in man or beast. A sound may also be a *signal* that evokes a response, such as the whistle that calls a dog to his master's side. On a higher level a sound may be a *symbol*, which is a signal or sign that stands for something. It has *meaning*. Languages are arbitrary systems of vocal symbolism, to which civilized cultures have also added visual symbols: writing. Symbols may also be tactile, such as the piece of sandpaper that is conventionally put on a bottle which contains poison so that it may be felt in the dark.

Pavlov's dogs learned to respond to the sound of a bell instead of to the taste and sight of meat by immediately producing a flow of saliva. The bell became a signal evoking a salivary response. Perhaps it was also an elementary symbol for the dogs, in that the sound came to stand for eating and evoked some of the sensations of eating; it could have had low-level meaning for them.

Compare, however, the human context of the dinner bell, and the quality of high-level symbolizing becomes clearer. A ringing bell is just as meaningless a sound to a baby as to a puppy. If a baby happens to grow up in a primitive society and does not hear a bell until a ship from the civilized world reaches his shores, it will still be a meaningless sound for

[8] *Ibid.*, pp. 85–88. [9] E. Sapir, *Language*, p. 7.

him on first hearing. Suppose, on the other hand, he has grown up to be an English or American factory worker. He has learned that when a particular bell sounds at high noon, this is the signal to knock off work and open the lunch box. But he has learned a good deal more than this. At 11:40 he is bored with his work and begins to feel hungry. He mutters to the man at the next bench, "When is that bell going to ring?" He may receive the reply, "I don't know. But now that you mention it, just thinking about it makes me hungry." It is not the sound of the bell that makes the second worker suddenly aware of the rhythmic contraction of his stomach muscles or causes him to swallow the excess saliva that has suddenly been released. It is the symbolic words "bell" and "ring." Other bells in other contexts, such as church bells, will have quite different symbolic connotations. They can become extremely full of meanings; for example, in the Italian countryside, the bells of a village symbolize village loyalty and village identity, called *campanellismo.* The village ties extend as far as the village bells can be heard. When the bells are silenced, there is the deep social sickness so feelingly portrayed in *A Bell for Adano,* by John Hersey.

So it is that almost all aspects of a culture come to be symbolically identified and symbolically transmitted from the old members of any society to its new members. So it is that the very way in which the members of a society see and understand the world in which they live is shaped by the symbol system that makes up their culture. There are many different kinds of symbolic representations, but the most important of all is language. For this reason, the next chapter is devoted in its entirety to the question of culture and language.

The integration of culture

The members of a society never exhibit *all* the behaviors of which we now know human beings are capable. This is one of the great lessons that modern anthropology has taught us. Many people think that what they do is *ipso facto* an expression of human nature. Little do they realize that other human beings have found quite different ways of doing the same thing. Or perhaps they do not do it at all. In the succeeding chapters of this book, the main varieties of known culture patterns are examined. The range of variability in surprisingly wide: "Anthropology holds up a great mirror to man and lets him look at himself in his infinite variety."[10] The variety of his known behavior is not really infinite, but it is impressively broad.[11]

The imperative of selection As each society builds its culture through the ages, it ignores or rejects many of the potential behavior patterns of which men are capable. Of course, this is partly due to the fact that the majority of these potential patterns remained undiscovered by most of the isolated societies of the past and hence were not available for inclusion in their cultures. Yet even if they had been available, many of them would necessarily have been excluded. Social behavior must be predictable. Expectancies must be realized, if men are to gauge their actions in terms of past experience. Men in society are men interacting. If everyone were liable to go off behaving in any one of the multitudes of ways in which human beings are capable of behaving, the result would be bedlam and disaster. Society is possible only in terms of a limiting order.

Limitation of ways of behaving is not only a social necessity but also an individual necessity. Experimental animal psychology, as well as psychiatry, has demonstrated that habit formation and habitual rewarding of psychological responses are necessary for individual mental health.[12] Behavior must be regularized to a high degree for effective functioning of personality.

Further, many behavior patterns are mutually contradictory and inherently incompatible. A people cannot enjoy free sexual license

[10]C. Kluckhohn, *Mirror for Man: The Relation of Anthropology to Modern Life,* p. 11.
[11]See J. P. Gillin, "Custom and the Range of Human Response" (*Character and Personality,* Vol. 13, 1944), pp. 101–134.
[12]S. J. H. Masserman, *Principles of Dynamic Psychiatry,* pp. 126–129.

and at the same time practice celibacy; no one has yet discovered how to eat his cake and have it too. This principle applies to thousands of other aspects of culture and is the basis of the *imperative of selection*, as summed up by Ruth Benedict:

The culture pattern of any civilization makes use of a certain segment of the great arc of potential human purposes and motivations. . . . The great arc along which all possible human behaviors are distributed is far too immense and too full of contradictions for any one culture to utilize even any considerable portion of it. Selection is the first requirement.[13]

Fundamental cultural postulates The selection of the customs that go to make up a culture is never wholly random and haphazard. Selection is made with reference to a set of deeply-lying assumptions, or postulates, about the nature of the external world and the nature of man himself. These assumptions as to the nature of existence are called *existential postulates*. There are also deep-lying assumptions about whether things or acts are good and to be sought after, or bad and to be rejected. These are called *normative postulates* or *values*. Both existential and normative postulates are the reference points that color a people's view of things, giving them their orientation toward the world around them and toward one another. The basic postulates provide the frame of reference for a people's *Weltanschauung*, or world view.[14] (See Chapter 34.)

The basic assumptions of a culture are necessarily consistent among themselves, although there are usually some exceptions. If a society is to survive, the gears of its culture must mesh, even though they may growl and grind.

In selecting its customs for day-to-day living, even in little things, the society chooses those ways which accord with its thinking and predilections—ways that fit its basic postulates concerning the nature of things and what is

desirable and what is not. If these ways are consistent with the basic postulates, and if these in turn are consistent with one another, integration is achieved. The culture is then a harmonious working whole.

To recapitulate:

1. Every culture represents a limited selection of behavior patterns from the total of human potentialities, individual and collective.

2. The selection tends to be made in accordance with certain postulates (dominant assumptions and values) basic to culture.

3. It follows that every culture exemplifies a more or less complete and coherent pattern, structure, or system of actions and relationships.

"The quality of a society," observes Otis Lee, "will vary with the quality of its basic values . . . with their suitability to its needs and circumstances, and with the consistency and thoroughness with which they are worked out."[15]

Some of the basic postulates of a culture may be explicitly stated by the people who hold them. Others are not explicitly stated, either because they are so taken for granted or because the people are so unused to reflecting about their beliefs that they are not themselves able to state them. In anthropology, when the social scientist is thoroughly familiar with the observed behavior of a society in all its aspects, he may generalize to the principles that underlie the behavior; thus he identifies the postulates for them,[16] like the linguist who analyzes a primitive language and formulates the rules and principles of grammar. The people who speak the tongue know only that one form is right and another is not, without being able to express the principles in so many words. There are striking parallels between general cultural and linguistic processes which are discussed in the next chapter.

---

[13]R. F. Benedict, *Patterns of Culture*, p. 237.

[14]E. A. Hoebel, *The Law of Primitive Man.* For comparison, see C. Kluckhohn, "The Philosophy of the Navaho Indians," in F. S. C. Northrop (ed.), *Ideological Differences and World Order*, chap. 17; also D. Lee, "Being and Value in a Primitive Culture" (*The Journal of Philosophy*, Vol. 46, 1949), pp. 401–415.

[15]O. Lee, "Social Values and the Philosophy of Law" (*Virginia Law Review*, Vol. 32, 1946), pp. 811–812; reprinted in O. Lee, *Freedom and Culture*, pp. 89ff.

[16]A detailed description of how basic cultural postulates are expressed in Cheyenne culture may be found in E. A. Hoebel, *The Cheyennes: Indians of the Great Plains.* Another example may be found in J. A. Hostetler, *Amish Society.*

Configurations of culture Although a culture is built up of elements and traits, the significance lies less in its inventory of traits than in the manner of their integration. For this reason we have phrased the definition of culture in terms of the "integrated system of learned behavior."

Benedict, who introduced the configurational idea into modern anthropological thought, has written of culture: "The whole, as modern science is insisting in many fields, is not merely the sum of all its parts, but the result of a unique arrangement and inter-relation of the parts that has brought about a new entity."[17]

This is a sound principle for the understanding of the nature of cultures and the

[17]Benedict, *op. cit.,* p. 47.

Fig. 2-2 Japanese and Gaucho greetings. Similar situations are culturally patterned in different ways. The Latin-American abrazzo *emphasizes emotional expressiveness, while the Japanese bow stresses the formality of status. (Left, Marc Riboud, Magnum; right, René Burri, Magnum.)*

uniqueness of divergent societies, for it is theoretically possible for two societies to possess identical inventories of culture elements and yet so arrange the relationships of the elements to one another as to produce two quite unlike systems of integration. By simple analogy, two masons may take two identical piles of bricks and equal quantities of mortar. Yet with these materials, one may build a fireplace, while the other builds a garden wall, depending on the way they integrate the bricks.

The configuration of a culture may be defined as its delineated contours as formed by the structural interrelation of all its elements. It presumes internal integration in accordance with some basic and dominant principles or value systems underlying the whole scheme. Thus Pueblo culture is characterized by collectivistic, ritual emphasis under priestly direction, while Plains Indian cultures emphasize individual self-realization through aggressive fighting against outsiders and hallucinatory vision experiences.

Cultural relativity All cultures differ in their basic postulates at some points. Each has gen-

eral features in common with all others, but in specifics every culture is different from every other in some respects. Some are very different. "Mankind is one. Civilizations are many," the great anthropologist Franz Boas used to say. The anthropological realization of this fact has led to the establishment of the *concept of cultural relativity,* which is closely related to the intensive anthropological use of the comparative method.

The concept of cultural relativity states that standards of rightness and wrongness (values) and of usage and effectiveness (customs) are relative to the given culture of which they are a part. In its most extreme form, it holds that every custom is valid in terms of its own cultural setting. In practical terms, it means that anthropologists learn to suspend judgment, to strive to understand what goes on from the point of view of the people being studied, that is, to achieve empathy, for the sake of humanistic perception and scientific accuracy. The anthropologist strives to assume the role of detached observer rather than that of apologist, condemner, or converter. He learns to laugh with people, not at them. He must have a real respect for human beings, whoever they may be. The student who lacks this trait—who cannot put aside all ethnocentrism, that is, the habit of uncritically judging other peoples' behavior according to the standards set in his own culture—can never become a first-rate cultural anthropologist. Ethnocentrism usually works toward the deprecation of others, a point made quite explicit in the complaint of a Bannock Indian headman in southern Idaho, who became jealous of my continuous attention to the neighboring Shoshones, among whom I was doing fieldwork. "Why do you spend all your time talking to them dirty Shoshones?" he demanded. "They don't know nothing. Why don't you talk to *us?*"

The functional nature of culture

The fact that each culture is made up of a multitude of selected traits integrated into a total system means that all parts have a spe-

cial relationship to the whole. Each part may have *its* specific form as, for example, a bow, a canoe, a pot, a marital arrangement, or a legal process. No one of these elements of culture exists in a vacuum, however, or stands as an isolated unit. It plays its part in contributing to a total life-way. The way it and all the other parts relate to one another and influence or affect one another forms the structure of the culture. The contribution that each part makes to the total cultural system is its *function,* in contrast to its form.

Thus the bow, whose form may be expressed in measurements and pictures, may function in meeting the needs of food getting and defense, in ritual symbolism in the religious and governmental systems, in fire making, and in musical activities. To understand all the functions of the bow in any culture, it is absolutely necessary for the anthropologist to follow through all its relationships to every other related aspect of the culture. He must do this for each unit of culture, to see finally how all units work to maintain the total lifeway of the people he is studying.

A strange custom may seem meaningless and incomprehensible, or tantalizingly exotic, at first acquaintance. Within its cultural setting, and in relation to the basic postulates of those who practice it, and in terms of its functions within the system of which it is a part, the significance of the custom becomes scientifically meaningful. It is no longer a queer custom, but a socially significant act—always with reference to the system or structure of which it is a part.

Functionalism emphasizes the dynamics operating within a culture. It is concerned with a good deal more than the mere description of habits and customs.

A. R. Radcliffe-Brown, who was one of the chief exponents of functionalism and who contributed a good deal to its development, has used a biological analogy to make its meaning clearer. In his words:

An animal organism is an agglomeration of cells and interstitial fluids arranged in relation to one another not as an aggregate but as an integrated whole. For the bio-chemist, it is a complexly integrated system of complex molecules. The system of relations by which these units are related is the organic structure. . . . The organism *is not* the structure; it is a collection of units (cells or molecules) arranged in a structure, i.e., in a set of relations; the organism *has* a structure. Two mature animals of the same species and sex consist of similar units combined in a similar structure. The structure is thus to be defined as a set of relations between the entities. . . . As long as it lives the organism preserves a certain continuity of structure although it does not preserve the complete identity of its constituent parts. . . . Over a period its constituent cells do not remain the same. But the structural arrangement of the constituent units of the organism does remain similar. . . . The life of an organism is conceived as the *functioning* of its structure . . . a cell or an organism has an *activity* and that activity has a function.[18]

The functions of each part are found in the contributions the part makes to maintenance of the life process of the whole organism. So it is with culture. The functions of each custom and of each institution are found in the special contributions they make to the maintenance of the life-way that is the total culture.

Malinowski emphasized that the interrelatedness of all parts of a culture means that the modification of any single part will inevitably produce secondary changes in other parts. Missionaries and officials of governmental technical-aid-and-development programs have often overlooked this simple principle, with the result that their efforts have had many an unforeseen and unwished for consequence. But even with the most intelligent awareness it is exceedingly difficult to foresee the ultimate social consequences of any act of induced cultural change.

The components of culture Cultures are built up of *behavioral norms*, or *customs*. They are sometimes identified as *culture elements*, which may be combined as *culture complexes*. Complexes may in turn constitute *institutions*. Norms may

[18]A. R. Radcliffe-Brown, "On the Concept of Function in Social Science" (*American Anthropologist*, Vol. 37, 1935), pp. 394–395. See also B. Malinowski, "Culture" (*Encyclopedia of the Social Sciences*, Vol. 4, 1931), pp. 621–646.

be classified according to the scope of applicability to the members of a societal population, namely, as *universals, alternatives,* and *specialties.* All these concepts are useful in the analysis of culture.

Behavioral norms and patterning Cultural behavior is organized and patterned. This means that it is ordinarily not random but repetitive and fairly consistent. It is customary. For analytical reasons social scientists prefer to think in terms of *norms* rather than *custom*, for "custom" has too many popular meanings. A norm is the average or modal behavior of a given type that is manifested by a social group. Statistically, it means either the average or the greatest frequency of a variable. If variation is observed in a certain type of behavior on the part of a population, a count may be made of the number of times each variation occurs in a given sample. The variations may be ranged in a continuous series in accordance with their degrees of likeness, with the most unlike forms at the two ends, or poles, of the scale. This gives the **range** of variability in the behavior. Next, the number of times each class of behavior occurs is plotted along the range of variability. This gives the *frequency distribution.* The frequency distributions may then be transferred to a graph which has the range of distribution as its base line and the frequency incidence for each class produces a *frequency-distribution curve* (Fig. 2-3).

In most situations, the curve shows a high point with a slope away on either side. This is a *bell curve.* In some situations, variation away from the high point will be in one direction only. This is a *J curve* (Fig. 2-4). A norm is a statistical expression of the most common class, called the *mode;* the average class, called the *mean;* or the middle class, called the *median,* in the total frequency distribution.

Customs are social norms statistically identified. They are that which is normal. When feasible, analyses of social behavior should be statistically based. Anthropological experience has shown, however, that it is not usually feasible to make rigorous statistical studies of all kinds of behavior. Consequently, when an anthropologist describes a custom, he is usually stating what appears to be the modal behavior. Only in extremely rare cases does he make an actual statistical count of all behavior over a given period of time to determine an arithmetically accurate distribution. Such precision may be ideally desirable but under the given situation either impossible or impractical. Modern canons of anthropology do insist on observation of the behavior described whenever possible. Yet sometimes it is not possible to observe what is recorded, since the behavior may have died out or may be secret, or the field worker may not be around at the particular time the event occurs. Therefore, to find out whether a given habit is modal or not, we frequently must take a people's word for it. They say this is what they always do, usually do, or would do if they did it.

Culture elements, complexes and institutions
A *culture element* is a pattern of behavior (or the material product of such behavior) that may be treated as the smallest unit of its order.

Anthropologists often speak of *culture complexes*. A complex is a network of closely related patterns. For example, the activities of a dance taken together form a dance complex; the activities of the hunt form a hunting complex; the activities of child training form a child-care complex.

The complexes that are woven together in relation to the basic interests of social living are called *institutions*. For example, those concerned with subsistence activities and the production and distribution of goods are called *economic institutions;* those concerned with sex, reproduction, and kinship are called *kinship institutions.*

Universals, alternatives, and specialties Norms that apply to every member of a society, such as the use of the fork among adult members of Western societies, are called *universals.* Although certain kinds of behavior may be required of everyone in a society, most cultures allow some degree of choice between norms for specific situations. These are known as *alternatives.*

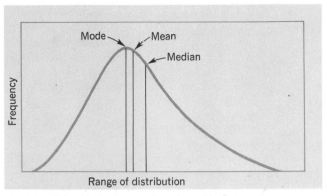

Fig. 2-3 Three kinds of norms in a skewed frequency-distribution curve.

Fig. 2-4 Model of a J curve. Hypothetical frequency distribution of homicides per male in an Eskimo community.

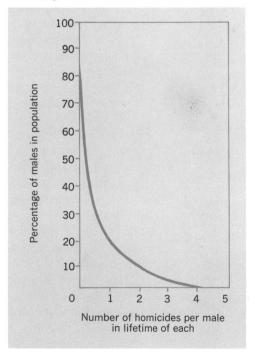

Thus, as a student, you may wear a four-in-hand, a bow tie, or no tie at all. A Cheyenne Indian could make a personal choice between a bow and arrow, a spear, or a club wherewith to smite the Crow. Each is a norm, but one does not exclude the other within the culture as a whole.

The traits that are restricted to a particular subgroup, such as the common tabus of medicine men or the hairdos of married women, are *specialties.*

The specialties of one group may be known to the other members of the society and yet not used by them, because they are not patterns for their behavior. Many American adult men know the Boy Scout salute, having once been scouts, but they do not use it as a form of greeting after they have left scouting behind. In a complex society, however, most specialties remain unknown to most of the people. This may be because the specialties require unique aptitudes or a rigorous course of training which is undertaken by only a few, or it may be that the specialties are the secret and hidden knowledge of a few, kept within their closed circle for the benefits that may be derived from secretiveness. The result is that no individual can ever acquire or manifest in himself all the elements of his society's culture. It means also that no anthropologist, even the most assiduous, can ever make note of, to say nothing of record, all the aspects of any culture, even the simplest known to man.

This, then, provides the answer to the question, often asked: "How can one speak of American culture when there is such a difference between the culture of New Yorkers and that of Kentucky mountaineers?—between the Italians of Lower Manhattan and the Scandinavians of Minnesota?—between the Yankees of Vermont and the *paisanos* of Monterey?" The universals shared by all Americans are the common binding and integrating elements of American culture and society. The specialties of the different regional groups and socioeconomic classes are merely internally differentiating elements.

The cohesive strength of a society is in part a product of the relative proportion of *universals* to *specialties.* In any analysis of a society and its culture, it is absolutely essential, in the interests of clarity and accuracy, never to generalize from the norms of a subgroup to make statements about the society as a whole, unless it has been observed that the norms of the subgroup are also characteristic of the whole. Americans who live west of the Hudson River and north of the Long Island Sound can appreciate the meaning ot this injunction if they will reflect on their feelings about European authors who write about America after a visit to New York City.[19]

Culture as construct or reality

Do cultures really exist, or do they exist only in the imagination of the social scientist? This is a question of epistemology (Gr. *epistēmē*, knowledge + *logos*, discussion), or the nature of knowing. The culture whole, or *the* culture of a society, is an abstraction of a high order. No one has ever seen or experienced a culture in its entirety. When we speak of a culture, we talk as though it were a neatly taped-off entity, when in point of fact each culture is woven into other cultures at the points where there are intersociety contacts.

The culture construct Cultures are constantly changing and modifying. Yet in anthropology we investigate a society on a field trip of greater or less duration, after which we write up a monograph describing its culture. In so doing, we fix for the moment those main lines of characteristic behavior that we have perceived and noted as though they were all taking place at any given moment. It is as though we stopped a fast action with a high-speed shutter to obtain an instantaneous picture of a continuous action. We get the main contours of the action frozen for an instant in what Linton called the *culture construct.*[20] It is a state-

[19]The analytical concepts of universals, alternatives, and specialties were introduced in anthropology by Ralph Linton. See his *Study of Man*, pp.272–275.

[20]R. Linton, *The Cultural Background of Personality*, pp. 43–46.

ment that lumps together descriptions of modal behavior, in which each mode typifies or represents what is actually a variable range of behavior produced in the members of a society by a given stimulus.

The real culture It should be realized, then, that what we deal with in anthropology is the *culture construct* rather than the *real culture* itself. The culture construct presents the real culture as accurately as scientific methodology permits.

The real culture is what all the members of a society do and think in all their activities in their total round of living, except for truly idiosyncratic behavior. The real culture, however, is never sensed by anyone in its entirety. It can be only partially perceived as it is ordered and translated into understandable terms by the anthropologist, the philosopher, or the novelist. This is why such radically different accounts of the same society and culture can be formulated by different reporters. Reality is never known raw, for it is always processed through one's instruments of knowing. A scientific knowledge of culture can never give us the real culture; it professes only to bring the culture construct as close to the real as the most advanced and reliable methods of anthropological research make possible.

The ideal culture *Ideal culture* consists of a people's verbally expressed standards for behavior, which may or may not be translated into normal behavior. Ideal norms are generally selected and phrased in terms of group well-being, and they are often violated when individual self-interest induces another course of action or even when hidden, or covert, values stimulate contradictory behavior.

An outstanding example of the clash between public and private interests is found in Malinowski's account of clan incest among the Trobriand Islanders:

If you were to inquire into the matter among the Trobrianders, you would find that . . . the natives show horror at the idea of violating the rules of exogamy and that they believe that sores, disease and

even death might follow clan incest. . . . [But] from the point of view of the native libertine, *suvasova* (the breach of exogamy) is indeed a specially interesting and spicy form of erotic experience. Most of my informants would not only admit but actually did boast about having committed this offense or that of adultery (*kaylasi*); and I have many concrete, well-attested cases on record.[21]

The natives manage to get away with it, provided they keep it from becoming a publicly recognized scandal, because they have a system of magic which insures immunity from the threatened diseases if a person has the proper charms. One segment of the culture provides the means for making a mockery of the other. Preservation of the clan is a social interest loudly acclaimed. Intercourse with a clan cousin is an individually motivated sport that is a genuine custom.

A similar conflict of norms existed among the Comanches, who married their young girls to older men. Ideally, it is said, the couple loved and respected each other—especially the girl her husband. Actually, a considerable number of romance-seeking wives ran off with dashing young warriors. This was against the law—for the law is on the side of the husbands. The Comanche husband could, and as a matter of fact had to, sue for damages. He could, and often did, kill his wife or at least cut off her nose. This was his privilege by law. But an interesting feature is that a deserting wife and her absconder always ran off with a war party, so they were consistently aided and abetted in flouting the avowed norms by fellow Comanches. It was a group custom to break the law.[22] We need not discuss here the gaps that exist between our own ideals of democracy and our practices that negate them, even though they may be tender spots. It is because of such ever-present gaps between the thought and the deed, between the ideal and

[21] B. Malinowski, *Crime and Custom in Savage Society*, pp. 79, 84.
[22] A number of cases are presented and discussed in E. A. Hoebel, *The Political Organization and Law-ways of the Comanche Indians* (American Anthropological Association Memoir 54; Contributions from the Laboratory of Anthropology 4, 1940), pp. 49–66.

the action, that the realistic social scientist will no longer take a people's say-so as valid evidence of the real behavior norm.

Society and culture distinguished

A culture is always carried and made manifest by a group, for no one individual ever knows or exhibits all the traits of any culture. Yet culture and the society are not one. A society is a people, while a culture consists not of people but of ways of acting. We may say that one belongs to a society but not to a culture.

A society, however, is more than just an aggregation of people. A society is bound together by an awareness of mutual belonging, by a sense of social and economic interdependence, and by the sentiments of consciousness of kind and of common interests. It has *esprit de corps*. Familiarity with animal societies shows us that wild herds and flocks have these same qualities on an instinctual basis. What distinguishes the human society is that it has these qualities *plus* cultural direction and control of the behavior of its members. A society is a permanent population of people acting in accordance with its culture.

Culture and societal maintenance

Cultures develop as answers to the problems of individual and group living. One imperative of living is to keep alive, and all surviving biological forms are so built that a sufficient number of the species stays alive long enough to reproduce a succeeding generation. Living forms, therefore, have a built-in survival capacity relative to the environments they have experienced in the past. Cultures consist, on the one hand, of set ways of meeting the survival needs of individuals. Because of the prolonged dependency of the human infant, a stable societal and group relationship is a biological prerequisite to continuance of the species. Cultures provide individuals with ways in which to hunt and fish, make fire and tools, defend themselves, relate to other members

of their society, cure their illnesses, and assuage their fears and anxieties. Cultures provide the individual with "proved" ways to meet the needs for food, shelter, safety, reproduction (sex), relaxation, and psychic security.[23]

Societies, too, have their needs which must be met by each culture if the societies are to survive. These have been identified as the "functional prerequisites of societal survival and continuity." The anthropologist John W. Bennett and the sociologist Melvin M. Tumin identify six such prerequisites:

(1) To maintain the biologic functioning of the group members; (2) to reproduce new members for the group; (3) to socialize new members into functioning adults; (4) to produce and distribute goods and services necessary to life; (5) to maintain order within the group, and between itself and outsiders; and (6) to define the "meaning of life" and maintain the motivation to survive and engage in the activities necessary for survival.[24]

Every cultural system therefore includes established ways of providing food, shelter, and health and of organizing sex relations, enculturation of individuals, the economy, technology, trade, government and law, war and defense, and a meaningful world view. (Part IV of this book is organized in terms of these institutions.)

It is not enough that a people *know how* to do things, however. It is also imperative that they find satisfaction in doing what they are to do. Men must *want* to eat, drink, and mate. Motivation on this level is so elementally physiological that societies have no great difficulty in eliciting such engagement from their members. The rewards of reproduction and enculturation of children are much less direct, however, and require adequate cultural provision. Not to work is easier than to work. To work in order to procure enough food is an automatic animal response to food deprivation. But if people are to be induced to work to satisfy secondary and derived wants in terms of self-gratification and social duty, there must be

[23] The psychological aspects of culture are discussed in Chap. 4.
[24] J. W. Bennett and M. M. Tumin, *Social Life*, pp. 45–59.

very special cultural rewards. Each society must learn how to provide the rewards that keep its workers working.

Cultures vary in the quality of the institutional devices they provide for societal survival. Traits that are ineffective or less effective in meeting the demands of the functional prerequisites reduce the efficiency and survival capacity of the society. Although cultural relativity teaches us that each custom or usage is valid in terms of its own cultural context and therefore should not be judged morally good or bad, the fact remains that one type of trait or another may be more or less effective in serving societal ends. Societies that invent and do not control lethal customs are doomed. Thus, if the notion that sex is evil and incompatible with the pure life were spread to all the members of a society, resulting in the practice of enjoined celibacy, that society would soon be extinguished because the secondary prerequisite, that of reproduction of new members for the group, would not have been met. Today, the great danger which threatens us all is the development through technology of the potentially lethal trait of uncontrolled use of atomic energy in war.

Cultures are man's means of improved survival, but cultures are limited by biological and social imperatives. They need not be implicitly successful.

Finally, the most human of all the functions of culture is to define the meaning of life and to maintain the motivation to keep going. The humanities are called "the humanities" because they search for the humane in man's work—that which provides the psychological commitment to life and society on the part of the animal being who has reached the state of development wherein he can demand to know: "What is it all about?"

Fig. 2-5   The Shakers. An American religious society that failed to survive because it developed a culturally "lethal" trait. Shaker doctrine suppressed sexual reproduction, and the society failed to reproduce its membership. (From the original in the Shaker Museum, Old Chatham, New York.)

SUMMARY

A culture is not a thing, nor is it a precise entity. Nevertheless, it is conceived of as having an existence and as being distinctive. It is expressed in individual behavior and exists only in the actions of people. Yet it transcends the individual, for the culture according to which the individual lives existed before his birth and continues its existence after his death. It consists not only of all the learned behavior manifested by the members of a society but also of patterns *for* the behavior of members of a society. Language and symbolism are major attributes of all cultures.

Anthropology demonstrates the vast range of behavior of which human beings have proved themselves capable. Yet no society could exist if its members were to indulge in all these behaviors. Some are directly contradictory to others and consequently are incompatible. Aside from this, sheer diversity of possible actions would make behavior so unpredictable that social conditions would be chaotic. To organize people's activities, the establishment of major lines of standardized behavior is a social imperative. Thus cultures are selecting and limiting.

Integration, the establishment of internal consistency in norms, is also an essential characteristic of cultures. Integration is achieved with reference to certain basic propositions or postulates about the nature of things and acts and about their goodness or badness.

The formulation of a culture by the anthropologist is a *construct,* an abstraction from the *real culture,* which itself can be perceived only partially. The *ideal culture* is a people's formulation of the standards of behavior it believes should prevail.

The components of culture are *culture traits, culture complexes,* and *institutions.* They are also identified as *universals, alternatives, specialties,* and *idiosyncrasies.* The elements and complexes of a culture are functional in that each part tends to be related to the others in ways which contribute to the operation of the whole culture. The differing ways in which variant culture traits are related to one another lend to each culture its unique overall quality, or configuration. It is through culture that each society develops a way of life which enables it to wrest sustenance and shelter from the physical world and to manage the relations of human beings to one another. Differences in basic postulates and in norms of conduct from one culture to another give rise to the anthropological concept of *cultural relativism,* which states that customs are to be recognized as valid in terms of the premises underlying the cultures of which they are a part.

"Culture," Kroeber and Kluckhohn concluded, "is a product; is historical; is selective; is learned; is based upon symbols; and is an abstraction from behavior and the products of behavior."[25]

SELECTED READINGS

Benedict, R. F.: *Patterns of Culture* (1937), Chaps. 1, 2, and 3, entitled "The Science of Custom," "The Diversity of Cultures," and "The Integration of Culture." An excellently written, classic treatment of culture and its configurations.

Kluckhohn, C., and W. H. Kelley: "The Concept of Culture," in R. Linton (ed.), *The Science of Man in the World Crisis* (1945), pp.78–102. An imaginary discourse between three anthropologists on the meaning of "culture."

Kroeber, A. L., and C. Kluckhohn: "Culture: A Critical Review of Concepts and Definitions" (*Papers of the Peabody Museum of American Archaeology and Ethnology, Harvard University,* Vol. 47, 1952). An encyclopedic survey and analysis of the concept of culture. Possibly not of much interest to the beginner, but a very useful guide nonetheless. Now available in a paperback edition (1964).

Spuhler, J. N.: *The Evolution of Man's Capacity for Culture* (1959). A symposium discussing factors relating to the development of the capacity to create and maintain culture.

White, L. A.: "The Symbol: The Origin and Basis of Human Behavior" (*Etc.: A Review of General Semantics,* Vol. 1, 1944), pp. 229–237. A stimulating analysis of the nature and significance of the process of symbolizing.

[25] A. L. Kroeber and C. Kluckhohn, "Culture: A Critical Review of Concepts and Definitions" (*Papers of the Peabody Museum of American Archaeology and Ethnology, Harvard University,* Vol. 47, 1952), p. 157.

Culture and language

chapter 3

Without language, culture among men would be wholly impossible. All sentient animals communicate, and some, like the bees and porpoises, apparently can do so extremely well. What is not clear among animals other than man is the extent to which their patterns of communication are learned. The human being learns his language just as he learns his culture; man is not born with a language. Thus language is "a distinctly human system of behavior based on oral symbols" which is "used to describe, classify, and catalogue experiences, concepts, and objects."[1] Language, therefore, is a special system of communication that is specifically oral and symbolic. And it is learned.

Cues and communication

Many ways of communicating exist that do not utilize language. Cries of warning and aggression, of contentment and affection, are forms of communication not limited to men. Or, on the human level, the dirty look, which may convey worlds of meaning, does not involve language. Gestures, too, are forms of communication, although these seem always involved with culturally defined habits. The nod of the head means "yes" to the American, but a single nod in the Middle East is a clear "no". Plainly, there are many ways of conveying messages of which language is but the major one for human beings.

[1] R. F. Spencer, "Language," in J. Gould and W. L. Kolb (eds.), *Dictionary of the Social Sciences*, p. 377.

All social behavior depends on the understanding of cues: events or things that have a conventional meaning. The responder who "reads" a cue is in a position to act in a predictable manner within a given situation. The understanding of cues is absolutely essential to effective participation in any social setting, be it animal or human. In order to have the inside view of a culture, one must know its cues like a native.[2] Language cues are spoken cues. They are able to rise to high levels of complexity—far beyond anything achievable in animal communication—because of man's capacity to generalize and abstract. It is interesting to note that man has no organs which have evolved especially to produce speech. Most mammals can make sounds and they have tongues, lips, and teeth. But only men have these body parts so combined as to produce the sounds of language. Apes, which are like men in their general facial and mouth structure, are capable of producing all the sounds that men make. Yet man's closest relatives have not developed patterns of speech. Rather than any special adaptiveness to speech as such, the human being possesses a brain which makes speech possible.

Culture and language, both learned, are the distinctive attributes of man. All men live in culture, but the culture of a modern Englishman is not the same as the culture of a Zulu. Similarly, all men have language, but English is not the same as Zulu, Chinese, or Eskimo. As cultures vary, so also do languages.

But language and culture do not necessarily go hand in hand. There are peoples who speak mutually unintelligible languages who share in the same cultural traditions. In the American Southwest, for example, the towndwelling Pueblo Indians, basically much alike in culture, speak languages related to four quite separate groupings. Unless a man from Zuñi learns Hopi, he really cannot communicate with a Hopi. Or, on the other side, peoples with very different cultures may be able to communicate through language across the barriers of cultural difference. Again, in the native American Southwest, the populous Navaho can converse quite readily with their Apache neighbors, even though the two have essentially different cultures. What is still more interesting is that both Navaho and Apache can make themselves understood in interior Alaska, thousands of miles away. The Athabascan speech family, to which both the Navaho-Apache and the interior Alaskan Indians belong, has apparently been spread fairly recently so that some degree of mutual intelligibility remains. Clearly, too, the cultures of the Southwestern desert dwellers differ greatly from those of the peoples of the sub-Arctic coniferous forest.

But language and culture may relate in special and subtle ways. The reason a people speaks the language it does depends to some degree on the accidents of history, on such factors as contact, migration, conquest, or isolation. As distinctly human phenomena, language and culture parallel each other in the ways they operate. It does not follow from a certain type of culture that a people will speak a certain language. Still the factors of growth and of structure which apply to culture have relevance to language as well, and the parallel between language and culture can be seen in their respective processes.

The origins of language

Tangible evidence justifies some educated guesses on the origins of culture, but we can find no artifacts that suggest when or how language might have come into being. Does the making of fire or a stone axe require language? Not necessarily, obviously, since society and social behavior can and do exist without language. But the development of traditions over time implies that some sophisticated means of communication beyond mere imitation or emotive expression proved necessary. Fashionable scholarship around the turn of this century devoted considerable time to speculation about the origins of language. Then

---

[2] This fact is demonstrated in a fascinating way in a popular book by E. T. Hall. He makes a point when he calls his book *The Silent Language*, but confuses the issue by so doing.

the question was abandoned as a fruitless pursuit, only to return at the present time as a realization of the ecological, social, and physiological preconditions of language has grown.[3] Most important, perhaps, is the precondition of human society, the fact of the long period of dependence of human young, as well as man's tendency to live together in groups.

But did the first hominids or prehominids actually speak? As the little Australopithecines (see Chapter 9) sat about cracking bones for marrow, did they share their thoughts orally? Who can say? There is even debate as to whether on not physiological evidence, taken from the impressions of brain cases of fossil men and suggestive of the development of speech centers, is reliable. But even if early man did at some point in time develop speech, there are still the problems of whether or not this was a single invention and where it may have taken place. It would probably be correct to infer that preconditions of human behavior which evoked language appeared variously where clusters of early human populations arose.

Richness of vocabularies It was once quite reasonable to assume that one existing language might be more archaic or more primitive than another. Yet this does not seem to be the case. Every language represents a finished product, a perfect system in the sense that each tongue is wholly adequate to all human situations. The ideas that a language can express are in some measure dependent on the interests and preoccupations of the society which develops it. It would be surprising to hear a discussion of logical positivism or cultural anthropology in Eskimo, but this does not mean that ideas of this kind cannot be expressed in Eskimo. English, similarly, must resort to circumlocutions to convey with exactness the subtleties of which Eskimo is eminently capable. Neither of these languages, nor any of the other 6,000 languages of the world, can thus be regarded as more archaic or primitive than another.

[3]See, for example, C. F. Hockett and R. Ascher, "The Human Revolution" (*Current Anthropology*, Vol. 5, No. 3, 1964), pp. 135–168.

It has sometimes been contended that a language has evolved further than others if it possesses a larger vocabulary. But one of the knottiest problems confronting the science of linguistics is to define the "word." Even in English, is "the" a word? Is "the man" one word or two? The verb "do" might be regarded as a word, but what of "does" and "did"? The latter case, to be sure, involves changing forms of the same element, but the very fact that the form changes raises some further questions about language and its nature. The speaker of English uses only a small fraction of the dictionary, or more properly, of the language lexicon. Many unwritten languages are far more elaborate in terms of the number of words employed by a speaker in normal converse. By such a standard, English might be regarded as more primitive. If Arabic has over 1,000 words for "sword," something cultural and stylistic is implied; the culture stresses poetry, and thus it is no surprise to discover an amazing array of synonyms and figures of speech.

Anthropologists are fond of pointing out that Eskimos have a large numer of words for "snow," each denoting snow of a particular state of being, such as softly-falling-snow, dry-wind-driven-snow, drifting-snow, powder-snow, wet-packed-snow, dry-packed-snow-suitable-for-cutting-into-blocks (for iglu building), ice-crust-surface-snow, and so on. It is perfectly true that we can linguistically express different conditions of snow through the use of modifiers, but the point is that Eskimos, whose very survival depends upon snow conditions, do not view snow as "crystallized water vapor" or "that beautiful white fluffy stuff that falls from the sky on some cold days," but rather as a series of *different* substances.

The American city dweller does recognize snow, sleet, and slush as three distinctly different linguistic categories for crystallized water in different states of being—because this much, and no more, is culturally significant to his comfort and well-being. Since the birth of wide popular enthusiasm for skiing in the United States, however, a skier's vocabulary for snow, similar in its distinctions to that of the Eskimo, has been borrowed from the Austrian Tyrol because the state of snow is important to ski culture. Hence we hear the terms *Pappschnee* (wet, heavy snow), *Kornschnee* (barley snow that has melted under spring sunshine and frozen at night), *Pulverschnee* (powder snow), *Fernschnee* (broad expanse of breakable crust), and so forth.

In our own equestrian subculture of cowboys a comparable example exists. To most Eastern city dwellers a horse is a horse. Not so to the cowpoke. It is a mare, stallion, or gelding in denotation of its sex; a grey, sorrel, piebald, strawberry roan, palomino, or white face, in denotation of its color.

The basic principle illustrated by these examples is that every language is adequate to express the needs of its culture. As the culture expands, the language expands. If the belief or knowledge system embodied in the culture requires the expression of abstract ideas, the language will provide the means of getting those ideas across, regardless of what syntax is involved. If a culture stresses rhetorical style, oratory, folktale, or poetry, these cultural interests will find their linguistic expression. No existing language is so primary as to contain half-formulated grunted thoughts or so limited in expressions as to suggest that it exemplifies the dawn of human speech. English, it is true, like other European languages, accompanies a culture in which there is great diversity of occupation and activity. Since each specialty has its specialized vocabulary, no one person can command the whole lexicon of the language. But every culture has its specialties, occupational or otherwise. If anyone still has the notion, which was so common in the nineteenth century, that primitive languages are childlike and inherently incapable of expressing complex thoughts and ideas, this error should be nailed and nailed hard. It is as false as the canard that was launched by the famous Army Captain John G. Bourke, that the language of the Apache Indians is so deficient in vocabulary that its speakers have to use gestures and signs to get their meaning across and con-

sequently they cannot converse at night unless they are around a campfire.

Writing Some languages are written, some are not. Indeed, the term "primitive" is usually held to be synonymous with "nonliterate." But when the anthropological linguist gives his attention to the components of a language, he is concerned only with the oral system, or more accurately, with the oral—aural, the spoken and the heard. Writing is not a part of language in any vital sense. English could be written equally well with Chinese characters. As it happens, it uses a Latin alphabet. Systems of writing are inventions going back to relatively recent times, to the Bronze and Iron Ages. Language had been in existence long before. Nor should we think that because a language lacks writing it is slovenly or debased. On the contrary, it is more frequently the unwritten language which preserves oral tradition with fidelity, which stresses correctness and precision of speech. Current usage in written as against spoken English is an exception.

The structure of language

Even if queries on the origins of language must remain only vaguely answerable, one can say a good deal about the nature of language structure. As we have said, any language is a finished system. It is a configuration, a whole equal to more than the sum of its parts. Each language emerges as a concise and distinct phenomenon, and each possesses definite boundaries. True, a language may have dialects, forms which are local and reflect variations in sound and word usage patterns. English, however, is still English, whether spoken by Midwestern Americans, or those of the Deep South, by the Englishman from Oxford or the Cockney cabdriver in London. The structure of the total language remains consistent. Each language, whatever the variations it permits within itself, has its definite boundaries; once these are crossed, a new language has come into being. English and German, for example, are closely related because they possess a near common ancestor and have, as a result, not only many words in common but distinctive elements of grammatical structure as well. Yet even though they do relate historically, English and German are wholly separate, so much so that only the trained linguist can find the basic similarities between them. French, Spanish, and Italian are very close to each other, with common sets of basic grammatical categories and vocabularies derived from the parent Latin, but each stands as a quite separate system of oral symbols, any one of which is unintelligible to the native speaker of another.

A single language thus stands apart as a discrete human phenomenon. The linguist, turning to the various forms of human speech, asks much the same questions of his data as does the anthropologist approaching cultures. A culture, too, is a whole and one may legitimately look for its precise boundaries. Just as the linguist may look for local patterns of dialect, so also the anthropologist, in his quest for understanding the regularities, the "grammar" of a culture, may concern himself with localized patterns of variation. It is worth stressing, in regard both to culture and to language, that the concern is with the predictable, with the elicitation of pattern. Language, in fact, appears to offer a more convincing example of this than does culture for the reason that language, by its very nature, cannot admit so many variables. One can readily supply—or predict—the missing words in such a sentence as *John and Mary are___to the movies.* Here, whether one chooses the verbs *go, walk, drive, come* or another among the host of other choices, one can predict from the nature of the sentence that the verb will contain an *ing* ending. The precise structure of each language permits variations, but they differ according to the linguistic system.

In thinking about language, as in thinking about culture, one may ask initially how the system works. In doing so, we place language at an end point in time with no concern for the origin of the finished product or for its relationships. The child learns the language of his group as it is spoken by those around him. The structure of English today is different from what it was in Chaucer's time, but the speaker

of English need not know the history of the language. *Hurricane* and *cigar* are good English words; as such, they have a meaning and function in the language and one need not be aware that they derive from an American Indian language spoken in the West Indies. To see language (or culture) as a temporal end product and to ask how the system operates at a given time is to look at structure, at the parts which interrelate to make up the whole. This approach is structural, or *synchronic.* In synchronic studies, languages are analyzed as each exists at a given moment in history.

The historical, or *diachronic,* approach poses a very different kind of question. Rather than "How does it work?" we ask "How did it get that way?" If the history of English as a language is the issue, then clearly, Chaucer's English, Shakespeare's English, as well as the earliest discernible forms of English must be taken into account. Further, one wishes to see the parts of English which relate to the Germanic ancestor, to Latin, to Norman French, or to the great speech family of Indo-European, of which English, German, French, Latin, Russian, and the languages of modern India are also descendants.

Both approaches, the synchronic and the diachronic, have relevance for the understanding of language processes. The historical relationships of language may provide a clue to cultural relations. Similarly, to comprehend a language as it is spoken—not only to speak and understand it but also to see it as a structured entity—may provide some leads to a greater awareness of how cultures, too, are organized.

Synchronic, or structural, linguistics Any language contains a distinctive series of patterns. Because language is oral and aural, the initial approach to a language is through its sound system by means of phonology (Gr. *phono,* sound + logy).

Phonology Every language has its own distinctive, idiosyncratic, and characteristic total series of sounds. A single sound in one language, or even a series of them, can appear in another. Taken as a total system, however, the sounds of a language offer a remarkable uniqueness. Linguistic science employs the term *phoneme* (Gr. *phonema*, a sound) to refer to these characteristic sound units in a given language. Some languages, such as Hawaiian, possess only a few basic sounds; others, such as Kwakiutl, may have considerably more. Rarely are there more than 45 to 50 basic sounds in any language, although some languages have considerably fewer.

A phoneme is thus the smallest sound unit of a language. But the sound alone, in isolation, is only a starting point. In the human speech mechanism, sounds, usually conventionally divided into vowels and consonants, not only appear in combination with each other, but in a given language, a sound is articulated or pronounced in a way peculiar to that language. The sound usually designated /t/ is pronounced by most speakers of English by placing the tip of the tongue on the gum just back of the front teeth (postdental). The sound is *stopped,* meaning that /t/, unlike /s/, cannot be continued, even though /s/ is pronounced in much the same position as /t/ in English. There are thus classes of sounds—those that are stopped, continued, nasalized, or trilled, along with possible combinations of these—as well as points of articulation—the use of the tongue, lips, teeth, vibration and resonance, and the various hard and soft parts of the oral chamber—to produce particular types of sounds. /t/ in English is not the same as /t/ in some other languages. In Tagalog, a Philippine language, for example, /t/ is pronounced with the tongue directly against the teeth. As between English and Tagalog this makes little immediate difference. But it could happen, and often does, that a language differentiates between a postdental and a dental /t/, /s/, or /n/, and the result can be most confusing, at least to an English speaker. Because he is used to a single postdental /t/, the English-speaker actually fails to hear the difference in the points of articulation. His own phonemes have not made him receptive

to two, three, or four, different locations of /t/.

Sounds in a language also follow a pattern of arrangement. English /sk/ is wholly compatible with the sound structure of the language. But the same sound is impossible to pronounce in Spanish, where an initial vowel must enter before /s/ followed by any consonant, as Spanish *escuela* (eskwela), off the same root as English *school* (sku:l). Bantu languages in Africa build many words beginning with /ng/ (for instance, *Ngbatu*). Not a single word in English starts so; it is against our rule which requires that /ng/ may be used only at the end of a phonemic series. Similarly, no language incorporates all the phonemes that are in use among all the tongues of mankind. Strongly fixed motor habits in forming our own speech make it extremely difficult to pronounce a foreign language like a native when it involves different habits. The difference between our /z/ and /th/ is only a matter of a few millimeters in the placement of the tongue. In /z/, the tip of the tongue rests against the lower edge of the gums of the upper dental arch. In /th/, it is between the teeth themselves. But how many English-speaking Frenchmen and Germans never succeed in mastering that little shift!

It should be clear that even so apparently simple a system as the sounds of language is fraught with difficulties. True, the number of sounds a human being can make are limited, and a person learns to follow the linguistic patterns of his group. But when secondary phonemes such as stress, or accent, tone, or pitch[4], length of vowel, presence or absence of resonance, throating, nasalizing, and many other possible factors are added to the basic patterns, we can readily see that no language is a simple system.

The sounds of a language, being adequate for that language, are thus relative to that particular language as a system. Languages are culturally determined systems not only in their sounds but in the ways in which they put these basic elements together in structured order.

[4]Consider, for example, how the voice rises and falls in Chinese, in many African and American Indian languages, or even in English.

Morphology and syntax It might be useful to compare a language to an organism. (Indeed, some anthropologists have treated culture in this way, although others are impatient with the analogy.) Suppose one considers a domestic cat. It is a mammal, of course, but it is also a specialized predator. It has, in addition to the features which permit assigning it to the class Mammalia, pointed ears, a set of rending and tearing teeth, a long tail used for balance, padded paws with retractable claws, and it is capable of great speed. It makes characteristic sounds. In general, the familiar cat is a good example of adaptation in the animal world, one well equipped with the tools to meet its needs for survival.

Proceeding to the analogy, we may say that the cat is a whole animal, different from all other animals which are specialized in their own ways. The biological morphology, or structure, of the cat, the parts making up the whole animal, are meaningless outside the context of the animal in its entirety. Dogs and cats have some similarities—both are carnivores, for example—but there is a world of difference between them. A language is also a whole system. It too has a structure, or morphology. To take the analogy further, the parts of language, like those of the cat, may be assembled in a particular way and reflect a special kind of adaptation. Some languages, but by no means all languages, build their meaningful concepts out of verbs, forming names for things and concepts, i.e., nouns, from stems that reflect action. Arabic and Hebrew are good examples of such a process. Others, such as many of the European languages, appear to stress things rather than actions. In English, any verb may be made into a noun. In fact, the tendency in English is to teach children the names of things first—"mouth," "head," "kitty," "doggie," and so on—and to introduce the child to verbs only later. Conversely, in Navaho, the child first becomes familiar with actions—"sitting," "running," "moving," and so forth. In Chinese, we can say that there are no nouns or verbs. Whether the concept expressed refers to a thing or an action (a noun or a verb) depends on its relations to other conceptual units expressed in an utterance. Just as animals differ in their morphology, so language structures vary in the ways that their component parts are put together. Just as a relative difference exists between dogs and cats, so relative differences exist among languages.

MORPHEMES The basic element in any language is the phoneme, but phonemic units are put together in various ways to form the elements of *structure,* or the *morphology.* If phonemes are basic units of sound, *morphemes* (Gr. *morphe,* form) are basic units of structure. The synchronic linguist, interested in determining the facts of the structure of a language, reduces the language first to its bedrock of sounds. He then notes that sound arrangements follow a pattern, that a clustering of certain kinds of discernible elements occurs. These may be actual words, although again, the problem of what constitutes a word in a given language poses some difficulties. More often, these clusters are parts that form units which are set off by the secondary phonemic element of *juncture.* Junctures are simply the breaks between words. The sentence *The man is eating* suggests these junctures. Almost no break occurs between /the/ and /man/, indicating that when the definite article is used in English, it is almost a prefix, that is, something bound to the element following. Between /man/ and /is/ and between /is/ and /eating/ there is a slight rest, a tiny hesitation that sets each element off. In French, for instance, the junctures are less apparent; other languages stress them more. The point here is that any language may have free morphemes (in this instance they equal words) or bound morphemes, that is, those which are in some way modified.

To illustrate what a morpheme is, let us look closer at the sentence just given—*The man is eating.* /man/ is a primary morpheme with the bound /the/; /is/ refers to the state occupied by some singular person or object; /eating/ consists of two morphemes—the root form /eat/ and a suffixed bound form /-ing/ which in English refers to an action going on, continuing, proceeding. Again, a sentence such as *Birds fly* consists of several morphemes. /bird/ is made plural by a bound suffixed /z/.[5] /fly/ is a single morpheme, but since it is preceded by the plural noun /birds/ it is not the same as /fly/ in /to fly/; a third person plural present tense is understood. The linguist can treat this as a "zero" morpheme, one in which there is no inflection but in which a distinct environment, in this instance, agreement between noun and verb, is held to prevail.

Is such a way of looking at language really any different from the way in which many of us have studied and learned languages—the method of the paradigm, where one encounters such patterns as *I hit, you hit, he hits?* Indeed it is, since by listing and categorizing the morphemes of a language, one obtains a total perspective on the potential range of variations in the whole system. Because languages differ so markedly from each other in the ways they put their concepts together, it is necessary to "get the feel" of the system by means of the morphology. It is here that the understanding of language cues begins. Since languages do differ, it is also necessary to obtain some sense of the meaning of the morphemes and the contexts in which they are used. Translation from one language to another is always difficult. Can one get all of the nuances, can one understand all that is conveyed in the oral-aural situation in a language that is not one's own? Morphemic analysis, which takes account of the language in its structural totality, offers a lead.

So far, little has been said about meaning in language. A morpheme, however, is a meaningful unit, not only in the sense that it may be a word with the psychological and emotive reactions that words evoke, but because it appears in environments with other morphemes to create meaningful forms.

A few examples chosen from selected languages may illustrate the point.

To an English speaker, the sentence *When I was going to the store, I saw a dog* seems infinitely logical and simple. In Turkish, a Ural-Altaic language that originated in Central Asia, the same thought possesses a rather different structuring, using morphemes solely Turkish and not in any way suggestive of English. The Turkish sentence is: *Magasine gittiğim zaman bir köpek gördüm.*

English uses eleven word units, with several more morphemes, while Turkish employs only five. The Turkish morphemes are: /magasin/ which means "store," with a suffixed /e/ "place to which action is directed"; /gittigim/ consists of a root morpheme /git/ "go," with a suffixed /*d(t)ik/ which is marked with an asterisk because it can never appear without some pronoun modification, but which refers to a continuous action in the past, and /-im/ referring to action by a first person "I," "my"; /zaman/ "time"; /bir/ "one," an indefinite single something; /köpek/ "dog," an indefinite noun (if the noun were definite, i.e., "the dog," the Turkish would be köpeği/, the /-i/ morpheme being used only where there is a definite direct object of a verb); /gördüm/ from a root morpheme /gör/ "see," plus /d(t)/ indicator of any part action, plus /-um/ action by a first person, again "I", "my."

In this case, what is the literal meaning of the Turkish sentence? One might render it into English, although meaninglessly: *To* (definite) *store my wenting time* (indefinite) *dog I saw.* Such a contrived rendition is scarcely necessary, since the Turkish sentence has much the same meaning as the English. We are simply attempting to convey the difference in the way in which concepts are put together.

SYNTAX   A language, however, is much more than a series of morphemes clustered haphazardly. Generally, morphemes, bound or free, follow some kind of ordered pattern. The pattern may be quite strict or fairly free. *Syntax* refers to *the arrangement of elements in phrases and sentences.*

---

[5] This also illustrates the problem of the change of a sound because of morphological factors. The rule in English is that if a noun ends in a vowel or a voiced consonant, i.e., a consonant which is accompanied with resonance, the suffixed /-s/ becomes itself voiced, i.e., /z/. A word such as *bee* (bij:) takes its plural as (bijz); *dog* /dawg/ becomes /dawgz/; but *cat* /kaet/ becomes /kaets/. This is true of any suffixed /-s/ in English, however variable the function of /-s/ may be. Its functions include: inflection of the third person singular verb, present tense; possession; and designation of number, i.e., the plural.

English, which has shed many of its inflections, or morphemic modifications, depends on a fairly rigid syntax. In the sentence *John and Mary to the movies went,* the hearer is at once aware of something wrong. But *John went the movies to Mary and* violates the rules of all English syntax and meaning.

When a language is more dependent on morphology, syntax may relax. In Latin, for example, the sentences *Canis ursum videt, Videt ursum canis, Videt canis ursum,* and so on through any other possible variations, all make good sense: *"The dog sees the bear."* The morphemic arrangement of /canis/ and /ursum/ make it completely clear that it is the dog which is doing the seeing and the bear which is being seen. Mandarin Chinese, and the Chinese languages generally, even more than English, have shed their morphology almost completely. For them, syntax has become a wholly necessary feature.

Languages thus vary tremendously in their structures, whether in sounds, in morphology, or in syntax. Some linguists have attempted to type languages according to the kind of morphology and syntax they possess, a process that is useful in showing the great potential range of human speech patterns. It also becomes eminently clear that one cannot read the structure of one's own language into another. What holds for English will not hold for even a closely related language.

Every language is bound by its own firm rules of grammar, and each speaker who wants to be understood must master the rules and abide by them. Language is a tyrant that does not permit much individual liberty, although there will always be great differences in individual skill in the use of a language.

One really intriguing point, however, is that although firm grammatical, that is, morphological and syntactic, rules control the use of language, the rules are not made by grammarians. They have been arrived at naïvely by generations of speakers who had no consciousness of what they were doing. Once certain elemental ways of shaping and combining morphemes were established, the mold for the future growth of the language was pretty well

set. Rules of grammar give consistency to the tongue; they integrate the use of vocal symbols. Yet, the tyranny of grammatical rules notwithstanding, no primitive man can state the rules of his grammar. He can only tell you that a certain thing must be said this way and not that way. It is only the sophisticated linguist who can analyze a language into expressly stated rules. A bright informant working with a field worker may discover some elemental rules for himself, however. This happened when I asked a Shoshone Indian how to say: *my house, his house, her house, our house, their house.* /gani/ is the morpheme for "house." In the informant's responses each word contained *ngani* preceded by a variety of personal pronoun prefixes. As I wrote down the words, a great light dawned upon him and he excitedly exclaimed, "Say! That /n/ in there must mean that something belongs to someone." On being assured that this was so (he had discovered the possessive infix), he marveled, "Well, what do you think of that? Here I've been talking Shoshone all my life and I never knew that /n/ in the middle of a word means it belongs to someone."

The rules of a language are unconsciously obeyed by its speakers. The normal way to learn any language is to become habituated to its unformulated rules through use of the language, not by learning the rules.

Semantics: the meaning of meaning The primary purpose of language is of course to communicate. Hence the question of meaning is always central. Semantics, the "meaning of meaning," is of interest on several different levels.

CROSS-CULTURAL COMMUNICATION One does not have to study a foreign language very long before he recognizes that certain concepts are untranslatable. The German adjective *gemütlich,* for example, is often translated as *comfortable.* But to the German speaker the ranges of meaning of *gemütlich* and of *comfortable* are quite different. A chair can be comfortable, but of itself it is never *gemütlich.* In English, I can be physically comfortable even though I am far from *gemütlich.* The German word (one actually related historically to the English *mood*) refers to a human state of mind, hence the comfort implied is purely a mental situation. The spirit of good fellowship, of lusty beer drinking, of joyous singing are also implied in the Bavarian *Gemütlichkeit* (with the noun-forming morpheme /-keit/ suffixed), all connotations which the English *comfort* can never suggest.

Between languages, meaning is constantly a problem. This is true not only on the level of words alone but in terms of the basic definitions that are resident in the structure of language. It has been contended that because Russian and English employ different built-in concepts of time—that is, time is differently expressed in the structure of the two languages—there is a basis for much misunderstanding on the international level. Whether or not this is so in this particular case, it is probable that the varying structures of languages do inhibit cross-cultural understanding. A case in point is provided by the Keresan-speaking Pueblo Indians of New Mexico. Suppose a missionary were to bring to these peoples his particular brand of religion. In the language, no idea can be expressed without containing the morphemes indicating whether the action described depends on experience undergone by the speaker or whether the speaker has his information from hearsay. If the missionary tells his listeners in Keresan that in the beginning God created heaven and earth, he cannot use the experienced mode—*he* was not there. His remarks can only imply, "So I've been told."

EMOTIONAL QUALITY IN MEANING   But what of meaning within a language? Every person, in any language, has his own *ideolect*, his particular style of speech, his favorite words and expressions, his particular set of images and thoughts which are evoked by words. Everyone can agree on the definition of "table"; what each hearer sees in his mind's eye may reflect a host of differing images, all of which, however, are acceptable tables. The field of psycholinguistics, which relates to the psychology of language, is as yet only in its infancy. Some

break-throughs have been made, to be sure, especially in the area of language learning. A speaker encodes an utterance, delivers it, and the hearer decodes it and responds. The linguistic system is internalized; the cues relate intimately to individual personality. It is clear from the experience of our own culture that some words are holy, some are obscene, some are proper for certain social occasions and improper for others. These distinctions indicate the continuing presence of the emotive quality of language. An expressed thought may be purely neutral, but it serves to relate the speaker to his cultural environment.

Meaning in a language poses some further problems. Just what does an utterance mean? The answer to this question depends in part on the social setting of the conversation, who is present, whether those present are men or women of superior or inferior statuses. The manner in which this problem is resolved depends on the demands of the cultural setting.

Finally, getting away from the emotive element in meaning, we should mention the purely academic issue of just what words do mean. Does one really express his primary thoughts with any exactness? Actually not, since the word is accompanied by a host of other culturally determined nonlinguistic cues. I do not have to say precisely what I think. Indeed, in our own and most cultures, care is necessary to avoid creating problems in social interaction. Some Americans prefer to say that a person has "passed away" rather than that he is "dead." And clearly, to say that he has "kicked the bucket" is in the most execrable taste. Meanings thus have social as well as psychological dimensions. Nowhere, perhaps, is the question of meaning so vital as in the specialized language of the law. Here exactness becomes imperative, a matter recognized not only by our own but by any society that has codified and verbalized its legal codes.

Culture and language

Several ways in which language and culture may interact have been suggested. We have said that every language is in itself a cultural phenomenon. Obviously, no one can speak instinctively. Language has absolutely nothing to do with biological inheritance; therefore, there is no inherent relationship between race and language. If, as is sometimes the case, a certain language is spoken only by the members of a given race, it is only because the racial population, having been isolated from other populations, developed its own mode of speech. Once the isolation breaks down, this need no longer be so. Eighteen million American Negroes speak English, but their ancestors of one and two centuries ago spoke only one or another of the African languages.

The fact that it is extremely difficult for English speakers to master some of the phonemes of other languages—ones that are used with ease by native speakers—does not mean that the native speakers have a natural proclivity to produce such sounds. It merely means, providing the adage is not taken too seriously, that "you can't teach old dogs new tricks." Once vocal habits are set, they become so firm that

to break them is quite a task. There is nothing in the physical structure of the members of any race, however, that makes certain populations genetically suited to the pronunciation of some phonemes and not others.

Therefore, if the question "What is the relation between race and language?" is asked, the answer is "None." On the other hand, if the question "What is the relation between culture and language?" is put, the answer is "A great deal." But in what ways?

Subgroup dialects (microlanguages) Most languages, although they are systems consistent within themselves, do have spoken variations that are used by different groups. Such groups may be localized, and in such instances the variety is recognized as a dialect or subdialect. Or such groups may be status groups within a society. Men employ certain speech usages that differ from those of women. In the same way, usages of adults differ from those of infants; those of professors from those of labor-

Fig. 3-1   A mother tongue can easily become a symbol of social and personal identity. Panjabi speakers demonstrate for a separate Indian state. (Marc Riboud, Magnum.)

ers; those of politicians from those of preachers. In Javanese, for example, socially inferior people address their superiors with one form of speech and are answered in another. Superiors use yet a third speech among themselves, while inferiors have still another.

The relation of language to cultural content

All languages are sufficiently expandable to make it possible for the members of any society to communicate the things they are interested in.

The fundamental ground work of language—the development of a clear-cut phonetic system, the specific association of speech elements with concepts, and the delicate provision for the formal expression of all manner of relations—all this meets us rigidly perfected and systematized in every language known to us. Many primitive languages have a formal richness, a latent luxuriance of expression, that eclipses anything known to the languages of modern civilization.[6]

The Sapir-Whorf hypothesis: language and thought habits

Every language is adequate to the needs of its culture insofar as the speakers of the language can communicate to each other the ideas and feelings that their culture makes it possible for them to have. But the very structure of a language subtly molds the way in which a people conceives of the nature of the world in which they find themselves. Philosophically, we know that man's idea systems are the screens through which he perceives reality. We saw in Chapter 2 how the basic postulates of each culture provide the assumptions about the general nature of things with which the members of each and every society view nature and themselves. Taken together, culture at large and language in particular grind the multiple lenses through which men view the world that surrounds them. Indeed, as Edward Sapir (1884–1939) was one of the first to perceive, in a real sense "language and our thought-grooves are inextricably interwoven, are, in a sense, one and the same."[7]

[6]E. Sapir, *Language*, p. 22.
[7]Sapir, *op. cit.*, p. 232.

We say we have mastered a language, but only in the present generation have we begun to perceive that the language we are born to speak in turn masters us to a considerable extent.

How does this identity of language and thought-grooves become manifest? Perhaps two illustrations will suffice.

English and Indo-European language speakers confront time as a divisible entity that falls "naturally" into a past, the present, and a future. Until Einstein pushed the special language of mathematics and physics into a new sphere that could not be described by any of these conventional Indo-European distinctions, time could not be thought of by any of us in any other terms.

Benjamin Lee Whorf, a chemical engineer and fire insurance executive, became concerned with the problem of how English words betray people into burning down buildings. He went on to demonstrate how the Hopi language, for one, creates an entirely different sense of time. But before we take a short look at Hopi time-sense, perhaps we should show how the English language can cause fire. One example from Whorf's argument will do:

In a wood distillation plant the metal stills were insulated with a composition prepared from limestone and called at the plant "spun limestone." . . . After a period of use, the fire below one of the stills spread to the "limestone," which to everyone's great surprise burned vigorously. Exposure to acetic acid fumes from the stills had converted part of the limestone (calcium carbonate) to calcium acetate. This, when heated in a fire decomposes, forming inflammable acetone. Behavior that tolerated fire close to the covering was induced by use of the name "limestone," which because it ends in "-stone" implies noncombustibility.[8]

Hopi syntax and conceptualization

In his study of the Hopi language, Whorf's analysis shows that Hopi verbs have no tense—no past, present, or future. There are no beads of time on the string of infinity, only validity forms, aspects, and clause-linkage forms. *Validity forms* assert the degree of authenticity of a statement

[8]B. L. Whorf, *Language, Thought, and Reality*, pp. 135–136.

(see also the Keresan example on page 42). In Hopi verbs there are three such degrees: that which denotes that the speaker *reports* a completed or an on-going event or that he *expects* an event will take place or that from his experience he *knows* the event is a regular thing. Aspect forms of Hopi verbs report the relative length of time an event lasts; clause-linkage forms relate two or more verbs to each other in terms of "later to earlier and of simultaneity" (whether they are happening together or before or after each other).

What is meant by *validity forms?* In a situation in which one of us sees a person run, we say, "He is running," a sentence in which the temporal *is* is important to our way of thinking (only an infant or a moron would say, "He running"). The Hopi, for his part, says, "wari," which means "running." Next—when we have just seen a person run, we say, "He ran." The Hopi says, "wari," which means "running." There is no difference between "wari" as running now and running that is just recently over. "Wari" is *a statement of fact about running.* That is all. But now comes a difference. If we saw a person run yesterday, we still would say, "He ran." The Hopi says, "era wari," or "remembered running." If the running is to take place in the future, we say, "He will run," thus putting it in another time category. Not so the Hopi. He still uses his timeless "wari," adding to it the suffix *kni,* to denote expectancy: "warikni," or "running expected." Finally, our own time grammar breaks down egregiously when we are confronted with the problem of timeless running, when we have to give expression to past, present, and future running all in one breath. We fall back on and do violence to our present tense by saying, "He runs," when reporting the activity of a track star, who may in fact be snoring in his bunk at the moment the statement is made. To cover this exigency the Hopi, because he has no tense commitments, says with much greater accuracy, "warikngue," or "running regularly occurs."

The Hopi language is also constructed without masculine and feminine genders; every-

thing is neuter. A Hopi therefore has no linguistic compulsion to dichotomize things like ships ("She's a beautiful tub") into masculine or feminine images. Here, again, appraisal of the real world is differently affected, largely because of mental habits formed by the nature of grammatical structure.

Shawnee syntax and conceptualization One more example of this principle makes reference to Shawnee, an Indian language spoken in the southeast woodland area of the United States.

Whorf confronts us with two English sentences:

1. I push his head back.
2. I drop it in the water and it floats.

The acts performed according to these two statements are quite unlike. In (1), the physical act is presented as the exertion of a force: subject → force → object. In (2), the emphasis is on an attribute of the object (it floats).

Shawnee language is so structured that in describing these same two events the Shawnee Indian sees and thinks of them in terms of similarity. How? To tell what happens in the first situation he says:

1. *ni*	*kwaškwi*	*tepē*	*n*	*a*
I	push back	on the head	by action of the hand	cause to a person

To tell what happens in the second situation, the Shawnee says:

2. *ni*	*kwašk*	*ho*	*to*
I	push back	at the surface of water	cause to an inanimate thing

Literally translated, (1) means, "I cause the head of a human being to be pushed back by action of my hand." Similarly translated, (2) means, "I cause an inanimate thing to be pushed back at the surface of water." Pushing against, a reverse force, is what Shawnee grammar induces the Shawnee speaker to see in *both* situations; not pushing and floating as separate phenomena. The Shawnee grammatical approach to what takes place is closer to the reality of the situation, as any student who learned Archimedes' principle in high-school physics knows.

In other words, it is not always that "sentences are unlike because they tell about unlike facts" (although, of course, in some situations other than those just mentioned, they may be unlike in fact). It may be that: "Facts are unlike to speakers whose language background provides for unlike formulation of them."[9]

Limitations of the Sapir-Whorf hypothesis   The Sapir-Whorf hypothesis, as it has been demonstrated by these Hopi and Shawnee examples, is very suggestive and exciting. But like every body of theory, this point of view has its adherents and its opponents. Whorf's ideas have actually been somewhat misunderstood. He does not say that because of the particular slant of the language the associated cultural form is predictable. His contribution lies rather in calling attention to the kinds of reality which a given group creates for itself. In some degree, this is a linguistic feature. Decisions are made because of the traps which language itself sets, as Whorf's concern with the imputed qualities that language imparts to substances that may be flammable or inflammable bears witness. People act according to the "realities" that their language provides.

It might be argued that Whorf is not really dealing with language at all. Rather, he is relating behavior to factors of perception and cognition, areas which the psychologists call their own. The Whorfian hypothesis, suggestive though it may be, is extremely difficult to prove. The coloring of behavior through language may indeed be indirect; what constitutes reality in a human situation does vary, and it can possibly be a function of linguistic system. Although one can readily see that Hopi and Shawnee, that any language, in fact, has its own peculiar ways of putting concepts together, we must recall that there are other groups

[9]*Ibid.*, p. 235.

which share the Hopi world, for example, whose linguistic structures are radically different.

It is said of Chinese that it lacks an orientation to time. In general, this is so, since Chinese does not have the same built-in tense systems that European languages have. Yet does this mean that the Chinese are indifferent to temporal sequences? Hardly. The language can and does express them. Chinese culture is characterized by a strong sense of rapport with nature; human actions are considered parts of a natural law. The culture sees itself as static; in its long past, China always stresses the stability of its society. The Chinese were eminent historians. Yet their history is different from that of European historical scholarship. The European stresses change and cataclysm; he is interested in "decline and fall," in periodic change. The Chinese historian, on the other hand, sees history as a smooth continuum, one in which cataclysm never intrudes. Clearly, decline and renaissance characterized Chinese history just as much as it did European history. Whether or not the unwillingness of the Chinese to see history in such terms is a function of their language must remain an open question.

The recent interest in the problems of cognition shown by anthropologists and psychologists may permit some greater validation of the Whorfian hypothesis. The differences among linguistic structures are striking. If there *is* an interaction between behavior in culture and behavior in language, as there doubtless is, many unsolved problems remain.

The growth and differentiation of languages

The origins of languages are lost in the distant past. The spoken word does not turn to stone—it leaves no remains for the archaeologist to unearth from an Eolithic or a Paleolithic site. Writing comes into being only after eons of language building have lapsed into the past. Words finally transcribed on stone or clay tablet, on papyrus, skin, or paper are manifestations of languages already millennia old.

Because all the people we can study have a developed language, there is no way to reconstruct the multiplex processes by which a people hit upon agreement as to the grammatical principles that they begin with. But languages, in spite of their inherent stability, inevitably change through time.

Diachronic (historical) linguistics Scientific study of the patterns of change in given languages is possible and feasible. This may be done in two ways. Once a language is committed to writing, the changes that occur may be followed through a sequence of documents. The other approach is to push the history of related languages back into prehistoric times through internal analysis of homologous languages. The major principle underlying this second method is similar to that used in reconstruction of organic phylogenies; namely, that forms which have in common a number of functionally similar qualities that is greater than the level of chance occurrence are genetically related.

The comparative method The criteria used in historical linguistics are morphemic and syntactic identities. The quickest way to get an indication as to whether or not two languages are related is to compare their vocabularies, or word forms. (Thomas Jefferson, even while President of the United States, prepared word lists to be sent out to explorers and traders living among the Indians so as to get the answer to the question of American Indian origins and relationships.)[10] By sheer chance, under the law of limited possibilities, they will possibly have some words in common. Nothing is so puerile as to argue that two tribes are related because one can say that they share a handful of words. There must be a concurrence in a significant number of words and their associated meanings.

What constitutes significance? Two languages that are clearly unrelated and also

phonemically unlike in structure will ordinarily share only 4 per cent of their total terms in like form and meaning. If it happens that the phonemic structure of morphemes in the two languages is similiar, then the concurrences may be double. It is therefore safe to hold that vocabulary identities of less than these percentages may be the product of nothing but chance, and the identities may not be taken as evidence of historical relationship. Conversely, it is the considered and well-supported judgment of linguists, as expressed by the American expert Prof. Joseph Greenberg, that:

It can be safely asserted that a resemblance of 20 per cent in vocabulary always requires a historical explanation and that, unless a similarity of a high degree of phonetic structure leads to the expectation of a high degree of chance similarity, even 8 per cent is well beyond what can be expected without the intervention of historical factors.[11]

By means of mathematical comparisons among three or more languages, it is possible to work out even sharper determinations of possible genetic relations along the lines just indicated.

Languages are apt to include a large number of words borrowed from other languages (e.g., in English, *totem, canoe, tobacco, tabu, automobile,* and so forth). Fundamental words such as pronouns and those representing parts of the body are most likely to retain their identity with the morphemes of their ancestry. Free borrowing from unrelated languages occurs more commonly in what are called the *cultural* (nonpersonal) *items.* Therefore, when the linguist is confronted by a group of languages that exhibit similarities greater than chance probability would account for in their fundamental vocabularies, while at the same time lacking similarities in their cultural vocabularies, he is certain that these languages were remotely derived from a common ancestor. If they had only recently come into contact with each other, the one would have borrowed words from the cultural vocabulary of the other before it would displace its own fundamental words

[10]Long vocabulary lists prepared by Jefferson are in the manuscript collections of the Library of the American Philosophical Society, Philadelphia.

[11]J. H. Greenberg, "Historical Linguistics and Unwritten Languages," in A. L. Kroeber (ed.), *Anthropology Today,* p. 270.

with those from an alien source. Thus another device for establishing historical relations between languages is available.

Sounds change over time. This means that the phonemic system of a given language does not remain constant. In seeking relationships among languages, the linguist with historical interests again may return to the bedrock of the language in question, its phonology. In comparing sounds between one language and another that he assumes to be related to it, he may observe a distinct pattern, a systematic change through the phonology of both. This principle was first elicited in the nineteenth century by Jacob Grimm, the same scholar who, along with his brother, Wilhelm, collected the famous fairy tales—not for purposes of entertainment, although that was a happy byproduct of their efforts, but to see historical relationships in the distributions of the stories. Grimm's *law of phonetic change,* set forth in 1822, made possible the designation of the great Indo-European speech family. Taking Sanskrit, the language of ancient India, as a kind of prototype of Indo-European, the brothers Grimm observed that systematic changes took place from one language to another as time went on. For example, the Sanskrit word *pitar* became *patēr* in Greek, *pater* in Latin, *vater* in Germanic (*v* is pronounced *f*), and *father* in English. Similarly, Sanskrit *bhrata* becomes Latin *frater,* Germanic, *bruder,* English, *brother,* and Russian, *brat.* These, of course, are only some obvious examples of what emerges as a complex and predictable series of patterns of sound changes. It can be seen that earlier Indo-European *p* may become *f,* that a weak *b* (bh) may also move to *f,* and the *f* may move back to *b.* Other regular modifications are demonstrable among the numerous Indo-European tongues, and similar relationships have been established for many other language groups.

This means that in comparing vocabularies for identities, exact phonemic similarity is not to be expected. The linguist, however, comes to recognize phonemic correlates that should be treated as identical. In cases where written documents extending over a number of centuries are available for related languages, it is possible to validate directly the specific functioning of Grimm's law and its derivatives.

Languages may also be related by comparison of their morphological and syntactic features. Thus an isolating language, such as Chinese, which sets up its words as simple monosyllables, is hardly likely to be related to such an extremely polysynthetic language as Eskimo, which builds up single words with as many as a dozen or more morphemes. More refined criteria, such as the presence or absence of gender, or inflection, and so forth, are also relied on.

Looking thus at Indo-European, it becomes possible to suggest some ultimate relationships. The speech phylum (family) has grown over a period of thousands of years, presumably from a single geographic center. Dialect changed to language as mutual intelligibility ceased; groups moved, forming their own variations on the themes of the original language. Once a parent language broke off from the main stem, it, too, was subject to further changes, giving rise to a kind of family language tree, with lesser branches off the main branches of the trunk. The process is analogous to genetic speciation and the radiating evolution of organisms, described in Chapter 8, except that language phyla cannot be traced back to one single original form, as is theoretically true of organic evolution. This comparative method has been applied to all of the world's languages so that in a general way, it is possible to see wide relationships. In Africa, among the American Indian, in Asia and the South Seas, classifications suggesting historical relationships have been made.

Thus, although the Cheyenne Indians live far out on the western Plains, because their language is Algonquian, we know that they are an offshoot of the great Algonquian group of tribes that dominated the northeastern part of North America. The linguistic fact confirms Cheyenne legend that they came from the vicinity of a great body of water in a wooded land to the east. The fact that the Navahos and

Apaches speak Athabascan dialects leads us to look for their original homeland far to the north in the woodlands of the MacKenzie-Yukon basin of western Canada, where all the tribes speak Athabascan.

Glottochronology The use of radioactive carbon counting as a means of reading the built-in "time-clock" for the dating of archaeological sites is one of the really exciting techniques developed since 1947. Equally exciting is the recently developed method for calculating the approximate time of the divergence of two dialects or languages from a common mother tongue. Thus the date at which the speakers of the dialects separated from each other can be established.

The fundamental premise of the method is that the basic vocabularies of a language change at a given rate. A basic, or fundamental, vocabulary is one which consists of words referring to universal "culture-free" phenomena, such as air, cloud, sun, rain, hand, foot, and so forth. Standard word lists of 100, 200, or more terms are used for comparison and analysis. Judgments are made according to established principles of linguistic analysis as to whether the two forms of a given word are cognate (i.e., of the same stock or origin) or noncognate. The relative number of noncognates to cognates is calculated. This provides a statement of the relative amount of change that has occurred since the two languages began to be separated from the original parent stock.

The rate of language change was first calculated on the basis of documented changes (noncognates) in a number of historic (written) languages. The replacement of terms in the fundamental vocabulary was measured at the rate of 19 per cent in a thousand years. The residue of cognates represents the rate of retention. The rate of retention actually varies among Indo-European languages from 86.4 per cent to 74.4 per cent per thousand years. This means that fundamental vocabularies may in fact change at rates of from 13.6 per cent to 25.6 per cent per thousand years. The average

figure is 19.5 per cent, but, for convenience, 19 per cent is still used.

By use of a standard algebraic formula for computation of time depth, the number of years which have elapsed since the languages became separated can be calculated within a limited range of probability.[12]

In a number of applications of the principle, the dates derived through glottochronology coincide nicely with historically known dates from the archaeological sites of the presumed ancestral populations. Glottochronology has useful possibilities in giving a measure of time precision to historical reconstructions. It is not reliable where no other supporting evidence is at hand, however. Its validity decreases outside the range of 500 to 2,000 years.

Lexicostatistics Glottochronology relates to a statistical method. In glottochronology, however, the issue is one of time, of actual dating. While some of its results are revealing and highly suggestive, questions have been raised about the accuracy of the dates obtained. For some languages, the method works well; for others, caveats must be observed. Putting aside, however, the question of dating, the issue of precisely when one language broke away from a parent grouping, if indeed such a thing did occur at a single point in time, the statistical summations that reside in the glottochronological word lists may have yet another utility. They begin to suggest hitherto unsuspected relationships between languages. To be sure, such relationships may be very ancient and one may be interested in the actual dating process. However, the problem of whether or not one language relates to another, easily resolved for Indo-European and languages with a long written history, is less readily apparent among unwritten languages where historical depth must be inferred. Lexicostatistic similarities (cognate words) shed some light on the matter.

[12]See S. H. Gudschinsky, "The ABC's of Lexicostatistics (Glottochronology)" in D. Hymes (ed.), *Language in Culture and Society*, pp. 612–623, for a succinct discussion of the assumptions and procedures to be followed.

We said that a treelike scheme can be used in formulating linguistic relationships. However, this is an older way of viewing language history, and, in the light of lexicostatistical formulations, such a pattern seems in some measure subject to rethinking. Morphological features, syntactic elements, as well as cultural items of the lexicon may spread by a process of diffusion. The suggestion that there is a parallel between diffusion of language and diffusion of culture has some further application. A language can assimilate new elements from without, whether these are in lexicon, element of sound, or element of structure. It is known that this happens to such an extent that some languages appear to take on the apparent structure of neighboring but unrelated languages. The linguist Morris Swadesh has formulated the concept of a "mesh principle," showing that diffused or convergent patterns may be operative among unrelated languages over wide areas. The reverse may also be true. Languages may remain apparently distinct from each other. Yet when compared lexicostatistically, using the basic word lists, relationships are beginning to be found between languages where previously none were thought to exist.

SUMMARY

Language is a distinctly human system of communication that is symbolic and oral. It must be learned, and it is an aspect of culture.

Every language is wholly adequate to all human situations. Thus, although there are thousands of languages spoken by primitive peoples, we cannot say that one language is more or less primitive, more or less developed than any other. Vocabularies vary in richness by stylistic and pragmatic criteria—not by primitiveness.

As a total, self-contained system, every language has its structure that can be analysed much as an ethnologist analyses a culture. The analysis of structure is the concern of *synchronic linguistics*. Structure begins with *phonemes*, the smallest units of sound on which a language builds. Sounds within a given language have regular patterns of arrangements that produce a *phonology*. The way phonemic units are combined constitutes the *morphology* or structure of a language, and *morphemes* are the basic units of structure. The patterned arrangement of morphemes in phrases and sentences makes up the *syntax* of a language. The range of variation in phonologies and syntaxes in the languages of the world is indeed tremendous. These are all linguistic problems. For the anthropologist as an anthropologist, the main language problem is one of *semantics*, or the meaning of meaning. What are the denotive and connotive intentions of speakers and informants? Major cultural communication takes place through language, and languages must *ipso facto* be understood, explicitly and implicitly.

The extent to which the syntax of a language preconditions, limits, and directs the thought patterns of the carriers of a given culture is the subject of the Sapir-Whorf hypothesis. Whether this is really a matter of linguistics or of the psychology of cognition is a moot question in this day.

Diachronic linguistics is concerned with the historic processes of growth and change in languages. The comparative method involves the compilation of vocabulary lists to establish genetic identities in languages and also traces patterns of phonetic shifts as dialects diverge and become new languages. On the assumption that basic vocabularies change at a fixed, determinable rate (analogous to the process of radioactive disintegration), *glottochronology* provides a method of determining the number of centuries which have passed since the speakers of two related tongues have branched apart. *Lexicostatistics* is a later development out of glottochronology. In this technique of the historical method, interest is shifted from time determinations to identification of statistical concordances which suggest historical affinities among languages which no longer have sufficient superficial similarities to be readily identifiable as related.

SELECTED READINGS

Carroll, J. B. (ed.): *Language, Thought, and Reality: Selected Writings of Benjamin Lee Whorf* (1956). Whorf's original essays in metalinguistics in a readily available form.

Gleason, H. A.: *An Introduction to Descriptive Linguistics* (rev. ed., 1961). A good workbook on how languages are put together and function.

Hall, E. T.: *The Silent Language* (1959). A popular and intriguing account of extralinguistic cues as they operate in cultural communications. Holds up for understanding what everyone acts upon but rarely is conscious of. Particularly helpful in its analysis of failure in cross-cultural communication because of unsophisticated awareness of meaning of cues on the part of business and public officials.

Hall, R. A., Jr.: *Linguistics and Your Language* (2d rev. ed. of *Leave Your Language Alone!* 1960). A penetrating, easily understandable exploration of process and function in languages.

Hockett, C. F.: *A Course in Modern Linguistics* (1958). A clear-headed introduction to the subject.

Hockett, C. F., and R. Ascher: "The Human Revolution" (*Current Anthropology,* Vol. 5, No. 3, 1964), pp. 135—168. A highly imaginative, hypothetical reconstruction of the origin of language during the transition from ape to man. Highly inferential and speculative, it is stimulating reading, but the thesis has not been discussed in this chapter because of its extreme tentativeness.

Lehmann, W. P.: *Historical Linguistics: An Introduction* (1962). Covers the techniques of reconstruction of the "genetic" relationships of languages, in addition to some of the results of the method.

Culture and personality

chapter 4

A personality is the integrated system of behaviors, learned and unlearned, that are characteristic of an individual. A culture is the integrated system of learned behavior patterns that are characteristic of the members of a society. The interrelations of the two have posed three kinds of problems for mutual study by psychologists and anthropologists: (1) How does culture affect personality? (2) How does personality affect culture? (3) How does personality response to specific cultural experience influence other aspects of the culture, or in what sense are individual personalities intermediary links in a chain of cause and effect between different parts of cultures?

Determinants of personality

A given personality is the product of many interacting factors, which may be classified under four main categories: (1) the constitutional characteristics of the individual (his biology, neurophysiology, endocrine system, body type, etc.); (2) the nature of the physical environment in which the individual lives; (3) the culture of which the individual is a part; and (4) the unique, or idiosyncratic, biological-psychological-social experience or history of the individual. These components are fused in the creation of each personality.

Constitutional characteristics The most obvious, although by no means the most important, factors in the determination of personality are the physical and mental capacities with which the individual is endowed at birth. These are the traits which are frequently termed "inherited" or "innate," although these labels are in themselves misleading and open to a variety of interpretations. Included are such factors as body build, intelligence, neurological make-up, presence or absence of deformities, and the like.

Morphological factors which can be readily seen as having a direct influence on personality are stature, weight, and physical appearance. The personality of a dwarf cannot be that of a giant. We must keep in mind, however, that the social meaning of a physical characteristic is culturally determined. In Western culture, big men are expected to be dominant in ascendant-submissive relations. Differing cultures attach their own particular and often widely differing meanings to such physical attributes as larger-than-average size.

To illustrate this point, we may contrast our situation and that of the Trobriand Islanders with respect to identification of physiognomy among kinsmen. In our culture every newborn baby is carefully evaluated by relatives and friends to see whether he looks like his mother or his father, or this uncle or that aunt, or this grandfather or that grandmother. We have a real obsession to find points of resemblance to kinsmen. Maternal kinsmen project maternal identities upon the infant. Paternal kinsmen project their counterparts. If the physical traits are quite definitely identifiable with those of one line or the other, the stimulus value is quite marked, and the role behavior may be definitely influenced one way or the other.

In the Trobriands, on the other hand, the dogma of the culture is that children do not and cannot resemble their mother or her kin. To hint as much is offensively bad taste. Yet resemblance to the father is always assumed and affirmed. Physical aspects of the father as well as aspects of his personality, but not of the mother, are thus transferred to the children. (Of course, a great many of the mother's traits are transferred to her children through association and learning.)

A queerer quirk in Trobriand culture is the dogma that brothers never look alike. Mali-

nowski once suggested, apropos of some Trobriand Islanders' remarks about how much a group of brothers looked like their father, that it followed from this that the brothers must look like one another. The natives made it plain that they thought he had very crude manners to make such a gauche remark.[1] Syllogistic reasoning could not stand in the face of culturally controlled perception. From the Trobriand point of view, any fool can see that brothers just never do look alike.

It may well be that certain kinds of temperament and body types tend to go together. The notion is deep in our folk beliefs.

Let me have about me men that are fat;
Sleek-headed men and such as sleep o' nights;
Yon Cassius has a lean and hungry look;
He thinks too much; such men are dangerous.

Redheads have fiery tempers. Blonds are dizzy. Fat men are jolly. But are they? Among anthropologists, Professors Earnest Hooton[2] and William Sheldon[3] have been leaders in a vigorous effort to put the issue to the test of science. Hooton measured and classified American prisoners and compared their bodily traits with those of a sample of the noncriminal population. He concluded as a result of the findings that men of distinctive types of body build have an affinity for certain types of crimes. Sheldon made a major contribution through the development of a photographic method in which the subject stands before a grid background; relative measurements may then be taken from the photo so that the individual may be typed for body form with relative ease. Much less successful has been Sheldon's attempt to develop a scale for classification of temperament which could be examined for association with specific body types.

That definite psychological correlations to distinctive body types exist seems to be likely enough. Yet in spite of the brave efforts of the

[1] B. Malinowski, *The Father in Primitive Psychology*, pp. 87–92.
[2] E. A. Hooton, *The American Criminal.*
[3] W. H. Sheldon and S. S. Stevens, *The Varieties of Temperament;* also W. H. Sheldon, S. S. Stevens, and W. B. Tucker, *The Varieties of Human Physique.*

Hootons and Sheldons, the technical problems of scientific demonstration have not yet been sufficiently mastered to allow us to say with any degree of confidence what such correlations may be in detail. No scholar has allowed for such important variables as social class, ethnic group, occupation, income, or diet in his researches, thus failing to account for a number of fairly obvious variables.

In much popular belief, racial biology is held to account for supposed psychological and behavioral characteristics of various races. This has been so thoroughly contradicted by scientific psychology and anthropology (see Chapter 14) that anthropologists working in the culture and personality field do not consider it worthwhile as an area of research.

Physical environment as a factor in determination of personality Anthropogeographers of the nineteenth century attempted to explain national character in terms of physical environment. Mountain dwellers are ruggedly individualistic, it was suggested. Enjoyers of temperate climates are creative and vigorous. Dwellers in the tropics are indolent and sexually precocious, and so on through a long list of stereotypes. Most early anthropogeographic work was so facile and superficial that it was tossed out, along with the concept of race as a determinant of psychological and behavioral characteristics, by twentieth-century anthropologists. Nonetheless, the mineral content of diet can and does affect the endocrine system of whole populations. Whether a people must adapt to an arctic, desert, or rain-forest environment is a factor of significant influence. Differences in the altitudes at which people live and the characteristic barometric pressures to which they must adjust are not without personality effects. Such matters are therefore not to be overlooked, and the imaginativeness of Professor John Whiting in seeking a causal relation between male initiation practices, multiple marriages, and climate is a good example taking the environmental factor into account (see page 328).

Cultural determinants of personality Cultural determinants set the patterns and limits for normal behavior within any society. In Miller and Dollard's phraseology, culture is ". . . a statement of the design of the human maze, of the type of reward involved, and of what responses are to be rewarded."[4] The operation of these determinants and the feedback effect of personality responses to them constitute the subject of the rest of this chapter.

Idiosyncratic features of individual experience Every individual has a unique personal history. Not all aspects of the society's culture are open to all persons, and differences in status mean differences in social opportunity and experience. These mean differences in status roles and personalities. Even more important, however, is the fact that persons of identical status never have the same experiences. The mother prefers one child over the other. One child burns his finger; another does not. One woman has an automobile accident; another does not. One infant falls in the river; another does not. No two persons ever have the same social experience, not even identical twins. From psychoanalysis we have learned how important the fortuity of history can be in shaping the direction of personality development.

Culture tends to standardize personalities by channeling the experience of all individuals along the same broad stream. But life is made up of so many instances, so many situations, such rich variety of experience, that absolute standardization can never be realized.

A comprehensive classification of personality determinants Personality is therefore to be understood as a behavioral synthesis of an individual's physical (including neural and glandular) constitution, the physicochemical character of his environment, the patterns of his culture, and his internalization of, and reactions to, his total life history in relation to people and things. These four categories are drawn on the basis of *levels within the natural order* and the nature of the individual's experience.

[4] N. Miller and J. Dollard, *Social Learning and Imitation*, p. 5.

A hint of the immense complexity of interacting factors that should ideally be understood may be obtained from trying to imagine all the steps which would be involved in getting all the data for just one person—to say nothing of a representative sample of a society. The model that accounts for this classifies determinants in terms of the criterion of *degree of universality among human beings*. The four categories based upon this principle are (1) the universal—those determinants which are relatively constant for all mankind, whatever the environment, culture, or race; (2) the communal—those determinants which are relatively constant and unique for all the members of a given society as opposed to the members of other societies; (3) the role—those determinants which are linked to different statuses within a society; and (4) the idiosyncratic—those determinants which are uniquely individual, in either constitution or life history. Combining these with the four determinants based upon the level of natural order gives fifteen major components of personality (Table 4–1).

This framework points the way for sifting out "group personalities." Thus the universal determinants, which apply to all mankind, produce what there is of "human nature" the world over. The communal traits lead to national or societal character types. The role determinants shape the distinctive personalities of persons belonging to various age, sex, occupational, class, and caste grouping within societies. The idiosyncratic determinants guarantee the uniqueness of every individual as long as men endure.

Child training and personality

"As the twig is bent, so grows the tree." A major factor in the development of the child as a person is the accumulation of innumerable pressures, most of them subtle, others not so subtle, that shape his images and his feel of the surrounding world. He strives to act in accordance with these understandings. The child's feel of the world and his gradually growing perception of what that world will give and

Table 4-1 The Components of Personality*

	determinants based on degree of universality among human beings			
determinants based on level of natural order	universal	communal	role	idiosyncratic
cultural	Incest tabu, kinship systems, property, magic, religion, housing, time reckoning, etc.	Special forms of kinship, property, magical and religious beliefs, etc.	Special roles culturally differentiated for status groups within each society	
social	Group life, child care	Size, distribution, density of population, etc.	Play groups, congeniality groups, cliques, etc.	Fortuitous experiences in social relations
biological	Birth, death, hunger, thirst, metabolic action, skeletal-muscular structure, basic drives, etc.	"Racial" variations of universal traits, health conditions of society at large, etc.	Age and sex differences, racially based class and caste	Individual peculiarities of stature, physiognomy, glandular functions, etc.
physical environmental	Atmospheric pressure, gravity, earth, sun, moon, stars, clouds, water, wind, precipitation, etc.	Local climate, topography, wild plant and animal life, other natural resources, etc.	Differential access to material goods by different status groups	Unique relations to flood, storm, lightning, and other physical phenomena

*Modified from C. Kluckhohn and O. H. Mowrer, "Culture and Personality" (*American Anthropologist*, Vol. 46, 1944), pp. 1–29.

what it demands serve as his guides for getting on.

All these perceptions have to be explored and tested. At the instant of birth, the world is nothing for the newborn infant. It is sensed only as a rude and sudden change from the all-encompassing perfection of the womb to the coldness of the air that first strikes him. His first response is a wail and not a laugh.

The world that awaits the child is a world of people who already have a multitude of cultural commitments concerning how to behave— people with culturally colored emotions, expectancies, and anxieties. It is a world of many physical things, some beneficial, even essential to human existence; some inexorably destruc-

Fig. 4-1 Steaming an Amahuacan child in banana vapor. Bananas are the staple crop of the Amahuaca tribe of the Peruvian rain forest. In celebration of the ripening of bananas, a great feast is held, during which small children are ritually treated so that they may become "like bananas," healthy and fast-growing. (Cornell Capa, Magnum; Robert Russell, Wycliffe Bible Translators, Inc.)

tive; some now one and then the other. Of these the infant is blankly ignorant. Of all these he must in time become knowledgeable.

Investigations of human adults show that much of their behavior consists of patterns derived from processes of conditioning in early childhood. Under ordinary circumstances the child's first experience, and his experience for some time thereafter, is in the primary conjugal family. This is his world. Margaret Mead, for one, has shown how this world differentially puts the imprint of its finger on him:

The Arapesh [of New Guinea] treat a baby as a soft, vulnerable, precious little object, to be protected, fed, cherished. . . . When the mother walks about she carries the child slung beneath her breast in a bark-cloth sling, or in a soft net bag in which the child still curls as he curled in the womb. Whenever it is willing to eat . . . it is fed, gently, interestedly.

Among the neighboring Iatmul head-hunters:

From birth the baby is handled as if it were a separate little entity capable of a will of its own. . . . As soon as the Iatmul child is a few weeks old, the mother no longer carries it everywhere with her . . . but instead places it at some distance on a high bench, where it must cry lustily before it is fed. . . . [T]he sense of the mouth is built up as an assertive,

demanding organ, taking what it can from a world that is, however, not unduly unwilling to give it. The child learns an attitude towards the world; that if you fight hard enough, something which will treat you as strong as itself will yield—and that anger and self-assertion will be rewarded.

And again:

The Mundugumor [another New Guinea tribe] women actively dislike child-bearing, and they dislike children. Children are carried in harsh opaque baskets that scratch their skins, later, high on their mother's shoulders, well away from the breast. Mothers nurse their children standing up, pushing them away as soon as they are the least bit satisfied. . . . Here we find a character developing that stresses angry, eager avidity. In later life love-making is conducted like the first round of a prize-fight, and biting and scratching are important parts of foreplay.[5]

Child training encompasses a good deal more than consciously directed education. As a biological organism, each individual is moved by a mass of impulses or drives. Many of these are innate, that is, inherent in the neurophysiological make-up. They are urges to action. These basic drives consist of internal tensions, physiological states of unrest producing urges to action. Those drives which lead to food seeking are labeled "hunger drives." Other basic intake drives are those centered on air and liquid (more specifically, water). Together, they constitute "oral drives." Behind these drives are basic physiological needs. If the drive-motivated activity fails to achieve the imperative intake, the organism is destroyed; it begins its decomposition toward its ultimate residue of inorganic compounds—"ashes and dust." Satisfaction of the basic needs is therefore an inescapable prerequisite to the continued life of the organism. Temporary dissatisfaction produces the tension state that is felt as a drive. Prolonged dissatisfaction builds the discomfiture to pain. Babies first get restless; then they howl. A hungry or thirsty adult may learn to bear the pain in stoic silence or to get relief in the fantasy of imagined food or drink, but this only alleviates the pain; it does not cancel

[5] M. Mead, *Male and Female*, pp. 65, 68–69. By permission from William Morrow and Company, New York.

Fig. 4-2 The Amahuaca child of the Peruvian rain forest enjoys close bodily contact with its father. (Cornell Capa, Magnum.)

out the fact that the need must ultimately be met.

A second type of basic drives that center on elimination of bodily wastes—the defecatory and urination drives—is classed as "anal drives."

The third category of basic drives centers on temperature control. There are limits to the tolerance of the human body for extremes of heat and cold. When external conditions approach such extremes, the individual is moved to reduce them by migrating to more equable climes, procuring clothing, building shelters, using fire, seeking coolants, or taking special foods or drink. If it gets too hot or too cold, the organism is reduced in efficiency until it dies from heat prostration or freezing.

A fourth set of basic drives is summed up in sex. In its crudest form, this is expressed in genital excitement, but of course the sex sensations are much more diffuse than that. The sex drives are powerfully sensational, but as far as the individual is concerned, their gratification is not directly necessary to survival, as are the other basic drives. Their direct gratification is essential to the reproductive survival of the group, however. The major contribution of psychoanalysis has been the demonstration of the manifold but not manifest significance of individual experience in the adjustment of the sex drives to the conditions of social living.

The ways in which these needs may be satisfied are always limited and standardized in every culture. No society permits its members to eat any which way at any time they please. No society permits its members to urinate and defecate whenever or wherever they get the urge. Sphincter control is always demanded. No society permits unlimited expression of the sex drive; on the contrary, all societies exert considerable social control in this matter.

Each person has to learn what kinds of responses to drive pressures lead to goal achievement and satisfaction of his needs. Antisocial responses—that is, culturally prohibited behavior—are punished through social efforts to extinguish them. The individual must learn to inhibit his impulse to act in prohibited ways and to habituate his behavior to culturally indicated ways.

The total process is called *enculturation* which is defined as conscious or unconscious conditioning occurring within that process whereby man, as child and adult, achieves competence in his culture. A well-adjusted personality is one who successfully gratifies his personal urges within the allowable expectancies of his social environment. In social psychology and sociology, the term of long-standing use that is synonymous with enculturation is *socialization.*

Human life is lived in a state of continuous tensions that may only be minimized, never permanently eliminated. The battle between inner urge and the channeled limitations allowed by culture is unending. "Inner psychic conflict would seem to be of the very essence of man."[6] Maturity in personality represents an acceptance of the terms according to which life can and must be lived in any given society. When a growing child has adjusted his behavior to the patterns of his culture, when its pertinent values, beliefs, and modes of action have become a normal part of his thinking and behavior, he has *internalized* his culture and has become thoroughly enculturated. His personality has matured.

Along the way he will have acquired many drives and attendant goals that were not in him at birth. These drives are not *basic* but are, rather, *acquired* or *secondary*. They are extensions of a more elemental need for warm social response. The goals are culturally symbolized in the social rewards that go with prestige status. Most men in most societies struggle to achieve and shape their personalities in accord with the demands of such acquired drives with as much intensity of action as the basic drives evoke.

Primitive education and enculturation Education, as opposed to child training, implies the more formal efforts of adults to mold the personalities of the young, but among primitive peoples the gap is nowhere as great as it is in American society. Primitives never make an issue over "education for life," as our school people do. In a tribal group, education *is* life. The father does not work in a factory or office the child never sees. The child is not shut up in a school away from the home for hours and days on end. In the simple camp or village, he is around and underfoot while all the fundamental activities of adult life take place. He

---

[6]A. I. Hallowell, "Psychological Leads for Ethnological Field Workers," in D. Haring (ed.), *Personal Character and Cultural Milieu*, p. 296.

can play with a bow and arrow until he is old enough to tag along on the hunt and learn by precept in action just how to handle it expertly. He can play around the older boys who are watching the herds until he is ready to herd himself. He can see and imitate the dancers until he himself is admitted to the dance. He can listen to the tales of tribal lore and myth as they are told until he knows them by heart. Most knowledge comes as a by-product of living, with one or another of the family members as a natural, nonprofessional instructor. And much is learned from play with other children who are just a bit older.

Formal learning is usually limited to the more esoteric or specialized aspects of religion and magic. Where tribal initiations are held, they almost invariably involve formal instruction in these affairs.

An example of the scope of such initiation education, from among the Tswana, is provided in the following paragraph by Professor Schapera:

All the eligible boys were initiated simultaneously in groups, kept secluded in one or more special "camps" (*mephatô*) away from all the villages for three months or so. The details of the ceremony were kept a profound secret from women and all other non-initiates, who were forbidden under penalty of severe assault and even death to approach too near to the camp. At the camp the boys were first circumcised in order of tribal precedence. They were then systematically taught a number of secret formulae and songs, admonishing them to honour, obey, and support the Chief; to be ready to endure hardships and even death for the sake of the tribe; to be united as a regiment and help one another; to value cattle as the principal source of livelihood, and so herd them carefully; to attend the *kgotla* regularly, as this was the place for men, and to look after its fire; to honour and ungrudgingly obey old people; and to abandon all boyish practices. Much of this instruction dealt also with the important topic of sex, the boys being taught the physiology of sex relations, the duty of procreation and other rules of conduct in married life, and the dangers of promiscuous intercourse with ritually "unclean" women. They were further taught tribal traditions and religious beliefs, and the tribal songs of war and self glorifica-

Fig. 4-3 Enculturation of Navaho children. Values are transmitted through the telling of myths and legends to the young. (Leonard McCombe, *Life Magazine.* © Time, Inc. All rights reserved.)

tion, and were made to participate in symbolic dances of many kinds. They were, moreover, subjected to starvation and blows, discomfort and actual torture, and rigorous and irksome taboos of many kinds, and were made to participate in strenuous hunting expeditions, all with the object of hardening them.[7]

The rituals of priests, and often of shamans, must ordinarily be taught on an apprenticeship basis, for these are frequently so complex, as well as secret, that they can be imparted only under isolated conditions which encourage strict attention and rigorous study.

[7] I. Schapera, *A Handbook of Tswana Law and Custom*, p. 106. By permission from Oxford University Press, London.

Fig. 4-4 Learning to dance in Bali. The teacher does not demonstrate but guides each movement. The Balinese does not learn by watching but by feeling. (Henri Cartier-Bresson, Magnum.)

C. W. M. Hart has pointed out that in most primitive societies, the education of children before puberty is left to the informal ministrations of parents and other relatives. In many societies, however, the boys are hauled off to a "bush school" at puberty to be put through a severe course of discipline and training in esoteric knowledge covering the "value system of the culture, its myths, its religion, its philosophy, its justification for its own entity as a culture."[8] Hart continues: "The initiation

[8] See C. W. M. Hart, "Contrasts between Prepubertal and Postpubertal Education," in G. D. Spindler (ed.), *Education and Anthropology*, p. 141.

schools are directed at imparting instruction that cannot be given in the home, under conditions as unlike home conditions as possible, by teachers who are the antithesis of the home teachers the boy has hitherto had."[9]

On the whole, it is safe to say that primitive children find their education less irksome than ours do. It demands less of them, and they can readily see the utility of what they learn because it is evident all about them in everyday living. They use their knowledge as they acquire it; they do not have to learn in a vacuum things that they will not have a chance to put to use for some years to come—or, perhaps, never.

Theoretical systems of culture and personality

The first anthropological studies on personality and culture were Malinowski's *Sex and Repression in Savage Society* and Margaret Mead's *Coming of Age in Samoa.* Malinowski tested Freud's theory of the Oedipus complex against the facts of Trobriand society. The Trobriand Islanders have a system of matrilineal clans in which authority over children is exercised by the maternal uncle (mother's brother), rather than the father. Malinowski asked the question: "In this type of social setting does a boy have incestuous desires for his mother and 'hate' his father as an authority figure and rival for the affections of the mother?" After analyzing Trobriand behavior and Trobriand mythology, Malinowski concluded that the answer is "No." It is the uncle who is resented and the sister (particularly the clan sister) who is the object of intrafamilial sexual interest. Therefore, the basic principle of the Oedipus complex exists, but its manifestation alters with the cultural complex.[10]

Mead's work in *Coming of Age in Samoa* was discussed in the first chapter (page 5) as an example of the use of the comparative method in anthropology as a substitute for laboratory-controlled experimentation to test hypotheses. It will be remembered that Mead's

[9] *Ibid.,* p. 140.
[10] B. Malinowski, *Sex and Repression in Savage Society;* also *The Father in Primitive Psychology.*

conclusion was that Samoan adolescents do not go through the period of psychological stress that characterizes American adolescence because Samoan culture is free of certain stress-producing features.

Neither Mead nor Malinowski expressed an explicit theory of culture and personality at that time (1928 and 1926, respectively). In 1934, however, Ruth Benedict published her famous *Patterns of Culture,* which became the theoretical prototype for a number of later "configurational studies." Subsequently, Abram Kardiner, a psychoanalyst, with the cooperation of Ruth Benedict, Cora DuBois, Ralph Linton, and other anthropologists, developed and published a "theory of basic personality structure" for handling questions of the effect of culture upon personality and vice versa. This, too, became the model for a number of studies. All these theoretical systems rest on intensive psycho-cultural analysis of one or a few tribes. John Whiting, a former colleague of G. P. Murdock in the initiation of the statistical method of cross-cultural studies (see pages 65–67), entered the lists in 1953 with the publication of a broader theory of culture and personality, in which specific hypotheses are put to correlational tests that are statistically devised.

Each of these theories will now be considered.

The configuration of culture and the ideal personality type The central thesis of Ruth Benedict's famous approach to this problem is that the ideological contours of a tribal culture are impressed upon individuals in terms of an ideal personality type. Each society has a more or less clear idea of what constitutes the "good man," the kind of man a person ought to be. The precepts, maxims, rewards, and punishments doled out by the *publicum* are directed toward molding all men in the image of the ideal. He who approximates the ideal is an object of social cynosure. The character of this ideal personality is equated with an abstracted tribal character structure.

In *Patterns of Culture,* Benedict purported to demonstrate the empirical validity of the theory by detailed descriptions of what she called the "Dionysian configuration," represented by the Kwakiutl Indians of the Northwest Coast of North America, and the "Apollonian configuration," exemplified by the Zuñi Indians of New Mexico.

The Dionysian and Apollonian concepts were phrased as follows:

The basic contrast between the Pueblos and the other cultures of North America is the contrast that is named and described by Nietzsche in his studies of Greek tragedy. He discussed two diametrically opposed ways of arriving at the values of existence. The Dionysian pursues them through "the annihilation of the ordinary bounds and limits of existence"; he seeks to attain in his most valued moments escape from the boundaries imposed upon him by his five senses, to break through into another order of experience. The desire of the Dionysian, in personal experience or in ritual, is to press through it toward a certain psychological state, to achieve excess. The closest analogy to the emotions he seeks is drunkenness, and he values the illuminations of frenzy. With Blake, he believes "the path of excess leads to the palace of wisdom." The Apollonian distrusts all this, and has often little idea of the nature of such experiences. He finds means to outlaw them from his conscious life. He "knows but one law, measure in the Hellenic sense." He keeps the middle of the road, stays within the known map, does not meddle with disruptive psychological states.[11]

The factual validity of Benedict's characterizations of Kwakiutl and Pueblo society is open to serious challenge.[12] She drew her configurations with the artistic license of a poet, rather than with the exactitude of a scientist. Nonetheless, her beautifully written exposition of her configurational theory has exerted great influence on anthropology, education, and public thinking from 1934 to the present. It is the most popular book on anthropology written thus far in the twentieth century. The effectiveness of the theory and of the analytical method was well substantiated in her wartime analysis of Japanese culture and national character,

[11]R. F. Benedict, *Patterns of Culture,* p. 72. By permission from Houghton Mifflin Company, New York.
[12]See V. Barnouw, *Culture and Personality,* pp. 41–48, for a bill of particulars.

published in 1946 under the title *The Chrysan-themum and the Sword: Patterns of Japanese Culture.*

Like culture, the ideal personality type is a construct. While it suffers from dangers of oversimplification, it nonetheless offers a fundamentally useful approach. For example, when we speak of the "national character" of a people we are really speaking of a collective ideal personality type. The French national character is different from the British, and the British is in turn different from the German. Plains Indians' personalities are typically strikingly unlike those of Pueblo Indians. The Benedict approach has pointed up and driven home the theory that the personalities of the majority in any society are largely reflections of the ideal personality presented by that society's culture.

The collective actions of a nation are to a certain degree the reactions of the ideal personality type to given stimulus situations. Accurate analyses of national character can aid in understanding national conduct. The problem from the point of view of social science is to see that such characterizations are validated by adequate empirical data and critical checking.[13]

The theory of basic personality structure and cultural projection Although the concept of basic personality structure developed by Kardiner originated in the concept of the ideal personality type, it developed from the latter and is not identical with it.[14]

Whereas the use of the concept of ideal personality type demonstrates the close interrelation between culture and personality, it presents a characterization that is essentially descriptive and nongenetic. It describes a type of personality without attempting to probe deeply into questions of how it got that way.

[13]Compare O. H. Klineberg, "A Science of National Character" (*Journal of Social Psychology*, S.P.S.S.I. Bulletin 19, 1944), pp. 147–162; and E. Beaglehole, "Character Structure" (*Psychiatry*, Vol. 7, 1944), pp. 144–162. Also M. Mead, "National Character," in A. L. Kroeber (ed.), *Anthropology Today*, pp. 642–667.

[14]A. Kardiner, *The Individual and His Society;* A. Kardiner et al., *The Psychological Frontiers of Society.* A concise summary of the historical development of the concept may be found in Kardiner's article, "The Concept of Basic Personality Structure as an Operational Tool in the Social Sciences," in R. Linton (ed.), *The Science of Man in the World Crisis*, pp. 107–122.

Kardiner, a psychoanalyst by training and in practice, has focused interest on the psychodynamics of personality and culture. The unique aspect of his approach is the way he undertakes to determine the effect of social institutions upon personality and of personality upon institutions.

Out of the interaction of this generalized psychoanalytic proposition that social institutions and personality do affect each other, and the anthropological materials on cultural determinism have emerged the following constructs: (1) Certain culturally established techniques of child treatment shape basic attitudes toward parents; these attitudes exist throughout the life of the individual. (2) The "group of nuclear constellations" of attitudes and behavior formed by the culturally standardized patterns of child treatment in any society, and persisting among the adults, is the *basic personality structure* that is characteristic of that society. (3) The complexes of child treatment are called *primary institutions*. (4) By means of the mechanisms of projection, the nuclear constellations derived from primary institutions are subsequently reflected in the development of other institutions such as religion, government, and mythology. Institutions derived as a result of projective systems are called *secondary institutions*.

The Kardinerian system is a limited system that attempts to establish two things: (1) the identification of the basic personality structure and the process of its formation as a reaction to child-care customs and (2) the carry-over effect of the basic personality patterns into certain of the larger institutional structures of the society.[15] In other words, Kardiner is striving to show how one phase of culture shapes personality and how the resultant personality in turn shapes other phases of the culture. He is really probing the interrelation between cul-

[15]Note that Kardiner's secondary institutions are institutions in the ordinary sociological sense (see p. 27). However, his primary institutions are what anthropologists usually call *trait complexes*. In a strict sense they are not institutions at all. This leads Kardiner in his later work to amend the concept of primary institution to read: "primary institution or related practices, whether institutionalized or not." (*The Psychological Frontiers of Society*, p. 25.)

ture and personality, not just the influence of culture on personality.

The method in its present stage of development is avowedly self-limited. It does not attempt to discover how the primary institutions, the child-care complexes, came into being. "The primary institution is treated as the taking-off point for the individual, not for the culture."[16] Furthermore, it assumes that various elemental aspects of culture, such as certain technologies (for example, basket making), may have no direct bearing on the basic personality structure. And yet further, it acknowledges that in many cultures certain institutions lie outside and are independent of the projective system.

On the positive side, a precept of psychodynamics which is essential to the whole scheme, and which we have not yet mentioned, is that the individual is not wholly the passive receptor of his cultural system. Culture is transmitted through learning, but the individual works emotionally upon what he experiences and what he is taught.

The point is that [direct] learning processes do not account for the integrative character of the human mind in so far as the emotional relationships of the individual to his environment are concerned. . . . In addition to direct learning processes, the individual builds up a highly complicated series of integrative systems which are not a result of direct learning.[17]

The integration of the personality, like the integration of a culture, is more than the sum of its parts.

Alorese culture and basic personality structure
It is quite impossible to convey the meaning of an operational application of the basic personality structure with anything like reasonable adequacy here. Yet a skeletal sketch will portray the idea better than none at all. We have selected Alor for the purpose, since it is the only one of the primitive cultures on which Kardiner has published results of psychodynamic analysis that is really based upon adequate data.[18] All his other analyses of primi-

tive cultures (Marquesan, Tanala, Comanche) must be recognized as experimental probing; the conclusions drawn from such probing must be treated as wholly provisional and indicative of potential results rather than final fact.

The Alorese, who live on the island of Timor in eastern Indonesia, are gardeners; their environment is that of the tropical forest. For women, the main cultural activity is gardening; for men, it is an endless round of wealth exchanges, the making and collecting of loans. Money, which in Alor consists of pigs, Javanese bronze vessels (*moko*), and gongs, is lent out at interest with tight bonds of obligation that bind the debtor to his creditor. Marriage and death, among other occasions, call for extravagant consumption of pork along with tremendous exchanges of *moko* and gongs. The heavy burdens of these occasions force the principals deep into debt.

Capitalism in Alor is primarily a vehicle for egotistical dominance over one's fellow men. In the family, the internal tensions and hostilities of the Alorese household fail to gratify the security needs of the infant child. Alorese culture is integrated about the basic insecurity of the individual. Dominance through credit control is an attempt at compensatory adjustment.

In like manner, Alorese war rests not upon any military interest. War is only a means of getting even, a sort of irritable gesture expressed not in any art of warfare but in a series of long-drawn-out feuds marked by cowardly assaults carried out by trickery and stealth. Women, as well as men, are the victims.

The Alorese child is neglected. He is wanted, not rejected, but he is neglected. The mother works, and works hard, in her scattered fields. After the fourteenth day following his birth, she has little time for her child. The father is away from home much of the time. The hunger pangs of the infant are irregularly and inconsistently met. The mother does not take the child to the fields with her; someone else around the house must tend him—the grandmother, an older child, or the father, if he is home. Several women may nurse him now and then; he is given gruel and premasticated

[16] *Ibid.*
[17] A. Kardiner, "The Concept of Basic Personality Structure as an Operational Tool in the Social Sciences," in R. Linton (ed.), *The Science of Man in the World Crisis,* pp. 109–110.
[18] C. DuBois, *The People of Alor.*

bananas almost from the outset. His hunger cravings are physiologically met, but no consistent image of any person upon whom he can depend for relief of hunger tensions is developed. Premasticated food may be given by anyone who wants to stop the infant's incessant bawling, but rejection and spitting out of such food, which is often observed, indicate that food thus given does not relieve the emotional tensions of the child. Hunger is more than an empty stomach.

Although the child is not left alone and is usually lugged around half-sitting in a shawl, he is not fondled or caressed by his parents to relieve his tensions. The mother or elder brother or sister, or whoever else is paying any attention to the infant, masturbates him to calm him down. This is merely a distraction and does not help to build the child's ego, for it is no more than an absentminded gesture.

In the primary institutions of Alor child feeding, there is no possibility of production of a parental image as a reliever of tensions. The intermittent appearance of the mother makes of her a tantalizing object who gives but inadequately the satisfactions so desperately needed.

Early childhood illnesses are indifferently

Fig. 4-5 Alorese children in the presence of adults. The lack of interest by adults is apparent, and the absence of adult response is evident in the behavior of the child. (Courtesy of Cora DuBois.)

treated and are aggravated by rough handling and irritating medication. The child learns to walk without assistance or encouragement. Again no one is available to enter into a relationship eliciting trust and dependence in response to receiving security and abetment. Defecation and urination are not brought under any particular coercive control. In this respect, Alorese child neglect is of a slight psychological benefit to the growing child. No anal eroticism is produced.

When weaning comes, the rejection of the child by its mother and mother substitutes, while not abrupt, is damaging. The breast-seeking child is pushed away or slapped. Then jealousy and rage are deliberately evoked by taking another child to the breast. Food is promised but not given. The adults think this is very funny.

These are the main lines of the primary institutions. What is the basic personality structure?

As children the Alorese are shy and reserved —they do not expect favorable response—but they readily fly into tantrums and become vituperative. Because they cannot obtain their desires or rewards in a direct way, they steal and forage as a regular thing. Aggression becomes canalized and predatory. The child, in turn, may reject his family by running away from home to live with some remoter relative.

This is the most extreme gesture of defiance and independence that the child is permitted and offers both a safety valve for pent-up aggressions and an

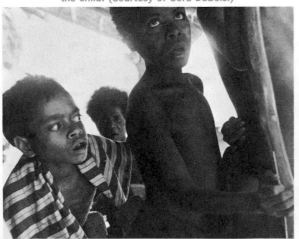

opportunity to sustain the hope that the child may find in one of its other relatives the long-sought-for kind parent.[19]

None of the childhood patterns build toward emotional solidarity within the family.

The ego development and social conscience of the adult are very weak. There is little self-confidence or sense of responsibility to others or to society. The adult male's relations to women are a projection of his almost complete defeat, as a child, in his relations to his mother. Husband-to-wife relations are bitter and nonintimate. Woman is the economic provider, and the male is dependent upon her. Yet he cannot really dominate her. Compensation is found in the elaborate activity of loans and exchanges, the functions of which are essentially to gratify the psychological rather than the production-consumption needs of the economy.

Warfare and religious institutions in Alor bear quite clearly the impress of the projective system. War is disorganized, fitful, and vengeful. Religion falls within the category of ancestor worship, as is characteristic of the cultures of this part of the world. But the ancestors are neither exalted nor revered. Their powers for good are not exaggerated, and the Alorese feel no desire to assuage them by suffering or renunciation in their names. Because there is no interest in, possibility of, or benefit to be derived from getting back in their good graces, there is no restitution by penance. One expects no more from the ancestral gods than one expects from parents.

Ancestors, however, want to be fed. Failure to feed the gods makes them angry—failure to feed the child was the supreme frustration. Angry gods punish their descendants. With great reluctance and only under the duress of misfortune, the Alorese make sacrificial food offerings to the ancestral spirits.

Religious art is careless and slipshod. Gods are projected "fathers" and "mothers." With no idealization of parents in the culture, there is no idealization of the gods. Representative carvings of ancestral deities are carelessly

[19] A. Kardiner et al., *The Psychological Frontiers of Society*, p. 156.

made, perfunctorily used, and quickly discarded. The dead are projections of the powerful and insistent creditors who bedevil adult life. In short:

The basic personality in Alor is anxious, suspicious, mistrustful, lacking in confidence, with no interest in the outer world. There is no capacity to idealize the parental image or deity. The personality is devoid of enterprise, is filled with repressed hatred and free floating aggression over which constant vigilance must be exercised. The personality is devoid of high aspirations and has no basis for the internalization of discipline. Individuals so constituted must spend most of their energy protecting themselves against each other's hostility. Cooperation must be at a low level and a tenuous social cohesion can be achieved only by dominance-submission attitudes, not by affection and mutual interest.[20]

Alor is a society with an old culture. It has survived for quite some time. This means that it has made the necessary minimal adjustments to the physical and biological imperatives. Yet that it is a precarious adjustment cannot be doubted; the continuance of the society must hang on a very thin thread. One of its strengths has been that the protection of island isolation has sealed it off from too much external competition.

As an object lesson in the interaction of culture upon personality and of personality upon culture, however, it is superb.

The Whiting-Child theory and correlational method J. W. M. Whiting, Harvard anthropologist, and I. L. Child, Yale psychologist, have combined Kardinerian-Freudian theory; the learning theory of Dollard and Miller, Skinner, Hull, and others; and the cross-cultural statistical techniques of G. P. Murdock to produce an intriguing approach in *Child Training and Personality*.[21] Although many hypotheses derived from psychoanalytic thought are used in this theory, the emphasis of the approach is on hypothesis testing—something in which psychoanalysis is woefully weak. The data for testing the hypotheses are drawn from the Human

[20] *Ibid.*
[21] Published in 1953.

Relations Area Files. These files consist of reproductions of all significant published data on more than two hundred selected societies representing all levels of cultural development and all major geographic areas of the world. The data are classified and indexed in such a way as to facilitate the collation of large quantities of facts for cross cultural comparison.

Essentially, Whiting and Child set the following propositions:

1. Child training is universal: "In all societies the helpless infant . . . must be changed into a responsible adult obeying the rules of his society."[22]

2. Societies differ in their rules and in their methods of teaching conformity to the rules. These differences have differential personality effects.

3. Specific qualities of personality effects are projected on adult institutions and influence their content.

So far, this is no different from Kardinerian theory. Now behavioral theory comes in.

4. Adults reward responses that correspond to culturally established patterns of behavior. Positive sanctioning (positive reinforcement) increases the tendency to repeat the approved response. Reponses that do not correspond to culturally established patterns of behavior are not rewarded and may be punished. Negative sanctioning (negative reinforcement) decreases the tendency to repeat the unapproved response.

5. The intensity of negative sanctions and the ages at which they are applied contribute to socialization anxiety. Approved responses bring drive reduction or satisfaction. Because they are rewarded, each successful repetition intensifies the satisfaction potential of the behavior.

6. Excessive frustration or excessive gratification in socialization results in negative or positive fixation. Fixation means that events of

[22] J. M. W. Whiting and I. L. Child, *Child Training and Personality*, p. 61.

a certain kind have greater or lesser psychological importance for someone who has had the fixating experience than for someone who has not.

7. Illness is anxiety-producing. Explanations of illness, or causes to which illness is usually attributed, are fantasy-colored by projection of fixations customarily established in the members of a given society by child-training experience.

For example, oral fixations will produce such "causes" of illness as eating and drinking (especially "poisonous" foods) or curses and other magical spells. Anal fixations will generate explanations of illness in terms of failure to hide one's feces or other personal waste.

A number of special hypotheses were refined for testing. The method consisted in giving numerical values on a scale of rating for degree of severity of socialization of oral, anal, sexual, dependent, and aggressive behaviors. This was done wherever possible for fifty selected societies. (Interestingly enough, middle-class practices in Chicago, which represented the United States in the sample, rated very high in severity and low in indulgence in virtually every measure of early child training. Americans are severe with, and demanding of, their children.) Each society was also classed, if the data warranted it, as *having* or *not having* oral, anal, sexual, dependent, or aggressive explanations for illness. Correlations were statistically derived between negative and positive fixations on the one hand and type of "disease theory" on the other.

The study established high correlations for the effect of severe, or negative, sanctions in producing illness projections. Positive fixations were not shown to be effective in influencing adult theory of disease causation.

Evaluation of the Whiting-Child method This method stands or falls on the validity of the value rating judgments made by the evaluators of the descriptive ethnographic reports. The evaluations are subjective and often rest on inadequate ethnographic data. Yet the judgments are processed as though they were "hard" quantitative units. Those who feel that a science must have numbers applaud the effort. Those who are skeptical of the value of the results are apt to think of it as "the method of putative precision." It does, however, produce a provocative new look at the materials.

Normality and abnormality

From the discussion of Alorese culture and its effects, it may be seen that what is normal behavior in that society would be looked upon by most Americans as unusual. In 1954, an Ojibwa Indian boy was sent down to the psychiatric ward of the University of Minnesota Hospital because he believed in spirits and thought people could be killed by shooting them with magic mollusk shells. He had been instructed in the mysteries of the Ojibwa Grand Medicine Lodge, or Midewiwin, by his grandfather. In Ojibwa terms, his beliefs are true and wholly normal. It is only when measured against our assumptions that he is "off the beam" and a subject for psychiatric treatment. To share the delusional beliefs traditional in one's own society is a normal phenomenon, Hallowell notes. To develop a private delusional system on one's own is what is abnormal. In its mild form this is neurosis. When it becomes so extreme that the individual loses contact with the reality order of his own society, it becomes a psychosis.

A number of Navaho incest cases, or what the Navaho believe are incest cases, collected by Professor Walter Dyk focus a sharp light on the cultural determination of psychoses.[23] In each case, the committer of incest became psychotic and developed a self-destruction-by-fire obsession. At night when others in the hogan relaxed their watchfulness in sleep, these poor psychotics burned off their hands or feet or lay on their bellies in the quiet embers of the hearth. In each case, the psychotic claimed to have committed incest. Navahos believe that

incest is punished by the fire madness. Psychiatrists are thoroughly familiar with the fact, however, that neurotics and psychotics may be convinced of their guilt for acts that they have never committed. It is clear that the Navaho psychosis with the self-destruction-by-fire symptom is a culturally determined abnormality; it is also quite possible that the incest guilt follows the mental aberration rather than causes it.

To a greater and greater extent, psychiatry is seeking the social roots of psychoses. Even medical practitioners are expanding their awareness of the etiology of seemingly organic diseases in sociopsychological maladjustment. "From concern with the individual as a biological unit psychiatry has progressed to a consideration of him as a social unit. . . . Psychiatry has become a social science as well as a medical science."[24]

Anthropology has proved that within limits "abnormals are those who are not supported by the institutions of their civilization."[25] This means that he who is abnormal in one society may be the approved ideal in another. Crashing Thunder, the Winnebago realist (see page 240), was a misfit in his tribal society, whose culture required visionary experience for success, but he had the personality equipment to make him a successful, hardheaded, two-fisted, go-getting businessman. Siberian shamans definitely have unstable neurotic personalities. In their society, they are leaders and men of influence. In our society, they would be crackpot members of the lunatic fringe, whom many judges would consider fit candidates for a mental hospital.

In our society, the habitually homosexual male is looked upon with emotionally intense hostility. His rejection by the normal elements of our world can be complete and devastating. His conflicts of guilt, remorse, and frustration may, in some cases, be enough to turn him into a psychopath no matter how healthy his early personality may have been. Homosexuality

[23]W. Dyk, *Navajo Field Notes* (unpublished).

[24]W. C. Menninger, "Psychiatry Today" (*The Atlantic Monthly,* Vol. 181, 1948), p. 65. An excellent book with this orientation is N. Cameron, *The Psychology of Behavior Disorders.*
[25]Benedict, *op. cit.,* p. 258.

usually accompanies a rejection of the normal social roles fixed for the two sexes.

In Plains Indian culture, the way out of the dilemma for the boy who found himself unable to meet the demands of the aggressive warrior role was that of the institutionalized *berdache,* or transvestite. At the time of the vision quest, he would be ordered by some tutelary spirit to take up a woman's role, to wear women's clothes, and to perform women's tasks. Because the order was a supernatural one, no blame was affixed to the transvestite. Indeed, although the half-men-half-women were looked upon with awe by children, they were respected and sought out by young men who hoped to procure love medicine from them with which to lure the affection of a desired girl. Thus, Plains Indian berdaches, while relatively rare, were not abnormal personalities because they were supported by their culture.[26]

Still another lead to the understanding of mental disorganization that may be derived from the cultural approach is an awareness of personal conflict resulting from the varying demands of the society's culture.

Mead phrased this very nicely in terms addressed to the problem of adolescent conflict but pertinent to the whole distressing miasma of uncertainty and the continuing demands for decision that our culture imposes upon all but the most circumscribed persons. Although the examples cited by Mead may sound dated (she was writing in 1928), the point endures:

Our young people are faced by a series of different groups which believe different things and advocate different practices, and to each of which some trusted friend or relative may belong. So a girl's father may be a Presbyterian, an imperialist, a vegetarian, a teetotaler, with a strong literary preference for Edmund Burke, a believer in the open shop and a high tariff, who believes that woman's place is in the home, that young girls should wear corsets, not roll their stockings, not smoke, nor go riding with young men in the evening. But her mother's father may be a Low Episcopalian, a believer in high living, a strong advocate of States' Rights and the Monroe Doctrine, who reads Rabelais, likes to go to musical shows and horse races. Her aunt is an agnostic, an ardent advocate of woman's rights, an internationalist who rests all her hopes on Esperanto, is devoted to Bernard Shaw, and spends her spare time in campaigns of anti-vivisection. Her elder brother, whom she admires exceedingly, has just spent two years at Oxford. He is an Anglo-Catholic, an enthusiast concerning all things mediaeval, writes mystical poetry, reads Chesterton, and means to devote his life to seeking for the lost secret of mediaeval stained glass. Her mother's younger brother is an engineer, a strict materialist, who never recovered from reading Haeckel in his youth; he scorns art, believes that science will save the world, scoffs at everything that was said and thought before the nineteenth century, and ruins his health by experiments in the scientific elimination of sleep. Her mother is of a quietistic frame of mind, very much interested in Indian philosophy, a pacifist, a strict non-participator in life, who in spite of her daughter's devotion to her will not make any move to enlist her enthusiasms. And this may be within the girl's own household. Add to it the groups represented, defended, advocated by her friends, her teachers, and the books which she reads by accident, and the list of possible enthusiasms, of suggested allegiances, incompatible with one another, becomes appalling.[27]

Fanatics are people who acquire fixations on one scheme of life, religion, or politics because they cannot thread their way through the maze of conflicting alternative demands that life imposes. They escape a breakdown by settling into a less complete form of sanity.

If the multiplicity of conflicting cultural demands drives to near madness people who are trained wholly within a single cultural tradition, how much more disrupting of the personality is the situation when people are subject to the demands of two or more unlike cultures. This is the case with immigrants to a country which is new to them.

Thus we see not only that culturally induced conflicts produce psychoses but also that the configurations of the cultures influence the kind of insanity that results.

[26]Cheyenne informants estimated that there were usually about five among the 3,000 members of the tribe.

[27]M. Mead, *Coming of Age in Samoa,* pp. 202–203.

SUMMARY

The personality of the individual is analogous to the culture of a society in that it is a sum of integrated behavior traits. The bodily constitution, physical environment, culture, and unique personal experience, as reacted to by the individual, combine to produce the total personality.

Enculturation encompasses all the processes by means of which the individual learns to internalize the norms of his culture. It requires selection among a multitude of kinds of behavior in which the individual has the urge to indulge and the elimination of a great many of them.

Basic drives result from biological needs that must be met. All cultures provide means of satisfactory drive reduction by presenting patterns for goal achievement. At the same time, each culture is the product of limited selection from the vast variety of potential human behaviors. The growing individual must learn to adapt his behavior to the expectancies of his society and to its peculiarities. The person who fails in this is a deviant and, under mental stress, may become neurotic or psychopathic. Mental abnormality, however, is a relative thing.

Ruth Benedict showed how ideal personality types reflect differing configurations of culture. Each culture puts its stamp upon the individual who develops under its influence. Most men reflect a common tribal or national type, mirroring their culture and society. Yet each is possessed of his own uniqueness that no culture can submerge.

The individual, in turn, responds to the specific requirements of his cultural experience by developing basic adjustment mechanisms of his own. The members of a society, exposed as they are to similar cultural experience, tend to develop similar constellations of adjustment. This is the basic personality structure. Kardiner and Whiting have developed special theories to account for the feedback effect of basic personality structures. Kardiner's method is psychoanalytic. Whiting applies a correlational technique using the Human Relations Area Files.

Personality and culture research has added great depth to anthropological understanding of behavior in human societies.

SELECTED READINGS

Aberle, D. F.: "The Psychological Analysis of a Hopi Life-history" (*Comparative Psychological Monographs*, Vol. 211, No. 107, 1951). This is a systematic interpretation in terms of general personality and culture theory of what took place in the life history of Sun Chief, the Hopi Indian whose autobiography was edited by L. Simmons (see below). Aberle's contribution is highly suggestive of illuminating examples. It should be read in connection with *Sun Chief.*

Barnouw, V.: *Culture and Personality* (1963). Useful as a general introduction to what has been done in the field and the methods that are used in relation to theory.

Benedict, R.: *Patterns of Culture* (1934). The classic formulation of the idea of cultural configuration in relation to ideal personality types. Persuasively written in fine literary style, it should not be taken as a reliable ethnography of the cultures discussed, although its major theme is acceptable.

Gladwin, T.: *Truk: Man in Paradise.* A detailed field study of personality in relation to culture in Micronesia, southwest Pacific. It is a fine model.

Haring, D. (ed.): *Personal Character and Cultural Milieu* (2d ed., 1956). A well-balanced anthology of technical papers written by professionals for professional reading. It will be hard going for the beginning student, but it is rewarding for those who want to go further into the subject.

Kardiner, A., et al.: *The Psychological Frontiers of Society* (1945). Contains a general statement of the Kardinerian theory, with description and analysis of the Comanche, Alorese, and Midwestern United States community.

Kluckhohn, C.: "The Influence of Psychiatry in America during the Past One Hundred Years," in J. K. Hall et al. (eds.), *One Hundred Years of American Psychiatry* (1944), pp. 489–618. Reprinted in D. Haring (ed.), *Personal Character and Cultural Milieu.* A useful historical summary of interdisciplinary cross-fertilization.

Lindzey, G.: *Projective Techniques and Cross Cultural Research* (1961). An excellent handbook on the various projective tests and how they have been used in anthropological studies, plus an objectively critical evaluation of each.

Mead, M.: *Male and Female.* (1949). Dr. Mead's most recent and provocative summing up of the interplay of culture and individual psychology in the shaping of men and women in seven primitive societies and the United States.

————and M. Wolfenstein (eds.): *Childhood in Contemporary Cultures* (1955). Applies culture and personality theory to growing up in a number of contemporary societies. Includes a number of interesting chapters.

Opler, M. K.: *Culture, Psychiatry and Human Values* (1956). Mental illness and culture expertly interrelated.

Simmons, L.: *Sun Chief: The Autobiography of a Hopi Indian* (1942). A fascinatingly rich and revealing document of personal experience. Not only does it give the inside view of what it means to grow up as a Hopi, but it also lays bare the severe personal conflicts caused by the need to integrate a single personality while living under two incompatible cultures.

Whiting, J. W. M., and I. L. Child: *Child Training and Personality* (1953). Spells out the theory, method, data, and results of their application of the correlational technique and use of cross-cultural data.

The growth of culture:
invention and diffusion

chapter 5

Culture is a system of learned behaviors. Although human behaviors can become standardized as habits or social usage, behavior is always variable, even when it is habit-bound. Because of this propensity to variability, it is impossible to fix behavior absolutely so that it never changes. Since culturally patterned behavior is learned and not fixed in the organism, it is modifiable and flexible. Therefore, cultures are changeable. Rates of change vary from place to place and from time to time. Some cultures have grown and changed with great rapidity; others have remained relatively stable for hundreds or thousands of years. In the next part of this book we see that the changes in Stone Age cultures from generation to generation were minuscule and that it took tens of thousands of years to develop even so simple a thing as a chipped-stone hand ax. Yet the culture of Japan changed from that of a feudal-peasant society to that of a front-rank industrial society in less than one hundred years. The problem of differential rates of culture growth intrigues and puzzles layman and scientist alike. Why did the Indians of North America not develop any culture comparable to that of nineteenth-century Europe? Why have African cultures lagged behind those of Asia? Truly satisfactory answers cannot yet be given, but certainly a start can be made. This is one of our recurring concerns throughout this book. At this point, let us consider the mechanisms of culture change and growth. An examination of cultural evolution follows in the next chapter.

Culture grows by accretion of inventions and the modification or replacement of old ways. An individual culture changes and grows by acceptance of inventions devised by members of its own society or by acceptance of new ways invented elsewhere and brought to the attention of its members through diffusion of ideas and behaviors.

Invention

What is an invention? Does it differ in any way from a discovery? These questions are not merely of theoretical importance for analytical purposes. They are of tremendous practical significance in the operation of modern patent law, under which an invention is patentable, while a discovery is not.

In the view of a United States District Court of Appeals, for example, a valuable patent on the process of irradiation of foodstuffs by exposure to ultraviolet light was invalid because it merely utilized a physicochemical process that has existed since life began. A distinction is drawn between the invention of a lamp for producing ultraviolet light and the discovery that exposure to ultraviolet rays increases the vitamin content of the exposed organic materials. The one is patentable—that is, subject to certain legal limitations; the other is not.[1]

A discovery is the act of becoming aware of something which has been existing but which has not been previously perceived. Vitamins and sunspots were discovered, not invented.

An invention is an alteration in, or a synthesis of, preexistent materials, conditions, or practices so as to produce a new form of material or action. We must, therefore, deal with new patterns of action that are translated into concrete form (material inventions), and also with inventions that remain in the realm of non-material action patterns solely. These latter are sometimes called *social inventions* or, by philosophers, *moral inventions*.

To illustrate the distinction between discovery and invention more fully, it might be noted that the first ninety-two elements, from hydrogen to uranium, were *discovered* by means of scientific perception. But the new transuranium elements, such as neptunium and plutonium, which have come into being since 1940, are truly *invented* elements. They were not found to exist in nature; they were produced as a result of human ingenuity in the development of techniques for separating neutrons from their elemental nucleus and causing them to enter another elemental nucleus without producing fission. New combinations of protons, neutrons, and electrons were produced —hence, the new elements.

To invent something involves a mental act, one which requires that two or more existing things be conceptually broken into parts and that one, or some, of the parts be modified or replaced or recombined so that a new structure exists. Homer Barnett, the anthropologist who has devoted more thinking and research to the problem of cultural innovation than any other in our time, uses the invention of producer gas as one example of this process:

Innumerable people have known that vapors emitted from crevices in certain parts of the earth are inflammable. About 1684, John Clayton verified reports of this phenomenon in Lancashire and then proceeded to produce such a gas himself. Conjecturing that

[1] *Vitamin Technologists v. Wisconsin Alumni Research Foundation* (*Federal Reports*, 2d series, Vol. 146, 1945), pp. 941ff.

there was a relationship between the gas, the earth's heat, and the coal deposits in nearby mines, he applied heat to coal placed in a retort . . . as a substitute for the earth. . . . Then, in a second step, he caught the released gas . . . in a bladder . . . formerly used for many . . . [other purposes], instead of letting it escape into the atmosphere. . . . He punctured the bladder with a pin, brought a candle flame near the vent, and so produced the precursor of gas lights and burners.[2]

Volitional invention of this order is a rational process of imaginative substitutions and recombinations. It represents the most sophisticated level of cultural modification. Such a process is characteristic only of highly complicated societies with a cultural bent toward dynamic change. Even among advanced civilized nations, relatively few include within their populations a great number of active, willful inventors.

Because invention is highly valued and richly rewarded in our culture, many aspiring minds struggle to find new relations as solutions to set problems. In the process of volitional invention, the inventor recognizes a need or thinks he sees an insufficiency in some form or function. He sets a problem for solution on the basis of this recognized need and proceeds from this point to attempt a rational solution in the form of a practicable invention.

Accidental juxtaposition and invention In the primitive world, volitional inventiveness is truly a rare occurrence. Conscious tinkering with the social structure or with gadgetary improvement is not the order of the day. Most primitive inventions are nonvolitional. They result from what Greenman has called *accidental juxtaposition.*[3]

The operation of the principle of accidental juxtaposition on the crudest level may be illustrated by the activities of Sultan, one of Köhler's famous apes. Sultan was presented with a problem—how to get a banana. He was also presented with two hollow bamboo sticks, neither long enough in itself to reach the banana. They were so fashioned, however, that one could be snugly fitted within the other to make a stick long enough to meet the need. An invention was called for, and the means were at hand. Sultan strained his simian brain for a solution, but the best he could work out was to push one stick toward the banana with the other. This failed to capture the banana. At length, like many another disgusted inventor, he gave up. His efforts at volitional invention were a flat failure. He dropped the sticks and turned his attention to less frustrating activities.

As he roamed around his cage looking for amusement, his attention was once more directed to the sticks. He picked them up and began to play with them in a casual manner and entirely without interest in the elusive banana. Suddenly he found himself holding the two sticks end to end. He pushed the one into the other. Lo, he had it! Accidental juxtaposition had resulted in a new set of relationships, a synthesized combination that constituted an invention. At this critical point, his intelligence was equal to the occasion. He could recognize a useful relationship when he saw it. Immediately he went to the bars, used his tool, and swallowed the banana.[4]

We actually know very little of the precise steps by which most primitive inventions came into being. Long archaeological sequences such as those established for Old World and Southwest prehistory reveal the external form of the gradual steps by which many artifacts have been developed over generations of time. A less empirical method, of which earlier anthropologists were quite fond, was to reconstruct the inventive steps by mesological inference. This is a most intriguing pastime, but too often the result is more "just so" story than objectively substantiated analysis worthy of scientific attention.

The Cheyenne Indian account of the invention of the tipi is of this order. Grinnell recorded that:

The first lodge of modern shape is said to have been suggested by a man who was handling a large poplar leaf, and quite by accident bent it into the shape of a cone—that is to say, of a lodge, such as are used today. As he looked at the leaf it flashed into his mind that a shelter like it would be better than those

[2]H. G. Barnett, "The Innovative Process" (*Kroeber Anthropological Society Papers*, No. 25, 1961), p. 32.
[3]E. F. Greenman, "Material Culture and the Organism" (*American Anthropologist*, Vol. 47, 1945), pp. 212ff.
[4]W. Köhler, *The Mentality of Apes*, pp. 130–133.

they then had. He showed it to the people, and they made lodges in the shape of this leaf, and have used them ever since.[5]

Although it is extremely unlikely that any Cheyenne Indian invented the conical lodge in this manner,[6] the story illustrates quite perfectly the operation of the principle of juxtaposition. Sultan's invention was the result of the close juxtaposition of two objects, the sticks; the supposed invention of the Cheyenne tipi was the result of the juxtaposition of two mental images, the cone formed by the leaf and the potential house. The two accomplishments together exemplify Greenman's final definition of juxtaposition:

The creation of a new implement as the sequel to the establishment of a close spatial relationship between two or more objects, or of a close temporal relationship between the mental images of two or more objects, by natural or artificial means without foreknowledge of the result.[7]

In the technical field, therefore, the creation of a new type of artifact as a result of juxtaposition is a mental reaction to a stimulus in the environment. For the most part, "the progressive evolution of technical forms had to wait upon such accidental juxtapositions."[8]

Of course, accidental juxtaposition can lead to inventive errors as well as to beneficial creativeness. The heavy freight of shibboleths, nonsense tabus, and false dogma carried through the ages by mankind results from erroneous association of images in juxtaposition.

Furthermore, mere juxtaposition does not in itself automatically generate an invention. The use, meaning, and function[9] of particular arti-

facts or social forms may be such as to block acceptance of new forms, uses, meanings, and functions that are proposed in conjunction with the new inventive ideas. Resistance to new inventions is proverbial, and inventors are by no means always heroes.

Anthropological data and historical fact combine to establish that invention is rarely discontinuous. Complex tools and institutions develop gradually as the result of contributions by many men over a considerable period of time. As an example of what primitive invention is not, the following flight of uninhibited imagination is noteworthy:

What vision some ancient fellow must have had to start this process [the domestication of corn]! Can you imagine some primitive hunter of long ago as he sat in the mouth of his cave after an unsuccessful hunt? This man's empty stomach had stimulated his mind and he began to reason, which is the process that distinguished this man from the animal he hunted. A bird was eating grass seeds before him. If only those seeds were as large in relation to the man as they were to the bird! Could they be made larger? Possibly by picking out the very largest seeds and those which tasted best, and planting them next year, he might have a larger plant with larger seeds. The process was started.[10]

The vast majority of human societies can claim relatively few inventions to their credit. Abundant evidence proves that most trait accretions occur through borrowing, and this leads us to a consideration of diffusion.

Diffusion of culture traits

When we find a particular trait or trait complex spread over a wide area and practiced by a number of different tribes, we are confronted with several theoretical possibilites. Each tribe may have invented the same trait independently; one tribe may have invented it, after which it spread to the others through borrowing; or several tribes may have invented it separately, after which it spread over the area.

We can safely say that the first hypothesis is an impossibility. Historical observation estab-

[5] G. B. Grinnell, *The Cheyenne Indians*, Vol. 1, p. 50.

[6] The Cheyennes did not acquire the conical skin tipi until well into the nineteenth century. Other Plains and Woodlands tribes had it before them, so it is quite certain that the Cheyennes borrowed the idea.

[7] Greenman, *op. cit.*, p. 215.

[8] *Ibid.*, p. 218.

[9] See H. G. Barnett, "Culture Processes" (*American Anthropologist*, Vol. 42, 1940), pp. 21–48. *Form:* how it looks to an objective observer; *meaning:* what a people think and feel about it; *function:* what it really does for them. See also R. Linton, *The Study of Man*, pp. 402–404, for a detailed discussion of these analytical concepts. Linton also distinguishes *use:* an ax is used to chop wood; it functions to satisfy the need for wood.

[10] F. C. Hibben, "Corn" (*The Atlantic Monthly*, Vol. 175, 1945), p. 121.

lishes that all peoples are always borrowing from others. We know, for instance, that Indians did not invent the domestication of the horse, nor the art of riding, nor halters, bits, reins, saddles, or any of the other accouterments of riding. They were all adopted from the Spaniards, first by the tribes of the Southwest frontier, who passed them on to the north and east.[11] An interesting fact to note is that the Western saddle, horn-pommeled and deep-backed, was copied from the Spanish saddle, as was the Indian's. But the Eastern riding saddle is copied from the English type that made its first appearance in the New World on the Atlantic Coast. The McClelland army saddle is a fusion of the two types.

Even such simple matters as hide dressing are acquired by borrowing. According to Grinnell:

When the Cheyennes first found the buffalo, they had no knowledge as to how to dress hides. Later, the Sioux on the east side of the Missouri showed them how to cut hides in two, dress them, and sew them together again. These they used as robes. After they reached the Black Hills the Kiowas and Comanches taught the Cheyennes how to dress buffalo-hides in one piece, and also showed them the use of a mixture for softening the hide.[12]

The diffusion of material culture Material culture and mechanical processes of technology are much more readily borrowed than ideas and abstract concepts.

No one has expressed this more impressively than the two missionaries to the Shipibo of the Upper Amazon, Fathers Girbal and Marques, who in 1792 wrote to their headquarters:

To reap it wholly and to bring to God all these heathens certain things are necessary, of which we are in need and of which we shall be in need. Send them to us; God and our most blessed father San Francois will know how to acknowledge it. . . . You

will find added to our letter a note of these requisitions. . . . 400 axes, 600 cutlasses, 2000 straight knives, 1000 curved knives, 4 quintos of iron, 50 pounds of steel, 12 books of small fish-hooks, 8000 needles, one case of false pearls, 500 flints and steels, 4 gross of scissors, 2 gross of rings, 3000 brass crosses, 1000 varas of calico to cover the skin of those who are naked, an assortment of colours to paint our church, a very immaculate Virgin and some ornaments. We also want two skins of wine, both for the celebration of the holy sacrifice and to stop diarrhoea and bloody flux among the infidels.[13]

Fathers Girbal and Marques sensed that if metal were first accepted, *then* these Stone Age gardeners might be ready to consider a new religion.

It does not take long to perceive the value of iron implements. Captain Cook, who was deified by the native Hawaiians in 1779, was later killed by them when he tried to recover one of his ship's longboats which had been stolen so it could be stripped of its metal parts. It was thirty years later that Hawaiians decided to abandon their old ideational order and social system for the culture presented by sailors and missionaries; they realized that the material and ideational aspects of that culture went together, and they wanted both.

The Tiwi of Australia, according to Hart and Pilling,

. . . were first drawn out of their hostile insularity by curiosity and the desire for iron, the same factors which had attracted them toward the Portuguese a century earlier. Iron looted from shipwrecks, channel markers, and the camps of casual visitors to the islands was not sufficient; the Tiwi desired a permanent avenue by which they could obtain the metal. The oldest Tiwi in the early 1950's stated that during the 1890's the Tiwi began to feel that opportunity was passing them by as they noted ship after ship sail in and out of Darwin; the islanders therefore came to the conclusion that they wanted a permanent European settlement in their midst, like the earlier Fort Dundas, for only in this way could they be guaranteed an uninterrupted source of iron.[14]

[11]C. Wissler, "The Influence of the Horse in the Development of Plains Culture" (*American Anthropologist*, Vol. 16, 1914), pp. 1–25; reprinted in Hoebel, Jennings, and Smith, *Readings in Anthropology*, pp. 155–173. F. Haines, "Where Did the Plains Indians Get Their Horses?" (*American Anthropologist*, Vol. 40, 1938), pp. 112–117; also "The Northward Spread of Horses among the Plains Indians" (*American Anthropologist*, Vol. 40, 1938), pp. 429–437.

[12]Grinnell, *op. cit.*, p. 52.

[13]Quoted in H. Hoffman, "Money, Ecology, and Acculturation among the Shipibo of Peru," in W. H. Goodenough (ed.), *Explorations in Cultural Anthropology*, p. 266.

[14]C. W. M. Hart and A. R. Pilling, *The Tiwi of North Australia*, p. 100.

It is much easier to establish a steel mill in a newly developing country than it is to diffuse the ideology and processes of democratic political culture—a simple fact, belatedly recognized by many who hoped for too much, too rapidly from American foreign-aid programs.

The diffusion of nonutilitarian culture Complex nonutilitarian cultural structures also spread through borrowing. In reconstructing histories of cultures, a number of similar traits are frequently found to have existed in two or more cultures. It is a canon of anthropological analysis that such similarities are the probable result of diffusion rather than of independent invention, especially if the group of traits have no inherent reason for existing as a complex.

Tylor was the first to formulate and apply this principle in a study of the diffusion of the ancient East Indian game of pachisi into prehistoric America, where it appeared among the Aztecs as *patolli* and in various other forms among other Indians.[15] Tylor undertook to prove the historical connection between the Asiatic and American forms of these games by "analysing such phenomena into constituent elements showing so little connection with one another that they may reasonably be treated as independent. The more numerous such elements, the more improbable the recurrence of the combination."[16]

The technique may be applied to any aspect of culture,[17] but there is a remarkable stability in myth complexes the world over.

Frazer's *Folklore in the Old Testament* is a fasci-

nating study of comparative distributions of Old World myth complexes and is challenging reading. For our demonstration of the application of the principle of diffusion analysis by means of internal congruity of traits, we shall use the "Tale of the Wandering Animals."

This story is familiar to all readers of Grimm's *Fairy Tales* as the "Musicians of Bremen." The old donkey, the worn-out hound, the abused cat, the rooster destined for the pot, and other rejected, decrepit animals all joined forces to go to the fair port of Bremen to become *Stadtmusikantern.* Night closed in on them as they found themselves deep in the woods. Frightening a band of robbers out of their hut, they made themselves at home, each in his favorite spot—the cat on the hearth, the rooster in the rafters, the dog on the doorstep, the donkey on the dungheap. The robbers sent back a spy in the darkness. But when he lighted the fire, the cat flew in his face; the dog chewed his leg as he fled through the door; the donkey planted a kick; and the rooster crowed his doom. The weak and despised creatures frightened away the robbers, who are symbolic of those who normally rule and dominate "the little man," and lived prosperously ever after in the nice snug little hut in the woods.

In Southeast Asia and Japan an ancient story is told, which in its simplest outline runs as follows.

An egg, a scorpion, a needle, a piece of feces, and a rice mortar (or any hard, heavy object) came together upon a journey. They entered the house of an old woman during her absence, and in order to do her harm, they disposed themselves in different places. The egg lay on the hearth, the scorpion in the water basin, the needle on the floor, the feces in the doorway, and the mortar over the door. When the old woman came home in the evening, she went to the hearth to light the fire, but the egg sprang up and smeared her face. When she went to the basin to wash, she was stung by the scorpion. Seized by terror, she rushed from the house, but the needle stuck in her foot, she slipped on the feces and was upset,

[15] E. B. Tylor, "On the Game of Patolli in Ancient Mexico, and Its Probable Asiatic Origin" (*Journal of the Royal Anthropological Institute of Great Britain and Ireland,* Vol. 8, 1879), pp. 116–129.
[16] E. B. Tylor, "American Lot Games as Evidence of Asiatic Intercourse before the Time of Columbus" (*Internationales Archiv für Ethnographie,* Vol. 9, supplement, 1896), p. 66. For a critical evaluation of Tylor's method, see C. J. Erasmus, "Patolli, Pachisi, and the Limitation of Possibilities" (*Southwestern Journal of Anthropology,* Vol. 6, 1950), pp. 369–387.
[17] F. Boas, *Tsimshian Mythology* (Bureau of American Ethnology, Annual Report 31, 1916), pp. 393–558. This is the classic study of the reflection of a people's material culture and social organization in their mythology.

and the mortar fell on her head, killing her.[18]

Here is the "Musicians of Bremen" all over again. Aarne justifiably concluded: "The concurrences between the tales are so significant that in my opinion we must conclude that the stories stand in an interdependent relationship in their origin."[19] He traced the story through India, into south Russia, up through Central Europe, and into Germany, where it arrived in the late Middle Ages.

Now let us shift our attention to the Northwest Coast of North America. A favored story of the Northwest Coast Indians has now a familiar ring. It is "Raven's War on the South Wind."[20] Raven is the mythological culture hero of this area, and the South Wind often brings too much rain from the ocean.

The South Wind, so the story runs, was blowing so incessantly that all the creatures had to stay in their huts. They could not hunt, and they were hungry. The smoke blew back down their smoke vents and made their eyes sore. At last Raven called a council of war to propose an attack on the Master of the South Wind. A special canoe was procured, and the war party made the journey to the home of the South Wind. They had trouble landing because the gale caused by the flatulence of the Master of the South Wind was so strong that they were nearly overcome.

But once ashore, Halibut and Flounder or Skate (all flat, slippery fish) arranged themselves according to Raven's orders just outside the South Wind's doorstep. Red Cod or the Wren went in and started a smudge (in another version, Mouse went in and bit the South Wind's nose). As the Master of the South Wind staggered from the house, he slipped on the fish and slithered down the beach, where the waiting animals tried to beat his brains out with clubs—which are as hard as a rice mortar or a donkey's hoof. The South Wind made a successful deal for his life—four days of good

weather to alternate with four days of bad.[21]

Here, then, is a basic plot in which pusillanimous animals overcome masterful human beings in their very houses by combining their own little natural aptitudes to undo mankind. No matter that men were the authors of the tale. It is the story of the little men triumphing over the big men who order their lives. Its appeal as a vicarious release of suppressed resentments is clear. The ludicrousness of the event provides an elemental sort of gusty humor. The story is too good to keep. It has a broad appeal because it meets a common need. From Asia it spread westward into Europe and northeastward into the northwest corner of North America. This, however, is not the end of its history. In post-Columbian times, variants of the "Musicians of Bremen" form of the tale were brought to the Eastern Indians by early trappers, and in the Plains and Woodlands these variants were adapted into a charming story known as "Big Turtle's War Party."

Thus, by word of mouth, crossing language barrier after language barrier, the "Tale of the Wandering Animals" has girdled the globe; penetrating North America from the west and from the east, it met itself along the rocky spine of the Western mountain area (Fig. 5-1).

The spread of tobacco may be followed from the New World to Europe and Africa, from Europe to the South Seas and Asia, and to Siberia, whence it went into Alaska even before it reached the Eskimos from the south. Although Indians 1,000 miles away had native tobacco, it had to travel some 15,000 miles around the world before the Eskimos were introduced to the habit of smoking. In this case, the essential factor was the difference between limited primitive transportation of an item that can be grown only in favored locales and the extensive communication established by European civilization with the Industrial Revolution.

[18]A. Aarne, *Die Tiere auf der Wanderschaft* (Folklore Fellows Communications, No. 11, 1913), p. 100.

[19]*Ibid.,* p. 162.

[20]Eleven versions are recorded in Boas, *op. cit.,* pp. 79–81, 658–660.

[21]An analysis in full detail is given in E. A. Hoebel, "The Asiatic Origin of a Myth of the Northwest Coast" (*Journal of American Folklore,* Vol. 54, 1941), pp. 1–12.

Fig. 5-1   Diffusion of the Asiatic "Tale of the Wandering Animals." A, original Asiatic center of origin; B, the "Musicians of Bremen" version; C, "Raven's War on the South Wind"; D, "Big Turtle's War Party."

Either by reliance upon historical data or by inferential reconstruction from distributional analysis, trait after trait may be followed through the course of its diffusion.

Dynamics of diffusion: selective factors   Diffusion is no simple, straight-line process in which a people put an idea on wheels, figuratively speaking, and give it a shove to send it on its way around the world.

Every spreading trait or complex, as it moves from one society to another, must face the test of its acceptability in the culture of the receivers; and if it is accepted, it is invariably reworked in form, use, meaning, or function. No people take an alien trait without altering it to some degree.

The fate of the Plains Indian sun dance illustrates this clearly. The sun dance is a fairly complex ritual shared by a score of tribes in the western part of the Plains area. The ceremony is most elaborated and developed among the Arapaho and Cheyenne. From these tribes,

according to Spier's classic analysis, the complex spread out among the other nomadic tribes.[22] In its core, the sun dance shows remarkable stability wherever it occurs. The fundamental form of the dance is universal within the area of its distribution. Nevertheless, considerable variation in content occurs from tribe to tribe. As Spier observed, strong systematic selection was exercised.

Selection often works in subtle ways that we cannot determine *ex post facto*. Some of the more obvious determinants, however, may be quite clear. Thus, two features of the Arapaho sun dance are the use of medicine bundles and the special roles played by the military fraternity of the man who sponsors the dance. Among the Wind River and Idaho Shoshones, neither of these occurs in connection with the dance. The reason is simply that the limited culture of the Shoshones has no military societies within their social structure and no priesthood of bundle owners. The Shoshones stripped the complex ritual down to the structure of their meager social framework. As they adapted it, the sun dance became primarily a purification and curing ceremony, designed to bring general well-being to the entire tribe. For the closely related Utes, the function and meaning were

[22]L. Spier, "The Sun Dance of the Plains Indians" (*American Museum of Natural History, Anthropological Papers*, Vol. 16, Part 7, 1921).

quite similar, although details, such as an increased emphasis on dreaming, varied.[23]

The Crows used the sun dance to generate war power against specific enemies. Revenge was the motif; a scalp, the object; a war party, the follow-up.

The Cheyenne sun dance was, and still is, a world-renewal ceremony. In the Cheyenne world view, the energy of the universe is being continuously used up and must be annually recharged mimetically through the ceremonies. Although the dance is pledged by one individual, the entire renewal effort is directed toward the welfare of all members of the tribe.

There is one recorded instance where the dance was "borrowed" by a tribe, tried once, and forever dropped. Urged on by their "messiah" and in need of "war medicine," the Comanches presented one sun dance that was to endow them with immunity to bullets. Soon after, they were thoroughly defeated in battle. The ritual had failed in its desired function, and it is improbable that it ever developed any meaning for them.[24]

Thus, the function and meaning of the sun dance varied as it was worked into one tribal culture after another. For the buffalo hunters in the mid-nineteenth century, its chief function was that of tribal integration. The scattered bands that eked out the winter separately were brought together in early summer for a grand socializing prior to the communal buffalo hunt. For individuals, the dance functioned to relieve anxiety. It also expressed a subconscious submissiveness to the supernatural through self-imposed hunger and thirsting and bloody immolation of the self to gratify the spirit forces. It functioned to make more probable the acquisition of power through visions by means of heightened social suggestion.

As the sun dances are performed on the reservations today, they function mostly as reinforcers of tribal integrity in the face of all the surrounding forces of disintegration.

The selective effect of ideology, or meaning,

on cultural diffusion and reinterpretation may be seen if we look at the celebration of the Fourth of July by the Crows and Cheyennes today. On the Crow reservation, a large crowd gathers at a racetrack. The betting is as spirited as the horses, the latter ridden by Crow Indians splendid in colorful jockey costumes. The shouting is loud. The fireworks are deafening. There is no sun dance. For the Crows it is dead.

At the Cheyenne reservation, a few miles away, a sun dance comes to its four-day climax. The dancers move through the ceremonial forms with somewhat weary dignity. The audience watches quietly. A neatly lettered sign reads: "Quiet. No Fireworks Allowed."

Why such a difference between two tribes of Plains Indians, whose acquaintance stretches back over many years and who currently live boundary to boundary?

It is obvious that both groups are celebrating the Fourth of July and that as citizens of the United States, they recognize this date as a symbol of American identity. However, each group has recombined certain elements of the national rite in such a way as to produce two very different kinds of celebration. The Cheyennes, with their age-old emphasis on world renewal and group solidarity, seem not so much to be celebrating the birth of our nation as seeking to revivify it through their tribal efforts. The basic meaning of the dance has changed little, although its form has worn a bit thin. The time of the dance has been changed from early June to July 4, signifying tribal integration into a new and larger society. School vacations and work schedules make this a convenient and natural date. Perhaps, too, the selection of the national holiday indicates that they are sufficiently identified with the larger society to wish to proclaim their membership in it and help keep it strong and vital.

The original function of the Crows' sun dance, to bring success in scalp-hunting, has long vanished. The meaning of the dance was too specialized to permit adaptation to contemporary conditions, and the Crows have held

[23]M. K. Opler, "The Integration of the Sun Dance in Ute Religion" (*American Anthropologist*, Vol. 43, 1941), pp. 550–572.
[24]E. Wallace and E. A. Hoebel, *The Comanches*, pp. 319–326.

no sun dances for several decades. But gambling and horse racing, with their attendant noisy clamor, are ancient pastimes. It was natural for the Crows to seize on the festive aspect of the Fourth and to make of it a noisy carnival as they, too, proclaim their identity with the United States.

• This fundamental anthropological fact—in cultural transference a trait or complex will be evaluated and rejected, or accepted and modified, in terms of the meaning it has for the receiving people—is one of the most difficult for professional civilizers to perceive and apply. This applies to teachers, Peace Corps volunteers, economic-development programmers, public health workers, and missionaries, whose numbers are steadily increasing. When this principle is ignored, the consequent mischief worked is often monumental.

Over one hundred years ago, a wise and not too doctrinaire Episcopalian missionary demonstrated his full recognition of this aspect of intercultural transference. Sensing the likelihood of misinterpretation of the Christian rite of

Fig. 5-2   Acculturation. English memorial sentiments are adapted to a traditional Kwakiutl carving of a chief in a frock coat embracing a copper shield. (Courtesy of Robert Gardner.)

communion by the Tsimshian Indians, among whom he was working, he was induced to omit the ritual from his services. Cannibalism among the Northwest Coast Indians, although quite different in meaning for the Indians, was too similar to communion in form and function. Not only in this but in other points as well did Duncan, the missionary in question, deliberately and as a matter of policy eliminate "many of the potential danger spots in Christian metaphysics for a native whose only basis for interpreting new belief was in terms of the old."[25]

Even with foresight, one cannot anticipate some consequences of interpretation of new phenomena in terms of old meanings. For example, the Dani tribesmen of the Balim Valley in western New Guinea (Irian) are active cannibals. American missionaries who entered the area in the 1950s discouraged the practice in their efforts to promote civilization and Christianization. As the Dani became familiar with eating canned goods, they quickly comprehended that a tin bearing a picture of beans on its label contained beans, that one picturing pears contained pears, and so forth. When one of the mission wives gave birth and cans of Gerber's baby food with pictures of healthy babies on the labels were flown in, the Dani's idea of the eating habits of American missionaries need not be guessed.[26]

Commonly, in diffusion and culture growth, the form of a trait or complex will remain the same, at least initially. But the meaning is almost certain to be altered, and, possibly, the use and functions also. Thus, an explorer may give an empty film spool to a native, who receives it with delight, puts it through the slit in his earlobe, and struts proudly, confident of his beauty. The form of the spool is unaltered, but its use is that of an ear labret; its meaning is aesthetic and perhaps also magical; and its function, that of prestige enhancement and ego gratification. The spool is thus culturally acceptable because it readily fits into the context of the native culture in a positive way.

[25]H. G. Barnett, "Applied Anthropology in 1860" (*Applied Anthropology*, Vol. 1, 1942), p. 24.

[26]Personal communication from a member of the mission organization, 1962.

The selective consequences of negative meanings Traits that have positive meaning in one culture may be blocked in diffusion because their forms are associated with negatively colored uses, meanings, or functions in the existing cultures of potential receivers.

At a Northern Cheyenne peyote meeting, the author once became interested in a decorative staff used in the ritual. It seemed to be carved with figures of bison quite similar to those of Franco-Cantabrian cave art. The thought was intriguing. Upon closer examination, however, the carved scenes proved to be of toreadors and charging bulls. There was also the Mexican eagle sitting on his cactus, but the snake in his claws had been scraped out with a knife. Black Wolf, the peyote leader, explained that the staff had come from Mexico, and he pointed out that the eagle is good medicine. The toreador confronting the bull suggested the vision-seeking Indian confronted by a bison. However, he said, "Those people down there worship snakes, but we don't. So we took the snakes out. We can't have any snakes in our ceremony." The Cheyennes, in point of fact, are not simply neutral with respect to snakes. In their mythology, the Horned Snake (or the Plumed Serpent) is a creature much to be feared and avoided.

Barnett has detailed a number of such rejections by several northern California tribes. When the bobbing of women's hair came into vogue, it met heavy resistance because that hairstyle was believed to cause death. Corsets and hairpins were rejected at first because they resembled the warrior's rod armor and the bone pins that he used in his hair.[27]

On a larger scale, the efforts of the Belgian administration in the Congo to make the Pygmies of the forest more economically self-sufficient by inducing them to take up gardening were rejected outright. A few Pygmies made the try on "model" plantations, and although they demonstrated the ability to cultivate, "they degenerated socially and physically at an alarming rate, losing all sense of individual or family responsibility and dying from sunstroke and

[27]Barnett, "Applied Anthropology in 1860," pp. 31–32.

Fig. 5-3 *A Tlingit prestigious possession—a working model of a sewing machine adorned with totemic figures. (From Robert Bruce Inverarity,* Art of the Northwest Coast Inverarity Indians. *Courtesy of the University of California Press.)*

stomach disorders."[28] These were merely symptoms; they were dying because they had accepted a new way of life utterly devoid of meaning. Other Mbuti "clearly see and state that once they abandon their nomadic forest existence they will cease to be Mbuti."[29]

For similar, though less drastic, reasons, the Navaho have refused through a thousand years of contact with the Pueblo Indians to adopt Pueblo architecture, even though it is structurally "better." To give up the hogan, or earth lodge, for an apartment in a pueblo-type settlement would require the abandonment of basic values that the Navaho hold dear. Such housing would make it impossible to live as a Navaho. As a people, they have stoutly refused to shed their identity simply for a better home.[30]

[28]C. M. Turnbull, "The Mbuti Pygmies of the Congo," in J. L. Gibbs, Jr. (ed.), *Peoples of Africa,* p. 313.
[29]*Ibid.*
[30]This is discussed in more detail in Chapters 15 and 16 pp. 236–237, 258.

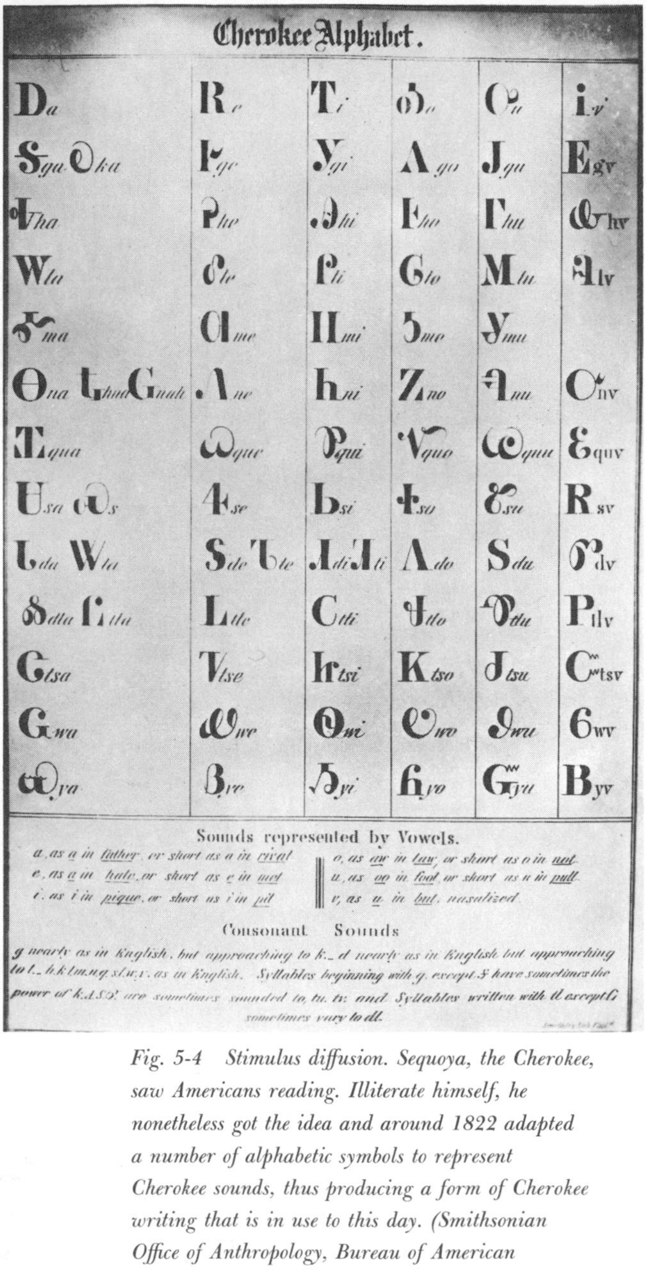

Cherokee Alphabet.

D_a	R_e	T_i	δ_o	O_u	i_v
$S_{ga} O_{ka}$	F_{ge}	Y_{gi}	A_{go}	J_{gu}	E_{gv}
∂_{ha}	P_{he}	θ_{hi}	F_{ho}	Γ_{hu}	Φ_{hv}
W_{la}	δ_{le}	P_{li}	G_{lo}	M_{lu}	Π_{lv}
δ_{ma}	α_{me}	H_{mi}	5_{mo}	y_{mu}	
$O_{na} t_{hna} G_{nah}$	Λ_{ne}	h_{ni}	Z_{no}	q_{nu}	O_{nv}
T_{qua}	ω_{que}	P_{qui}	V_{quo}	ω_{quu}	$\mathcal{E}_{quv}$
$U_{sa} \omega_s$	4_{se}	b_{si}	Φ_{so}	$\mathcal{E}_{su}$	R_{sv}
$L_{da} W_{ta}$	$S_{de} \mathcal{T}_{te}$	$J_{di} \mathcal{I}_{ti}$	Λ_{do}	S_{du}	$\mathcal{G}_{dv}$
$\delta_{dla} \mathcal{L}_{tla}$	L_{tle}	C_{tli}	Ψ_{tlo}	$\mathcal{P}_{tlu}$	P_{tlv}
G_{tsa}	V_{tse}	Ir_{tsi}	K_{tso}	J_{tsu}	C_{tsv}
G_{wa}	ω_{we}	O_{wi}	O_{wo}	9_{wu}	6_{wv}
ω_{ya}	B_{ye}	δ_{yi}	f_{yo}	G_{yu}	B_{yv}

Sounds represented by Vowels.

a, as a in father, or short as a in rival *o, as aw in law, or short as o in not*
e, as a in hate, or short as e in met *u, as oo in fool, or short as u in pull*
i, as i in pique, or short as i in pit *v, as u in but, nasalized*

Consonant Sounds

g nearly as in English, but approaching to k. d nearly as in English but approaching to t. h.k.l.m.n.q.s.w.y. as in English. Syllables beginning with g, except Ɠ have sometimes the power of k.A.S.9. are sometimes sounded to, tu, tv; and Syllables written with tl except L sometimes vary to dl.

Fig. 5-4 Stimulus diffusion. Sequoya, the Cherokee, saw Americans reading. Illiterate himself, he nonetheless got the idea and around 1822 adapted a number of alphabetic symbols to represent Cherokee sounds, thus producing a form of Cherokee writing that is in use to this day. (Smithsonian Office of Anthropology, Bureau of American Ethnology Collection.)

These examples demonstrate that the pre-existing biases of the members of a receiving society facilitate or block the accepting or borrowing of any new cultural possibility. The compatibility of a new way with the basic postulates and derived corollaries underlying the receiving culture is of vital importance. On the other hand, the acceptance of materials of apparently neutral significance but of demonstrated technical efficiency, such as iron or tractors, may ultimately lead to value and postulational disruptions that were never anticipated. The successful development of lunar and interplanetary rockets, for example, obviously holds undreamed-of cultural consequences in store. Yet we seem quite willing to take our chances on what the penetration of space will mean for the future.

The selective consequences of cultural indifference The selection of culture traits in accordance with their compatibility with a specific set of cultural postulates and related cultural values leads not only to negative rejection. It may also result in the neutral nonacceptance of alien possibilities because of indifference. A thing or an idea may be seen or encountered and yet not be borrowed, adapted, or even desired. It meets no felt need of a people; or its usefulness is not perceived by them; it rings no bell. Their interest is in other things or ideas. Loren Eiseley astutely comments of the Maya, who were capable of inventing such an abstraction as the concept of the zero, plus a hieroglyphic symbol to represent it:

These men who could predict eclipses never learned to weigh or to use the wheel for transportation, though wheeled toys were in use among their neighbors. No better example could be utilized to reveal that a given society has just so much energy and interest at its disposal, and that its intellectual achievements will move in the path of its deepest motivations. The Mayan intellect centered upon a divine mathematics that controlled the human world, just as different cultures, including our own, have pursued reality in other shapes and guises.[31]

[31]L. Eiseley, "In the Beginning Was the Artifact" (*Saturday Review*, Dec. 7, 1963), p. 52.

Stimulus diffusion A very special type of diffusion has been discussed by Kroeber under the heading *stimulus diffusion*.[32] This occurs when the general idea of a culture trait or complex is transferred from one people to another without a transmission of the actual detailed content. The content of the pattern is more or less wholly invented by the borrowers of the idea. Sequoya, the Cherokee inventor of the syllabary used by the Cherokees for writing their tongue, got the idea of writing from contact with whites, but he did not learn to write the English language. He took some alphabetic symbols directly from English, modified some, and invented others. His English symbols, however, bear no relation to the English phonetic system. He made them stand for Cherokee syllables. He took the idea, but not the form of writing.

Stimulus diffusion as a process stands midway between independent invention and genuine diffusion. Awareness of a need or an inventive possibility is stimulated by contact with a trait or a complex from an alien source. The stimulated people, who lack the trait, attempt independently to invent an equivalent of it.

Culture change, growth, and evolution A culture changes whenever a modification of any established pattern occurs among its component parts. This may or may not involve growth. Arts and usages are frequently lost without a functionally analogous replacement. When new elements increase the complexity of the total system of a culture, change is producing growth. Whether growth of a specific kind is good or bad is a matter of value judgment. In general, because cultures are, in the long run, adaptive mechanisms subject to natural selection, culture growth is more often positive in its social consequences than negative. Culture growth that is continuous and enduring leads to cultural evolution, the subject of the next chapter.

Acculturation occurs when a culture undergoes drastic alterations in the direction of conform-

ity to another culture from which it borrows numerous traits or principles. The acculturating society, although drastically modified, retains its discrete identity. It becomes adjusted to, but not assimilated in, the dominant society. All developing nations around the world are in the process of whirlwind acculturation to the technological, military, scientific, and political aspects of Western civilization. The relevance of anthropology to this portentous process is examined in the last chapter of this text.

SUMMARY

Invention differs from discovery. Discovery produces new knowledge, it is true, but invention creates a wholly new relationship among things. All culture is the product of invention, but no culture is the product of inventions created solely by its builders. An inventory of traits in any culture shows more borrowed than independently invented elements. In the process of diffusion, each people selectively adopts or rejects the alien culture traits or complexes with which it comes in contact. This is done on the basis of the uses, meanings, and functions that it attributes to the new traits. A major problem in modern public health, technical aid, and missionary programs is the understanding of the intended beneficiaries' attitudes toward new proposals. This can be done only in terms of the concepts of use, meaning, and function already in existence among the receiving people.

Borrowing and the stimulus of new ideas are essential to cultural vitality, but too rapid an acceptance of diffused culture patterns often destroys the way of life of a people.

SELECTED READINGS

Barnett, H. G.: *Innovation* (1953). The most intensive effort so far at systematic analysis of the processes of culture growth.

[32]A. L. Kroeber, "Stimulus Diffusion" (*American Anthropologist,* Vol. 42, 1940), pp. 11–20.

Greenman, E. F.: "Material Cutlure and the Organism" (*American Anthropologist,* Vol. 47, 1945), pp. 211–231.

Hodgen, M. T.: *Change and History* (1952). Shows how technological advance within England varied by districts during the Industrial Revolution. Pinpoints the particular towns and parishes where technological innovation took place.

Kroeber, A. L.: *Anthropology* (rev. ed., 1948), chaps. 11 and 12, entitled "Some Histories of Inventions: The Interplay of Factors" and "Culture Growths and Spreads." Contains many interesting examples.

————: *Configurations of Culture Growth* (1944). The greatest effort by a modern anthropologist to cope with the problem on a broad historical scale by use of anthropological concepts and tools of analysis. Kroeber's aims are those of Spengler and Toynbee, but his results are much more acceptable, according to the canons of an empirically based, analytical science.

Singer, S., E. J. Holmyard, and A. R. Hall (eds.): *A History of Technology* (1954). Definitive. The most comprehensive summary of invention and the steps that have occurred in the development of material culture. In three volumes.

From the time of the American Revolution to the end of World War I, the idea of the evolution of culture as the key to the story of man was the definitive concept of social history. It began in speculative thought about the "savages" of the New World, who had been revealed to European consciousness by the explorations of Columbus and those who followed him. It was enlarged when Magellan, Cook, and their counterparts discovered the peoples of the islands of the vast Pacific. It was fed by the opening of Africa. The problem for the thinkers of the Age of Enlightenment was the same as that which was touched upon in the last chapter: How could they account for the vast gap that was observed between life-styles of the primitive tribes of the uncivilized world and those of the peoples of ancient and modern civilizations?

Evolutionary thought in the eighteenth and nineteenth centuries

Rationalists quickly discounted and rejected the common notion advanced by a number of theologians that savages were human beings who had degenerated from a state of original grace and well-being. This idea was a simple extension of the doctrine of the Fall of Man. The great enlightened scholars of the eighteenth century thought otherwise. They believed in human progress that advanced by well-defined steps toward perfection, and they were imbued with a stirring enthusiasm for the prospects of systematic human advancement in the years ahead. To them, the newly discovered savages were primitive men who, for whatever reasons, had lagged in the climb up the ladder of human improvement.

The eighteenth- and nineteenth-century view of social evolution as developed by historians and philosophers of history was first formulated by the Scottish historian and churchman William Robertson (see also pages 509–511), who in 1777 wrote: "In every part of the earth, the progress of man hath been nearly the same; and we can trace him in his career from the rude simplicity of savage life, until he attains the industry, the arts, and the elegance of polished society."[1] In France, Montesquieu, Voltaire, Condorcet, and Comte all built on the idea prior to 1835. Hence, contrary to common belief, the formulation and establishment of the principle of evolution in the fields of sociology and anthropology were not in imitation of Darwin. Herbert Spencer, in England, had clearly fixed and formulated his

version of the principle of evolution some years before Darwin published his masterwork. Indeed, all scientific knowledge of the period was leading toward evolutionism. Spencer was influenced not only by his predecessors in social philosophy but also by the work of the embryologist von Baer and the geologist Lyell. From Malthus's *Essay on Population*,[2] Spencer derived the principle of the survival of the fittest. Darwin, too, was stimulated from the same source, for, as he acknowledged:

In October 1838 . . . I happened to read for amusement "Malthus on Population," and being very well prepared to appreciate the struggle for existence which goes on . . . it at once struck me that under these circumstances favorable variations would tend to be preserved, and unfavorable ones to be destroyed. The result would be the formation of a new species.[3]

Darwin felt the need of some principle to explain the biological facts he had long since sensed; quite by accident he read Malthus, whose ideas juxtaposed to, and then combined with, his own inspired the greatest thought invention of the era. Before this, Malthus had found in an essay by Benjamin Franklin the critical stimulus for the formulation of his theory of the reproductive capacities and consequent competition for survival of living things.[4]

Nineteenth-century lineal evolutionism The aim of the nineteenth-century cultural evolutionists was to put flesh on the skeleton of prehistory that the archaeologists of Europe were so assiduously exhuming from the earth. How did ancient man organize his life, and what changes in social culture accompanied technological evolution?

Lewis Henry Morgan (1818–1881) reacted to his firsthand knowledge of the Iroquois Indians in much the same way as had the French Jesuit missionary Lafitau one hundred years before. Lafitau (1681–1746) had seen in the

[1] W. Robertson, *History of America*, as quoted in A. I. Hallowell, "The Beginnings of Anthropology in America," in F. DeLaguna (ed.), *Selected Papers from the American Anthropologist: 1888–1920*, p. 15.

[2] T. R. Malthus, *An Essay on the Principle of Population.*
[3] F. Darwin (ed.), *The Life and Letters of Charles Darwin*, Vol. 1, p. 83.
[4] B. Franklin, "Observations concerning the Increase of Mankind," in *The Interests of Great Britain Considered.*

society of American Indians a clue to the understanding of ancient cultures when he wrote his *Customs of the American Savages Compared with Customs of Early Times.*[5] Morgan took a similar position in his *Ancient Society, or Researches in the Lines of Human Progress from Savagery, through Barbarism to Civilization.* Morgan's thesis was well summed up in his own words:

Commencing, then, with the Australians and Polynesians, following with the American Indian tribes, and concluding with the Roman and Grecian, who afford the highest exemplifications respectively of the six great stages of human progress, the sum of their united experiences may be supposed fairly to represent that of the human family from the Middle Status of savagery to the end of ancient civilization. . . . So essentially identical are the arts, institutions, and mode of life in the same status upon all continents, that the archaic form of the principal domestic institutions of the Greeks and Romans must even now be sought in the corresponding institutions of the American aborigines. . . . This fact forms a part of the accumulating evidence tending to show that . . . the course and manner of their development was predetermined, as well as restricted within narrow limits of divergence, by the natural logic of the human mind and the necessary limitations of its powers.[6]

The essence of lineal evolution as summed up by Morgan is as follows: (1) Culture evolves in successive stages, which are (2) essentially the same in all parts of the world, from which (3) it is to be inferred that the order of the stages is inevitable (predetermined) and their content limited because (4) mental processes are universally similar among all peoples (that is, there is a psychic unity of man). In other words, when confronted with the conditions of stage A, men universally respond by inventing the cultural forms of stage B, in reaction to which they then produce stage C, and so forth through the ages. The only difference is in the rate of speed with which they move through the several stages. (See Chapter 35 for a more detailed discussion.)

[5] J. F. Lafitau, *Moeurs des sauvages amériquains comparées aux moeurs des premiers temps*, Paris, 1724.
[6] L. H. Morgan, *Ancient Society*, pp. 17–18.

Sir Edward Burnett Tylor (1832–1917), the leading English evolutionist of that time, put the same set of ideas even more succinctly than Morgan. In 1888 he wrote:

The institutions of man are as distinctly stratified as the earth on which he lives. They succeed each other in series substantially uniform over the globe, independent of what seem the comparatively superficial differences of race and language, but shaped by similar human nature acting through successively changing conditions in savage, barbaric and civilized life.[7]

This concept of evolution is called *lineal evolutionism* because it emphasizes a straight-line course of development for all societies. It is also called *parallelism* because it posits that all societies, even if they were completely isolated from one another, would pass through parallel stages of evolution.

Morgan tried to show what happened in the evolution of technology, property, kinship, and political structure. Tylor concentrated on religion. Among other early cultural evolutionists, Bachofen, McLennan, Lang, Frazer, Westermarck, Brinton, and Haddon stand out as leaders.[8]

Evolution in Communist theory In the field of political philosophy, Karl Marx was greatly stimulated by Morgan's evolutionary thesis. He found the key to history, according to his close companion, Friedrich Engels, in the study of the American Indian. After Marx's death, Engels wrote a book based on Marx's notes and ideas, bearing the title *On the Origin of the Family, Private Property, and the State in the Light of the Researches of Lewis Henry Morgan.* Marx

[7] E. B. Tylor, "On a Method of Investigating the Development of Institutions: Applied to Laws of Marriage and Descent" (*Journal of the Royal Anthropological Institute of Great Britain and Ireland,* Vol. 18, 1888).
[8] E. B. Tylor, *Researches into the Early History of Mankind; Primitive Culture; Anthropology.* Morgan, *op. cit.* J. K. Bachofen, *Das Mutterrecht.* J. G. McLennan, *Primitive Marriage; The Patriarchal Theory.* A. Lang, *Myth, Ritual, and Religion; The Making of Religion; Social Origins.* J. G. Frazer, *The Golden Bough; Totemism and Exogamy.* E. Westermarck, *The History of Human Marriage.* D. G. Brinton, *Religions of Primitive People.* A. C. Haddon, *Evolution in Art.*

and Engels used Morgan's scheme of lineal evolution as the framework upon which to build an account of the linkage between private property, the monogamous "patriarchal" family, and the state as the exploitative institutions that, the theory holds, are responsible for the exploitation of workers and the degradation of women. It is this work which established Morgan and cultural evolutionism as official theoretical dogma in Communist thinking and which largely characterizes Soviet ethnology to this day. The pen of Engels undertook to turn nineteenth-century evolutionism into an ideological weapon to speed the downfall of capitalism and to assure the triumph of the Communist proletarian society as the next logically inevitable stage of cultural evolution. Evolution was to make manifest destiny of *The Communist Manifesto.*

The Boasian reaction

With the turn of the century, a strong reaction, led by Franz Boas in America, set in against much of the work of these men.

The main line of the Boasian attack was in terms of the numerous errors in fact that were exposed by careful empirical field study. To a considerable degree, the nineteenth-century cultural evolutionists were more social philosophers than empirical scientists. They grasped the large idea of evolution and then moved in to formulate detailed schemes of the development of various aspects of culture without waiting for sufficient factual data. Indeed, except in the case of Morgan, they hardly bothered to raise a finger to add to factual knowledge by means of field studies. Truly, they earned the epithet "armchair anthropologists." Too much of their work rested on a priori premises and uncritical handling of the tales of travelers and accounts of officials and missionaries, who were themselves in most cases without scientific training. They mistook masses of library references for critical scholarship. Above all, they blindly ignored the great variability of cultures in terms of their patterning of inner details and their adjustments to different types of ecological environments.

With Boas, anthropology came to be firmly grounded in empiricism. Primitive cultures were fast disappearing. The job was to get in the field and make objective studies before the sands of time ran out. As factual knowledge scientifically obtained began to come in and to be collated, the known errors in the current evolutionary schemes began to pile up.

As the recognized errors increased, so did the Boasian rejection of evolutionism as it was then practiced.[9] To pull the pillars from under the edifices of lineal evolutionism was often a major interest of American anthropologists, and in some extreme instances, the enthusiasm for the truth that Boas insisted upon was too readily converted into a scorn of all theory.[10]

Scientific caution so hypertrophied to scientific negativism, that in 1939 Kluckhohn reported the mental state of American anthropologists to be such that "to suggest something is 'theoretical' is to suggest that it is slightly indecent."[11]

R. H. Lowie's great work, *Primitive Society,* published in 1920, seemed to put the *coup de grâce* to Morgan. By 1925, English, American, German, and French anthropologists had turned completely away from any interest in the evolution of culture. In England and France, anthropologists were absorbed in functional analysis of living cultures. The subject was dead and buried.

Cultural evolution today

The simple fact remains, however, that cultures have evolved in generally similar ways. The data derived from archaeological research all

[9]In an outburst of antievolutionistic fanaticism, such a highly respectable American anthropologist as Berthold Laufer could be so immoderate as to write of lineal evolutionism, "the most inane, sterile, and pernicious theory ever conceived in the history of science." B. Laufer, "Review of: R. H. Lowie, *Culture and Ethnology*" (*American Anthropologist,* Vol. 20, 1918), p. 90.

[10]"I must confess that I am in a state of mind where I would no longer give a dime for a new theory, but I am always enthusiastic about new facts." *Ibid.*

[11]C. Kluckhohn, "The Place of Theory in Anthropological Science" (*The Philosophy of Science,* Vol. 6, 1939), p. 333.

over the world demonstrate for anyone who has eyes to see that, wherever local archaeology has any prehistoric dimension, local cultures have "evolved." If the record goes back far enough, it shows the simple material technology of hunters and gatherers, who had no metals, no domesticated plants or animals, no weaving, no pottery, no writing, no permanent house structures, no public buildings—a culture of illiterate people of meager development. Such a society falls under the rubric _savage;_ its culture lacks domesticated plants and animals and writing. Because of limited technology and food-getting techniques, savage society is limited both in numbers of people and in the elaboration of social institutions. In later archaeological levels, domesticated plants and animals appear, permanent housing shows up, weaving and pottery are apt to be present, and settlement patterns indicate an increase in sizes of populations. Everything points to some degree of elaboration of culture. Such people are classed as _barbarians:_ those whose culture contains domesticated plants and animals and settled villages or homesteads, but no writing, cities, or monumental ceremonial centers. The highest archaeological levels reveal all these things and a good deal more. They yield the remains of _civilizations:_ societies whose cultures include agriculture and cities; diversified craft specialties, including metallurgy; monumental, ceremonial, and governmental structures; writing; and an inventory of innumerable additional items. Civilized cultures may or may not be more "moral" than savage or barbarian cultures. In anthropology, the word "civilization" refers only to a degree of complexity of culture, although civilizations do show qualitative differences in moral characteristics when compared with primitive societies, and these are discussed in Chapter 36. Anthropologists reserve judgment on the ethical goodness or badness of the differences.

The primitive world was the world before the invention of writing. Most of the span of human experience occurred during this time. The archaeological record testifies to an orderly pattern of cultural development within the prehistoric era, that is, before the time of written records. By inference, patterns of social culture must also show some regularities of development. The task of studies in cultural evolution is to determine the content of such patterns, if possible.

The pendulum of Boasian antievolutionism had completed the swing of its arc by 1945, and a new look at cultural evolutionism became possible. Since then, two sorts of neoevolutionism have emerged.

Specific evolution   A refinement of the idea of cultural evolution was introduced in 1960 by Marshall Sahlins, who calls it _specific evolution,_ "the historic development of particular cultural forms . . . phylogenetic transformation through adaptation."[12] In specific evolution, the concern is with the sequence of changes in the cultural history of specific societies; for example, what actually happened in the development of American culture between 1776 and 1965? In what specific senses were these modifications responses to the potentialities of the North American continent and its mastery? Or how, specifically, were Pueblo Indian cultures changing and modifying between A.D. 100 and 1850? This is more than history, for specific evolution is concerned with more than a chronicle of events; it wants to know how the _cultures_ changed. It is really cultural history or Boasian _historical reconstruction_ under a new name in a theoretical framework more congenial to thinking in evolutionary terms.

Multilineal evolution   As developed by Professor Julian Steward, multilineal evolution searches for parallels in specific evolution. It does not attempt, at least in its present stage, to develop a comprehensive set of evolutionary principles to cover the growth of culture from earliest prehistoric times to the present. Rather, it deliberately narrows its scope to focus on parallel developments in limited aspects of the

[12]M. Sahlins, "Evolution: Specific and General," in M. D. Sahlins and E. R. Service (eds.), _Evolution and Culture_, p. 43.

cultures of specifically identified societies. It undertakes to determine whether identifiable sequences of culture change occur in the same order in independent cultures. When such apparently similar sequences are identified, it then seeks to determine whether like causes have produced them.

Multilineal evolution is essentially a methodology based on the assumption that significant regularities in cultural change occur, and it is concerned with the determination of cultural laws. It is inevitably concerned also with historical reconstruction, but it does not expect that historical data can be classified in universal stages.[13]

Multilineal evolutionary studies aim to examine whole cultures in detail to see what specific social forms do in fact take shape on different levels, that is, degrees of complexity, of social integration. It expects great diversity in detail but assumes the probability of limited generalizations with respect to directions of evolutionary change.

General evolution General evolution differs from multilineal evolution mainly in the level of its formulations. It attempts to establish evolutionary trends for culture *in toto* rather than for limited cultures of comparable types, as does multilineal evolution. Its formulations are consequently much broader in scope. They are of the type that V. Gordon Childe, Leslie White, Robert Redfield, and Elman Service, among others, have formulated with respect to the great changes in culture that accompany the development from Paleolithic to Neolithic to Metal Age technological bases.[14] General evolution does not assume that every culture develops exactly comparable details in cultural patterns on comparable levels of technology. But it does hold that broad-scale trends in the succession of cultural forms are demonstrable.

To study the general evolution of culture is to examine the courses along which human societies have arrived at more distinct patterns of behavior to fulfill more distinct functions. In writing on the "reality of social evolution," MacIver has said: "The main interest of the evolutionary method is not the modification of specific form into specific form but the emergence of a variety of more specific forms from the less specific."[15]

The process of specific social change and cultural modification in a particular society is not *general cultural evolution*, which must be studied with reference to many forms.

Failure to hold fast to this principle has engendered confusion among both the earlier cultural evolutionists and their critics. Morgan, as Lowie has shown, did reconstruct unknown aspects of ancient societies in terms of his general evolutionary formula.[16] Morgan's analysis of American Indian house types was wholly vitiated because he had a predilection for an a priori scheme of the evolution of clan and family; he specifically attributed earlier matrilineal clans to the patrilineal Ojibwa, for example, because, according to his scheme, it had to be that way.

Tylor, too, as Lowie has indicated, was guilty of the same error, though less crassly than Morgan.[17] At times, therefore, the early evolutionists did treat specific and general cultural evolution as if they were one and the same thing. This is the fatal error.

One thing that evolution as a working tool does not do, and cannot do, is formulate a line of specific detailed development through which all species or societies must pass. A whale and a dog are both mammals, and each is the product of evolutionary divergence, but the detailed phylogenetic histories of the two species are quite unlike, and the one cannot be transferred to the other. In sociocultural terms, the history of any particular society does not recapitulate the evolution of culture. It cannot, for evolution covers the differentiation of cul-

---

[13] J. H. Steward, "Evolution and Process," in A. L. Kroeber (ed.), *Anthropology Today*, p. 318.

[14] Or as indicated for legal evolution by the present author in "The Trend of the Law," in E. A. Hoebel, *The Law of Primitive Man*, chap. 12.

[15] R. M. MacIver, *Society: Its Structure and Changes*, p. 424.

[16] R. H. Lowie, "Lewis Henry Morgan in Historical Perspective," in *Essays in Honor of Alfred Louis Kroeber.*, pp. 171–172.

[17] R. H. Lowie, "Evolution in Cultural Anthropology" (*American Anthropologist*, Vol. 48, 1946), pp. 229–230.

tures as wholes and of institutions and customs within them. No one culture ever embraces all the patterns of all cultures, either past or present. From this it follows that the *history* of a given society cannot be reconstructed from general patterns of evolution.

It has not been difficult to demonstrate that diffusion and the accidents of historical contact between peoples with different levels and forms of culture play hob with any serial scheme of cultural development *for particular cultures.* Cultures grow, as was shown in the last chapter, mostly through acquisition of diffused traits. Whether a particular people is exposed to one or another form of a trait is often the result of sheer accident. The Cheyennes were clanless hunters and gatherers in their early habitat in the woods of the western Great Lakes region. When they moved west to settle among the Arikara in the Missouri River Valley, they learned gardening from their sedentary neighbors, and there is evidence that they acquired the rudiments of a maternal clan system. Had their migration led them southward to settle among the gardening Omahas, who have paternal clans, it is quite probable that they would have copied gardening and acquired the rudiments of a paternal clan organization.

The theory of general evolution does not hold that any particular culture must go through the entire sequence of established evolutionary development. It recognizes full well that the remaining Stone Age tribes of the interior highlands of New Guinea will leap across all the intervening stages of culture into the Modern Age in the next 25 to 50 years. This will be the result of the brand of forced diffusion brought about by technical-development programs.

The theory of general evolution relates to the evolution of culture as an attribute of humanity. It does not provide a blueprint that each culture follows in specifics.

The energy theory of cultural evolution White has emphasized that one important consequence of cultural evolution is the progressive increase in the amount of energy put under

control for utilization by men.[18] The potential daily average energy output of a healthy man is estimated as equal to approximately 50 pounds lifted 1 foot in 1 second, or roughly $1/600$ horsepower-hour. With infants, the sick, and feeble adults taken into account, the daily amount of energy per capita available in the earliest societies was approximately $1/1,200$ horsepower-hour per person. For a very primitive local group, this would amount to an energy utilization of no more than $1/24$ horsepower-hour of energy a day for the entire society. Not much could be accomplished. As long as man was restricted to such a level, the development of culture was destined to be limited. This condition prevailed throughout the Old Stone Age and was characteristic of all societies before the development of hoe culture and the domestication of animals.

The great revolution of the Neolithic Age was wrought by the domestication of plants and animals. Domestication of plants increased man's control over solar energy, which is stored in plants. Domestication of animals made him an exploiter of animal energy. More efficient tools reduced energy waste, and new tools made possible new applications of energy. All culture expanded rapidly; the mode of life changed from that of hunters to that of gardeners and pastoralists. Old institutions and customs went down, and new ways had to be worked out. The savages became barbarians.

The Bronze and Iron Ages are but extensions of the Neolithic Age, which fulfilled its potential in the urban revolution. Metal was substituted for stone. Increased efficiency of tools, leading to stepped-up productiveness in handicraft industries and gardening, gradually expanded the cultures of the Old World.

The next cultural revolution awaited the harnessing of steam, the invention of the internal-combustion engine, and the artificial production of electricity. With the Industrial Revolution, feudalism gave way to modern capitalism. The reorganization of society and culture shook the

[18]L. A. White, "Energy and the Evolution of Culture" (*American Anthropologist*, Vol. 45, 1943), pp. 335–356. See also W. F. Cottrell, *Energy and Society;* and Sahlins and Service, *op. cit.*

modern world through and through. The repercussions are still with us.

In 1945, the most stupendous energy conquest of all time was accomplished. Einstein's theory of the equivalence of mass and energy ($E = mc^2$) indicates that 1 kilogram (2.2 pounds) of matter, if it could be converted entirely into energy, would release 25 billion kilowatt-hours of energy, or approximately 33 billion horsepower-hours. Splitting the uranium atom, as was first done in 1945, converted 0.1 of 1 per cent of the uranium mass into energy. Thirty-three million horsepower-hours of energy could then be released from one kilogram of uranium.[19] And this was but the beginning, for not only has the efficiency of techniques for splitting the atom been improved, but also we have learned since then how to release energy through fusion of the hydrogen atom.

Each new mastery of energy is in itself a cultural achievement. Once incorporated into a culture, it has innumerable feedback effects—it causes a chain reaction of new cultural developments. Every major breakthrough in energy control has initiated vast cultural, and frequently social, revolutions in its wake.

The Atomic Age is upon us. Wild and wonderful interplanetary frontiers are opening. Around the world, unrest, turmoil, and discontent are the widespread symptoms of coming change and new cultural patterns. Everything is in flux. Before discussing this, however, we shall put the concept of cultural evolution to work in studying prehistoric man and culture, the subject of Part 2.

SUMMARY

Rationalist thinkers of the seventeenth, eighteenth, and nineteenth centuries formulated the idea that the newly discovered primitives of the world were laggards on a ladder of progress from savagery, through barbarism, to civilization. They postulated that all peoples had begun at the bottom of the ladder originally.

Spencer, Morgan, and Tylor developed detailed theories and schemata of evolutionary sequences between 1850 and 1875. By 1920, these theories had been generally rejected as unrealistic by field-working anthropologists of the Boasian and French-English functionalist schools. Archaeological evidence, plus a changing social climate, finally led to a revival of interest in the evolutionary theory of culture after 1945. Contemporary theories of cultural evolution are specific, multilineal, or general. The major differences among them are that the theory of specific evolution focuses upon adaptive modification through time of single cultures, while multilineal evolutionary studies try to formulate parallel sequences of development that hold good for limited groups within specific cultures. General evolution deals with the order of development of *new* cultural forms out of older forms—not for any specific cultures necessarily, but for cultures at large.

The energy theory of cultural evolution is a subtheory within that of universal evolution. It holds that progressive mastery of energy sources triggers increasingly complex cultural developments and is consequently the key factor in cultural evolution.

SELECTED READINGS

Childe, V. G.: *Man Makes Himself* (1942) and *What Happened in History* (1946). Two books on the evolution of culture by the distinguished British prehistorian who established the concept of the urban revolution.

Coon, C. S.: *The Story of Man* (1955). A very well-written, panoramic view of the worldwide growth and diffusion of the major cultures, with emphasis on the Neolithic complex.

Cottrell, W. F.: *Energy and Society* (1955). A searching application of the energy theory of society.

Linton, R.: *The Tree of Culture* (1955). Similar to Coon's book in scope and organization, but more detailed.

Morgan, L. H.: "Social Evolution," in Hoebel, Jennings, and Smith, *Readings in Anthropology* (1955), pp.

[19]H. D. Smyth, *Atomic Energy for Military Purposes*, pp. 2, 224.

356–364. Should be read in conjunction with R. H. Lowie's article in the *Readings,* "Lewis Henry Morgan in Historical Perspective."

Redfield, R.: *The Primitive World and Its Transformations* (1953). A stimulating discussion of the changes in moral and social outlook that are fostered by the shift from primitive to urban life.

Sahlins, M. D., and E. R. Service (eds.): *Evolution and Culture* (1960). Four disciples of Leslie White formulate a "manifesto" for the evolutionary revival in cultural anthropology.

Service, E. R.: *Primitive Social Organization* (1962). Under-takes to state modern ethnographic materials in the framework of general evolutionary theory. This book offers more empirical data and less theory than White's work, suggested below.

Steward, J. H.: *Theory of Culture Change: The Methodology of Multilineal Evolution* (1955). An exposition of a contemporary approach to the study of cultural evolution.

White, L. A.: *The Evolution of Culture* (1959). White's comprehensive statement of the theory of general evolutionism. The unilineal theory given twentieth-century expression.

Part 2/ The evolution of man and culture

Man's place among the primates

chapter 7

Anthropologists might well recite the lines of Alexander Pope as the first incantation of their creed:

Know then thyself, presume not God to scan,
The proper study of mankind is man.[1]

This interest in man, however, does not keep anthropologists from studying apes and monkeys, either as fossils or as living social groups. For although it is true that if you want to learn about man, you should study man, it is also true that new light, and more light, may be thrown upon man and the nature of man through knowledge of his near relatives and his ancestors. Consequently, anthropologists study primates and fossil man to unfold man's biological background, seeking what may be learned about the prehuman roots of social and physical existence. To this end, we discuss in this chapter the reasons that man is placed among the primates and then summarize the facts of primate behavior as they bear on the problem of the evolution of man and culture. As we proceed in this and later chapters, many questions of classification arise. Hence, an understanding of classifications needs first attention.

Problems in classification

In the comic strip, a flying object evokes the cries, "It's a bird! It's a plane! It's Superman!" What is perceived of the flying form depends on how much or how little of it is discerned and on the discriminating powers of the ob-

[1] Alexander Pope, "An Essay on Man," epistle 2.

server. In prehistoric paleontology, when a very primitive and fragmentary fossil of a new type of hominoid is first discovered, the cries characteristically go up: "It's an ape!" "It's a man!" "It's a half-ape!" Sides are chosen. The battle lines of cephalic calipers and comparative morphology are drawn, and the war of words begins. The result has been dubbed by George Gaylord Simpson the "chaos of anthropological nomenclature." In commenting on the situation, he wryly but cogently observed:

It is of course also true that the significance of differences between any two specimens has almost invariably come to be enormously exaggerated by one authority or another in this field. Here the fault is not so much a lack of taxonomic grammar as lack of taxonomic common sense or experience. Many fossil hominids have been described and named by workers with no other experience in taxonomy. They have inevitably lacked the sense of balance and the interpretive skill of zoologists who have worked extensively on larger groups of animals. It must, however, be sadly noted that even broadly equipped zoologists often seem to lose their judgment if they work on hominids. Here factors of prestige, of personal involvement, of emotional investment rarely fail to affect the fully human scientist, although they hardly trouble the workers on, say, angleworms or dungbeetles.[2]

Many hominid fossils have been discovered or first identified by amateurs or semiprofessionals for whom the urge to convince the world that they have found a new form of man or ancestor of man is well-nigh irresistible. Each stakes his claim by posting a new genus, or at least a new species, label on his creature. Others counter with what they consider to be more suitable labels according to their judgments. And so a single find may receive a variety of Latin sobriquets, and a number of different finds which should properly be grouped within a single classification are put into separate pigeonholes with different names. The history of the first famous finds of Java man (see pages 147–151) is an example of

what has too often taken place. His discoverer, Eugene Dubois, named the fossil *Pithecanthropus erectus:* genus, *ape man;* species, *upright.* Three decades later, a leading American evolutionist, Henry Fairfield Osborn, argued that the specimen was not an ape at all, but that he belonged to an ancient fossil race which had crossed the threshold of humanity without having evolved far enough to be classed as *Homo;* therefore, he proposed to call him *Paleoanthropus trinilensis:* genus, *ancient man;* species, *of Trinil* (the locality of discovery). Today, the consensus of European and American specialists is to designate the type as *Homo erectus erectus:* genus, *man;* species, *upright;* variety, *upright.*

If, therefore, inconsistency and contradiction among the names and classification systems used in this text and previous editions of this book and among the nomenclatures of other authors occur, there is nothing for it except to understand the provisional nature of all classifications.

However, science struggles continually to supplant unreason with reason, and dogma with objectively sustained theory. In this process, zoologists have arrived at a logical international formulation of rules and methods for making scientific classifications.[3] Prehistorians have in the past played so fast and loose with the naming of human fossils that they have at last been driven to order their prehistoric storehouse. In 1962, an international symposium on the problem was convened under the auspices of the Wenner-Gren Foundation for Anthropological Research. It was not the aim of the symposium to formulate a code of primate classification, but much debris was cleared away, and we were provided with a nomenclature that should serve as a standard until such time as new knowledge and further accumulation of sober experience make changes necessary. The detailed results are to be found in the volume edited by S. L. Washburn, *Classification and Human Evolution.* The taxonomies of man used in this text follow the consensus presented by the Wenner-Gren symposium.

[2]G. G. Simpson, "The Meaning of Taxonomic Statements," in S. L. Washburn (ed.), *Classification and Human Evolution,* pp. 6–7. By permission of the Wenner-Gren Foundation for Anthropological Research, New York.

[3]N. R. Stoll et al., *International Code of Zoological Nomenclature;* G. G. Simpson, *Principles of Animal Taxonomy.*

Principles of taxonomy

The significance of the names attached to primates and fossil men will be easier to comprehend if the more basic principles of taxonomy are kept in mind.

Grades of nomen, or designation In a well-run museum or laboratory, each specimen gets its serial number for individual identification. This is its *primary nomen* (N_1), or designation (nomenclature). It tells us absolutely nothing about the object except where its listing should be found in the acquisitions catalogue and where one may hopefully search for it in the collections. It says nothing whatsoever of scientific significance. In modern American archaeological practice, N_1 now includes designation by state, county, and site, plus feature (room, stratum, and so on, within the site) and serial number within the feature. For example, 42-To-29, D346 would read: "Utah, Tooele County, Site No. 29, Feature D, Item 346." This is an excellent finder designation, but it is still scientifically mute.

When an analyst identifies the item as a mammalian bone, however, he begins to tell us something of significance. He has identified it with a *population*: "a group of possible observations or of individuals united by some common principle."[4] This is the *secondary nomen* (N_2), of which the specimen is a sample. The population theoretically exists as all potential instances of the thing in question. The population is therefore never seen or sensed in its entirety. Its characteristics are inferred from the available samples.

The *tertiary nomen* (N_3) is that of the *taxon*, a group of real, or existing, specimens with which the taxonomist can actually work. It is the actual group to be classified in a higher or lower position in the systematic *hierachy of categories*, which constitutes the final taxonomy that is used as a general frame of reference.

The *category designation*, or *quarternary nomen* (N_4), expresses more specific relationships. In the system now in use, the category levels are

[4]Simpson, "The Meaning of Taxonomic Statements", p. 2.

ranked in a descending sequence as follows:

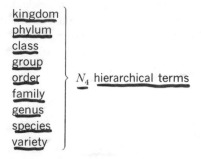

kingdom
phylum
class
group
order
family
genus
species
variety

N_4 hierarchical terms

Intermediary categories are frequently established by use of the prefixes "super-," "sub-," and "infra-," for example,

superfamily
family
subfamily
infrafamily

Organisms are assigned to a given rank category on the basis of common characteristics shared by other organisms assigned to that category. Within such a rank, smaller groups are frequently distinguishable on the basis of differences in specializations, and so on down the rank hierarchy. Thus, the lower the rank order of a group, the more specific are the common specializations of the members of that group, and the more similar they are.

It is entirely possible to classify living organisms without reference to evolutionary development, as did Karl von Linné (1707–1778), the great Swedish naturalist who devised the basic system of classification in use today. The Linnean system was synchronic: it treated all forms on a single time plane. Today, however, biologists use taxonomy to imply common ancestry as well as physical resemblances. Two separate ideas are involved in this statement. The first rests upon the zoological proposition that two or more animal forms showing a large number of significant similarities in form and function must be more or less closely related. The second proposition is that close relationship means common ancestry. Further, the greater the detailed similarity in form and function, the more definite is the commonness of ancestry. The neo-Linnean system as now used not only groups organisms according to similarities but also implies a good deal about evolutionary relations between living forms in terms of common ancestral types and closeness of collateral relationships.

Criteria used in zoological classification Similarities of structure, function, development, and evolutionary history all enter into the classification of organisms. _Structure_ refers to bodily form, or _morphology; function,_ to the manner in which an organ works in the maintenance of the organism as a whole; _development,_ to the sequences in the growth process, or life history, of the individual organism; and _evolutionary history,_ to the sequences of development in the ancestry of the type.[5]

The taxonomy of man

Modern man, therefore, consists of a large number of specimens which have been measured, dissected, X-rayed, and so forth for a vast number of physical characteristics. Insofar as each specimen has his individual identification (be it name, catalog number, or Social Security number), it has its N_1. Immediately each is identified as a type of any kind, and put in a population (N_2). With all the studied specimens lumped together as a particular type of man, it has an identity in a taxon (N_3). When the taxon is assigned to the category *Homo* in the hierarchical rank of genus, it receives one of a number of N_4 (hierarchic terms) that relate it to other genera on the same level and to families above it and species below it.

Zoologists and physical anthropologists conventionally use Latin terms for hierarchical labels, such as Hominoidea (*oidea,* as an ending = superfamily) and Hominidae (*idae,* as an ending = family). For purposes of simplification in this introductory discussion, we shall follow the less professional but acceptable Anglicized terms "hominoid" and "hominid."

[5]Individual development is called *ontogeny,* while the historical evolutionary development of the type is called *phylogeny.*

It is not difficult to identify man as to kingdom, phylum, and class. Each primate is clearly a member of the animal kingdom, not of the vegetable kingdom. Because of his spinal cord and nervous system, he belongs to the _phylum_ of chordates. His spinal column of bony segments and the associated skeletal structure put him in the _subphylum_ of vertebrates. His practice of nourishing the young on nutrient fluids generated by the female gives him membership in the _class_ of mammals. Because the unborn young are developed in the maternal womb, he qualifies for membership in the _subclass_ of eutheria, within which he is identified as belonging to the _group_ of placentals, since the fetus is nourished directly from the bloodstream of the mother through the placenta.

Within the _order_ of primates, taxonomists identify two _suborders:_ (1) the anthropoid, which includes all apes, monkeys, and man, and (2) the prosimian, which includes the tarsier, the lemur, and the tree shrew—the most primitive in development of the primates.

Within the suborder of anthropoids are two _infraorders:_ (1) the catarrhines (Gr. *kata,* downward + *rhis, rhinos,* nose), the Old World anthropoids, whose nostrils are usually narrow and closely spaced, and (2) the platyrrhines (Gr. *platys,* broad + *rhis, rhinos,* nose), the New World monkeys, whose nostrils are usually flat and widely spaced. Man is clearly a catarrhine. The catarrhines in turn subdivide into two _suprafamilies:_ (1) the hominoids (man and the apes) and (2) the cercopithecoids (Gr. *kerkos,* tailed + *pithekos,* ape), which include baboons, macaques, vervets, and langurs. The hominoids group into three _families:_ (1) hominid, man; (2) pongid, the great apes; and (3) hylobatid, within which fall the gibbons. Finally, the hominid family today has but one surviving _genus, Homo._ It also produced one other known *genus, Australopithecus,* long since extinct. There are two living genera of pongids: (1) *Pan* and (2) *Pongo. Pan* is now considered to be made up of at least two species: (1) the chimpanzees and (2) the gorillas. The genus *Pongo* includes only the orangutans.

The hierarchy of categories for the primate order is schematized in Fig. 7-1, and the position of man within it is clearly discernible.

Common name	Genus	Family	Superfamily	Infraorder	Suborder	Order
Tree shrew Lemur				Lemuriformes	Prosimii	PRIMATES
Loris				Lorisiformes		
Tarsier				Tarsiiformes		
New World monkeys				Platyrrhines	ANTHROPOIDS	
Macaque Baboon		Cercopithecines	Cercopithecoids	CATARRHINES		
Langur		Colobines				
Gibbon	*Hylobates*	Hylobatids	HOMINOIDS			
Orangutan	*Pongo*	Pongids				
Chimpanzee	*Pan*					
Gorilla						
Ape-man	*Australopithecus*	HOMINIDS				
MAN	*Homo*					

Fig. 7-1   Taxonomic classification of man in relation to other major primate groups.

The characteristics of primates

We must now backtrack a little and ask: "When is a mammal a primate, or what is distinctive about primates within the mammalian class and placental group?"

There is no absolute answer, for as Le Gros Clark has put it: "It is peculiarly difficult to give a satisfying definition of the Primates, since there is no single distinguishing feature which distinguishes all the members of the group."[6]

The differences between primates and other

[6]W. E. Le Gros Clark, *History of the Primates,* p. 45.

Fig. 7-2 Skeletal modifications in the shift from pronograde (horizontal) to orthograde (vertical) posture. The spine gets a double curve; the rib cage projects, rather than forming an underslung basket —thus the viscera are poorly supported in man, and the abdominal wall often ruptures; the pelvis broadens and becomes bucket-shaped; and the skull balances delicately above the vertebral column.

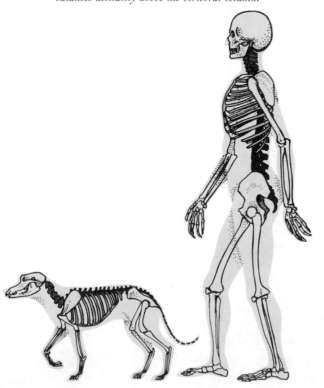

mammals are relative; they exist mainly in degree rather than in kind. Among the lower primates, the major morphological differences are those which are associated with tree life; among the hominids, they are those which result from adaptations leading to upright posture and intensified manipulation. In major respects they are as follows:

1. Brain: Increasingly complex as one ascends the primate scale.

2. Eyes: Located well forward on the skull, rather than back and toward the sides. The back of the eye socket is closed and encircled with a bony ridge, whereas in other mammals it is open at the sides and rear. Vision is stereoscopic and very acute.

3. Face: Snout and jaws are reduced in size. Olfactory sense and dentition are also reduced.

4. Hands: (*a*) Forepaws are prehensile. The five-toed characteristic of primitive mammals is retained, but the toes have a marked flexibility that makes extensive grasping possible. (*b*) Claws have become flat nails on the top of the digits. (*c*) Digits have soft, fleshy pads on their undertips, richly provided with sensory nerves. Primates can feel and manipulate.

5. Hind paws: Retain five flexible toes, while big toe is especially strengthened as a pincer. In hominids the foot is more clublike and acts as a weight-carrying base.

6. Forearms: Exhibit a high degree of flexion; that is, with the elbow steady, they may be rotated clockwise or counterclockwise through almost a full circle.

7. Reproductive traits: (*a*) Adults are sexually active the year around rather than only during well-defined rutting seasons. (*b*) Female normally bears but one offspring at a time instead of a litter. (*c*) Generally, the female has but two mammary glands. (*d*) Postnatal development is relatively much more prolonged.

Morphological and functional characteristics of the hominids Man, as the most highly developed primate, possesses all the above characteristics in their most clearly distinguishable forms. This means that he has by far the largest and most complex brain, eyes set fully forward in completely enclosed sockets with the back walls of the orbits fully formed, the smallest jaw relative to the braincase, the fewest teeth, the most fully shrunken bony structure of the snout, the most flexion of the fore limbs, and the most upright posture of all primates. The special and distinctive modifications which man has developed in his evolution away from the more primitive and generalized primate ancestral type are detailed as we proceed with the examination of the fossil and contemporary representatives of the hominids in succeeding chapters.

Less obvious similarities and distinctions among the primates have been identified as the result of more and more refined laboratory techniques for blood and genetic analysis. The main results follow.

Blood precipitates Refinements in serology, or the study of blood, have given additional dimensions to the criteria of identification of man as a primate. Serum vaccines are produced by injecting foreign organisms into the bloodstream of a host animal, which produces antibodies specific to the alien organism. The white part of the blood, the serum, is extracted to be used as a vaccine for the specific. If dog blood is injected into a host, the resulting serum is specific for dog. When this antidog serum is mixed with dog blood, it produces a white precipitate. Weaker precipitation occurs when antidog serum is mixed with the blood of any canine, but no precipitate occurs at all if it is mixed with noncanine blood. *Only the blood of closely similar animals reacts to the vaccine serum of a member of its order.* Thus, antihuman-specific serum produces a white precipitate when mixed with ape blood and a weaker precipitate when mixed with the blood of monkeys, but no precipitates at all when mixed with nonprimate bloods. Even more specifically, the ape's reactions to ABO, RH, and MN blood-type serums of human beings are much the same as man's. It is evident that the chemical structure of human blood and that of apes and monkeys is quite similar—and somewhat different from that of all other warm-blooded creatures.

Serum protein patterns Current work is greatly refining the methods of serologic proof of man's relationships to other animals. By means of a process of electrophoresis, the proteins of various blood serums may be separated into from nineteen to twenty-five components that show characteristic shapes and patterns. In this process, a serum is mixed in a gel, which is placed between a positive and a negative electrode; an electric current flows between the electrodes and through the gel. The positively charged serum proteins move toward the negative pole, and the negatively charged proteins move toward the positive pole. The proteins move at differing speeds, according to their molecular weights. A filter placed before each pole traps the proteins, collecting them according to their rates of motion. The similarities of serum protein shapes among man and the other primates are shown in Fig. 7-3. Inspection reveals that the patterns of man, the gorilla, and chimpanzee are very much alike, while those of the gibbon and the orangutan are distinctly different. The serum patterns of other animals are found to be very unlike those of the hominids. The cellular structure of blood protein thus confirms the more gross anatomical identification of man with the primates.

Chromosome patterns The genetic structures called *chromosomes* vary in numbers and in gross form among different plants and animals. The chromosome forms of man and the apes show close similarities, although the African chimpanzee and gorilla are more similar to man than the Asiatic orangutan and gibbon are. All are much more similar than any other animal chromosome forms.

Such similarities in detailed form indicate a close relationship among the primates as a whole and between man and the great apes in particular.

Ontogenetic development At various stages of human embryonic development, structures such as the notochord, gill arches, and gill grooves are present. They represent important features

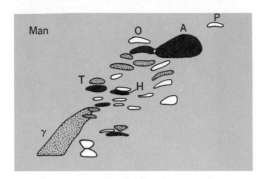

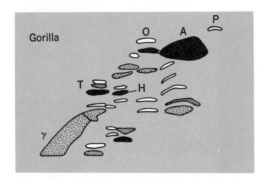

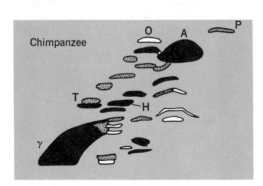

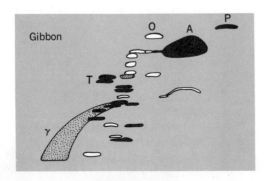

of certain early evolutionary forms that are not present in the fully developed human being. In broader terms, the human embryo passes through successive stages roughly similar to an undifferentiated cell mass, a coelenterate, a worm, and a generalized fish with the foundation of gill arches in its neck region. Finally, it takes on mammalian qualities and is ultimately born a human child (although even a proud parent frequently finds it difficult to agree that a newborn infant really looks like a human being).

As first formulated by K. E. von Baer (1792–1876), these facts were expressed in the following proposition, called "Baer's rule": The younger the embryos of different animals, the more alike they are; the older the embryos, the more distinctive they become. Ernst von Haekel (1834–1919) subsequently reformulated Baer's rule into a "biogenic law," which states that the embryonic development of each individual is a compressed recapitulation of certain major features of the development of the species. This is the origin of the commonly stated principle, "ontogeny recapitulates phylogeny," or "each individual climbs its own family tree."

Overstatement of the theory by uncritical early evolutionists brought it into disrepute among biologists, but the fact remains, in the view of Dobzhansky, that: "Yet making allowances for overstatements and exaggerations it remains true that many features of human ontogeny make no sense at all except on the assumption that they are retentions of the developmental patterns of remote ancestors."[7] More important for the question of taxonomy is the accepted fact that the suc-

[7]T. Dobzhansky, *Mankind Evolving: The Evolution of the Human Species*, p. 165.

Fig. 7-3   The close similarity of shapes of the proteins found in the blood serum of man and in that of the great ape is one type of evidence of their close evolutionary origins. (After Morris Goodman in Sherwood L. Washburn (ed.), Classification and Human Evolution. *Aldine Publishing Co. Copyright © 1963 by the Wenner-Gren Foundation for Anthropological Research, Inc.)*

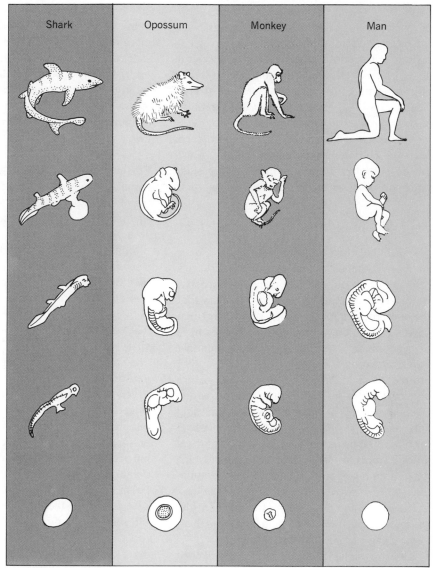

| Shark | Opossum | Monkey | Man |

Fig. 7-4   Ontogenetic development in the shark, opossum, monkey, and man. Marked morphological differentiation among genera occurs late in fetal development. (Modified from the American Museum of Natural History.)

cessive stages of embryonic morphology of man and the apes and monkeys are very similar until quite late in fetal development, when they begin to diverge significantly. In other words, the prenatal morphological similarity of man, apes, and monkeys reinforces their grouping in common categories.

Evolutionary history: the fossil record   Remains of ancient organisms are occasionally preserved in earth layers of different ages. Such remains are known as *fossils*. They may be reconstituted

shells or skeletons that have become permeated with mineral materials from the surrounding deposits or metamorphosed by pressure and heat. Or they may be casts of imprinted molds left by the original organism. They may also be preserved specimens found in tar pits, logs, permafrost layers (permanently frozen earth), or glacial ice. The fossil record, as it has been fitted together, adds time depth to the biological picture. It frequently yields the actual ancestral types from which relatively similar living forms of organisms could have been derived. It provides the _diachronic_ proof, or proof through time, of common ancestry for common types by placing the solid evidence of gradual divergence from the common types before our very eyes. The fossils of prehuman primates and prehistoric man are described in the next four chapters.

The living primates

The fact that man and the living simians have so many detailed traits in common provides rational evidence of their common ancestry. However, this must not be taken to mean that the numerous kinds of monkeys, apes, and men have *one* common ancestor. The primates have enjoyed seventy million years of evolutionary development as a distinctive order. During that protracted span, hundreds of primate genera and varieties have existed. It is therefore wrong to speak of any of these forms as *the* missing link, as though there were just one ancestral form. It must be realized at the outset that there are a number of series of missing links which make a complex pattern back to remote antiquity. *There is no common ancestor, but many ancestral predecessors.* A complete family tree of man, the apes, and the monkeys would include a truly bewildering number of fossil ancestors.

All living higher primates carry some of their common heritage into the present, but the fact that the apes have certain traits today does not necessarily mean that man's early ancestors also had them. Apes, too, have evolved and changed during the past several million years, and they have developed their own distinctive specializations, such as the overgrown canine tusks, which were not characteristic of earlier primate ancestors. At no time, then, did man pass through an evolutionary stage in which he exhibited all the characteristics now displayed by the living apes or living monkeys.

Phylogenetically, one may think of apes as our backward cousins and of contemporary monkeys as our even more remotely related and more retarded distant relatives. Our true ancestors can be known only from the fossils given up by the rocks of earlier Cenozoic times. Consideration of our fossil progenitors is reserved for the next chapter, however. We shall first take a brief look at our contemporary cousins, the living primates.

Prosimia: the tree shrew, the tarsier, and the lemur A few shy species of surviving genera of the oldest of primate types survive in out-of-the-way places in the tropical belt of the Old World. Tree shrews are rather widely distributed throughout South and Southeast Asia. The tarsier is located in north-central Indonesia (Borneo, Celebes, and the Philippines). Lemurs survive only in Madagascar.

The tree shrew The tree shrew is superficially much like a squirrel, with his furred tail and sharp-clawed digits. Yet with his generalized incisor teeth, which are not of the gnawing type developed by rodents, his greater mobility of fingers and toes, his relatively larger brain, and his greater acuity of vision, he is—though still an insectivore—an insectivore that shows notable primate propensities. Indeed, in a number of details of skeletal and muscular construction, he shows specific lemuroid leanings.

All in all, in the judgment of Le Gros Clark: "It seems very probable that the tree shrews represent in their general structure a tolerably close approximation to the earliest phases in the evolution of the primates from generalized mammalian ancestors."[8]

The tarsier The tarsier, so named because of the extreme development of the tarsal bones in his ankles, exhibits many of the general features of early primates, and in spite of his specializations, he could be very close to the original ancestral type. He is smaller than the lemur. He sports a small nose and large, goggly eyes—the better to see at night—and a free upper lip

[8] W. W. Le Gros Clark, *op. cit.,* pp. 43–44.

like that of monkeys and man, a lip that can be curled. He has full flexion of the neck, which can be swiveled in a complete half circle. These are all traits that point in the direction taken by the higher primates.

The evolutionary adaptation of the tarsier is all for the trees. He has, for example, developed round, platterlike toetips and fingertips with increased friction surfaces for clamping onto boughs. Like other primates, he does not have to dig in with sharp claws to climb and move about. Safe hand-and-foot contact is made much more quickly without claws, even though it may seem that squirrels and birds do all right in this respect. His most remarkable specialization, however, is the elongation of his tarsals. This gives him extra-effective leverage for sudden, propulsive jumping, while at the same time the toes at the end of his foot retain their prehensility for grasping.

The lemur The lemur looks rather like a little raccoon, except for his befingered hands and feet. His long snout, with its wet, doglike nostrils, is more generalized mammalian in character than it is primate, as are his large, movable ears and split upper lip. But the lemur's brain, his prehensile "hands," and his flexible limbs mark him as a lowly type of primate. He is a timid little beastie who spends the greater part of his life in the trees and is active mostly at night. In evolutionary morphology, the lemur occupies an approximate midpoint between insectivores and monkeys. He is a primitive primate, but not the most primitive of the forms that we would place in the primate order.

The tree shrew, the tarsier, and the lemur are three examples of what the first Paleocene primate ancestors were like, the tree shrew coming closest to the probable ancestral prototype.

The monkeys The living monkeys fall into two main infraorders within the suborder of anthropoids. These are the platyrrhines and the catarrhines, as already noted.

The platyrrhines The platyrrhines are found only in the New World. They are notable mainly

Fig. 7-5 *Living prosimia are the most primitive of all primates and the most similar to man's earliest primate ancestors. [After Maurice Wilson in W. E. LeGros Clark,* History of the Primates. *Courtesy of the Trustees, British Museum (Natural History).]*

Fig. 7-6 New World Capuchin monkey. The broad, flaring nostrils mark it as a platyrrhine. (Courtesy of the American Museum of Natural History.)

Fig. 7-7 Old World Colobus monkey. The narrow, downward-pointing nostrils mark it as a catarrhine. (Courtesy of the American Museum of Natural History.)

for their flat faces and long, frequently prehensile tails. Because their alley leads away from the main line of human evolution, we need not give further attention to them.

The catarrhines The Old World catarrhines divide into the hominoids, which include man and the great apes, and the cercopithecoids, which today are seen in the form of macaques, langurs, vervets, and baboons.

Of these the macaques are probably the most generally familiar, for they have by far the widest distribution. They cover a wide belt running all the way from Japan through China, Southeast Asia, India and western North Africa, and Gibraltar. (British tradition has it that as long as the "Barbary apes" live on Gibraltar, the Rock will remain in English hands.) Over fifty species and hundreds of varieties of macaques are alive today, and there is no point in trying to describe them in general terms. Macaques can be seen in numbers in the monkey house of any zoo. They are usually equally at home on land and in trees.

Langurs are Asiatic monkeys, confined in their distribution to Tibet, India, and Ceylon and eastward to Java. Their territory overlaps that of the macaques, but it is more restricted, probably because of their more specialized adaptation to a vegetarian diet.

The baboons and the vervets (mandrills) are ground dwellers who have adapted their way of life to open country rather than to forests. With their large muzzles, quadrupedal gait, and moderate-sized tails, they are anatomically quite remote from man, in spite of the fact that they utilize a terrestial habitat.

The great apes The living pongids consist of the African gorilla and chimpanzee along with the Indonesian orangutan. The Malayan gibbon is classed separately as a hylobate.

Almost all the distinctive features of adult apes are tied up with the fact that they have become adapted to a semierect posture combined with brachiation. In their mode of getting about from branch to branch and tree to tree, they have greatly modified their technique from

Fig. 7-8   Asiatic great apes. The orangutan (*left*) and gibbon (*right*) are highly adapted to arboreal existence in Southeast Asia. (Orangutan, Courtesy of the American Museum of Natural History; gibbon, Ylla, Rapho Quillumette Pictures.)

Fig. 7-9   African apes. The chimpanzee (*left*) and gorilla (*right*) are semiadapted to ground dwelling and more closely related to man. (New York Zoological Society.)

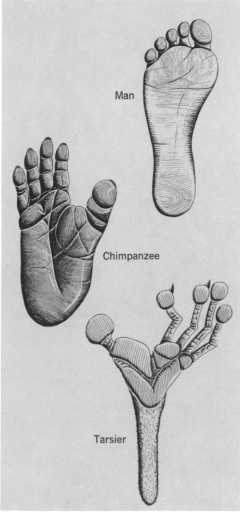

Man

Chimpanzee

Tarsier

*Fig. 7-10   The undersides of primate feet, showing
strengthening of big toe, reduction of grasping
powers, and solidification of the foot as a walking
and standing base in man. (Josef Biegert in
Sherwood L. Washburn (ed.),* Classification and
Human Evolution. *Aldine Publishing Co.
Copyright © by the Wenner-Gren Foundation for
Anthropological Research, Inc. Courtesy of the author.)*

that used by the ancestral primates and still
retained by the monkeys. Instead of running
and springing, they <u>brachiate</u>; that is, they
move by swinging from the fore limbs. They
also walk on the ground to some extent.

Many skeletal and muscular adjustments
have accompanied these two changes in basic
living habits—arm-swinging and semierect walking. The feet have lost some of their mobility
and a considerable amount of their prehensility. The leg bones are much stouter and have
much more pronounced dorsal ridges (the *linea
aspera*) for anchoring the flexing muscles that
run to the thigh and pelvis. The ilia in the pelvis
have flared out, and the whole hip structure has
become shorter and wider. The spine has become more massive and rigid, with fewer vertebrae. The shoulders have broadened, the chest
has become more like a barrel and less like the
prow of a ship, and the breastbone has become
short and stubby.

The fore limbs of the apes have become
enormously elongated and strengthened relative to the length of the body, for this pair of
limbs bears most of the brunt in getting about
in the trees. Their hands have become more
handlike, while they have lost their tails—externally, that is, for a vestigial tail is still to be
found in the coccyx, as it is in man.

In the skull, the occipital condyles, the
hinges on which the skull articulates with the
spine, have moved from a position far back on
the occipital bone forward to an intermediary
position. The related *foramen magnum*, or great
opening, through which the spinal cord passes
from the cranium as an appendage of the brain,
has also moved forward and downward from a
vertical orientation to one that forms an acute
angle with an imaginary horizontal base line.

In adult males, especially, the heavy chewing
and neck musculature is attached to remarkable
bony ridges that form sharp crests along the
top of the skull and across the occiput.

Concerning dentition, the apes have cusp
patterns for the upper and lower molars similar
to those of man. The canine teeth of the apes
are very different from man's, however, for the
apes possess conical, daggerish canines pro-

jecting well beyond the surface level of the lower teeth and overlapping them.

The brains of these creatures, while far inferior to those of the hominids in mental capacity and development, are far superior to those of all other animals.

Primate behavior Until 1958–1960, very little was known about the behavior of wild chimpanzees and gorillas in their natural habitats. Little is still known scientifically about the comparable behavior of gibbons and orangutans. Now, however, the daily lives of wild chimpanzees and gorillas have been painstakingly scrutinized by trained observers for a number of months.[9]

In essence, research done in their natural habitat shows the great apes to be exceedingly timid and nonaggressive. It took Jane Goodall fourteen months of almost daily, quiet contact before the chimpanzees of the Gombe Stream Reserve on Lake Tanganyika would accept her presence without disturbance and flight.[10] Gorillas became habituated to the presence of a peaceful man in the vicinity much more readily, however. African apes have apparently survived by keeping out of harm's way. Populations are small aggregations (sixty to eighty chimpanzees and two to thirty gorillas), divided into subgroups among which individuals readily transfer their membership. Each primary group focuses about a large, dominant adult male, who is clearly the leader. Males are dominant over females, and dominance hierarchies exist within the sexes; yet chimpanzees and gorillas are remarkably tolerant in personal relations, and there is little fighting to establish or maintain dominance. Accession to authority, mildly exercised, seems to be readily accepted.

The infant-mother dependency-protective relation is close and attentive for three years. Adults of both genera, but particularly gorillas, "gave one the impression of having an independent and self-dependent temperament, appearing stoic, aloof, and reserved in their

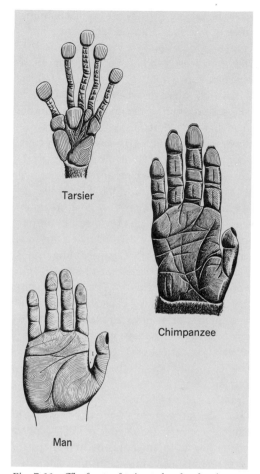

Tarsier

Chimpanzee

Man

Fig. 7-11   The fronts of primate hands, showing relation of thumbs to fingers in the retention of prehensility. (Josef Biegert in Sherwood L. Washburn (ed.), Classification and Human Evolution. *Aldine Publishing Co. Copyright © 1963 by the Wenner-Gren Foundation for Anthropological Research, Inc. Courtesy of the author.)*

[9]See I. DeVore (ed.), *Primate Behavior. Field Studies of Monkeys and Apes,* for generalized comparative accounts of the studies and their results.
[10]*Ibid.,* p. 428.

affective behavior."[11] They are social creatures, but they are not sociable. Social organization is minimal and loose, and yet very cohesive in that individuals rarely tend to get very far apart. Communication within the proximate group is accomplished more by means of bodily and facial gesture than by sounds. On the other hand, subgroups that are out of sight of one another regularly indicate their locations by calls.

Goodall has emphasized the tool-using propensities among the chimpanzees under her observation, but somehow these activities do not strike one as very impressive. Wild chimpanzees prepare stems which they insert in termite holes until they are full of clinging insects, which they then bite off. Captive chimpanzees will occasionally throw sticks and stones, with very poor aim, at "enemies." The apes, in spite of their manifest learning capacities in circuses and the laboratories of experimental psychologists, do not under natural circumstances produce very notable cultural contributions.

The eating habits of the apes are largely vegetarian, and six to eight hours a day is required to collect enough plants and fruit to sustain their large bodies. Goodall has seen an occasional chimpanzee devour a freshly killed baby monkey or infant antelope, which apparently represents a bit of the omnivorous impulse that came to be so characteristic of the hominids and so significant in the evolutionary adaptation that ultimately produced man.

ANTECEDENTS OF CULTURE   It is impossible for an outside observer to *know* what takes place in the mind of a chimpanzee, but Kortlandt may not be overimaginative when he observes:

The chimpanzees were unceasingly alert and curious. They seized every opportunity to bring variety into their lives, taking different paths down the hill on different occasions and continually changing their gait and their mode of locomotion. They were fascinated by everything new and unusual. They carefully examined all the objects I laid in their path and even collected some of them. Once I saw a chimpanzee gaze at a particularly beautiful sunset for a full 15 minutes, watching the changing colors until it became so dark that he had to retire to the forest without stopping to pick a papaw for his evening meal.

Another respect in which the animals resembled human beings was in their doubting and uncertain nature. They appeared to ponder such problems as whether to turn to the left or the right, or whether or not a papaw tasted good. Often, just like laboratory chimpanzees puzzling over a difficult problem in an intelligence test, the chimpanzees I observed scratched themselves elaborately while making these decisions.[12]

Man's ancestors surely had this capacity to ponder over problems in an even greater degree, and it is the ultimate key to his culture-creating capacity. When fully flowered, it is the glory of man.

Before we leave the living primates, however, it may be well to note four important and socially significant traits that apes and monkeys obviously share with the precursors of man: (1) group sociability and year-round association of the sexes; (2) prolonged infant dependency and protection of the females and their young by the males; (3) incipient food sharing; and (4) rudimentary conceptualization without the capacity for speech. These traits provided the basic behavioral elements for the first rudimentary societies and "culture."

Building upon this base, the hominids achieved very early (1) a transition to hunting and meat eating; (2) upright posture and regular reliance upon toolmaking and tool using; (3) family grouping with local bands; (4) out-group mating (consciousness of incest sensitivities); and (5) speech. The first two of these hominid traits we derive from the fossil record. The last three are inferred from our knowledge of primitive human societies. Let us now turn to the fossil record.

SUMMARY

Classification is man's way of simplifying his world of experience. Scientific classification is the process of identifying common characteristics inherent in a number of differing phe-

[11]G. B. Schaller, "The Behavior of the Mountain Gorilla," in *ibid.*, pp. 345–346.

[12]A. Kortlandt, "Chimpanzees in the Wild" (*Scientific American*, May, 1962), pp. 128–134.

nomena and of grouping them accordingly. It is the search for the like in the unlike. Classifications are always arbitrary constructions of the human mind in that the taxonomist decides which traits are sufficiently alike and significant to be included among the attributes of a class. A good taxonomy must be empirically sound; that is, the traits that it uses for classification must be genuine characteristics of the subjects to be classified and not imputed by the prejudices of the observer. Nevertheless, there is always a subjective act of judgment in every assignment of a specimen to a given category within a system of classification. However, scientifically educated people accept the proposition that a living human being should be classified among the primates as an anthropoid, catarrhine, hominoid, and hominid.

Primates are mammals possessing highly complex brains, stereoscopic and sharp vision, a sense of smell and snout that have been reduced in acuity and size, prehensile forepaws (with nails and fleshy pads), hindpaws that have become feet with a big toe, and forearms with total flexion. They have no rutting season, two mammary glands, usually one offspring at a time (normally no litters), and a long period of postnatal development.

In addition to such gross morphological and functional characteristics, which are shared by the prosimia, monkeys, apes, and men, a number of special common traits have been revealed through advanced techniques in scientific laboratories. These include blood precipitation reactions, serum protein patterns, chromosome patterns, and similarities in ontogenetic development.

Finally, the fossil record reveals many transitional forms that link the present fossils phylogenetically through geologic time.

The living primates are represented by the prosimia (the tree shrews, the tarsiers, and the lemurs) and by monkeys, apes, and men. The prosimia, which are the most primitive in form, are quadrupedal tree dwellers of small size. Monkeys exist in hundreds of varieties and more than fifty species. They, too, are mostly arboreal forest dwellers (particularly in Africa)

and are quadrupedal, although the members of a number of genera, such as baboons and vervets, are terrestrial. The great apes are limited to only four genera—those to which the chimpanzee, gorilla, orangutan, and gibbon belong. These large, tailless creatures are forest dwellers, but the members of the African genera, the chimpanzee and the gorilla, spend more time on the ground than in trees, and they can walk in a semiupright position. When moving about in trees, they brachiate rather than run along branches on all fours.

All nonhuman living primates subsist on leaves, shoots, berries, and insects. Chimpanzees occasionally kill and eat the meat of the young of defenseless monkeys and antelopes, but man is the only modern primate who is an habitual meat eater. He alone is the great toolmaker and tool user, the talker and thinker, who lives more by culture than by instinct.

SELECTED READINGS

DeVore, I. (ed.): *Primate Behavior: Field Studies of Monkeys and Apes* (1965). A very useful summary of recent field studies of primate behavior written by a number of the people who have done the original research.

Goodall, J.: "My Life among the Wild Chimpanzees" (*National Geographic,* Vol. 24, No. 2, 1963), pp. 272–308. If you want to know what patience, resourcefulness, controlled courage, and skill it takes to do a really successful field study of chimpanzees, this article will tell you. Illustrated with excellent color photographs.

Hooton, E. A.: *Man's Poor Relations* (1942). No longer up to date, but still a great handbook of information on primates.

Schaller, G. B.: *The Mountain Gorilla* (1963). The most comprehensive account of gorillas in their natural habitat in the Belgian Congo (1959 to 1960).

Simpson, G. G.: *Principles of Animal Taxonomy* (1961). An expert coverage of the subject.

Washburn, S. L. (ed.): *Classification and Human Evolution* (1963). The papers of the 1962 Wenner-Gren symposium on classification of the hominoids. It contains a number of excellent papers by foremost students of the primates.

Evolution
and the primates

chapter 8

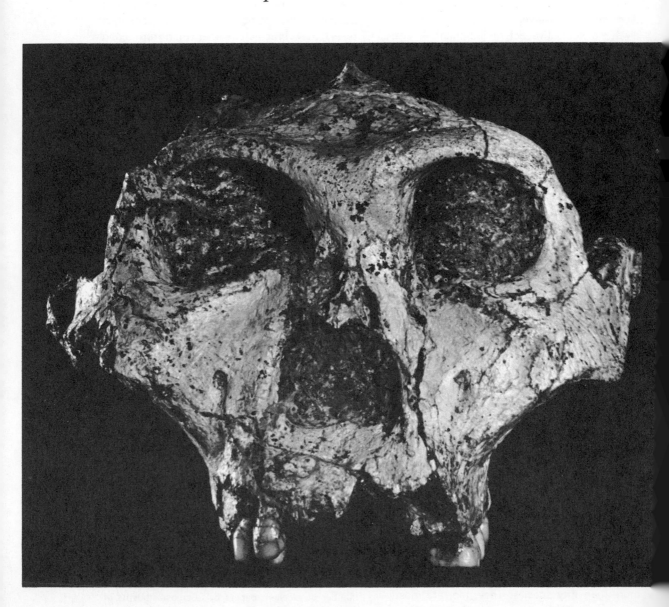

Two thousand years ago, the Latin poet Horace, gave us the classical version of the evolution of human culture and the concept of a lowly beginning for man:

When men first crept from out earth's womb, like worms,
Dumb speechless creatures, with scarce human forms,
With nails or doubled fists they used to fight
For acorns or for sleeping-holes at night;
Clubs followed next; at last to arms they came,
Which growing practice taught them how to frame,
Til words and names were found, wherewith to mold
The sounds they uttered, and their thoughts unfold;
Thenceforth they left off fighting, and began
To build them cities, guarding man from man,
And set up laws as barriers against strife
That threatened person, property, or wife.
'Twas fear of wrong gave birth to right, you'll find,
If you but search the records of mankind.[1]

What the classical ancients dimly understood, we can now see in finer detail and clearer outline, for the last century of research in the physical, biological, and anthropological sciences has done much to dispel the misty fogs that have so long shrouded our past. No longer need we rely on myth and fancy to understand something of our origins. With the tools of archaeology to provide the fossil evidence, the techniques of physics and botany to prove the antiquity of the fossils, and the science of genetics to reveal how evolution takes place, we have a firmer hold on the reality of the past than was the case a century ago.

The problem for science today is to reconstruct in more certain detail the lines along which man has developed in evolution from the simple, single-celled organism that first came into being in the Archaeozoic era two billion years ago and to determine the processes at work in shaping him and his modes of life.

In this chapter, we discuss certain factors of biological evolution as they relate to the primates, namely, the dating of fossils, the mechanics of evolution, and the fossils of the prehominid primates.

[1]*The Satires, Epistles, and Art of Poetry of Horace,* Conington's translation (7th ed.), p. 12.

Geology and the antiquity of the primates

Stratigraphy is the analysis of geological deposits in terms of discernible layers. Derivative time sequences are inferred from the relative positions of the strata, for the underlying strata are older than those overlying them—barring serious disturbances of the earth. In any local site, the relative ages of major geological strata are ordinarily clear. But in no single locality is one likely to find the entire sequence of major strata for all geologic periods. The master key is then built up by matching overlapping sequences. Once the key is established, the relative position of an isolated geological stratum can be determined by matching it to the homologous stratum in the key. Stratigraphy thus makes it possible to tell the relative ages of rocks and of the fossils and archaeological materials that may be contained within them. This in turn makes it possible to place the sequences of the evolutionary development of life forms in time by means of hard facts.

Geologic eras and periods The time that elapsed from the beginning of our universe to the birth of the earth is *cosmic time; geologic time* began with the laying down of the first sediments and extends to the present. Major blocks of geologic time are called *eras.* Eras are brought to a close by drastic changes in earth conditions, called *revolutions.* The five geologic eras and their dominant life forms are indicated in Table 8-1. Minor changes in earth conditions, called *disturbances,* take place within eras, producing the subdivisions of eras, called *periods* and *epochs.* The evolution of the primates occurred entirely within the final geologic era, the *Cenozoic.* Within this era are six epochs: the *Paleocene,* the *Eocene,* the *Oligocene,* the *Miocene,* the *Pliocene,* and the *Pleistocene.* The Miocene, Pliocene, and Pleistocene epochs are of critical importance for man's immediate antecedents, and Pleistocene geology is crucial for the study of man himself, for this is the period in which the hominids finally evolved.

Table 8-1   *The Geologic Eras, Beginning Dates, and Dominant Life Forms That First Evolved in Each Era*

geologic eras	beginning date of era (before present)	duration of era	dominant life forms developed in era
Cenozoic	75 million years	75 million years	Man, primates
Mesozoic	200 million years	125 million years	Land plants, seaweeds, mammals, reptiles, amphibians, fish
Paleozoic	500 million years	300 million years	Invertebrates
Proterozoic	1.5 to 2 billion years	1.5 to 3 billion years	Metazoa, protozoa
Azoic	4.5 to 6 billion years	3 to 4 billion years	No life; first cells not yet formed

NOTE: Each life form continued into all subsequent eras.

The Pleistocene epoch   The Miocene and Pliocene were warm epochs; the first moist, the second dry. The Pleistocene was an unstable epoch of alternating cold and moderate warmth.

During spans of extreme cold, snow that falls in high altitudes or in high latitudes of the northern hemisphere does not melt off in the short, cool summers. It accumulates year by year, packed down by its own weight, until it is metamorphosed into ice. Although ice is a solid, it has a low viscosity, which enables it to flow downgrade, scouring mountain valleys and spreading outward from the massive ice cap over vast areas. The locking of water in the ice, during glaciations, lowers sea levels around the world by several hundred feet. The great glacial weight upon the continents and the lightened weight of the water in the ocean basins cause continental subsidence and changing of land contours. Temperate and tropical zones outside the frigid glacial areas shift and change, forcing extensive migration and new adaptations by plant and animal life. The Pleistocene has been a time that tested and stimulated the adaptive capabilities of man and hastened his evolutionary development.

The long heaps of debris left at the points where glacial advances ceased (called *morains*), outwash deposits, and river terraces all correlate with specific glaciations. Changes in flora and fauna also correlate with glacial and interglacial phases. Thus, the geochronology within the Pleistocene can be fairly precisely determined in many local areas of the world today. The major climatic cycles within the Pleistocene produced four primary advances of the ice sheets, called *glaciations*. In Europe, these are named after Alpine valleys, while in North America they are known after the states in which their effects are most prominent.[2] For our purposes, it is sufficient to refer to them by numbers, using Roman numerals for glaciations and Arabic numerals for interglacials (Fig. 8-1).

Dating prehistoric remains   Concern with evolutionary sequences makes it important to know which forms of life came after which. For these purposes, the *relative dating* of materials is sufficient. Often, however, it is not possible to link a deposit in one part of the world directly with another elsewhere so as to be able to say with certainty which is the older. This, then, may

[2]Günz, Mindel, Riss, and Würm, in Europe, and Kansan, Nebraskan, Illinoisan, and Wisconsonian, on the North American continent.

seriously inhibit the establishment of evolutionary sequences, if two crucial fossils or cultural deposits happen to be involved. In such instances, absolute dating is a great help. In *absolute dating,* exact or approximately exact ages may be established. When such dates are available, relative ages are then readily determinable. Absolute dates are therefore always desirable, if not always attainable.

Physicochemical dating Early in this century, Lord Rutherford and his coworkers at Cambridge University, England, demonstrated that uranium and thorium gradually disintegrate to become nonradioactive lead. Rates of decay were established and expressed in years of half-life. A *half-life* is the span of time necessary for 50 per cent of a given amount of uranium or thorium to disintegrate to lead isotypes. Table 8-2 shows the half-lives and the residual products of the five radioactive minerals known to occur in some rocks. In 1907, the idea was born that if the ratio of residual lead to radioactive elements could be determined in representative rocks, the age of the original formation of the rocks could be determined. For example, if the number of atoms of uranium 238 in a rock is equal to the number of lead 206 atoms, it means that one-half of the original uranium 238 has converted to lead 206; a half-life of uranium 238 has elapsed, and the rock is 4.5 billion years old (assuming no contamination or other upsetting factors). Recent derivations indicate a probable age of 4.5 billion years for the earth, and 4.9 to 6 billion years for our portion of the universe. In archaeology, potassium 40–argon 40 (K-A) readings are potentially important, since under optimum

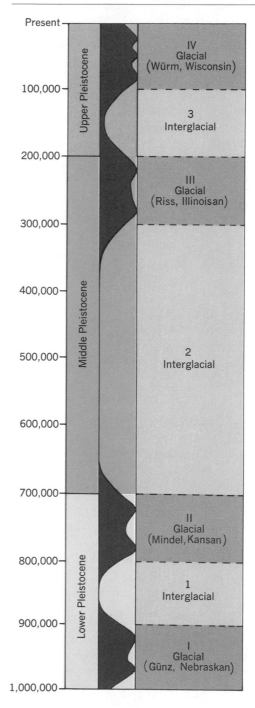

Fig. 8-1   The Pleistocene time scale, with European and North American nomenclature for major glacial phases. The prolonged second interglacial is sometimes called the "great interglacial." The conventional time scale of one million years is used, although potassium 40–argon 40 dates indicate the possibility that the age of the Pleistocene may have to be doubled.

Table 8-2   *Radioactive Elements and Their Disintegration Products, with Their Half-lives, Used in the Measurement of the Age of Rocks*

radioactive element	nonradioactive decay product	half-life, in millions of years
Uranium 238	Lead 206, helium	4,500
Uranium 235	Lead 207, helium	710
Thorium 232	Lead 208, helium	13,900
Potassium 40	Calcium 40, argon 40	1,310
Rubidium 87	Strontium 87	50,000

conditions they can fix dates between one hundred thousand and two million years by virtue of the relatively short half-life of potassium 40.[3]

CARBON 14 DATING   Immediately after World War II, a new possibility for dating archaeological materials was conceived by the nuclear physicist W. F. Libby. The method is based on the same principle of disintegration of radioactive elements, but instead of being applicable solely to rocks, it is usable with organic materials: wood, bone, and seeds and other forms of plant life. It also works with the charcoal from prehistoric campfires, the remains of man's dinners (animal bones and seeds), and the bones of his very self, provided they are not too fossilized.

Carbon 14 (C^{14}) is formed in the stratosphere when neutrons freed by cosmic rays bombard atmospheric nitrogen. The nitrogen becomes transmuted to radioactive C^{14}. Atmospheric movements are assumed to mix C^{14} evenly throughout the earth's air. Plants absorb C^{14} from the air; animals absorb it from the plants they eat. When a plant or animal dies, the absorption of C^{14} ceases, and its disintegration begins. The half-life of C^{14} is now calculated at 5,730 ± 40 years.[4] The number of radioactive emissions per minute, as measured by specially devised counters, indicates the amount of C^{14}

still residual in a specimen. From this, its age may be calculated. Carbon 14 dating presents a number of technical problems, and its readings need to be used with care. It is also limited by the fact that it is reliably effective only up to 30,000 years, although recent improvements in technique indicate that usable readings up to 70,000 years may be available.[5]

Biological analysis   Certain characteristics of plant and animal life associated with geological strata may also be used to establish the age of prehistoric remains and the climatic conditions under which they evolved.

POLLEN ANALYSIS, OR PALYNOLOGY   The analysis of the relative frequencies of different kinds of pollen is also a useful supporting technique for relative dating. It is particularly useful in reconstructing local climatic conditions in recent deposits. Core drillings are taken of the bottoms and underlying alluvial deposits of "live" and "extinct" lakes. The percentage of pollen grains of different plants in each 100-pollen-grain sample is determined. Fluctuations in the kinds of trees in the location can then be read, and climatic inferences suggesting a date, relative or absolute, may be drawn from the results.

DENDROCHRONOLOGY   Dendrochronology (Gr. *dendron*, tree + *logy*, study of), or tree-ring dating, exploits the fact that trees grow faster in wet years than in drought years, provided

[3]H. Brown, "The Age of the Solar System" (*Scientific American*, April, 1957, S. A. Reprint 102); A. Knopf, "Measuring Geologic Time," (*The Scientific Monthly*, November, 1957), pp. 225–236. And see especially F. Hole and R. F. Heizer, *An Introduction to Prehistoric Archaeology*, chap. 10.
[4]Libby's original figure was 5,568 years.

[5]See Hole and Heizer, *op. cit.*, for other less commonly used physicochemical methods.

their roots are not waterlogged. This, in turn, shows in the annual growth rings of some types of trees, especially pine. The basic technique is very similar to that used in building a stratigraphic master key, except that instead of matching layers of types of rock, growth rings of comparable thickness belonging to trees that grew in the same area are matched. The method is neat and precise, but it is applicable only in a limited number of environments. So far, keys going back 1,500 years in the American Southwest and 4,000 years in Nevada have been worked out. Efforts are being made to apply the method to Turkey and other semi-arid regions.

PALEONTOLOGY Paleontology (Gr. *palaios,* old + *onta,* existing things) is the study of past life through fossils. Associated flora and fauna add another dimension to chronological analysis. Woolly mammoths are Ice Age mammals, which do not occur in deposits laid down in warm Mesozoic times. Consequently, the mere presence of such fossils in a deposit indicates that the stratum is almost certainly post-Mesozoic and is likely to be of the Pleistocene epoch. In favorable instances, the total assemblage of fossil plants and animals may indicate rather clearly whether it is a Lower, Middle, or Upper Pleistocene deposit.

Taken separately, or in combination as circumstances permit, such techniques as those just presented help to take the guesswork out of prehistoric dating. As additional experience with physicochemical methods leads to greater precision and reliability, the replacement of inference with direct facts will be achieved. Having indicated the nature of the time scale within which evolution has taken place, our next task is to review some of the major mechanisms by means of which evolution occurs.

Genetics and evolution

How do species come into being through a gradual process of evolution over many generations of time? Only when this is understood can we begin to answer the more specific questions concerning the origins of man: "How did the primates develop from simpler mammals?" "How did the different genera of fossil men derive from the primates?" "How do the many types of fossil and living primates—including man—relate to one another?"

The answers have been found in Mendelian genetics, Darwin's principles of natural selection and adaptation, and studies of cellular reproduction. Considering the complicated nature of cell chemistry and biparental reproduction, it is hardly possible to do more than touch on the basic genetic principles that are relevant to our anthropological concerns. Those who wish to know more may find additional details in sources on genetics.

Cellular reproduction Up until 100 years ago, the idea of spontaneous generation of life such as maggots was commonplace in Europe and America. By the middle of the nineteenth century, however, microscopic study of living organisms was demonstrating that all organisms are communities of cells and that every cell is the offspring of preceding cells. The pattern of inheritance is different for uniparental and biparental organisms. Because primates are of the biparental type, only the second pattern need be considered here.

Mitosis The mature human body is made up of trillions of cells, all organized in an integrated system. Every one of these cells is the product of repeated reproduction of a single pair of sex cells (*gametes*). The fusion of a male gamete, or sperm, with a female gamete, or ovum, produces a *zygote,* or fertilized egg. At this early point in an organism's life history, it receives the basic genetic materials that will largely determine the nature of the molecular structure of all its subsequent cell development. The organism itself grows by multiplication of additional cells through cell division, or fission. In multiple-celled organisms, all cells contain nuclei, and each nucleus contains genetic materials in a substance called *chromatin.* The particular kind of cell division that occurs among metazoa is known as *mitosis* (Gr. *mitos,* thread) because it is characterized at one stage by the formation of threads out of the chromatin. The threads in turn break up into microscopically visible bodies of distinctive shapes, which are known as *chromosomes* (colorable bodies). The cells of man produce forty-six chromosomes in twenty-three pairs. In mitosis, chromosomes split longitudinally into two separate halves, which then migrate to opposite poles in the cell, whereupon the cell itself divides into two new daughter cells, each of which contains identical chromosomal complements of twenty-three pairs. By means of mitosis, each chromosome produces an exact replica of itself that is repeated in all the trillions of cells that subsequently mature to form the organism—except for the sex cells. Gametes go through a special process of self-reproduction called *meiosis* (Gr. *meioun,* to make smaller).

Meiosis   The *diploid* state occurs when there is the normal chromosome complement of paired chromosomes characteristic of all but sex cells. Fertilization joins two gametes, which, if the sex cells were diploid, would double the chromosome count every generation. To prevent this from happening, sex cells have a special process of self-reproduction, in which a gamete receives only one of the chromosomes out of each pair. Human gametes have only twenty-three chromosomes. Whether it is the chromosome from the father or that from the mother which goes into any given gamete is apparently a matter of chance. As a result, there is *variation* among the offspring of any mating pair.

Mitosis produces hereditary stability and is the basis of continuity of organic life. *Meiosis* ensures continuity but introduces an element of variation among offspring. *Variation is the first key to evolutionary change.*

Genes in heredity   Chromosomes are exceedingly gross units of hereditary reproduction, for they are constituted of an undetermined number of smaller units, called *genes.* Genes in turn are known to be constituted of combinations of deoxyribonucleic acid (the now-famous DNA),

ribonucleic acid (RNA), and several types of proteins. Variations in the molecular structure of DNA constitute the hereditary determinants in genes. The DNA code, or molecular structure, sets the pattern for subsequent molecular synthesis in cell formation.[6]

A gene is thought of as that minimum part of a chromosome (1) which functions to control a single chemical synthesis in a cell; (2) which, when its own molecular structure changes (mutates), alters just one trait of a cell; or (3) which can separate from its own chromosome and transfer, or "cross over," to the other chromosome in the pair in a reproductive cell. In other words, a gene is a unitary segment of the continuous molecular chain that constitutes a chromosome. Traits are the product of the genes that an organism inherits. The traits that can be detected as characteristic of an organism develop, under the direction of genes, according to the DNA code in the genes interacting with the total cellular environment of the organism and the external environment that impinges on the organism. More briefly, organic traits are the product of gene patterns as limited by environment.

Mendelian inheritance   The Austrian monk Gregor Mendel (1822–1884), breeding peas in the garden of the Augustinian monastery in Brünn, Austria (now Brno, Czechoslovakia), knew little of the cellular mechanisms outlined above, but he discovered laws for the inheritance of traits that hold for all living things. He noted that when two pure lines of unlike peas (for example, smooth versus wrinkled surfaces) were crossed, all the offspring were smooth. But when the hybrid offspring were mated with one another, smoothness and wrinkledness showed up as distinct traits in a definite proportion of 3 to 1. Furthermore, in all subsequent hybridizations, the characters of smoothness and roundness were inherited independently and recombined in all possible

[6]The Watson-Crick model, which presents a theoretical concept of DNA molecular structure, is described in contemporary biology and genetics texts. Good expositions may be found in P. B. Weisz, *The Science of Biology* (2d ed., 1963), chap. 18; and R. C. King, *Genetics* (2d ed., 1965).

ways. He also showed this to be true of other traits such as color.

THE LAWS OF MENDELIAN INHERITANCE In explaning his observations, Mendel reasoned that the sperm and the egg each contain "factors" that control the development of traits. These are the modern genes. Further, he reasoned, each plant must get at least one factor from each parent plant. Therefore, there must be two factors for each trait in the offspring. But only one factor could be passed on when the offspring mate, so there must be a reduction of the two factors to one in the sperm and egg. How it was done, he did not know, but he predicted meiosis as a process. He further noted that the redistribution of factors among the offspring was entirely random and also that differences in the effects of the factors influenced specific traits. For example, the factor for smooth skins is dominant over that for wrinkled skins when the two forms of this factor are combined in the cells of an offspring. Because the hereditary factors transmitted through reproductive cells are separable units and are inherited as such, Mendel's first law of inheritance is called the *law of segregation.* Phrased in modern terms, in which "gene" is synonymous with *"factor,"* it states: "Genes do not blend, but behave as independent units. They pass intact from one generation to the next, where they may or may not produce visible traits, depending on their dominance characterists. And genes segregate at random, thereby producing predictable ratios of traits in the offspring."[7]

Mendel's second law expresses the fact that inherited gene pairs for a given trait are not influenced by the inheritance of, or the failure to inherit, any other specific genes *located on other chromosomes.* The genetic controllers of traits are independently assorted among offspring and express their traits independently of the location of other genes on other chromosomes. This is the law of *independent assortment.* It explains how each individual, except identical twins, may receive a unique *total* combination of inherited traits. The possible number of gene

[7]Weisz, *op. cit.,* p. 684.

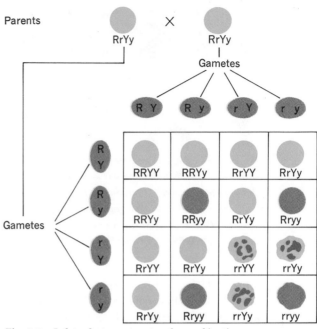

Fig. 8-2 *Independent assortment and recombination of genes. In this model, each parental gamete contains a heterozygous combination of dominant and recessive genes for round (R) and wrinkled (r) shape and for yellow (Y) and green (y) color. In meiosis, the genes are segregated and independently assorted and recombined in the differing combinations indicated in the block diagram. (Paul B. Weisz,* Elements of Biology. *Copyright © 1965 by McGraw-Hill Book Company.)*

combinations for any twenty-three hypothetical traits in man that are controlled by genes located on different chromosome pairs is 2^{23}, or more than eight million different gamete combinations. In fertilization, the fusion of two such gametes gives the mathematical possibility of $8,000,000 \times 8,000,000$, or more than sixty-four trillion gene combinations. Since many more than twenty-three different traits are controlled by genes located on different chromosome pairs, the number of possible differing total trait combinations is more than astronomical. Here, then, is a second major Mendelian source of variation.

The third law of Mendelian inheritance was discovered not by Mendel, but by T. H. Morgan

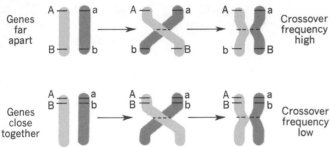

Genes far apart

Crossover frequency high

Genes close together

Crossover frequency low

Fig. 8-3   Crossing-over as a form of genetic variation. Genes that are far apart in locus on their chromosomes are more apt accidentally to cross over and become "misplaced" than genes that are close together. (Paul B. Weisz, Elements of Biology. Copyright © 1965 by McGraw-Hill Book Company.)

(1866–1945), the first of the great geneticists at Columbia University, early in the present century. It is the law of *lineal order of genes;* namely, the genes for specific traits are located in regular sequences along a chromosome, and they are linked together by chemical bonds, so that they are all normally inherited as a chromosome group. When chromosomes match up in the zygote, they ordinarily bond in parallel strands. Sometimes, however, they twist across each other, and a segment of each chromosome may become detached at the point of crossing-over. Each detached segment "joins" the chromosome of its opposite number, and a switch of chromosome segments is effected. The genetic code of each particular chromosome in the pair is thus altered. Although genes are independently assorted in inheritance, their relative positions on the chromosomes are important, for genes influence one another's effects in the development of traits. Crossing-over, by changing the proximity of specific genes, can alter their combined effects and so modify cell structure and somatic form, thus producing yet another source of variation.

GENOTYPES AND PHENOTYPES   Each individual receives two matching genes of each type, one from each parent. The separate genes that match or pair with each other at the same chromosome locus are *alleles* (Gr. *allelon,* of one another). The total complement of genes trans-

mitted to a zygote makes up its *genotype* (Gr. *gen,* to reproduce + *typos,* blow), or the genetic constitution of a given organism. When the pair of alleles for a given trait in an organism is the same (that is, both dominant or both recessive genes), the condition is called *homozygous* (Gr. *homos,* like + *zygotos,* yoked). The trait then directly manifests its genetic base. When the pair of alleles for a given trait in an organism is unlike (one dominant and one recessive gene), the condition is *heterozygous* (Gr. *heteros,* unlike + *zygotos*). The appearance of an organism is the sum of its traits; this is known as the *phenotype* (Gr. *phainein,* to reveal + *typos*). Because recessive genes are masked in heterozygous genotypes, their presence is not directly revealed in the phenotype and can be determined only by their known occurrence among the ancestors or descendants of a particular organism. This has certain evolutionary consequences of importance that are noted on pages 124 and 125.

Mutations   The genetic variations occurring among individuals in the transmission of traits from one generation to another, discussed above under Mendelian Inheritance, all operate as a *sexual recombination of genes.* Additional variations also occur as a result of internal changes in the molecular structure of genes themselves. This is the alteration of the DNA code, which changes the control effect of the gene over cell growth. When such changes are sufficiently stable to be inherited in the genes of the offspring, they are called *mutations.*

FREQUENCY OF MUTATIONS   The average frequency of mutations is estimated as possibly 1 in 100,000 genes. But because a single human gamete may contain some ten thousand genes, it is possible that one gamete in ten contains a spontaneous mutation.[8] A gene mutation that is lethal in its effect may cause the early death of the organism, as is often the case with the mutation that produces hemophilia. The individual then has no chance to reproduce, and the mutant gene is not passed on through heredity. Such mutations have no significant evolutionary consequences unless

[8]King, *op. cit.,* p. 201.

they are linked to other genes, which are consequently lost because of the lethal mutation.

If the mutant gene happens to be recessive, there will be no visible trait effect in the generation in which the mutation occurs. Its effects will show up in homozygous genotypes in later generations, in very low frequencies. If, on the other hand, the mutation is dominant and not lethal, it will establish its phenotypic effects immediately. These same effects will be inherited by a majority of the organism's offspring. Since mutations, even though they occur wholly by chance, take place regularly and repeatedly, nonlethal forms may, under given conditions, become established in a *Mendelian population.*

Mendelian populations and gene pools A Mendelian population is a localized grouping of members of a given species who interbreed mostly among themselves but occasionally with members of sister populations. All the genes possessed by all the members of the population constitute its *gene pool.* The gene pool is therefore the reservoir of genetic materials available to the population for the genotypic inheritance of the next generation. Because of the reproductive processes of mitosis and meiosis, the tendency is for the organisms of a particular species to convey the gene pool relatively unchanged to succeeding generations.[9] Such stability preserves the species and works against evolution. *Evolution means change in the genetic structures of populations.* Phenotypic changes occur from generation to generation as a result, and the bodily forms and living processes characteristic of the population are modified thereby. But what lends direction to the change?

Variation, natural selection, and adaptation The factors that upset genetic equilibrium are (1) mutation, (2) natural selection, (3) population mixture, and (4) genetic drift. Of these, the first two are the most important as evolutionary

[9]The Hardy-Weinberg law states that if mating within a population is random, if mutations do not occur, and if the population is large, the frequencies of genes in a gene pool will remain constant from generation to generation; a condition of genetic equilibrium will be maintained, and there will be no evolution.

processes. To Charles Darwin (1809–1882) and Alfred Wallace (1823–1913) goes the main credit for the first comprehensive formulations and systematic explanation of species origin in terms of developmental sequences. Darwin, in particular, demonstrated that inheritable variations are *differentially* affected by the environment in which a population lives. In his own words:

It may metaphorically be said that natural selection is daily and hourly scrutinizing, throughout the world, the slightest variations; rejecting those that are bad, preserving and adding up all that are good; silently and insensibly working whenever and wherever opportunity offers, at the improvement of each organic being in relation to its organic and inorganic conditions of life.[10]

In modern terms, if among individuals carrying new genes some survive and have offspring of their own, the new genes are added to the gene pool, and the characteristics of the population are changed by that much. If, however, they fail to survive to reproduce because of the effects of the new gene in the local environmental setting, the new variation does not alter the gene pool, and no impact on its future results. If, in addition to surviving, the individuals who possess the new genes and their resulting traits survive with greater relative frequency than those who do not have them, the chances are they will increase the frequency of the new genes in the population from generation to generation.

Natural selection is the operation of any environmental factors upon genetic variations that result in *differential reproduction.* Those variant individuals which reproduce and survive most frequently are the best adapted to the environment; from generation to generation, they contribute a progressively larger proportion of descendants in the population. Eventually their genes may become preponderant in the population, and the modal phenotypes of the population will be altered. In such a situation, those gene carriers which are most positively responsive to the environment in terms of their reproductive capabilities have survived,

[10]C. Darwin, *The Origin of Species* (Macmillan edition), p. 78.

and the population becomes better *adapted* to its environment.

In the evolutionary context, the important questions to be asked about a mutation are whether its survival value is negative (lethal) or positive (adaptive) and, in either case, to what degree. *Population genetics* is the study through which gene frequencies and the *survival quotients,* or *reproductive potential,* of different genes in specific environments are mathematically determined. Such quotients are indicators of rates of evolutionary change. Obviously, a mutation has to have a high selective advantage and frequency, as well as the quality of dominance, to change the physical character of a population very rapidly in a stable environment.

The effect of population mixture Miscegenation between two populations with differing gene pools results in new combinations of genes in the offspring generations of the mixed populations. Although we have been talking as though each gene were responsible for a single trait, genes actually work in concert to influence the development of many phentoypic traits. The new phenotypes can become characteristic of the population either because of continued *hybridization* or because the hybrids have a higher survival and reproductive quotient than the nonhybrids. Eventually a new taxonomic type may result, as has been the case in recent centuries with the American Colored and South African Colored populations (see Chapter 13).

The selective effect of environmental changes Environments as well as genes are to some extent unstable. Any environmental change will alter the selective effect upon the gene pools of all the populations inhabiting such an altered environment. Environmental variation is therefore just as important and necessary to evolution as genetic change. But an environment is also biological as well as geological. Any change in plant or animal life is itself an environmental change affecting everything else in the environment. Every evolutionary change has a feedback effect that produces

environmental changes for other organisms. Hence, evolution has progressively speeded up from geologic era to geologic era, as the cumulative effect of organic changes is felt.

Adaptive effects of sickle-cell anemia Whether or not a given mutation has a selective disadvantage always depends upon the specific environment with which the population has to contend. An example that has excited much interest among geneticists and anthropologists is the discovery of a mutant recessive gene that causes a blood disorder known as *sickle-cell anemia,* so named because the defective blood cell is sickle-shaped. The homozygous genotype is believed to be 100 per cent lethal, and homozygotes for this gene die in childhood. However, in its heterozygous state, in which a person receives a normal dominant gene from one parent and the recessive mutant gene from the other, the genotype is not lethal. Heterozygous children do not die because of their single sickle-cell gene. The factor that has intrigued modern scientists is that the heterozygotes have a special immunity to malaria. In the malaria zones of the Old World tropics, thousands of homozygous dominants die from, or are seriously impaired by, malaria. Heterozygotes with one recessive sickle-cell gene are malaria-resistant and get on much better than those who have no sickle-cell gene at all. They suffer neither from anemia nor from malaria.

In a malaria-ridden environment, it is thus advantageous for the population to have the sickle-cell mutant in the gene pool, even though it means that every child born a homozygote is doomed to an early death, a sacrifice necessary to the maintenance of the population. The mutation is a curse for the homozygote and a blessing for the fortunate heterozygote.

Malaria eradication removes the selective advantage of the sickle-cell mutant; hence, its very low frequency in nonmalarial zones, as compared with those where the disease is still rampant.[11] The presence of malaria works selectively to maintain the recessive sickle-cell

[11]See A. C. Allison, "Aspects of Polymorphism in Man" (*Cold Spring Harbor Symposium in Quantitative Biology,* Vol. 20, 1955), pp. 239–255.

gene in a population. Therefore, evolution in the direction of sickle-cell anemia as a trait is maintained among populations that live in malarial zones, and it ceases if malaria is eliminated.

Genetic drift It is also possible for an isolated population to experience a change in its original genetic composition without the effect of mutation or natural selection. This is the result of the *Sewall Wright effect,* named after the great contemporary American geneticist who demonstrated the workings of *genetic drift,* as it is also called.

Suppose a small group of people (or any other organisms, for that matter) migrate to a new territory and subsequently lose contact with their ancestral group. Suppose, further, that in later generations more groups break off from the descendants of the original immigrants to make their homes elsewhere and that they, too, become isolated as populations.

In a situation in which the gene frequency for a given trait is only 15 per cent for the original population, it could easily happen that by sheer chance no more than 5 per cent of the migrants carry the gene. In the gene pool of the emigrant population, the frequency of this gene is automatically reduced by two-thirds. The gene pools of the original and the new societies are different by that much. Furthermore, in the absence of intermarriage, mutation, and changes in factors of natural selection, the change would remain constant indefinitely. Now suppose that in the course of time, a handful of descendants of the emigrants move on to new territories. There is only a 5 per cent frequency of the gene in the total pool of their parent population. By chance, it is possible that none of them will carry the gene. In that event, the gene would drop out of the population entirely. The new population would henceforth be absolutely different from its ancestors in the trait that the gene in question produced.

Drift may also move in two or more directions simultaneously. Fig. 8-4 is a simplified model of how this may take place. Let us assume equal frequencies of two alleles, x and y. In the model, each x and each y represents a

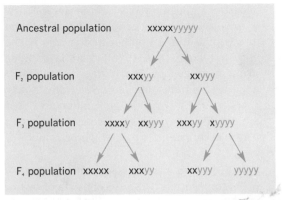

Fig. 8-4 Hypothetical genetic drift (Sewall Wright effect) in a series of subdividing populations. The genetic character of two populations with a common ancestry may change without mutations solely by operation of the laws of chance in the distribution of genes.

gene frequency of 10 per cent in the total gene pool of the original population. Therefore, we begin with five x's and five y's. Assume that the population divides equally; half the people pack up and move away entirely. By chance it hypothetically happens that one population contains three x's and two y's, and the other population two x's and three y's. Now, let us follow the three-x, two-y population. It inbreeds; then its children decide to split up, and half of them migrate. The chances are one in five that the migrating group will carry away a ratio of four x's to one y, leaving the home F_3 generation with two x's to three y's. The migrants inbreed; then half their children carry on the tradition of breaking away and moving on. The chances are one in five that the migrating group will carry away a ratio of five x's to zero y's, leaving the home F_4 generation with a ratio of three x's to two y's.

The third generation of isolating migrants has lost all its y genes. In the character that y determines, it has nothing in common with its racial ancestors. On the two-x to three-y side of the F_2 generation (the right of the model), similar splitting and isolating migrations can produce a population totally devoid of x. From the original equally heterogeneous ancestral population have come several new ones with varying proportions of x and y, one that is pure x, and another that is pure y. The ancestral group has spawned at least three races: a mixed one like itself, a pure x, and a pure y. All this has occurred without any changes in the original gene structures, but through the roll of the genetic dice when group fission occurs and the resulting groups inbreed.

Speciation   We have already referred several times to "species." A *species* consists of one or more populations whose members are capable of intrabreeding among themselves. Simultaneously, they are incapable of interbreeding with members of other species. Genetically, species members can exchange genes through reproduction. Nonspecies members cannot.

Speciation occurs when two or more groups from an original population become isolated from one another and, in adaptation to their separate environments, go through sufficiently great genetic modifications that their genetic molecules are incapable of interacting on one another. This is the process that produces the branched-tree, or dendritic, effect on phylogenetic charts (see Fig. 8-8, for example). The result is *differential evolution* through *adaptive radiation.* Most new species are formed in this manner. In limited conditions, however, such as on a small island, a species may change through time without producing additional species. A new species simply replaces the original through straight-line change, known as *transformation.*

In the evolution of the hominoids, the lines of man, gorilla, chimpanzee, orangutan, and gibbon were simultaneously radiating from a common ancestral species in the Miocene era.

Extinction   The fossil record is replete with the eloquent testimony of species that had their day and survive no longer. Extinction is the outcome of failure to readapt to rapid environmental change. Again, remember that the appearance of new organisms in an environment is just as much a change as an alteration in climate or elevation of the earth's surface is. Extinction of one type of organism may

open an ecological niche for a new organism to move into by its own means of adaptation.

Radiant evolution has progressively diversified the forms of life from its "simple" beginnings in the Proterozoic era. New forms have generally become more complex and more heterogeneous. The primates represent the most complex of all living orders. By virtue of his nervous system, man is the most complex creature of all. He is the product of the interacting forces that have just been summarized. Our next task is to trace out the phylogeny of the anthropoid branch of primates.

Fossil primates from the Eocene to the Pleistocene

The opening epochs of the Cenozoic era were long, moist, and warm. The Eocene, lasting from sixty until forty million years ago, was a time of extensive forests that provided a rich habitat for myriads of unobtrusive, small tree-dwelling primates, who evolved from the insect-eating, long-snouted, sharp-eared, ground-dwelling mammals of the order Insectivora. The prosimia proliferated.

Eocene prosimia   The *prosimia* (before simians) were the earliest primates. Today fifty or sixty fossil genera of prosimia have been found in the northern hemisphere of the Old and New Worlds. Initially, the adaptive success of the prosimia was remarkable in the development of grasping paws for running on branches and of sharp vision for gauging jumping distances. Then they fell upon bad times. During the Oligocene, environmental changes were such that in North America and Europe they were "selected out"—extinguished. Perhaps they were outdone adaptively by the rodents, who could exploit the grasslands of the north more effectively and who could certainly outbreed any primate. However, the prosimia did successfully maintain themselves in Central and South America, where subsequent evolution produced the New World monkeys but no hominoids. In South Asia and Africa, the prosimia carried through the critical late Eocene and Oligocene periods to provide the ancestral stock for the anthropoid lines to come. It is presumed that tree living gave a selective advantage to those primates who varied in the direction of stereoscopic vision. The admonition to "look before you leap" was as valid then as now. Larger brains would also help in acrobatic judgment. Whatever the reasons, vision was becoming stereoscopic, and brains larger.

The Oligocene catarrhines We have no Oligocene fossil primates whatsoever from Europe. In Egypt, however, the story is very different. A famous fossil bed was laid down at Fayum, near Cairo, in early Oligocene times. The deposits are alluvial sedimentary strata related to the rise and fall of the Mediterranean shoreline.

Two jaw fragments and a few other bones, collected at Fayum at the beginning of this century, represent two Oligocene fossil genera, *Parapithecus* and *Propliopithecus*. On the basis of its dental pattern, *Parapithecus* has long been accepted as a true hominoid, sufficiently generalized in its dental structure to have been of the type that could have been ancestral to the cercopithecoidal Old World monkeys. Since 1960, extensive excavations at Fayum by Yale University anthropologists have turned up parts of over one hundred primate individuals, which when fully studied should reveal a good deal more about the Oligocene anthropoids than is known at present. For one thing, the single *Propliopithecus* jaw had been thought for fifty years to represent a protohylobate, or gibbonoid, ancestor. Now it is evaluated as a generalized hominoid. This would make it a representative of the Oligocene ancestral pool from which man and all later apes evolved. It is generally accepted as representing one of the types from which all living hominids—apes and man—are very probably descended.[12]

[12]In the second edition of this book (*Man in the Primitive World*, pp. 38–40), the Boule-Strauss hypothesis was presented in detail. It held that the evolutionary line leading to man separated in Oligocene times from a monkeylike ancestor, rather than in Miocene times from an apelike ancestor. This hypothesis implied that man's ancestry links directly with that of Old World monkeys and does not pass through a hominoid stage shared with the apes. Recent chromosome and serologic analyses show that this is quite impossible. The Boule-Strauss hypothesis has failed to gain further acceptance and is, indeed, so generally ignored by specialists in this decade that discussion of it has been dropped from this book.

The Miocene hominoids The twenty-million-year Miocene was an era of environmental conditions once again highly favorable to the arboreal primates. The climate was mild, generally moist, and wetter than today. Rain forests (a more elegant word for scientific use than jungle) covered much of Asia, Africa, and even Europe in the lower altitudes. Higher plateaus were richly grassed and sprinkled with open tree areas; they were pleasantly cool. Over wide spaces, the country was verdant and rich in vegetable foodstuffs. The cercopithecines were on hand, and the stage was set for the great primate evolutionary outburst that would produce the immediate hominoid precursors of modern apes and man.

The result, in the Miocene, was the production of the manifold genus of *Dryopithecus*, from which derive the pongids (orangutans) and members of the genus *Pan* (chimpanzee and gorilla). Another Miocene fossil ape, very closely related to the dryopithecines, was the African genus *Proconsul*. *Pliopithecus* is a third important Miocene fossil hominoid genus, and *Oreopithecus* is yet another.

Dryopithecus The first dryopithecine fossil fragment was described by the French paleontologist Edouard Lartet in 1856, three years before Darwin's *Origin of Species*. For many decades the one significant feature of the dryopithecine family that could be fixed upon with certainty was its dentition, notably the much-talked-about "*Dryopithecus* Y-pattern" of the molars. As with some of the constellations of the heavens, it takes a good imagination to see the "pattern" to which the name applies. However, the molar teeth of Old World monkeys and baboons, when looked at from above, have four peaks, or cusps. The deep valleys between them are in the form of a plus sign. The molars of living hominids, on the other hand, usually have an additional fifth cusp. The extra valleys made by the presence of the fifth cusp form a Y between cusps 3, 4, and 5, (Fig. 8-5).

Any fossil ape that has this pattern is sure to be closely related to man and the modern apes. If he lived in the Miocene, he could easily be

home-like

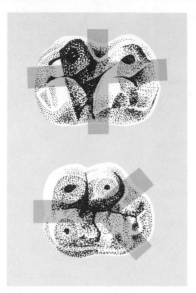

Fig. 8-5 The "dryopithecus Y-pattern," formed by the fifth cusp in the molar tooth (below). distinguishes the hominoids from all other primates. The above tooth is a four-cusp molar of a baboon which shows the four cusp + pattern. (Adapted from Elwyn L. Simons, "The Early Relatives of Man," Scientific American.)

Fig. 8-6 Proconsul africanus. The reconstructed skull of a fossil Miocene ape as seen from the side. [From a drawing after J. T. Robinson in W. E. Le Gros Clark, History of the Primates. Courtesy of the Trustees, British Museum (Natural History).]

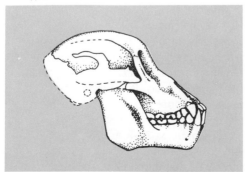

ancestral to all later hominids, extinct and living. Innumerable dryopithecine teeth and skeletal fragments have been found in Europe and Asia, but unfortunately no complete skulls or skeletons. Details of the genus's bodily structure are therefore lacking.

Proconsul In Kenya, Africa (mostly on Rusinga Island, near the eastern shore of Lake Victoria), L. S. B. Leakey, who has devoted his life to the discovery and interpretation of prehistoric primates, has discovered several species of Miocene fossil apes of a single genus, called *Proconsul* in honor of a popular ape named Consul who was a long-time resident of the London Zoo. *Proconsul* signifies "before Consul," which is certainly true enough.

The nearly five hundred *Proconsul* individuals that have been discovered come in three distinguishable types, which Leakey has identified as separable species: *Proconsul africanus* (a small, gibbon-sized type), *Proconsul nyanzae* (a chimpanzee-sized form), and *Proconsul major* (who could match a gorilla for size).

Proconsul africanus is the best preserved and therefore the best known. It is small-brained when compared with man, but it had already achieved a cranial capacity that put it between the range of the gibbon and the chimpanzee (100 to 400 cc). Its teeth are pongid. Its limbs, hands, and feet are considered to be those of a creature which could either brachiate in the trees or get about on the ground on all fours. It probably did both, but the fact that it could do either shows that the gorilla-chimpanzee pattern of life was already being established by these Miocene apes, who were beginning to exploit the ground as a possible habitat.[13] But more important in the Miocene stage of evolution is the apparent fact that *Proconsul* got about in the trees by swinging from the branches rather than by running along them, as all earlier primates did. This is a primate adaptation that accompanies increasing body size in the direction of the hominoids. It, in turn, leads to adaptive radiation that selects for modification in

[13]For details, see W. E. Le Gros Clark and L. S. B. Leakey, "The Miocene Hominidae of East Africa" (*British Museum Fossil Mammals of Africa*, No. 1).

the direction of hands rather than paws. The basis for manipulation and tool using was being laid. The earliest seeds of culture were about to be planted.

Oreopithecus *Oreopithecus* is an Old World anthropoid who has graced the storage trays of European museums for over one hundred years. The type specimen, a jawbone with teeth, discovered in Tuscany (central Italy) in 1860, was for decades looked upon by most students as a fossil Old World monkey (cercopithecoid). A German specialist, G. Schwalbe, in 1916 argued that the teeth showed sufficient hominoid character to warrant identifying the type as an extinct genus of anthropoid ape. In 1958, *Oreopithecus* burst from the museum closet to make world news. Dr. Johannes Hurzeler, of Basel, Switzerland, had reopened the *Oreopithecus* question and had resumed digging in the lignite beds of the Pontine marshes in 1954. Within a few years, he had found the partial remains of at least four dozen individuals. But the great prize was the recovery on Aug. 2, 1958, of an almost complete specimen in very good condition (Fig. 8-7). Hurzeler hailed *Oreopithecus* as a primitive hominid and early ancestor of man. Considering the age (Upper Miocene–Lower Pliocene), this was news, indeed.

More sober evaluation, however, leads to a less ebullient conclusion. W. L. Strauss, Jr., has carried through a thorough comparative analysis of the original fossils. In his view, *Oreopithecus* is clearly a hominoid. Whether or not, within the hominoids, it falls in the hominid family is a moot question. Its teeth prove it to be definitely not pongid. But the postcranial (from the neck down) skeleton is that of a full brachiator. Therefore, either it is hominid, or a new oreopithecid family must be established for it. The decision "is essentially a matter of taste."[14] G. G. Simpson, to whose judgment most scientists give great weight, has examined the *Oreopithecus* teeth himself and is convinced that they have too many nonhominid peculiarities to warrant putting them in the hominid class. He sees

Fig. 8-7 A complete and nearly perfect fossil of *Oreopithecus*. (Courtesy of Johannes Hurzeler, Natural History Museum, Basel, Switzerland.)

Oreopithecus as an early ape that separated from a *Propliopithecus* ancestral base during the Oligocene to evolve in a hominid direction along its own separate course, becoming extinct in Pliocene times and making no direct contribution to modern apes or man.[15] This is the interpretation accepted in the phylogenetic pattern of primate ancestry diagramed in Fig. 8-8.

The Pliocene hominids During the mid-1930s, a combined Yale–Cambridge University expedition carried out intensive explorations in the famous fossil beds of the Siwalik Hills along the northern border of India and West Pakistan.

[14]W. L. Strauss, Jr., "The Classification of Oreopithecus," in S. L. Washburn (ed.), *Classification and Human Evolution*, p. 174.

[15]See G. G. Simpson, "The Meaning of Taxonomic Statements," in Washburn, *op. cit.*, pp. 21–22.

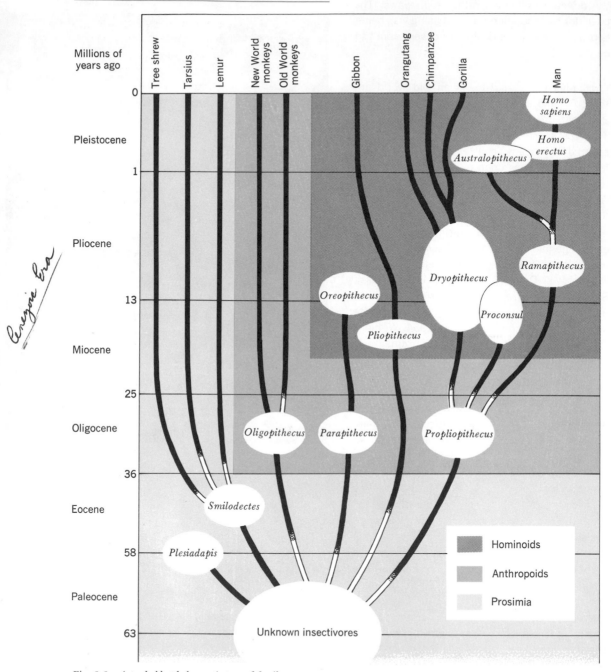

Fig. 8-8   *A probable phylogenetic tree of fossil primates. The antecedents of* Oreopithecus *are highly problematical; the species could be derived from* Propliopithecus.

Among the finds were remains of numerous dryopithecines of several different types. One of these is of great potential significance—*Ramapithecus brevirostis.*[16]

Ramapithecus The major piece of this specimen is a part of the upper right cheek (maxilla). It contains the root of the lateral incisor, both premolars, and the first two molars. A left canine and a third molar, as well as the premolars and the first and second left molars, have been found separately. These provide samples of all the *Ramapithecus* teeth except the incisors. Enough of the maxilla is present to allow quite accurate reconstruction of the upper jaw:

According to this reconstruction the palate is arched, as in man; the canine was no larger than the first premolar, and was thick mesiolabially as in man, instead of spatulate, as in apes; and the ratio between the sizes of the front teeth (premolars and canines) and those of the cheek teeth (premolars and molars) is roughly the same as in man, and not as in the apes, which have relatively large front teeth. Enough of the maxilla is preserved to show that the upper jaw was more manlike than apelike in its depth and degree of prognathism.[17]

The conclusion to be drawn from this is that *Ramapithecus* had developed dental features that point strongly in the direction of man. If additional finds at some future date show a skull with an adequately protohuman cranium and a pelvis indicating at least partially upright posture, then we could be quite sure that in *Ramapithecus* we have an early ancestor of man, as distinct from the pongids, in Pliocene India.

Africa has turned up a close cousin of *Ramapithecus* in the discovery by Leakey, in 1961, of a similar fragment of upper right maxilla containing a couple of molars and premolars. A canine tooth was found separately. This specimen has been dated at fourteen million years by K-A analysis and falls within the Early Pliocene range. So far as presently reported, there is nothing to distinguish it as a separate genus

from *Ramapithecus.*[18] The find is very important, however. It proves that *Ramapithecus* is not a freak specimen, and it demonstrates that similar protohominid populations were emerging from the dryopithecine matrix in both East Africa and the Indian subcontinent at the same time.

SUMMARY

The accumulation of facts by biology in all its branches and by paleontology, geography, and anthropology overwhelmingly demonstrates that the earth and all the living forms upon it have been undergoing persistent evolution.

The antiquity of human antecedents is established through stratigraphy and geochronology based upon the rates of disintegration of radioactive elements, pollen analysis and tree-ring counts, and chemical content of fossil materials. Life began some two billion years ago in unicellular form. The evolution of life has consisted in the continuous development of greater and greater complexities and varieties of cell aggregations. The process is the result of genetic variation and adaptation to specific environments through natural selection. The continuity of life is maintained by cellular reproduction involving mitosis, which is the process wherein chromosomes are formed and split longitudinally into two halves, each of which goes to a new daughter cell, thus replacing the original cell with two exact replicas. In bisexual reproduction, however, gametes, as a result of meiosis, receive only half the usual number of chromosomes, so that when male and female gametes join, the fertilized egg, or zygote, will have the normal complement. Which chromosome goes into which gamete is a matter of chance. Thus all individuals are unique genotypes, and variation occurs. Genes are the units

[16]Rama is a legendary Hindu culture hero. Other closely related dryopithecine types discovered in the Siwalik beds and named by G. E. Lewis were *Sivapithecus, Bramapithecus, Sugrivapithecus,* and *Paleosimia.* Siva and Brama are highly revered Hindu gods. Sugri is a monkey god. Taxonomically, these names are neutral. Culturally, they are in questionable taste.
[17]C. S. Coon, *The Origin of Races,* p. 205.

[18]Leakey, whose dedicated enthusiasm has led him to the discovery of more important precursors of man than any living scientist, also overenthusiastically (some think) tends to give each of his new local finds at least a new species status, if not that of a new genus, too. In this case, he has done both. Hence, he calls his specimen *Kenyanthropus Wickeri,* after Kenya and Mr. Fred Wicker, on whose farm the fossil was found. See L. S. B. Leakey, "A New Lower Pliocene Fossil Primate from Kenya" (*Annals and Magazine of Natural History,* Vol. 14, 1961), pp. 689–696.

of DNA molecules that determine specific traits. They have a standard alignment along the chromosome body. But in the formation of new chromosome pairs, parts of chromosomes may be realigned through crossing-over. When this happens, more variation results.

In addition to variation produced by gene recombination in bisexual reproduction (Mendelian variation), gametic variation is produced by mutation, population mixture, and genetic drift.

Evolution occurs whenever natural selection acts upon genetic variations to produce differential reproduction, that is, when organisms possessing certain genes are more able to survive and reproduce themselves than other organisms in the population. A Mendelian population is a localized group of species members who interbreed (exchange genes). Enduring changes in the gene pool of a population caused by natural selection produce adaptation to the environment on the part of the population. When two or more groups from an original population become isolated and adapt to different environments to the point where they can no longer interbreed, speciation has occurred. Evolution has then produced two new organic species. This is the process of adaptive radiation, through which branching, leading to more and more living forms, has taken place.

The ancestry of all primates goes back to some primitive Late Mesozoic mammal from which the prosimia of the Eocene period of the Cenozoic era were derived. The prosimia radiated over both hemispheres, but under Oligocene conditions most types became extinct. Modern prosimia are represented by living tree shrews, lemurs, lorises, and tarsiers, among others. In Late Oligocene times, anthropoidal precursors evolved in Africa (and probably Asia) and are known in part from the fossils of *Propliopithecus* and *Parapithecus*.

Cercopithecoids evolved separately from one another in the Old and New Worlds after the Oligocene, and New World monkeys have only a remote relationship to man. Old World monkeys are more closely related to man, but they are not in themselves ancestral. In Miocene times,

the protohominoid *Dryopithecus* came into existence. *Proconsul* is an African Miocene ape with the dentition, the brain, and apparently the brachiating equipment to qualify him as a close ancestor to the ancestral type. *Ramapithecus,* as representative of our Pliocene precursors, is apparently sufficiently human in dentition to indicate that hominid ancestors were already distinguished from the pongids in Miocene times, twelve to fourteen million years ago. *Oreopithecus* might have sired an entirely unique stem of men or apes if the genus had survived the Middle Pliocene, which it did not.

A long gap of ~~thirteen~~ 10-11 million years exists between *Ramapithecus* and the appearance of the first man-creatures in the Pleistocene. The fossils to fill that gap are yet to be discovered.

SELECTED READINGS

Aitken, M. J.: *Physics and Archaeology* (1961). A professional handbook on the application of physics to problems of archaeological dating.

Clark, W. E. Le G.: *The Antecedents of Man: An Introduction to the Evolution of the Primates* (1960). A detailed and thoroughgoing anatomical summary. Neither overtechnical nor overeasy to read, but sound and understandable.

Dunn, L. C.: *Heredity and Evolution in Human Populations* (1960). A relatively simple introduction, written for the layman by a leading scientist.

Dobzhansky, T.: *Genetics and the Origin of Species* (1936). This book provides the basic biology and ideas behind many of the recent developments in the modern scientific approach to the study of human races.

———: *Mankind Evolving: The Evolution of the Human Species* (1964). Written almost three decades after *Genetics and the Origin of Species,* it presents the lastest findings and expresses Dobzhansky's humane reflections on "whence and whither mankind."

Hole, F., and R. F. Heizer: *An Introduction to Prehistoric Archaeology* (1965). This guide to archaeological methods, prepared for the nonprofessional, includes excellent sections on stratigraphy and dating.

Simpson, G. G.: *The Meaning of Evolution* (1965). An outstanding contemporary exposition and interpretation of organic evolution.

The transition

to man

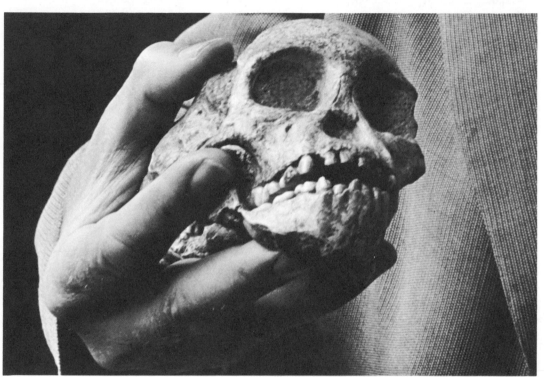

chapter 9

The Miocene provided the seedbed for the pro-
liferating growth of the prehuman anthropoids.
The Pliocene tested their survival capacities to
the utmost, for it was a time of climatic catastrophe for all Africa. The Miocene rains stopped,
and for more than ten million years an incredible desert, which very likely linked the Sahara
of the north and the Kalahari of the south,
smothered the vast continent in searing heat
and choking sand and dust. It imposed an even
more excruciating survival test on the evolving
primates than would the freezing climates of

the north in the Pleistocene epoch, which was to follow.

In the high hills flanking the southern shoulders of the Himalayas, and perhaps on the flanks of the high equatorial mountains of Africa, there was, however, sufficient moisture to sustain the grasses, shrubs, and trees necessary for a primate environment. Thus the proto-hominids survived until the resumption of rains and snowstorms in the Pleistocene, when in Africa verdure again returned to the lowlands and lakes and streams were filled.

The significant effect of the Pliocene climate on primate evolution would seem to have been the shrinkage, and even disappearance, of the Miocene forests and the resultant premium placed upon genetic adaptability to terrestrial living. Those primates which could come down from the trees and move about on the ground sufficiently well to get from grove to grove in search of food and security would have had, by and large, the best chance to survive and perpetuate their kind. What actually happened in the Pliocene can be only inferred, for the ten-million-year gap between *Ramapithecus* and the next higher fossil hominoid remains for the time being a lost chapter in the history of the primates. By the very end of the Pliocene, however, an upright ape man or very ancient and exceedingly primitive type of man had evolved. His remains have been found in Early Pleistocene deposits in Africa and Indonesia. These are the australopithecines.

The two species of Australopithecus

"Austral" refers to south, not to Australia, for the only thing *Australopithecus* has in common with Australia is a location in the southern latitudes. Although the several discoverers of the various australopithecine fossils enthusiastically named four or five different genera from their finds, in addition to a couple of further species, the consensus of scientific opinion now recognizes but one genus, *Australopithecus*, and two species, *Australopithecus africanus* and *Australopithecus robustus*. (But, see page 142, below.)

Australopithecus africanus In 1924, Raymond A. Dart, professor of anatomy at the University of Witwatersrand, reported the find of a nearly perfect juvenile primate skull in the quarries near Taung, Rhodesia. Its association with numerous extinct Pleistocene fossils, including monkeys, made its antiquity apparent. The specimen was six years old, as indicated by its teeth. Its face, as well as the frontal region of the calvarium, was intact. The larger part of the braincase had been dislodged and lost in the mining operations, but a perfect fossil endocranial cast revealing the size and shape of the brain itself was attached to the face (see Fig. 9-1). The anatomical character of the first *Australopithecus* as a type was difficult to determine with certainty because species characteristics are not too definite in the young; much surer comparisons can be made with adult skeletons of the same sex. Nonetheless, Dart felt safe in identifying a new genus of hominoid, to which he gave the name with which we are now familiar. Subsequently, in 1936 and thereafter, other *Australopithecus* fossils were found at Sterkfontein, Makapansgat, Swartkrans, and Kromdraai —all in South Africa—and the validity of the first Taung specimen as representative of a new genus was thoroughly established.[1] The Sterkfontein site produced the almost complete cranium of a sixteen- to eighteen-year-old, plus another fragmentary skull. Makapansgat has produced three fragmentary craniums. About two hundred teeth have been recovered from these three sites; nothing is ambiguous about our knowledge of either craniums or dentition.

Morphology of the cranium The skulls of *Australopithecus africanus* present a generally simian

[1] The first Sterkfontein find was made by Robert Broom in 1936. Broom named it *Plesianthropus*, but it is clearly an *Australopithecus africanus*.

When Dart discovered the remains of a fossil man ape at Makapansgat in 1951, he thought it was somewhat different from his Taung *africanus*, and he misinterpreted the coloration of the associated animal bones as being due to burning. Although there was no direct evidence of the use of fire by the man ape, he decided that he had had things cooking in his time, and so he ebulliently named him *Australopithecus prometheus*, "bringer of fire." Subsequently, *A. prometheus* has been more soberly relegated to *A. africanus*, which is distinction enough.

quality, with small braincases and protruding, chinless jaws. Within the small cranium of *Australopithecus africanus*, the brain assumes moderate proportions, varying from about 450 to a maximum of 700 cc. Gorilla brains run from around 300 to a recorded maximum of 685 cc, while the chimpanzee-orangutan range is 290 to 475 cc. The average brain of *Australopithecus africanus* is thus larger than that of the chimpanzee but not that of the gorilla. Relative to body size, however, the brain of *Australopithecus africanus* is distinctly larger than that of the massive gorilla and somewhat larger than that of the chimpanzee or orangutan.

A question may be raised as to the validity of comparisons based on mere brain size, since it is well established that no correlation exists between brain size and mental ability within the present human species except in pathological cases of microcephaly and macrocephaly. Nevertheless, among the several primate genera and in comparison with even lower animal forms, brain volume, cortical surface area, and the relative development of the different parts of the brain are determinable and significant indicators of relative mental capacity and degree of environmental adaptability—including, of course, the ability to produce culture. It will be seen that the higher fossil hominids all have relatively large brains; in the case of modern man, the minimal size (except for microcephalic idiots) is 1,000 cc, whereas the largest nonpathological brains run to 2,000 cc. The human mean is approximately 1,500 cc for males and 50 cc less for females.

The skull of *Australopithecus africanus* presents a high, fairly rounded cranial vault when compared with that of the gorilla. The next feature that excites interest is the low position of the occipital bony ridge for the attachment of neck muscles, the occipital torus. This phenomenon is distinctly hominid rather than apelike. The mammalian skull hinges on the atlas (the first cervical vertebra) by means of two bulbous knobs, the occipital condyles. In quadrupeds these are located on the vertical rear wall of the skull. In apes they are at the back of the skull but moved forward and oriented on a slanting

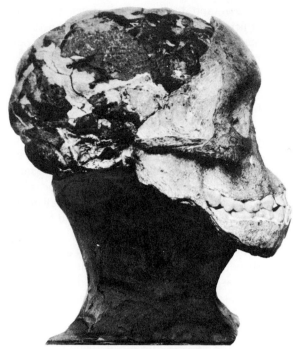

Fig. 9-1   The fossil skull of the Taung *Australopithecus africanus* discovered by Dart. The natural cast of the brain is easily seen. (Courtesy of the American Museum of Natural History.)

plane. In *Homo sapiens* they are well under the skull, beneath the auditory meatus and horizontally oriented. The position of the occipital condyles of *Australopithecus africanus* approximates their position in man and is therefore hominid rather than pongid in quality. The position of the occipital condyles is functionally related to the orientation of the foramen magnum. It follows that in this feature, too, the australopithecines are hominid. In apes the mastoid structure is weakly developed, if at all. In man and the australopithecines, it juts down as an inverted pyramid. The australopithecines may well have been the first sufferers of mastoiditis, or infection of the mastoid sinuses, although there has been no report as yet that any of the extant skulls show pathology of the region.

All these traits combine to indicate that in spite of the apparent general primitiveness of the cranial appearance of *Australopithecus africanus* and the puniness of his brain, the structure of his cranium exhibits generalized hominid features and predicates upright posture like man's.

When we look at the lower facial structure and the jaws of the australopithecines, we note that the snouty protrusion of the face combined with the small cranium presents a general apelike quality. Attention to certain details, on the other hand, gives a different impression. The upper palate is hominid for the most part. The alveolar arch is rounded and short instead of deep and narrow, as is that of the apes. There is no simian shelf behind the symphysis, and some individuals show the merest beginnings of a chin. There is no gap, or diastema, between the frontal incisors and the canines, except for a slight one in some individuals. The canines do not flare out, nor do they show a tusking overlap in any degree. More than this, the immature fossils of *Australopithecus africanus* indicate a tendency toward early replacement of the deciduous teeth by the permanent dentition—a trait which is characteristic of the hominids and which is progressively more marked the higher one goes in the primate order. This development is a function of the lengthening of the growth period relative to the total lifespan.

The dentition of the australopithecines apparently links them to man, for in addition to the traits just mentioned, the incisors are small and hominid. The canines, as can quickly be noted in Fig. 9-1, are wholly unapelike and very hominid. The single-cusp, cone-shaped, and pointed premolar that is so characteristic of modern apes in wholly absent.

The pelvis and upright posture It has thus far been indicated that the sum of hominid traits in the australopithecine skulls may be taken to outweigh the pongid traits. On the evidence from the skulls and dentition alone, we are probably confronted with an upright, ground-living, primitive creature who was more man than ape, in spite of his dim brain and protruding snout.

It does not take much brains to get up and walk, but it does require a proper skeletal and muscular structure to do so. Certain modifications of the pelvis and of the leg and foot bones and related muscles are called for. The modifications that ultimately came to mark the human skull in conjunction with upright posture are largely secondary to the posture itself.

Among the earliest hominoids, it was the spinal-chest-shoulder-forearm complex that first underwent marked modification through adaptation to brachiation. Then, as the australopithecine ancestors of the hominids took habitually to the ground, the next great segment to be generally modified was the pelvic–lower-limb complex. Modification of the jaw-face-cranial complex (particularly the great enlargement of the brain) came later in the phylogeny of man and *Homo sapiens* precursors.[2] It is now held, with a sound basis of evidence, that the complex of features related to upright posture is the most important morphological characteristic of the hominid line and the preliminary condition for the later mental development that came to characterize the genus *Homo.* "The total morphological pattern of the limbs and pelvis in the known representatives of the Hominidae thus presents a criterion by which these are distinguished rather abruptly from the known representatives of the Pongidae."[3]

What of the pelvis and legs of *Australopithecus?* Twenty-three years after Dart's discovery of the infant Taung skull, the Sterkfontein site yielded a pelvic bone amid a welter of other skeletal remains, which fortunately also included a thighbone (femur) and a shinbone (tibia). The next year (1948), the site at Makapansgat produced a pelvic bone of an adolescent (presumably belonging to the teen-ager whose jaw had previously been discovered in the same spot). In 1950, yet another pelvis came from Swartkrans, and in 1953 a complete pelvis was dug out at Sterkfontein. Even a quick glance at Fig. 9-2 shows how hominid

[2]S. L. Washburn, "The New Physical Anthropology" (*Transactions of the New York Academy of Sciences*, Vol. 13, 1951), pp. 298–304. See also W. E. Le G. Clark, *The Fossil Evidence for Human Evolution*, pp. 11, 13–14, 123.
[3]Le G. Clark, *op. cit.*, p. 12.

the fossil pelvis of *Australopithecus* is. The adaptive modifications of the pelvic configuration that make it functionally effective for upright posture and walking are basically as follows:

1. The extension of the lateral attachment of the gluteal musculature of the buttock in a broadening of the ilium. This produces an adequate balancing effect for the upper portions of the body, which rest on the sacrum.

2. The downward swing of the iliac crest in the sacral area. This places the point of attachment of the gluteus maximus behind (instead of lateral to) the hip, improving the effectiveness of its extensor function in erect walking.

3. The shift of the sacrum (on which the spinal column now rests) upward and closer to the hip socket (acetabulum). This improves stability in transmission of the weight of the trunk to the hip joint and also provides a certain amount of basinlike support for the internal organs that now rest in the abdominal-pelvic basin.

4. The new ruggedness of the anterior iliac spine. This provides a first rooting for the ligament (the iliofemoral) that extends to the femur to provide countertension to the gluteus maximus in erect standing.

5. The shortening of the distance between the ischial tuberosity and the acetabulum. This brings the anchorage of the upper end of the hamstring muscles into a position behind the hip joint rather than under it, a further aid in the maintenance of upright posture.[4]

The *Australopithecus* leg bones also show conformity to the demands of upright posture. He stood more like a man than an ape. In the words of Coon: ". . . as far as the femur is concerned the Australopithecine from Sterkfontein, at least, could have either walked or run erect, as he pleased, and if his ancestors had ever brachiated in the trees, no trace of the brachiating type of adaptation remained on their femurs once they had become anatomically suited for life on the ground."[5]

The general skeletal structure of *Australo-*

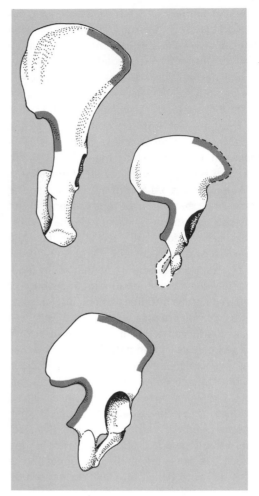

Fig. 9-2   The right pelvic bones of a chimpanzee (above), Australopithecus robustus *(center), and man (Bushman) (below) show the changes that occurred with evolution to upright posture. The broadening of the iliac crest and the downward flare of the sacroiliac spine are particularly evident. (After R. Broom,* Finding the Missing Link, *C. A. Watts and Co. Ltd.)*

pithecus africanus therefore reveals a small, 50- to 90-pound individual who stood and ran on his hind legs. This and his mode of life tell us that he was really agile and quick-footed, so that some anthropologists, with his discoverer in mind, call him "the South African Darter."[6]

[4]*Ibid.,* pp. 151–152. The main reason for including these anatomical details in a general anthropology text is to indicate the nature of the evidence that is considered by the expert.
[5]C. S. Coon, *The Origin of Races,* p. 246.
[6]This sobriquet was coined by Professor Jesse D. Jennings.

Life and culture of *Australopithecus africanus*
It is not enough to know from his skeleton that *Australopithecus africanus* has passed from apehood into early manhood, for one wants immediately to ask: "Did he have a culture?" The answer is: "Yes, definitely!"

Dart has stoutly claimed since 1947 that *africanus* was not only a "darter" but also a "basher." In biblical times, Samson slew a thousand Philistines with the jawbone of an ass. Dart has quite convincingly demonstrated that *africanus* was a slayer of baboons and other game and that he used a thighbone of an antelope as a bony bludgeon. He may, somewhat like Samson, even have used half the lower jaw of an antelope.[7]

Africanus's environment was that of the moderately well-watered savannah, a country of scattered shrubs and trees among lush grasses. It was prime grazing country and was well stocked with game, but it had little to attract a large tree-dwelling primate. *Australopithecus africanus* was not a tree dweller—his hands were freed by upright posture, he could run quickly, and his teeth, like ours, were those of a meat eater.[8]

Africanus may have started to eat meat when he scavenged for carrion in competition with vultures and hyenas, but he was far beyond that by the time he left his own bones in the caves of South Africa. *Africanus* seems to have been a wily predator. He had crossed the Rubicon from prehominid herbivorousness to hominid carnivorousness.

On behalf of these South African australopithecines, Dart stoutly argues that they used

[7]See R. A. Dart, "Predatory Implemental Technique of the Australopithecines" (*American Journal of Physical Anthropology*, Vol. 7, 1949), pp. 1–16; "The Predatory Transition from Ape to Man" (*International Anthropological and Linguistic Review*, Vol. 1, 1953). The argument for *Australopithecus africanus* the killer is given in great detail and with no little vehemence by Robert Ardrey in his *African Genesis*, especially chaps. 7, 9, and 10. Per contra, see S. L. Washburn, "Australopithecines: The Hunters or the Hunted?" (*American Anthropologist*, Vol. 59, 1957), pp. 612–614.

[8]If a skeptic asks: "Are the teeth of vegetarian Brahmins in India any different from ours?" the answer will be that the Brahmins have not been off a meat diet for more than one or two hundred generations, and they do not have to chew raw roots and uncooked bulk greens.

weapons in a patterned way—not *stone* tools, to be sure, but clubs of bone. How else could one account for the myriads of clobbered baboon skulls in the caves in which *Australopithecus africanus* is found? Out of one collection of fifty-two *Parapapio* skulls, forty-eight, or ninety-two per cent, had fractured crania. Most of the fractures are on the left frontal region of the baboon skulls, and many bear the imprint of a dual point of impact. Using the reasoning of the expert in forensic medicine testifying on a case of presumptive criminal homicide, Professor Dart argues that the circumstantial evidence shows death by frontal attack with a double-knobbed crusher wielded by right-handed individuals.

A count of the fossil bones from the *Australopithecus* breccia taken from the cave of Makapansgat shows that 11.2 per cent are thighbones of antelope. This is far above the normal proportion of thighbones in ordinary collections of fossilized antelope skeletal material, and of these thighbones, 90 per cent are pieces from the knee end (the joint that has double-knobbed condyles). This end most naturally serves as a club. Half antelope jaws with their sharp molar teeth (a vicious weapon) are also found in numbers out of proportion to reasonable expectancy had they not been brought into the cave.

These were apparently the weapons of *Australopithecus africanus,* the lively hunter, for *no stone tools have been found in the lower, or early, australopithecine breccia of the South African sites.* This, however, is not the problem that some prehistorians make of it. As adaptive devices, the saw-toothed jawbones and knobby bone clubs of *Australopithecus africanus* in South Africa could certainly have served their needs more efficiently than the Oldowan pebble tools (see page 142) associated with the australopithecines in East Africa.

Australopithecus robustus The creature that Broom first discovered at Sterkfontein in 1948–1949 and called *Paranthropus* (Gr. *para,* near + *anthropos,* man) is today recognized as *Australopithecus* but as a different species from *afri-*

canus. He is bigger, bulkier, and more muscular, and above all, he has larger molar teeth. Hence, his species name: *robustus.*

The cranial bones of *robustus* are thick, and the braincase itself is not larger than that of *africanus.* Instead of the rounded forehead of *africanus,* however, *robustus* has a sloping forehead, which leads back to a sagittal ridgepole, a medial crest like a gorilla's (Fig. 9-3). This makes it clear that he was heavy-jawed, for the sagittal crest anchors the thick muscles that work the masticatory movements.

Robustus' teeth also fit the same picture. The chewing and grinding teeth (premolars and molars) are very large, larger than human teeth in a number of length and breadth measurements. His incisors, or biters, are not larger than those of *africanus,* however. His immense molars have enamel 3 millimeters thick, three times as thick as in *africanus* and man. They are worn down and pitted, as if from chewing gritty food—specifically, roots. J. T. Robinson, who statistically analyzed over 375 teeth of *Australopithecus robustus,* concludes: "All the features of *Paranthropus* [*Australopithecus robustus*] dentition, as far as size and proportion are concerned, may be explained on the assumption that selection has retained as large a chewing area in the grinding teeth as is consistent with reducing jaw size at the expense of the less important teeth (incisors and canines) in a large vegetarian."[9]

Finally, *robustus* has added a unique sixth cusp to his molars. It is rare among hominids, but invariable with *robustus.* It may turn out to be an important diagnostic feature for linking him to fossils elsewhere, whatever its functional significance was for the living creature.

The pelvic remains are similar to those of *africanus,* except that they are larger. The long bones indicate a much heavier body size (100 to 150 pounds, as against 50 to 90 pounds for *africanus*).

Differences in adaptation *Australopithecus robustus* is pictured as a somewhat slow, plodding

[9]J. T. Robinson, "The Dentition of the Australopithecinae" (*Transvaal Museum Memoires,* No. 9, 1956), pp. 149–149.

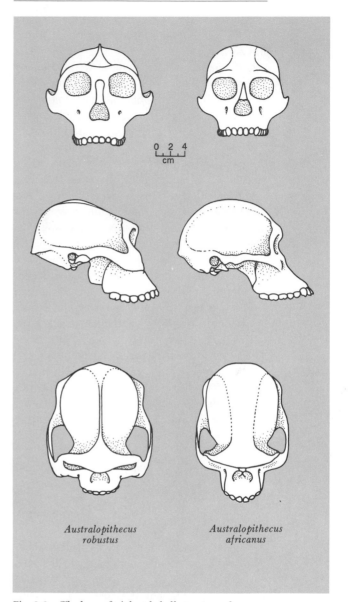

Fig. 9-3   The heavy facial and skull structure of Australopithecus robustus *contrasted with that of* Australopithecus africanus. *Both specimens are females. (After J. T. Robinson, in F. Clark Howell and François Bourliere (eds.),* African Ecology and Human Evolution. *Aldine Publishing Co. Copyright ⓒ 1963 by the Wenner-Gren Foundation for Anthropological Research, Inc.)*

type who went poking about with a digging stick or with his bare hands, prizing out roots and eating berries and fruit in a rather pleasant, if slightly dampish, pluvial world. He was a stream and lake hugger, who lived in Middle Pleistocene times probably equivalent to the second glaciation. *Africanus* adapted to fairly dry climates in Early Pleistocene times, and he probably had no love for groves and vines. *Robustus* was not averse to a bit of meat, but the fossils associated with him show that he took the easy pickings and was no great hunter. His culture was essentially that of the collector and small-game hunter. *Africanus's* culture was that of the game hunter and collector.

Clearly, these two species represent divergent branches of an unknown Pliocene ancestor who had probed the open edges of forests for living space. *Africanus* is earlier in the known South African cave sites, but he is clearly a more advanced type phylogenetically than *robustus*. *Robustus* was still largely a vegetarian, but he had achieved uprightness. *Africanus* shared the upright trait, but he was a carnivore with hominid dental and cranial features. He was evolving rapidly in the direction taken by man. He was also a bone-tool user, if not a maker of stone tools.[10] Both forms had effected the critical evolutionary adaptation of bipedalism, thus fully freeing the hands for potential tool using. But only *africanus*, through his response to the potentialities of savannah life, made the shift to meat eating.

The vegetarian commitment of the Oligocene and Miocene apes had deprived the australopithecines of any possibility of effective predatory development as killers with fang and claw. It is important to emphasize that in spite of the fearsome-looking fangs of gorillas, chimpanzees, orangutans, and baboons, there is absolutely no evidence from the modern reports on primate behavior that these are used for

defensive purposes against nonprimate predators. Temperamentally, they are not fighters. The security of prehuman primates apparently lies in prudence, caution, and bluff. But the adaptive change of *Australopithecus africanus* that gave him his taste for meat does seem to have been the critical catalytic factor in early human history, for this is associated with tool use and tool production. *Africanus* entered upon the exploitation of weapons and tools as extensions of the arm and started our ancestors on the road to cultural adaptation. If Dart's interpretation of the bones and jaws found with the South African *africanus* fossils is correct (and the case he has made is impressive), *africanus* had killing and cutting tools in profusion. Whether he "made" them or simply used them is beside the point. If they served his purpose well, they were an effective *cultural* adaptation sufficient at that time and place for survival. What is to the point is that henceforth all homonid evolution is simultaneously biological and cultural in mutual interaction: "Human evolution can be understood only as a product of interaction of these two developments."[11]

Thus, the change in diet of *africanus* placed a greater premium on tool using. Tool using is enhanced by superior intelligence, and a selective factor in favor of those with greater brainpower was probably operative on the australopithecine populations. J. T. Robinson sees the higher and lateral developments of the frontal area of *africanus* skulls, as compared with those of *robustus* skulls (see Fig. 9-3), as evidence of *africanus's* response, for the frontal lobes of the brain are the locality of the "associational" and "thought" processes.[12] This, in turn, if one follows the reasoning of E. A. Hooton, would have contributed to the reduction of the canine teeth, along with a simultaneous shortening and broadening of the jaw. Enlargement of the brain broadens the calvarium, spreading the condyles apart at the rear. Reduction of the snout requires reduction of the canines for

---

[10] At Sterkfontein, which has yielded more *africanus* fossil specimens than any other site, no stone tools have been found throughout the greater depth of the deposits, but in 1956, and subsequently, Chellean-type hand axes were found in association with *africanus* in the topmost breccia. Whether he or another creature made them is an undetermined question.

[11] T. Dobzhansky, "Evolution: Organic and Superorganic" (*The Rockefeller Institute Review*, Vol. 1, No. 2, 1963), p. 1.

[12] J. T. Robinson, "Adaptive Radiation in the Australopithecines and the Origin of Man," in F. C. Howell and F. Bourliere (eds.), *African Ecology and Human Evolution*, pp. 410–413.

purely mechanical reasons, if no other.[13] Brace and Montagu, on the other hand, speculate that because the canines of *Australopithecus africanus* ". . . do not project as significant defensive weapons . . . one can infer that the ancestors of the australopithecines had been using tools as defensive weapons for a long enough time so that the accumulation of random mutations could result in the reduction of the canines toward the level of the incisors."[14]

The Brace-Montagu hypothesis concerning reduction of the canine has the weakness of resting on the wholly nonempirical assumption that hominoids with tusklike canines use, or used them as fighting fangs.

The Olduvai australopithecines

Our knowledge of the australopithecines was opened by the discoveries in South Africa. It has been given new dimensions and fitted into a larger picture by the rapidly accumulating discoveries at Olduvai, Tanzania, in East Africa.

Olduvai Gorge Olduvai Gorge has been called "the Grand Canyon of human evolution." It is not so awe-inspiring to see, but it is stupendous in its yield of fossil man and prehistoric cultures, extending from the earliest Pleistocene times well toward the end of the period. The gorge is cut from west to east into the west wall of the Great Rift Valley. It is now a dry canyon in wild country, lying midway between Lake Victoria and fabled Mt. Kilimanjaro, 150 miles by air southwest of Nairobi. Here a series of water and wind-laid strata rest upon a bed of volcanic lava. The restless earth in this territory elevated the land surface in Late Pleistocene times, and a prehistoric river cut through the strata, exposing their surface faces from bottom to top. The weathering faces of the canyon continually expose the fossils and artifacts buried within the beds.

The stratigraphy of Olduvai presents five major strata, or beds. Bed I contains Lower Pleistocene fossil fauna such as the modern elephant, the one-toed horse, the cow, and a number of Pliocene survivors such as three-toed horses, mastodons, and antlered giraffes. It was laid during the first African pluvial during a time of rising and falling lake levels. Some strata are lake bottoms, with fish, crocodile, and hippopotamus remains. Others are land surfaces. Both lakes and land were periodically showered with volcanic ash. Bed I varies from 18 to 105 feet in thickness. The upper strata of Bed I indicate a time of interpluvial dryness and subdesert.

The absolute age of Bed I is a highly moot question. The K-A dates derived at the University of California in 1961 indicate an approximate age of 1.8 million years for the lowest sections of Bed I and one million years for the upper portions. On this basis, and on the basis of some comparable K-A dates for presumed Early Pleistocene strata in the Rocky Mountains, it may be necessary to double the million years conventionally allowed for the onset of the Pleistocene. However, as yet there are too many inconsistencies in the K-A results for Olduvai and other sites to warrant unreserved acceptance of their validity.[15] Therefore, we shall continue to use the one-million-year approximation for the onset of the Pleistocene and the antiquity of the lower levels of Bed I at Olduvai, with the understanding that it remains a provisional figure and may well have to be revised upward.

Between Beds I and II is a break that geologists call a *disconformity*. This means that the upper surfaces of Bed I were eroded away and that Bed II was subsequently laid down at a later date—in this case one hundred to several hundred thousand years later. Bed II is a thick (60 to 80 feet), wet-climate layer of clay and silt lake deposits. It represents the mid-Pleistocene pluvial in Africa. Then comes another disconformity caused by geologic faulting. Bed III represents a time of violent erosion (indicating sporadic runoff of heavy occasional rains in a generally dry country, such as occurs in New

---

[13] E. A. Hooton, *Up from the Ape* (rev. ed.), pp. 163–167.
[14] C. L. Brace and M. F. A. Montagu, *Man's Evolution*, p. 227.

[15] See F. C. Howell, "Potassium-Argon Dating at Olduvai Gorge" (*Current Anthropology*, Vol. 3, No. 3, 1962), pp. 306–308.

Fig. 9-4   Excavations in progress in Bed III at Olduvai Gorge during 1963. Hand axes protrude from the face of the cut above the heads of the workers. (Courtesy of Rupert Murrill.)

Mexico and Arizona today). Bed IV is another layer of lake deposits, with fish, crocodile, and hippopotamuses. It represents a Late Pleistocene pluvial phase, possibly equivalent to the fourth glacial. Figure 9-6 shows a diagrammatic cross section of the Olduvai beds. All these beds are rich in fossils and artifacts.

Fossil and cultural remains at Olduvai   Bed I is a hominid deposit. In 1960, L. S. B. Leakey and Mary Leakey discovered fragments of a child consisting of three pieces of the calvarium, parts of the mandible with all teeth, an upper molar tooth, and a set of hand bones. On the same floor with the child, crudely chipped stone tools of quartz rocks had already been discovered. This is the famous Oldowan pebble (or chopper) culture, which extends all the way through Bed I and into Bed II and which is also widespread elsewhere in Africa and in Asia.

THE OLDOWAN BED I PEBBLE (CHOPPER) CULTURE There is not much to describe in this oldest of known lithic (stone) industries. In Leakey's summing up:

The Oldowan culture has from time to time been referred to as a "pebble culture," and this description is

to some extent correct, for the vast majority of the implements of this culture are in fact made from water-worn pebbles. It must, however, be clearly understood that other forms of raw material were also used by the makers of this culture. Specimens occur which have been made from nodules of chert, and others from rough irregular lumps of quartz and quartzite, and there seems to be little doubt that sites containing assemblages of this culture might be found where tools made of actual water-worn pebbles were entirely absent.

The commonest tool type of the Oldowan culture is a crude chopper, varying in size from about the dimensions of a ping-pong ball to that of a croquet ball. The chopping edge is made by removal of flakes in two directions along one side of the pebble or other lump of stone which has been chosen, the intersection of the flake scars resulting in an irregular jagged cutting edge.[16]

The most important feature of the tools is that they are, indeed, intentionally constructed. There is a plan and a purpose, an idea and its execution, in these simple worked stones. A hominid was coordinating mind and hand to improve his means to achieve his goals. If one definition of man is *a primate who is capable of the manufacture of definite tools,* then there were indeed manlike creatures at Olduvai when Bed I was being deposited. His pebble tool was a kind of hacking knife—a chopper of sorts, used in all likelihood to cut up joints of meat, which was eaten raw. (There is no evidence of the use of fire in the Bed I deposits.)

Australopithecus africanus or Homo habilis?   In addition to the juvenile of Bed I, remains of several other individuals of a similar type have been found by the Leakeys in Bed I, plus a very fine specimen of an adult *Australopithecus robustus* skull.[17] There is a real division of opinion over

[16]L. S. B. Leakey, *Olduvai Gorge,* p. 34.
[17]This is the specimen that Leakey first called *Zinjanthropus* (Arabic *Zinj,* East Africa + Gr. *anthropos,* man). It is frequently referred to as such in the literature, but there is general agreement that this particular individual is an australopithecine.

Fig. 9-5   Schematic representation of stratification and representative fossil and cultural finds at Olduvai Gorge. (Tools after L. S. B. Leakey, *Olduvai Gorge,* Cambridge University Press.)

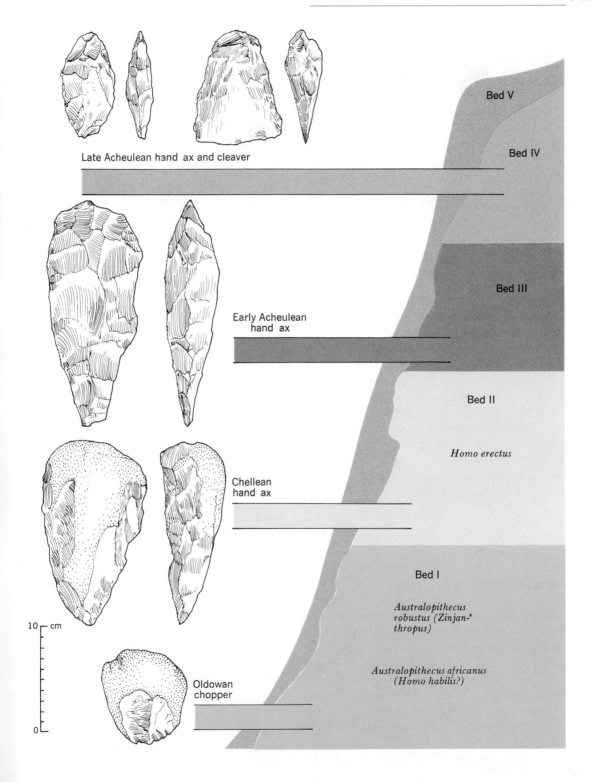

Late Acheulean hand ax and cleaver

Bed V

Bed IV

Early Acheulean
hand ax

Bed III

Bed II

Homo erectus

Chellean
hand ax

Bed I

*Australopithecus
robustus (Zinjan-
thropus)*

*Australopithecus africanus
(Homo habilis?)*

10 ⌐ cm

0 ⌐

Oldowan
chopper

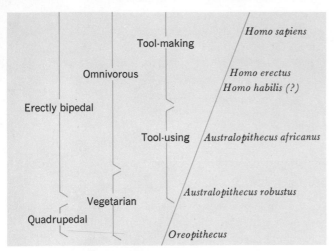

Tool-making

Homo sapiens

Omnivorous

Homo erectus
Homo habilis (?)

Erectly bipedal

Tool-using

Australopithecus africanus

Australopithecus robustus

Vegetarian

Quadrupedal

Oreopithecus

Fig. 9-6 Diagrammatic representation of the prevailing theory of the evolutionary relations of hominids (austrolopithecines) and hominins (Homo). Posture, diet, and toolmaking and tool using are shown as operative factors correlated to primate types. Note that the threshold between the quadrupedal and bipedal stages is a major one and that the break in the line marks off two essentially discontinuous zones. Note also that this is not a family tree, but an adaptive grid. (Modified from J. T. Robinson, in F. Clark Howell and François Bourliere (eds.), African Ecology and Human Evolution. *Aldine Publishing Co. Copyright © 1963 by the Wenner-Gren Foundation for Anthropological Research, Inc.)*

the interpretation of the non-*robustus* fossils from Bed I. Most paleontologists and prehistorians accept the Bed I group tentatively as a local population of *Australopithecus africanus*, but Leakey and his two associate physical anthropologists, P. V. Tobias and J. Napier, have opted for membership in the genus *Homo* for the little Olduvai Bed I hominids on the grounds that (1) their estimated cranial capacity of 643 to 724 cc gives a mean of 80 cc more than the largest known capacity of the australopithecines, (2) their small teeth and cranial contours give a "total pattern more markedly hominized than that of *Australopithecus*," and (3) they indubitably

produced the Oldowan tools.[18] They therefore named this population *Homo habilis* (L. *habilis*, apt, skillful), the "handy man." This position holds that any hominid who has achieved the psychocultural-organic level is *ipso facto* to be welcomed into the brotherhood of man. However, whatever anthropologists choose to call the Bed I hominids does not alter the facts one way or another, and the ultimate taxonomic decision will reveal more about our state of mind than it does about the early Olduvai fossils. It is simply a matter of how broadminded we become in defining the qualifications for membership in the genus to which we assign ourselves.

The facts, in short, are that an improved form of australopithecine, akin to *africanus*, lived at Olduvai early in the Pleistocene, at least 1 million and possibly 1.85 million years ago. He almost certainly made the simple Oldowan stone tools and an occasional bone tool,[19] and he ate a variety of bits of game and tortoises.

Other australopithecines A similar type seems to have existed among the australopithecines of South Africa, where J. T. Robinson has sorted some bones out of the trays containing *robustus* remains from Swartkranz, which are in his view different from both *africanus* and *robustus*. They include upper and lower jaw pieces with teeth (apparently from the same skull), a nearly perfect lower jaw from another individual, and some cranial fragments. In 1961, Robinson and Leakey were both convinced that the fragments represented an advanced hominid of the same grade as the Olduvai Bed I form.[20] Another apparent representative of the group was found in 1961 at Lake Chad in West Africa; it is probably of Lower Pleistocene age (but nothing like the two million years at first claimed for it). Yet another sample is reported from Tell (Mound)

[18]P. V. Tobias, "Early Man in East Africa" (*Science*, Vol. 149, 1965), p. 27. See also, S. Tax (ed.), "The Origin of Man" (*Current Anthropology*, Vol. 6, No. 4, 1965), pp. 342–438.

[19]See S. Cole, *The Prehistory of East Africa* (rev. ed.), p. 121.

[20]This is the form that Robinson named *Telanthropus* (Gr. *tele*, far, remote + *anthropos*, man). J. T. Robinson, "The Australopithecines and Their Bearing on the Origin of Man and of the Making of Tools" (*South African Journal of Science*, Vol. 57, 1961), pp. 3–13.

Ubeiyada, in Israel, associated with Oldowan tools and the fossil debris of both large and small Pleistocene mammals whose bones had been split and flint-scratched.

AUSTRALOPITHECINES IN ASIA No australopithecines have ever been found in Europe, and considering how intensively the prehistory of Europe has been explored, it is not very likely that one ever will be.

It is otherwise in Asia. Two fragments of lower jaws were found in 1941 and 1952 in Lower Pleistocene beds in Java at Sangiran. They are larger and thicker than any definitely hominid jaw. In size and other characteristics the teeth are australopithecine. Particularly significant is the identical cusp pattern including the sixth cusp of *Australopithecus robustus,* which the Java specimens share with the African australopithecines. Von Koenigswald, who made the first discovery, felt he had a human type in his hands and named it *Meganthropus* (Gr. *mega,* large + *anthropos,* man) *paleojavanicus* (*paleo,* ancient + *Java*). The consensus, however, is that these Java individuals are australopithecines of the *robustus* type, although Tobias, in pressing the case for the concept of *Homo habilis,* agrees with von Koenigswald that while the Java specimen in question ". . . has some strong resemblances to australopithecines, it shows several features in which it has advanced beyond the australopithecine grade."[21] Here again, it is a matter of viewpoint. One thing. is certain: an australopithecinelike form existed in Southeast Asia at the same time that a similar form existed in Africa.

Thus, this advanced type of australopithecine, or *Homo habilis* (as one may choose), had a wide African distribution and a possible foothold in Asia. He has, as of now, no other competitor as the immediate precursor of all subsequent forms of fossil man and, ultimately, of *Homo sapiens.* Whether or not he is significantly different from *Australopithecus africanus* can wait on more discoveries for final settlement. If the claim of a position for him in the genus *Homo* finds ultimate favor, then in due time we may also expect *Australopithecus africanus* to be given

[21]Tobias, *op. cit.,* p. 25.

membership in the club as another early form of *Homo*—on the assumption that he did utilize bone clubs and tools. *Australopithecus robustus,* however, is not likely to make the grade unless future finds provide overwhelming evidence that he too used or made tools. As it stands, he is looked upon as a side branch who failed to make the transition.

SUMMARY

The australopithecines of South and East Africa are the first upright, bipedal hominid fossil primates. Of the two recognized species—*Australopithecus africanus* and *Australopithecus robustus*—*africanus* is the older. Morphologically, *africanus* is rather small (50 to 90 pounds) and agile. His calvarium is smooth and broad, with a rounded frontal contour, and it housed a brain varying from 425 to 700 cc—larger than any ape's, but smaller than the minimum for *Homo sapiens.* His dentition consists of canines and molars that are relatively much reduced in size—the dental equipment of a meat eater, which the fossil animal bones associated with his own fossils show him to have been. He had evolved from normal primate vegetarianism to become a predatory hunter, who apparently in South Africa used bone clubs and antelope jaws as smashers and slashers, and at Olduvai produced a stone tool inventory (the Oldowan). From his use of such tools, we infer that he had a genuine culture.

Australopithecus robustus normally grew to almost double the size of *africanus.* His heavy jaw housed massive masticatory molars, which were worn down by chewing gritty roots and vegetables. His forehead was low and recessive, running back to a strong sagittal crest.

At Olduvai Gorge, Tanzania, a number of australopithecine fossils have thus far been found. Those in Bed I are associated with an Oldowan lithic industry; they were unquestionably toolmakers and meat-eating hunters. Except for the *robustus* specimen of Bed I, the others are small and of a brain size that is estimated to run up to 725 cc by Tobias, who, with Leakey and Napier, takes the position that these forms should be classed as *Homo habilis* on the basis of their purported toolmaking dexterity. This view has not won general acceptance, however; most prehistorians prefer to look upon the Olduvai Bed I toolmakers as *Australopithecus,* and probably *africanus.* Whatever the ultimate taxonomic outcome, the australopithecines of Africa (excepting, perhaps, *robustus*) had the essential attributes of man—upright posture, a larger brain than those of apes, a taste for meat, and a hunter's culture with the tools with which to hunt, fight, and butcher. They were at least protomen, if not already men.

Forms of *Australopithecus robustus* also lived in Java during the Early Pleistocene, although one view maintains that the two Java specimens in question are variants of the *Homo habilis* type. Either could be right.

SELECTED READINGS

Ardrey, R.: *African Genesis: A Personal Investigation into the Animal Nature of the Origins of Man* (1961). This is a skillfully written book that tells the story of the australopithecines in the setting of a theory of animal behavior emphasizing the aggressive aspects of competitive adaptation. The book has been vigorously attacked by those who disagree with the social implications of the theory, but that aspect aside, it is informative and interesting, even though polemic and one-sided.

Cole, S.: *The Prehistory of East Africa* (rev. ed., 1963). Chapters 1 to 4 provide the best popular introduction to the setting and background of the Olduvai australopithecines.

Coon, C. S.: *The Origin of Races* (1963), chap. 7 (pp. 217–304). Covers the physical anthropology of the australopithecines in great and judicious detail.

Dart, R. A.: "Cultural Status of the South African Man-Apes" (*Smithsonian Institution Annual Report,* 1955), pp. 317–338. Dart's summation of the case for *Australopithecus africanus* as a bone-tool user.

Leakey, L. S. B.: "Very Early East African Hominidae and Their Ecological Setting," in F. C. Howell and F. Bourliere (eds.), *African Ecology and Human Evolution* (1963), pp. 448–457. A brief statement of Leakey's views on the subject in 1962.

Robinson, J. T.: "Adaptive Radiation in the Australopithecines and the Origin of Man," in F. C. Howell and F. Bourliere (eds.), *African Ecology and Human Evolution* (1963), pp. 385–416. Presents a succinct summary of the probable origins and relations of the two types of australopithecines. Robertson persists in clinging to the designation *Paranthropus* instead of adopting *Australopithecus robustus.*

Tax, S. (ed.): "The Origin of Man" (*Current Anthropology,* Vol. 6, No. 4, 1965), pp. 342–446. Contains a detailed account of the K-A (Potassium 40–Argon 40) method of dating, plus results for Olduvai Gorge and elsewhere, plus eleven additional articles on the australopithecines and *Homo habilis* (mostly reprints). A handy but highly technical compendium of data and viewpoints.

Tobias, P. V.: "Early Man in East Africa" (*Science,* Vol. 149, 1965), pp. 22–33. Presents the case for the *Homo habilis* taxonomy for the Olduvai Gorge Bed I australopithecines and gives a compact summary of the finds.

Pressing hard upon the later <u>australopithecines</u> were the first hominids that every scientist now agrees were men. This is the group known as *Homo erectus erectus,* which means that they were very upright men. In Java, *Homo erectus* was, for awhile at least, contemporary with *Australopithecus robustus* (or *Homo habilis?*), whose Lower Pleistocene presence in Southeast Asia was noted in the last chapter. *Homo erectus* long outlived *Australopithecus* and continued his evolution well into the Middle Pleistocene, until he, in turn, was supplanted by *Homo sapiens.*

Two varieties of *Homo erectus* have been established: (1) *Homo erectus erectus,* or <u>Java man</u>, and (2) *Homo erectus pekinensis,* or <u>Pekin man.</u>[1] Java man is the older and more primitive representative of the species.

Homo erectus erectus

Java man was discovered in 1891 in sandstone and conglomerate deposits in the valley of the Solo River near Trinil in central Java. His discovery was the result of a deliberate search for primitive fossil man on the part of the Netherlander Eugene Dubois (not by "two boys," as the *New York Herald Tribune* once reported it).

Dubois first recovered a fossilized and very primitive calvarium of a hominoid (Fig. 10-1), along with some primate teeth. A year later, he found a fossilized primate femur at the same level 15 yards away.

[1]A third variety, *Homo erectus mauritanicus,* has been tentatively proposed on the basis of a specimen found in 1954–1955 at Ternefine, Algeria, and called *Atlanthropus mauritanicus* by its discoverer, Camille Arambourg. See pp. 156–157 for a discussion of this fossil variety.

Fig. 10-1   A cast of the calvarium of the first specimen of Homo erectus erectus *found by Eugene Dubois in Java and originally known as* Pithecanthropus erectus. *(Smithsonian Institution.)*

Dubois named his find *Pithecanthropus* (Gr. *pithekos,* ape + *anthropos,* man: ape man) *erectus* (L. upright). He described it as an intermediate type, much more developed in the direction of modern man than any ape, but falling short of manhood—a form that was presented as the evolutionary link between man and ape. A "missing link" had been found.

For at least two decades, skeptics expressed doubt that the femur and calvarium belonged to one individual and that a being with so primitive a skull could walk on his two hind legs, head up. By 1920, however, the validity of association of the leg bone and skull was generally accepted, and the fossil was viewed as a human prototype.

Von Koenigswald's Java finds   For nearly half a century, Java man stood alone. Then in the mid-1930s, the assiduous and systematic efforts of G. H. R. von Koenigswald in Java brought forth a rich harvest of finds, all confirming the validity of Dubois's original contribution and expanding our knowledge of many aspects of the total morphology of Java man, which could originally be reconstructed only by inference and projection. Between 1936 and 1941, when the Japanese invasion put a stop to von Koenigswald's work, seven new representatives of Java man were found in close proximity to the old Trinil site, except for an infant skull found at Modjokerto in eastern Java. The origin

of von Koenigswald's other Java men is Sangiran, about 20 miles from Trinil. A helpful feature of the Sangiran site is the occurrence of a differential stratigraphic geology in which an upper Trinil layer rests on an older fossil-yielding stratum of black clay labeled *Djetis.* Five of the seven new individuals come from this lower Djetis level, which, on the basis of its mammalian fossil assemblage, is Early Pleistocene (possibly First Interglacial).

The new assemblage of Java fossils includes a full skull (the Modjokerto infant), two complete and two partial calvariums, an excellently preserved upper jaw and teeth, three fragmented lower jaws, and a number of miscellaneous teeth.

Morphology of Java man   On the basis of this abundant assemblage, it is now possible to be quite specific about the human qualities of Java man.

Cranial characteristics   The Java cranium (Fig. 10-2) is quite unlike that of the australopithecines. Instead of the relatively high and rounded cranial vault, which characterizes the latter, Java man has a flat, receding forehead that slopes back from beetling browridges. The supraorbital torus is massive. The temporal regions behind the orbital area are very constricted and narrow, and the greatest breadth of the skull is far back toward the occiput and low down in the temporal area. Although there are no saggital and occipital crests, such as are found in the adult male chimpanzee and gorilla, the roof of the skull is markedly gabled, and the occipital region is angular. The mastoid process is only slightly developed, while the foramen magnum is far forward under the skull, much as it is in *Homo sapiens.* These are indicative of at least semiupright posture combined with heavy neck and jowl musculature to support a powerful chewing jaw.

The palate is huge, and there is a strong facial prognathism conforming to massive jaws with recessive chin devoid of the human dental eminence (prow). At the same time, it does not show the slightest trace of a simian shelf. The teeth are intermediate in size between those of apes and those of *Homo sapiens,* but they are preponderantly hominid. Their pongid elements are the presence of a slight canine-incisor diastema in some, but not all, individuals and the large size of the molar teeth relative to those in the front of the dental arch.

The cranial capacities of the Java skulls are not exactly known, since none of the skulls is complete. However, the adult range is from 775 to approximately 975 cc. This puts the Java man well above the apes and australopithecines, but just below the normal minimum for *Homo sapiens,* whose range of brain volume is 1,000 to 2,000 cc. The average brain of modern man is 1,500 cc for males and 1,450 cc for females.[2] Endocranial contours indicate a relatively weak development of the frontal lobes. The largest cortical areas are localized in the parietal, or motor-control, regions.

Homo erectus erectus could not have exhibited a very great intellect, and yet in spite of his heavy face and low-browed character, he was too brainy to be an ape. In the more expansive mood of the second half of the twentieth century, the rubric "man" has been quite unanimously readjusted to include him, and he is accorded full taxonomic status in the genus *Homo.* Dubois's *Pithecanthropus* label has been dropped.

[2]Men do have more brains than women, but this does not mean that they are smarter. Within the species, brain size within the normal range has no functional significance. Men's brains are larger because their bodies are generally bulkier (sexual dimorphism).

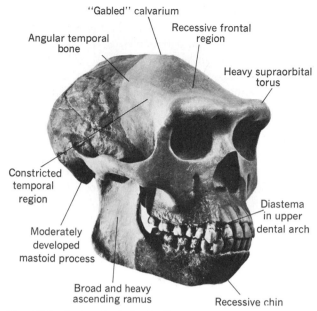

Fig. 10-2 **Restored skull of** *Homo erectus erectus.* **(Courtesy of the American Museum of Natural History.)**

Fig. 10-3 The range of cranial capacities of Australopithecus, Homo erectus erectus, *and* Homo sapiens. *The gap between the australopithecine maximum and the minimum for* Homo *is apparent.*

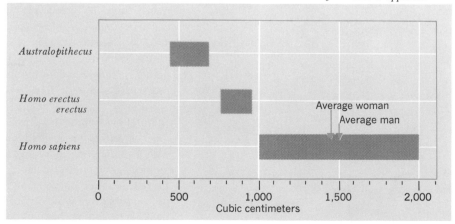

The femur The first-discovered femur of Java man excited particular interest and won for him the species designation *erectus*. In all respects it is a human type of leg bone, one that goes with bipedal, orthograde posture: it is long and slender and has a ridge (the linea aspera) running down the dorsal side for the anchorage of the hamstring muscles, which are so important in the upright position.

Recent fluorine analysis confirms the contemporaneousness of all the femurs with the skull and with the extinct Pleistocene mammals that come from the same deposit. In addition, the later Pekin finds conform to the same kind of skull-leg complex.

These facts, plus the now well-authenticated

Fig. 10-4 Comparison of femurs in the chimpanzee (left), Homo erectus pekinensis *(center), and modern man (right). (From a drawing after Franz Weidenreich, in G. H. R. Von Koenigswald,* The Evolution of Man. *By permission of The University of Michigan Press.)*

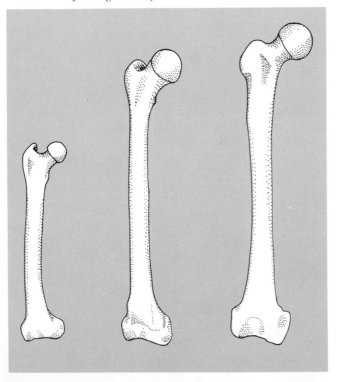

fact that *Australopithecus* also was upright, indubitably establish the erect posture of Java man. Thus, he shared this human trait with *Australopithecus* but outdid him in brain capacity; hence, he is placed higher on the phylogenetic tree.

Early and late Java man We mentioned that at Sangiran, Java, where von Koenigswald first worked from 1936 to 1939, two distinct geological strata are identifiable. The top layer is the same as that which had yielded Dubois's Java man at Trinil. Hence, it is called the *Trinil bed.* The Trinil animal fossils and geology show it to have been laid down in a mid-Pleistocene pluvial period, probably equivalent to the second glacial.

The lower stratum contains earlier types of fossil fauna identified as post-Villefranchian and therefore early Middle Pleistocene or, possibly, late Lower Pleistocene. Because they are older than the Trinil beds, these are probably first interglacial. These deposits are the *Djetis* beds.

This geological detail is important because two of the known Java skulls of *Homo erectus* come from the Trinil beds, and two from the older Djetis bed at Sangiran. It establishes the long continuity of evolutionary development in *Homo erectus erectus* in Southeast Asia. The somewhat more rugged quality of the fossils from the Djetis bed suggests that its type was morphologically, as well as temporally, more primitive than the *erectus* forms from the Trinil beds. Further, the *Australopithecus robustus* jaw and fragments (page 145), found in the Djetis beds and called *Meganthropus paleojavanicus* by von Koenigswald, indicate possible simultaneous occupation of the same territory, or *sympatry* (Gr. *sym*, together + *patriotes*, countryman), by australopithecines and early *Homo erectus.*

Cultural evidences No stone or bone artifacts have as yet been recovered in direct association with the remains of Java man. However, a stone-flake industry, called *Patjitan*, is known from the upper portions of the Trinil beds in other parts of Java. The implements are crude, heavy scrapers or chopping tools with ⊔ shaped edges such as those which characterize adzes. The Patjitan choppers are early representatives in Java of the great Eastern *chopper-tool tradition*, which extends through Java, Burma, India, and Pakistan to the Valley of the Indus and north through China and into Japan.[3] Pointed "pebble" tools similar to those of the Oldowan are also included in the inventory of the tradition. It is reasonable to infer that Java man was a toolmaker. He lived in the open, and he had not yet mastered fire. He has not left us such direct evidence of his hunting prowess as *africanus* has, for the locations of the Java finds are neither caves nor campsites. However, his later descendants in Java (Solo man) and his close relatives in China (*Homo erectus pekinensis*) were great hunters and evidently enthusiastic eaters of human brains (see pages 154 to 155). There is little doubt that Early *Homo erectus* in Java was a predator, as was *Australopithecines africanus*. He had the teeth of a meat-eating hominid as well.

Homo erectus pekinensis

Pekin man is so similar to Java man in physical characteristics that he is now classed in the same genus and species. He is simply a later and improved variety of the same type.

Early Java man, it will be remembered, comes from the Djetis beds, which are probably first interglacial. Later Java man comes from the Trinil beds, which were laid down in a pluvial climate, probably second glacial.

The great home site of the original Pekin finds, called Choukoutien locus 1, was a vast cavern with a lofty ceiling 100 feet above the floor and was 1⅔ times as long as a football field. During its prolonged use through a time of relatively stable climate, it became filled from bottom to top with bones, muck, and tools. The great cave was one of those water-made limestone caves, not unlike the South African australopithecine sites, produced in pre-Pleistocene times. During the long Middle Pleistocene (second interglacial), it was a refuge as well as a refuse dump for *Homo erectus*. In the

years preceding the Japanese invasion of China, between 1924 and 1939, fourteen different skulls, some facial bones, quantities of teeth, and eleven limb bones had been recovered— the remains of forty or more individuals. The diggings also showed ample evidence of the use of fire and yielded a plentiful supply of simple stone tools and other evidences of cultural activities. Of Pekin man we know a good deal, although, as usual, not as much as we would like to know. The fossils were all lost in the Japanese invasion of December, 1941.[4] Fortunately, Franz Weidenreich had sent excellent casts to the United States before World War II, and his detailed monographs on the fossils are so superior that they make the total loss of the original fossils less of a catastrophe.

Once the war was over and the revolution which followed was completed, the new Chinese government continued the fine tradition established by the old Chinese geological survey. The recovery of fossil man in China goes on through the work of the Institute of Vertebrate Paleontology and Paleoanthropology in Peiping, and since 1949 there have been numerous additional discoveries of *Homo erectus* as well as of fossilized early *Homo sapiens* and some forms that appear to be transitional between *erectus* and *sapiens* in China.[5]

The evidence shows that Pekin man had at least four traits that went beyond those of his south-country cousin in Java. He had a distinctly larger cranial capacity; he had fire— which was one reason he could live in caves; he had better tools and weapons; and he seems to have had a penchant for eating other Pekin men. How are these things known?

Morphology of Pekin man Comparison of Fig. 10-5 and 10-2 shows the superficially observable similarity and the singular differences between *Homo erectus erectus* and *Homo erectus pekinensis*. There is the similar heavy supraorbital torus,

[3] The Burmese form of the tradition is known as *Anyathian;* in Pakistan it is the *Soan;* in China it is the *Choukoutienian.*

[4] W. W. Howells tells the story in some detail. For the interesting facts of this intriguing little tragedy, see his *Mankind in the Making,* pp. 166–168.

[5] Kwang-chih Chang, "New Evidence on Fossil Man in China" (*Science,* Vol. 136, No. 3518, 1962), pp. 749–760.

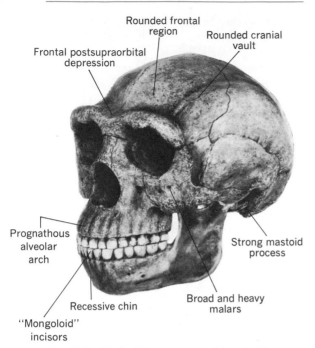

Rounded frontal region

Rounded cranial vault

Frontal postsupraorbital depression

Prognathous alveolar arch

Strong mastoid process

Recessive chin

Broad and heavy malars

"Mongoloid" incisors

Fig. 10-5 Skull of *Homo erectus pekinensis*. (Courtesy of the American Museum of Natural History.)

the recessive forehead, the constricted frontal region, the angular occiput, the protruding face, and the massive jaw with a weak chin. In *pekinensis*, however, there is no diastema of the upper dental arch. The most significant difference is in the size and contour of the calvarium. There is a marked expansion of the brain itself, and the braincase has enlarged and rounded out to accommodate it. The cranial capacity of Pekin man overlaps that of Java man but attains volumes well above that of the latter. The Pekin cranial vaults run from 850 to 1,300 cc capacity with a mean of about 1,075 cc. Pekin man has thus far outstripped the great apes and *Australopithecus*. His smallest-brained members had cerebrums nearly as large as those of the most brainy Java man, and the cerebrums of his "big domes" equaled those of the average modern man. *Pekinensis*, as his culture reveals, was a hominid of reasonable intelligence and abilities.

The relative geographic isolation of Pekin man shows up in a number of highly peculiar

osteological characteristics. The first of these is the so-called Mongoloid shovel-shaped incisor, which is scoop-shaped on the posterior surface. This produces a ridge across the back of the cutting edge and down the sides. Java man entirely lacked this characteristic, but it has survived as a diagnostic feature of modern members of the Mongoloid race, including many American Indians. All the grinding teeth (molars and premolars) have enlarged pulp cavities extending downward into fused roots, a condition known as *taurodontism* (Gr. *tauros*, bull + *dontos*, tooth). This feature is not exclusively distinctive of *pekinensis*, however. European Neandertals have it, as do many American Indians, Eskimos, and South African Bushmen. The Pekin canine teeth are large, but as is true of the rest of the teeth, they are definitely human.

Two other features of the mouth are notably distinctive of *pekinensis*. One is the mandibular torus, a heavy bony ridge inside the lower jaw from the canine to the first molar on each side (the lingual surface). It is a common characteristic of subarctic peoples; more than half the Eskimo population has it, and prehistoric Japanese, Chinese, and Scandanavians, among others, reveal the trait in proportions running from one-fifth to two-thirds of their populations. In all likelihood, these peoples were heavy skin chewers, as Eskimos are known to be; skin chewing is a technique that keeps wet boots and clothing from becoming unwearably stiff. The heavy, deep, but polished wear, characteristic of all adult Pekin teeth, may indicate the cultural pattern of heavy chewing of soft, but tough, materials.

The other mandibular feature is the presence of multiple foramina mentalia, the openings in the lower jawbone beneath the first and second premolars, through which pass the nerves and blood vessels to serve the muscles and other tissues of the chin and lower cheeks. Most human beings have only one foramen on each side of the jaw—not so *pekinensis*. In the seven recovered inferior maxillae of Pekin man, all have from two to five such openings. Among all the hundreds of known fossil men, none but *Homo erectus pekinensis* and the fossil men of Ternifine, Algeria, and of Heidelberg, Germany, have more than one. This could have been a special adaptation to the hearty use of masticatory muscles, particularly for distribution of the facial blood with less crowding of the major veins and arteries.

The body and limb bones of *pekinensis* have a few distinctive features of the kind that characterizes some local populations as against others, that is to say, racial differences. Yet, taken as a whole, the skeleton is indistinguishable from that of *Homo sapiens* today. Just as the australopithecines developed upright posture and other bodily changes far in advance of their cranial development, so *Homo erectus* achieved the modern level of bodily development while he still had a moderately primitive brain, teeth, and face. The evolution of the postcranial (below the skull) skeleton of man was thus completed 500,000 years ago. *All subsequent evolution, except for minor racial variations, has been concentrated in the brain and head.* This is to be expected, for once the hominid had risen to the psychocultural-organic level, his organic adaptations became concentrated primarily in his culture-creating apparatus, the brain.

Culture of Pekin man Unlike the South African caverns that yield the australopithecine remains, the Pekin cave deposits do not reflect drastic climatic changes. The indicated climate was slightly cooler than the present one, but definitely not glacial.

There is no way of knowing whether Pekin man habitually made the Choukoutien caves his home base or whether he just periodically visited them, but that he camped out in the caves again and again is clear. Deliberately broken and split bones of animals are found by the thousands throughout the deposits; ashes and scorched bones give testimony of the first-known hearths of mankind. The quantities of worked choppers show the continuation of the australopithecine tool tradition.

Pekin man dined mostly on venison. Two-thirds of the animal bones with which his personal and cultural remains are intermingled are those of two species of the fallow deer. The deer obviously did not walk into the caves themselves, nor would they have been dragged into them in such numbers by the other predators with whom man struggled for possession of these sites. Other gentle game that graced his menu included sheep, antelope, roebuck, small horses, and camels. But *Homo erectus pekinensis* was clearly a more wily and ferocious hunter than this inventory alone would indicate. Making up another sizable part of the solid remains of his garbage are the bones of elephants, rhinoceroses, bison, and water buffalo—creatures which would have left him alone if not bothered and certainly would not have invaded the caves themselves. He could have killed these huge beasts by means of fire drives, stampeding them over cliffs in wild panic before deliberately set grass fires or lines of men, women, and children waving flaming brands. He might also have trapped them individually in pitfalls, or, like the Congo Pygmy, he may even have brought down the great elephant by hiding near the game trails and leaping up under the belly of the lumbering beast, thrusting fiercely into the vitals of the soft underbelly with a fire-hardened wooden spear, and dodging to safety behind sheltering rocks or trees. Or, like the Pygmies, he might have collected the carcasses of the big game that had stumbled to their deaths through disease or old age. More than likely, he fed on the meat of dead big game, racing to consume it before it was eaten by hyenas, jackals, and ants.

As for the monster cave bears, saber-toothed tigers, leopards, and giant hyenas, whose fossil bones—also burned and sometimes split—are mingled throughout the debris, it is hard to believe that he fought them face-to-face, although he might have. He had the brains to be cunning and the courage to drive these great predators from the caves to make room for himself. Masai and other East African hunters have traditionally proved their manhood in this century by provoking a lion to charge and awaiting the final leap crouched upon the ground, holding a spear aslant with butt planted to receive the shock as the lion impales himself upon the point. Pekin man could have done the same. True, he had no iron spearheads, or even flint, but he did have the fire with which to harden a wooden point, and with his chopper tools he could skin any beast and hack up its meat.

Mastery of fire With fire, Pekin man could cook the meat and improve its digestibility and its nutritious effectiveness. He may have faced times of famine and starvation, but in the main he prospered. He held his caves at Choukoutien off and on for 200,000 to 300,000 years (600,000 to 300,000 before present), on the one-million-year Pleistocene scale. When he was displaced, the odds now indicate that it was because he himself had evolved to become *Homo sapiens.*

It may be too much to attribute his success to his mastery of fire, but there is good reason to believe that this was a key factor in his ecological adaptation. The Greeks knew the importance of fire to mankind. Prometheus dared as Pekin man dared. According to the myth, fire was the cherished possession of the gods and was not meant for men. When Prometheus stole it from the lightning of Zeus and gave it to man, the gods could not take the gift away, but they condemned Prometheus, the fire-bringer, to the torture of the damned, chaining him hand and foot to a rock, belly exposed to the tearing beak of a vulture. The Greeks were not alone in seeing fire as a divine possession that man could steal by his wits alone; the myth is one of the primeval *Elementargedanken* of all mankind. The story of the theft of fire is told in one form or another in virtually all societies, primitive and civilized.[6]

Pekin man, too, was probably a "fire stealer" rather than a fire maker. At any rate, no fire-producing instruments have come from his caves. Lignite and coal beds, which lie close to the surface and could have been subject to spontaneous combustion, lie near to Choukoutien. And, of course, lightning sets fire to trees. The precious tending of the "eternal ember" of

the family fire was surely a matter of great concern and could well have been the focus of simple, early ritual anxiety.

Lithic industry The chopper tools of Pekin man did not reach the level of technical excellence that was being attained by *Homo erectus* at the same time in Africa and Europe, where the Chellean-Acheulean tradition was well under way (see pages 157–158). The Pekin, or Choukoutien, industry, as described by Kenneth Oakley,

. . . consists principally of roughly broken quartz, with a few crudely flaked pebbles of greenstone, quartzite and cherty rocks. . . . Only a small percentage of these are recognizable as tools, but these include chopper-like cores and flakes trimmed as points and scrapers. The industry proved to be practically uniform throughout the thickness of the . . . deposits. . . . Most of the raw material was evidently collected from the bed of a nearby stream, but crystals of quartz with well formed facets were found among the tools, and these must have been sought by Pekin Man in the granite hills some miles away to the northeast or south of the Choukoutien caves.[7]

It is as though, having got hold of fire, the cultural adaptation of Pekin man stabilized as an adjustment to an unchanging environment and he had little impulse to improve his stone-tool industry. Another possibility, of course, is that he may have concentrated on wooden weapons. More probably, however, in terms of what we know of the dynamics of culture growth, the stability of his long interglacial environment, and his relative geographic isolation from what was going on among other peoples (he was living on the very eastern margin of the human world of his time), shielded him from changing selective pressures and isolated him from new ideas generated elsewhere.

Cannibalism Lastly, there is the matter of cannibalism. Cannibalism, or *anthropophagy* (Gr. *anthropos,* man + *phagos,* to eat), is of three kinds, classified according to the dominant motivation.

The first is *ritualistic* and *incorporative.* It in-

[6]See "Sun Snarer" (*Standard Dictionary of Folklore, Mythology and Legend,* Vol. 2, p. 1089).

[7]K. P. Oakley, *Man the Tool-maker,* p. 113.

volves the idea that the special qualities of the victim are contained in a bodily essence, which the feaster may incorporate into his person by eating the bodily substance. In some cultures the transference may be made without cannibalistic ingestion. Head-hunting, such as that in Melanesia or among the Ifugao of Luzon in the Philippines, is practiced to secure the head, which contains the "soul stuff"; this is incorporated in the souls of the slayers through ritual transference.

The second form of cannibalism may be called *gustatory*. Men eat men because they think they are good eating. This kind of sentiment and practice had a sporadic but widely scattered distribution in recent times. It was common in Oceania and parts of Africa, especially among the Congo tribes. In both places, prisoners were penned and fattened for the feast, like the hand-stuffed geese of France. Gustatory cannibalism occurred also in parts of South America, but not among the North American Indians.

The third form of cannibalism is *survival cannibalism*. It is a final recourse of starving people. Eskimos practiced it without pleasure. In the words of a King William Island Eskimo speaking to the great Knut Rasmussen:

Many people have eaten human flesh, but never from any desire for it, only to save their lives, and that after so much suffering that in many cases they were not sensible of what they did. . . . But we who have endured such things ourselves, we do not judge others who have acted in this way, though we may find it hard, when fed and contented ourselves, to understand how they could do such things. But then again how can one who is in good health and well fed expect to understand the madness of starvation? We only know that every one of us has the same desire to live.[8]

There is no way of knowing what kind of cannibalism Pekin man indulged in, but that he ate human brains and the marrow of the long bones of his fellow men seems quite evident. First, the recovered bones of *Homo erectus* in the Choukoutien caverns were found scattered helter-skelter throughout the deposits, just as were most of the animal bones; both kinds of bones are fractured and split. This could be

[8]K. Rasmussen, *Across Arctic America*, pp. 223–224.

done to produce tools, but most of the bones are unworked and unused. Nor are these river-terrace deposits, in which the bones could have been scattered by running water. The bodies of men and animals had been dismembered, and the bones smashed and tossed aside by those who crouched and cooked about the campfires.

More significant is the fact that in all five of the skulls of Pekin man, the *foramen magnum* at the base of the braincase had been artificially enlarged so that it would admit a fist. The operation was the same as that performed on a number of skulls of Middle Pleistocene *Homo sapiens* (see pages 170–171) and in much later times by the producers of the Black Duck culture of prehistoric Minnesota (Fig. 10-6). The Minnesota Indians, however, worked with more finesse than Pekin man. Rather than smashing the long bones, they did a neat surgical job and buried bones and skulls together. The interment indicates that this was probably a case of ritual cannibalism.[9]

Homo erectus mauritanicus

Homo erectus in the West is apparently first represented by the famous Heidelberg jaw, found in 1907 in first interglacial sands. This massive chinless mandible (Fig. 10-7), with very modern teeth, remains an isolated phenomenon for its time and place. There is insufficient evidence to prove its exact relationship to Java or Pekin man. Heidelberg man is earlier than they, apparently contemporary to the australopithecines, but not of them. If more representatives of his kind are found, there will indeed be established yet another variety of *Homo erectus: Homo erectus heidelbergensis*. In the meantime, as has been the case for sixty years, we make note of him but do not know quite what to do with him.

On the other hand, recent finds in Algeria and at Olduvai Gorge add new and solid dimen-

[9]As late as 1900, five Winnebago Indians in Wisconsin, seeking to prove their manhood and to obtain supernatural war power, went on the warpath by train to kill a Potowatamie Indian, whose heart they cut out and cooked and ate. See Paul Radin (ed.), *Crashing Thunder: An Autobiography of an American Indian*, chap. 22.

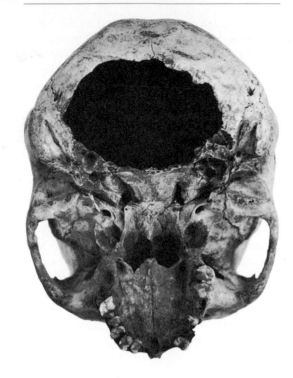

*Fig. 10-6   Prehistoric American Indian skull (above)
with basal hole for extraction of the brain. Portion
of human femur (below) with hole for removal of
the marrow. Both are from the Minnesota Black
Duck culture. (Courtesy of the Museum of
Anthropology, University of Minnesota.)*

sions to the picture of Lower Pleistocene early
man and his accomplishments. At Ternifine,
Algeria, during the second glaciation, there was
a watering hole where men and animals con-
gregated for their dawn and evening drinking in
mid-Pleistocene times. The men waylaid antelope, zebras, and giraffes; they feasted on elephants, rhinoceroses, giant baboons, and hogs;
and they contested with the saber-toothed

tiger. It was the same story as at Choukoutien
and Olduvai—the story that would be repeated
throughout the Pleistocene for one-half million
and more years, except that at Ternifine and
Olduvai, the remains of the animals were not
dragged off to a cavern but were simply tossed
onto the ground or into the water. Stone tools
were occasionally lost in the pond, resting amid
the debris of bones. Also, some human skulls
were lost in the deepest layers. In 1954–1955
C. Arambourg found three human jaws in good
condition and the fragment of a parietal bone.
The materials are too fragmentary to give definitive results, but the expert view is that the
heavy jaws and the teeth have much in common
with those of Pekin man, while at the same time
exhibiting some similarities to features of *Australopithecus robustus*. As is so common with the
discoverers of new fossils, Arambourg was convinced that he had a new genus of man. He
named it *Atlanthropus mauritanicus*. However, Professor William Howells predicted in 1959: "It
seems probable that most people will accept
Professor Arambourg's assertion that the Ter-
nifiners are closely related to Pekin and Java
man, and will therefore reject his new genus."[10]
The contemporary consensus of professionals
is expressed in the summing up by Bernard
Campbell for the 1962 Wenner-Gren Foundation
conference on classification: ". . . it seems clear
that, together with other Middle Pleistocene
N. African fossils,[11] they may represent a variety of the species *Homo erectus* which can reasonably be associated as a single subspecies."[12]
This species is now named *Homo erectus mauritanicus*, and it is the Western counterpart of *Homo
erectus pekinensis*.

In 1960, in the middle of Bed II at Olduvai
Gorge at a level which yields a K-A date of
500,000 years, Leakey found a fossil skull that
shows "certain superficial characters such as a
very large brow ridge and relatively low vault,

[10]Howells, *op. cit.,* p. 180.
[11]That is, the 1953 discovery in the quarry of Sidi Hbd er-
Rahman at Casablanca; the Smugglers' Cave discovery in 1935
at Temara, Morocco; and the Rabat skull of 1933.
[12]B. Campbell, "Quantitative Taxonomy and Human Evolution," in S. L. Washburn (ed.), *Classification and Human Evolution,*
p. 66.

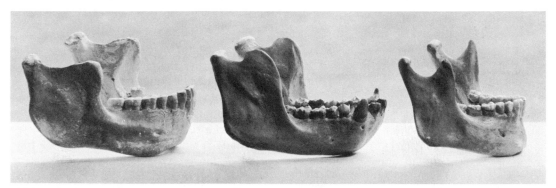

Fig. 10-7 Heidelberg jaw (left) compared with the jaw of a chimpanzee (center) and the jaw of a modern man (right). (Courtesy of the American Museum of Natural History.)

which recall the Pithecanthropicines."[13] Although Leakey seems to prefer not to think of the new find from Bed II as *Homo erectus,* most anthropologists do think so, pending the detailed analysis of the skull. It is presumed to be an East African representative of *Homo erectus mauritanicus* and the Olduvai successor to the australopithecines (*Homo habilis?*).

The Chellean-Acheulean hand-ax tradition

Between Bed I, which contains the Oldowan assemblage, and Bed II is a geologic break. Bed II represents a long interpluvial period, which is probably coeval with the interpluvial mid-Pleistocene deposits of the Choukoutien caves. From the bottom of Bed II at Olduvai to the very top of Bed IV, thousands upon thousands of stone artifacts have been recovered that express a tradition evolving in unbroken sequence from the time of the late australopithecines, through *Homo erectus,* and into the time of *Homo sapiens.* This is the Chellean-Acheulean hand-ax tradition, which is found throughout much of Europe and Southwest Asia, as well as throughout most of Africa.

Hand axes are made of the remaining heart of a lump of stone after a number of flakes have been struck off the surface from two or more directions. The residual core has two faces (hence, the designation core-biface) because it is wider than it is thick, and it tapers to a thin edge around all, or a large

[13]L. S. B. Leakey, "East African Fossil Hominoidea and the Classification within This Superfamily," in Washburn, *op. cit.,* p. 43.

part of, its circumference. Such implements must have been held in the clenched fist, and are thus appropriately called *coup de poing* (blow of the fist) by French prehistorians. Germans call this instrument a *Faustkiel,* or fist ax, although its typical pointed cutting edge is the edge of a pick ax rather than of a wood-chopping ax. Certainly, one must not be misled by the name into thinking of the tool as a wood ax, for it most likely was carried in the fist as a weapon and also used as a butcher's cleaver and bone smasher.

The type station (a type station is the place of discovery of prehistoric remains that are considered standard for a specific culture) for the earliest discovery of the Lower Paleolithic hand-ax culture is Abbeville, a village near Paris, where Boucher de Perthes (1788–1868) was collector of customs when he made the discoveries that established European prehistoric archaeology early in the nineteenth century. Hence, the first manifestations of the hand-ax tradition in the Lower Paleolithic are identified as *Abbevillian,* or *Chellean,* after the town of Chelles. The terms "Abbevillian" and "Chellean" are synonymous and apply to the first stages of the hand-ax tradition. In its improved and refined form, the Chellean becomes the *Acheulean* (named after the type station of St. Acheul, in France), which finally fuses with a flake tradition, known as the *Levalloisian* (after Levallois-Perret, a suburb of Paris), to become the *Mousterian* (after Le Moustier) tradition of Neandertal man in Late Pleistocene times.

The Chellean industry of Bed II At the very bottom of Bed II at Olduvai, half of the artifacts are "indistinguishable from the types found in Bed I, and in appearance characteristic of the Oldowan culture."[14] However, half of the artifacts represent a distinct evolutionary advance over the types of tools found in Bed I and are hand axes of the Chellean 1 type. "Some of these crude hand-axes," writes Leakey, "are made of large pebbles and others are made of lumps of quartz and lava, but all of them agree in having, as an essential characteristic, flaking in three or four different directions and the intersection of two jagged cutting edges . . . in a point at one end."[15] (See Fig. 9-6.)

At a second level, 10 to 15 feet above the base of Bed II, the hand axes have taken on a specialized quality (Chellean 2):

The butt ends are thick and massive and usually with a marked flattening on the lower face. Running along the upper face is a steep ridge which is usually more or less central in the anterior part and curves markedly—but irregularly—from about the centre of the butt-end. On the lower face the flattening, which is so marked in the posterior half, is sometimes carried forward the whole length of the specimen, but in other examples is replaced by a sharp ridge formed by the intersection of flat scars in two directions at a steep angle.[16]

Twenty feet above the horizon that yielded stage 2 are found the implements of Chellean 3. These are

. . . large thick hand-axes more or less triangular but sometimes roughly oval in outline when viewed from above. The lower face is remarkably flat . . . due to careful flaking which usually extends over the whole inferior face. The upper face has a more

or less defined central keel anteriorly, so that a section through the anterior part of the specimen is roughly triangular.[17]

Near the top of Bed II, 10 feet below Bed III, is an artifact level in which the instruments show a quality of refinement of technique that adumbrates the Acheulean. This, however, takes us into the cultures associated with *Homo sapiens,* the subject of the next chapter.

The elaboration of the great hand-ax tradition of the West was not localized solely at Olduvai Gorge, but it does seem now as though East Africa may well have been the homeland from which it spread to Europe and Southwest Asia. The Western representatives of *Homo erectus* were tens of thousands of years behind their Eastern congeners in the acquisition of fire, but they ran far ahead of them in the development of stone technology. The cultural differentiation of East and West was well under way in Middle Pleistocene times. The African hand-ax makers lived in the open in an equable clime. Pekin man was a caveman for whom fire was a necessity and nicely made tools were not. This is not to say that the East Asian *Homo erectus* invented control of fire so that he could inhabit caves. Rather, he discovered that use of fire made caves inhabitable, and he adjusted his living habits accordingly and effectively. *Homo erectus* in the East and West was building toward higher developmental levels on a common biological heritage and a diverging cultural tradition.

SUMMARY

Java man (*Homo erectus erectus*) is found in two distinct strata (the Djetis and Trinil beds) of the Lower Pleistocene age. The Java men of the lower-lying Djetis bed overlapped with a local representative of *Australopithecus robustus.* Java man had a maximal cranial capacity just short of the minimum for *Homo sapiens,* while his minimum cranial capacity exceeds that of the most capacious australopithecine skulls. His skull is angular with a recessive forehead behind heavy browridges. The jaw is massive,

[14] L. S. B. Leakey, *Olduvai Gorge,* p. 34.
[15] *Ibid.*
[16] *Ibid.*
[17] *Ibid.*

but the teeth are more hominid than otherwise. The structure of the femur indicates upright posture.

No cultural remains have been found in the same deposits with Java man fossils, but the presence of chopper tools in the Trinil beds elsewhere in Java implies his continuation of the pebble-chopper tradition begun by the australopithecines (or *Homo habilis*) at Olduvai.

Pekin man (*Homo erectus pekinensis*) is a more developed kinsman of Java man, who inhabited the Choukoutien caves throughout the protracted second interglacial period. He produced chopper tools in somewhat greater variety but did not advance stone technology to any great degree. His triumph lay in the taming and use of fire and in the advancing of big-game predacity. He seems also to have been a consumer of the brains and marrow of his own kind—that is, a cannibal.

In Africa, fossils at Olduvai and in Algeria establish the distribution of *Homo erectus* from the Atlantic to the Pacific in Lower and Middle Pleistocene times in the form of the subspecies *mauritanicus*. However, the technological tradition of Western *Homo erectus* was building on the hand-ax tradition unassociated with the use of fire. The implications of this cultural bifurcation between East and West for later Paleolithic development are explored further in the subsequent chapter.

SELECTED READINGS

Cole, S.: *The Prehistory of East Africa* (rev. ed., 1963), chap. 5, "The Hand-ax Makers." Covers a number of manifestations of the Chellean in Africa, with an interesting account of the fabulous site of Olorgesalie.

Coon, C. S.: *The Origin of Races* (1963), chap. 9, "Pithecanthropus and the Australoids," and chap. 10, "Sinanthropus and the Mongoloids." Much detailed comparative data on all the *Homo erectus* finds.

Clark, W. E. Le G.: *The Fossil Evidence for Human Evolution* (1955), chap. 3. The analysis of the Java and Pekin fossils contained in this chapter will fill in many additional details not included in our discussion. The writing is fairly technical, but still understandable by the nonprofessional. Clark still classifies the two forms of *Homo erectus* as *Pithecanthropus erectus* and *Sinanthropus pekinensis*, but this should produce no difficulties if the nature of the synonyms is kept in mind.

Leakey, L. S. B.: *Olduvai Gorge* (1951). A handsomely illustrated book on the evolutionary sequences of the hand axes at Olduvai. Unfortunately, it ignores the flake-tool components of the Chellean-Acheulean complex and therefore gives a distorted impression of the tradition as a whole.

Oakley, K. P.: "On Man's Use of Fire, with Comments on Tool-making and Hunting," in S. L. Washburn (ed.), *The Social Life of Early Man* (1961), pp. 176–194. A good summary of the data on the first evidences of man's use of fire and the implications to be drawn therefrom.

Prehistoric Homo sapiens and the Upper Paleolithic Age

chapter 11

The evolutionary shaping of man that resulted in the production of *Homo sapiens* was a slow process. The development of his culture through the long Lower and Middle Paleolithic proceeded at a snail's pace. It took one million or more years for man to develop his stone technologies from the level of the Lower to the Upper Old Stone Age. The process had been started by the australopithecines. The foundations of that process were consolidated by *Homo erectus* in Africa and Asia, with a major diversification between the Eastern chopper-tool tradition and the Western hand-ax–flake-tool tradition. During the Middle Pleistocene (second interglacial, third glaciation), the Clactonian and Levalloisian flake-tool tradition and the Chellean (Abbevillian) — Acheulean — Mousterian traditions evolved and interacted in the West. As in earlier times, hunting and gathering were still the source of human sustenance, but the techniques were slowly changing, and man's brain was changing even more rapidly. Upright posture was no longer his predominant feature. Man's brain caught up with, and surpassed, his morphological development. He was becoming more and more the toolmaker and the thinker.

By the middle of the long second interglacial period, about 500,000 years ago, the mental development of man had expanded to the point where the first group of fossils that contemporary paleontologists are willing to classify as *Homo sapiens* (Gr. *homo*, man + L. *sapiens*, intelligent) had established themselves. In this group are the Steinheim, Swanscombe, and Fontechevade remains.

Homo sapiens steinheimensis

The Steinheim fossil was discovered in southwestern Germany, not far from Stuttgart, in the summer of 1936. It came from second interglacial gravels containing extinct Pleistocene fauna such as *Elephas antiquus* and Merk's rhinoceros. The skull and face are well preserved, although twisted and compressed by the pressure of the overlying gravels or possibly by a crushing blow. Nonetheless, they are in good enough shape to allow for clear identification of their qualities. The forehead is moderately recessive behind sharp supraorbital ridges. The occipital region is less angular than that of Pekin man; it has a very slight occipital ridge, and the mastoids are small but sharp. The cranial capacity of 1,150 cc is at the lower end of the range for modern man. The face is relatively small, and the overall dental configuration is human. It is the skull of a *Homo sapiens*.

The Swanscombe skull No artifacts have been found at Steinheim, but at Swanscombe the situation is very different. The Swanscombe fossil comes from a second interglacial terrace of the Thames River. These terraces yielded the first-known Lower Paleolithic hand ax, a beautiful Acheulean specimen found at Gray's Inn Lane, London, in 1680. They have for generations constituted a happy hunting ground for relic hunters and dealers in stone "spearheads" who have looted tens of thousands of Lower Paleolithic tools from these deposits. The usual early interglacial Boreal forest fossil fauna (including *Elephas antiquus, primigenius,* and *cervus,* Merk's rhinoceros, *Megaceros,* bison, and horse) abound to prove, along with analytical geology, that the terrace gravels were laid down in second interglacial times.

A sample of the men who hunted these beasts, roughed out the hand axes with which they were killed, and knocked off the stone flakes with which they were butchered was finally found in 1937 by Alvan T. Marston, who had been keeping close watch on the removal of the gravels from the pit since 1933. Marston first found a human occipital bone embedded in the face of the gravel workings 24 feet beneath the present ground surface. Nine months later, after the pit face had been worked back 8 yards, the left parietal of the same skull was found at the same level. Fluorine analysis has proved the bones to be as old as those of the extinct Pleistocene mammals. Here is unimpeachable evidence of the nature of early man in Britain.

Because the muscular markings are light in comparison to the size and thickness of the skull, it is inferred that the individual was a female. The estimated cephalic index of 78 indicates a medium-rounded head; the occipital diameter is very broad. Within the thick-boned cranium was housed a brain of approximately 1,325 cc, just about the modern female average. Even more significant is the modern complexity of cortical convolutions shown on the endocranial cast. The foramen magnum is located well under and forward on the cranium.

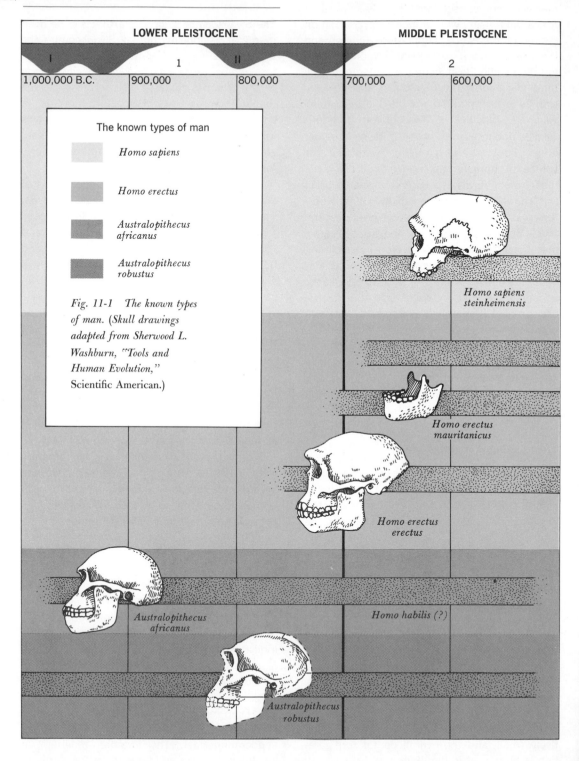

LOWER PLEISTOCENE			MIDDLE PLEISTOCENE	
I	1	II	2	
1,000,000 B.C.	900,000	800,000	700,000	600,000

The known types of man

Homo sapiens

Homo erectus

Australopithecus
africanus

Australopithecus
robustus

Fig. 11-1   The known types
of man. (Skull drawings
adapted from Sherwood L.
Washburn, "Tools and
Human Evolution,"
Scientific American.)

*Homo sapiens
steinheimensis*

*Homo erectus
mauritanicus*

*Homo erectus
erectus*

*Australopithecus
africanus*

Homo habilis (?)

*Australopithecus
robustus*

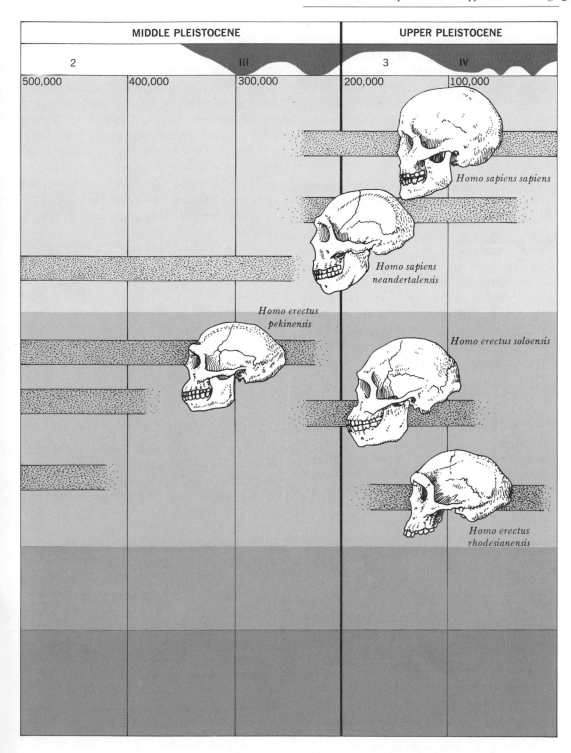

MIDDLE PLEISTOCENE			UPPER PLEISTOCENE	
2		III	3	IV
500,000	400,000	300,000	200,000	100,000

Homo sapiens sapiens

Homo sapiens neandertalensis

Homo erectus pekinensis

Homo erectus soloensis

Homo erectus rhodesianensis

The Swanscombe woman was upright and human-brained. Although we have no evidence concerning her face, teeth, or bodily structure, she is certainly a member of the genus *Homo;* and, indeed, Morant concluded after detailed study, there is nothing about the fragments that would justify excluding her from the species *sapiens.*[1] She is a British representative of *Homo sapiens steinheimensis.*

The Fontechevade skulls The two skulls found at Fontechevade in southeastern France in 1947 by Miss G. Henri-Martin are also *Homo sapiens steinheimensis.* Associated with a Late Clactonian industry called *Tayacian,* and separated from an overlying Mousterian level by a seal of limestone, these skulls are clearly interglacial, possibly third rather than second. The Fontechevade cranial capacity equals the modern average: 1,460 to 1,470 cc. The skull is long, broad, and low, but in the words of Henri Vallois, who analyzed the Fontechevade finds: "The essential fact is the absolute absence of a supraorbital torus: the glabella and the brow ridge are less developed than in the Upper Paleolithic Europeans, or even the majority of Europeans today. They recall, in their general configuration, skulls of female Europeans; there is no nasion depression, and the brow ridge does not extend down to the upper border of the orbit."[2]

The inference to be drawn from these large-brained Middle Pleistocene fossils is that the evolution of man had achieved its present biological plateau in Europe and Africa by second interglacial times. Populations of *Homo erectus* were still present, but sufficient genetic modifications were widespread, so that many individuals were clearly becoming *Homo sapiens* phenotypes. Keeping in mind the principles of genetic variation, natural selection, and adaptive radiation (Chapter 8), it is only reasonable to hold that there would be just a few manifestations of sapienization at first among predominantly *erectus* populations. Gradually, as the selective advantages of *sapiens* traits began to take effect, higher percentages of *sapiens*-type genes would be established, until at last they characterized whole populations. This was fully achieved by the time of the third interglacial but was well under way in second interglacial times.

Homo erectus had very nearly completed the skeletal adaptation to upright posture. After the achievement of full human cranial capacity by *Homo sapiens steinheimensis,* the major changes are in the face and dentition.[3] These facial and dental adaptations of man that occur with *Homo sapiens* appear to be closely related to his improving skill as a hunter, toolmaker, and user of fire and, ultimately, to drastic changes in dietary habits. The possible mechanics of these changes are discussed a bit later, after a consideration of the actual cultural developments that occurred.

Middle Pleistocene cultures

Whether light had spread from the old *Homo erectus* of China or whether it had been an independently kindled idea in the West, *Homo sapiens* at Swanscombe had fire. At least, carbonized vegetable matter and fire-crazed (surface-crackled) flint are closely linked to the debris of the Swanscombe workshop. Strong evidence of the use of fire on other Middle Acheulean horizons in Europe and western Asia confirms the attribution of fire to *Steinheimensis* wherever he lived.[4]

The Acheulean tradition It is hardly probable that *steinheimensis* developed the Acheulean hand-ax industry that is found in such profusion in the Thames second interglacial terraces.

[1]G. M. Morant, "The Form of the Swanscombe Skull" (*Journal of the Royal Anthropological Institute,* Vol. 68, 1938), pp. 67–97; K. P. Oakley, "Swanscombe Man" (*Proceedings of the Geologists' Association,* Vol. 63, 1952), pp. 271–300; reprinted in the *Yearbook of Physical Anthropology,* 1952, pp. 40–70.
[2]H. V. Vallois, "The Fontechevade Fossil Men" (*American Journal of Physical Anthropology,* Vol. 7, No. 3, 1949), p. 352.

[3]See L. C. Brace and M. F. A. Montagu, *Man's Evolution,* pp. 255–264.
[4]K. P. Oakley, "On Man's Use of Fire, with Comments on Tool-making and Hunting," in S. L. Washburn (ed.), *The Social Life of Early Man,* pp. 176–193.

This probably occurred in East Africa. When Steinheim man followed the retreating second glaciation into western Europe, he brought knowledge of the hand-ax and flake-tool techniques with him.

At Olduvai, the evolution of the hand ax continued through Bed III (third pluvial) and into Bed IV. In these later deposits, the hand axes were produced by application of a much more controlled flaking technique than was used earlier. This involved a finishing process wherein, instead of striking a blow on the core with a hammerstone to remove flakes, it is struck with the round edge of a stick, bone, or horn. The force of the blow is diffused so as to remove thinner flakes in the desired direction. This method of flake removal is called the *cylinder-hammer technique*.

The invention of the cylinder-hammer technique made possible the manufacture of thin, symmetrically refined hand axes of the Acheulean type such as the sample from Olduvai Bed III shown in Fig. 9-5 (page 143).

Above all, the effect of these developments was economy of raw material, not that there was necessarily any shortage of raw rock. Yet, the more suitable cores have to be searched for, and it is more economical to produce a lasting and more efficient tool by use of improved techniques than to bang out a new hand ax with crudely removed flakes whenever one is needed.

Flake tools as a part of the Chellean-Acheulean complex Although archaeologists write of the "core-biface hand-ax complex," it must not be forgotten that man has never confined himself to the manufacture and use of only one type of weapon or tool. The maker of a hand-ax implement *ipso facto* produces quantities of flakes. He has no interest in most of them, and a workshop floor near a good source of raw materials will be littered with thousands of unused chips and flakes. But the flintworker and his women would not be human if they failed to pick up appropriately shaped flakes suitable for cutting and scraping wood and hides. The evidence is perfectly clear that the early bands of *Homo sapiens* who produced the hand axes also used many flake tools.

Thus, although Leakey himself has contributed to the common distortion of the image of the core-biface hand-ax complex by discussing hand axes only in his beautiful monograph on Olduvai Gorge, Professor Hallam Movius, Harvard's distinguished Old World archaeologist, properly notes:

> In the immediately overlying beds [Bed II at Olduvai] pointed chopping tools appear which are regarded as the forerunners of the true bifacial hand-axes that have been reported from the next series of deposits, *in association with various types of massive flake tools.* . . . In Bed III the pointed hand-axes of Middle Acheulian type are associated with cleavers . . . *and proto-Levalloisian flakes.* This developmental sequence culminates in the Late Acheulian of Bed IV, where, in addition to the finely made hand-axes, there are rectangular-shaped cleavers *and a fully developed Levalloisian flake industry* [italics added].[5]

The Levalloisian flake tradition The pattern and technique for producing Levalloisian flakes are sufficiently significant to require special attention. The important point is that Levalloisian flakes are not simple fragments of sharp rock that are by-products of hand-ax production and subsequently convenient to use. They are the primary object of the flintworker's intention when he picks up a flint nodule to begin his task. The procedure is called the *striking-platform-tortoise-core technique*. It involves the following steps, which are also illustrated in Fig. 11-2:

1. An oval-shaped flint nodule is flaked around its edge to remove irregularities and to give it symmetry.

2. The patina, or surface shell, is removed from one side by a series of blows directed along the edge toward the middle so that the surface of the nodule resembles the surface of a tortoise shell, rather than that of a potato. When this task is completed, the worker gets ready to remove the flake from the core.

[5]H. L. Movius, Jr., "Old World Prehistory: Paleolithic," in A. L. Kroeber (ed.), *Anthropology Today*, p. 178.

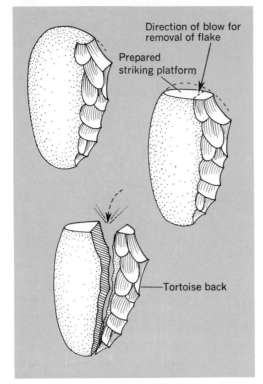

Direction of blow for
removal of flake

Prepared
striking platform

Tortoise back

*Fig. 11-2 The manufacture of a Levalloisian
flake. After the surface is shaped and a striking
platform is prepared, the flake is removed with a
single blow. Edges may be resharpened after use.
Such a tool, which is ready for immediate use
without further preparation, was probably used
as a skinning knife or skin scraper.*

3. A striking platform is next prepared by
removing a flake from one end of the nodule
roughly at a right angle to the long axis of the
nodule. In terms of our own experience, we
might think of the way in which we knock off
one end of a soft-boiled egg with a sharp blow
of a table knife. The end of the egg becomes
flat; likewise, the end of the nodule. This flat
plane forms the Levalloisian prepared striking
platform, or facet.

4. The tortoise back is removed with one
clean blow delivered obliquely to the striking
platform. The flake comes off in a single piece:

hump-chipped on the back, smooth on the
front, with clean, sharp edges. These may be
resharpened with pressure flaking after use.

The Levalloisian technique, which appears
during the second interglacial in France and is
associated with Middle Acheulean hand axes,
is the most efficient technique ever devised for
the production of a good flake implement with
a lasting sharp edge that is suitable for re-
sharpening. It ultimately becomes the basis of
most of the developed technologies of Neandertal man. In its most refined state, it replaced
the hand-ax tradition almost entirely in the
industries of the Upper Paleolithic.

The distribution of the Lower Paleolithic
hand-ax–Levalloisian flake cultures in Africa,
Europe, and the Middle East sheds indirect
light on the ecology of the Middle Pleistocene
in the Old World.

Whereas *Australopithecus* was a savannah
dweller, the early *Homo sapiens* producers of
the Acheulean-type complexes seem to have
adapted to open forest life. Where the interglacial forests stopped, the distribution of
the Acheulean hand ax and Levalloisian flake
stopped.

The Clactonian flake tradition On the northwestern fringe of the area of hand ax distribution, outside the forest areas in what might
be called peripheral glacial tundra, there lived
men who preferred to make sizable cutting and
chopping implements.

A localized industry, first identified at Clac-
ton-on-the-Sea in East Anglia (southeast England), lends its name to this tradition. The
flakes are large and consistently show an
oblique 130-degree angle from the striking
facet to the bulb of the removed face. Clactonian flakes are prepared by steps more or
less similar to those used in the Levalloisian
technique, except that the tortoise-back effect
is not produced, and the flakes often have
broad chopper edges. Such chopping tools are
the functional equivalent to the Acheulean
hand ax. The earliest Clactonian assemblages
are found in second glacial gravels.

Homo sapiens neandertalensis

The first Neandertal[6] skull was found on Gibraltar in 1848, before the time of Darwin. It was viewed as an interesting specimen, but its significance struck no responsive chord. The fossil after which the Neandertal subspecies is named was found in a cave in the Neander Valley near Düsseldorf, Germany. The year was 1856, three years before the publication of Darwin's *Origin of Species,* and the specimen was just in time to take its place in the excited debates which enlivened the latter half of the last century. The evolutionists hailed him as an intermediary, submodern fossil man. The conservatives sourly held that he was nothing but a pathological freak, probably a peasant. It was even suggested that he might have been a stupid Roman legionnaire of the less soldierly kind who crawled off in the cave for twenty winks and liked it so much that he stayed there. The discovery of two more skulls of the same genre at Spy, Belgium, in 1887 put an end to all such scurrilous reflections on the character of the man of the Neander Valley. It then became clear that a different order of man had been in Europe in earlier times and, further, that he was the producer of the Old Stone Age cultures, the antiquity of which had been established through the efforts of the French archaeologist Boucher de Perthes.

Immediately after the turn of the century, Neandertal men, women, and children began to rise from their graves in profusion—from France and Spain to the Crimea, and later from Palestine and North Africa, until there was no

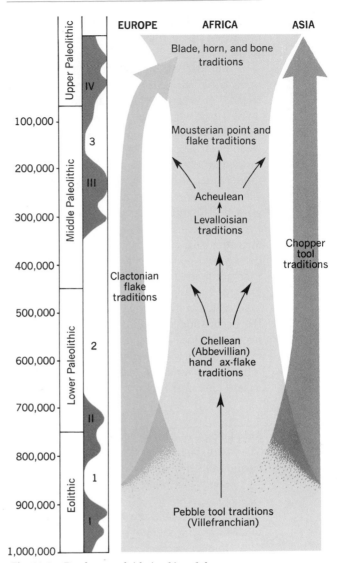

Fig. 11-3   Developmental relationships of the major industries of the Paleolithic age in the Old World. All of these industries begin in the Villefranchian pebble-tool traditions. The Chellean (Abbevillian) hand-ax-flake tradition and the Clactonian flake tradition develop separately and fuse in the Mousterian traditions. The Asiatic chopper-tool traditions remain separate.

[6]The original spelling of this word was "Neanderthal." However, early in this century in Germany an Imperial Commission of Philologists, with authority to streamline the language in the interests of Teutonic efficiency, recommended that since German is quite consistently spelled as it is pronounced, the unsounded *h* should be dropped from all *th* combinations except in *der Thron.* For a group of professors to tamper with the seat of the then Emperor would be lese majesty. Less respectful German wags said they were afraid that the monarchy might collapse if the *h* were removed from the throne. Be that as it may, prehistorians are not philologists, and most of them cling to the archaic *h* in "Neanderthal." See also H. Vallois, "Néanderthal-Néandertal?" (*L'Anthropologie,* Vol. 55, 1952), pp. 557–558.

doubt that Neandertal man had been a very important figure who had really gotten around in his time.

A number of contemporary experts look upon *Homo sapiens steinheimensis* as a "pre-Mousterian" or "early Neandertal man."[7] By so doing, they emphasize the evolutionary continuity from *Homo sapiens steinheimensis* to the Neandertal subspecies of *Homo sapiens*, who lived in the third interglacial and the first half of the fourth glacial (200,000 to 25,000 years ago). But the *Homo sapiens* of the second interglacial were not Neandertals, "progressive" or otherwise. They are, however, in all probability the ancestral stock from which the Classic Neandertals evolved under the highly selective environmental conditions of the third glaciation in Europe. The important thing about Neandertal man is that with the full possession of fire and the occupation of caves, he was able to hold his own in the subarctic conditions of climate in glacial Europe. Earlier men had regularly retreated to Africa or Asia Minor when the ice sheets took over, but not the Neandertal.

Morphology of Homo sapiens neandertalensis
The more distinctive skeletal features of the Neandertals are specifically:

1. Long, low, wide, and capacious cranium (1,300 to 1,600 cc)
2. Cranial base acutely oriented upward with tilted foramen magnum
3. Bun-shaped or angular occipital profile
4. Large facial area
5. Semicircular supraorbital ridges fused above the nose and with the temporal regions
6. Convex curvature of the upper jaws, fusing directly with the cheekbones without forming a suborbital depression (canine fossa)
7. Short, massive spinal column
8. Long, vertical dorsal spines on the cervical vertebrae

9. Limited forward curvature of the cervical and lumbar areas of the spine
10. Heavy, short upper arm (humerus) with a massive head
11. Pronounced curvature of the radius (bow bone in the forearm)
12. Broad, flattened ilia in the pelvis
13. Highly curved thighbone of massive structure
14. Short shinbones
15. Short forearm relative to upper arm
16. Very short leg in proportion to thigh

In appearance the Neandertal was a short, massive-chested, round-shouldered, forward-stooping, powerfully armed, bullnecked, beetle-browed, broad-nosed, flatheaded character, who would, as Professor Howells says, "go to the foot of any posture class in the nation, but he would, notwithstanding, be a dangerous person to face in any wrestling match."[8]

The Levalloiso-Mousterian culture of Neandertal man The work and cultures of the widely scattered groups of Neandertal men brought a final culmination to the technology and way of life of the Lower and Middle Paleolithic ages. Man had become man, but he had not yet made the breakthrough to a really diversified food-getting technique. He had, however, greatly improved his flint-flaking techniques. He had thoroughly domesticated fire, and he carried or produced it wherever he went. With fire, he could drive and keep the great and ferocious Late Pleistocene beasts of prey from the rock shelters and caves he frequented at night and in stormy weather. With fire, he could avoid freezing to death—most of the time. With fire, he made hard-tipped wooden spears—undoubtedly his most used and most reliable weapons. With his refined flint sidescrapers, he had the wherewithal to work animal skins into a proper condition for tanning. Whether he did in fact so use the sidescrapers or whether he handled them merely as knife blades, we have no way of knowing. Tanning requires knowledge of the chemical properties of tanin, which is necessary

[7]For example, F. C. Howell, "The Evolutionary Significance of Variation and Varieties of 'Neanderthal' Man" (*The Quarterly Review of Biology*, Vol. 32, No. 4, 1957), pp. 333–336.

[8]W. W. Howells, *Mankind So Far*, p. 168.

to soften the skin and convert it from rawhide into leather. No tanned leather has ever been found in Mousterian sites.[9]

In spite of real improvements in technique, the tool kit of Neandertal man was still essentially that of his antecedents of the Chellean and Clactonian complexes 500,000 years earlier. He had not learned how to work bone into implements other than the pressure-flaking tool. Nor could he haft a point on a spear. But he had a great brain, agile hands (as shown by his delicate retouching of tool edges), and a fierce will to live, sustained by what must have been incredible courage. We can infer that his introduction of intentional burial of the dead within occasional caves reflects the first dim dawning of a belief in a spiritual essence as an attribute of being human (see Chapter 32). The act may be read as a projection of the will to live into a belief in some form of afterlife. Neandertal man was *Homo sapiens* on the verge of forming his first complex symbolic concepts. He was still a Middle Paleolithic hunter—a low-level savage, indeed—but he was also man thinking, or *Homo sapiens.*

To leave inference and to get to the hard facts of archaeology, the Chellean-Acheulean hand-ax tradition continued right into the Mousterian assemblages of the Neandertals. In Europe, however, the hand axes become much reduced in size and relatively fewer in number in relation to flake tools.

The Mousterian tool complexes of the Neandertals of western Europe fused the Clactonian and Levalloisian traditions to produce characteristic retouched sidescrapers and triangular points. Out of the tortoise-back idea, the Neandertals evolved the small discoidal core. This is not much of an invention, but it is something.

In South Africa, the Congo basin, East Africa, the Nile Valley, and the Horn, local variations on the Acheulean hand-ax–Levalloisian flake complex were developed through the entire Middle Paleolithic, lending further testimony to

the basic efficiency and viability of the Western Pleistocene hunting-subsistence complex.[10]

Similar specializations pushed across Asia Minor into the Indus Valley, where they mixed with the Late Soan versions of the chopper-tool tradition.

Neandertal man and modern man An incredible amount of confusion has been engendered by the "Neandertal problem." The problem is: What is the evolutionary (phylogenetic) relation of Neandertal man to modern man?

For a third of a century (ca. 1900 to 1935), the dominant theme was that (1) Neandertal man is a distinct species of the genus *Homo,* morphologically represented by the "classic" type discovered in the cavern of La Quina; (2) this species evolved rather directly from the pithecanthropine forms of Asia without "modernization"; (3) somewhere, somehow, in Asia Minor or North Africa, modern man of the species *sapiens* evolved and developed the basic Upper Paleolithic culture (Chatelperronian), moved into Europe during the middle of the fourth glaciation, and proceeded to exterminate the Neandertals with pestilence and war in the matter of a few millennia; and (4) because "Neandertal" traits are so rare in late Upper Paleolithic skeletons, and thereafter, species differences must have made racial interbreeding impossible. This is the "theory of hominid catastrophism."[11]

One thing is certain: the Middle Paleolithic (Mousterian), Classic Neandertal type disappeared from the scene around 30,000 years ago.

In the 1930s, two events set in motion a reevaluation of the whole question of the historical relation of Neandertal man to modern man.

1. The discovery of the Swanscombe and Steinheim fossils showed the existence of a type of man in Europe in second interglacial times with "little indication of specifically Neanderthal

[9]The Mousterian tradition is named after the rock shelter of Le Moustier, near Les Eyzies in the Dordogne (the "capital" of Paleolithic Europe) in France.

[10]For details, see S. Cole, *Prehistory of Africa* (rev. ed.), pp. 141–166.
[11]See C. L. Brace, "The Fate of the 'Classic' Neanderthals: A Consideration of Hominid Catastrophism" (*Current Anthropology,* Vol. 5, No. 1, 1964), pp. 3–46.

morphology."[12] Mid-Pleistocene man in Europe and North Africa is not a Neandertal prototype in a narrow sense.

2. The characteristics of a number of fossil individuals discovered in Palestinian caves by Dorothy Garrod and Theodore McCown were published.[13] On Mt. Carmel, near the Sea of Galilee, two caves have yielded Early and Middle Mousterian cultural inventories in association with several dozen human skeletons, or rather, parts of skeletons.

The remarkable aspect of the Mt. Carmel population is its variability. From the lower levels of the Tabun Cave came a girl who is similar to the Swanscombe-Steinheim type of *Homo sapiens*. In the upper levels of the cave were genuine *Homo sapiens sapiens* (contemporary modern men) and others with mixed Neandertal and *Homo sapiens sapiens* traits. These fossils are of the early last pluvial in the Middle East, contemporary to the Neandertals of the first part of the fourth glacial epoch in Europe. In the light of the then-prevailing theory, the discovery of primitive *Homo sapiens* types, of fossils with mixed Neandertal–modern *Homo sapiens* traits, and of fossils that were similar to the Cro-Magnon type of *Homo sapiens* (see page 172), was extremely surprising.

McCown and Sir Arthur Keith proposed that a basic Neandertal population was evolving into modern man. They examined and rejected an alternative hypothesis that the Mt. Carmel population represented the hybridization of a population of Neandertals with a population of modern *Homo sapiens*, both having originated separately elsewhere (the place being left undetermined). The obvious possibility that evolutionary divergence and hybridization were occurring simultaneously seems to have been ignored.

At any rate, it was proved that modern *Homo sapiens* and Neandertals hobnobbed in the Holy Land 30,000 or more years ago. The either-or theory could no longer hold up.

Leaving aside the details of the long argument,[14] and limiting ourselves to the most reasonable interpretation of the known facts, we arrive at the following conclusions.

The term "Neandertal" is confined to the type of fossil man associated with the Mousterian tradition in Europe and Southwest Asia— the type called Mousterian or Classic Neandertal. It does not extend to the fossil populations of the second interglacial in Europe represented by the Steinheim-Swanscombe-Fontechevade series.

The Neandertal category of man, thus cut down to size, is to be understood as simply a very distinctive and specialized cold-climate subspecies of *Homo sapiens*, an archaic local race of Late Pleistocene man that got "selected out" when the special subarctic climate to which it was adapted ended in Europe. The Neandertals were then replaced by the culturally better-adapted *Homo sapiens sapiens*, who came to compete for the same *Lebensraum*.

Neandertal man, when so defined, does not represent a stage through which all forms of *Homo sapiens* have passed. He is seen as a specialized variety derived from the same *Homo sapiens* base as contemporary *Homo sapiens sapiens*. This relationship is indicated in Fig. 11-4. In this chart it is not implied that all early *Homo sapiens* were of the *steinheimensis* variety. The Steinheim subspecies is the only one we know at this time; therefore, it represents the basic *Homo sapiens* pool in the second interglacial.

Homo erectus soloensis and *Homo erectus rhodesiensis*

The first of these two special varieties of *Homo sapiens* was found in the Ngandong beds, which overlie the Djetis and Trinil beds in Java. Eleven fragmentary skulls and two tibia of Solo man were found just 6 miles from Trinil, on the Solo River, in 1931–1932. The geological matrix places the fossils in the Upper Pleistocene.

Every one of the skulls had been subjected to

[12] F. C. Howell, *op. cit.*, p. 334.
[13] T. D. McCown and A. Keith, *The Stone Age of Mt. Carmel*, Vol. 2, *The Fossil Remains from the Levalloiso-Mousterian*.

[14] Brace, *op. cit.*, gives a comprehensive coverage. Unfortunately it is tinged by an injudicious polemicism that must be discounted by the reader.

postmortem butchery. In all but one instance, the face had been hacked off entirely, and no lower jaws were found at all. In all but one skull, the foramen magnum had been enlarged by a stick or bone that was inserted in the hole and then pressed upon. Apparently, Solo man was keeping up brain cannibalism. The skulls all lay bottom up, which means that they had been carefully placed. They were not water-rolled, which means they were found where they had been left. And they were in such good condition, apart from intentional mutilation, that the absence of any loose teeth or other parts of the body, except for the two shinbones, indicates they had been carried in their butchered condition to the river bank. For a feast, or as ritual sacrifices? We cannot say.

Viewed superficially, Solo man is an improved *Homo erectus* (see Fig. 11-1). The skulls are thick-boned. The browridges are heavy but do not form a massive, continuous shelf. The profile is generally that of *Homo erectus*, but the brain is much larger. The range of the Solo cranial capacities is from 1,035 to 1,255 cc, with an average, combining both sexes, of about 1,100 cc. This puts the type in the same range as *Homo erectus pekinensis* and in the lower ranges of *Homo sapiens.*

Morphologically, the traits of Solo man are very close to those of Java and Pekin man.[15] Therefore, the taxonomy of Solo man should place him within the *Homo erectus* group. Dobzhansky[16] and Campbell[17] place Solo man in the *Homo sapiens* category. The reason seems to be that, like Rhodesian man, he lived too recently to be classed as a *Homo erectus*. Taxonomies are properly made only on the basis of genetic traits, however. So if a few enclaves of *Homo erectus* lived beyond their "proper" time as evolutionary laggards, they ought not to be upgraded just for that.

Rhodesian man was blasted loose from his

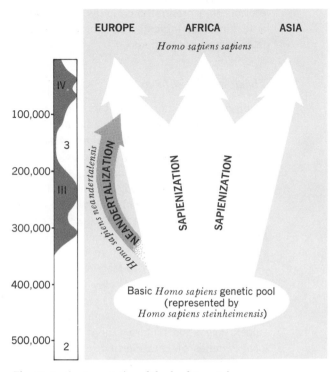

Fig. 11-4   *A representation of the developmental relations of the three species of* Homo *during the second half of the Pleistocene. During the Middle Pleistocene, gene flow among the* Homo sapiens *populations of the three continents established the genus. Continuing intensification of* sapiens *traits through speciation produced* Homo sapiens sapiens *in Upper Paleolithic times. Extreme selective effects of the glacial environment in the north produced the Neandertal subspecies (*Homo sapiens neandertalensis), *which was reabsorbed into the* Homo sapiens sapiens *pool during the later phase of the fourth glacial, and so became extinct. (Modified from F. C. Howell.)*

[15]F. Weidenreich, "Morphology of Solo Man" (*American Museum of Natural History, Anthropological Papers*, Vol. 43, Part I, 1951), p. 227.

[16]T. Dobzhansky, *Mankind Evolving*, p. 179.

[17]B. Campbell, "Quantitative Taxonomy and Human Evolution," in S. L. Washbunn (ed.), *Classification and Human Evolution*, p. 66.

stony bed in Broken Hill Mine, Northern Rhodesia, in 1921. He represents another Upper Pleistocene variety of *Homo erectus* with the moderate brain size of 1,280 cc. Like *soloensis*, he has heavy *erectus* brow ridges, discontinuous over the nose; a recessive, low-domed calvarium with a strong occipital ridge and angular roof; and weak mastoids (Fig. 11-1). The lower face projects to a prognathous upper alveolar arch, a feature that indicates possible ancestry to later African populations.

Homo sapiens sapiens

European and American writers have, in the past, been prone to think of early *Homo sapiens sapiens* in the image of Cro-Magnon Man. Because he lived in Europe, produced excellent art a good twenty thousand years ago, and was so large-brained, high-domed, upright, and energetic and so much more obviously like a northwestern European in appearance and capabilities than *Homo sapiens neandertalensis*, it has been too easy to say he *is* modern man.

The fact is that the Cro-Magnon fossil group is but one manifestation of *Homo sapiens sapiens*. It is not the only type that lived in the Late Pleistocene and produced a manifestation of Upper Paleolithic culture. There are also the local varieties of Late Pleistocene *Homo sapiens sapiens* found as fossils at Grimaldi and Chancelade, in France, and at Brünn and Predmost, in Czechoslovakia. In Africa, there is the Boskop type in the south. In Southeast Asia, there is the Wadjak predecessor of later Australoids. And in China, the man of the upper cave at Choukoutien is also a *Homo sapiens sapiens*, as are a number of other more recently discovered specimens.

Hereafter, when we speak of modern man, we refer to *Homo sapiens sapiens*.

The morphology of modern man   What, in generalized terms, are the morphological traits of modern man?

His skeletal features are different from those of his *Homo sapiens* predecessors only in those traits which are associated with the final attainment of upright posture. The long bones of the legs lose their curvature and become characteristically more slender and less robust. The iliac wings of the pelvis become more smoothly rounded and tilted more toward the rear. The radius in the forearm is much less bowed, and the humerus becomes relatively longer and generally more delicate. The scapula broadens out at the top and is relatively less elongated.

The modifications of major significance leading to *Homo sapiens sapiens*, however, are found in the brain and the skull. It is, after all, the brain that is the generator of the culture-creating capacity, and it was with the emergence of modern man that the slow-working Lower Paleolithic cultural experience suddenly became activated, and civilization was at last created.

Modern man exhibits a globular braincase and a marked reduction of the face and lower jaw (see Fig. 11-1). The new forehead makes room for the enlarged frontal lobes of the brain. The supraorbital ridges virtually disappear; the occipital torus becomes residual. The mastoid process is more pronounced as a muscular anchor. The foramen magnum is horizontally oriented and well forward under the braincase.

Mastication, except in the special circumstance of Eskimos, has become for man the cooker functionally much less significant. The molars are persistently smaller, and the old *Dryopithecus* Y pattern of five cusps is frequently replaced with a four-cusp structure that produces a + pattern.[18] Smaller teeth are set closely in a reduced dental arch surrounding a smaller palate. A broadening of the skull increases the relative width of the span between the maxillary condyles. The more active tongue (modern man is "the great talker") requires maneuvering room within the jaw. At the same time, the bowed region of the lower jaw (symphysis of the inferior maxilla) must remain strong. The modern jaw is subject to a great stress of lateral compression by the inward pull of the pterygoid muscles, which run from the condyloid processes to the upper walls of the palate. The two sides of the jaw could easily crack where they are joined together at the chin. Reinforcement of the jaw in *Homo sapiens sapiens* is achieved in the thickening of the symphysis. Hence, the chin, the appropriate symbol of manliness.

Another feature of modern man that relates

---

[18]C. S. Coon, *The Origin of Races*, pp. 360–364, gives details on the relative frequency of the + in lower and upper molars (the first, second, and third molars differ) by populations.

to a reduction of the chewing function is the dimunition of the temporal muscles. The zygomatic arches that bridge the temporals are reduced, and the face is narrowed, Eskimos excepted. The whole face is drawn back under the frontal part of the cranial vault, as well as being reduced in size. The eye sockets are located under the bulb of the frontal bones rather than under the ridge of a supraorbital torus. Finally, of course, the nasal bridge is pronounced to a greater or lesser degree, depending on the racial subvariety.

The stature of some varieties becomes notably larger than that of any premodern populations, while in the case of a few special subvarieties (Bushmen and Pygmies), there is a regression in size.

The brains of all forms of modern man are large (1,000 to 2,000 cc), with complex cortical surfaces.

The origin of modern man It is unlikely that modern man originated in any very precisely localized spot. There was no Garden of Eden, except in an allegorical sense. Although the Smithsonian's physical anthropologist, Ales Hrdlička, argued that modern man evolved directly from Neandertal man, and although this same thesis is currently propounded by C. L. Brace, its probable validity is not so very great. Neandertal man enjoyed an intensive but limited distribution in the West. Third interglacial, non-Neandertal *Homo sapiens* existed over a wide area of the Old World. Of modern man, Dobzhansky writes: "*Homo sapiens sapiens*, was from the beginning a wanderer and a colonizer. . . . Toward the end of the Pleistocene he is already a cosmopolite who appeared in eastern Asia, Australia, Africa, and America."[19]

Modern man represents a continuing evolution of Middle Pleistocene *Homo sapiens*, with a certain amount of gene flow among various populations. Geographic isolation and differential natural selection were sufficient to produce different races, but there was apparently enough genetic interaction so that *Homo sapiens sapiens* was developing as a subspecies all

[19]Dobzhansky, *op. cit.*, p. 180.

through Africa, Asia Minor, and the outer edges of Asia more or less simultaneously.

Modern man does not appear to have developed in Europe, where *Homo sapiens neandertalensis* held the stage through the first advance of the fourth glacial. But he does, indeed, displace Neandertal man during the milder interstadial phase following the first crest of the fourth glaciation. In view of the very limited persistence of any distinctive Neandertal traits in subsequent Late Pleistocene populations, it does not seem that the Neandertals had much of a chance to contribute to the enduring gene pool. In our diagram representing the phylogenetic relation of the Neandertals to the rest of *Homo sapiens* (Fig. 11-4), an indication of interchange is shown in the upper left corner. If the Neandertals were not exterminated through war and disease, they were at least biologically swamped by their more adaptive cousins, the more sapient subspecies of *Homo sapiens*.

The taxonomic inventory of the hominids

The contemporary classification of the known types of man that is used in this text is that formulated by Campbell for the 1962 Wartenstein Symposium on *Classification and Human Evolution*,[20] with two exceptions: we have followed Weidenreich and Coon in classifying the Solo and Rhodesian men within the species *erectus*, and we have made room for *Homo habilis* as a possible species.

In this system, shown in Table 11-1, there are two genera, four or five species, and eight subspecies of man, fossil and living. All are now extinct except *Homo sapiens sapiens*.

Upper Paleolithic cultures

The replacement of the Lower and Middle Paleolithic hand-ax–flake-tool technologies in the Late Pleistocene was achieved by Upper Paleolithic blade and horn technologies. The hand ax disappeared. Boneheaded spears and reindeer-

[20]Campbell, *op. cit.*, pp. 66–69.

Table 11-1   *The Taxonomic Inventory of the Hominids*

genus	species	subspecies
Australopithecus	*A. africanus* *A. robustus* *H. habilis(?)*	
Homo	*H. erectus*	*H. erectus erectus* *H. erectus mauritanicus* *H. erectus pekinensis* *H. erectus soloensis* *H. erectus rhodesianensis*
	H. sapiens	*H. sapiens steinheimensis* *H. sapiens neandertalensis* *H. sapiens sapiens*

horn harpoons became the chief weapons, while a veritable hardware store inventory of specialized blade tools was developed. A blade tool is a narrow, elongated flake struck in quantities from a pyramidal core by applying a bone or wood punch to a flat surface on the core (near its edge), and then hitting the punch a sharp blow to remove the flake. From these were produced chisels, drills or awls, endscrapers, notched blades, and a variety of points. Thick flakes with humped tortoise-backed keels and fine edge retouching served as planing tools or scrapers. (See Fig. 11-5 for examples of all these types.)

The occurrence of these special forms varies

Table 11-2   *Upper Paleolithic Cultures and Their Durations*

radiocarbon dates	tradition
B.C.	
15,000 to 8,000	Magdalenian
18,000 to 15,000	Solutrean
22,000 to 18,000	Gravettian (Upper Perigordian)
28,500 to 22,000	Aurignacian
32,000 to 28,500	Châtelperronian (Lower Perigordian)

from site to site, and from time to time through the interstadial and final advance of the fourth glacial. The specialist is much concerned with the identification and analysis of these numerous local assemblages. As an introduction, however, the simplified model of Upper Paleolithic sequences in southwestern France, offered by Grahame Clark,[21] will still do as a frame of reference. It is presented in Table 11-2. Obviously, the radiocarbon dates should not be taken as so absolutely exact as they look. None of these cultures began or stopped at a given millenium.

The Upper Paleolithic age and *Homo sapiens sapiens* made their first appearances together, in Southwest Asia and Europe around 35,000 B.C. The earliest known manifestations of the Upper Paleolithic took shape quite suddenly in Iraq (Shanidar Cave), Afghanistan (Kara Kamar), Israel (Mt. Carmel), and Cyrenaica, North Africa (Haua Fteah). The earliest C-14-dated Upper Paleolithic sites in Western Europe fall about 2,000 years later, at Arcy-sur-Cure in the Yonne area of France. Some prehistorians suggest that this implies an origin of the Upper Paleolithic culture complex in Asia Minor, followed by rapid diffusion westward via migrating *Homo sapiens sapiens*. More reliable dates are needed before jumping to such a conclusion, however. Yet one

[21]G. Clark, *World Prehistory*, p. 51.

thing is certain. Wherever Upper Paleolithic assemblages are found, the associated hominid remains are always those of fully modern man.

The first phases of the Upper Paleolithic are seen in the Chatelperronian, Aurignacian, and Gravettian traditions.

The Chatelperronian: 32,000–28,500 B.C. This incipient Upper Paleolithic tradition is not very richly represented among known archaeological assemblages, and there is a diversity of opinion as to whether it may have evolved locally in France or was developed in Southwest Asia from whence it may have diffused westward. The latter alternative is perhaps the most probable. At any rate, although the Chatelperronian does not show the high degree of specialized elaboration that marks the succeeding Upper Paleolithic cultures, it does include the elongated flake blade that is the hallmark of the Upper Paleolithic. The distinctive Chatelperronian blade has a curved cutting edge. The back edge, on which finger pressure would be applied in use, is blunted with fine transverse chipping (Fig. 11-5). Simple, pointed bone tools were also produced, but there was none of the art that became so important in the Gravettian and Magdalenian, later on.

The Aurignacian: 28,000–22,000 B.C. Unlike the Chatelperronian, which is sparsely distributed, Aurignacian industries are numerous in southwestern France and Central Europe. The distribution of these industries, which ranges from France, where it appears quite suddenly, through Hungary to the caves of Israel, Iraq, and Afghanistan, strongly suggests a point of origin in Southwest Asia. The occurrence of a hybrid Mousterian-Aurignacian tradition, known as the Szeletian, in Hungary, Slovakia, and Moravia, testifies to the probable fusion of an indigenous Middle Paleolithic population and migrating Upper Paleolithic men from the southeast.

In Europe, as in the Middle East, Aurignacian man was a cave dweller. He had fire, of course, and was an avid hunter and skin dresser. His tool kit was characterized by elongated, parallel-sided flakes which were triangular in cross-

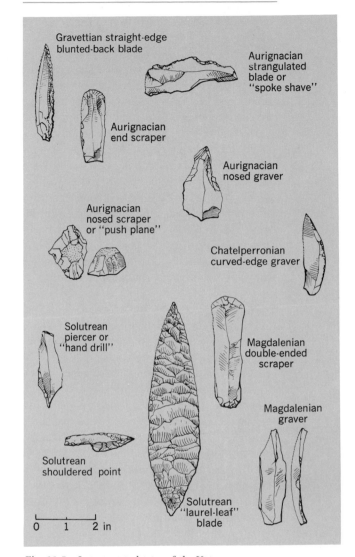

Fig. 11-5   Important tool types of the Upper Paleolithic cultures. A large variety of specialized flake instruments for cutting, boring, engraving, and scraping is characteristic of Upper Paleolithic artifact assemblages. [After Kenneth P. Oakley, Man the Tool Maker. *Courtesy of the Trustees, British Museum (Natural History); shouldered point and laurel-leaf blade after Robert J. Braidwood,* Prehistoric Men. *Copyright © 1964 by the Chicago Natural History Museum.]*

section and retouched to give steep, rounded working ends (Fig. 11-5). Also included were tools known as *gravers*, or *burins*—elongated blades with one end coming to a sharp-pointed chisel edge. These tools were used for working wood, bone, ivory, antler, and soft stone. Burins are the implement of the carver. Humpbacked "nosed scrapers" (Fig. 11-5) were also produced from small cores. Aurignacian blades lack the transverse fine flaking that blunts the back edges of Chatelperronian and Gravettian blades—a small feature that demonstrates how large small cultural differences can loom. Finally, the makers of the Aurignacian assemblages produced bone "javelin héads" having fine, sharp, piercing points and cleft bases for fixing the bone heads into wooden shafts.

The Gravettian: 22,000–18,000 B.C. The Gravettian tradition flourished during a brief amelioration of the frigid climate of the fourth glaciation. In East Europe, the interstadial climate softened sufficiently to permit the creators of the Gravettian cultures to live in skin tents or oval huts on the loess plains of Hungary and South Russia. Although Gravettian blades have some features in common with the Chatelperronian (and for this reason French archaeologists hold that the one is an outgrowth of the other, both together constituting what they call the Perigordian), the gap in time between the end of the Chatelperronian and the onset of the Gravettian makes this unlikely.

Gravettian flint workers produced delicate slim blades with dull back edges which are so refined that they are often likened unto penknife blades. Burins were produced in large variety, and Mousterian-like points with the added feature of biface retouching (i.e., the removal of flakes from both faces of the artifact) appear. An added innovation can be seen in points that are worked down to a tang at the base. The tang, like that on modern knives, was probably for hafting a handle to the blade.

Gravettians not only relied on flint-working, but applied their flint carving tools to ivory, bone, and antlers in profusion to make awls

and lanceheads, spatulas (perhaps used to beat snow from clothes and tents?), scoops, and shovels. They also produced decorated pins and bracelets of ivory, plus beads of clay, bone, iron, and stone—and pendants—to be worn about the neck by both men and women. These decorative objects were incised with rows of dots and parallel lines in complex geometric designs. The Gravettians were truly skilled artisans. More than that, they were artists who modelled small animals in clay and carved excellent stylized human (mostly female) figurines in ivory. They planted the seeds of artistic creativity that were to flower so gloriously in the Magdalenian of France between 15,000 and 10,000 B.C. As an extra flourish, the Gravettians innovated the practice of burial of the dead, with their personal ornaments and in full clothing, sprinkled with red ochre.

The Solutrean: 18,000–15,000 B.C. Immediately overlying the Gravettian strata in some parts of France is a distinctive culture named after the site of Solutre. Its main feature is the biface laurel-leaf point, which in its most developed form is the epitome of the flintworker's technique anywhere in the world at any time (Fig. 11-5). Solutrean workers also produced excellent barbed and tanged arrowheads, delicately worked over both surfaces (like the laurel-leaf points) by means of carefully controlled pressure flaking. Bone and ivory pendants, beads, bracelets, and long bone pins, plus red, yellow, and black pigments indicate the probability of body painting and ornamentation in the Gravettian manner. But although some examples of sculpture and paintings have been found in Solutrean deposits, it still remains true that the Solutreans had little interest in art. Nevertheless, it may be said of Solutrean man that he was a true artist in flint working. At the height of his technique, the Solutrean workman gave form, rhythm, and symmetry to his products beyond the needs of utilitarianism. The best of his willow-leaf and laurel-leaf points are the results of precocious effort.

The distribution of Solutrean sites is erratically scattered across southern France to Hungary. In many places within this area, it does not appear at all. The Solutrean correlates, in time, with a very cold phase of the fourth glacial. It seems to be a slightly aberrant Upper Paleolithic culture that intrudes as a brief, alien interlude in the Gravettian-Magdalenian sequence. In its interaction with the Gravettian, it may have provided a kind of stimulus—a challenge that gave impetus to the Gravettian trends which flowered in the rich exuberance of the Magdalenian.[22]

The Magdalenian: 15,000–10,000 B.C. The Magdalenian tradition carries on and elaborates the bone-working propensities of the Gravettians, producing an intriguing series of barbed harpoons out of the bone javelin point. In the Lower Magdalenian, these harpoons were fashioned with a single row of barbs carved out along one side only. In the Upper Magdalenian, the barbs were fashioned to alternate along both sides, and a "swallow-tailed" base was developed to facilitate hafting into the wooden shaft which held it (Fig. 11-6). Magdalenian man also invented the dart thrower, or *atlatl* (the Aztec name by which it is frequently known), thus applying the principle of the lever for greater projectile force.

The flint artifacts of the Upper Magdalenian became modified in the direction of greater delicacy and the splinterlike sharpness of their cutting points to be used in the engraving and carving of art objects. Planing tools that undoubtedly served to remove the tissue from the underside of skins in preparation of animal hides for robes and clothing were also numerous. These same planes also could have been used to work down bone and ivory preparatory to final carving and engraving in artistic output.

Upper Paleolithic art It is in the field of art that the accomplishments of the men of the Upper Paleolithic have led to the sobriquet "Paleolithic Greeks." The aesthetic sensitivity and technical proficiency of these ancient cave dwellers are truly awe-inspiring. They surpassed

[22]P. E. L. Smith, "The Solutrean Culture" (*Scientific American*, Vol. 211, No. 2, 1964), p. 94.

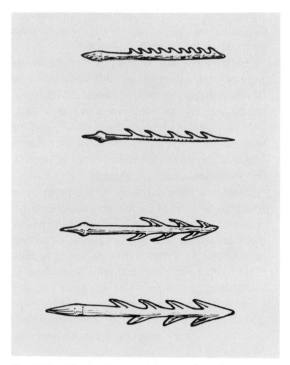

Fig. 11-6   The double-rowed, barbed, bone harpoons of the Late Magdalenian evolved from Early Magdalenian single-rowed harpoons.

many later primitives in ability, while some of their sculpture compares favorably with good modern works. They were versatile, too. Painting, engraving, sculpture, and modeling were familiar media of expression, and they were skilled in all these fields. Their art began in experimental crudeness and developed steadily to the sure technique of masters. It offers a rich field for the study of developmental processes in art because the sequences in improvement are clearly discernible in archaeological series.

Although they represent different techniques, engraving and painting were closely integrated by the Gravettian-Magdalenian artists. They developed hand-in-hand to produce closely similar forms of expression. It appears that when an engraving was made first, its incised lines were always painted in afterward. Sometimes a wall surface was given a paint wash, after which the engraving was incised. The effect was to set out the engraving in fresh contrast to the painted background.

Early Gravettian engravings and paintings were no more than crude, stiff outlines. Later Gravettian pictures were more accurate representations, and in the Lower and Middle Magdalenian, skill in composition, contour, and the use of polychrome was reached. Some comparative examples from the four phases of Gravettian-Magdalenian art are given in Fig. 11-7.

Sculpture does not show such a progressive trend, since most of the known examples reveal reasonably good technique, whatever the phase. Mural sculpture was wall engraving developed to produce medallion types of low and high relief. The best work, however, was done in sculpturing in the round on bone, antler, and ivory, in shaping such articles as dagger grips and dart throwers in animal and bird forms. The most famous example of plastic modeling

is a family group of a bison bull, cow, and calf from the cavern of Tuc d'Audubert.

Much light is shed on the beliefs and mentality of Upper Paleolithic man by the art that he produced. If ever an art reflected the spirit of its culture, it was this. There has been much argumentative exchange of opinion between utilitarian-minded anthropologists and those who insist that art be evaluated as an end in itself. Anthropologists have insisted on the magico-religious utilitarianism of the art. Aesthetes have insisted that it manifests the essential artistic genius of its makers. Both are right, but to an anthropologist the anthropologists seem more so, for they see the cultural functions of art as being more significant than the aesthetic.

Upper Paleolithic art had the gross purposes of filling men's stomachs and of maintaining the population by serving as a magical aid in hunting and procreation. But besides being a means to these ends, it was also an end in itself. The Upper Paleolithic artist produced not merely images, but beautiful images. He not only strove to produce magically efficacious representations of the goals of his desires but

Fig. 11-7   Four phases of Upper Paleolithic art.

Early Gravettian

Late Gravettian

also developed artistic skill for the intrinsic pleasure it gave him.

It is likely, however, that magical purposes never left his mind. This is especially evident in the case of his mural art, which is rarely found where it may easily be seen. The Upper Paleolithic artist did not adorn the walls of his home or the entrance to a cavern. On the contrary, his works of art are found deep in the earth's bowels, in the dark, mysterious caverns where the artist worked by the fitful smoky flare of a stone lamp. There he drew his animals: the woolly mammoth, bison, reindeer, wild cow, bear, woolly rhinoceros, horse, and ibex—most of them long since extinct in Europe. Again and again he painted red gashes on their bodies, gashes dripping with blood. He often showed projectile points piercing their flesh. Sometimes he drew hunting clubs beside the beasts. In Europe, he rarely drew actual hunting scenes, but contemporary artists who lived in eastern Spain to the south of the Pyrenees did. His paintings were effigies designed to play their part in imitative magic. In one form or another, he almost certainly performed mystic rites before his pictures, as the contemporary Austra-

lian aborigines do, and as the Winnebago Indians of Wisconsin did not so long ago (see page 240).

Not all magic is intended to do harm; some of it may be wholly beneficent. This is particularly true of fertility magic, magic that constitutes the main content of fertility cults. The Gravettians were especially fond of statuettes of pregnant women, of whom the Venus of Willendorf (Fig. 11-8) is the most famous. The parts of her torso that swell with pregnancy are given lavish exaggeration. The face, arms, legs, and feet are ignored. The artist has composed her with selective interest. The detail of her coiffure and that of the Venus of Brassempouy (Fig. 11-9) show that hairdo had its social, and probably cult, significance 20,000 years ago and that the hairdresser existed as an artisan long before our era.

Females were the more frequent objects of artistic representation, but masked male dancers were sometimes portrayed.

We may summarize by saying that the Upper Paleolithic art of Europe was a vividly representational art—an art of flesh and blood—and a

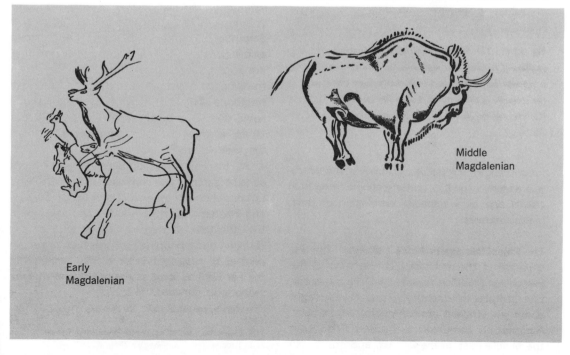

Middle
Magdalenian

Early
Magdalenian

Fig. 11-8 The Venus of Willendorf. A Gravettian goddess of fertility. She represents the idealization of a reproducing mother in which nearly every curve on the statuette is the segment of a perfect circle. (Courtesy of the American Museum of Natural History.)

functional art which aided in survival and which was eagerly used by a hunting people living in a glacial age as a symbolic expression of their major interests.

The Paleolithic age in Africa and Asia   The distribution of the archaeological remains of the Paleolithic tradition reveals that the basic culture complex as an entirety must have brought about an efficient environmental adjustment. Aurignacian complexes are found throughout the Middle East, in the Crimea, and on up into

Siberia, where they are associated with remains of semi-subterranean houses. Eastward, these complexes extend into India to the boundary of the old Acheulean and East Asian chopper- and flake-tool complex. Aurignacian and Gravettian traditions also occur in East Africa and the Mediterranean coastal areas as the Capsian tradition.

In Africa, the Middle Paleolithic Acheulean traditions went through a number of local developments, but a general Upper Paleolithic complex, called the *Sangoan,* spread over South Africa and the Congo basin. Related local traditions of East Africa and the Cape regions are known as *Fauresmith* and *Stillbay,* respectively. As a forest tradition, the Sangoan could not do away with the hand ax, as the Upper Paleolithic traditions of Europe did. Thus, in the Sangoan, the hand ax of the preceding Acheulean tradition was elongated to take on the form of a pick or broadened along the cutting edge and narrowed at the butt to take on a form very similar to a modern steel ax. The chipped-stone type is called a *tranchet* (Fr., anvil cutter). The more generalized hand ax evolved into two specialized artifacts in the Sangoan. The Sangoan equivalent of the Mousterian point consists of elongated biface lanceheads that are analogous to Solutrean blades far to the north. The Sangoan also included tanged and shouldered points that are analogous to those found in the Solutrean tradition. In other words, the Upper Paleolithic traditions of most of Africa evolved in much the same directions as those of Europe and Asia Minor, while at the same time developing certain distinctions.[23]

As for East and Southeast Asia, Movius's concise summary is sufficient: "Uninfluenced by contemporary innovations in Africa, Europe, and Western Asia, the archaic and very primitive tradition of making implements of the chopper and chopping-tool varieties either on pebbles or roughly tabular blocks persisted in the Far East as long as the practice of making stone tools survived."[24]

[23]For details, consult S. Cole, *The Prehistory of Africa,* pp. 164–196.
[24]H. L. Movius, Jr., "Old World Prehistory: Paleolithic," in A. L. Kroeber (ed.), *Anthropology Today,* p. 181.

Paleolithic migration to the New World Long before the Pleistocene ended, migrant bands of *Homo sapiens sapiens* crossed the land bridge at what is now the Bering Strait and moved down an ice-free corridor along the Mackenzie River Valley. They spread out across the Plains and around the face of the Wisconsin glacial lobes into the eastern part of the United States. Others pushed steadily southward; by 10,000 years ago, they had spread through Mexico and Middle America, over South America, and down to the very tip of the southern continent.

A *Homo sapiens sapiens* skull of 18,000 years ago was unearthed at Midland, Texas, in 1954, and there is evidence of a chopper-scraper Paleolithic complex of fourth glacial antiquity all through the West.[25]

The world was now man's home.[26]

SUMMARY

As the glacial age approached its final climax, man was evolving toward his present state.

Homo erectus was already becoming *Homo sapiens* during the course of the long second interglacial in Europe. The earliest transitional form is represented by *Homo sapiens steinheimensis*. Neandertal man evolved from the basic *Homo sapiens* pool to produce a specialized subspecies of *Homo sapiens* (*neandertalensis*) in the West. *Homo sapiens sapiens*, modern man, emerged outside Europe during the third interglacial and was fully established in Africa, Asia Minor, and South Asia by the beginning of the fourth glaciation. He arrived in Europe during the fourth glacial interstadial, quickly replacing the Neandertal subspecies.

The tool traditions begun by *Homo erectus* were continued by his immediate *Homo sapiens* successors. The Western traditions of Chellean and Clactonian axes and flake tools flowed smoothly into the Acheulean-Levalloisian complexes, and ultimately into the Mousterian tra-

Fig. 11-9 The Venus of Brassempouy, a stylistically "modern" fragment from Upper Paleolithic times. The hairstyle is quite different from that of the Venus of Willendorf. (Courtesy of the Musée des Antiquités Nationales.)

ditions of Neandertal man. Parallel developments occurred in Africa and South Asia outside the sphere of the Neandertal subspecies of *Homo sapiens*.

Homo sapiens sapiens, however, quickly developed flake and horn or bone inventories of specialized artifacts all over the northern half of the Western Hemisphere. He dropped the hand-ax tradition. In Africa, refined and specialized axes were developed in the Upper Paleolithic Sangoan.

In Asia, east of India, the chopper-tool and flake complex continued quite unmodified as long as the ancient Paleolithic hunting traditions survived.

[25]See R. F. Spencer, J. D. Jennings, et al., *The Native Americans*, chap. 1, for a clear and succinct summary of early man in the New World.
[26]Excepting, of course, that the Pacific Islands and other hard-to-get-to spots were not to be inhabited until later.

It is reasonable to infer that the tribes of the Upper Paleolithic had fully developed cultures on a level comparable to that of any recent society of skilled hunters such as the Bushmen, Eskimos, or nomadic Plains Indian tribes. They had the full mental equipment for development of religion and magic, familial and kinship systems, government and rudimentary law, folklore and mythology, and dance, painting, and sculpture. Although they are thought of as cave dwellers, they also built semisubterranean houses.

Wherever he went, *Homo sapiens* took fire and fire making with him. The remains of his art and his consistent burial of his dead give evidence that his imaginative intellect had achieved the humanistic level. Although organically he was still an animal, he had unconditionally climbed to the level of the *psychocultural-organic.*

He quickly spread out to inhabit the entire world. He was now ready to move beyond direct dependence on wild plants and animals as a savage hunter and gatherer. In his more germinal centers of cultural creativity, he stood ready to domesticate plants and animals and to revolutionize his life as a farmer and a founder of cities.

SELECTED READINGS

Brace, C. L.: "The Fate of the 'Classic' Neanderthals: A Consideration of Hominid Catastrophism" (*Current Anthropology,* Vol. 5, No. 1, 1964), pp. 3–46. A strongly colored, but highly informative, coverage of the question: What were the Neandertals and what happened to them?

Breuil, H.: *Four Hundred Centuries of Cave Art* (n.d.). Profusely illustrated, with descriptive analysis of the total range of Upper Paleolithic mural art by the great master of European prehistory.

Burkitt, M.: *The Old Stone Age* (4th ed., 1963). Chapters 9 through 14 describe the Upper Paleolithic cultures and art in some detail. Chatelperronian, Aurignacian, and Gravettian cultures are all described under the heading "Aurignacian," but the reader will be able to correlate Burkitt's descriptions with the categories used in this text.

Clark, G., and Piggott, S.: *Prehistoric Societies* (1965). Chapters 4 through 6 summarize the most modern view of the cultures of the Upper Paleolithic in the context of the cultures of recent hunters and fishers.

Coon, C. S.: *The Origin of Races* (1963). Page 472 to the end of the book catalogs and describes all the Upper Pleistocene fossils from Asia, Europe, and Africa.

Movius, H. L., Jr.: "Old World Prehistory: Paleolithic" in A. L. Kroeber (ed.), *Anthropology Today,* (1963), pp. 163–192. An authoritative summary of what is known of Old World manifestations of Paleolithic culture.

The dawn
of civilization

chapter 12

Homo erectus lived as a predator and developed toolmaking. The predatory way of Stone Age life was raised to a high level by *Homo sapiens sapiens* in the Late Pleistocene caves of Europe. Then, with the waning of the glaciers, he became a gatherer of small foodstuffs, fish, shellfish, and game, rather than a roving big-game hunter with an artistic flare. Around 9000 B.C., in the Middle East, he shifted from hunting and food gathering to intensive foraging and hunting, in which a band focused upon seed and vegetable collecting supplemented by hunting and fishing. Vegetation became a primary source of sustenance once again in human affairs. Big-game hunting continued in some parts of the Old World, as it did east of the Rockies in North America, but the diminution of many of the great Pleistocene mammals and their final disappearance from numerous areas of habitation forced most groups of men to change their living habits. They settled down in permanent locations and developed the *Mesolithic era of intensive foraging* as their form of adaptation to new environmental situations.

Intensive foraging led to the domestication of plants and animals, and to the establishment of settled farming communities. In their early phases (*ca.* 7500 to 4800 B.C. in the Middle East), these developments produced the *Early Neolithic era of incipient agriculture.* As the complex was expanded and refined through time, it became the *Full Neolithic era of developed agriculture* (4800 to 3800 B.C. in the Middle East). In time, ceremonial and market centers became towns and cities. Bronze was accidentally invented, and the first metallic tools and weapons were produced. Writing evolved from pictographic notations (see pages 303–306), while specialized artisans made diverse quantities of goods. Priests and kings organized religion and government. The urban revolution was on, the world of primitive man was being transformed, and the first civilizations were taking shape in the *Bronze Age era of regional development and florescence* (3800 to 2000 B.C. in the Middle East). In due course, organized states struggled for dominance and survival throughout a *Bronze and/or Iron Age of cyclical conquests* (2000 B.C. to 1 A.D. in the Middle East, continuing to the fall of Rome, A.D. 450, in Europe). South Asia and Middle America were following parallel courses at roughly the same time but whether they did so independently or in interaction, as well as the extent of their independence or interaction, is a much investigated and debated question.

The Mesolithic era of intensive foraging

In Africa, Europe, Asia Minor, and Asia, the lithic hallmark of Mesolithic technology is the microblade. Microblades were minute-to-small flakes of more or less geometric form that were set in a row along a piece of wood or bone to give a durable cutting edge to harpoons, swords, and, above all, sickles. Braidwood and Willey have summed up this distinguishing feature of technology as "the ecumenical . . . spread of the habit of producing microliths or bladelets for the making of composite tools."[1]

Equally important to the complex was the introduction of milling stones for grinding seeds. They may be of either the mortar-and-pestle type or the hollow-slab-and-rubber type. In America, this latter combination is called by the Mexican-Spanish names *metate* and *mano.* In English usage, *quern* or grinding stone is the term used.

The Natufian culture of Palestine In the Near East, where the Old World Mesolithic began, the complex has been thoroughly explored in the upper layers of the Palestinian caves and in open sites at Karim Shahir and Shanidar in Iraq. These sites date from around 9000 B.C. The Natufian assemblage, as it is called, contains flints of which 80 per cent are microliths. The rest are familiar survivors from the Upper Paleolithic—backed blades, awls, scrapers, and picks. Sculpture in stone, and bone awls, needles, and harpoon heads are particularly reminiscent of the Solutrean and Magdalenian work of an earlier age. So also is the inset blade "machete" with its animal-head haft, shown in Fig. 12-1. Other stone artifacts include metates, basalt pestles, hammerstones, and net sinkers. Bone fishhooks are also numerous. A distinctive sheen on many microliths results from the abrasive effect of thousands of stems of grass upon the surface of flint. A flint edge may crush and sever the cellular structure of a stem of long grass or wheat, but each living stem in turn takes its microscopic toll from the crystalline structure of the blade.

Although the Natufians of Palestine lived in caves and rock shelters where these were available, they also constructed round stone-walled

---

[1] R. J. Braidwood and G. R. Willey, "Conclusions and Afterthoughts," in R. J. Braidwood and G. R. Willey (eds.), *Courses toward Urban Life,* p. 333.

houses with plastered bell-shaped storage pits beneath the floors. Not only were the Natufians foragers, but they were also the earliest men known to store surplus harvests against lean times. They also took good care of their dead. At Mount Carmel, eighty-seven individuals were buried in one cemetery outside the rock shelter. Another Natufian population at Eynam made a large, round tomb with plastered walls to house its dead. Religion and the belief in immorality were incontrovertibly part of the Natufian life-way, and the souls of the dead were inseparably linked to the local territory in which the band, no longer wanderers, was rooted. Speaking of the Natufian tradition, Jean Perrot tells us:

The assemblage conveys the impression of an economy still essentially based on hunting and fishing and, by comparison with the preceding assemblages, on the intensified collection and consumption of seeds (including probably wild wheat and barley). We have no clear evidence of cultivation, but, from the subsequent development in Jericho, it is not unreasonable to infer that the economy of late Natufian times was already oriented toward the cultivation of cereals in the zone of their natural habitat.[2]

The Khartoum Mesolithic in Africa

The Mesolithic complex took many forms in varying local situations as it diffused south, east, north, and west. Four thousand years after the Natufian, it was well established along the upper reaches of the Nile in the form of the Early Khartoum, of which Desmond Clarke says:

In the mesolithic so-called Early Khartoum culture (5000–4000 B.C.) we see a group of very specialized food collectors, dependent upon food resources derived from the Nile and living in large "village" settlements along river banks. The stone industry, which is adapted to both hunting and fishing, is based on small blades and tools and includes some microliths and large crescents, the crescent adze flake, bone harpoons, net sinkers, and grindstones. Although these people grew no crops and had no domestic animals, their pottery, with its characteristic wavy line decoration, is a good indicator of a sedentary type of life.[3]

[2] J. Perrot, "Palestine-Syria-Cilicia," in Braidwood and Willey, *Courses toward Urban Life*, pp. 150–151.
[3] J. D. Clarke, "Africa South of the Sahara," in Braidwood and Willey, *Courses toward Urban Life*, p. 14.

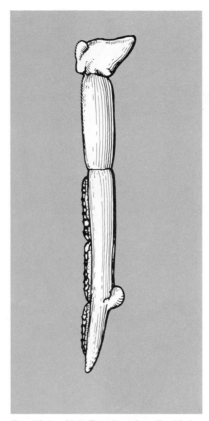

Fig. 12-1 Natufian "machete" with inset microlith blades. [After Kenneth P. Oakley, *Man the Tool-Maker*. By permission of the Trustees, British Museum (Natural History).]

Note that the introduction of pottery here, as in a number of other places, antedates the domestication of plants and animals.

Marginal Mesolithic manifestations When the microlithic tradition became established north and west of the Middle East, it included special adaptations to the forest environments that had replaced the glaciers. Mesolithic microlith traditions became established along the river deltas and shores of North Europe. The small flakes were set in harpoons and were used as arrowheads, rather than as sickle teeth, for these people harvested berries, which needed no cutting, rather than grasses; they were men

Fig. 12-2 Neolithic axes from northern France. Ax heads are roughed out by flaking and finished by polishing. Resilient staghorn sockets combine leverage with shock-absorbing elasticity. (Courtesy of the American Museum of Natural History.)

of the forests. Hence, their more characteristic tool is the straight-edged flint ax. The ax head, called the tranchet, was shaped by symmetrically chipping a flint nodule and partially smoothing the surfaces with an abrasive polishing stone while giving it a well-ground cutting edge. The finished and hafted ax was a great improvement over the old Lower Paleolithic hand axes, for the energetic force of the blow was increased many times—not only because of the leverage of the handle but also by virtue of the fact that the blow could be swung harder

without risk of injury to the hand, as had been the case when the hand itself held the ax head (Fig. 12-2).

The introduction of the bow in this complex also attests to the rising mechanical sophistication in hunting instruments. The presence of skeletons of domesticated dogs is a possible indication of the intensive nature of the hunting aspect of the culture. Man and dog may already have entered into a mutual-aid compact as a hunting team. If not, they were at least keeping company. At any rate, the predatory facet of the Paleolithic cultures continued in the Baltic specialization of the Mesolithic. Dugout canoes hewn from solid logs were another adaptive device. They made it possible to penetrate the swamps for hunting and to get from one shore settlement to another. But, "there are no mortars, pestles, or any stone implements other than such items as flint points and scrapers to suggest the exploitation of plants."[4]

The man of the lake and river cultures of the European woods was not exploiting farinaceous (cereal) plants because he was a forest dweller; hence he had no use for the equipage of the grassland peoples far to the south. Yet he

. . . was no longer a migrating, nomadic hunter. He had become specialized as a hunter of *Standwild*[5] and as a fisherman who rounded out his diet with fruits; he operated from relatively solid huts, which could not readily be disassembled and re-erected farther along the route, and thus was inhibited, just as by the dugouts, from transportation over a wider region.[6]

The European northerner was making no contribution to the agricultural revolution by domesticating new plants or animals. Nonetheless, he was working out a settled pattern of environmental exploitation of the woodland environment to the limits of his Mesolithic capabilities. In so doing, he shaped a way of life that was to be important to the men of the northern latitudes for a long time to come.

[4]H. T. Waterbok, "The Lower Rhine Basin," in Braidwood and Willey, *Courses toward Urban Life*, p. 233.
[5]That is, nonmigratory animals.
[6]H. Schwabedissen, "Northern Continental Europe," in Braidwood and Willey, *Courses toward Urban Life*, p. 260.

India and China to the east took up their manifestations of the Mesolithic, apparently in the Middle Eastern tradition, but the archaeology of this era is as yet too fragmentary there for much to be said about it.

The Mesolithic complex in the Americas Only the shadowiest outlines of the earliest arrivals in North America have been limned in the record of New World archaeology, but evidence is at hand to indicate the presence of hunters equipped with a Lower Paleolithic stone tradition[7] perhaps as early as 30,000 to 40,000 years ago.

Ten thousand years ago, Mesolithic food foragers were well established in the dry areas of the Western United States and in Mexico. Their traditions took the form of a complex called the *desert culture*. It became established in the Western desert area of the United States around 9000 B.C. (possibly earlier) and extended from Canada deep into Mexico. J. D. Jennings, who defined the desert culture early in the 1950s, summarizes its traits as follows:

. . . cave and overhang locations for settlement, bark or grass beds, seasonal gathering, intensive exploitation of resources, small—seed harvesting and special cooking techniques, basketry (twined predominant), netting and matting, fur cloth, tumpline, sandals (moccasins rare), atlatl, pointed hardwood dart shafts, varied (relatively small) projectile points, preferential use of glassy textured stone, flat milling stone and mano, a high percentage of crude scraper and chopper tools, digging stick, fire drill and hearth, bunt points, wooden clubs, horn-shaft wrenches, tubular pipes, use of olivella and other shells, vegetable quids.[8]

The presence of deer-hoof rattles and medicine bags is evidence of shamanism (see pages 479–482). Most significant, however, is the use of shoulder-blade grass cutters as the analogue of the Old World microlith sickle. The presence of grinding stones in all sites further confirms

Fig. 12-3   Ornaments of the late Bronze Age. Neolithic north woodsmen of the Baltic region creatively expressed their aesthetic interests in gold and bronze jewelry, among which bracelets and pins were important. (Photograph by Lennart Larsen of the Danish National Historical Museum, Copenhagen.)

the fundamental importance of seed harvesting in the new life of postglacial man in the New World and the Old. Hunting of small animals rounded out the subsistence diet of these early Americans. In Utah and Nevada (the Great Basin), climatic variations did not seriously alter the ecology, which remained consistently marginal desert around the fluctuating lake shores. Population has always been sparse and meager in this area, which is incapable of supporting grasses outside the limited edges of freshwater basins. Hence, the desert culture remained virtually unchanged from 9000 B.C. to A.D. 1850 and did not contribute to the development of agriculture in the Western Hemisphere.

The Mesolithic foraging complex of the New World developed quite independently of that of the Old World, so far as one can tell. The situation seems to have been one of parallel development. Small bands of men were settled in favorable locales near good sources of water and were squeezing their land for all it was worth in terms of plants and readily accessible fish and small game. As Emil Haury has written of the people of the desert culture: "The long and inti-

---

[7]American archaeologists also call this phase the *lower lithic, protolithic, percussion stage* and the *pre-projectile stage.* See A. D. Krieger, "Early Man in the New World," in J. D. Jennings and E. Norbeck (eds.), *Prehistoric Man in the New World*, pp. 42–51.

[8]J. D. Jennings, "The Desert West," in J. D. Jennings and E. Norbeck, *op. cit.,* pp. 154–155.

mate experience of a wide range of plant life undoubtedly saved them during adverse climatic shifts, for changing the dependency from desirable to less-desirable, and perhaps hardier, plants was made relatively easy."[9]

In the Middle East, in Mexico, and perhaps in Southeast Asia, such intimate environmental knowledge led to the domestication of plants and animals: the phase of cultural development known as *incipient agriculture,* which occurred during the Early Neolithic age and is the immediate prelude to the dawn of civilization.

The Early Neolithic era of incipient agriculture

The domestication of both plants and animals was a gradual process that took place in a number of different parts of the world along independent lines. Domestication consists merely in controlled cultivation and husbandry. A domesticated plant is one that is useful to man and is cultivated by him. Dandelions are noxious weeds in the lawn to most persons, but cultivated dandelions may be purchased from vegetable stands in city areas settled by Italian-Americans. The first steps in plant cultivation were probably taken in the area of weed elimination and control (a weed is any plant that is held to be undesirable). A patch of wild plants was tended, and weeds were cut or uprooted. The Kwakiutl Indians' care for their wild clover patches is an example of this. Clover beds were the properties of specific families who dug them for their roots. The main roots, however, were never dug, and pieces that were not considered good for food were, if they had been dug up, replaced in the ground for future growth.[10]

Real domestication begins, however, when seeds, roots, or shoots are deliberately planted or are stored from one season to the next for later planting. Not only does this call for foresightedness and self-restraint (you cannot eat

your seed and plant it, too), but it also requires preparation of the soil. The idea of plant domestication was hard to come by, but once established it spread over all continents and the isles of the Pacific in a matter of 8,000 years. Even before the age of exploration, during which European traits were disseminated around the world, the bulk of mankind's societies consisted of preagricultural gardeners.

Lightly forested upland grass areas may strike the reader as strange places for the origins of primitive gardening, but new evidence does not support the old theory that gardening first began in irrigation oases of the arid river valleys of the Old and New Worlds. Irrigation comes later, and it is where the grasses grow naturally but not too densely that the process of plant domestication begins. Primitive wild wheat and barley grow in a natural state at elevations of from 2,000 to 4,300 feet above sea level in the Anatolian highlands of modern Turkey and on the hilly flanks of the Fertile Crescent, which swings from the Nile along the eastern edge of the Mediterranean and down the Tigris and Euphrates Rivers (see Fig. 12-4).

Çatal Hüyük A *hüyük* in Turkish is a mound built up by generations of village or town life on a given spot, such as the one Schliemann found at Troy. Ever since excavations were begun at one such hüyük in southern Turkey in 1961, under the direction of James Mellaart, the picture of Early Neolithic culture has been undergoing rapid change. The first three years of work (1961 to 1963) were sufficient to establish that barley, wheat, lentils, and peas were thoroughly domesticated and were producing surplus yields in Anatolia by 6385 B.C. $\pm$ 101 years,[11] sheep were domesticated and sheared for wool, which was woven into fine cloth. Cattle were domesticated by 5800 B.C. $\pm$ 92 years. An amazingly rich inventory of specialized handicrafts included beautifully worked wooden bowls

[9]E. W. Haury, "The Greater American Southwest," in Braidwood and Willey, *Courses toward Urban Life,* p. 112.
[10]E. S. Curtis, *The Kwakiutl,* p. 43.

[11]Carbon 14 dates for Çatal Hüyük were graciously made available by F. Rainey, director of the University of Pennsylvania Museum. They have since been published in *Radiocarbon,* Vol. 7, 1965.

and boxes; baskets; obsidian and flint daggers, spearheads, lance heads, arrowheads, knives, scrapers, awls, and sickle blades; jewelry of bone, shell, and copper; obsidian mirrors; and bone awls, punches, knives, ladles, spoons, bowls, spatulas, bodkins, belt hooks, toggles, and pins. This was a creative and well-off people.

The town itself (for that is what existed at Çatal Hüyük) was a solid community structure of adjoining rooms not dissimilar to the Indian pueblos of the Southwestern United States. Like the pueblos, the rooms had to be entered through an entrance in the roof, which also served as a smoke vent for the fires in the hearth and oven on the floor beneath. This structure made a defensive citadel of the community house, and the doorless and windowless walls of mud brick gave added protection from flooding by the river on whose banks the prehistoric town stood.

Numerous shrines are scattered throughout the complex, with full-sized clay cattle heads protruding from the walls, statuettes of a fertile mother goddess accompanied by a son and daughter, as well as of a bearded consort god seated on a bull. Layer after layer of religious murals, painted on the walls and plastered over to make way for the next painting, bespeak a vital and highly developed cult and religious belief system, much concerned with the mystery of life and death. Life-associated scenes, done in symbolic red paint, are on the west walls of the shrine rooms. Death scenes created in black paint are on the east side.

Mellaart expressed puzzlement after the conclusion of the 1963 dig that no workshops had been exposed among the two-hundred rooms that had by then been excavated:

Somewhere in the mound there must be the workshops of the weavers and basketmakers; the matmakers; the carpenters and joiners; the men who made the polished stone tools; the beadmakers . . . the flint and obsidian knappers . . . the merchants of skin, leather and fur . . . the workers in bone . . . the carvers of wooden bowls and boxes; the mirror makers; the bowmakers . . . the merchants and traders who obtained all the raw material; and finally the artists—the carvers of statuettes, the modelers and the painters.[12]

It could well be, however, that the town itself was a ceremonial and administrative nucleus for a number of farmsteads and cottage industries dispersed about the countryside—a regional community. Future excavations will provide the answer.

Mellaart's view that the city's wealth depended on its control of a well-organized trade carries conviction. The heart of the trade appears to have been the obsidian that came from the volcanoes some 50 miles away—obsidian that found its way to Jericho and Jarmo (see below) and to Cyprus in the Mediterranean. Clearly, the social, political, and theological structure of Çatal Hüyük and the environs over which it held sway was strong. It would seem that the people of the town were too specialized in trade, politics, and religion to have spent much time in farming. They hunted for sport and game food; bones of wild animals are profuse in the refuse dumps, and excavations in 1965–66 uncovered wall paintings of hunts containing hundreds of human and animal figures. But compact as it is, it hardly seems likely that a town which covered only 1/20 square mile (32 acres) could have housed so diversified a productive system within its confines.

The town at Çatal was burned out and rebuilt a number of times between its Early Neolithic founding *ca.* 6500 B.C. and its final abandonment in the Hittite period *ca.* 1900 B.C.

One cannot help being impressed, on the basis of what is now known from the excavations at Çatal Hüyük, at how rapidly the transition from Paleolithic hunting bands to regionally organized communities occurred, once the domestication of plants and animals—the food revolution—had taken place in the Middle East. The rapidity with which the cultural explosion occurred indicates how much more fully *Homo sapiens* was utilizing his intelligence potential

[12] J. Mellaart, "A Neolithic City in Turkey" (*Scientific American*, Vol. 210, No. 4, 1964), p. 99.

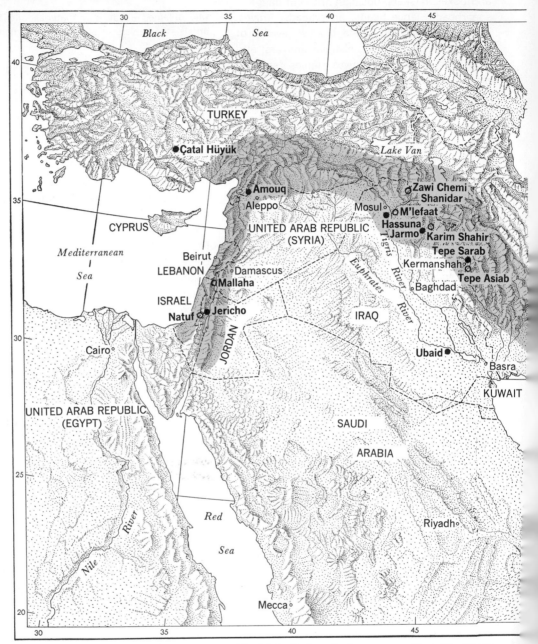

Fig. 12-4 Early agriculture communities of the Middle East. The major known sites in Anatolia and the Fertile Crescent. (Adapted from Robert J. Braidwood, "The Agricultural Revolution," *Scientific American.*)

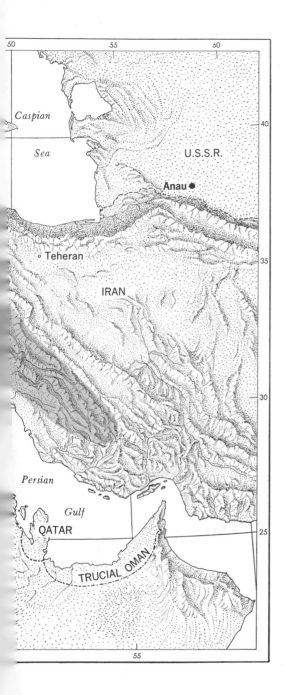

than he had in Late Paleolithic times. Once man had evolved a nervous system capable of producing language and culture on anything more than the most rudimentary level—and this was achieved in the *Homo sapiens* of third interglacial times—cultural adaptation was henceforth the product of cumulative experience, limited mostly by the productive potential in food and energy control that could be marshaled. This has been true for at least the last 100,000 years of human experience. There is little indication, which can only be indirect, of genetic change in man's nervous equipment during all the time that cultural development has moved on apace.

Jericho and Jarmo   During the 1950s, prior to the discovery of what lay beneath Çatal Hüyük, Jericho and Jarmo were two sites of intense interest and excitement. Jericho is actually the biblical city that rested on top of Tell es-Sultan (*tell* is the Arabic equivalent of the Turkish *hüyük*).

Jericho   Underneath the 70 feet of debris and dirt, the English expeditions, directed by Miss Kathleen Kenyon, uncovered a fortified town at 900 feet below sea level, where an ancient spring creates an oasis. On the bedrock are the clay-paved floors of Natufian huts whose burned posts have given a carbon 14 date of 7800 B.C. ± 21 years.

In higher levels, the huts covered 10 acres and were surrounded by a stone wall 6 feet thick and 12 feet high with a 30-foot tower at one point. The oasis was a valuable spot and thus a mark for marauders, and it was heavily defended. The village, or a section of it, was burned out, and its charcoal has been given a carbon 14 date of 6850 B.C. ± 210 years. It is thus several centuries older than Çatal—assuming the carbon 14 dates to be comparably correct.

Although actual grain from Jericho has not been reported on, serrated sickle blades and a specialized wedge-shaped metate attest to its well-established use as food. House compounds consist of walled, rectangular rooms built of adobe bricks and organized around a central courtyard, where outdoor cooking was done.

Fig. 12-5 A goddess from Çatal Hüyük giving birth. (Courtesy of Arlette Mellaart.)

Fig. 12-6 Skull of early Neolithic man from Jericho with face modeled in clay. (Photograph by Kathleen Kenyon, from Kathleen Kenyon, *Digging up Jericho*, Ernest Boon Ltd., London. Courtesy of the Jericho Excavation Fund.)

The household pattern was different from that at Çatal, for here the town was enclosed by a fortified wall. Beautifully modeled reproductions were made of heads of the deceased (Fig. 12-6) and were buried in clusters. Yet in spite of their skill in ceramic sculpture, the Jerichoans made no pottery, and their technological inventory was in no way comparable to that of Çatal to the north. Jericho was marginal to the centers of early domestication of plants and animals.

Jarmo   Jarmo, a village-farming community in northeastern Iraq, was brought to the center of the stage by Robert Braidwood, of the Oriental Institute and department of anthropology at the University of Chicago. Braidwood has enlisted the able collaboration of expert geologists and biologists in his study of the total cultural and ecological setting as it existed around 5600 B.C., when domesticated wheat and barley had just been established in this area. Jarmo is but one of dozens of Early Neolithic incipient agriculture village sites dotting the countryside in Iraq. Its significance derives from the fact that it was the one selected for intensive excavation.

Braidwood and Howe give a summary of Jarmo's revelations:

1. It does yield positive traces of a village-farming community way of life; several-roomed rectangular houses within villages of some degree of permanence; the remains of at least domesticated wheat, barley, probably the dog and the goat, and possibly even the sheep, with the pig appearing in the upper levels; the conventional artifactual traits of the "neolithic," with pottery appearing before the phase is completed. As they pertain—by reasonable but *not* absolutely guaranteed interpretations—to food production, these artifacts are querns and rubbing stones, mortars and pestles, flint sickle blades with sheen, occasional subfloor storage pits, a peculiar form of oven, possibly for the parching of grain, a few large celts (hoes?), and an occasional large pierced stone ball (digging stick weight?). Overwhelmingly, however, it is the demonstrated presence of the plant and animal domesticates and the apparent year-round permanence of a village of perhaps twenty-five well-built houses that make Jarmo impressive for our present purposes. It should remain clear, however, that a very significant portion of the Jarmo subsistence pattern still depended upon collected foods.

2. Jarmo does indicate firm traces of longer-range trade, especially evidenced by the great bulk of obsidian (closest natural flow near Lake Van in Anatolia) in its chipped-stone category. We suggest that this first indication of a bulk carrying trade—with its implications of attendant exchanges of ideas—may well presage a reversal of the above-mentioned trend toward regional specialization and localized intensification.[13]

Conspicuous among artifacts from Jarmo are the pecked and abraded stone mortars, pestles, and grinding stones—the millers for the wheat and barley that the Jarmoans had tamed. Compared with the dwellers of Çatal Hüyük, the hill villagers of Jarmo were somewhat "backwoods"; their culture was a good five hundred years behind that which was being enjoyed at Çatal. Comparisons of Çatal, Jericho, and Jarmo indicate the rapid establishment of village and town settlements based upon an incipient agricultural foundation, with specialization sustained by trade in which the villages served as regional market centers. Such comparisons also indicate that the domestication of plants probably occurred first in Anatolia rather than on the hilly flanks of the Fertile Cresent, as had been thought in the 1950s.

Fig. 12-7 Excavation site at Jarmo. The grid pattern of test pits may be clearly seen. This makes it possible to get a statistically representative sample of the contents of the entire site without expending the time, effort, and money to strip the entire area. (Courtesy of Robert J. Braidwood; from Scientific American.*)*

The domestication of wheat and barley   Charred kernels of wheat and barley and impressions of kernels in clay are the proof of domestication of plants at Çatal and Jarmo. The wheats at Jarmo are *Triticum aegilopoides* (wild einkorn, which has a single seed per spikelet) and *Triticum monococcum* (domesticated einkorn). Wild einkorn is still a common grass in many parts of Asia Minor, and domesticated einkorn is still cultivated in hilly regions with thin soils in the Middle East, although it is much inferior to the free-threshing strains of hybrid wheat which have been found at Çatal and which were introduced into Europe from Anatolia during the sixth millennium B.C.[14] In

[13]R. J. Braidwood and B. Howe, "Southwestern Area beyond the Lands of the Mediterranean Littoral," in Braidwood and Willey, *Courses toward Urban Life,* p. 138. Note, however, that such trade at Çatal Hüyük antedates Jarmo by 1,000 years. (By permission from the Werner-Gren Foundation for Anthropological Research, New York.)
[14]Mellaart, *op. cit.,* p. 97.

other words, plant husbandry in Neolithic Turkey was well in advance of that to the southeast, as were other domestic arts.

Two-row barley (*Hordeum spontaneum*) is present in quantity at Jarmo. Six-row barley, a less primitive form, occurs further south and also at Çatal Hüyük to the northwest. Barley is usually found associated with wheat throughout the Old World Neolithic and later phases of culture. Wheat, however, is the foundation crop and "staff of life" for all the Old World village-farming communities and civilizations. Barley is an adjunct. Carbonized field peas, lentils, and vetchling at Çatal and Jarmo show that these early horticulturalists also had the wherewithal for basic vegetable soup, and the remains of their pottery show that they had the vessels in which to cook it.

The domestication of animals   The animal remains at Jarmo include the skeletons of goats, sheep, cattle, pigs, horses, asses, and dogs, all of which inhabited the highland in a wild state. Dogs had already been domesticated elsewhere during the Mesolithic, but there is no certain evidence that they were at Jarmo, although pottery models of doglike figures with upturned tails would indicate the canine presence. Changes in the shape of the horns of goats at Jarmo indicate that only these animals were domestically bred, but neither the cow nor other animals were domesticated at Jarmo. However it is clear that sheep and cows were domesticated at Çatal by the time Jarmo was founded. The high proportion of butchered young billy goats is further indirect evidence that the goats at Jarmo were domesticated. Immature males were evidently slaughtered for eating, while only a few were kept to mature as breeding studs. Females were allowed to grow up for breeding and possibly for milking. Milk would have provided a very good food supplement for the lean preharvest seasons.

The kind of ecological specialization that leads to pastoralism has recently been discovered at Tepe Sarab, a herder's campsite of the same age as Jarmo, which lies about 100 miles to the southeast at an elevation of 3,000 feet. It has goats, but no metates or manos. The Tepe Sarabians apparently traded goats and possibly cheese for meal in the lower-lying farm villages.

The Full Neolithic era of developed agriculture

The Full Neolithic—the phase of cultural evolution in which man depended mainly on gardening and the exploitation of domesticated animals for food and sustenance—came out of the simple beginnings of the previous era, as prehistoric men experimented with selective breeding and domestication of more plants and animals. Communal life focused in the village or town, and although it may have been necessary to move the villages periodically as fields became exhausted, except for full pastoralists and marginal hunters, the nomadic way of life was gone.

Domesticated plants and animals Wheat and rye, plus the goat, sheep, and dog, as already indicated, had been domesticated by the end of the era of incipient agriculture. During the era of developed agriculture, the remaining basic cereals, rye, flax, and millet were added to the list of domesticated plants of Asia Minor, western Asia, Africa, and Europe. Wheat, however, remained the fundamental foodstuff.

In Southeast Asia, apparently because of stimulus diffusion (see page 83), the cultivation of rice was developed as the staple food source for Neolithic societies located in the tropics, where wheat and barley will not grow. Yams and taro were also added.

Wild Paleolithic cattle (*Bos primigenius*) provided the stock from which, by 3500 B.C., the humped domestic cattle of India and Mesopotamia were derived. The cult of the sacred cow, already established at Çatal by 5500 B.C., spread with domesticated cattle in a great arc from eastern Africa, through Egypt and Mesopotamia, and into India.

The pig did not fare so well, and it was not domesticated at Çatal. It was hunted in Mesolithic times and has continued to be throughout historic ages. But the pig is nonmigratory, and could be herded only by thoroughly settled farmers. As Zeuner writes: "It is indeed difficult to imagine how a nomadic community, and even tribes that changed their habitations twice annually according to the season, could cope with the art of pig-driving, since the animal is notoriously unaccommodating in this respect."[15] Neolithic farmers achieved domestication of the succulent pig at the same time that they domesticated the cow, however.

Although wild horses were of much interest to Upper Paleolithic artists, no horses were domesticated in Mesolithic times. Horses are free-spirited and skittish. There is nothing timid about them, and taming a wild horse is no gentle operation. Possibly the first domestication of the horse occurred in the Steppe country of southwestern Russia and Asia, where gardeners found their country becoming desiccated and so

[15]F. E. Zeuner, *A History of Domesticated Animals*, p. 260.

combined sporadic gardening with horse no-madism. This took place around 2500 B.C. As a way of life, it swept across the Steppes and spawned the later Mongol hordes of historic times.

Other domesticates of the Neolithic Old World are the buffalo and yak, elephant, camel, ass and mule, cat, ferret, mongoose, rabbit, and dormouse. It is not likely that birds were domesticated in Neolithic times, however.

Artifacts In contrast to Paleolithic hand axes, Neolithic adzes and axes were generally hafted to a handle. In Scandinavia, this was ingeniously done by gluing the polished stone ax head (celt) into a staghorn socket, which in turn was hafted to a wooden handle. The softer socket acted as a shock absorber to reduce the likelihood of splitting the handle as well as to cut down the shock that would jar the wood-cutter's arm with each heavy stroke. Elsewhere in the Neolithic, wooden drills and wet sand were commonly used to drill holes through stone ax heads into which the handle could be fitted.

War clubs and maces became differentiated from industrial axes. In the Middle East, they were pear- or ball-shaped. In North Africa and the Danube region, disk-shaped club heads were more prevalent. This type spread to the north in Middle Neolithic times.

A prevalence of flint arrowheads throughout all Neolithic deposits, except for those of the Lower Neolithic in the Balkans and parts of the Near East, attests to the wide use of the bow and arrow for both hunting and war. In the area where the bow was little used, baked-clay sling pellets show that the weapon with which David felled Goliath was not just a Hebraic device, by any means. Daggers of flint and bone, as well as the familiar scrapers and blade sickles, continue well into the Bronze Age.

Perhaps most significant of all is the manifold development of pottery, which fits in with the making of gruel, so important to the diet of Neolithic man. Early Neolithic pottery is usually plain and undecorated, and the forms are sim-

Fig. 12-8 Early Neolithic pottery from Halaf. (Courtesy of The University Museum, Philadelphia.)

ple and clean-lined. The body color of the clay varied from area to area, according to the nature of the natural clay and the additives put into it (see pages 270–271, on the techniques of pottery making). Although plain ware continued to be used for kitchen purposes, painted and decorated pots were usually developed quite rapidly. The possibilities for distinctive variations led to numerous distinctive local types. Thus, Graham Clark describes the Late Neolithic pottery of Tell Halaf, in Assyria, as:

. . . outstanding on account of the variety of its forms and above all of its painted decoration and because of the excellence of its firing; but it was still hand-made, and there is no reason to think it was necessarily or even probably made by whole-time potters. In addition to dishes and flasks the forms included bowls with sharp-shouldered bodies and flaring necks and bowls and flasks on hollow stands. The decoration comprised geometric patterns like triangles, chevrons, lozenges, chequers, stars, Maltese crosses, quatrefoils and rosettes; stipples, including egg and dot; and stylized representations of men and animals, including designs based on the bull's head. It was applied to a buff or cream slip by glaze paint. At the climax of the industry the decoration was polychrome; red, orange, yellow and black paints being used, sometimes highlighted by white spots. The pottery was apparently fired to temperatures up to 1200° C. in great domed kilns with rectangular annexes. . . .[16]

Settlements More important than pottery or artifacts were the new gardening techniques that were developed in the Full Neolithic in the

[16]G. Clark, *World Prehistory*, p. 86. (By permission from Cambridge University Press, Cambridge, England).

great river valleys of Mesopotamia (the Euphrates and Tigris), Egypt (the Nile), and western Pakistan (the Indus). In the fertile floodwater lowlands, it was possible to carry on intensive gardening to the extent that continuous settlements could develop along the Nile, while in Mesopotamia and Pakistan, full cities emerged. The development of towns into cities changed the whole scheme of life for more and more of humanity from that time onward. Civilization means "city making." Where civilization took over, the primitive tribesman moved into town and became an urbanite (of whom the most sophisticated were "urbane") or he remained on his land as a satellite peasant villager. Of the first towns and cities, the essential characteristic described by Henri Frankfort is worth noting:

Now one may say that the birth of Mesopotamian civilization, like its subsequent growth, occurred under the sign of the city. To understand the importance of the city as a factor in the shaping of society, one must not think of it as a mere conglomeration of people. Most modern cities have lost the peculiar characteristic of individuality which we can observe in cities of Renaissance Italy, or Medieval Europe, of Greece, and of Mesopotamia. In these countries the physical existence of the city is but an outward sign of close communal affinities which dominate the life of every dweller within the walls. The city sets its citizens apart from the other inhabitants of the land. It determines their relations with the outside world. It produces an intensified self-consciousness in its burghers, to whom the collective achievements are a source of pride. The communal life of prehistoric times became civil life.[17]

Although in America, the Maya built a civilization without cities, and although Egypt, too, achieved a civilized level before it developed cities, it is reasonable to hold with the great English prehistorian V. Gordon Childe that the food-producing revolution of the Mesolithic and Early Neolithic ages laid the basis for the urban revolution of the Late Neolithic age and the Bronze Age. The urban revolution fostered the aspects of civilization that have been of enduring significance for humanity.

[17]H. Frankfort, *The Birth of Civilization in the Near East*, p. 48.

The urban culture of Mesopotamia: Al Ubaid and the Sumerian civilization

The events that took place in the Tigris-Euphrates Valley serve as a good model of the process of urban evolution in its early phase and of the making of cities and the development of civilized ways of life. For this reason, the major aspects of the emergence of Sumerian civilization (4000 to 500 B.C.) are surveyed in the next pages.

The Ubaid phase The alluvial delta of southern Iraq offered neither timber nor stone, but it was rich in soil and water. At Al Ubaid, an early village, located on a low rise of land near the Euphrates, was settled around 4000 B.C. by Iraqi highlanders who brought a well-developed subsistence economy of developed agriculture into the river bottoms with them. They had microlithic sickles or a new type of sickles made of hard-fired clay. They made themselves simple wattle-and-daub-walled huts (see page 255) with palm-stalk frames. They also made Quonset-type huts of reed bundles set vertically and arched to meet along the center top, a type of construction that survives in the Euphrates delta to this day in great numbers. But elsewhere, more impressive Ubaid towns were constructed of adobe bricks, such as at Çatal Hüyük, 1,300 years earlier.

The coming Bronze Age was adumbrated by the presence of a few cast-copper tools and axes and more numerous fired-clay copies of them. Forecasting a most important feature of the early civilizations were the sizable temple structures of the Ubaid towns. Monumental public works of a religious nature were the most visually prominent feature.

The Sumerian protoliterate phase As the name of this phase indicates, it is marked by the appearance of the earliest writing. The evidence is found in the temples in the form of clay tablets bearing signs and pictograms incised with reeds. The predynastic texts have not yet been deciphered, but the contents of those of the early dynasties are prosaic and hardly religious. Yet they shed a flood of light on the role of the temple priests as organizers of work and society. The tablets list wages paid and goods received and often include lists of names. Religion was obviously of extreme importance, as attested by the very large temples constructed on artificial mounds.

Pottery had for some time been turned on a wheel and produced commercially in quantity for daily use. Copper and silver bowls and dishes were now wrought for ceremonial use or display. Statues were carved and used in association with the temples. Clearly a vigorous cultural flowering was under way.

The Sumerian early dynastic phase: full civilization (3200 to 2800 B.C.) Technologically, the most significant development is the harnessing of the ass and oxen to solid-wheeled chariots and to plows and carts. Agricultural efficiency was reaching a peak, while trade and wars were spreading. Each citizen, whether artisan, fisher, or soldier, was, in the early phases of development, also a part-time farmer. As the culture expanded, some soldiers and governmental officers became full-time professionals, as were a number of the priests and traders.

The city was the political unit in relations with the outside world. In the protoliterate phase, it had governed itself in matters of war and intercity relations through a democratic town council. Matters of boundary conflicts, safe conduct, and irrigation were its main concern. Internal organization of town activities focused on the temples. Each city "belonged" to a god, and every citizen belonged to a temple district and served the god of his temple. Allotments of land, work assignments, and raw materials were designated by the head priest-administrator of the temple district. Each workman had to deliver a specified amount of produce; anything beyond this was his own. Some goods went to maintain the priests, and much was redistributed among the producing populace. Thus, the division of labor and the economic exchange that are necessary to effective civilization were achieved—in this case without a market system. A fair part of the Sumerian

Fig. 12-9   Stages in the development of cuneiform writing. Visual symbols impressed in clay gave the first permanence to the spoken word. (Courtesy of The University Museum, Philadelphia.)

cities' output was exported in exchange for precious stones, metals, and incense for the temples and for necessities for the people. The head priest-administrator of the temple of the god of the city distributed major tasks among the various temple units. In this way the walls were maintained, as well as the irrigation systems that were being elaborated for more effective food production.

In Sumer, in the early dynasties, the system of exaction of labor was not particularly exploitative. People were in effect taxed for producing more than they themselves were allowed to keep. But through highly organized effort, each received or retained a good deal more than he could have produced on his own or than his Mesolithic progenitors had been able to enjoy. He was induced to play his part wholeheartedly by acceptance of an elaborate theology of catastrophism and beneficence. Floods and pestilence were common disasters. Anxieties born of human insecurity and intellectual concern with cause and effect had elaborated the supernatural in explanation and relief of tensions. Gods properly served could benefit rather than punish man, and the Sumerian willingly served.

Every urban civilization must find some way of getting surpluses out of farmers and workers. Otherwise, a society could never build above

Fig. 12.10   A group of alabaster Sumerian temple statuettes from the Abu Temple in Tell Asmar, Iraq. In the theocratic system of Sumerian civilization, the gods and their priests were of first-rank importance and were given visual manifestation. (Courtesy of The Oriental Institute, The University of Chicago.)

the lowest Mesolithic levels. Many later civilizations used force and gross exploitation, but in Sumerian cities this was not the case. The symbols on seals and in art all referred to the gods, and the gods, as Frankfort says, "were also symbols of a collective identity. Each city projected its sovereignty into the deity which it conceived as its owner."[18] Yet even in Sumer at the city of Lagash, the priests were in time so enriching themselves that the political arm had to put a rein on them. In turn, some political heads (*ensi*) became extorters themselves.

Sumer does not represent in detail the world view or social structure of Egypt or the Indus civilizations or of the myriad of civilizations that

[18]Frankfort, *op. cit.*, p. 57.

were born in Sumer's tradition as indirect inheritors of the "great idea." Egypt seems to have developed independently and simultaneously, but that is another story. Sumer, however, is the archetype of Old World civilizations.

[prototype]

Characteristics of early civilization

In this account, Sumer serves the purpose of epitomizing the process of the urban revolution that followed hard upon the food revolution. It exemplifies the ten characteristics of early civilization specified by Childe:[19]

1. The great enlargement of an organized population means a much wider level of social integration (organized social interaction) than ever occurred in any prehistoric tribal society of food gatherers and hunters.

2. Social means for collection of "surplus" production of farmers and artisans are devised to produce a central accumulation of goods for "managed" use.

3. Specialization of production among work-

[19]V. G. Childe, *The Dawn of European Civilization; What Happened in History; Man Makes Himself.*

ers is instituted, along with systems of distribution and exchange of goods.

4. Specialization and exchange are expanded beyond the city in the development of far-reaching trade.

5. Monumental public works in the form of temples, palaces, storehouses, and irrigation systems are constructed and maintained through the centrally organized use of surplus productive time not devoted to food production or basic manufactures.

6. Highly developed art forms give expression to symbolic identification and aesthetic enjoyment.

7. The art of writing is developed to facilitate the process of organization and management. It is later expanded to other uses, especially theological and protoscientific.

8. Arithmetic, geometry, and astronomy are developed as rational thinking techniques. This constitutes the initiation of exact, predictive science.

9. Well-structured political organization comes about in which membership based on residence replaces political identification based on kinship.

10. A privileged ruling class of religious, political, and military functionaries organizes and directs the whole system.

All this, as we have described it for the first 1,000 years of Sumer's evolution (Ubaid through the early dynasties), took place in what Julian Steward identifies as a regular phase of civilizational development in early times, and labels *the era of regional development and florescence*. It is a time in which the first magnificent realization of the human potential is seen, the first era of cultural creativeness on the grand scale.

The Bronze and Iron eras of cyclical conquests

Once well established, the early civilizations consistently turned to war and conquest, as characterized in the last 2,200 years of Sumerian history (2800 to 550 B.C.).

The diagnostic features of this era, according to Steward, are the emergence of large-scale

Fig. 12-11   A map of Nippur incised in a clay tablet. (Courtesy of The University Museum, Philadelphia.)

militarism, the extension of political and economic domination over wide areas (or empires), a strong tendency toward urbanization, and the construction of fortifications. In the social structure, priest-warriors constituted the ruling groups, usually under a divine monarch, whose importance is revealed in elaborate status burial. Social classes now tended to become frozen into hereditary classes, in contrast to the society of the previous era, which probably permitted individuals some upward mobility through personal achievement. Gods of war became prominent in the pantheon of deities.

There were no important technological changes in the era of cyclical conquest. Bronze appeared in Peru, Mesopotamia, and Egypt, and was used for weapons and ornaments, but it contributed little to the production of food or other goods and added no new forms of energy to the culture. Iron, though not an Iron Age culture, appeared in China. The principal change in manufactures was a strong trend toward standardization and mass production, with a concomitant sacrifice of aesthetic freedom and variety. Large-scale trade within the empires, and even beyond, brought the beginnings of a special commercial class, but coin-

Fig. 12-12 Bronze Age pictographs from Sweden.

conquistadores of Spain, early in the sixteenth century.

But here we bring our studies of Old World prehistory to a close, for in the era of cyclical conquests, writing is developed in the Old World, and *history* begins.

Parallel developments in the New World

While the hillmen of the Near East were taming wheat and barley, and subsequently chick peas, beans, lentils, rye, flax, and sundry vegetables, and so laying the foundations for the first civilizations of Mesopotamia and the Nile, the American Indians of the highlands of southern Mexico were engaged in the same process at almost the same time.

During the first half of this century, it was believed that corn was wholly the product of the crossing of one or another of two tassel grasses (teosinte or *Tripsacum*) with an unknown wild grass. No wild corn had ever been discovered. In the 1950s, however, the picture suddenly changed when the pollen of wild corn was unexpectedly discovered in borings of 80,000-year-old soil taken from the prehistoric lake bottoms where Mexico City now stands. Corn did exist before man came upon the scene.

The oldest known corn at the time had been uncovered in Bat Cave, New Mexico, in 1948. It had a carbon 14 date of from 2000 to 3000 B.C. The Bat Cave corn was primitive when compared with the corn Indians were growing when the Spaniards first arrived, but it was far from being wild corn, and it was obviously by no means the earliest domesticated corn.

Ten years later (1958), R. S. MacNeish began a dedicated and systematic search for the natal place of corn. Two years of searching out caves and rock shelters in the Guatemalan and Honduran highlands and the hill country of Chiapas in southeastern Mexico brought no results. But in 1960, the thirty-ninth cave tested in Puebla, Mexico, paid off handsomely. Minuscule corncobs, no bigger than a filter tip and bearing kernels that were best studied under a

age and an efficient monetary system were not yet developed.[20]

Civilizations rose and fell, prospered and faltered. Conquerors rode back and forth across the lands with sword and fire. Artisans learned how to smelt iron to make better weapons and improved plowshares and pots. In the New World, there was no smelting of iron, and there were no horses, but the cycles of conquest ran their courses there, too, until the great civilizational edifices of Middle America and the Andes were brought down in crashing ruins by the

[20] J. H. Steward, *Theory of Culture Change*, p. 195.

magnifying glass, were found. They and their pollen were the heads of wild corn. Their carbon 14 date goes back to 5000 B.C. This was not cultivated corn, but the Mesolithic foragers of Mexico were harvesting the parent of modern corn 7,000 years ago.

The culture sequence in the valley of Tehuacán sketches out the first headings of the story of incipient agriculture in that part of the New World. The sequences are as follows: From 6700 to 5000 B.C., foragers had domesticated mixta squashes and avocados. They also collected wild beans, chile, and amaranth, but they had no corn.

Between 5000 and 3500 B.C., corn was domesticated, as were amaranth, the jack and common bean, chili, black and white zapotes, maschata squash, and the water-bottle gourd. The populations of this period were not assiduous farmers, for these foods appear to have constituted only about one-tenth of their total diet. For the rest, they hunted and trapped small game.

By 3400 B.C., a marked change is seen; settlements of pit houses (see pages 255–256) replaced caves and rock shelters. The farming village was established in America, and one-third of the food of the inhabitants was made up of garden produce, including the plants previously mentioned as well as runner beans and the dog.

Eleven hundred years later (2300 B.C.), a number of varieties of hybridized corn and pumpkins had been bred, and the first pottery was made (note how much earlier it was present at Çatal Hüyük and Jarmo). Irrigation agriculture began slightly later, at about 700 B.C. By

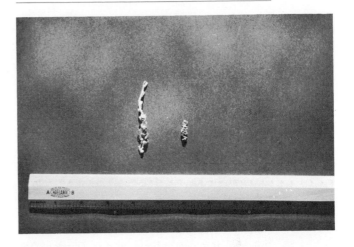

Fig. 12-13   Stages in the evolution of corn in the valley of Tehuacán, Mexico. Wild corn (top) was first discovered in 1960; it dates from ca. 5000 B.C. Successive improvement of breeds through domestication and crossbreeding is revealed in later prehistoric finds (middle and bottom, early hybrid corn, ca. 3500 B.C., and early modern corn, ca. 1500 B.C.). (Courtesy of Richard S. MacNeish.)

A.D. 700, true cities, under dynastic Mixtec rulers, were flourishing in the valley of Tehuacán, and 85 per cent of all food was agricultural in origin.

This is the sequence for only one valley in Mexico.[21] Variations in the pattern and dates for first appearances may be discovered elsewhere in the future. Nonetheless, the essential story is there. Squashes, beans, and maize were domesticated, in that order—and all between 7000 and 5000 B.C. They became the "triumvirate that forms the basis of much of American Indian agriculture."[22] They provided the nutritional source for the energy that went into building the civilizations of the Olmecs, Toltecs, Aztecs, Mayas, and Incas, as well as those of many lesser-known groups.

In South America, the domesticated potato became the staple for Andean peoples, while in the Amazonian rain forests, techniques for growing and processing manioc were developed to meet special environmental conditions (pages 247–248), much as the Southeast Asians developed rice culture in lieu of wheat and barley as their special adaptation of agriculture to the requirements of their physical environment.

New World cultures did not build extensively upon domesticated animals until the Spanish introduced the horse, sheep, and cattle. Andean tribes domesticated the llama and alpaca—whose wild ancestors were native American camels—and the iguana and vicuna. The llama was bred and used largely as a beast of burden, and the alpaca largely for its wool. Guinea pigs, those gentle little beasties, were domesticated for food in the Andes.

The independent domestication of cotton in the semitropical parts of Asia and the Americas produced a new source of fiber for weaving. Cotton was substituted for the flax that was domesticated earlier in the Middle East as a source of thread for weaving, in addition to the fleece of goats and sheep.

[21]R. S. MacNeish, "The Origin of New World Civilization" (*Scientific American,* Vol. 211, No. 5, 1964), pp. 29–37.
[22]G. F. Carter, "Origins of American Indian Agriculture" (*American Anthropologist,* Vol. 48, 1946), p. 1.

American Indians also had the dog, apparently domesticated independently from the Mesolithic dog of the Old World. It was a food source for some tribes[23] and a tabued animal for others.

SUMMARY

The end of the fourth glaciation brought a new type of cultural response from *Homo sapiens sapiens.* He shifted from predominant reliance on predatory hunting of big game to intensive exploitation of the vegetative and small-game and fish potentials of his local environment. He settled down and quickly domesticated plants and animals. The processes were essentially similar in the Old and New Worlds, except that the microlithic sickle, so prominent in the Old World, was not developed in the New.

Old World domestication led to the development of a number of farinaceous cereals, of which wheat and barley were first and basic. In the New World, the focus was on maize, squashes, and beans. The Old World also developed its own legumes. The domesticated dog was shared by both hemispheres, but the Old World provided more domesticable animals, and hence, pastoralism emerged as a secondary environmental adjustment there.

Over a span of several millennia, the small, settled farming village of the era of incipient agriculture gave rise to towns as centers of political and religious operations, staffed by priests and chiefs, along with their subordinates. Specialization in crafts contributed to the development of the towns as market centers. As efficiency of production was stepped up through the era of regional development and florescence, cities emerged in many parts of the Mediterranean, South Asia, and China. The urban revolution was on, and civilization was achieved. Complex social structures on a broad level of integration produced a new order of living for man. Writing was invented, and the replacement

[23]High Forehead, my Cheyenne Indian friend and interpreter, used to say: "With us, a nice, fat, boiled puppy dog is just like turkey at Thanksgiving to you people."

of the prehistoric world of primitive man by the historic world of civilized man was under way.

SELECTED READINGS

Braidwood, R. J., and G. R. Willey (eds.): *Courses toward Urban Life* (1963). Contains many excellent papers covering the manifestations of the eras of intensive foraging and incipient agriculture in all parts of the world. Each paper is written by an outstanding pioneering expert in the field.

Brew, J. O.: "The Metal Ages: Copper, Bronze and Iron," in H. L. Shapiro (ed.), *Man, Culture and Society* (1950), chap. 5. A good introductory summary.

Childe, V. G.: *The Dawn of European Civilization* (6th ed., rev., 1958). The classic statement of Childe's thesis.

Clarke, G.: *World Prehistory* (1961), pp. 76–239. This book provides a comprehensive description of many specific cultures that manifest the transition to the Early Neolithic. It is clearly written and is recommended as a more extensive treatment of the subject than could be provided in this introduction to anthropology.

Flannery, K. V.: "The Ecology of Early Food Production in Mesopotamia" (*Science,* Vol. 147, No. 3663, 1965), pp. 1247–1256. Collates data and new theory in a useful synthesis.

Frankfort, H.: *The Birth of Civilization in the Near East* (1951). A scholarly treatment that relates classical archaeology to Braidwood's researches. More up to date than Childe's work.

Helbeck, H.: "Domestication of Food Plants in the Old World" (*Science,* Vol. 130, No. 3372, 1959), pp. 365–372. Describes the recent evidence prior to the finds at Çatal Hüyük.

Kenyon, K.: *Digging up Jericho* (1957). Exactly what the title says it is.

Life, Editors of: *The Epic of Man,* sec. 2, "The Coming of Civilization," pp. 67–227. Particularly useful and inspiring for its superb color photographs of sites, artifacts, and art objects. The descriptive text and paintings reconstructing characteristic aspects of life in the different civilizations help to convey the tone of the time and place.

MacNeish, R. S.: "The Origin of New World Civilization" (*Scientific American,* Vol. 211, No. 5, 1964), pp. 29–37. A popular and well-illustrated account of the discoveries in Tehuacán Valley, Mexico, and the cultural series that led to emergent civilization in the New World.

Zeuner, F. E.: *A History of Domesticated Animals* (1963). Discusses the basic facts relating to the domestication of each variety of animal all across the board, including birds, fishes, and insects.

All living human beings belong to a single sub-species. This means that in all their major biological characteristics, they have more features in common than they have distinguishing differences. It is in this sense that we recognize the biological commonality of the human race.

At the same time, most individuals appear physically different from others in a number of discernible traits. This, of course, is true to some degree even within every family of brothers and sisters. If such differences were evenly distributed around the face of the globe, they would be noted merely as representing individual variation among human beings, and that would be that. The fact is, however, that certain distinctive traits tend to cluster in populations that have lived predominantly in one part of the world or another. It is these populations and the people directly derived from them that we have in mind when we speak of "races."

So much evil and so much of man's inhumanity to man has clustered, in recent centuries, around the whole idea of race, that some anthropologists have urged the abandonment of the concept entirely. F. B. Livingstone and C. L. Brace, in particular, have recently urged this, proposing that scientists content themselves with plotting the frequency occurrences of physical traits in continuous distribution from one continent to another, without grouping them according to races. The majority of anthropologists believe, nonetheless, that a scientific concept of race can be useful and valid.[1]

The definition of race

First, let us establish exactly what "race" means in scientific terms. It should be remembered, at the beginning, that this concept is only another category in biological classification (see pages 97–101, on classification). It is a means of breaking the subspecies of man into smaller biologically determined units. The anthropological definition of race with which we shall work is as follows: *A race is a human population that is sufficiently inbred to reveal a distinctive genetic composition manifest in a distinctive combination of physical traits.*

There are four components in this definition: (1) population, (2) inbreeding, (3) genetic composition, and (4) physical traits. Each of these is examined in turn.

Human populations In Chapter 7, a population was defined as "a group of possible observations or of individuals united by some common principle" (page 99).

[1]F. B. Livingstone, "On the Non-existence of Human Races" (*Current Anthropology*, Vol. 3, 1962), p. 279; C. L. Brace, "On the Race Concept" (*Current Anthropology*, Vol. 5, 1964), pp. 313–314, and following discussions.

Geographical races The kind of population that is commonly meant when we talk about race is an aggregation of people who have inhabited in the past, and who still do inhabit to a great extent, a given continent or a large section of a continent. Such populations tend to be sufficiently isolated from the inhabitants of other continents so that they have more common ancestors among themselves than they share with other populations on other continents. If they do not, they cannot be distinguished as a race, for there will be nothing distinctive· about their genetic composition. In point of fact, however, in spite of vast movements of peoples, continental populations do reveal distinctive gene pools (genetic composition). As a result, it has been customary to recognize a Caucasoid race, which was located largely in Europe, India, and North Africa and which has since 1600 extended itself to become the majority population in North America, Australia, and New Zealand. Likewise, the Negroid race of Africa south of the Sahara has been long identified in all racial classifications. So, too, the Mongoloid race of Asia is clear-cut and continentally associated. The American Indian population is sufficiently similar to the Mongoloid so that many older racial classifications grouped the American Indian under the Mongoloid rubric. The old, popular classification of white, black, yellow, red, and brown linked each of these "races" to one or more large continental masses. The brown race inhabited the island chains of Indonesia and the east-central Pacific.

This "old-fashioned" set of races, crudely conceived as it was, was based on a certain amount of fact. Continental, or other populations occupying significantly distinctive geographical areas have usually inbred for a long enough time to develop genetic differences through the operation of the processes of genetic variability, natural selection, genetic drift, and limited mixture.

In current anthropological usage, such races are called *geographical races*. A geographical race is therefore a human population that has inhabited a continental land mass or an island chain sufficiently long to have developed its own distinctive genetic composition, as contrasted to that of other continental populations. A modern classification of geographical races is given on pages 215–218.

Local races Within a continent, there may be barriers to easy intermixture of the continental population. Thus, the people of the North Baltic area interbreed among themselves to a much greater extent than they do with the people of the Mediterranean belt of southern Europe. They can be distinguished as identifiable subpopulations, localized over broad areas *within* a continent or island chain. This produces a lower-level classification of races, such as the Nordic, Alpine, and Mediterranean within the Caucasoid. Some physical anthropologists would push the analysis further and distinguish even more localized *local races* in the Balkan area, for example, where an unusual cranial shape, called "sugarloaf," and certain other physical features are common. They identify a so-called Armenoid race. The Basques of the Pyrenees are another good example of a local race. There is no agreement on just how many local races one could identify in the world. Garn and Coon, who originally formulated this approach to racial analysis,[2] suggest that the number might be about thirty.

Microgeographic races It is also possible to identify extremely isolated, tightly inbreeding small populations and set them off as genetically distinctive from other populations. How many such groups one might come up with becomes very much a matter of how one wants to cut the pie of population genetics. Clear-cut examples on which there would be no disagreement, however, would be the descendants of the mutineers of the Bounty who lived in absolute isolation on Pitcairn Island from 1788 to 1808 and have had very little outside contact since then.[3] The Kentucky mountaineers, in the southern Appalachians, constitute another

[2]S. M. Garn and C. S. Coon, "On the Number of Races of Mankind" (*American Anthropologist*, Vol. 57, 1955), pp. 996–1001. Also S. M. Garn, *Human Races*, chap. 2.
[3]See H. L. Shapiro, *The Heritage of the Bounty*,

example, and the polar Eskimos of northwest Greenland, who were so isolated that they did not know any other population existed anywhere, are another.

How many races of mankind are there living today? By now it should be clear that there are few or many, depending on where the dividing lines are drawn and on what criteria for identification of populations are used.

The significance of inbreeding The members of a given race are more like one another in certain physical traits than they are like other human beings because they possess certain genes in common which other populations do not have, or which they have in greater or lesser quantity. These genes have been distributed among the members of a racial population through interbreeding among its members—or intrabreeding within the population. The population shares a gene pool that is not exactly the same as the gene pool of other populations. Inbreeding is the result of isolation and limited mobility. Isolation among men is the consequence of geographic circumstance and social distance.

Space and physiographic features are the primary geographic stimulators of inbreeding. North American Indians did not mate with Australians because 12,000 miles of ocean separated them. When we consider that the polar Eskimos numbered no more than a few hundred individuals, we can realize how close their inbreeding had to be. In fact, in almost any of the smaller primitive tribes, and this includes the majority of all tribal groups, every person is apt to be a genetic relative of every other.

Social isolation is man-made. It exists in the form of endogamous rules and practices that forbid or discourage intermarriage between populations or social groups, while requiring or encouraging marriage within such groups. Any other kind of social practice that discourages social interaction between populations also establishes social distance and hence contributes to inbreeding. Caste endogamy, for example, insofar as it is strictly enforced (the penalty for violation of customs or rules is to be outcast), produces a micro race of each caste. Endogamy is discussed further under Preferential Mating in Chapter 22.

Geographical and social mobility are the dissolvers of race, as geographic and social isolation are its generators.

Distinctive physical traits The question of what constitutes a realistic combination of distinctive physical traits poses the greatest difficulties. Which traits legitimately go into the combination, and which must be left out?

Obviously, considerable overlapping of single traits occurs among the different races. Only the Negro has a distinctive lip, for instance, which means that a generalized lip form occurs in all other races. Black hair distinguishes the Negro from the blond Nordic, but not at all from the multitudinous Mongoloids. Thus the fact that any one of the physical traits found to be characteristic of a race may be found in other races has in itself neither positive nor negative significance. Any suggestion that the presence of a single trait in two different races indicates genetic affinity between the races would be absurd. The fact that certain Melanesians possess "Semitic" noses cannot be used as evidence of Semitic ancestry of those Oceanic Negroes. On the other hand, neither can it be said that this nose is not an important element in the cluster of distinctive traits that characterizes each of these groups.

The whole concatenation of traits marks the race. Yet an individual person rarely possesses all the traits that characterize his race. If, for purposes of illustration, we say that a particular race has twenty-five traits in a distinctive combination, this does not mean that every person who properly is a member of the racial population possesses all twenty-five traits.

The Swedes, for example, are a notably homogeneous population with unusually distinctive physical traits: flaxen hair, blue eyes, light skin, long heads, and so on. Retzius and Furst, in 1898, in measurements of 45,000 Swedish army recruits, found that only 11 per cent possessed *all* the traits that go to make up the dis-

tinctive Nordic combination; 29 per cent had all the traits except that they were roundheaded. Some years ago, the statue of an average Harvard undergraduate was produced by sculpting a figure according to the average physical measurements of the Harvard student body. But only 1 in 1,024 Harvard students would have conformed to this imaginary type.

Should we not conclude from this that a combination of traits ascribed to a race involves an imaginative idealization of types that rarely occur in any given individual? Those who would wish away races answer "Yes."

Race-conscious persons hold images of racial types in their heads. To them, a particular racial type consists of all the distinctive traits of that race in combination. When these persons associate an individual with a given race because that individual has one or more of the type traits, they either overlook the presence of nontypical traits or impute the type traits to the person being considered. Correction of such false perception is a matter of social psychology. The scientifically oriented observer will make no such error because he knows that a race is statistically determined on the basis of biologically derived data.

Frequency distribution of variable traits Statistically, any student of elementary biology knows that all morphological traits are variable. He also knows that each trait is limited in its range of variability, that the variables tend to cluster around a norm or mean, and that the occurrence of extreme forms of the variable becomes less frequent the farther they vary from the norm. Statistically, when plotted for frequency distributions, variables usually form a humpbacked curve with the same number of units falling on each side of the mean. This is the old, familiar frequency curve. In a normal distribution curve, the mean (average) coincides with the mode (variable of greatest frequency) and the median (midpoint between the two extremes of the range). In a skewed or lopsided curve, these three types of norms will not coincide (see Fig. 2-3, page 27). In such a case, physical anthropologists usually use the mean as expressive of the physical trait characteristic of the group. Thus, according to Hooton, the mean stature for Ainus is 157.9 cm (5 feet 3 inches); for Negritos, 150 cm (4 feet 9 inches); for Nilotic Negroes, 175 to 180 cm (5 feet 10 inches to 6 feet); and for Nordics, 172 cm (5 feet 8.8 inches).[4] We can properly say that the Ainu and Negrito races are short and that the Nilotic Negroes and Nordics are tall.

In detailed, specialized studies, physical anthropologists usually give the total range of distribution with coefficients of deviation. Figure 13-1 illustrates comparative distributions with respect to the relative statures of Navaho Indian and white American girls of college age (sixteen to twenty-four years; average age twenty years). These comparative data show some overlapping in the ranges of distribution for the two groups. Some Navaho girls are taller than some white girls. However, although 5 per cent of the Navaho girls are less than 4 feet 9 inches (1,500 mm) in stature, not a single white girl is shorter than this. On the other hand, although 28 per cent of the white girls are more than 5 feet 4 inches (1,640 mm) tall, not a single Navaho girl exceeds this height.

The average (mean) stature of the Navaho girls is an even 5 feet [1,556 mm; Probable Error (P.E.) $\pm$ 2.81; Standard Deviation (S.D.) 41.70 $\pm$ 1.99]. The average (mean) stature of the white girls is 5 feet 3 inches (1,628.05 mm; P.E. $\pm$ 3.75; S.D. 55.59 $\pm$ 2.65).

The shortest Navaho girl is 4 feet 8 inches (1,420 mm) tall, and the tallest Navaho girl stands 5 feet 3-3/4 inches (1,640 mm). Among the white girls, the shortest of the group is 4 feet 11-3/4 inches (1,520 mm), and the tallest is 5 feet 9 inches (1,760 mm). The range of variability between the shortest and the tallest Navaho girl is 7-3/4 inches; between the shortest and the tallest white girl, 9-3/4 inches.[5]

It can be seen that the difference between the average heights of the two groups is approximately 3 inches. Thus, the difference between the tallest and the shortest within

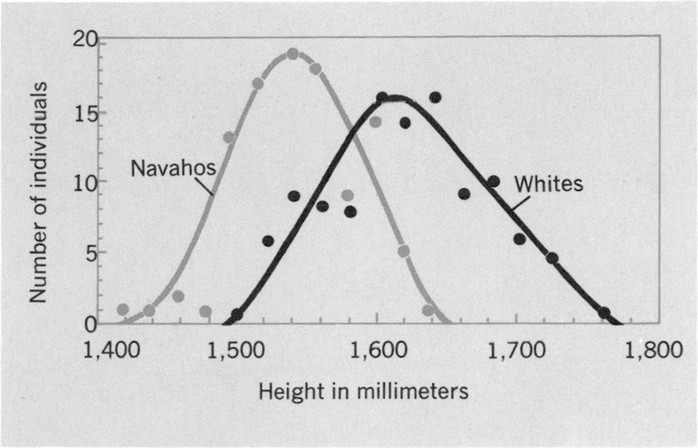

Fig. 13-1 Frequency distribution of stature among 100 Navaho and 100 white American girls of college age.

each of the groups is greater than the difference between the means of the two groups.

A recent tendency among some anthropologists has been to emphasize that in such single traits, the groups are more akin to each other than the extreme members within one of the groups are. This is perfectly true, and it should serve to warn us against overemphasis on racial differences, but it does not wholly negate the significance of the differences that are to be discerned in the averages.

The distribution of statures among the little Congo Pygmies, the Japanese, and the lanky Nilotic Negroes reveals racial characteristics in bodily length in even sharper terms. In the samples represented in Fig. 13-2, there is absolutely no overlap between the Pygmies and the Nilotics. The Japanese cluster, for its part, is clearly distinct from the other two.

Frequency distribution of blood types Traditional physical anthropology dealt only with appearances. Because appearance does not reveal the true genetic composition of the majority of individuals at a given moment, and since race is controlled by heredity, obviously anthropologists in the past have been only scratching the surface. They were, as Washburn states, "chiefly concerned with sorting the results of evolution." Today the application

[4] E. A. Hooton, *Up from the Ape*, pp. 503ff.
[5] M. G. Steggerda, "Physical Measurements on Negro, Navajo and White Girls of College Age" (*American Journal of Physical Anthropology*, Vol. 26, 1940), p. 420.

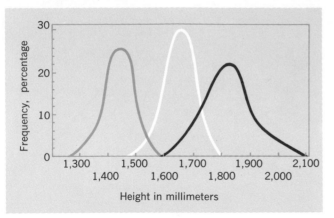

Fig. 13-2   Frequency distribution of stature among 98 Congo Pygmies, 109 Japanese, and 115 Nilotic Negroes (Dinka tribe). (Modified from Boyd, *Genetics and the Races of Man*, p. 297.)

of genetic principles to the study of race makes it possible to sort the results more exactly and, even more important, to move toward a more adequate understanding of how races develop and why. The best progress made to date has been through identification of blood-group genes and through the study of their population distributions.[6]

Almost everyone is familiar with the existence of the O, A, B, and AB blood types. Blood is classified according to its agglutinative reactions, i.e., according to whether the hemoglobin (red blood corpuscles) clump together when mixed with alien blood. Two classic blood clumpers, A and B, were the first to be isolated. They are antigen A and antigen B. Type O blood is immune to the effect of both antigens; hence it can ordinarily be used in transfusions to any other basic blood type. (O-type persons are universal donors.) Type A can be transfused to types A and AB, but not to type B. Type B can be transfused to types B and AB, but not to type A.

Soon after blood types were discovered, it was noticed that the percentage frequencies of the four types were not the same for different

phenotypic races. First, it was observed that most European populations run from forty to fifty per cent O, from 30 to 40 per cent A, from 8 to 12 per cent B, and from 1 to 6 per cent AB. In sharp contrast, some American Indian tribes revealed almost all O, little A, and virtually no B. The Utes, for example, run 98 per cent O, 2 per cent A, and zero for B and AB. As against Europeans, here is surely a clear-cut hereditary population difference. Among the Mongoloids of Asia, the samples thus far tested show roughly around 30 per cent O, A, and B, with a small residue of AB. Local populations within the larger geographic populations just mentioned vary in O, A, B, and AB distributions to some extent, but the major differences tend to run as indicated.[7]

The advantage of blood types as genetic criteria of race is that they are discrete traits. A type is either present or absent in a person. It is neither ambiguous, as is "olive skin," nor continuously variable, as is stature. Therefore, the gene distribution in the population for a number of blood types can be precisely calculated, and these distributions vary by population.

In addition to the classic blood types, numerous other agglutinators have been discovered. These include the M and N types and the Rh negative and positive, as well as several subtypes—the Lewis, Lutheran, Kell, Duffy, Kidd, and others.

The A antigens have been found to fall into two subtypes A_1 and A_2. It is significant that the A occurring in American Indians, Asiatics, Pacific Islanders, and Australoids is all A_1.

Rh-negative genes occur in about 15 per cent of Europeans. They are absent among the Asians, Australians, Pacific Islanders, and American Indians who have been tested to date. Once again, the Mongoloid affinity of the American Indian is apparently confirmed.

Beyond blood groupings, not much progress has thus far been made in isolating easily identifiable genes for use in racial classifications. A peculiar and interesting gene is the one

---

[6]A review of the discussion of genetic factors in evolution (pp. 119–126) is strongly recommended at this point.

[7]For the method of calculating gene frequencies in a population, see H. H. Strandskov, "Genetics and the Origin and Evolution of Man" (*Cold Spring Harbor Symposia on Quantitative Biology,* Vol. 15, 1951), pp. 1–11.

Table 13-1   Summary of Distribution of Major Blood-group Systems among the Geographical Races of the World

blood-group system (alleles in parentheses)	description of phenotype frequencies
A, B, O (including A$_1$ and A$_2$)	O most common group; over 50% of individuals in most populations are of this type. B nearly absent in aboriginal America and Australia, and progressively more common in Europe (15%), Africa, India, and Asia (up to 40%). A$_2$ practically limited to Europe.
MNS, U (or S^u)	American Indians almost exclusively M. N most common in Australia and the Pacific. MS and NS absent in Australia. U negative rare and apparently limited to Africa.
Rh (R$_1$, R$_2$, R$_0$, r', r, etc.)	Rh-negative individuals (rh) rare or absent in most of the world, but approximately 15% of Europeans are Rh-negative. Of the Rh-positive alleles (R$_1$, R$_2$, etc.), the R$_0$ form is found primarily in Africa (up to 70%).
Duffy (Fy^a, Fy^b, Fy)	Most Australians and Polynesians and 90–99% of Asians are Duffy-positive (Fy^a). 90% of Indians, 85–90% of most American Indians, 65% of populations of England and America, and 27% of American Negroes. Fy^a very low in Africa, but the gene Fy extremely common (>80%).
Diego (Di^a, Di^b)	Diego-positive (Di^a) individuals limited to Amerindians (2–20%) and Asians. Di^a absent in Europe, Africa, Australia, Micronesia, and Polynesia and in Eskimos.
Kidd (Jk^a, Jk^b)	Kidd-positive (Jk^a) most common in West Africa and American Negroes (>90%), North American Indians (70–90%), and Europeans (approximately 70%) and least common in Chinese (50–55%).

SOURCE: S. M. Garn, *Human Races,* p. 47.

that determines the ability to perceive a bitter taste in phenylthiocarbamide (PTC).

The allele for tasting ability (T) is inherited as a Mendelian dominant over the nontasting allele (t). Seventy per cent of the population of the United States are tasters, and 30 per cent are nontasters. In terms of gene frequency, this means that 55 per cent of the United States population carry the t gene.[8] Within a sample of Navaho Indians, on the other hand, the proportion of nontasters is only 2 per cent. The frequency of the t allele in this Navaho

population is $\sqrt{0.2}$, or 14 per cent. This is definitely a significant racial difference. Although not enough different populations have as yet been tested for T, t, the indications are, according to Boyd, "that the results for the tasting gene parallel in general what has already been observed for the Rh negative and A$_2$ genes, that is, that European populations tend to differ rather strikingly from Mongoloid populations. In both cases there is insufficient information about the Africans."[9]

[8]The frequency of a recessive gene in the gene pool is equal to the square root of the genotypes for the recessive gene in the population: $\sqrt{0.30} = 0.55$.

[9]See W. C. Boyd, *Genetics and the Races of Man,* p. 281; F. S. Hulse, *The Human Species,* chap. 12, provides a comprehensive summary of blood-type distributions as of 1963, including a number of useful maps.

In summary, on the basis of gene-frequency occurrences for various blood types and PTC, Boyd suggests five major contemporary races similar to those commonly identified by bodily traits (morphological phenotypes). These are the Caucasoid, Negroid, Mongoloid, American Indian, and Australoid. The American Indian is closely linked to the Mongoloid, but the presence of the B agglutin gene among the Mongoloids and its absence among American Indians suggest sufficient racial differentiation of the American Indians since their migration to the New World to warrant a separate racial category in genetic terms.

The origin of racial differences

Races differentiate within the human species as a result of four factors: (1) gene mutation, (2) natural selection, (3) genetic drift, and (4) population mixture. The mechanisms according to which each of these factors works have already been described in Chapter 8; however, some of the more probable consequences of environmental adaptation through the effect of mutation and natural selection can now be considered.

Ecological rules and racial adaptation Three biological rules of long standing have recently been reexamined by Coon and others in terms of their applicability to human races. These are Gloger's rule (1833), Bergmann's rule (1847), and Allen's rule (1877). They are stated as follows:

1. *Gloger's rule*. "In mammals and birds, races which inhabit warm and humid regions have more melanin pigmentation than races of the same species in cooler and drier regions; arid regions are characterized by accumulation of yellow and reddish-brown phaeomelanin pigmentation. . . . The phaeomelanins are subject to reduction in cold climate, and in extreme cases also the eumelanin" [polar white].
2. *Bergmann's rule*. "The smaller-sized geographic races of a species are found in the warmer parts of the range, the larger sized races in the cooler districts."

3. *Allen's rule*. "Protruding body parts, such as tails, ears, bills, extremities, and so forth, are relatively shorter in the cooler parts of the range of the species than in the warmer parts."[10]

Gloger's rule and the skin color of man Do tropic dwellers in fact have more melanin pigment than those who habituate colder and drier climates?

Most human beings have relatively light-colored skin, which, if not covered by clothing, tans in strong light as a response to natural ultraviolet radiation. Those exposed constantly to sunlight become quite dark the year round. Those who live in middle latitudes go through an annual cycle of skin coloring, tanning in the summer and bleaching in the winter. In order to ascertain the standard (unmodified) skin color of a person, skin-color tests must be taken on the underside of the upper arm, near the armpit. The capacity for variable pigmentation has obvious adaptive advantages, within limits. It permits ultraviolet rays to penetrate the skin and produce vitamin D, which is beneficial. Overexposure to radiation is painful and dangerous, however. Sunburn and sunstroke are only immediate consequences. Skin cancer which has a higher incidence among persons who are continually over exposed, is a longer-range consequence.

Black skin color results from high melanin content. It is fairly constant and subject to little or no seasonal variation. The original geographic distribution of this genetic trait is along the tropic regions of the Old World within 10 to 20 degrees of the equator. In the non-forested regions of this area, the functional adaptive usefulness of black or near-black skin under the high and constant equatorial sun is clear. However, much of the equatorial region in which the black peoples live is gloomy rain forest, and has been in the past, at least in postglacial times. Much larger areas are open parkland, desert, and water. It is here that the adaptation of black skin was probably effected. In the Americas, the Amazon valley is jungle,

[10]C. S. Coon, "Climate and Race," in H. Shapley (ed.), *Climatic Change*, p. 14.

and the more open areas of the western equatorial region have a heavy, permanent cloud cover. This, and the fact that the local populations have not been very long in these regions, should account for the absence of black pigment in the New World.

At the opposite extreme of the color spectrum is the sunburning, nontanning variety of skin that is confined to a very small minority of the population of the cloudy areas of northwestern Europe and their migrating descendants. It has no discernible adaptive advantage over the more common variable-color skin. Presumably it survives in North Europe because under prevailing climatic conditions, its selective disadvantage is not lethal—as it can be elsewhere.

Bergmann's rule and human body size Bergmann's rule for warm-blooded animals expresses the fact that the smaller the skin area relative to total body volume, the lower the loss of body heat, and vice versa. A short and stocky Eskimo physique conserves body heat, while the long, lanky body of the Nilotic Negro (Fig. 13-3, left) helps to dissipate it. Differences in the numbers of sweat glands and capillary control of blood flow are also significant factors. Bergmann's rule applies with moderate consistency to human beings. Heavier populations are concentrated in the north, while slighter ones are found in equatorial regions (except for Pacific Islanders, who bask in the comfortable trade winds).

Allen's rule and human bodily extremities The shape of the protruding parts of the body facilitates or inhibits heat loss and heat retention. Populations in hot climates do have larger extremities. Desert Negroes as well as desert Caucasoids have long limbs and slim torsos. The forehead and hands are the concentrated sweat areas. A long, narrow head and long hands function to effect heat dissipation, which is especially important for the brain. Negro populations are uniformly long-headed and long-handed. Heat control in the hands and feet is good deal more than a matter of sweating, however. The capillary system in the hands acts like the thermostat at the head of the engine block in a water-cooled automobile, which controls the flow of water to the radiator according to temperature. In high temperatures, arterial blood returning to the heart flows through the close-to-the-surface veins on the back of the hand. When the temperature drops below a critical threshold, vasoconstriction shuts down the flow to the surface arteries, while vasodilation opens it to the deeper-lying ones. Thus internal heat, carried in the blood, is conserved. Recent experiments indicate population differentials related to environment in this respect.

The cranial features of Mongoloid populations are all adaptations to extreme cold: round heads; flat cheekbones; small, flat noses; heavy layers of subcutaneous fat; and fatty double eyelids, which produce the characteristic Mongoloid internal epicanthic fold, or so-called slant eye (see Fig. 13-3 right). Theoretically, these adaptations took place among the Northeast Asian populations during the Upper Pleistocene. They are, of course, highly characteristic of Eskimos and many other North Asian local races.

It is clear that in a number of features, the effect of selective adaptation in the development of geographical races can be identified. It is also true that experimental observation has thus far been too limited and research techniques too undeveloped to make it possible to account for many of the identifiable physical characteristics of populations. Much more needs to be known about human physiology and the details of geographic locations and climatic conditions encountered.

A modern classification of races

Thus far, we have referred to races by the names that were conventional in anthropological usage until 1950. A new nomenclature based on the principles just presented is now gaining acceptance in the United States.

Coon, Garn, and Birdsell, in 1950, proposed

Fig. 13-3 The long-limbed Batutsi of Burundi, with their small torsos, exemplify bodily adaptation to hot, humid climates. This body shape produces the largest skin area relative to total body volume. Surface radiation is maximal and body heat is more effectively dissipated. On the other hand, the short-limbed Eskimos, with their large, heavy torsos, exemplify bodily adaptation to cold climates. This body shape produces the smallest skin area relative to total body volume. Surface radiation is minimal and body heat is more effectively preserved. (Left, United Nations; right, courtesy of the American Museum of Natural History.)

a classification of races based upon the idea of geographical races identifiable as Mendelian, or inbreeding, populations.[11] Garn subsequently refined the application of the concept and presented a classification of living races in nine major categories:

1. European: population of Europe, North Africa, and the Middle East and their worldwide descendants

2. Indian: population of the Indian sub-continent

3. Asian: population of Siberia, Mongolia, China, Japan, Southeast Asia, and Indonesia

[11]S. C. Coon, S. M. Garn, and J. B. Birdsell, *Races: A Study of Race Formation in Man.*

4. Micronesian: population of the western Pacific Islands from Guam to the Marshalls

5. Melanesian: population of the western Pacific Islands south of Micronesia, extending from New Guinea to Fiji

6. Polynesian: population of the eastern Pacific Islands from Hawaii to New Zealand and Easter Island

7. American: population of "Indians"

8. African: population of Africa south of the Sahara

9. Australian: population of aboriginal Australians

Garn[12] has also formulated a classification of living local races, which we have regrouped under their geographic races and renumbered as follows:

I. European
   1. Northwest European: population of Scandinavia, northern France and Germany, the Low Countries, the United Kingdom, and Ireland
   2. Northeast European: population of Eastern Baltic, Russia, and modern Siberia
   3. Alpine: population of central France, southern Germany, Switzerland, and northern Italy, to the Black Sea
   4. Mediterranean: population surrounding the Mediterranean, eastward through Asia Minor

II. Indian
   1. Indic: population of India, Pakistan, and Ceylon (Note: Garn calls this race Hindu, but inasmuch as Hindu properly identifies a religion, we feel that Indic is more appropriate.)
   2. Dravidian: aboriginal population of southern India

III. Asian
   1. Classic Mongoloid: population of Siberia, Mongolia, Korea, and Japan
   2. North Chinese: population of northern China and Manchuria
   3. Turkic: population of western China and Turkestan

4. Tibetan: population of Tibet
   5. Southeast Asian: population of South China through Thailand, Burma, Malaya, the Philippines, and Indonesia
   6. Ainu: aboriginal population of Japan
   7. Eskimo: population of northern maritime fringe of North America and ice-free fringes of Greenland
   8. Lapp: population of arctic Scandinavia and Finland

IV. Micronesian (no local races distinguished)

V. Melanesian
   1. Papuan: population of mountain highlands of New Guinea
   2. Melanesian: population of coastal area of New Guinea and most of the other islands in the Melanesian archipelago

VI. Polynesian
   1. Polynesian: aboriginal population
   2. Neo-Hawaiian: nineteenth- to twentieth-century blend of Polynesian, European, and Asiatic

VII. American
   1. North American (Indian): aboriginal population of Canada and the continental United States
   2. Central American (Indian); population of the Southwestern United States, Mexico, and Central America to Brazil
   3. South American (Indian); population of all South America, except Tierra del Fuego
   4. Fuegian: population around the Straits of Magellan
   5. Ladino: new Latin-American population resulting from blending of Mediterranean, Central and South American (Indians), Forest Negroes, and Bantu
   6. North American Colored: eighteenth- to twentieth-century population blended of Northwest Europeans and Africans

VIII. African
   1. East African: population of the East African Horn, Ethiopia, and Nilotic Sudan

[12] *Ibid.*, pp. 127–132.

2. Sudanese: population of the Sudan, except for Nilotics
3. Forest Negro: population of West Africa and most of the Congo
4. Bantu: population of South Africa and adjacent parts of East Africa
5. Bushman-Hottentot: surviving post-Pleistocene population in South Africa
6. Pygmy: small-statured population living in the equatorial rain forest
7. South African Colored: population of South Africa produced by a blend of Northwest European and Bantu, plus some Bushman-Hottentot

IX. Australian
   1. Murrayian: aboriginal population of southeastern Australia.
   2. Carpentarian: aboriginal population of central and northern Australia

The Negrito populations are sporadically scattered throughout Southeast Asia, Indonesia, and New Guinea. They thus straddle several normal geographic areas, and cannot be placed in any one of the major categories.

Salient features of the geographic and more important local races

European (formerly Caucasoid) The European race is not actually white. It belongs to the group possessing varying pigmentation. Eye color varies from light-blue to dark-brown. Hair is blond to black and of fine to medium texture; it may be straight, wavy, or curly, but it is rarely kinky and never woolly. The males tend to grow hair on their chests, arms, legs, and faces as well as on the tops of their heads. The nose is narrow and high, rarely broad or flat. Although the forehead is usually sloping, the face is not prognathous. Chins tend to jut, and lips are thin. Stature is medium to tall.

Northwest European (formerly Nordic) This population is low in pigmentation. Hair is blond, ranging from a flaxen color to light-brown; eyes are blue, gray, or hazel. Head form is dolicho-cephalic; the face is also narrow and angular. Jaws and chin are usually prominent; the nose is narrow and usually high. Hair is sparse on the body and thin on the head, and it usually falls out in adult males. In form the hair is straight or wavy but seldom curly. The body is tall and slender; the torso is relatively small, and the legs are long. The chest is usually shallow and flat.

Alpine These people are brachycephalic (roundheaded) and have broad faces with sharp, square jaws. They are brunets; eyes and hair are brown to black, and the skin is olive-hued. The nose is well padded with adipose tissue at the tip, and it tends to be broad. The body is usually solid and heavy, rarely exceeding medium stature. Alpine men grow fine dark beards, and if hair on the chest indicates masculinity, they have more of what it takes than any other Europeans.

Mediterranean The Mediterranean is also a brunet, but unlike the stocky Alpine, he is usually slight of stature. He tends to be slight in youth and fat in maturity (this applies to the female also). The race is dolichocephalic (narrow- and long-headed) with narrow, high foreheads unmarked by any protrusion of a supraorbital ridge. Hair is black or dark; it is usually handsomely wavy and is rarely straight. Although luxuriant on the head, it is sparse on the face, limbs, and body. Eyes are brown; the skin is light-brown or pale olive. Noses are narrow and high-bridged.

Northeast Europeans This is a round-headed, broad-faced population, with thin lips; gray-blue eyes; straight, light-colored hair; and light-colored skin. Stature is short and the bodies heavy.

Indian

Indic The fact that India is a subcontinent isolated from the rest of Asia by vast mountain ramparts qualifies its population for consideration as a geographical race. The population is, in fact, made up of hundreds of local races and microgeographic races. Tribal and caste endogamy has split the population into numerous intrabreeding groups separated by great social distances that are more inhibiting than geographical distances.

In the north of India, skin color is variably light. In the south, it may be very dark. Stature is short, except in the extreme northwest, where there has been much European (mostly Middle Eastern) intermixture.

Most Indians are brunets, and the hair is usually wavy. Body hair on males is moderately frequent. The head is almost always dolichocephalic. Eyes are dark-brown and large. Body build is gracile.

In traditional classifications by anthropologists, Indians are grouped within the Mediterranean race.

Dravidian This population is heavily pigmented, with dark-brown skin, brown eyes, and black, wavy hair. The head is dolichocephalic; the face is narrow. Stature is short (mean of 5 feet 2 inches), and the torso is slight in build. Dravidians are believed to be the archaic inhabitants of India and remotely related to the Australians.

Asian (formerly Mongoloid) The most outstanding Asian physical trait is the slant eye, more elegantly known to anthropologists as the internal epicanthic fold. The infants also have a unique feature, the "Mongolian patch," which is a purplish, triangular area of skin at the base of the spine. Skin color is brown or yellowish-tan. Eyes are brown or dark-brown, and the hair is black. It is very coarse and straight, growing long on the head and scarcely at all on the face or body. Most Asian populations are brachycephalic. The cheekbones are broad and high, while the nose is squat and low-bridged, thus giving a flat-faced appearance. While their body trunks are fairly long, heavy, and broad, they are usually short and squat in stature, because their legs are short.

Micronesian This population resulted from a blending of Southeast Asians and Melanesians. It is medium-statured, brown-eyed, and dark-skinned. Hair is black and frequently frizzy. The head is brachycephalic to mesocephalic.

Melanesian (formerly Oceanic Negro) The peoples of the Black Islands are black in skin color (some are brown) and hair color. The hair is long and frizzy; hence the nickname "Fuzzy-Wuzzies" given them by American soldiers in World War II. The head is usually dolichocephalic, and the nose is high and broad (sometimes called Semitic). Eyes are dark and set in a very prognathous face, which has notably thick lips. Body hair is scanty. Stature is medium and the body well-formed.

Polynesian When, at some future date, miscegenation blends all the races of man into one standardized variety, that variety may reasonably be expected to look somewhat like the aboriginal Polynesians. Such a prospect is genuinely gratifying, for rare is the person who dissents from the judgment that they are a handsome and comely people of great ability. Yet the Polynesians are thoroughly mongrelized; predominantly they are of Indic mixed with Melanesian and South Asian stocks. The race is very similar to the Malayo-Indonesians except that the stronger Mediterranean heredity gives a wavy form to the hair, elongates the face and body, lightens the skin, and produces a high nose. African traits show up in a tendency to fullness of lips. The dominant roundheadedness of the Asian characterizes most Polynesians. Hair grows luxuriantly on the head, but, as is to be expected in an Indic-Asian-Melanesian mixture, it is scanty on the face and body. As well-fed islanders, they have developed large and powerful bodies.

American (formerly Amerind) The Indians of the Americas are highly variable in stature, head form, and details of facial features. In general, however, they reveal their Asian ancestry in a predominance of brachycephaly; brown eyes; black, usually straight hair; thin lips; broad, high cheekbones; occasional internal epicanthic fold; and yellow or reddish-brown skin covering a broad and heavy body. Blood-type

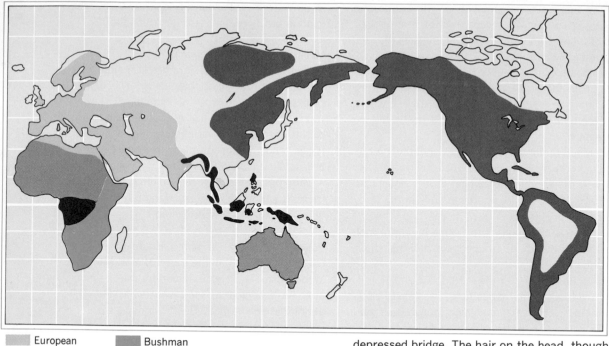

European
Asiatic
African

Bushman
Australian
Pygmy

Fig. 13-4   The distribution of the major macrogeographic races of mankind in the Mesolithic age. Note how the presence of glaciers limited the distribution of mankind. (Adapted from William W. Howells, "The Distribution of Man," Scientific American.)

frequencies, as already noted, differ markedly from those of the Asian, however.

African (formerly Negro)   Africans are the possessors of the darkest pigmentation of all mankind; nevertheless, few Africans are actually black. Most are dark-brown or brownish-black in skin color. Hair is prevailingly black, coarse, wiry, and tightly curled, kinky, or woolly. With few exceptions, heads are long and narrow. The occipital region juts out, as does the lower portion of the face, which in appearance is accentuated by the thick, everted mucous membrane that forms the lips. The African nose is broad, with flaring wings and a broad, deeply

depressed bridge. The hair on the head, though thick, is short in length, while the male beard is sparse; body hair is rare. Stature is medium tall. The forearm is long, and the legs are thin (i.e., the calves do not ordinarily develop thick musculature).

East African   The East African is notable among Africans for his slender body build and tall stature (with a mean of 5 feet 10 inches and taller) and for his high, narrow head and straight nose.

Bushman-Hottentot   This remnant population has a dolichocephalic to mesocephalic head with a smallish, triangular-appearing face. The nose is very low and broad, beneath a low, sloping forehead. The eyes frequently have an internal epicanthic fold. Skin color is yellow-brown. The hair grows in tight "peppercorn" spirals close to the scalp. Stature averages only 5 feet. The body is slight and prone to fatty buttocks (steatopygous).

Australian   The fact that European Australians call the dark-brown Australians "blackfellows"

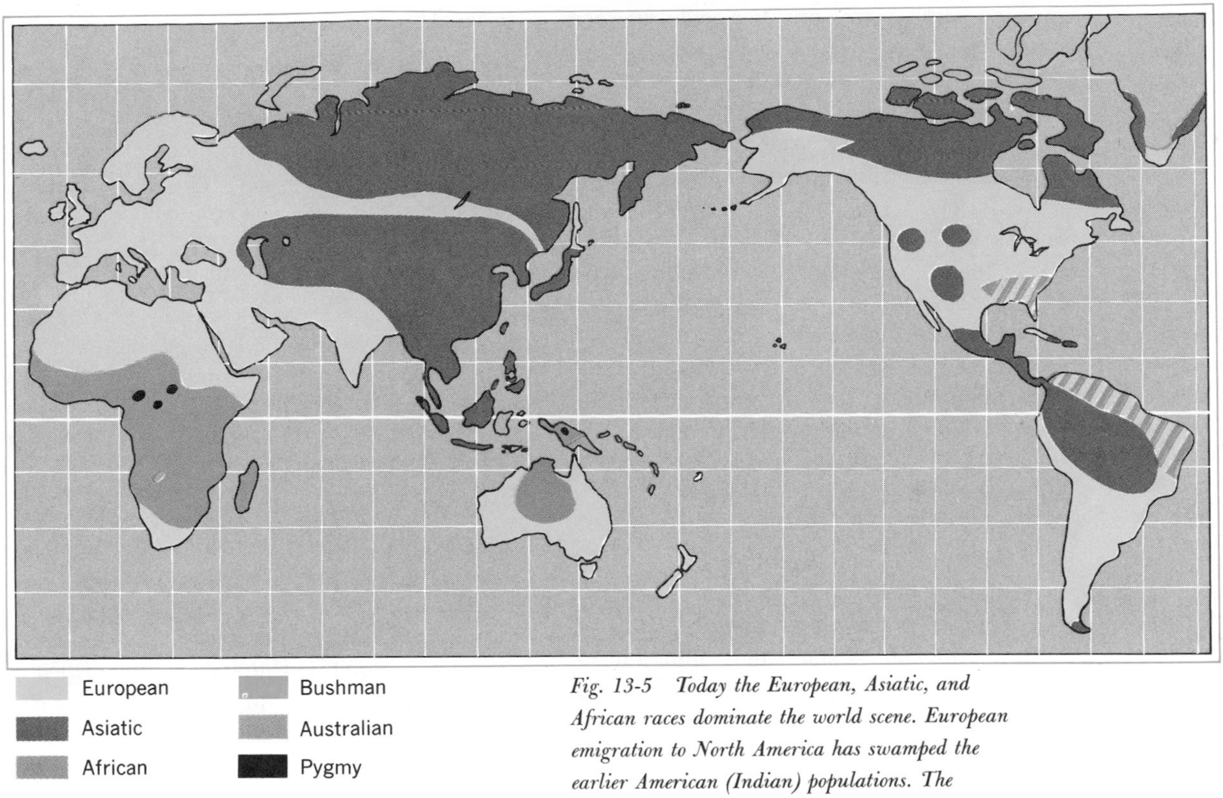

European

Asiatic

African

Bushman

Australian

Pygmy

Fig. 13-5 Today the European, Asiatic, and African races dominate the world scene. European emigration to North America has swamped the earlier American (Indian) populations. The aboriginal Bushmen of Africa and the Australians have suffered a similar fate. (From William W. Howells, "The Distribution of Man," Scientific American.)

leads to the easy error of thinking of them as Negroes. They decidedly are not, for there is a strong reddish cast to their dark skin. The hairiness of their heads and bodies and the waviness of their hair indicate a strong possibility of archaic Dravidian relations.

The Australian aborigine is physically a "lowbrow." His forehead slopes back from the heaviest supraorbital ridges to be found in any surviving race. His skull is narrow and houses a brain that is notably smaller in volume than that of any other living race. His face juts forward, and his dental arches even more so. His dark-brown eyes are set beside a deeply depressed nasal root, below which the broad thick tip of the nose flares up in a great bulb. The whole face is compressed from symphysis to nasion. The Australian is neither very short nor very tall. He grows a slender, short body on a pair of pipestem legs.

This descriptive typology does not cover all the local races or spell out all the descriptive details, but it should serve in distinguishing the more notable populations of the world.

The historical divergence of races

The prevailing view among anthropologists, and that expressed in this book, is that modern man spread throughout the Old World through migratory radiation. The general hotbed of original sapienization probably cannot be pinpointed for the reason that it could have been spread over a fairly large area of Africa, Asia Minor, or South Asia. It is assumed that there was a moderately steady gene flow among the *Homo erecti* who were evolving into *Homo sapiens*. It is also inferred that *Homo sapiens sapiens,* equipped with more effective cultures and sharper brainpower, overwhelmed or absorbed all other species and varieties of hominins. Radiating in all directions from the old heartland, he quickly spread over the entire globe. As modern man spread about the world, large residual blocks remained in Africa and Asia. Processes of selective differentiation began among them and were intensified through the tens of thousands of years that followed after *Homo sapiens sapiens* first emerged. But racial differences within the subspecies remain quite minor when looked at from a zoologist's point of view. They are all secondary in quality. The biological unity of modern man is more significant than the diversity.

The Weidenreich-Coon hypothesis The 1963 publication of Carleton Coon's *Origin of Races,* an impressive piece of scholarship, loosed a storm of vituperation about the author's head. In his Herculean assay of fossil man and primate evolution, Coon committed himself to elaboration of the *polyphyletic theory* of the origins of modern races, which had been formulated by the late Franz Weidenreich between 1935 and 1950. Weidenreich, it will be remembered, capped his distinguished career with his brilliant studies of the fossils of Pekin and Java man. He decided that the contemporary Asian population is directly descended from *Homo erectus pekinensis.* In this theory, the Australians are held to be lineal descendants of *Homo erectus erectus.* The antecedents of the Asians and Australians are seen as running in separate, parallel lines back to the *Homo erectus* level, with no common *Homo sapiens* ancestral link. Coon proposed in his book that the Europeans evolved through the group of European Middle Pleistocene fossils that we have identified as *Homo sapiens steinheimensis.*

Two major races are posited by Coon for Africa, going back to Middle Pleistocene origins: a Congoid (or Negro) and a Capoid (or Bushman). Proto-Capoid fossils are very ancient, but proto-Congoid fossils are few and late.

Coon sets his theory to trace five racial lines,

"each as old as man himself,"[13] back to *Homo erectus:* This is a possible alternative theory, but its genetic validity has been challenged.[14]

In an earlier decade, Professor Coon's theory would have evoked academic arguments but no public storm. In the emotional climate of the racial integration movement in the 1960s, however, one sentence of his introduction raised a hurricane. It reads:

However, it is a fair inference . . . that the subspecies who crossed the evolutionary threshold into the category of *Homo sapiens* have evolved the most, and that the obvious correlation between the length of time a subspecies has been in the *sapiens* state and the levels of civilization attained by some of its populations may be related phenomena.[15]

As Coon reads the fossils, the European (Caucasoids, including the Indians of India) made it across the line first—by several hundred thousand years—and created the first civilizations. Negatively, he sees no fossil evidence for any antiquity of the African subspecies (excepting the Bushman-Hottentot local race) and makes no conclusive statements about their origin except that they "appeared as if out of nowhere" very recently.

Segregation propagandists made the most of it, and integrationists excoriated the professor. Dead bones can provoke live issues.

SUMMARY

Racial differences are the expression of variations in gene distribution in semi-isolated populations. Isolation can be the result of geographic or cultural factors. Traditional physical anthropology classified races according to the relative frequency of physical traits that are externally measurable in populations. Modern genetic anthropology includes counts of gene frequencies of blood types and a limited number of other genetically identifiable characters. This makes it possible to get around the ambiguity

[13]Coon, *The Origin of Races,* p. viii.
[14]See T. Dobzhansky, "Review of C. S. Coon, *The Origin of Races*" (*Scientific American,* Vol. 208, No. 2, 1963), pp. 169–172.
[15]Coon, *op. cit.,* p. x.

caused by phenotypes and by the continuous variability of many of the traits morphologically measured. The findings of gene analysis have not of themselves, however, required any marked modification of the traditional major racial groups.

The starting point for any racial study and classification is a geographically identifiable intrabreeding population. This can lead to identification of races on a continental level, in which case nine major races can be distinguished. In addition, classification can be approached on the basis of identification of smaller intrabreeding populations called *local races*. This produces thirty or more possible races. It can also be done on the basis of identification of very tightly intrabreeding, isolated populations called *microgeographic races*, of which there is a large but undetermined number.

Selective adaptation among human populations seems to result in some operation of Gloger's, Bergmann's, and Allen's rules of bioecological distributions.

As social interaction and physical mobility have increased in recent years, a trend toward miscegenation has set in that will undoubtedly blur racial distinctions as gene pools mix.

SELECTED READINGS

Birdsell, J. B.: "The Origin of Human Races" (*The Quarterly Review of Biology*, Vol. 38, No. 2, 1963), pp. 178–189. A dispassionate and well-considered critique of Coon's polyphyletic theory of race origins.

Boyd, W. C.: *Genetics and the Races of Man* (1950). A thorough book by a pioneer authority in the field.

Coon, C. S. (with E. E. Hunt, Jr.): *The Living Races of Man* (1965). The most comprehensive and interesting work on the origin, character and distribution of contemporary races.

————, S. M. Garn, and J. B. Birdsell: *Races: A Study of Race Formation in Man* (1950). An easily understandable, short examination of selective adaptation and its effects in producing races.

Dobzhansky, T.: *Genetics and the Origin of Species* (3d ed., 1951). This book provides the basic biology and ideas for much of the recent developments in the modern scientific approach to the study of race.

————: *Mankind Evolving* (1962). Chapters 9 and 10, "Polymorphism, Class, and Caste" and "Race" are excellent discussions of race building and racial classification.

Dunn, L. C., and T. Dobzhansky: *Heredity, Race, and Society* (1951). An elementary and popular treatment.

Garn, S. M.: *Human Races* (1961). The newest and most clearly written authoritative treatment of the subject.

Hulse, F. S.: *The Human Species* (1963), chaps. 11, 12, and 14. A good general summary with reasonable detail. Particularly useful for its summary of blood-type distributions among the populations of the world as of 1963.

"Origin and Evolution of Man" (*Cold Spring Harbor Symposia on Quantitative Biology*, Vol. 15, 1951). Technical papers summarizing developments in theory and research by geneticists and physical anthropologists.

Shapiro, H. L.: *Race Mixture* (1953). A genuinely authoritative treatment of the findings of science on the results of racial interbreeding.

UNESCO: *The Race Concept* (1952). A balanced evaluation of the idea of race: what it is and what it is not.

Race and cultural capacity

chapter 14

In 1777, when the American Colonies were struggling to win their war of independence, William Robertson (see pages 509–510), the clearest thinker of the eighteenth century in terms of modern anthropology, wrote in Scotland:

A human being as he comes originally from the hand of nature, is everywhere the same. At his first appearance in the state of infancy, whether it be among the rudest savages, or in the most civilized nations, we can discern no quality which marks any distinction or superiority. The capacity of improvement seems to be the same and the talents he may afterwards acquire, as well as the virtues he may be rendered capable of exercising, depend, in a great measure, upon the state of society in which he is placed. To this state his mind naturally accommodates itself, and from it receives discipline and culture. . . . It is only by attending to this great principle, that we can discover what is the character of man in every different period of his progress.[1]

Time has not altered, nor the doctrines of racism impaired, the clarity of this simple truth. Nonetheless, the question of differential racial capacities is still with us, for racism is a highly virulent force in the world of today.

Racism is the doctrine that assumes as self-evident the proposition that "one group has the stigmata of superiority and the other has those of inferiority."[2] Science presupposes that superiority and inferiority must be determined by careful sifting of all the evidence that can be marshaled on the subject. Prejudiced opinion

[1] W. Robertson, *History of America*, Vol. 1, pp. 368–369.
[2] R. F. Benedict, *Race: Science and Politics*, p. 5.

Table 14-1   Human Racial Types Ranked According to Subhuman Primate Characteristics

trait	most apelike	less apelike	least apelike
Cephalic index	Asian	European	African
Cranial capacity	African		Asian, European
Eye color	African, Asian		European
Nasal index	African	Asian	European
Hair form	Asian	European	African
Hair length	European, Asian		African
Body hair	European		African, Asian
Lip form	Asian	European	African
Lip color	Asian	European	African
Facial prognathism	African	European	Asian
Eye form	European, African		Asian

and demagoguery do not provide acceptable bases for determining the facts.

The question of biological superiority and inferiority of races

The debate over whether some races are superior or inferior to others raises the basic question: "Superior in what way?" Nilotic Africans are superior in stature to Negritos; Northwest Europeans are obviously superior in average stature to Pygmies. Nevertheless, this is not the kind of superiority on which the "racial issue" turns. The alleged superiority or inferiority is a functional one. Do some races have a superior capacity for cultural attainment? Are they inherently more intelligent? Do they have an inherently greater capacity for leadership and domination that justifies their control and exploitation of allegedly less fortunately endowed races?

To what conclusions does the anthropological consideration of the facts of physical anthropology, race psychology, anthropogeography, sociology, and cultural history lead in the search for the truth?

Anatomical comparisons   First, are some races more advanced in biological evolution than others? A positive answer would indicate gen-

eral functional superiority. *Homo sapiens* is unquestionably more advanced than *Homo erectus,* and there can be no gainsaying his functional superiority. Further, contemporary *Homo sapiens* is undoubtedly more functionally adapted to survival under modern conditions than the classical *Homo sapiens neandertalensis* was. However, all living races are members of the *Homo sapiens sapiens* group, and functional differences between the varieties of *Homo sapiens sapiens* are not so obvious.

Comparison with subhuman primates   Southern gentlemen argued in the antebellum debates on slavery that Africans were physically and spiritually subhuman and devoid of souls and therefore were not subject to the moral injunction against enslavement of human beings. Some people still argue that their body proportions, facial projection, and flat, broad noses indicate either retarded or advanced evolutionary development—that such features are prima-facie evidence of biological inferiority or superiority. Such arguments prove nothing at all. A comparison of the three primary races will quickly show why (Table 14-1).

This is by no means an adequate balance sheet; innumerable detailed features of anatomy could be listed. All we have undertaken to demonstrate is that with respect to the superficial traits on which popular judgment is based, no race comes out ahead of the others. Africans are most "apelike" in five of the selected traits, whereas Europeans come closest in three. But Africans are least apelike in six of the traits, and Europeans are least so in only three. *This whole argument turns out to be puerile.*

Comparisons of brain size   Attempts have been made to correlate racial intelligence with average brain size. It is a fundamental fact of evolution that brain size and complexity increase relatively with each successive emergent animal form. Functional adaptability increases with larger and more complex brains, as we compare one genus with another. Within the European race, several methodologically sound studies correlating brain size with school and university grades have been made. Klineberg, on consideration of these studies, concludes: "In general there appears to be an exceedingly small, though positive correlation between head size and intelligence."[3] However, judicious interpretation explains this difference as being due to good conditions of nurture, which produce brighter people as well as larger stature, which in turn is consistently correlated with larger brains. If this is true, the correlation between brain size and intelligence is due to external factors, not inheritance.

When the problem of brain size as related to racial intelligence is tested, the results are wholly inconclusive. The average brains of Australians, Pygmies, and Africans are smaller than those of Asians and Europeans. In the case of the Pygmies, this is a function of small body size. Racists have seized on the generally smaller brain size of Africans as evidence of inferiority. But on the basis of such reasoning, we should have to acknowledge the large-brained Eskimos as our intellectual superiors and include the African Zulu and AmaXhosa along with them. The extinct and primitive Neandertal would also rate as our equal if not our superior on this score.

In the case of Neandertal man, anatomical

[3]O. H. Klineberg, *Race Differences*, p. 80.

evidence indicates possible qualitative inferiority of the brain due to the relative smallness of the frontal lobe and the simplicity of convolutions. It has not yet been possible to establish similar deficiencies for any of the living races.

Comparisons of body odor   Another popular basis for assumption of racial superiority is body odor. We know little or nothing about the biochemistry of human perspiration. We do not know what produces diversity of body odor. Diet is definitely a factor, but there is a good possibility that inherently different organic functions are also important.

A tentative conclusion to the effect that distinctive body odors may be inherent racial traits does not carry a correlative conclusion that a particular odor is superior or inferior to another. People are merely prone to accept their own body odor because they are used to it. But it is common to react obsessively to the unpleasantness even of one's own aroma, if we are to judge by popular response to soap advertising and the flourishing sale of deodorants.

Psychological comparisons   The really crucial issue is whether or not the mental processes and psychological aptitudes of different races are inherently different. Then follows the problem: If they are different, is it possible to determine whether the psychological traits of some races are inferior to those of others? Animal breeders and fanciers are thoroughly familiar with inherent differences in temperament, physiological functioning, and learning capacities among breeds or varieties within the same species of animal. It must be recognized that a similar possibility exists in the case of the human animal. Inasmuch as the nervous system of man is a part of his biological system, it is quite possible that inherent differences in the structure and functioning of the nervous systems of different races do exist.

There are three possible approaches to the scientific solution of this problem: (1) neurological analysis of the anatomy and physiochemical functioning of the nervous systems of different races, which, unfortunately, calls for a refinement of laboratory technique far beyond that yet developed by neurologists; (2) controlled psychological experimentation, in which the cultural and environmental factors are held constant or eliminated, so that the inherent functional capacities of different races may be measured; and (3) anthropological analysis of the cultural accomplishments of different races.

The limitations of cross-cultural use of intelligence tests The Australian possesses the world's rudest culture, but since he is in an isolated location, this does not prove his inherent incapacity to do better. The psychologist Porteus attempted a serious evaluation of native Australian endowment by means of a large variety of tests and observations.[4] His psychological results are utterly inconclusive, except to demonstrate the power of cultural influences in causing differential behavior. For instance, the solution of problems by the individual acting alone is the basis of most psychological tests. Porteus found to his dismay that it is difficult to get Australians even to attempt to solve a problem alone, since they are used to acting and thinking in concert. All problems in tribal life are debated and worked out by the council of elders until a unanimous decision is reached. The natives even felt that Porteus should have helped them solve the tests, especially when in one group they had made him a tribal member! Speed has no meaning to the Australian, whose skill in the hunt demands "sustained muscular control, and undivided attention, an extreme sensory wariness, inexhaustible *patience and concentration of purpose.*"[5] Yet speed is an important factor in many intelligence tests. Hence, the results of such tests, which naturally show the Australian up poorly, have no validity. There can be no doubt that tests designed to take full account of skills that are important in the native Australian environment would measure differences between individual natives with reasonable significance. It is equally likely that Australians would obtain a higher rating than Europeans if both were subjected to these tests.

Such results would be just as unfair to whites as the present tests are to the Australians.

Results of intelligence testing in the United States Since 1918, there has been a flurry of activity among experimental psychologists attempting to measure inherent race differences. Hundreds of experiments of varying worth have been undertaken. Many of the earlier ones have been analyzed and summarized in the books of Garth[6] and Klineberg.[7]

Tremendous interest was first raised by the published results obtained from the Army alpha and beta tests of World War I. Subsequently, hundreds of tests of various races and nationalities were undertaken during the 1920s. American Colored and Asians rated definitely lower on these tests than Europeans. On the Binet tests, the Colored IQ averaged around 99; the American (Indian), 75.3; the Chinese and Japanese, 99; and the European, 100. Since Terman, who had the prestige of authority behind him, had expressed the opinion that the Binet scale is a true test of native intelligence, it seemed that the inferiority of Negroes and other non-European races had been scientifically proved. At last, in the eyes of its proponents, social discrimination justified by racial superiority seemed to have an irrefutable *raison d'être.*

More experience with the tests has sobered the psychologists, however. Their own work has demonstrated that emotional maladjustment, amount of schooling, language facility, and kinds of attitudes (motivation) toward the testing process drastically alter performance on the tests. Criticism from anthropologists evoked a realization that tests designed on the basis of one type of cultural experience are not valid when applied to persons trained under markedly different cultures. Our comments on Porteus's experience with Australians illustrate this. Intelligence and aptitude tests measure innate ability and experience, modified by emotional and cultural factors.

The first warnings against uncritical use of

[4]S. D. Porteus, *The Psychology of a Primitive People.*
[5]*Ibid.,* p. 64. Italics are the author's.

[6]T. E. Garth, *Race Psychology.*
[7]Klineberg, *op. cit.*

the results of the Army tests in racial interpretation of differential intelligence appeared in Yerkes's original presentation of the data.[8] It was shown that Coloreds from the North rated much higher than Coloreds from the South. The Army testers observed that this fact could be due to better economic, social, and educational opportunities open to Coloreds in the North. Thus they gave implicit recognition to the effect of environment on intelligence-test performance. They also noted that the difference could be taken to mean that naturally intelligent Coloreds leave the South (selective migration). It was further noted that the median scores of Coloreds from some Northern states were higher than those of white draftees from some Southern states. Since Northern whites obtained higher grades on intelligence tests than Southern whites, the inference was rather clear that the better general educational and economic environment of the North was the crucial element.

THE KLINEBERG STUDY OF NEW YORK SCHOOL-CHILDREN, 1935   The Army testers had left open the question of whether the high performance of Northern Coloreds was due to their innate capacity or to the more favorable environment of the North. The problem was tackled by Klineberg in the 1930s. The first step was to obtain the school records of Colored children in Charleston, Nashville, and Birmingham. The percentile rankings of children who were known to have left for the North were compared with those of children who stayed in the South. Klineberg found: "The migrants as a whole were almost exactly at the average of the whole Negro school population in these three Southern cities."[9]

Next, Klineberg and his assistants measured 3,000 Southern-born Colored children in the schools of New York City. Five different standard intelligence and performance tests were used. It was found that the IQ and other ratings of new arrivals (less than one year's residence in New York) were lowest and that these ratings improved in regular progression with each additional year of residence in New York, until the same level as that of the Colored children born in the North was reached. The factor of mixed ancestry was properly taken into account, and a check was made to determine that the more recent arrivals were not of inferior rating in the South.

The Klineberg studies demonstrated conclusively that the lower IQ ratings of Southern Coloreds are in large measure an IQ *retardation* caused by inadequate schooling and a cultural environment different from that presupposed by the standard intelligence tests. Modification of education and cultural environment in the direction of that enjoyed by whites, in the case of New York City Coloreds, narrows the gap between the IQ averages of white and Colored children. The gap was not wholly closed, for Klineberg found that twelve-year-old New York Colored schoolchildren were still six to eighteen months lower in "mental age" than white children of the same chronological age. The deleterious effects of separate and unequal educational and cultural opportunities, against which the United States Supreme Court's antisegregation decision of 1954 was directed, are clearly evident.

It remains perfectly true that the bulk of intelligence tests give higher median IQ ratings to American Europeans than to American Coloreds.[10] But it is just as true that:

The widely accepted belief in the hereditary group differences in intelligence which the test results seem to demonstrate must for the present be regarded as unproved. If intellectual differences between racial and social groups do exist (and this point is still debatable) the testing technique is nevertheless incapable of proving their existence.[11]

The reason lies in the pervasive influence of very subtle cultural differences that the tests cannot control.

[8]R. M. Yerkes (ed.), "Psychological Examining in the U.S. Army" (*Memoirs of the National Academy of Sciences*, Vol. 15, 1921).
[9]Klineberg, *op. cit.*, p. 184.

[10]H. E. Garrett, "Negro-White Differences in Mental Ability in the United States" (*The Scientific Monthly*, Vol. 65, 1947), pp. 329–333.
[11]O. H. Klineberg, "Mental Tests" (*Encyclopedia of the Social Sciences*, Vol. 10, 1933), p. 326.

THE DEUTSCH-BROWN STUDY OF NEW YORK PRI-
MARY GRADE CHILDREN, 1964 The 1935 findings
of Klineberg remain unaltered three decades
later. IQ ratings cannot be taken literally because of the differential effects of home experience and the cultural environment on individual
development. A large number of recent studies
have attempted to get at the degree of influence
of differences of sociocultural experience on
racial IQ ratings. A very good example is the
research on children of American Colored and
European races in New York City. The children
were first- and fifth-graders. Home background
data were obtained, and ratings of socioeconomic status were worked out. Three SES
(socioeconomic status) groups, ranging from
low to high, were formulated. In the lowest
group, there was an IQ (Lange-Thorndike Test)
differential of six points in favor of Europeans
(97.24 to 91.24). The gap increased to 10.7
(105.59 to 94.82) in the highest SES group. As
socioeconomic level goes up, the children of
both racial backgrounds show higher IQs, but
the improvement for Europeans is much
greater. Deutsch and Brown, the investigators,
interpret these results to mean that the influence of racial membership tends to become
increasingly manifest and crucial as the social-
class level increases:

In other words, it is much more difficult for the Negro
to attain identical middle or upper-class status with
the whites, and the social class gradations are less
marked for Negroes because Negro life in a caste society is considerably more homogeneous than is life for
the majority group. . . . there are fewer variegated
family activities, such as eating together or taking
trips, in the Negro as opposed to the white groups.[12]

Two social variables in these populations of
primary grade children that correlated positively
with the IQ differentials for race and socioeconomic status were the frequency of broken
homes (no father in the household) and the
amount of preschooling the child had had (early
educational opportunity for development).
There was no father in 43.9 per cent of the

Colored homes at the lowest economic level, as
against 15.4 per cent for the Europeans. At the
highest SES level, only 13.7 per cent of the
Colored homes had no father present, but every
European child in this group had the benefit of
a father in the house. Children of both races
who came from a home with a father present
performed appreciably better.

Deutsch and Brown sum up their results in
these words: "The conclusion is inescapable
that the Negro group is a socially deprived one.
It would seem probable that when behavorial
scientists have been able to classify and measure the elements and variables in social deprivation, the observed differential in intelligence
test scores between Negro and white samples
will be accounted for."[13]

Conclusions regarding psychological-test results
On May 17, 1954, the United States Supreme
Court, relying heavily on the evidence of sociopsychological studies of the order just cited,
ruled that racially segregated schools are another factor that tends, as the court said, "to
retard the educational and mental development
of Negro children and to deprive them of some
of the benefits they would receive in a racially
integrated school system."[14]

The ameliorating effect of greater equaliza-
tion of cultural factors through integration of
educational opportunity was reported by O. Car-
michael, superintendent of schools of Louisville,
Kentucky, who declared that the IQ ratings of
Colored children in all grades in the Louisville
schools had improved significantly during the
two years following integration. There was "a
slight improvement for the whites; a substantial
one for the Negroes." Klineberg himself surveyed the dozens of comparative test results
that covered both Colored and white populations in the United States between 1935 and
1964. He noted that there is indeed in most
instances, but by no means all, a gap in the

[12]M. Deutsch and B. Brown, "Social Influences in Negro-
White Intelligence Differences" (*The Journal of Social Issues*, Vol.
20, 1964), p. 27.

[13]*Ibid.,* p. 35.
[14]Quoted in O. Klineberg, "Negro-White Differences in Intelligence Test Performance: A New Look at an Old Problem"
(*The American Psychologist,* Vol. 18, 1963), p. 201.

test ratings of whites as against those of Coloreds. But he also noted that in every instance in which factors modifying the social disadvantages of the Colored are introduced, the IQ ratings of the Colored show marked improvement and the gap decreases. "I can only conclude," says Klineberg at the end of his 1964 review, "that there is no scientifically acceptable evidence for the view that ethnic groups differ in innate abilities. This is not the same as saying that there are no ethnic differences in such abilities."[15]

In summary, the evidence from psychology is largely negative. It demonstrates several points: (1) So-called "intelligence tests" measure innate skill plus cultural experience. No test has yet been evolved that can eliminate the cultural factor, and differential ratings of the various races in intelligence tests must be critically evaluated. (2) Aptitude tests do reveal racial differentials in visual, motor, and vocal skills, but these too are subject to cultural influences that have not been eliminated in tests and measurements. (3) Many skills of intelligence and aptitude definitely change when the cultural environment changes.

The whole result of scientific race psychology has been to throw the explanation of significant behavior differences among people of different races over into the field of cultural experience. The findings of psychology harmonize with those of anthropology and history, which we treat simultaneously in the next section.

Race and culture history

It is the judgment of anthropologists that all races are equally capable of cultural development and that culture operates independently of racial heredity. How, then, it is often asked, can it be that some races are culturally more advanced than others? How does one account for the fact that the Africans did not attain civilization until it was brought to them by Europeans? Is it not true that the highest modern civilizations have been developed by the European whites?

Three principles must be grasped in formulating the answers to these questions: (1) Although all cultures are fundamentally similar in their nuclear cores, the range of cultural variability as manifested by human societies is truly remarkable. Limits to the range of culture are imposed by the physical nature of man. These limits are so basic and so generalized, however, that they are common to all races of man. The forms of variation are the result of the processes of culture growth, not of racial predisposition. (2) The behavior and cultural ingenuity of different peoples within any given race are so variable that obviously the racial factor can be of little importance. (3) The same people may exhibit astounding cultural energy at one period of their history and be almost wholly devoid of it at another. Peoples who have been culturally quiescent for centuries suddenly burst into a veritable fury of cultural development without any determinable change in racial composition. The Japanese are the most spectacular example in modern times.

In European history, the facts confound the racists again and again. Cicero said of the Britons: "Do not obtain your slaves from the Britons, for the Britons are so stupid and so dull that they are not fit to be slaves." Yet what was to be the relative position of Cicero's descendants and the Britons 2,000 years later? The Romans also considered the Germans inherently incapable of high civilization.

It is easy for North Europeans and their descendants to forget how late they came to the forefront of civilization and cultural development. The centers of cultural invention did not shift to North Europe until after the Renaissance, only 500 years ago. During the Dark Ages, the Maya Indians of Central America showed greater cultural accomplishments than the European whites.

The history of the Uto-Aztecans is also pertinent. The Aztecs, Comanches, and Shoshones are all Indians who speak similar languages indicative of a common historical background. They are racially quite similar, and 700 years

[15] *Ibid.*, p. 203.

ago they stood as lowly hunters and gatherers at the bottom of the cultural scale, living in the western deserts of North America and possessing a meager cultural equipment. Historical events radically altered their basic characters and cultural development.

The Aztecs wandered southward until they settled in what is now Central Mexico in the midst of several high cultures that had been greatly influenced by the Mayan tradition. In A.D. 1325, they founded Tenochtitlan (the present Mexico City), and 175 years later they were overlords of the land: maize growers, road builders, astronomers, artists, and possessors of a city with public buildings of cut stone so magnificent that stout Cortez cried out that in all Andalusia there was nothing to compare with its glory.

The Comanches wandered into the southwestern plains at a somewhat later date. There they acquired Spanish horses and guns and came into contact with the warlike tradition of the Plains tribes. They became truculent, nomadic robbers and fighters, so violent that to this day the plainsman's saying, "as wild as a Comanche" is still heard in the West.

The Shoshones, who retain the attitudes and culture once shared with the Comanches, obtained neither guns nor horses. They were regularly mauled by the Blackfeet, who had guns and horses, so they timidly hid out in the desert —peaceable, because they dared not make war. They developed a strong inferiority complex, and they are the only Indians the author has ever worked with who welcomed the coming of the whites. "If the white man had not come, there would be no Indians left," they said. By Indians, they meant themselves.

As circumstances found them, the Aztecs and Comanches had become definitely superior people, and the Shoshones miserable by any man's count. But race was a constant element. The accidents of culture history had frowned upon the hapless Shoshones.

What causes cultural spurts is a complex and difficult question that must be analyzed in terms of cultural process. Outstanding among the multitude of factors is cross-fertilization of

cultures, the stimulation of new ideas and new ways of coping with the environment. Isolated peoples always stagnate, whether they are Asian, African, or European. But the bent of the culture is important too—a backward-looking, ancestor-worshipping culture is not readily amenable to change and further development. The physical environment is also influential. All these can be shown to be active factors. But since it cannot be shown that races differ in the possession of hereditary mentality and capacities, because the performance of different groups within a single race ranges from high to low, and because the performance of a single racial group varies so markedly through time, it becomes evident that race per se is of small moment in cultural achievement. <u>Culture, not race, is the molder of human societies.</u>

SUMMARY: THE UNESCO STATEMENT ON RACE

In summary and conclusion, we can do no better than cite the closing paragraphs of the *Statement on Race,* formulated in 1950 by an expert panel of physical anthropologists and geneticists convened in Paris by the United Nations Educational, Scientific, and Cultural Organization. It reads as follows:

We have thought it worth while to set out in a formal manner what is at present scientifically established concerning individual and group differences.

(a) In matters of race, the only characteristics which anthropologists have so far been able to use effectively as a basis for classification are physical (anatomical and physiological).

(b) Available scientific knowledge provides no basis for believing that the groups of mankind differ in their innate capacity for intellectual and emotional development.

(c) Some biological differences between human beings within a single race may be as great as or greater than the same biological differences between races.

(d) Vast social changes have occurred that have not been connected in any way with changes in racial type. Historical and sociological studies thus support the view that genetic differences are of little significance in determining the social and cultural differences between different groups of men.

(e) There is no evidence that race mixture produces disadvantageous results from a biological point of view. The social results of race mixture, whether for good or ill, can generally be traced to social factors.[16]

SELECTED READINGS

Count, E. W.: *This Is Race* (1950). A comprehensive selection of writing on race from all parts of the world.

[16]For the entire statement, see H. L. Shapiro, "Revised Version of UNESCO Statement on Race" (*American Journal of Physical Anthropology,* Vol. 10, 1952), pp. 363–368.

Klineberg, O. H.: *Race Differences* (1935). An eminently sound appraisal of race psychology and the interpretation of psychological testing of races.

Myrdal, G. S.: *An American Dilemma* (1944). As close to a definitive study of the effect of culture on racial behavior in the United States, *ca.* 1940, as it is possible to come. The work is the product of the combined efforts of a special team of able social scientists.

Simpson, G. E., and J. M. Yinger: *Racial and Cultural Minorities* (rev. ed., 1955). An exceedingly comprehensive and well-documented coverage of the whole subject of ethnic groups. Chapters 5 to 8, on the cultural factor in prejudice and on the consequences of prejudice, are particularly relevant.

Part 4/ Primitive culture and society

Man eats to live. The cravings of hunger are sensory stimuli that provoke the organism into food-getting activities. Ingestion of food is an absolute necessity to the maintenance and functioning of the organism. Food as fuel to be released as energy is necessary to bodily action. Food as repair material to replace the continuous loss of substance from the body is necessary to bodily maintenance. True foods are either <u>energy yielders</u> or <u>non-energy yielders</u>, and man must get an adequate intake of both. The latter supply inorganic materials for body replacement. In addition, man must take in indigestible materials, called <u>roughage</u>, to assist the passage of true food and its residues through the alimentary canal.

Food getting is a physical imperative; subsistence, a fundamental interest; and hunger, a diffuse primary drive.

The society that fails to solve the problems of development of minimal subsistence techniques is doomed. The ghost of Malthus haunts all mankind. In the ghastly light of the twentieth-century population explosion, the ghost becomes ever more restless.

The subsistence resources available to a people depend upon three factors: the natural environment, culture, and population. People who subsist by collecting and gathering roots, berries, seeds, and insects are for the most part directly dependent upon what the natural environment offers for the taking. People who have acquired the techniques of planting, cultivating, and harvesting crops, or of the husbandry of animals, and who have mastered methods of cooking or otherwise changing the chemicophysical substance of natural products so as to make them useful or more desirable as foods are less directly dependent upon the natural offerings of their physical environment. As man learns to expand his food-producing resources through cultural techniques and devices, he pushes back the specter of starvation and lays the base for the expansion of society, but only insofar as food production can keep ahead of population increase.

Cultural ecology

Ecology is the study of the mutual relations between organisms and their environment. Human ecology is concerned with the ways in which man relates to his environment and how his activities affect it.[1] Cultural ecology, as defined by Julian Steward, seeks to explain the origin of particular cultural features and patterns that characterize different areas, rather than to derive general principles applicable to any cultural-environmental situations.[2]

The natural environment does not determine absolutely the nature of the foodstuffs a society can enjoy. Deserts can be made to bloom and bear fruit. Hothouses can be built in the arctic, and ice cream can be frozen on a

Pacific isle. Yet only quite advanced cultures make such things possible. Nor do food-getting techniques dictate the details of all aspects of culture. Great variations occur in the cultures of hunting peoples and, more especially, of gardeners.

Modern anthropology rejects the cruder aspects of environmental determinism espoused by the anthropogeographer of an earlier day. Nonetheless, the nature of the physical environment does influence the materials and modes of subsistence of any people, especially primitive peoples.[3]

These, in turn, are intimately related to the ways in which the family and kinship, political structure, and religious and ceremonial interests are organized and expressed. The physical environment does not determine directly what the culture of a people will be, but it does indeed limit its nature. Indirectly, the environment is a powerful factor in cultural selectivity and innovation. Nonetheless, the culture and the food preference and work habits that it sustains are important determinants of the ways in which a people utilize their physical setting. Particularly significant is the world view of a people (see Chapter 34).

The Navaho and Pueblo Indians The cultural ecology of the Navaho and Pueblo Indians aptly illustrates the significance of world view in a people's use of its environment. These tribes occupy the same part of the southwestern desert in New Mexico and Arizona. They have been neighbors ever since the Navahos moved down from Canada 1,000 years ago. Both practice gardening and pastoralism, and yet their utilization of the environment and their social systems are very different. The Pueblos live in compact masonry villages housing 100 to 1,500 people. Most of their villages have not moved in centuries. They garden with intensive proficiency and exhibit more interest in religious and ceremonial control of weather and crop control than they do in the mechanics

[1]O. C. Stewart, for example, has shown how the practice of setting fire to the prairies by Indians drove back the forests in North America. See his "Fire as the First Great Force Employed by Man," in W. L. Thomas (ed.), *Man's Role in Changing the Face of the Earth*, pp. 115–133.

[2]J. H. Steward, *Theory of Culture Change*, pp. 30–42.

[3]A. L. Kroeber, *Cultural and Natural Areas of Native North America*, represents the quintessence of anthropological analysis of the relation of cultures to geographic features of regional areas.

of gardening itself, although their gardening techniques are very effective. Dominance of the group over the individual is tight and relentless. The political system is that of a totalitarian theocracy. The Navahos, on the other hand, live in widely dispersed hogans (semisubterranean earth lodges; see Chapter 16), and their main interest is fixed upon sheep. They also garden, but only in a minor way. They do virtually nothing about weather control or crop fertility. Their supernatural interests rest in the maintenance of personal health. They have no centralized government,[4] or even chiefs. Their social system is highly atomistic. Navahos and Pueblos are as unlike as night and day, despite their identical physical environments.

Both are limited in their gardening to natural watercourses, since the annual rainfall is too meager. Both do some hunting, but neither could make hunting a major subsistence source, for game is too sparse in their environment. Obviously, neither makes or uses boats or does any fishing. But these are negative examples of environmental limitation. The number and degree of differences and, especially, the elaborate richness of Pueblo culture, however, show how much more important in cultural ecology is the quality and degree of development of the culture itself than the mere physical environment.

The Ruanda of the Congo Ruanda society also illustrates that culture patterns relate to, but are not determined by, the physical environment. Like the Ankole, whose social system is discussed in some detail in Chapter 27 (pages 408–409), the Ruanda constitute a prime example of a conquest state. The rulers are Tussi tribesmen, extremely tall Nilotic invaders and militaristic cattle herdsmen. Their government, their wars, their whole lives are centered around their cattle. Gardening is beneath their dignity and reserved for the Hutu, a racially distinct population of Bantu-speaking horticulturalists, who were the earlier inhabitants of the country.

[4]Under the influence of the Indian Reorganization Act of 1934 (the so-called New Deal for Indians), the Navahos organized as a federally chartered corporation and have operated under a tribal council since that time.

The Hutu are absolutely barred from ownership of cattle and are exploited by their Tussi overlords. Yet a third group, another distinct population, is the Twa, Pygmy forest dwellers and hunters, who exist as henchmen of a sort to the Tussi. The three tribes were originally separate social entities, each with its own subsistence technique. After the Tussi conquest, which was completed several centuries ago, they were forcibly consolidated into a single society using the different ecological niches (grasslands, open forest garden areas, and heavy forest hunting territories) in accordance with the culturally determined usages of the three groups. In 1958 and 1963, thousands of Tussi were slaughtered in ferocious uprisings after the Congo gained its independence, as the Hutu, who greatly outnumber their erstwhile overlords, threw off the yoke of servility.

Levels of subsistence techniques

In Part 1, as we followed the evolution of man and culture, we saw how the earliest hominids lived by hunting and gathering throughout the entire Paleolithic age. Then, shortly after the end of the Pleistocene, when *Homo sapiens sapiens* was fully established, he quickly shifted to Mesolithic hunting and foraging, out of which the Neolithic era of incipient agriculture and the Bronze and/or Iron Age era of intensive agriculture followed. It was also indicated that some populations made the ecological adaptation of primary reliance upon pastoralism. As a way of life, it is neither earlier nor later than agriculture; it is an alternative that is turned to when physical and social conditions make it the more rewarding path to pursue.

The levels of subsistence techniques arranged from bottom to top in the order of their evolutionary priority *and* the degree of complexity of cultural integration that characterizes each is as follows.

4. Intensive agriculture or pastoralism
3. Agriculture or pastoralism
2. Hunting and foraging
1. Hunting and gathering

Table 15-1   *Frequency of Levels of Subsistence Bases in 565 Cultures Distributed by Continents*

subsistence	Africa	Mediterranean	Asia	Pacific islands	North America	South America	total
plow agriculture	0	49	54	14	0	0	117
pastoralism	23	27	16	0	8	5	79
developed agriculture	82	2	5	58	42	46	235
foraging	2	0	0	15	5	11	33
hunting and gathering	9	0	10	12	55	15	101

NOTE: The Mediterranean and Asiatic cultures are based mostly on plow agriculture; African societies rely on gardening (developed agriculture) and pastoralism; Pacific Islanders are predominantly gardeners, as are the peoples of South America; and North Americans are equally hunters and gardeners. SOURCE: A. D. Coult and R. W. Habenstein, *Cross Tabulations of Murdock's World Ethnographic Sample*, p. 32.

When Columbus opened all the world to the spread of European civilization, there were no peoples left in Europe or the Mediterranean areas who were still on the first three levels of subsistence. The Lapps had become intensive reindeer pastoralists. Across the north of Siberia, the Samoyed and Yukaghir hunters held a thin fringe, while the Gilyak on the northeast coast were a tribe of hunters and fishers. Africa was given over wholly to pastoralists and food-growing peoples, except for the Bushmen, Congo Pygmies, and a few other scattered groups. All Indonesians, except for a few small groups, were gardeners or agriculturalists.

Agriculture in the Old World attained a continuous distribution from Europe and the Mediterranean scrub forests of North Africa into India, Southeast Asia, and throughout the Pacific, except for Australia and Tasmania.

In North America, all the prairie and Eastern woodland tribes south of the Great Lakes and the St. Lawrence River raised maize, beans, and squashes. The Indians of the Southwest were intensive gardeners and growers of maize.

Even in the Great Plains, settled villagers gardened in the river bottoms, and there were few hunting tribes on the far reaches of the Plains themselves. Hunting and foraging were characteristic of California, the Great Basin desert, the woodlands of Canada, and the arctic wastes inhabited by the Eskimos. Texas and northern Mexico were still mostly exploited by food foragers, but the rest of all Central and South America was given over to intensive agriculture, except for the extreme southern part of the continent, where hunters and gatherers eked out a marginal existence.

In the nineteenth century, Neolithic and Iron Age agricultural techniques had so diffused around the world that of 565 cultures in Professor G. P. Murdock's world ethnographic sample, 235, or 41 per cent, of the societies represented practiced developed agriculture, while an additional 117, or 20 per cent, used the plow. This means that 61 per cent, or nearly two-thirds, had assimilated food *growing* as their subsistence base. A mere 6 per cent (33) were engaged in foraging, which indicates that once domestication of plants had been achieved, the transitional type of foraging subsistence survived only among peoples living in marginal environments. Seventy-nine, or 13 per cent, of the sample were pastoralists, and 101, or 18 per cent, were living as hunters.[5] In recent modern times, it can be seen, most primitive peoples were gardeners or developed agriculturalists.

None of the categories of subsistence techniques, it must be emphasized, is absolutely exclusive. All food economies are mixed, to a greater or lesser degree. Gardeners still hunt and fish. Pastoralists raid or exchange meat for flour. Even an atomic, industralized society such as ours includes agriculture, pastoralism, fishing, and hunting within its activities. When we identify a subsistence economy as agricultural or pastoral, it means only that this is the predominant food source. A hunting and gathering economy is just that, however.

Hunting and gathering Hunters always rely to some extent upon berries, nuts, and roots to round out their diet. But they are distinguished from collectors and gatherers in that they are predominantly predatory carnivores in their subsistence habits. Man is omnivorous by nature. This more than any other single trait distinguishes him from his vegetarian anthropoidal relatives. The revolutionary meat-eating habit first took hold in the evolutionary development of the australopithecines.

It is difficult for man to down his animal victims without the aid of tools. In almost all hunting situations, he relies upon some inventive device to assist him in bringing down his quarry. Thus he uses clubs, spears, darts, arrows, deadfalls, pitfalls, snares, nets, weirs, hooks, axes, knives, and poisons to accomplish his ends. He may enlist the aid of a dog, or mount a horse or camel. He may fashion a boat to bring him to his quarry. Whatever the device he may use, hunting techniques are those of assault (shooting, spearing, clubbing, axing, stabbing), trapping and snaring, the pitfall, and poisoning. Shooting, while the most commonly preferred technique among recent primitives, was probably the last of these methods to appear in human prehistory. The bow was not invented until late Paleolithic or early Neolithic

[5]Data are derived from A. D. Coult and R. W. Habenstein, *Cross Tabulations of Murdock's World Ethnographic Sample*, p. 32.

Fig. 15-1 Fish traps on the Congo River at Stanley Falls, near Stanleyville, Congo. Elaborate scaffolding of lashed poles to support the basket traps attest to a high degree of cooperative organization and primitive technical skill. (Courtesy of the American Museum of Natural History.)

Fig. 15-2 Bison herds on the North American plains often stretched to the horizon. Drives and surrounds were tribal methods of killing large numbers for the winter meat supply. Individual hunters sometimes used wolf skin disguises to get within bow shot and to lessen the danger of attack from wounded animals. (Courtesy of the American Museum of Natural History.)

times. Neandertal man had clubs, spears, and hand axes. While there is no direct evidence that he utilized traps and snares or pitfalls, it is likely that he had invented simple devices of this order. There is no way of knowing whether he wittingly used poisons or not.

Because it is so efficient a weapon, the bow had attained almost worldwide distribution by the seventeenth century. The skill of most primitive hunters in tracking game to bring them within bowshot is so well known as not to bear repeating here. Devices of disguise are cleverly used in some tribes. Bushmen artists have depicted disguised bowmen stalking the unwary ostrich. Western Indians were wont to wear antelope skins to approach that fleet and shy beast. Cheyennes shot eagles on the wing by hiding under grass in a pit from which they slowly rotated a stick with a bit of cloth on the end. This aroused the curiosity of the king of birds, who warily soared lower and lower until the patient hunter could spring from his blind for a shot.

Fig. 15-3 The close of an elephant hunt. Except that they possess ironheaded, rather than flint-pointed, spears, and that the environment is semitropical rather than glacial, these Mandari hunters of the eastern Sudan, Africa, could be reenacting an Upper Paleolithic mammoth hunt of 30,000 B.C. (From Peter Molloy, The Cry of the Fish Eagle, *Michael Joseph Ltd.)*

In the jungles of Malaysia and South America and in the woodlands of the southeastern United States, the blowgun with dart is often preferred for the hunting of small game and birds. The heavy jungle growth inhibits any long-distance shooting, and in such a setting darts are often more effective than arrows, especially in South America and Indonesia, where they are poison-tipped.

The ritual of the hunt The hunting of larger animals is not usually a matter of technique pure and simple. Ritual and magic are evoked to reinforce the hunter, whose anxiety for personal safety and fear of failure are overriding. Much of the cave art left by Cro-Magnon man is eloquent, if mute, evidence of this. His painted figures of animals frequently show them wounded and pierced by darts. We do not know what ritual formulas gave efficacy to Cro-Magnon animal effigies. But a Winnebago Indian tells of a very holy hill in Wisconsin in which there was a cave wherein lived twenty spirits, called *Those-who-cry-like-babies.*

My father had control of them [says Crashing Thunder in his autobiography] and when he wished to bless a man he would take his bow and arrows and, holding them in his hands, lead the man around the hill and into the lodge (i.e., into the hill). There he would look for a stone pillar, and upon it, at about arm's length, he drew the pictures of a number of different animals. My father possessed only one arrow, but that one was a holy one. Then dancing around the stone pillar and singing some songs, he finished by breathing upon the pillar. Finally he walked around it and shot at it and when he looked at the stone, it had turned into a deer with large horns which fell dead at his feet. . . . My father was a very famous hunter and my brother wished to be like him.[6]

Whaling among the Eskimos and certain Northwest Coast Indians is assuredly one of the bravest and most technically skillful hunting-by-assault accomplishments of any primitive people. To reinforce his hunting skills, to give social recognition to the outstanding hunter, and merely in consequence of his belief in the spirit nature of whales and all the denizens of the ani-

[6]P. Radin (ed.), *Crashing Thunder*, pp. 27–28.

mal world, the Alaskan made of whale hunting not only a hunt activity but also a cult of magical and religious observances.

Lantis's analysis of the Alaskan Whale Cult[7] has revealed it as a complex of technological, economic, sociopolitical, magico-religious elaborations. The Whale Cult is only one example among the many that come to our attention when we observe actual subsistence activities by means of fieldwork. Whale hunting, then, in addition to the actual chase, which involves skilled use of boats, paddles, harpoons, lines, and floats to locate, trail, attack, destroy, and land the great sea monster, is worked into a web of behavior and beliefs that includes the following chief elements:

1. The headman of a whaling crew is a headman of the local group. Whaling leadership is integrated with social leadership.

2. Distribution of the parts of the whale is regulated by customary usage in accordance with which the boat owner, harpooner, and others hold particular rights.

3. Initiation into the Whale Cult is through a long, arduous period of instruction in which the young whaler learns the rituals and songs and seeks a vision.

4. Special amulets to ensure good luck are used in the whale hunt and are hidden away in a secret cave between seasons. Knowledge of such caves and of the use of the amulets is passed from father to son.

5. Whaling songs are sung. They are private incorporeal property (see pages 423–424).

6. The season of whaling is a special ceremonial and tabu season. The whalers are isolated from the main village. They are unclean, must sleep in the open, and (in northern Alaska) must not eat raw meat.

7. Whalers must be sexually continent before and during the whaling activities.

8. All those left in the village during the actual hunt must neither sleep nor work.

9. The wife of the chief whaler must remain quietly at home without eating, "in order to draw the whale to her."

10. Corpses or parts of the bodies of deceased whalers are used in ceremonial preparation for the hunt or are carried in the whaleboat.

11. All gear must be repaired and cleansed before the onset of the whaling season; otherwise the whale will be offended.

12. When the whale is hauled ashore, it is given a symbolic drink of water by the whaler's wife.

13. As the whale is cut up, certain parts of its body are ceremonially handled, and very special rituals are performed to return the whale's spirit to the sea unangered. It is given food, and no disturbing noises are permitted.

14. The length of the ritual period following a whale killing is the same as for a human death (3 to 5 days).

This is only a brief sketch of the Whale Cult complex, but it should serve to indicate how much more there is to hunting than tracking and killing.

Hunting and foraging Foraging differs from gathering in the intensity of the dependence upon wild seeds, fruits, and roots. Instead of using wild plant life to supplement a predominantly meat diet, the forager relies upon hunting to supplement a predominantly vegetarian diet, but he has not yet domesticated plants.

To illustrate the subsistence techniques of a group of hunters and foragers, we might describe the activities of one or another Australian tribe, or the Tasmanians, Semangs, Andaman Islanders, African Pygmies, or African Bushmen. Any of numerous California tribes would do equally well, as would one of the three main tribes of Tierra del Fuego. However, we take the Great Basin Shoshones as our exemplars.

The Shoshones In 1860, Abbé Domenech noted of the Great Basin Shoshones: "According to the season, they emigrate from one place to another to seek miserable roots, which form their only nourishment; even animals are seldom to be found there."[8] It is because of their

[7]M. Lantis, "The Alaskan Whale Cult and Its Affinities" (*American Anthropologist,* Vol. 40, 1938), pp. 438–464.

[8]E. Domenech, *Seven Years' Residence in the Great Deserts of North America,* Vol. 1, p. 242.

root-grubbing activities that the Shoshonean food gatherers are known throughout the Western states as *diggers*. Steward lists over one hundred species of seeds, roots, and nuts known to have been eaten by the Shoshones.[9] Roots were extracted with a simple pointed digging stick, or dibble. Seeds were collected with the aid of a woven basket and a fanlike beater with which to knock the grass seeds into the basket. Of all the delectable seeds offered by the desert, those of the sunflower were the most prized. Roasted lightly and ground on a stone metate, they were reduced to an oily paste, which tasted, according to the Shoshones, "just like peanut butter." In fieldwork among the members of the H3kandika (Seed Eater) Shoshones, who live on Bannock Creek in Idaho, gallon jars of peanut butter make most acceptable presents. They stimulate memories of olden days. Pine nuts also played a great part in the social economy of the various Shoshones—with results that we shall look into under Land Ownership (see Chapter 28).

Not only was the environment exploited for roots, berries, and nuts, but insects were looked upon as an epicurean godsend. Regular communal grasshopper drives were organized. A sizable pit, 3 or 4 feet deep and 30 or 40 feet across, was laboriously prepared. Then men, women, and children formed a large circle, which converged slowly on the pit as they drove the grasshoppers before them with brush beaters. A good drive netted countless grasshoppers, which could then be roasted to provide a feast of plenty.

Ants were a more favored delicacy because of their pungent flavor when properly prepared. In March, when the ants had left the larva stage but were not yet up and around, a woman would scoop up an entire ant nest in her large scallop-shaped winnowing basket. With dextrous and wonderful manipulation, she shook the basket so that the ants gathered in its heel, while the sand and dirt bounced off the outer edge. When only ants remained, she scooped

up hot coals with the basket. Rapidly jouncing them in the air, she kept the coals and ants turning together and the basket from burning up. When at last the legs were burned from the ants and their bodies properly toasted, her motions were deftly altered; the ashes bounced off the edge of the basket, while the ants once again foregathered in its heel. They were then dumped upon a grinding stone, rolled out, and reduced to a delectable paste—from the Shoshone point of view. (This recipe is known as Shoshone *antipasto*.)

Small rodents were trapped by means of simple deadfalls. Rabbit hunting took the form of a great communal hunt under the direction of a hunt chief.[10] Nets were set up, and beaters drove the quarry into the waiting meshes. Soft robes were plaited from thin strips of rabbit fur for winter use. Antelope were occasionally hunted in much the same way, but with the addition of magical lures and antelope disguises worn by the hunters. A fence of brush supplanted the nets of the rabbit hunt.[11]

Deer, mountain sheep, and mountain goats were sometimes pursued alone by the most energetic hunters. A hunter with much endurance would chase a deer or sheep for two whole days until exhaustion of the quarry made it possible for him to get close enough for a shot. Should this seem like incredible exertion, perhaps the motivation can better be appreciated if we quote Lewis and Clark on the meat hunger of the Shoshones. One of the expedition's hunters had killed a deer on Friday morning, Aug. 16, 1805. The Shoshones accompanying Captain Lewis, after a pell-mell race to the spot where Lewis's man had dressed the deer,

. . . all dismounted and ran tumbling over each other like famished dogs; each tore away at whatever part he could, and instantly began to eat it; some had the liver, some the kidneys, in short no part on which we look with disgust escaped them; one of them who had seized about nine feet of the entrails was chewing at

[9] J. H. Steward, *Basin-Plateau Aboriginal Sociopolitical Groups* (Bureau of American Ethnology, Bulletin 120, 1938), pp. 21–32.

[10] Communal rabbit hunts extend down through the Southwest into the pueblos, where participation is not only a lark but also a religious duty, and into the various groups of the Gila River area.

[11] Antelope and buffalo drives were performed by the Plains tribes in a somewhat similar manner.

one end, while with his hands he was diligently clearing his way by discharging the contents at the other.[12]

This method of eating "sausage" was still remembered by my Shoshone informants in 1934.

Shoshone deer hunting was much like that of the Tarahumara Indians of Mexico, of whom Bennett and Zingg report:

Hunting deer consists of chasing the deer for two days—never less than one day. The Tarahumara keeps the deer constantly on the move. Only occasionally does he get a glimpse of his quarry, but he follows it unerringly through his own uncanny ability to read the tracks. The Indian chases the deer until it falls of exhaustion, often with its hoofs completely worn away.[13]

Fear of starvation constantly haunted the Shoshones. Like the Eskimos, they sometimes took a desperate last resort in cannibalism. But cannibals were feared and hated, and occasionally lynched.[14]

It would be an error to conclude from the above remarks that the Shoshones were devoid of all fastidiousness. They would and will eat neither dogs nor coyotes, for Coyote is a supernatural culture hero—a lovable rapscallion who figures in many a myth as an Indian equivalent of Tyll Eulenspiegel. He is the younger brother of Wolf, whom some Shoshones look upon as the Supreme Deity.[15] To kill a coyote or his cousin the dog is unthinkable; to eat them, impossible. Modern Shoshones, in 1934, were even loath to eat the surplus Navaho sheep sent them by the government. Skinned sheep look too much like flayed dogs.

Bands of food gatherers are necessarily seminomadic. They must cover wide areas to skim off sufficient provender to keep them alive. But a given band tends to stay within its own familiar territory because (1) any animal may secure food and water more efficiently if it knows the land; (2) all human groups practice some storage of food; (3) they may also practice conservation of food resources; (4) their movements are hindered to a certain extent by their possession of material goods; and (5) property concepts are universal among mankind; tacit agreement allocates to each group its landed property unless the equilibrium is upset by war and migration.[16]

Intensive agriculture Rainfall and the seasons control the basic patterns of primitive agriculture outside the tropical rain forests. There are four major crop complexes that have been developed by man. Two are basically adapted to dry uplands and seasonal variation in climate; two are adapted to tropical rain forests. One of each type is found in the Old World and the New. Thus, a suitable agricultural combination exists for all environments except those which are too extremely cold or too absolutely dry to support intensive plant life.

The Old World upland-seasonal complex is the old Neolithic farinaceous one centered on wheat, barley, flax, rye, and millet. These crops are fall-sown, make a large part of their growth of stalk and leaf in cool weather, and complete their maturity during the long summer days of warmest weather. These climatic adaptations made easy the diffusion of such plants into northwestern Europe. In the European lands, there was still the same condition of a cool, moist starting period, although the start was shifted to spring, and maturity still took place during the long days of midsummer.[17] Old World cereals are sown broadcast. New World plants are individually planted in hills.[18]

The Old World wetland complex centers around rice cultivation or the growing of such tubers as yams or taro. The New World dryland-

[12]M. Lewis and W. Clark, *History of the Expedition of Captains Lewis and Clark, 1804–05–06*, Vol. 2, p. 401.

[13]W. C. Bennett and R. M. Zingg, *The Tarahumara*, p. 113.

[14]E. A. Hoebel, *The Political Organization and Law-ways of the Comanche Indians* (American Anthropological Association, Memoir 54, Contributions from the Laboratory of Anthropology, 4, 1940), p. 141.

[15]R. H. Lowie, "The Northern Shoshone" (*American Museum of Natural History, Anthropological Papers*, Vol. 11, Part 2, 1909), pp. 233ff.

[16]J. H. Steward, "The Economic and Social Basis of Primitive Bands," in *Essays in Anthropology in Honor of Alfred Louis Kroeber*, p. 332.

[17]C. Sauer, "American Agricultural Origins," in *Essays in Anthropology in Honor of Alfred Louis Kroeber*, p. 285.

[18]The modern use of long rows, or drills, is a modified improvement on this practice.

Fig. 15-4   Anuak tribesmen thresh millet with hand flails on a raised platform. The loosened grain falls through the floor of the platform to the ground below. The chaff blows away during the fall. Thus the seeds are separated from stalk and chaff by a method that in this part of the world probably goes back to the prehistoric Neolithic Age. (United Nations.)

Fig. 15-5   Grinding corn with mano and metate in Otovalo, Ecuador. (From Collier and Buitron, The Awakening Valley, *The University of Chicago Press. Copyright 1949 by The University of Chicago Press. Copyright under International Copyright Union. Photograph by John Collier, Jr.)*

season plants are the maize-beans-squash complex and in the Andean region, the potato. The New World tropical wetland complex centers on the cultivation and processing of manioc.

Forest agriculture: the slash and burn technique
Lightly forested highlands may strike the reader as strange places for the origins of gardening. Clearing forests is hard work, and it would seem at first careless thought that open country would be more suitable. However, two factors militate against horticultural origins in open lands. Deserts are deficient in water, even if the soil is friable. Archaeological evidence does not support the thesis that gardening first began in "irrigation oases" of the arid river valleys in the Old and New Worlds. Grasslands are impenetrable to planting by peoples who do not have heavy plows. Even our own pioneers avoided the heavily sodded prairies, until special sod-breaking plows were developed (which was not so long ago). Although the best grain-producing lands in the world are the American and Russian prairies, they have become so only under modern conditions. Tropical rain forests can be made to support gardens by primitive men, but the environment was not conducive to the first efforts at plant domestication. Archaeological evidence and botanical facts do not indicate great antiquity for domesticated jungle plants.

Clearing the forest for planting requires energetic labor; it is not for lazy men. But for people who are not rushed for time, it can be effectively done with primitive tools by the "slash and burn method." Each tree is girdled by cutting a ring through the bark and cambium layer. Death follows. The dead trees may then be burned out or left standing. Their leafless branches no longer shade the ground. The weedless floor of the virginal forest is a light rich humus, and the gardeners simply plant among and around the dead stumps. Stumps are a serious nuisance only to the farmer with a plow.

DRY-RICE CULTIVATION IN BORNEO   As practiced by the Siang Dyaks of central Borneo, whose methods are typical of dry-rice cultiva-

Fig. 15-6 Dyaks planting dry rice. Slash and burn horticulture in Borneo. The jungle has been felled and burned to open a gardening space. A cooperative work group is using refined dibbles to make holes for the seed rice among the fallen logs and remaining stumps. (Courtesy of William W. Conley.)

tion, each man selects a sloping plot for clearing and planting. If it is a new one, he cuts partially through the trees on the lower side of the slope. Large key trees at the top of the plot are then felled so as to smash down the lower trees. All are trimmed, left to dry, and, after several weeks, burned. In all this he is usually helped by neighbors, whom he must help in turn. Work parties often get drunk on rice wine at lunchtime, when the party phase washes out the work aspect of the joint undertaking.

Planting is done by poking holes in the ground with a pointed stick, after which a couple of grains of rice are dropped in. Weeding is done occasionally, but it is so disheartening a task that most gardeners prefer to clear a new field every two or three years. In Borneo, where culture is primitive and communities small, there is still more than enough land to support this method of land use.[19]

MAIZE CULTIVATION AMONG THE MAYA High cultures that support large populations may enjoy no such margin of safety. The *milpa* system, as it is known among the Mayas, was

(and still is)[20] basically similar to the *ku, kaingin,* or *jhum* system, as it is known in Borneo. In J. E. Thompson's account in *The Civilization of the Mayas,*[21] we read that:

The Maya system of agriculture was primitive. Land suitable for agriculture was prepared by burning off trees and undergrowth. After the first rains, the sower, with a bag of seed and a sharp-pointed stick, crossed and recrossed the field, making a hole with his stick in the ground at every pace, and throwing a few grains of maize into the pit. . . . At the end of the season the field was abandoned, and next year the Maya farmer marked out a new piece of land to be cleared and sown. In the course of time and with the large increase of population that undoubtedly occurred, the Mayas must have been driven farther and farther afield in search of virgin soil. The exhausted soils nearer home must have been resown

[19] J. H. Provinse, "Cooperative Ricefield Cultivation among the Siang Dyaks of Central Borneo" (*American Anthropologist*, Vol. 37, 1939), pp. 77–102; reprinted in part in E. A. Hoebel, J. D. Jennings, and E. R. Smith, *Readings in Anthropology*, pp. 141–150.

[20] See R. Redfield, *The Folk Culture of Yucatan*, pp. 115ff.
[21] (Field Museum of Natural History, Anthropology Leaflet 25, 4th ed., 1942), p. 15.

after shorter and shorter periods of recuperation. In time the yield of the district would have fallen below the level of consumption, and, faced with evacuation or starvation, the people chose the former.

In this we have one of the theories to account for the decline and abandonment of the great urban centers of the Old Empire of the Mayas (A.D. 320 to 890). Morley has advanced the theory that intensive slash and burn gardening

Fig. 15-7   Ifugao rice terraces in Northern Luzon, The Philippines. (John Launois, Black Star, for PepsiCo International.)

by the ancient Mayas resulted in the invasion of grasses that converted the tropical forest of southern Yucatán to tough sod savanna. With their primitive dibbles, they were unable to pierce the sod, he thinks, and so by the natural consequences of their own efforts, they were driven from their cities.[22] Thompson's present view, however, relies on less direct factors than the effect of *milpa* farming on the soil or vegetation. Old Maya cities were not urban centers of population concentration. They were religious and court centers supported by *milpa* farms more or less evenly distributed for miles around, not clustered like European peasants beneath the walls of citadels. Such a pattern requires a pacifistic state of society. It is quite possible that the upset of the delicate social balance by the introduction of war forced the abandonment of Mayan centers in southern Yucatán around A.D. 900.[23] Whatever the true explanation, high cultures rest precariously if the base is *milpa*.

Wet-rice agriculture   Wet-rice irrigation was probably developed in India some three thousand or more years ago, whence it spread into China, Southeast Asia, and western Indonesia. Prior to its penetration of Indonesia, yams, taro, and millet were the staple crops of this part of the world. In the central islands of Indonesia (the eastern Lesser Sundas and the southern Moluccas), American maize introduced in post-Columbian times has won out over rice as the staple crop, but in the extreme east, where Indonesia merges into Melanesia, sago prevails. Rice cultivation belongs to the Asiatic, not the Oceanic, province.

Wet-rice culture requires extensive water control and irrigation systems, which sustain and require heavy population density combined with societies that are confined to specific localities because of the amount of work that is required to build and maintain the system. Some of the most populous areas of the world are those of wet-rice-growing societies in the Orient.

The economic organization of irrigation cultures is too complex for us to attempt to ana-

[22]S. G. Morley, *The Ancient Maya*, pp. 71–72.
[23]J. E. S. Thompson, "A Survey of the Northern Maya Area" (*American Antiquity*, Vol. 2, 1945), pp. 2–24.

lyze here. Barton has given us a useful study of the Philippine Ifugaos,[24] to which the reader may refer, and Linton has published some illuminating materials on the social adjustments that were forced when a primitive dry-rice culture changed over to wet-rice techniques in Madagascar.[25]

Forest agriculture: the manioc complex The use of manioc as a basic foodstuff by Amazonian Indians reveals a genuine ingenuity. Sweet manioc, which grows wild, gives relatively small yields. The domesticated forms with large yields contain much poisonous prussic acid. This necessitates a leaching process of some complexity before the manioc tubers can be converted to edible cassava. The roots, after being dug, must be sliced and fermented to free some of the poisons. Next they are pulped on hand graters and then wrung dry of liquids. The dried pulp must then be ground to a flour and heated to free the remaining volatile poisons. Safe bread can then be baked.

The Kuikuru of central Brazil grow eleven varieties of manioc, all of which are poisonous. Yet manioc makes up 80 or 85 per cent of their diet, according to the estimates of Robert Carneiro, who has given us a thoughtful analysis of their system.[26] The heavy rain forest is opened for gardens exactly as we have described. Before 1900, stone axes and the jaws of the piranha were used to girdle the trees. Now trade axes, machetes, and brush hooks are used. Plants are allowed to grow for 1-1/2 years to get a maximum starch output, although they could be harvested in one-half year. From their fixed village, the Kuikuru cultivate about 95 acres from among the 13,500 acres of rain forest that is available to them.

Fig. 15-8   Manioc processing in the Amazonian rainforest. The pulp of the manioc is squeezed free of poisonous juices in a woven tube which contracts when stretched lengthwise by pushing down on the bar. (Cornell Capa, Magnum, from Matthew Huxley and Cornell Capa, Farewell to Eden, *Harper & Row, New York.)*

[24]R. F. Barton, "Ifugao Economics" (*University of California Publications in American Archaeology and Ethnology,* Vol. 15, No. 5, 1922).
[25]R. Linton, "The Tanala," in A. Kardiner, *The Individual and His Society;* also "The Tanala: A Hill Tribe of Madagascar" (*Field Museum of Natural History, Anthropological Series,* Vol. 22, 1933).
[26]R. L. Carneiro, "Slash and Burn Cultivation among the Kuikuru and Its Implications for Cultural Development in the Amazon Basin," in *The Evolution of Horticultural Systems in Native South America: Causes and Consequences—A Symposium* (Anthropologica Supplement No. 2, Caracas, 1961), pp. 47–67.

Men do the gardening and have to put in only two hours at agricultural labor and 1-1/2 hours at fishing, daily. The remaining 10 to 12 waking hours are spent in dancing, wrestling, loafing, or other informal means of recreation. They could grow much more food as surplus with the available time and land. But the jungle has not favored extensive trade, so no more is raised than is required to eat well. There is no population pressure or other immediate reason to dig in harder. Carneiro empha-sizes that the mere possibility of food surplus is not enough to engender the kind of activity that produces it and so leads to elaboration of other parts of the culture and an expansion of its scope and complexity.

To an even greater degree than is true of hunting technology, gardening techniques tend to become woven into elaborate tapestries of magic and religion.[27] Gardening gives greater food leeway to man than hunting, but the very fact that it leads to greater populations brings about two direct consequences: (1) There is a greater stake in the success of the food crop, and (2) supernaturalism is embellished as a projective aid to crop security. Where the magi-cian once reigned, the secular experts of the United Nations World Food and Agricultural Organization enter to wrestle with the problem of how best to grow food for all mankind.

Pastoralism All gardeners have some domes-ticated animals. They may or may not be eaten. Indeed, so frequent is the abjuration of the flesh of domesticated animals among their primitive masters that Lowie concluded that "the original reasons for keeping animals were not practical ones."[28] Domesticated animals are kept as pets, for emotional reasons, or as objects of religious sacrifice. However, pigs, goats, and dogs, although not eaten, are not as economically useless as is often imagined. Hambly notes that goats, for instance, are ubiquitous and neglected in Africa; they are neither milked nor used extensively as a meat supply. But "goats pick their own food supply, and since they are almost omnivorous in their selection of vegetable food, there is no cost of maintenance."[29] What Hambly failed to note is that in their omnivorousness, goats are good garbage disposers. So are pigs and dogs, a fact that has led Ashley-Montagu to suggest this as

the original reason for the domestication of dogs in Neolithic times.[30]

The fact that most primitive peoples ignore or are ignorant of the half-dozen practical uses for domestic animals seems to be what led Lowie to his conclusion.

The known utilitarian uses to which domes-tic animals can be put are (1) consumption of their meat and blood; (2) use of their hides; (3) use of their hair or wool for weaving or felt-ing; (4) milking and dairying; (5) load carrying or pulling; and (6) riding.[31]

The Chinese do not milk cattle and will eat no cheese or dairy products (although they are not averse to beef as food). East Africans make a cult of sour milk along with adoration of sacred cows and just plain cows. Africans, for all their preoccupation with sour milk, rarely acquired the art of cheese making, and butter is less often eaten than smeared in the hair or used for oiling the body. Beef is eaten only occasionally. Women may toil under heavy loads, but cattle must not be burdened or set to pulling loads. In East Africa south of Abys-sinia, the art of riding was totally unknown to the native peoples. So, although the cult of the cow is the dominant theme of most East Afri-can cultures, the use of the cow falls far short of full realization of all potentialities.

Of course, we, in our use of horses, reverse the situation. We ride them, make them haul burdens, and pet them. But we neither milk nor eat them. The mayor of New York City in 1943 insisted that the eating of horseflesh is "immoral and uncivilized," and upon these lofty if narrow-minded principles he forbade the selling of horsemeat as a wartime measure to relieve an acute meat shortage.

Pastoralism is an adjustment to ecological factors on the part of advanced primitives. For-est dwellers cannot become pastoralists, and dwellers in the grasslands and deserts cannot readily become gardeners. Men strive to pene-trate all habitable areas of the globe. In dry grass and steppe areas, men on the lower levels

[27]See B. Malinowski, *Coral Gardens and Their Magic,* for an ex-haustive analysis of this aspect of Trobriand culture.
[28]R. H. Lowie, *An Introduction to Cultural Anthropology,* pp. 51–53.
[29]W. D. Hambly, "Source Book for African Anthropology" (*Field Museum of Natural History, Anthropological Series,* Vol. 26, Part 2, 1937), p. 596.
[30]M. F. Ashley-Montagu, "On the Origin of the Domestication of the Dog" (*Science,* Vol. 96, 1942), pp. 111–112.
[31]C. D. Forde, *Habitat, Economy, and Society,* p. 401.

of economic development may be hunters and foragers. If they move on to higher levels, they must become herders. Only when civilization reaches the point where the plow is produced may agriculturalists successfully move into the more favorable semiarid regions.

Pastoralism in Africa   Pastoralism is preeminently an Asian-African economic complex. In Africa it covers the whole Sahara, where it centers on the camel and the horse, as in eastern Arabia. In the northern Sudan and most of East Africa, it combines with hoe culture, and in the extreme south, the Hottentots and Hereros live on their cattle. The great Asian Steppes, from the east shores of the Caspian to the boundaries of China, and from the Himalayas to the arctic wastes, support such eminently pastoral peoples as the Kazaks, Tartars, Altai, Kalmucks, and Mongols.

In India the cow is sacred, but in East Africa it is the heart and core of life. The cattle do not represent wealth; they *are* wealth. As Elizabeth Marshall Thomas has written of the pastoral Dodoth of East Africa, among whom the women are millet growers:

For the Dodoth, cattle are the warp of life. They are the only wealth, the foundation of economic and social stability, the origin of all human ties. . . . Cows give milk. This is drunk daily, and churned into butter, and curdled with cow's urine into a salty cheese. Oxen give their blood. . . . People drink the blood raw after squeezing it with their fingers to break the clots, or they cook it with green millet flour into a delicate delicious pudding, as airy as a soufflé. Cowhides make sleeping mats and clothing. Cow dung makes flooring. Fresh cow urine, in its sterile steam, washes dirty hands or cleans utensils or softens leather or curdles milk for clabber or speeds the making of ghee. The first morsel a baby eats in his life is a drop of butter. From then on, he will be involved with cattle; every day and night of his life his nostrils will be filled with their sweet odor, his ears with their vibrant voices; and when he dies, if he dies at home, his body may be wrapped in the hide of one of his oxen and buried in the soft earth of their pen.[32]

[32]E. M. Thomas, "The Herdsmen" (*The New Yorker*, May 1, 1965), p. 52. (By permission from *The New Yorker* and Alfred A. Knopf, Inc., New York.)

This passage conveys a small touch of the significance of cattle for African pastoralists, but the intensity of emotional identification of a man for his cattle, although it may be written about, cannot really be sensed by an outsider. An indication of the complexity of exchange of cattle at marriage may be found in the example concerning the Nuer tribe on pages 346–347.

Transhumance   Marked seasonal fluctuations in rainfall frequently force pastoralists into semiannual movements, called *transhumance*. P. H. Gulliver describes this for the Jie tribe, neighbors of the Dodoth:

The pastoral cycle is briefly as follows: by about the middle of the rainy season the stock camps are all located in the eastern region, where, by that time, new grass has grown sufficiently and surface water collects in pools and stream beds. Camps are scattered throughout the region. Dairy herds are at their largest in the homesteads, and milk supply is at its peak. As the dry season sets in, both grass and water quickly become exhausted and camps must shift westward. There is an irregular migration of the camps, for it is entirely the responsibility of each herd owner to determine the timing and direction of movement as he assesses the situation. At first in the western region water supplies are sufficient to allow a wide-spread scatter of camps, but as the time of the last rains recedes, surface water dries up and camps are compelled to converge on one or another of the half-dozen permanent watering places for the remainder of the season. The choice of watering place is a matter for each herd owner to decide, although usually he tends to put his camp near the same one each year. Nevertheless, some readjustment of locations does occur each dry season when some places tend to become overcrowded or when men decide to shift for personal reasons. With the onset of the next rainy season it again becomes possible for camps to scatter through the western region as fresh grass and water are available. Then there is a shift back to the east, where the rains come a little later.[33]

In the New World, only the Navahos became real pastoralists—and that only in modern

[33]P. H. Gulliver, "The Jie of Uganda," in J. L. Gibbs, Jr. (ed.), *The Peoples of Africa*, p. 162. Copyright © 1965 by Holt, Rinehart and Winston, Inc. Used by permission.

times with sheep acquired from the Spanish. In the southern Plains, such tribes as the Comanche became quasi herders, but not pastoralists, in the mid-nineteenth century. Their horse herds numbered in the thousands, but horses were eaten only occasionally, were never milked, and were used mostly for riding and trade and as prestige tokens akin to the war bonnet. A man so identified with his favorite horse that the killing of such an animal was treated as murder. It required a revenge killing of the horse killer, even as a man would avenge the death of his brother.

SUMMARY

An elemental feature of every culture is a complex of techniques for production, consumption, and distribution of food. The physiological need for anabolic replacement of used-up energy supplies in the body imposes a biologic imperative on every society to organize its culture so that at least minimal food requirements are met, if the society and its culture are to survive. The ecological adjustment of a culture to the physical environment in which it operates is therefore of prime importance. Consequently, the culture areas of the world are, in large measure, also food-getting or subsistence areas.

The simplest and most primitive cultures of mankind are those whose subsistence economy is based predominantly upon hunting and gathering—the cultures of the food gatherers.

The vast majority of contemporary primitives share in the great Neolithic complex of gardening. Pastoralism represents a specialized adjustment to physical environments that are not suitable for gardening by people who possess only primitive horticultural techniques, or it may be joined to gardening in a mixed economy.

All primitive peoples reinforce their rational food-production methods with religious and magical practices that function psychologically to strengthen their sense of assurance that the food quest will not fail disastrously, and so they allay the ever-present gnawing anxiety that their means of survival may not suffice. Many of the rituals also serve to reinforce, symbolically and in action, the interdependence and group solidarity of the members of a society and its lesser collective units.

Although there remains a possibility that the idea of the domestication of animals and the cultivation of plants may have spread from the Old World into the New, the only domesticated animal brought from the Eastern Hemisphere into the Western in pre-European times was the dog. Because the specific plants cultivated by American Indians were (with the possible exception of cotton) entirely indigenous to the Western Hemisphere, and because the techniques of cultivation used in the New World were quite unlike those established in the Old World, we infer that New World horticulture (and, hence, the New World Neolithic complex) developed independently of Old World influence.

SELECTED READINGS

de Schlippe, P.: *Shifting Cultivation in Africa: The Zande System of Agriculture* (1956). A modern study based on anthropology and agronomy with very enlightening results.

Forde, C. D.: *Habitat, Economy, and Society* (1937). Contains condensed descriptions of the subsistence activities of a number of tribes and the relation of their social structure to such activities. Also presents a general comparative summary of the subject.

Hill, W. W.: *The Agricultural and Hunting Methods of the Navaho Indians* (Yale University Publications in Anthropology, No. 18, 1938).

Malinowski, B.: *Coral Gardens and Their Magic,* Vol. 1 (1938). A masterful and detailed study of the interrelation between social organization, supernaturalism, and gardening among the Trobriand Islanders.

Richards, A. I.: *Land, Labour, and Diet in Northern Rhodesia* (1950). How the Bemba tribe makes its living.

Steward, J. H.: *Basin-Plateau Aboriginal Sociopolitical Groups* (1938). The ecology and livelihood of the peoples of the Great Basin desert.

Housing

chapter 16

One might think that after a million years of experience, man would have mastered the housing problem. After all, of the basic needs of mankind, that for shelter is one of the most elementary. That the majority of humanity does not enjoy decent, healthy housing is a sad reflection on man's technical and social incapacities. Rural hovels and crowded, dirty city tenements do put a roof overhead, but so does a doghouse. Rationalized, functional dwellings are within human vision but still out of reach for all but a few.

In the realm of housing, man has remained throughout the ages strangely conservative. Again and again, he has modified his dwellings not at all or only with the most perverse obstinacy when improvements were known or at hand. Certainly, he has not concentrated his interest or attention on the problem of providing functionally sound housing to anything like the degree of assiduity with which he has attacked problems of myth making, religion, art, song, and dance. If this sounds like gross exaggeration, consider the Navaho in his wood and dirt hogan making intricate sand paintings and performing his nine-day chants. Consider the Australian with his bush windbreak putting on elaborate initiatory rites. Or consider the earth-lodge Pawnee with his elaborate hako ceremony.

It must be concluded that so physically elemental is the need for shelter that it is easily and simply satisfied. The feelings of insecurity and inadequacy that myth, magic, and religion strive to overcome are so deep and diffuse that elaborate cultural inventions are devised to relieve them. Further, man's earliest childhood experiences are closely associated with the particular type of dwelling possessed by his family. Basic habits are linked to a definite form of dwelling, and changes in house patterns mean changes in individual personality and, indeed, in family and kinship structures and function. More than that, changes in house form may very well necessitate changes in the entire societal structure.

As we indicated in the last chapter, if the Navahos were to give up their widely scattered and separated hogans for the consolidated, communal dwellings of the pueblo, they would have to reorganize their lives and stop being Navahos as they now know themselves. They could not continue their present amorphous system of social organization or nurture their individualistic separateness. Contemporary Pueblo Indians, as they become Americanized, tend to build small individual houses away from the old communal structure. This takes place because in the rural West, the original American pattern of separatistic dwellings is still closely tied to personal individualism and family exclusiveness, both important features of American private-property-based society. But at the very time that Pueblo Indians are gradually abandoning their communal apartment houses as a step in Americanization, industrial urbanism is forcing a greater and greater percentage of the American population out of separate dwellings and into mass-housing structures and cooperative apartment houses and condominiums.

Morgan's theory of housing and social organization

The intimate and subtle relations between house forms and the functional manifestations of individual, familial, and kinship behavior and the more general aspects of social and eco-

nomic institutions have been grossly neglected in anthropological and sociological literature. Almost a full century ago, Lewis Henry Morgan attempted a pioneer study in the relation between house form and social living.[1] His keen mind perceived the possibility of close interrelations, but his study was vitiated by his preconceptions. His study of house forms and house life was tailored to fit his assumptions. The pertinent presuppositions were: (1) The gens (clan) was universally "the unit of social organization ánd government, the fundamental basis of ancient society."[2] (2) Since food and house hospitality are universal among American Indians, it follows that the law of hospitality implies common stores and communistic living in large households.[3] (3) "These and other facts of their social condition embodied themselves in their architecture."[4] From these premises, Morgan attempted to demonstrate that the housings of the Iroquois, the Pueblo Indians, and the Northwest Coast tribes were manifestations of primitive communism. The individualistic Ojibwas in their one-family huts gave him a momentary pause. They certainly were not practicing communal living in the nineteenth century, but he thought they must have done so in ancient times.

In all this, Morgan grappled with some truth and a large amount of error. Social organization and type of dwelling *are* interrelated. Emphasis upon kinship tends to gather relatives under a common roof. This, however, is not necessarily a communistic unit. It may be merely a joint-family household. And the clan, as we shall see later (Chapter 24), is not characteristic of the more primitive levels of human society.

Somewhat later, Wilhelm Wundt[5] expressed a different theory of the influence of dwelling types upon social forms. He observed that occupation of a small cave by a single family must have produced separatistic social atti-

[1]L. H. Morgan, "Houses and House Life of the American Aborigines" (*Contributions to American Ethnology*, Vol. 4, 1881).
[2]*Ibid.*, p. 2.
[3]*Ibid.*, p. 61.
[4]*Ibid.*, p. 105.
[5]W. Wundt, *Völkerpsychologie*, Vol. 7.

tudes and behaviors. On the other hand, occupation of a large cave by several families would tend to produce the joint family as a communal type of social organization. All subsequent dwelling forms and arrangements, he thought, continue to reflect this basic contrast between the single family unit and the multiple family dwelling. For Wundt the impress of early cave life was indelibly stamped upon subsequent social history, but such speculative reconstruction of prehistoric psychology is not in keeping with modern anthropology.

Caves Caves have served as homes for man since the earliest Pleistocene times. If not too damp, they serve as comfortable shelters from beasts, weather, and prowling enemies. Archaeologists always probe cave sites when looking for remains of ancient man because the chances of finding some human refuse in a cave are always good. Not that there is the least evidence that primitive men suffered from agoraphobia, nor is there much empirical evidence to support the psychoanalytical notion that our earliest ancestors preferred caves because in the snug, enveloping darkness of the comfy cavern these unsophisticated people subconsciously recaptured the ineffable sense of security once enjoyed in the prenatal state—for it is, in fact, in the womb alone that the perfect environment is enjoyed. If a cave was the best adjustment to his psychic needs that primitive man could work out, his was a sad state indeed.

We need not waste our sympathy, however. Although caves have served man well as homes (and the time may again come when any number of us will be grateful for a good, deep cave), caves are few and men are many. There never were enough to go around. More than that, caves have a number of serious disadvantages as homesteads. They may not be well situated with respect to water and game. They cannot be moved around, and in consequence they inhibit the nomadic tendencies that are so characteristic of hunters and gatherers. They are always unhealthy spots. Garbage accumulations are bothersome. If dampness is present,

arthritis threatens, as well as rheumatic fever.

No, even Old Stone Age man chose an open campsite, climate permitting, and by and large, mankind has preferred building shelters and houses to curling up in nature's holes in the ground. After all, our primate relatives do not patronize dens. Every one of them sleeps above ground. Chimpanzees, gorillas, and orangutans fashion nests on the ground or in trees. Of these the orangutan does the best job:

Just before dark the animal stands upright on a forked branch, using one arm as a support and with the other drawing in distant branches, breaking them,

Fig. 16-1   The nomadic Rendille of East Africa transport the framework and covering of their beehive shaped tents by packing the parts in a traditionally standardized way on the backs of donkeys. (East Africa Tourist Agency.)

Fig. 16-2   The Bushman brush shelter provides daytime shade and some protection from the wind, the prime necessities for life in the Kalahari Desert of South Africa. It also identifies the family base, even though it is minimal in architectural sophistication. (Peabody Museum, Harvard University.)

Fig. 16-3   Gabled tree houses in eastern New Guinea are constructed to provide nighttime security against sneak attacks. (Courtesy of the American Museum of Natural History.)

and piling them up all around him until he is in the center of a circle of twigs 45 cm or more in height. He then breaks off smaller twigs and puts them across to form the floor of the nest; next comes a process of stripping leaves from the branches to line the nest. These are pressed into the crevices. Finally, the orang lies down and draws over himself and interlaces the remaining twigs, which are piled up, so that a dome-like roof covers him completely.[6]

Windscreens   There are no universal house forms among men, but the simplest homes of wandering food gatherers are not much more than nests. Murdock describes the usual Tasmanian shelter as "a simple windbreak, constructed of interlaced boughs or strips of bark in the form of a crescent and open on the leeward side."[7] This is the exact counterpart of the Shoshones' windbreak used in summer wanderings. The natives of Patagonia huddled before similar shelters made of skins. For more permanent settlements, beehive-shaped grass houses, called *wickiup*, were the Shoshones' highest attainment in housing.

The Arunta *wurley* is no more than a lean-to constructed of leafy branches laid against a horizontal pole supported in the crotches of two upright sticks set into the ground 6 to 8 feet apart. In the jungles of the Malay Peninsula, Negrito Pygmies build lean-tos of palm leaves on a frame very much akin to the *wurley*. The hut of the African Bushman is only a dome of light sticks not more than 5 feet high and thatched with straw (Fig. 16-2).

Huts   Thus the homes of the most primitive peoples of modern times are hardly more ingeniously devised than the nests of the great apes. They are little valued and readily abandoned—hardly to be considered real property. However, they have possibilities. Elaborations of these little hovels of grass and sticks have served to house the greater part of mankind in the eras of precivilization. Throughout the vast areas of the tropical rain forests and the woodland areas, pole and thatched houses made of vegetation prevail. They may be semispheric

[6]E. A. Hooton, *Man's Poor Relations*, pp. 124–125.
[7]G. P. Murdock, *Our Primitive Contemporaries*, p. 5.

domes, such as the Ojibwa bark *wigwam* or the South African hut of the Zulu and Hottentot, or they may be cones, such as the Shoshonean adaptation of the Plains Indian *tipi*. But more commonly, they will be found to be oblong, gabled structures formed by joining two lean-tos at the ridge in the form of a pup tent. The gabled structure, however, is almost always raised on walls. By such simple means, the internal cubage, or volume of usable living space, is greatly increased without much additional effort. The additional effort is nevertheless great enough so that except for certain Mongolian tribes, only sedentary peoples expend it. This means that such houses are generally confined to those people who have attained a gardening economy or who have a dependable localized source of food such as fish. In Indonesia and Melanesia and again in South America, such houses are raised on stilts as a protection against vermin, floodwater, and excessive dampness during the rainy season, and often as a defense against marauders (Fig. 16-3). In the coastal areas of the Melanesian Islands, pile dwellings are commonly built over the waters of lagoons, just as the Neolithic lake dwellers of Switzerland built their homes on the shores of the sub-Alpine waters.

The walls and roofing of primitive houses are variously made of snow, thatch, bark, mats, hides, felt, mud, planks, or stones. Thatch and mats prevail in tropical forest regions but in the Puget Sound area, mat houses were common for summer use. Bark was extensively used in the Eastern (temperate) woodlands of North America. Hides were in common usage on the Plains and among Eskimos for summer tents. Felt, used in the same manner as mats or hides, finds preference among Mongols and culturally related Asians. Mud is used either as covering for earth lodges in temperate or subarctic regions or as wall material in regions where rain will not reduce such a house to a puddle too quickly (Fig. 16-5). Plank houses were concentrated on the Northwest Coast of North America and nearby Siberia. Stone houses were built only by extremely sophisticated primitives—Mayas, Aztecs, Incas, et al.,

Fig. 16-4 Pile dwellings of the coastal Moros of the island of Solo, Philippines. Notice the double outrigger canoes and the early age at which boys learn to swim by themselves. (Philippine Tourist and Travel Association.)

in Central and South America; Pueblo Indians in the Southwest; and the early predecessors of Mediterranean civilization.

The pit house The technique of sinking the floor of the house into the ground before raising the superstructure above it represents a distinctly different line of development in house forms. This technique is adapted to the conditions of temperate climates with cold winters.

Fig. 16-5 Construction of the rectangular, gable-roofed house with mud-on-wattle walls of the prehistoric Middle Mississippi Indians. (Chicago Natural History Museum.)

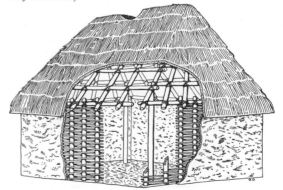

For obvious reasons, it never occurs in the tropical areas where the ground is too wet. The semisubterranean house has two advantages: (1) it is easier to keep warm, and (2) it can be made roomy without raising high side walls. The first reason is the functionally effective one, since many primitive people have solved the problem of getting sufficient inside height when building above ground.

The earliest known house sites, which date from the Mesolithic period (*ca.* 10,000 B.C.) at Campigny in France and elsewhere, are shallow pits over which half-dome superstructures were apparently raised.

Among recent primitives, the pit house has found greatest favor with numerous peoples of western North America and North Asia. The description of the pit houses seen by Lewis and Clark just below The Dalles of the Columbia River could very well have applied to the Campignian house types of 14,000 years ago:

They are sunk about eight feet deep and covered with strong timbers, and several feet of earth in a conical form. On descending by means of a ladder through a hole in the top, which answers the double purpose of a door and a chimney, we found that the house consisted of a single room clearly circular and about sixteen feet in diameter.[8]

Almost identical words describe a traveler's view of the pit dwellings of the Samoyed tribes of Siberia: "They lived in little, half underground lodges, with circular upper parts and

[8]M. Lewis and W. Clark, *History of the Expedition of Captains Lewis and Clark, 1804–05–06*, Vol. 2, pp. 253–254.

Fig. 16-6   Cross section of a prehistoric Mogollon pit dwelling: A, entrance; B, smoke hole; C, excavated earth wall. (Chicago Natural History Museum.)

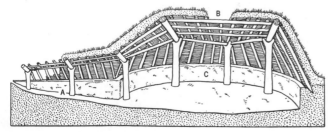

without windows. In the middle of the latter there is a hole, through which smoke and people pass."[9]

Here we have the parallel occurrence of two similar culture traits on separate continents. In this case, they do not represent independent inventions, however, for the combination of facts covering their archaeological distribution and details of structure indicates clearly that this mode of dwelling, which was in frequent use in Late Pleistocene Siberia and survived into the present century among the sedentary fishing cultures of that bleak land, was carried into western North America by very early migrants from the Asian mainland.[10]

Pueblos: the development of a communal house form   From the pit house to the great five-storied apartment buildings of the Pueblos of the Southwest United States is a great distance to travel in the span of a millennium.

Three main archaeological patterns of prehistoric culture have been found in the Southwest. The first is the Anasazi, of which the living Pueblos of today are a part. Because of its geographical localization on the high plateaus of northern Arizona and New Mexico and southern Utah and Colorado around the Four Corners,[11] it is sometimes referred to as the *Plateau culture.* It must not be confused with the ethnologists's Plateau Culture Area, which is located on the Columbia River Plateau. The second is the Hohokam, also called the *Desert culture* because of its location in the central and southern Arizona deserts. The third is the Mogollon-Mimbres, also known as the *Mountain culture* because of its association with the mountainous area of southeastern Arizona and southwestern New Mexico. In their earliest known phases (about 2,000 years ago), each of these cultures included pit houses as the dwelling type (Fig. 16-6).

[9]Olearius, *The Description of a Journey in Moscovia*, pp. 167–168.
[10]See W. Jochelson, "Past and Present Subterranean Dwellings of the Tribes of North Eastern Asia and North Western America" (*Proceedings of the 15th International Congress of Americanists*, 1907).
[11]The only place in the United States where four states touch each other.

The evolution of the Anasazi pattern begins with what is known as the *Basket Maker period* (A.D. 100 to 500). Basket Maker houses were constructed of inclined posts, poles, and twigs laid horizontally to form a dome around and above a saucerlike pit 10 to 20 feet in diameter. The frame was plastered over with mud. Individual houses were built in small groups, either within shallow caves or in the open.

In the succeeding Modified Basket Maker period (A.D. 500 to 700), pit houses still prevailed. They now consisted of a framework of four or five uprights supporting a flat roof. Entrance was gained either through the smoke hole over the fire pit or through a projecting passageway on the south side of the house. A low ridge of mud separated the south from the north half of the house. A new feature that marked this period, however, was the long, flat-roofed structure of poles and mud that contained two rows of contiguous rooms. Some of these buildings were in the shape of crescents. Two lines of architectural development had emerged.

In the period of the Modified Basket Maker, the pit houses were used for ceremonial and dwelling purposes. The multiroomed surface houses were apparently used mostly for storage. Later, in the Pueblo periods, the pit house evolved into the underground ceremonial chamber, or *kiva*. The aboveground storage rooms became the multiple apartment houses for which the Pueblo Indians are justly famous. The climax was reached between A.D. 1000 and 1300 in the Pueblo III period. To this period belong the famous cities in the caves, including Cliff Palace in Mesa Verde National Park (Fig. 16-7). Of the open sites of this period, Pueblo Bonito in Chaco Canyon, New Mexico, is the best known. These buildings contained hundreds of rooms built of coursed masonry walls rising often to four stories. The modern pueblos are merely shrunken survivals of the Great Period.

There is a close nexus between the communal houses of the Pueblos and the general configuration of Pueblo culture. The pueblos of the Great Period were defensive citadels as well as domiciles. The outer ground-level walls of the open-site pueblos were blank surfaces with no doors or windows. To enter a house, one had to climb to the roof and go down the smoke hole, as in the pit house. To the hostile outer world the pueblo turned its back. It faced inward upon the court, in which the public dances of its rich ceremonialism occurred. The great building formed a compact, architecturally integrated, in-turned whole. The members of the pueblo were forced to live in the closest intimacy with one another; not just the members of one family, but all familes, all clans were piled together in a great heap. The cooperative emphasis of Pueblo life was required by the nature of their housing, if nothing else. And, of course, their housing could not have come into being had they not simultaneously been developing cooperative values. But the crowded intimacy of Pueblo living seems also to have left its impress in the form of excessive touchiness, backbiting, fear of witchcraft,

Fig. 16-7   The Cliff Palace at Mesa Verde, in Southwestern Colorado, was constructed over a millennium ago. The many round ceremonial chambers, called kivas, *are indicative of the complexity of religious organization in this multiple dwelling that housed an entire village. (Courtesy of the American Museum of Natural History.)*

and factionalism. "Chronic cabin fever" is the diagnosis of W. W. Hill. "Cabin fever" produces centrifugal forces pushing toward breakup of the pueblo. Well-integrated religio-ceremonial structures counteract this tendency to a great degree in Pueblo society. In the political sphere, however, the Pueblos have failed in the development of governmental mechanisms that combine reasonably centralized authority with flexibility in the handling of divergent interests. This is, of course, the eternal problem of healthy government. In the case of the Pueblos, their compact form of housing contributed to an intensification of the imperative need for political skill.

We would agree with the conclusion of Steward in speaking of the Basket Maker and Pueblo I cultures: "It is difficult to reconcile the division of the early villages into small house clusters with any other social unit than the unilateral lineage or band."[12] Steward and Titiev[13] both suggest that a movement of consolidation of independent clans or bands in Pueblo II times resulted in the building of communal houses. "The formally separated small groups are amalgamated, but do not lose their social and ceremonial integrity."[14] And because these formerly discrete groups did not lose their integrity when compressed into the larger pueblo units, plus the irritability engendered by too close living, vindictive factionalism is an inherent aspect of Pueblo life. Quarreling has led again and again to the breakup of pueblos and the establishment of new settlements. The hundreds of ruined pueblos that make the Southwest an archaeologist's paradise are rich testimony to the long Pueblo struggle to adjust their house forms to their social conservatism.

Earlier in this chapter we remarked that the Navahos could not adopt the Pueblo house form and remain Navahos in spirit and action. We have seen something of the difficulty the

Pueblo Indians themselves have had to reckon with in the solution of their housing problem. Those who have wondered how it is possible for the Navahos after centuries of contact with the Pueblos—centuries in which they have absorbed much of Pueblo ritual imagery and arts—to live even yet in wretched log and mud hogans, when they have for so long had the exemplar of Pueblo masonry houses before them, may find the answer in the Navaho's devotion to his form of social organization. Present-day Navaho social forms are undoubtedly much closer to those of the society that was enjoyed by the Basket Maker and Pueblo I peoples than the modern social forms of the Pueblo Indians are. The scattered Navaho communities of individual hogans are not greatly different from the ancient open-site pit-house villages of the Anasazi.

The Plains Indian earth lodge   Far to the northeast in the great valley of the Missouri River and its drainage, the advanced, sedentary gardeners (the Village tribes of the Plains: Mandan, Hidatsa, Arikara, Omaha, Pawnee) lived in so-called "earth lodges" that were impressive enlargements of the pit-house idea. In construction, a stick was thrust into the ground where the fireplace would be. This served as the focus for a 10- to 30-foot rawhide rope that was used to describe a complete circle. The sod within the circle was removed, and the floor was excavated about 1 foot deep. Crotched poles 10 feet high were set within the circle every 8 feet or so and joined with horizontal beams. Midway between this circle of posts and the fireplace, four to eight large crotched pillars were raised in a square or circle. These, too, were joined by beams. Posts for an entrance hall were also set. Palisaded walls of split posts were laid against the frame. Long, tapering tree trunks formed the roof. Above the fireplace, a 3-foot smoke opening was left. Outside the walls and roof, willow withes were horizontally lashed and then covered with a heavy thatch of coarse grass. Over this was placed a thick coating of sod laid to lap like shingles. Thus by combining logs, thatching, matting,

[12] J. H. Steward, "Ecological Aspects of Southwestern Society" (*Anthropos*, Vol. 32, 1937), p. 99.
[13] M. Titiev, "Old Oraibi" (*Papers of the Peabody Museum of American Archaeology and Ethnology, Harvard University*, Vol. 22, No. 1, 1944), pp. 96–99.
[14] *Ibid.*, p. 96.

and mud, a truly impervious, if lightless, habitation was manufactured. To the Omaha Indians, an earth lodge was a mansion, tangible evidence of social importance, for "the erection of this class of dwelling required considerable labor, hence only the industrious and thrifty possessed these lodges." Others lived in tipis. Usually only one family was housed in a lodge, but if there were two, each took one side.[15]

Joint-family houses of the Jivaro and Iroquois Indians The buildings of the Great Pueblo period were properly communal dwellings. Communal houses of a different sort occur in parts of Southeast Asia and South America and in interior New Guinea. The notorious head-shrinking Jivaros of eastern Ecuador exemplify the South American pattern. The unit of Jivaro social organization is the patrilineal family group living under a single roof. "Such a household is quite independent and self-sufficient, being subservient to no one."[16] The typical Jivaro house is about 75 feet long and some 40 feet wide, ellipitcal in shape, with parallel sides and rounded ends. The walls are made of 10-foot laths of palm or bamboo lashed vertically to the frame. The roof is thatched. At each end of the house is a door of heavy planks, which must be lifted and set aside to gain entrance. These doors are barred from the inside. An interesting sexual dichotomy reserves one door for men only and the other for women. In like wise, one half of the interior is for men, and the other half for women. Each man has his private sleeping platform against the wall on his side; each woman has her platform on the woman's side. Women's platforms are enclosed with mat walls, but the men seek no such privacy. Thus, within the *jivaria* separation is based upon sex. Although several conjugal familes may be living in a single house, they are not spatially separated on a family

basis. Most lamentably, we know nothing about interpersonal relations within the household group or about how the Jivaros manage their sex lives.

In Jivaro society there are no clans, villages, or other forms of social organization beyond the isolated household, except a loose and amorphous federation of five or six households under a common war leader.

In the long house of the Iroquois Indians, we find an internal organization more typical of joint-family households. The structure of an Iroquois long house is something like that of a Quonset hut. A roof of slabs of dried bark is laid on vertical walls. The house may be enlarged or shortened merely by adding or removing sections at either end. Doors are at the ends, with an open passage down the entire house, which in one instance was 100 yards long—the length of a football field. On either side of the passage were cubicles about 12 feet wide and deep, closed on the sides but wide open to the passageway, like the long corridor of bedrooms in the Tuileries. Murdock refers to these as apartments.[17] More seemingly, they were compartments. At the back of each was a sizable shelf, 6 feet deep and the width of the cubicle. Here a whole conjugal family slept at night. On the back wall was a shelf for utensils, and between each living compartment and the next was a storage closet. A number of closets were kept at either end of the house, too.

Who lived in this big building, and what were their arrangements? Each long house "belonged" to a lineage of related women. At the head of the long house was an influential older woman. The household certainly included all her daughters and their husbands and children. It usually included her sisters and their familes as well, and also the families of her married granddaughters. All the women of the long house, in theory at least, belonged to the same clan. The long house bore the name and clan insignia of its dominant matrilineal family (except in the case of the somewhat virilocal Seneca tribe). Married men were supposed to

[15]A. C. Fletcher and F. LaFlesche, *The Omaha Tribe* (Bureau of American Ethnology, Annual Report 27, 1911), p. 88. See also G. R. Wilson, "The Hidatsa Earthlodge" (*American Museum of Natural History, Anthropological Papers*, Vol. 33, 1934), p. 5.
[16]M. W. Stirling, *Historical and Ethnographical Materials on the Jivaro Indians* (Bureau of American Ethnology, Bulletin 117, 1938), p. 38.

[17]Murdock, *op. cit.*, p. 298.

move into the long house of the wife, but the son of an influential mother married to a girl from a family of less account might choose to stay in his mother's home. And since the Iroquois were given to adoption of captive enemies as replacements for dead relatives, there were always some of these in the household.

The women could throw their husbands out at any time. For the dispossessed divorcé, there was nothing to do but pick up his gear and leave. He had no legal claim on children or home.

The social organization of the Iroquois long

Fig. 16-8 *The ground plan of a Jie household. All the yards lettered A belong to the wives of one man; the B's are the yards of the wives of a brother; and C's yards of yet another brother, and so forth. The entire homestead is physically and socially a tight unit, discrete among all the other homesteads of the tribe. (From P. H. Gulliver, in James L. Gibbs, Jr. (ed.),* The Peoples of Africa, *Holt, Rinehart & Winston, Inc., New York, 1965. By permission.)*

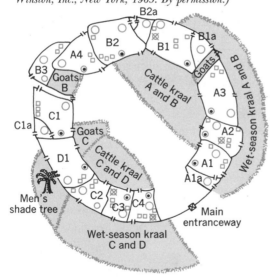

-I⊢ Palisade fence and doorway

~~~ Bush fence and gateway

○ Main house

▢ Granary basket

○ Hut for calves

⊕ Kitchen   Total population of homestead: 56

Usual number of residents: 40-45

house was that of a joint matriarchate (see the discussion of the composite unilineal family, pages 364–366). Segregation within the long house was not, as among the Jivaro, by sexes but rather by conjugal families. Each woman had her cubicle, which was shared by her husband and children. Eating was partly a joint-family, partly a separate-family, affair. Each conjugal family shared a cooking fire with the occupants of the opposite compartment. Down the center of the passageway lay a hearth for each pair of families.

Iroquois long houses could encompass quite a conglomeration of relatives, but they did not pose the onerous dilemma that bedeviled the Pueblos. Living was close, but the entire village was not housed in one building. A village consisted of several to many long houses within a protective palisade. A number of villages together made up a tribe (whereas among the Pueblos, each village was usually a tribe in itself). The six original Iroquois tribes made up the Iroquois nation. Loyalties reached out far beyond the lineage group in the long house. Further, the Iroquois were militant expansionists. They could release their internal tensions in outward aggression.

As the cultural environment of the Iroquois changed under the impact of white colonization of their country, the long-house organization began to break down, giving way to log houses of smaller dimensions, until, by 1800, the long house as a dwelling form was no more.[18]

In Southeast Asia, where long houses are common,[19] they tend to be associated with clans. Where the village unit is formed on territorial rather than kinship bonds, as in Java and the Philippines, each family has its own separate house. The lineage and joint family do appear to go together. Morgan had a certain amount of truth to back him up. But lineages and clans do not by any means always live in

[18]W. N. Fenton, "Locality as a Basic Factor in the Development of Iroquois Social Structure," *Symposium on Local Diversity in Iroquois Culture* (Bureau of American Ethnology, Bulletin 149, 1951), pp. 35–54.

[19]E. M. Loeb and J. O. M. Broek, "Social Organization and the Long House in Southeast Asia" (*American Anthropologist,* Vol. 49, 1947), pp. 414–425.

long houses, while some clanless people do. The relationship is not absolute.

The compound homestead of African pastoralists The joint households just described are those of gardeners who live in wooded areas where long timbers are available and where the only problem is protection of human, not animal, life. African pastoralists give a different form to the joint-family homestead. In their ecological setting, materials for large buildings are frequently rare, and a major need is to protect both people and stock from raiders. The homestead of the Jie, whose seasonal cycle was described in the previous chapter, may be taken as generally typical (Fig. 16-8).

A Jie homestead ordinarily contains the families of from six to eight men, all descendants of one grandfather. The social base of the household is therefore the patrilineage (see pages 371–372). Families are polygynous (see pages 361–363). All the wives, their children, and the married sons with their wives and children live within the compound—thirty to forty people in all. The compound is a palisaded pole brush fence in which the only openings are small apertures 3 feet square. Anyone entering must crawl on his hands and knees, presenting his head for a death blow in case he is not welcomed.

Ringing the inner side of the wall is a series of fenced yards—one for each married woman. Here she has a small thatched hut with no windows, which is used only for sleeping in rainy weather. Otherwise, sleeping, cooking, and eating are done in the open yard, although some wives build themselves a kitchen hut with open sides. Every woman's yard also contains a small house for young cattle, and this is used as an emergency kitchen if there is no regular one. Each yard also has at least two large plastered baskets on stilts for storage of grain. The yard of each wife is her own domain. Although the yards of the co-wives of a common husband are adjacent to each other, no door leads directly from one to another. It is necessary to go out into the cattle pens to achieve passage to any other yard. The cattle

and goat pens (kraals) take up about half the interior courtyard of the homestead. Here the livestock is herded at night, except in the rainy season, when they are kept in outside kraals.

The homestead is the base of a corporate lineage that inherits and owns all the cattle in common. The unity of the lineage as against all the rest of the world is clearly symbolized and reinforced by the very nature of the homestead.[20]

SUMMARY

All cultures contain patterns for the physical establishment of a home. House types are variable in structure, depending upon the nature of the local climate and materials, the kind of subsistence economy indulged in, and the nature of the social organization of the society and the kinds of aggressive threats it must face from enemies.

Nomadic peoples in the jungles, semideserts, and arctic wastes ordinarily throw together simple, temporary shelters. Settled peoples in the wet lands build fixed abodes of wood and thatch; in the dry lands, stone and mud are more commonly used. The pit dwelling is a northern-latitude phenomenon of the European Neolithic and later Siberian and western North America areas.

In societies built around the joint-family or localized lineage, a single housing unit may serve as a common dwelling in many cultures both prehistoric and contemporary. Such joint-family houses exemplify the close interrelationship between social and architectural forms. The fact that the Navahos rely on the individual hogan and the Pueblo Indians use the communal apartment house, even though both tribes have simultaneously inhabited the same area for 1,000 years, also illustrates the effect of general configuration upon architectural forms. Small family huts consolidated within a compound reflect a nice adjustment of the requirements of a lineage type of social organization and a pastoral ecology.

[20]For more detail, see P. H. Gulliver, *The Family Herds.*

SELECTED READINGS

Beals, R., P. Carrasco, and T. McCorkle: *Houses and House Use of the Sierra Tarascans* (1944). An excellent study of the relationship between architectural and social forms in highland Mexico.

Fortes, M.: *The Web of Kinship among the Tallensi* (1949), chap. 3, "The Homestead and the Joint Family." A model study of the functional interrelation of home and family.

Loeb, E. M., and J. O. M. Broek: "Social Organization and the Long House in Southeast Asia" (*American Anthropologist*, Vol. 49, 1947), pp. 414–425. A useful analysis of the relation between lineage and homestead.

Murdock, G. P.: *Our Primitive Contemporaries* (1934). Sections in each chapter devoted to the ethnography of a tribe describe a variety of house types.

Steward, J. H.: *Theory of Culture Change* (1955), chapter entitled "Ecological Aspects of Southwest Society." Includes a highly suggestive historical treatment of the relation of dwelling patterns to social organization.

Waln, N.: *The House of Exile* (1933). A beautifully written novel giving the inside view of life in a traditional Chinese compound household.

Handicrafts

chapter 17

The workaday world is the world of the tool manipulators. Man is a toolmaker and a tool user. He performs few operations with his bare hands or feet. *Australopithecus* fashioned the first tools, the forerunners of the vast fabricating machines of modern technology. From the first clumsy artifacts of one million years ago to the satellites now in orbit, man has steadily improved his mechanical devices in a continuous effort to meet his physical needs and psychic wants more satisfactorily.

Stone implements

Almost all primitive peoples were dependent upon stone as the material from which to make cutting and scraping implements. The greater part of the prehistoric span of man's existence in the Old World was the Stone Age. In North and South America, although the peoples of high culture knew metallurgy, it is proper to say that all the Indians were Neolithic men, as were all the Oceanic peoples of the Pacific. It must be remembered, however, that on coral islands, rocks other than flint had to be used. Africa south of the Sudan was given over to tribes with stone technologies, while many of the Sudanese Africans were well advanced in ironworking and bronze casting.

The course of European Paleolithic and Neolithic cultures has already been sufficiently described (see Chapters 10, 11, and 12), so we need not discuss stone artifacts here.

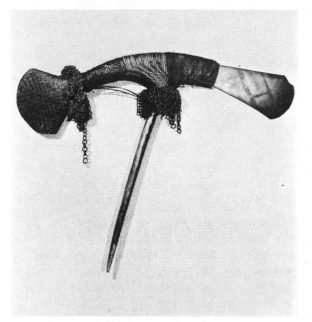

Fig. 17-1 Polished stone ax from the Mt. Hagen district, New Guinea. An example of artistic overelaboration of a utilitarian object. (American Museum of Natural History collection; photograph courtesy of The Museum of Modern Art.)

Wooden implements

In Chapter 10 it was asserted that Paleolithic man relied as much upon wood for artifacts as he did upon stone. This statement is based on inference from recent primitive cultures rather than direct archaeological evidence. Wood is perishable, and yet all primitives make considerable use of it. Eskimos use relatively less than most peoples, for the simple reason that trees do not grow in the arctic. Northwest Coast Indians, endowed as they are with excellent workable cedar, have turned wood to an unusually great number of uses. A Northwest Coast inventory would include plank houses, wooden totem poles, adze handles, canoes, paddles, clubs, bows, arrows, helmets and slat armor, bowls, dishes, spoons, boxes, rattles, batons, and masks in a profusion of carved and painted varieties.

Eastern woodland Indians preferred to use the bark of the birch for canoes, boxes, and housing. Plains Indians seized upon hides. Pueblo Indians use wood only sparingly, for, skillful in pottery making, they prefer utensils of clay and homes of adobe and stone. Tropical tribes in Africa, Oceania, and South America, who find themselves in rain forests with plenty of wood at hand, use it extensively. Polynesian wooden clubs are a sophisticated transformation of the cave man's bludgeon.

The drill A universal and fundamental use of wood that should not be overlooked is in fire making. It is widely used as a fire starter around the world. By setting the drill in a wood socket and pouring dry tinder about it, it is possible to generate enough heat by friction to start a fire. Hand rotation, strap, bow, and pump methods are all used. The fire plow is a simpler but less efficient device. Named by Tylor the "stick and groove method," the implement consists of a grooved board lying on the ground and a blunt stick, which is pushed back and forth with vigorous pressure until friction-generated heat kindles fire—a method concentrated primarily in Polynesia. In Indonesia the fire saw, a variant form, is preferred. In this method, a piece of split bamboo is sawed so rapidly that the dust ignites.

Drilling through solid stone has been within the capabilities of most primitive peoples since Neolithic times. The drills are ordinarily nothing but wooden rods or tubes rotated between the hands or by mechanical means. Wet sand does the actual cutting. But think how many drills must be used to go through a 2-inch piece of basalt. Although rotation between the hands was unquestionably the most primitive and earliest drill technique, it is probable that Neolithic man hit upon the bow drill, since he had the bow and arrow. Also, in later Neolithic times he produced many polished ax heads with drilled transverse haft holes. However, in modern times hand drilling has had a much wider distribution than use of the bow drill, even among peoples who possess the bow and arrow; thus it by no means follows automatically that the one leads to the other. The trick of the bow drill, as every Boy Scout who has passed his fire-by-friction test knows, is to wind the bowstring once around the drill, hold the top of the drill in a hand socket, and then saw back and forth with the bow like a cello player. The Eskimo takes a bite on the socket instead of a handgrip. The strap drill works on the principle of the bow drill, except that there is no bow. The ends of the working thong are simply held in the hands and drawn back and forth. A clever refinement is the pump drill. By first winding up the string on the drill shaft and then pushing the crossbar down, a spin is imparted to the drill. The momentum given to it by the stone or pottery flywheel automatically rewinds the string. Another downward push keeps it spinning.

Fig. 17-2   Carved Maori war club from New Zealand showing the curvilinear decoration so characteristic of Maori art. (Compare with Figure 18-4 on page 284.) By contrast, this Easter Island (Polynesia) canoe paddle is designed and decorated with elegant simplicity and beauty. (Left, courtesy of the Peabody Museum, Salem; right, courtesy of The Museum of Primitive Art.)

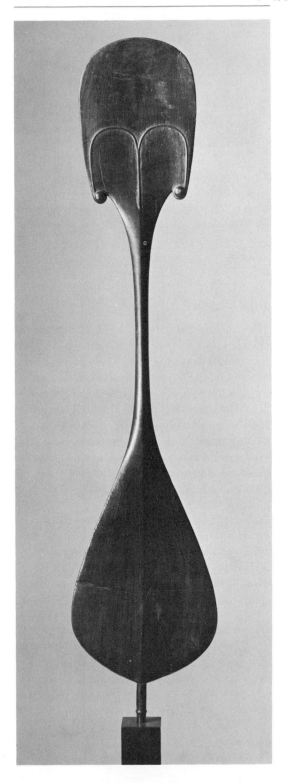

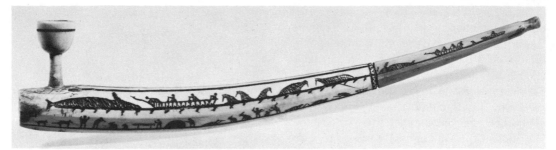

Fig. 17-3   Eskimo pipe of walrus tusk ivory
decorated with scenes of whale, walrus, and seal
hunting. The designs are etched into the surface of
the ivory and rubbed with lampblack to produce the
black-on-white contrast. (Courtesy of The Brooklyn
Museum.)

Bone and shell

The skeletons of vertebrates and the shells of
crustaceans find their uses in primitive material
culture. Unworked shells make serviceable if
not durable scrapers and saucers. Caribbean
Indians rubbed heavy seashells into polished
celts like those of stone. The long bones of
birds and animals, splintered and polished to a
smooth point, have always found favor as per-
forators and awls, and the earliest needles were
made of slivers of bone. Fishhooks made of
bone occur almost everywhere. Harpoon heads

of bone, antler, or ivory were characteristic of
Magdalenian man and Eskimos alike.

One of the most interesting bone implements is the garden hoe produced by Indians
in the eastern Plains area from the shoulder
blade of the bison. The scoop-shaped scapula
was lashed at right angles to a wooden handle
and used exactly as we use a hoe today. Alaskan Eskimos use whale scapulas as handleless
snow shovels.

Traps

Traps and deadfalls have been previously mentioned as primitive food-getting devices. The
ingenuity of such machines, as in the Arawak
Indian bow-and-arrow trap shown in Fig. 17-4,
occasionally reaches remarkable proportions.
This is an unusual variation of the much more
common spring trap, in which the animal puts
his head into a noose to get the bait, releases
the trigger, and is hoisted, if not by his own
petard, at least in consequence of his own
action. Deadfalls are forms of traps in which
the animal who tugs at the bait releases a trigger that literally brings down the roof on his
head.

Fish weirs, commonly used on the west
coast of North America, in South America, and
in the African Sudan, consist of fencelike ob-
structions across a river or lagoon, and are
designed to lead the fish through a funnel into
a large basket or crib (see Fig. 15-1). Although
he can wriggle into the funnel, the poor fish
cannot reenter the narrow spout.

To detail all the trap forms devised by clever
primitives is impossible here. Probably all
recent primitives have utilized some means of

Fig. 17-4   Arawak Indian bow and arrow set-trap.
The tripper string is stretched across a game trail
so that when brushed against by an animal the
trigger is pulled and the arrow released with deadly
effect.

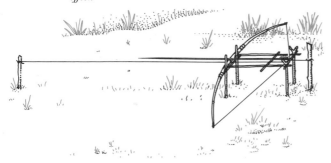

trapping or snaring animals. It is also likely that man in the Early Paleolithic was already catching his dimwitted animal brethren with crude but carefully prepared snares.

Bags and baskets

All human beings use artificial containers. Skin pouches or bags may serve to meet this need. Primitive containers may also be made of wood or of plastics, such as clay. But of all these possibilities, baskets, which are containers made of interwoven reeds, grass, or shredded bark (bast), have by far the widest distribution.

Basket making is a truly ancient craft. Direct archaeological evidence yields basketry remains from the Neolithic sites of Europe, and in the Southwest, elaborate basketry skill gave the name Basket Maker to the potteryless pre-Pueblo inhabitants of the area.

The simplest basketry container (made by the marginal food collectors, the Fuegians and other southern South Americans, the Australians, and Bushmen) is a loose, open-weave bag such as that used to package onions and oranges in the United States.

Bags of genuine netting are not so much woven as worked out in crochet patterns. *Knotless netting*, as this technique is called, occurs throughout a large part of the Western Hemisphere and in Oceania and Australia.[1]

A basket differs from a bag in that it is at least semirigid, if not actually stiff. It is built upon its own frame, or its foundation is formed as it is made. The body is produced by the interlocking of long strips or threads of fibrous materials such as dried reeds, grasses, split cane, or shredded bark. Basketry materials can be found in all environments inhabited by man.

Plaiting The simplest basket-making method is that of wickerwork or plaiting. Every reader of this book has done plaiting with paper in kindergarten. It is the alternating over-and-under technique (Fig. 17-5). However, virtuosity

[1] D. S. Davidson, "Knotless Netting in America and Oceania" (*American Anthropologist*, Vol. 37, 1935), pp. 117–134.

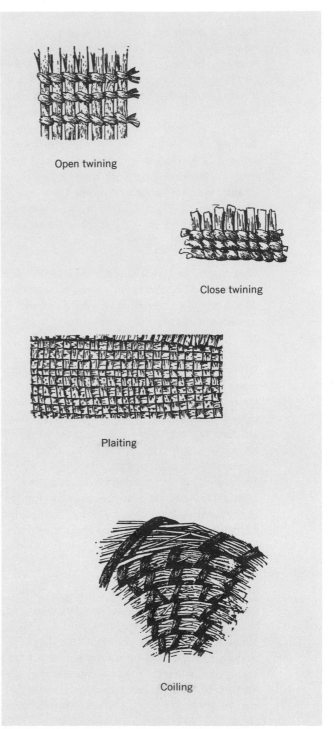

Open twining

Close twining

Plaiting

Coiling

Fig. 17-5 Basketry techniques: open twining, close twining, plaiting, and coiling. (After Wissler.)

such as that displayed by the Hopi of Third Mesa[2] in producing wicker trays of sumac and rabbit brush is not kindergarten work. In method, plaiting and wickerwork are alike, except that plaiting is done with very soft and pliable materials, and wickerwork with stiff materials.

Twilling Twilling is plaiting with variations. Instead of plaiting in and out, over one under one, the basket maker goes over two or more strands and under two or more. Each row is offset from the one next to it, so the effect produced is that of a series of staircases or slanting lines.

Wrapping Wrapping utilizes a slightly different technique. The foundation of the basket consists of stiff parallel rods. A pliable strand is turned or wrapped once around each rod in a continuous series. It is used relatively little.

Twining This is a more complicated basket-making method. In its simplest form, two strands of pliable material are simultaneously woven in and out between parallel foundation strands. As each strand is passed between two foundation strands (from over to under, and vice versa), it is given a half twist (Fig. 17-5). The foundation strips are thus firmly bound on both sides in a way that gives much strength to the weaving. Soft grasses or strips of rabbit fur twined in this way produce a clothlike material. In fact, twined rabbitskin robes to be worn in the winter were the sole clothes of many peoples of the Great Basin and California.

Coiling This is the most sophisticated and painstaking of all basketry methods. As a technique it has little in common with plaiting, twilling, and twining, except the use of a foundation of one or more rods or a bundle of grass. Presumably it represents a distinct inventive idea. A spiral coil of the foundation material is

built up like rope coiled on the deck of a ship by a careful sailor. It is permanently bound by a strand of pliable material wrapped around the bundle that is to be sewed into position. A hole is then punched through the outer edge of the coil already in place. The binding strand is pushed through this hole and back up around the outside coil to hold it in place. Figure 17-5 shows this method better than words can describe it.

Coiled basketry has a sporadic distribution about the surface of the globe that suggests independent invention in several areas. A continuous distribution occurs from Northeast Asia through Alaska, down through the Mackenzie-Yukon area into the Great Basin, California, and the Southwest. In extreme isolation, the Labrador Eskimos and the Tierra del Fuegians also make it. In the Old World, the coiling technique occurs in Africa, Indonesia, and Australia.

Twined and coiled baskets are used to hold not only dry stuffs but also water. To carry water in a basket may seem as silly as bailing with a sieve, but if baskets are closely woven and sealed with clay or pitch, they will do. The Shoshone Indians make their drinking-water baskets slightly permeable like Western water bags. Enough liquid seeps through to keep the water cool by evaporation, and a gentle flavoring of pine gum makes a delectable desert drink.

In North America there is a close association between tightly twined and coiled basketry and stone boiling as a method of cookery. Preheated stones are grasped with wooden tongs and held in the basketful of water. The heat of the stones brings the water to a boil. In the Plains area, a pouch of skin suspended on four stakes was used in the same way.

Conversely, where pottery is well developed, basketry is not used for cooking purposes. Once the techniques are known, pottery is quicker and easier to make than baskets. More than that, it is more efficient for cooking purposes, since it may be put directly over the fire.

The Pomo Indians of California are acclaimed as the world's finest basket makers. Not only did they use the three basic basket-

[2] The Hopi villages are located on three mesas in northeastern Arizona. From east to west, the mesas are named First, Second, and Third.

making techniques, but they also practiced five kinds of twining (plain, diagonal, three-strand, three-strand braided, and lattice). Coiling was done on a one- or three-rod base. The variety of forms, however, is too great to describe here (Fig. 17-6).[3]

There are also many modifications on the basic patterns practiced by various people in different parts of the world. The reader interested in the details should go to the classic work of Mason on American Indian basketry.[4]

Pottery

The making of pottery is one of the higher accomplishments of primitive life. Paleolithic man never achieved it, for not until Mesolithic times was the first pottery invented. The earliest migrants to North America left Asia before the technique of pottery making had spread to Siberia. There are no shards associated with the earliest prehistoric finds on this continent. Not until the Modified Basket Maker period (A.D. 500 to 700) did the people of the Anasazi culture, who were later to become such skilled potters, start to make ceramic vessels.

In Central America and the Andean region, archaic pottery making began earlier. It is most likely that pottery was independently invented in one or another part of this area, whence it spread out to other parts of the New World. Patagonians and Tierra del Fuegians never received the invention, while basket-making Californians and Shoshones rarely found the urge to copy their neighbors in the Southwest. Northwest Coast Indians were satisfied with their baskets and wooden boxes, and the Indians of the Canadian woodlands utilized bark utensils.

All peoples of Africa make some pottery, but it has received scant attention as an artistic

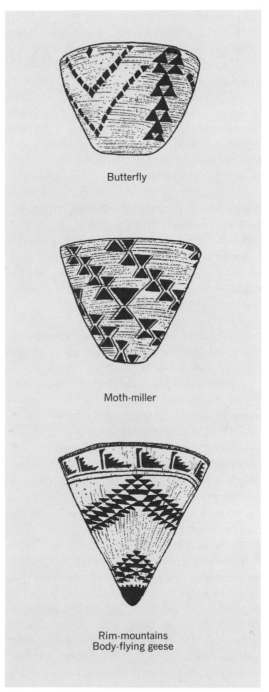

Butterfly

Moth-miller

Rim-mountains
Body-flying geese

Fig. 17-6 Basketry designs of the Maidu Indians, neighbors of the Pomo of California. (After Boas.)

[3] See S. A. Barrett, "Pomo Indian Basketry" (*University of California Publications in American Archaeology and Ethnology*, Vol. 7, 1908).

[4] O. T. Mason, *Aboriginal American Basketry* (United States National Museum, Report, 1904), pp. 171–548. For a discussion and analysis of ethnological problems in basketry, see G. Weltfish, "Prehistoric North American Basketry Techniques and Modern Distributions" (*American Anthropologist*, Vol. 32, 1930), pp. 454–495.

craft on that continent, where woodworking, metalworking, and weaving are of more interest to the natives.[5]

The potter's art extends across Asia through Indonesia into the Pacific. Good pottery is made in Melanesia and Guam, and in Palau and Yap in western Micronesia, but to many Micronesians and the Polynesians it became a lost art. Polynesians hit upon the substitute device of the stone pit oven for cooking purposes.

In general, except for the gap just mentioned, the distribution of primitive pottery follows the distribution of gardening and agriculture. Food gatherers and hunters are too far removed from the centers of pottery invention to have received the art by diffusion, or, because of their nomadic life, they have rejected clay pots as too burdensome.

Pottery-making techniques   A primitive potter must successfully complete six steps in the making of even the simplest pot:

1. He must know where to find decent clay. Surely the reader, as a child, has hopefully made at least one crude clay vessel, only to have it crack and crumble upon drying. Clay is a disintegrated rock consisting essentially of hydrous aluminum silicate with various impurities. The relative proportions of silica and aluminum oxide, plus the nature and quantity of the impurities, determine the quality of the clay for pottery purposes.

2. The clay must be prepared: (a) Most primitive potters first dry the clay and then pulverize it so that coarse extraneous materials may be sifted out. Clay of homogeneous texture is thus procured. (b) The mechanical and chemical composition of the clay is usually adjusted by the addition of tempering materials, which may be powdered shell, mica, quartz, sand, or even crushed potsherds. Tempering serves to give the clay a workable and binding consistency. It also prevents cracking and checking on drying. Archaeological specimens indicate

that the earliest Neolithic potters did not add artificial temper to their clay. (c) The clay must be moistened to a proper working consistency.

3. The clay must next be shaped into a vessel.

4. After this is completed, the pot must be air-dried.

5. Decoration, if any, is applied before or after drying, depending upon the nature of the decorative process. Glaze may be added at this point.

6. The final and critical step is the firing of the pot.

Steps 3, 5, and 6 deserve to be discussed in some detail. There are three possible methods of shaping pottery vessels, all of which were known to primitive man. The least used, but possibly the oldest, is to mold the clay about a basket or gourd, which becomes burned out in the firing process. This method is wasteful of labor and baskets: truly a long way to a pot. Modeling may be done either from a solid lump of clay or from built-up coils that have been rolled out like long snakes. Either process may be performed with or without a paddle and dolly. And either method may be used with or without a potter's wheel.

The potter's wheel need not be a true wheel; i.e., it does not have to be round in circumference. It can be a square platform—or octagonal. But it must embody the basic principle of the wheel, namely, a plane rotating on an axle. No American Indians, not even the sophisticated Mayas, Incas, or Aztecs, were ever able to discover this principle for themselves. Hence, all American Indian potters were wheelless.

In the Old World, the potter's wheel appears to have been invented in Egypt some five thousand years ago. It spread throughout Bronze Age Europe and eastward through India. In using the wheel, the lump of clay is centered directly over the axle, and in the hands of a skillful worker, the revolving mass seems miraculously to grow up and out into a vase.

In the coiling of pottery, a piece of clay is always first laid down as a base. Pueblo Indians start the bottom coils in a tray or pottery bowl to provide a support and a turning base.

[5]Omitted from the scope of this statement are the ancient civilizations of the Lower Nile and Asia Minor.

Other peoples invariably use a flat rock or piece of board. If the pot is to be a large one, it must be set aside to dry for awhile when the side walls are half built so that it will become stiff enough to hold its shape. When the whole pot has dried to a leathery consistency, it is pressed smooth with the worker's fingers or with a rounded dolly of stone or clay held against the inside wall while the outer surface is patted or rubbed into shape.

Attractive corrugated ware for household use was made by prehistoric Pueblo Indians, who, instead of obliterating the coils, pinched or pressed down the outer rounded edges.[6] A much more primitive decorative device was to pat the surface of the pot with a cord-wrapped paddle, imparting to it a textilelike surface.

In the European Neolithic, cord imprints were applied in horizontal series to what the Germans have called *Schnurkeramik.* The other great class of European Neolithic pottery was produced by scratching in bands of incised lines or punctate dots, the so-called *Bandkeramik.* More sophisticated artisans obtain decoration through slip, painting, method of firing, and sculpture. A slip is a surface wash of very fine clay, which when baked, produces a smooth finish. Use of a clay of different composition from the body produces a different exterior color. Painted designs are put on before firing. The paint changes color in baking.

All primitive pottery is baked or fired, but a kiln is not necessary for this purpose, and few primitive potters have them. Several pots are fired at once to save labor. They are simply piled up in inverted fashion (the bottom ones resting on rocks) and covered with a heap of wood or dry dung, if that is available. The latter makes a very hot fire; even without the use of bellows, temperatures of 1200 to 1700°F are produced.

If the potter wants to turn out creamy ware or shades of buff, brown, orange, or red, he does not inhibit or smother the fire. He knows air produces those colors, according to the chemistry of the clay. All combustible materials in the clay are oxidized. If he wants black pottery, he smothers the fire with wet grass, peat, wood, or powdered dung. The oxygen in the clay is thus driven out by reduction, and carbon deposited by the smoke produces black coloration.

Glazing was known to few primitives. It is attained by applying a slip or painted design of lead oxide, silica, or salts in solution. At high temperatures, they fuse and impart a glassy luster.

The final technical step in pottery making (porcelain) was never attained by any primitive people. Invented by the civilized Chinese, who developed it into a high art imitated by Europeans, chinaware is nothing but very thin pottery made of pure pipe clay (kaolin) fired at such high temperatures that it fuses throughout.

Weaving

Weaving is an outgrowth of netting and basketry. Its product is textile fabric. It differs from basketry in that the strands used are so pliable and fine that they must be worked on a loom,[7] which is a device for holding the warp[8] threads taut. Such strands are, of course, string or thread made of animal or vegetable fibers. They may also be strips of fur, although woven fur robes are not considered to be true cloth.

The manufacture of twine is universal in human culture. In the most primitive method, fibers are simply rolled between the palms or between the thigh and the hand. Spindles were independently developed in Egypt, and much later in Central and South America. The primitive spindle is nothing more than a long, narrow stick with a stone or pottery collar near one end that keeps the thread from running off. A rough string of fiber wound several times about the spindle and held taut with the left hand is tightly twisted and simultaneously wound around the spindle, which is spun with

---

[6]See R. Bunzel, *The Pueblo Potter* (Columbia University Contributions to Anthropology, Vol. 8, 1929), for a comprehensive analysis of an important pottery complex.

[7]Knitting and crocheting are special forms of close netting, not weaving.

[8]The *warp* is the group of parallel-lying foundation threads over and through which the *weft,* or *woof,* is woven at right angles.

Fig. 17-7 Guatemala Indian woman wearing hand woven blouse and skirt, spinning cotton thread with a hand-twirled spindle. (Photograph by Esther Bubley for PepsiCo International.)

the right hand (Fig. 17-7). Several spinnings are needed to produce an even thread.

In spite of the fact that cord or thread making is universal, weaving is not. Although an ancient art in the Mediterranean area, India, Indonesia, and prehistoric Europe, it did not extend deeply into the tropical forests of Africa (although it is practiced in the Sudan), nor was it known to the Bushmen. We have already noted that it was a lost art in most of Polynesia, where its absence was adequately met by bark cloth (as it was in the African Congo). In Melanesia and the Micronesian Caroline Islands, a limited amount of weaving was done, but here, too, the preference was for bark cloth. There was no weaving in primitive Australia.

In the Americas, the Andean region around A.D. 1200 became the center for some of the finest and most complicated handwoven fabrics the world has ever known (Fig. 17-8). The direction of the textile industry became one of the chief interests of the Inca government, which levied taxes, fines, and tribute in cloth. Great stores of perfect cloth, well preserved in the high, dry climate, have been recovered by modern archaeologists and collectors.

Archaeological stratigraphy gives a clear sequence for the development of looms in this area. The belt loom was the earliest (Mochica culture, A.D. 600 to 700). It was followed by a horizontal frame loom supported on stakes, which is to this day preferred by Aymara Indians. Finally, it was followed by a vertical four-pole frame loom built against the wall.

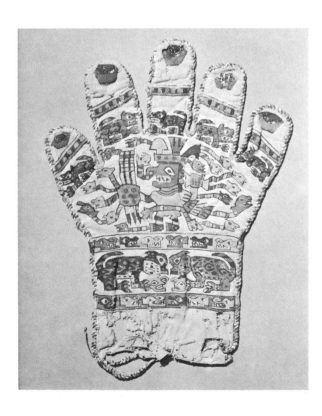

Fig. 17-8 A thousand-year old woolen glove woven in tapestry technique; from the pre-Inca culture of Tiahuanaco, Peru. The central figure is adorned with serpent-like plumes and is surrounded by jaguars and jaguar heads. (Courtesy of The Brooklyn Museum.)

From the Inca center, true loom weaving is distributed north and south along the Andean cordillera, and up through Central America and Mexico into the Southwest (Fig. 17-9). Simple frame weaving is done in the Amazonian basin, as is belt loom work; frame weaving occurs in the Gran Chaco and the Pampas, but disappears completely in the extreme south. Native American cotton is the chief material used from the Southwest down through South America.[9]

Weaving was absent in California and the Plains area, but very primitive suspended-warp weaving was done on the Northwest Coast and in the woodlands of the Mississippi Valley and the Southeast.

Suspended-warp weaving is done without a true loom. It calls for finger weaving without the aid of a heddle. Chilcat blankets from the Northwest Coast are the most famous product of this kind of weaving (Fig. 17-10). The warp of shredded cedar bark is suspended free-hanging from a horizontal pole supported on two uprights. The weaving is done from top to bottom, as the weaver works the woolen weft in and out with the fingers.

True looms must meet two needs: (1) they must keep the warp taut, and (2) they must have some arrangement whereby a whole group of warps can be lifted at once, so that the weft may be passed through the *shed* (the open space between the lifted warps and the dormant ones) in one movement. When the lifted warps are released, the shed closes as they fall back into place, and the weft falls automatically into its over-and-under position.

The device that performs this function is

[9]See L. M. O'Neale, "Weaving," in J. H. Steward (ed.), *Handbook of South American Indians*, Vol. 5, *The Comparative Ethnology of South American Indians*, pp. 97–138.

Fig. 17-9 Navaho woman at hogan entrance weaving a blanket on a suspended warp loom. (Smithsonian Office of Anthropology, Bureau of American Ethnology Collection.)

Fig. 17-10 A Chilcat Indian chieftain from the Northwest Coast of North America. The face and eye design, seen both in the carved wooden helmet and the blanket, is highly characteristic of the art of the Northwest Coast. The woolen weft of the blanket is woven on a warp of shredded cedarbark. (Courtesy of the American Museum of Natural History.)

known as the *heddle*. The most primitive heddle is a simple stick, which need be only a little wider than the *web* (the breadth of the warps). One heddle is passed under every other warp. The remaining warps are manipulated by means of one or more additional heddles. By alternately lifting each heddle, the warps can be shifted to speed up the weaving. After the weft is passed through the shed by means of a *bobbin*, it is hammered tightly against the woven material with a flat stick (the *batten*) or a comb. Design patterns are woven in by use of more than two heddles or by laying in differently colored wefts and warps.

The belt or waist loom solves the problem of warp tension by tying one end of the loom to a pole and the other to a belt around the weaver's waist. Larger looms may have a four-pole frame, or the warp poles may be lashed to ceiling or floor.[10]

Felting

Weaving and spinning are two ways to interlock fibrous materials to form a compact cloth covering; felting, in which animal wools are matted together by wetting, beating, forming in sheets, compressing, and drying, is another.

Because of the relatively greater complexity of the weaving process, it was at one time assumed that felt was the earlier invention. But the world-wide distribution of weaving as against the limitation of felting to Asia and Europe makes it clear that felting is a special and later invention. For all their skill in weaving, and in spite of the fact that they possessed an excellent supply of wool in the llama and alpaca, the Andean Indians never felted at all. Of course, felting is possible only where woolly animals provide a source of materials.

Bark cloth

In such tropical areas as Indonesia, Oceania, Central Africa, and Central and South America, bark fibers are used as equivalents of wool. The principle underlying the manufacture of

felt and bark cloth is the same: a sheet of material is produced by matting fibers so tightly that they adhere permanently. However, geographical distribution and analysis of the complexes make it quite clear that bark-cloth manufacture was independently invented and not derived from felting or vice versa.

A full comparative study of bark-cloth techniques in all parts of the world is yet to be done.[11] But in general the process is the same everywhere. The fibrous inner bark of a suitable tree, such as the paper mulberry (which is cultivated for the purpose in Polynesia), is stripped, scraped, and beaten out with a grooved wooden mallet or paddle on a wood anvil. It may or may not be soaked in water as a part of the preparatory process. Where it is, there is no limit to the size of the cloth that can be made, since one piece may readily and effectively be "felted" into another.

Indonesians and Polynesians decorate their *tapa* cloth with stamped designs carved into wooden blocks and printed over the surface of the material in brown vegetable dyes. Polynesian block-print designs have been fashionable for some time in sports shirts and casual clothes in the United States.

Metallurgy

Metallurgy is scarcely a primitive craft, for it requires the kind of technological knowledge that is more closely allied to civilization than to savagery. Yet preliterate people did acquire metalworking skill. This was probably true of the Europeans, as well as of the peoples of the Mediterranean and Asia, during the prehistoric Bronze and Iron Ages. It was true of many Africans, and also of the Peruvian Indians and Indonesian peoples. All were close to the threshold of civilization.

The beating out of gold nuggets or chunks of pure copper does not constitute metallurgy.

---

[10]See C. Amsden, "The Loom and Its Prototypes" (*American Anthropologist*, Vol. 34, 1932), pp. 216–235.

[11]An excellent prototype of such a study was done by Raymond Kennedy, who demonstrated that the internal congruity of technical steps and linguistic terminology associated with bark-cloth manufacture in Polynesia and Indonesia is such that it must be inferred that Polynesian bark-cloth manufacture originated in Indonesia. See his "Bark Cloth in Indonesia" (*Journal of the Polynesian Society*, No. 172, 1934).

Indians in the copper-rich regions of Lake Superior made tubular arrowheads and spearheads of beaten native copper. Copper pieces are found in mounds of the prehistoric Hopewell culture of Illinois and Ohio. Eskimos fashioned a few rare tools out of the iron residue of meteorites found on the frozen surface of the ground. But not a single North American Indian knew how to smelt a metal.

The Mexicans, who knew how to melt gold nuggets with the aid of blowpipes, came close to the secret of the reduction of ores. The Peruvians found the secret in the smelting of copper and tin, which were mined from hills looked upon as sacred shrines. Inca metalworking processes included smelting, alloying (bronze), casting, hammering, repoussé, incrustation, inlay, soldering, riveting, and cloisonné.[12] Skill in goldworking by the highly honored profession of goldsmiths was the bait that brought the gold-greedy conquistadores down upon the hapless Indians.

The Africans have concentrated upon the more prosaic tools of the blacksmith's forge. From iron smelted in little clay blast furnaces with hand bellows, they shape such utilitarian tools as knives, adzes, axes, and hoes; even tools may be shaped with artistic love when they are to be endowed with symbolic value. Bronze casting in West Africa reached a peak of artistic perfection in the work of the Bina at Benin that has made the Benin masks precious collectors' items. The Benin method of casting is the "lost-wax," or cire-perdue, technique, in which a model is first made of wax and then covered with clay. The wax is then melted out to make room for the molten metal. When the clay molds are broken, the casting is freed (Fig. 17-11).

Fig. 17-11   The bronze casters of Benin produced complex compositions by first modelling in wax over which a clay mold was pressed. Molten bronze, poured onto the wax, melted and replaced it, thus taking on the form of the mold. (Courtesy of The Brooklyn Museum.)

SUMMARY

Tools are artifactual extensions or substitutes for human limbs and other features of the body. With tools, man adapts his activities to a more efficient exploitation of his environment without reliance on genetic changes to achieve the result. This is the reason why some biologists, as, for example, Julian Huxley, think that biological evolution has finally come to an end with modern man. We adapt through culture rather than through biological changes of our bodily inheritance.

Stone and wooden tools are as old as man. Bone implements date from the Old Stone Age and are found in all parts of the primitive world. Pottery and weaving represent high arts not developed until Neolithic times, but they subsequently spread to virtually all humanity. Felting and the production of bark cloth are interesting specialized primitive methods of pro-

[12]J. H. Rowe, "Inca Culture at the Time of the Spanish Conquest," in J. H. Steward (ed.) *Handbook of South American Indians,* Vol. 2, *The Andean Civilizations,* p. 246.

ducing fabrics used as body covering. We can say that an age of handicrafts began in the Paleolithic age and lasted until the Industrial Revolution in Europe. For most of humanity that age is dying only now; yet the demise is to be hastened by the great technical-assistance programs for so-called "backward" countries. These programs are designed to supplant handicraft technologies with modern industry, for handicrafts, although they have served humanity well for a million years, do not greatly increase man's energy output. They require a heavy output of time and effort for a relatively small return in food or other consumable goods. Except as handicrafts survive as specialized arts in advanced civilizations, handicraft technology is synonymous with a primitive mode of livelihood, but it is one that often reveals remarkable ingenuity and technical skill combined with high aesthetic quality.

SELECTED READINGS

Amsden, C. E.: *Navaho Weaving* (1949). From sheep to blankets in all their varieties.

Blackwood, B.: *Both Sides of Buka Passage,* (1935), chap. 10, "Useful Crafts." Material culture and its social uses among a Melanesian people.

Bunzel, R.: *The Pueblo Potter* (1929). A comprehensive analysis of an important handicraft complex.

Mason, O. T.: *Aboriginal American Basketry.* (1904). A complete survey of American Indian basketry.

Sayce, R. U.: *Primitive Arts and Crafts* (1933). Succinctly summarizes the field.

Singer, S., E. J. Holmyard, and A. R. Hall (eds.): *A History of Technology,* Vol. 1, *From Early Times to the Fall of Empires* (1954). Encyclopedic and detailed in its coverage, it is a mine of fact and information.

Trowell, M., and K. P. Wachsman: *Tribal Crafts of Uganda* (1953). Comprehensive, well illustrated, and especially good on musical instruments.

Clothing and ornament

chapter 18

In all times and climes, man undertakes to effect what he believes are improvements upon his bodily appearance. His cosmetic accomplishments, both primitive and civilized, are wonderful if not always beautiful to behold. The time and effort that have gone into painting, pricking, scarring, puncturing, and otherwise mutilating and deforming the human body for aesthetic and status reasons are beyond all calculation. We shall leave it to sociologists and economists to calculate how many billion dollars are spent per year on clothes and cosmetics in this most advanced of civilizations today.

The undressed man

People who wear little or no clothing in no way contradict what has just been said. Be he ever so unclothed, man is never unadorned. If he wears not so much as a G-string, he certainly sports a nose, ear, or lip plug, or bears his tattoos or scarifications, or paints his face, or curls his hair, or cuts it off, or blackens his teeth, or knocks them out, or perhaps merely files them to a point.

Fig. 18-1 Bodily decoration of an Amazonian youth of the Amerakaeri tribe. Painted stripes, bead necklace and armlets, and feathers through his nose make up the costume in which he waits his turn to dance at a tribal festival. (Cornell Capa, Magnum.)

The sense of modesty Modesty is merely a habit, not instinct. The discomfiture that is felt when one's sense of modesty is disturbed is a diffused neurophysiological upset of a large part of the nervous and organic system, shock-stimulated by a behavior situation that contrasts sharply with those to which a person has been intensely habituated. And of course, there is more than the element of mere habit in the total situation. There has also been a strong ideational indoctrination that penalties, social or supernatural, accompany any departure from the habituated pattern. Apprehension of dire consequences contributes much of the tone of fear and anxiety that colors the feelings of immodesty. As late as 1936, for example, old-timers among Comanche males felt acutely uncomfortable and indecent if they thoughtlessly went out without a G-string, even though fully clothed in pants and shirt.

A favored tale among anthropologists is that of Baron von Nordenskiold, who in his Amazonian travels undertook to purchase the facial plugs of a Botocudo[1] woman, who stood all unabashed in customary nudity before him. Only irresistible offers of trade goods at long last tempted her to remove and hand over her labrets. When thus stripped of her proper raiment, she fled in shame and confusion into the jungle. After all, the close identification between the Botocudo as a person and the *botocudo* as a plug is such that to become unplugged is most un-Botocudo.

Such circumstances make it perfectly clear that the use of clothing does not rise out of any innate sense of modesty, but that modesty results from customary habits of clothing or ornamentation of the body and its parts.

Among primitive peoples, the use or nonuse of clothing is more or less functional, although not wholly so. People who dwell in the tropical

---

[1] "The *Botocudo* owe their name to the large cylindrical wooden plugs worn by men and women alike in the ear lobes and lower lips. These cylinders, of light wood (*Chorisia ventricosa*), were 3 to 4 inches (7.6 to 10 cm) in diameter and 1 inch (2.5 cm) thick. The ears were perforated at the age of 7 or 8, the lips a few years later." A. Métraux, "The Botocudo," in J. H. Steward (ed.), *Handbook of the Indians of South America*, Vol. 1, *The Marginal Tribes*, p. 534.

rain forests tend to get along with a minimum of clothing. This is true in Africa, the Americas, and Oceania. Generally, however, the men wear some sort of a pubic covering, a suspensory or supporter. It is hardly necessary to seek magical reasons for the widespread use of this device, as was done by the early anthropologist Waitz,[2] and after him by Sumner.[3] Notions of mystic shielding of the male sex organ from evil influences are more likely to be secondary developments. Certainly, the conspicuous coverings of gleaming shells, gourds, bark, hide, cloth, or grass do not serve to divert attention but rather to attract it.

An alternative to the rigid sheath is a small apron of leather, grass, or cloth worn in front, or fore and aft, or between the legs and about the waist. Such a garment is frequently worn by women as well as men. It is the basic, and often the only, bit of clothing worn by most primitive peoples.

The use of robes When warmth is needed, something more must be added. Most races of mankind are so relatively hairless that they need artificial insulation. Hence, we rob the animals of their hairy covering—skin and all. The trapper flays the beast and prepares the hide, the tailor shapes it, and the lady of fashion slips the skins of animals over her own when she makes her winter excursions. Wool coverings are also produced at the expense of animals, but not necessarily by lethal methods.

Shoshones weave rabbit-skin robes, as did the early prehistoric Basket Makers. African Bushmen provide themselves with skin cloaks. The Yahgan of Tierra del Fuego wore a small sealskin, sea-otter, or fox cape as the sole protection against a nasty subantarctic climate—except for a small pubic covering worn by women. The Ona of the same area and the nearby Tehuelche sported longer and larger capes. The Tasmanians wore no proper cloak, but the men were given to draping and tying sundry strips of fur around their shoulders and limbs. For the most part, the Tasmanians

Fig. 18-2 Lip and ear labrets displayed by a Suia male, Brazil. (Emil Schulthess, Black Star.)

smeared themselves with grease and red ochre for protection against cold, as did the Fuegians. The Central Australians, like the Tasmanians, deviate from the norm of hunters and gatherers who live in the temperate zone in that they have no cloaks. They seem never to have hit upon the idea of wearing skin for clothing. For the men, a conspicuous pubic tassel suspended from a belt of human hair and armbands of twisted fur suffice. A woman is dressed if she has a string of beads around her neck.

When we turn our attention once again to South America, we find that the fur mantle is worn by Patagonians and Indians of the Gran Chaco in inclement weather. The famous woven wool ponchos of the Andean Indians are undoubtedly a cultural elaboration of this more primitive covering.

In North America, the buffalo-hide robe of the Plains Indians was also a form of cape, a large one, later to be replaced by the trader's blanket, which is to this day the symbol of the conservative Indian, the "blanket Indian," who clings to the old ways. Even in the rugged Northeastern woodlands, the draped robe was

[2]F. T. Waitz, *Anthropologie der Naturvölker*, Vol. 6, pp. 575–576.
[3]W. G. Sumner, *Folkways*, pp. 432, 456.

the chief item of winter clothing, besides leg-gings and moccasins. In the Southeastern states, the natives went naked except for a loincloth. When cold did sweep down from the north, they, too, cast on a loose robe or cape of fur.[4]

The tailored man

We may conclude, then, that tailoring, was not one of the more widely esteemed human arts. Most of mankind, including such sophisticates as the Greeks and Romans, have done quite well without it. The feature that is unique about tailoring is that by means of sewing, clothing may be made more or less to fit the human frame. The very idea of tailoring is "fit," and "well-tailored" means more fit rather than less. In temperate and arctic climates, it is func-tionally advantageous to have tailored clothes. The insulating efficiency of clothing is greatly enhanced by the closed, tubular effect of the tailored garment, which gives little room for the play of chilly breezes upon the body. In the tropical rain forest or torrid desert, the very advantages of tailored clothing become its disadvantages.

Two factors, therefore, combined to limit the pre-Columbian distribution of tailored cloth-ing to Europe, northern Asia, and the northern half of North America: (1) selective adjustment to climatic factors and (2) the fact that tailor-ing is an advanced technique, which the Fue-gians, who certainly could have used warm garments, failed to invent.

That cultural improvements are not *ipso facto* beneficial is incidentally demonstrated in the debilitating effect of the introduction of Euro-pean clothing among the Yahgan, of whom Cooper writes:

The clothing of the Yahgan seems to us utterly inade-quate, given the climatic conditions—temperatures commonly around and well below freezing point in winter, high winds, frequent snow, hail, sleet, and cold rain—but in view of the seeming role played in their decline by introduced European clothing and their relative good health prior thereto, perhaps their clothing was reasonably well-adapted to the environ-ment.[5]

In this case, we would observe that it is not so much that their clothing was reasonably well adapted (which it was not) as that they were physiologically well adapted to a *specific* environmental situation. The adjustment was more biological than cultural. The introduction of tailored European clothing and other ele-ments was a cultural modification that so altered the total environment of the Yahgans as to disturb disastrously the biological balance between them and their physical world. Inexo-rable extinction apparently stalks them.

This, of course, has been a common conse-quence of culture contact when very primi-tive peoples find their environment drastically unsettled by incursive elements emanating from a suddenly presented, unlike, and higher culture.

The diffusion of tailoring To return to the problem of the distribution of tailored clothing, it was made originally among the arctic and subarctic peoples of Siberia and North America and the ancient Chinese. The distribution in North America, as Wissler pointed out,[6] was coterminous with the distribution of caribou; in Asia the association was coterminous with the reindeer. Although the Northwest Coast Indians could easily have adopted the tailoring technique (they did sew boxes together), they did not do so. The northern bison hunters of the Plains did, however, make loosely tailored shirts and dresses of the modified poncho type.

Real tailoring is done by the Eskimos and Indians of the Canadian woods. Coats are fitted with genuine sleeves and necks. Eskimo gar-ments with the fur turned in and the outer skin dyed and decorated are not only func-tional but also aesthetic.

[4]For a detailed account of the clothing of Southeastern Indians, see J. R. Swanton, "Southeastern Cultures," in E. A. Hoebel, J. D. Jennings, and E. R. Smith, *Readings in Anthropology*, pp. 117–122.

[5]J. M. Cooper, "The Yahgan," in J. H. Steward (ed.), *Handbook of South American Indians*, Vol. 1, *The Marginal Tribes*, p. 87.
[6]C. Wissler, *The American Indian*, p. 62.

The diffusion of tailoring in prehistoric times raises several unsolved problems. Did it spread from the ancient civilization of China to the Siberian barbarians, and from there to the east and west? Or did the primitive skin workers of northern Asia develop it, from whence it came to the Chinese?

The westward diffusion into Europe proper did not occur until a number of centuries after the conquests of Caesar. And finally, since the bursting of the confines of Europe in modern times, when tailored clothing became the symbol of the European conqueror, human creatures in all parts of the world have now enclosed their bodies in suits and dresses. The lovely tapa sarong of the Polynesian has given way to the missionary's Mother Hubbard. But, having "civilized" the Polynesian out of the sarong, we moderns have taken its charms for our own.

Shoes and hats

A properly dressed American would rarely think of making a public appearance without shoes. The nether extremities must be covered. Further, many men and most women still consider that some kind of headgear is de rigueur on more or less formal occasions. Shoes and hats, like tailored clothing, are functional of course, but they may also be status symbols.

Among primitives, footgear is more common than headgear. The status functions of headgear can be served readily enough by hairdos. The protective functions of hats are also notably less important than the protective function of shoes. Here again, the physical environment is an important factor in influencing the adoption of an element of material culture.

The problem of fabricating a foot covering that will stand up under the wet rot of the tropical jungle is practically insoluble. Even our best efforts with all the resources of science are still not very satisfactory. Jungle primitives prefer to go barefoot. An unshod foot dries more quickly and comfortably than one encased in a soaking and muddy moccasin. For this reason, the highly sophisticated Indians

of the Northwest Coast rain forest went barefoot, even in southern Alaska.

The simplest footgear is a piece of hide folded about the foot. When tailored, it becomes a moccasin of the type made famous by the North American Indians. Further development of this form produces the boot. The so-called "arctic boot" is an adjunct of true tailoring. This is not at all surprising, since anyone skilled enough in cutting and sewing to make a boot is *ipso facto* skilled enough to tailor clothing, and vice versa. Further, the same climatic circumstances that lend to tailored clothes their functional value do the same for boots. People who have to plod around in snow and cold find high tops more comfortable. Who enjoys walking through the snowdrifts in oxfords? However, we have learned in anthropology not to expect that necessity necessarily mothers invention. The Indians of the North American boreal forests (the Canadian woodlands), who make tailored clothing and are confronted with heavy snows, make moccasins instead of boots, in spite of the fact that the more northerly of these Indians have contact with boot-wearing Eskimos. The boot of the Eskimos, worn from Greenland to Alaska, was undoubtedly borrowed from the Siberian herders and hunters. It is quite definitely an Asian trait.

The high, thigh-length, Cavalier-style riding boots of the Tehuelche Indians of the Patagonian pampas (whence comes its name, the "Patagonian boot") are apparently a post-Columbian adoption. The early, horseless "foot Tehuelche" wore a kind of moccasin stuffed with straw.[7] Because of its association with the horse, a post-Columbian acquisition, the Patagonian boot is hardly to be considered an independent primitive invention. But it is interesting to note that similar boots were not adopted in the Amazon, where the natives still prefer to go barefoot, or in the Andean region, where the prehistoric sandal holds sway.

[7] J. M. Cooper, "The Patagonian and Pampean Hunters," in J. H. Steward (ed.), *Handbook of South American Indians*, Vol. 1, *The Marginal Tribes*, p. 144.

The sandal is the other type of primitive footgear that finds great favor. In its simplest form, it is a piece of leather roughly fitted to the sole and held firm by thongs passing over the foot.

Sandals with woven fiber soles were very popular with prehistoric Southwestern and Great Basin Indians. Wissler noted that "in eastern North America moccasins were discarded when walking in the rain, in wet grass, or upon moist ground."[8] This was also true of the Incas with their rawhide-soled sandals, which would become soft and squishy when wet, and then hard and out of shape when dried. Wissler thought he detected a link between the wearing of sandals and the wearing of woven clothing in both the Old World and the New. The fact is, however, that in prehistoric North America, the production of woven sandals antedates the weaving of cloth by thousands of years. Such sandals are an aspect of the making of baskets, not of textiles.[9]

The hairdo

One of mankind's most intense concerns is with the coiffure. We do not know when the earliest prehistoric men and women first began to play with the cranial hair. Archaeological evidence from the Upper Paleolithic in Europe decisively demonstrates that Cro-Magnon man and his contemporaries laid great emphasis upon the female hairdo. In the Gravettian statuette of the Venus of Willendorf (Fig. 11-8, page 180), no facial features were carved by the artist. He had no interest in a pretty face. But the pattern of the hairstyle is meticulously incised. This trait of the Venus of Willendorf in the Gravettian epoch, more than twenty thousand years ago, was not a mere accident but a strong feature of the culture, for a similar degree of care was lavished upon the hair pattern of the female head from the Grotte du Pape at Brassempouy (Fig. 11-9, page 181).

All recent primitives, from those of the

lowest cultures to the highest, treat the hair. Add to this the fact that all civilized people do likewise, and we see that this trait is universal in human culture.

Hairstyles and social status   The trimming and arrangement of the hair are not merely matters of decoration and ornamentation; in culture after culture, such treatment serves to symbolize social position. The most basic status represented in the treatment of the hair is that of sex. Males and females within any given society almost without exception have different ways of fixing the hair. In America, the cultural pattern with its attendant symbolic quality is still so strong that short-haired women are considered mannish and long-haired men effeminate—at least by most individuals over thirty.

Less universally, hairstyles are used to indicate age status. Omaha Indian boys had their heads shaved close, with isolated tufts of hair left here and there. Men either wore their full head of hair lying loose or shaved it off, except for a continuous roach along the sagittal line. At one time in our society, young girls wore their hair down until after adolescence, when they were privileged to put it up.

Among the Omahas, the shaved head of the boys indicated more than just age status, for the patterns of the remaining tufts were different for the boys of each clan. "The cutting of the hair was done, it was said, in order to impress on the mind of a child, as in an object lesson, the gentes [patrilineal clan] to which a playmate belonged."[10] This selfsame practice is widespread among Sudanese West Africans. There the pates of children are divided into patterns of diamonds and squares formed by parting the hair and gathering it into tightly tied tufts. In Africa, the various patterns indicate different social affiliations. Some of the styles, the tightly pulled pigtails all over the head, for example, can be seen on small children among American Coloreds, who have long since lost all vestiges of African clan organiza-

[8]Wissler, *op. cit.*, p. 65.
[9]*Ibid.*, p. 64.

[10]A. C. Fletcher and F. LaFlesche, *The Omaha Tribe* (Bureau of American Ethnology, Annual Report 27, 1911), p. 198.

tion; the practice apparently[11] expresses no more than a style convention that is but a survival of the old practice. A definitely New World symbolism has arisen among American Coloreds in the matter of hair form. The passion for hair-straightening and kink-removing compounds among American Coloreds reflects an identification of nonkinky hair with the social status of whites.

The varieties of hair decoration are so multifarious the world over that it is not possible to attempt a distributional summary here. Mention should be made of the localized Melanesian custom, particularly in New Ireland, of bleaching out black hair to a reddish orange with lime. This phenomenon confounded any number of American G.I.'s when they were first confronted with it in the South Pacific.

A closing comment on this subject reemphasizes the vital significance of the relation between hair treatment and formal social position. We have all heard the colloquialism, "They really let their hair down and had a good time." Do we actually let down our hair? Only figuratively. What is let down are the customary restraints that keep us within our more cautiously preserved social roles. Let-down hair is ordinarily hidden from the public view, as is the "uncensored" personality.

Fig. 18-3   Elaborate hair and bodily decoration of the wife of a Makere chieftain, central Sudanese area, Africa. (Belgian Government Information Center.)

Ornaments and ornamentation

Cosmetics and jewelry Americans spend an estimated billion dollars on cosmetics in a normal year. It is not the primitive but the universal man in us that accounts for this seeming extravagance. From a lofty, ascetic point of view, cosmetic aesthetics seem basely barbaric. But lotions, pastes, powders, pigments, and synthetic essences to alter the texture, color, feel, and smell of the external surfaces of the human body are neither primitive nor civilized. They are the universal cultural responses to the basic human need for favorable response. They are designed to heighten the stimulus intensity of the physical presence of one person upon the touch, smell, sight, and perhaps taste of others. Those others are usually of the opposite sex, but not exclusively so. If personality is the social stimulus value of an individual, then cosmetics intensify personality.

Body paint Rouge is the most common cosmetic for two reasons: (1) red ochre (iron oxide) occurs in many places and is readily procurable, and (2) red is the primary color with the longest wavelength perceptible to the human eye, the color with the greatest natural stimulus value. When mixed with grease, it may be harmlessly applied to the human body. Yellow, black, blue, and white are the other favored colors.

Body painting among primitive peoples is for the most part limited to special occasions.

[11]There has been no investigation into the possible functional significances of hair arrangements in American Colored children.

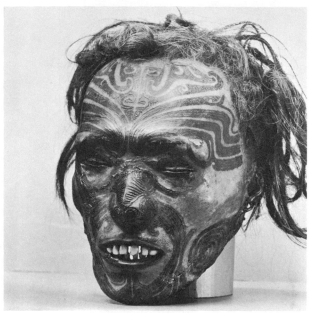

Fig. 18-4   *The elaborate tattooing of a living Maori is vividly preserved on the mummified head which he lost in battle and which was kept by his conqueror for its* mana. *(Courtesy of the American Museum of Natural History.)*

Fig. 18-5   Delicate cicatricizing on the chest and forehead of a pubescent Bankutshu Congolese girl. (Pix, through Belgium Government Information Center.)

Such occasions are, of course, usually ritual and ceremonial. These events are out of the ordinary, and painting changes the individual from an ordinary person to a man of distinction. War paint is usually linked to magical potency and serves less to frighten the enemy than to bolster the faint heart of its wearer. Thus, much of primitive cosmetic practice takes on symbolic values.

Tattooing   The trouble with paint and cosmetics, as every woman knows, is that its application is not lasting. The solution hit upon by many peoples is tattooing. In North America, light tattooing is found among the Eskimos, continuing down the West Coast and into South America. The two high centers of the art, however, were Polyneisa and Japan. Curiously, the status associations of tattooing in Polynesia and the civilized world are just reversed. Among Americans, soldiers and sailors in the lower ranks, longshoremen, and unskilled laborers are usually the persons who get themselves tattooed. Among people of higher status, it is definitely considered *déclassé*. But within the lower classes it serves as a symbol of masculinity and toughness.[12] In Polynesia, the higher the social status, the fuller the tattooing. It extended over face, body, and limbs, and in some overenthusiastic cases, even to the tongue. The process was long, drawn out, and painful, but socially rewarding (Fig. 18-4).

A tattoo is made by puncturing the skin with needles carrying an indelible dye—usually carbon black. This posed a problem for the Africans and Australians. No white dye for tattooing was ever discovered by them. The solution hit upon in Africa and Australia was to incise the skin instead of puncturing it. Then by rubbing ashes, grit, or other irritants into the wounds, scar tissue can be encouraged to form, so that a series of raised lumps remain in a permanent visible pattern.

In Central Australia cicatrization, or *scarification*, as the process is called, is a part of the

[12]In contemporary American illustrative advertising, we might note that when the emphasis is on the "manly" associations of the product, a very discreet hand tattoo may be desirable.

adolescent initiatory rites for boys. The patterns are simply parallel rows of lines on the chest and back, but they are absolutely necessary to manhood. So important are they as symbols of manhood that individuals voluntarily repeat the operations in later life to keep their scars large and fresh.

In Africa, scarification among the Congo Bantus is usually part of the initiatory rite.[13] The designs are in some instances elaborate geometric patterns.

Traditional German corps (fraternity) students and university men gave great kudos to dueling scars, which reputedly had much sex appeal. A wound that did not fester and leave a glaring scar was a dead loss. So important were the duel-born scarifications that persons who had no such scars have been known to slash themselves with razors and rub salt in the wounds to create the impression that they, too, bore the scars of honor.

Decorative deformations and mutilations Tattooing and scarification are only superficial ornamental embellishments impressed upon the body. Piercing of the nasal septum, the lips, or the ears, so that sundry bones, feathers, shell, wood, or metal ornaments may be shoved through them, extends from the most primitive to highly civilized peoples. The invention of the screw and spring clip has only recently obviated the need for ear puncturing among American women, who find the functionally atrophied external ear a convenient appendage from which to dangle pretty baubles.

Incas, in South America, and Baganda, among others in Africa, gradually extend the ear lobes to receive thin disks as much as 6 to 8 inches in diameter. Inca nobility wore disks of gold. Baganda women, with their huge lip labrets, are familiar to all circus sideshow visitors. Separation of the cervical vertebrae and extension of the neck in ringed brass collars by Burmese women is another familiar distortion.

Cranial deformation was much esteemed

[13]See Chap. 21, pp. 328–329 for a discussion of cicatrization, circumcision, and clitoridectomy as important symbols of status transition through initiatory rites.

Fig. 18-6   Punan girl, Borneo, with slit earlobes distended by heavy decorative brass rings. (Courtesy of William W. Conley.)

as a mark of beauty by various Northwest American Indian tribes (viz., the Flatheads of Idaho) and also by the Incas and other Andean peoples, who bound a flat board against the frontal region of the head of a baby in the cradleboard in order to produce a recessed forehead and a high, peaked occipital. Binding with cloth to produce long heads was also practiced.

Circumcision and subincision are not so much mutilations for ornamentation as they are mystical and status operations. The one is the removal of the foreskin of the penis; the other, a slitting of the skin and urethra along the length of the male sex organ. Among the Central Australians, these operations, which are often fatal, symbolize masculinity in a male-dominated and ideologically masculine society; like scarification, they are performed without anesthesia and with flint knives on adolescent boys as a part of initiation into manhood. Most

Fig. 18-7 Filed incisor teeth embellish the smile of a Ticuna mother in Peru. (Cornell Capa, Magnum.)

African tribes also circumcise at adolescence, and for similar reasons. Circumcision is an absolutely required status mark of the Islamic male and orthodox Jew.

Filing or knocking out of incisor teeth occurs in scattered distribution from Australia up through Melanesia and Indonesia, and over into Africa. Prehistoric Europeans and American Indians spared themselves this mark of

distinction. Of all the decorative blemishes imposed by man upon himself, this is perhaps the most foolish. Scarification, tattooing, and circumcision may be painful, but except as they cause death through infection, they do not inhibit the healthy functioning of the body. The deliberate destruction of the teeth does just that to a certain extent.

Yet, as this discussion has shown, what is lost physically is gained socially. Mind triumphs over matter. No matter if the psychic satisfactions are not rational. The need that is met is elemental. The fashion and jewelry industries, the cosmetic manufacturers and purveyors, and the beauticians may rest secure that their services have a future—one that is as long as all mankind's.

SUMMARY

The sense of bodily modesty is a habit and not an instinct. Human beings cover, decorate, or mutilate their bodies for a variety of reasons, chief among which are status identification (symbolic advertising of social position), protection against inclemency of climate, real or imagined self-beautification or enhancement, and magico-religious requirements.

SELECTED READINGS

Elwin, V.: *The Tribal Art of Middle India* (1951). For illustrations and descriptions of bodily adornment.

Hambly, W. D.: *The History of Tattooing and Its Significance* (1925). A broad survey.

Wissler, C.: *The American Indian* (1938), chap. 3, "The Textile Arts." A brief summary.

chapter 19

The urge to beautify is one of the most interesting and unique, and certainly one of the most remarkable, characteristics of the human being. It is, as seen by Justice Oliver Wendell Holmes, "one of the glories of man that he does not sow seed and weave cloth, and produce all the other economic means simply to sustain and multiply other sowers and weavers. . . . After the production of food and cloth has gone on a certain time, he stops producing and goes to the play, or he paints a picture or asks unanswerable questions about the universe, and thus delightfully consumes a part of the world's food and clothing."[1] Unlike so many of the basic drives that may be more or less directly linked to the imperatives of biological survival, the aesthetic and artistic drives are much more obscure in their origins and functions. Man could survive without art; yet man and art are inseparable. To be artless is to be dehumanized. Not without reason are the arts and belles lettres known as the *humanities.*

A working definition of art suitable for anthropoloical purposes is given by E. G. Burrows in his work *Flower in My Ear: Arts and Ethos in Ifaluk Atoll:* ". . . art is any human activity or product (artifact) that emphasizes form beyond all requirements except those of a distinctive pleasure that the manufacture and contemplation of form can give. By form is meant a perceptible relation of parts to a whole. The distinctive pleasure it gives is here called 'aesthetic experience.' "[2]

[1]O. W. Holmes, Jr., "Law in Science and Science in Law" (*Collected Legal Papers*), p. 212.
[2]Page 11.

One function of art as art is to release tensions by enabling the artist to externalize some of his emotions and ideas in an objective way. The release of the tensions brings satisfaction and pleasure. The viewers of the art object, if it has meaning for them, are stimulated to sensuous perceptions that likewise produce emotional responses ultimately resolving into pleasurable feelings of euphoria and balance. This is not to deny, however, that the artistic experience may be highly disturbing and may even cause the artist great discomfiture while it runs its course. The expression of art begins in a state of tension, and the process of translating these feelings of tension into high artistic form is not an easy one.

Thus even from the individualistic point of view, art never exists literally for art's sake alone. It exists for psychophysiologic reasons. And because our scientific knowledge of the physiology of emotion is still crude, we understand little of the workings of the artistic impulses. Aesthetics, the study of beauty, remains almost entirely a branch of philosophy, for beauty is still subjective, as far as our understanding of it goes.

But art may not be seen in its entirety if analyzed only from the individualistic point of view. Art is also a social expression, and inevitably it becomes a part of culture. Further, since man is always a creature of society and the child of culture, art *ipso facto* serves social as well as individual interests and needs. Art is inextricably tied to religion and magic—and to politics. It cannot help expressing and reflecting social relations and systems. It can serve to sustain them, as Renaissance art so notably served Christianity or as art in Russia, which is expected to evoke Socialist sentiments in Soviet citizens. It can also aim at their destruction, as does the anarchist art of those who hold modern civilization to be so false and meaningless that the honest artist can only lampoon it.

What is primitive art?

The only safe answer to this question is that primitive art is the art of primitive peoples. It is impossible to define primitive art merely as crude art, for some primitive forms of artistic expression are exceedingly complex. It is impossible to label it as "childish," for some primitive art is precocious in technique and sophisticated in ideology. It is impossible to identify it as naturalistic, for some primitive art is highly stylized and conventionalized. The art of primitive peoples runs a wide gamut from technical clumsiness to high skill, from childlike simplicity to confusing complexity, from naturalism and realism to conventionalized abstraction.

Even when we eliminate the more florid forms of primitive art from our consideration and concentrate on the arts of the most primitive of known peoples, this is still true. Bushman art is naturalistic and full of vitality (Fig. 19-1). Australian art is highly stylized and in certain forms is abstract and symbolic. Eskimo art is naturalistic and technically quite sophisticated. Shoshone art is almost nonexistent.

No qualities that universally characterize primitive art can be adduced from the art of primitive peoples, unless it is that no primitives ever solved the problem of perspective—with which most of them never dealt.

The so-called "primitivists" in recent Occidental art are not true primitives. In stripping down their art forms to what they see as essential simplicity, they are not necessarily emulating primitive art, even though they have been consciously influenced by the art of certain primitive peoples, especially African sculpture.

The "primitives" of early American painting

Fig. 19-1 Bushman rock painting. The dancers.

cannot be considered truly primitive either. They were only the untutored early representatives of an American offshoot of the European cultural tradition. They are called primitives simply because, in the early nineteenth century they had reference to only a very limited art history, and because they were crude in their technique.

Since, as most art students now agree, an art can be the product of a culturally primitive people without itself being primitive, primitive art must be defined by extra-artistic means, viz., its association with a preliterate culture.

Decorative art Decorative art is the work of the artisan, not the artist. It is the embellishment of an artifact. Plains Indian moccasins were embroidered with dyed porcupine quills. Later, when traders made colored beads available, beadwork replaced quillwork. Basket makers found that variations in twilling produced interesting and pleasing designs within the structure of the basket. They discovered that the use of varicolored fibers made possible tasteful coil and twill work (Fig. 17-6, page 269). Potters discovered that slips, painting, and sculptural detail made infinite variety a possibility in ceramic production. Clay vessels can be mere household articles, or, by attention to decorative line and form, they can be transformed into objects of pure beauty (Fig. 19-3). Rawhide boxes could have been left as crude and undec-

Fig. 19-2 Australian bark painting. The successful spearing of the kangaroo expresses the idea of magical effect by association. The hunter who possesses this pictorial talisman hopes to strengthen his luck by its use. (From Australia. Aboriginal Paintings—Arnhem Land, *New York Graphic Society. Courtesy of UNESCO.)*

Fig. 19-3 Stylized naturalism expressed in a pre-Columbian vase from Mexico. (Courtesy of The Museum of Primitive Art)

Fig. 19-4 Northwest Coast Indian carving on the handle of a spoon fashioned from a mountain-sheep horn. (Courtesy of the American Museum of Natural History)

orated as our corrugated shipping cartons. But Plains Indians preferred to decorate them with geometric designs in color.[3] A lime spatula could be a simple stick, but the natives of eastern New Guinea prefer to carve out a handle with painstaking skill. Northern Shoshones were content with roughed-out spoons of mountain-sheep horn, whereas Northwest Coast Indians worked intricate totemic designs into their handles (Fig. 19-4).

These are all examples of decorative embellishment—modification in line, form, or color of useful articles—which is superfluous in the sense that such modifications do not contribute to the utilitarian effectiveness of the article. But they please their owner, impress his guests, and whet the acquisitive appetites of museum collectors.

A valid principle seems to be that as soon as a people solves the fundamental technical problems in the production of an artifact or tool, the artistic impulse begins to assert itself. The more aesthetically endowed individuals begin to play with the surface in an effort to increase the pleasing potentials of the object.

As a rule, technique must be mastered before decorative art worthy of being called art develops. Beyond mastery of technique, the more leisure the subsistence techniques and resources of a people's culture allow, the greater the likelihood of decorative embellishment. This must not, however, be taken as a bald assertion that leisure produces art. It may, or it may not. Surplus energies and time may be directed into other channels to satisfy other interests, such as war, trading, or games.

Decorative art may be purely *formal,* or it may be *representative.* Formal decoration is characterized by its concentrated emphasis upon form and design without reference to meaning or thought. Examples of this would be the perfect shaping of a pottery bowl, the turning of a beautiful rim. Designs in coiling, weaving, and twilling that come out of the arrangement of warp and weft, and the introduction of decorative bands about the rims of baskets through the process of binding the edges to avoid raveling, are further examples of formal decoration that results primarily from industrial technique. However, formal decoration not imposed by technical needs is used universally. Decorative bands incised or painted about the neck of a pot or the edges of a box are purely *superimposed* on the functional structure of the artifact. Such formal design elements are not extensions of technique, but rather expressions of the universal *feeling for form* that prompts man to emphasize the form of his object.

Thus, the ubiquitous formal decorative art that has been so assiduously studied by anthropologists and so generally spurned by art historians ("because it is not *pure* art") springs from two fundamental sources. As Boas has put it, such art "is not necessarily expressive of purposive action"; i.e., the artisan is not consciously producing an artistic product. Rather, this art is based upon "reactions to forms that develop through mastery of technique." Secondly, "the formal interest is directly due to the impression derived from the form. It is not expressive in the sense that it conveys a definite meaning or expresses an aesthetic emotion."[4]

Art styles

Decorative art may also be representative; i.e., the design or figure may portray some object. It presumes to represent the real thing. If the representation is faithful to the original model, it is said to be *natural,* or naturalistic, as European cave art is, or as the delightful dancing figures with their long limbs, narrow torsos, and fluid movements conceived by the Bushman are. The meaning of *style* in representative art can be quickly grasped by comparing Egyptian naturalistic representation of dancers with the Bushman's. Figure 19-5 shows us an extraordinary example of style in Zapotec sculpture from Oaxaca, Mexico.

The same people were also capable of marked naturalism. The term "style" means a departure from absolute naturalism. Artists

[4]F. Boas, *Primitive Art,* pp. 62–63.

Fig. 19-5 Decorative elaboration. Terra-cotta funeral urn from Oaxaca, Mexico. (Courtesy of the American Museum of Natural History.)

always compose their creations to some degree. Documentary photography, as well as the snapshots of most amateurs, is not art. But by selective lighting, screening, and retouching, photography can be made to approach art. A textbook line illustration of an anatomical specimen is a scientific representation, but hardly ever art. Style denotes a standardized selective modification of the real image in a way that produces an aesthetically effective and distinctive representation (Fig. 19-6).

Style in Northwest Coast art One of the most distinctive of all primitive art styles is that which originates on the Northwest Coast of North America and is exemplified in the carving and painting of masks, totem poles, boxes, rattles, dishes, spoons, canoes, houses, and other objects. Exaggerations in representative art have led not to geometric design but to a unique stylization in which a body form can still be distinguished, in spite of the fact that it is weirdly

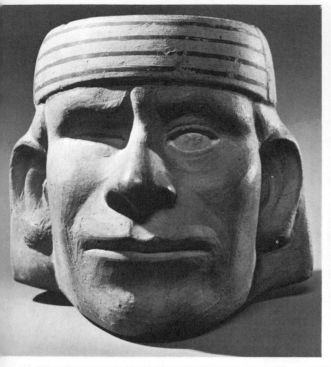

Fig. 19-6 *Stylized naturalism. Above left, effigy jar from Mochica, Peru. Above right, wooden headdress from Tlingit, Alaska. Lower left, "tino" figures from Nukuoru Island, a Polynesian Society located in eastern Melanesia. Height 14 inches. (Above left, photograph by Charles Uht, courtesy of The Museum of Primitive Art; above right, courtesy of the American Museum of Natural History; lower left, courtesy of the Bernice P. Bishop Museum.)*

distorted in size and arrangement. All Northwest Coast art objects are utilitarian in intent, and therefore the decorative element is more or less subordinated to the object. This is definitely not free art.

The effects of this subordination of the art to the object are most interesting. The artist is given, so to speak, a decorative field that he must cover. He abhors blank spaces. He also wants all his decorative elements to represent some aspect of animal life. Hence, he is impelled to dissect, dismember, distort, and remold his creatures to fill the space whether it is the surface of a box, bowl, wooden hat, or rattle. Distortion becomes such that the representation is in the end a caricature. But sheer design does not annihilate representation wholly, because the impulses of the Northwest Coast artist are not unalloyedly aesthetic. Totemic heraldry, with its rich mythology of clan and lineage origins from heroic animal ancestors, pervades most Northwest Coast art. The representative art portrays not just an animal but an animal that symbolizes some mythical or historic event in the social background of the artist. This interest in the art counterbalances the tendency for caricature to get out of hand. The device by means of which this purpose is made effective is the standardization of certain immutable symbols based on one or a few outstanding anatomical traits of the natural creature portrayed. Thus, no matter how weird the distortion in the interests of design or in the flight of imaginative fancy, the message to be conveyed by the representation cannot be lost in meaningless form and line.

The marks of the beaver in Northwest Coast art are the most readily recognizable—his flat, scaly, mud-slapper tail and his efficient cutting teeth. These are always present in any artistic representation of the beaver. In Fig. 19-7 we see a Haida Indian totem-pole beaver. He may be quickly recognized by his two great incisors and his crosshatched tail, which, since the pole is to be viewed from the front, is curled up between his legs, for otherwise it could not be seen. Since the beaver is a woodworker, he is often, but not always, shown with a chunk of a log in his paws. One other important landmark is the projecting ear. Although it will be observed that stylization of the face is in the direction of the human visage (all the mythological creatures talk, think, and act like human beings), the ears above the head are certain, distinctive evidence that a nonhuman animal is represented.

The bear in Fig. 19-7 fills in a square design area. Again the ears prove him to be an animal. The teeth are bear teeth, but the most important mark is found in the long claws. Notice, too, that the bear looks as though he had been split down the back and then opened to fill out the flat space.

The best example of the use of this tricky device is in the treatment of the shark, shown

Fig. 19-7   Northwest Coast Indian art. Haida: top left, carved totem-pole beaver; top right, painted bear on a flat surface; bottom, painted shark or dogfish. (After Boas.)

in Fig. 19-7. The distinguishing shark features, which are all on the face, are (1) a large mouth, drawn down at the corners, (2) many sharp teeth, (3) gill slits on the cheeks, (4) large round eyes, and (5) a high, tapering forehead on which are drawn two circles like eyes and gill slits to form a pseudo subface. Since these features are all best seen from the front, the shark head is never shown in profile. Yet the side of the body must be shown in profile. In order that symmetry may be attained, the artist has split the fish down the back and folded the two sides out to the right and left of the head. What looks to us at first glance like wings are the outspread right and left sides of the shark's body. So that a large void is not left beneath the body, the pectoral fins are much enlarged; and then to keep the whole within the confines of the rectangular decorative area, the split tail is turned down and inward at both ends of the body.

Thus we see how the Northwest Coast artist, with great skill and ingenuity, compromised and balanced his hunter's interest in animal anatomy, his artistic interest in design, his abhorrence of blank spaces, and his totemic mythology into a sophisticated art style. In the struggle between representation and symbolism, neither won. Northwest Coast art is both representative *and* symbolic.

Variation in styles An interesting aspect of primitive art is the occurrence of different art styles within the same culture, each style associated with a specific aspect of the culture and not transferable to others. On the Klamath River, among the Yurok Indians, naturalistic representations are permissible on woodwork but absolutely tabu on basketry, where only geometric patterns are allowed. Why? Naturalism in basketry designs is sure to bring bad luck, especially eye trouble, as happened to a woman once, according to the old wives' tales.[5]

Sculptured representations of Cook Islands

[5] L. O'Neale, lecture, *Seminar in Psychological Approaches to Culture,* University of California, Spring, 1941.

Fig. 19-8 Carved wood representation of a clan deity from the Cook Islands, Polynesia. (Courtesy of The Peabody Museum, Harvard University.)

deities reveal a nice contrast of styles between two closely related objects. Private gods, belonging to individual persons, are represented by grotesque but utterly realistic figurines that are carved in a highly stylized manner and yet are essentially naturalistic. Lineage and tribal deities, on the other hand, "were usually represented by highly abstract wood carvings most of which bear no recognizable relation to the human figure."[6] The group deities are highly stylized and abstract (Fig. 19-8). The knobby projections running down the body should be viewed from the left. Then they may be seen as a series of highly conventionalized human heads and figures.

A most interesting example of symbolic abstraction is found in the worship of ceremonial tools as representing the god of a cult of craftsmen. The superbly fashioned adze from the Cook Islands (Fig. 19-9) is the apotheosis of their basic tool. They literally worshiped the tools with which they worked. Nevertheless, the Cook Islanders, although their craftsmanship was suffused with religion and magic, knew that good work calls for good tools and that unnecessary decorative embellishment can impair function. Therefore, although their tools and objects of use are created with a strong feeling for form, they are rarely decorated. All the decorative effort goes into the deified objects.

In this context, the mastery of functional form by the Micronesians should be mentioned. Only a people who have "found their aesthetic expression in fine craftsmanship and functional design rather than elaborate decoration"[7] could produce such an exquisitely modern piece as the wooden dish from the Matty Islands shown in Fig. 19-10.

Religion and art

Religion and art are by no means inseparable, but for deep-rooted reasons they have a strong affinity.

In essence, religion is subjective—a matter of belief. Yet the covert concepts of religious

[6] R. Linton and P. S. Wingert, *Arts of the South Seas,* p. 27.
[7] *Ibid.,* p. 71.

Fig. 19-10   Shallow wooden dish from Matty Islands, Micronesia. A fine example of functional art. (Courtesy of The University Museum, Philadelphia.)

Fig. 19-9   Ceremonial adze. Cook Islands, Polynesia. (Courtesy of The Museum of Primitive Art.)

belief are always translated to overt ritual and ceremonial forms. Religion needs objectifying, and art is an outstandingly effective medium. By artistic embellishment, the paraphernalia of religion and magic may be lifted out of the realm of ordinary artifacts or activities to become endowed with the qualities of the unusual that should be associated with the supernatural —the sacred.

Yet even more important than the elaboration of religious paraphernalia is the representation of the spirits and gods. Gods are imaginative conceptions who exist in belief. If the belief can be translated into concrete form, it becomes more real and convincing. Paintings and statues objectify the subjective concepts of the divinities. The presence of a god at a ceremony is more directly felt by the majority of men if he is there in solid stone or wood looking down on the believers. The visual religious art of any primitive people communicates eloquently without sound. Edmund Leach has stated it well:

It is intended to be understood. And in the ordinary way it will be understood by the audience for whom it is designed. For the audience for which a primitive

Fig. 19-11   Bella Coola double mask of British Columbia shown in its open position (top) and closed position (bottom). (Courtesy of the American Museum of Natural History.)

artist works is composed of members of his own community steeped in the same mythological tradition as himself and familiar with the same environment of material fact and ritual activity; the primitive artist can therefore afford to communicate in shorthand; symbols have the same basic significance and the same range of ambiguity for artist and audience alike.[8]

Leach goes on to observe that the European art critic who tries to understand primitive art is forced to concentrate on its form alone, without reference to its meaning; he is blissfully ignorant of the religious and mythic content of the object he is trying to analyze.

Masks and rituals   Primitive religious sculpture is in the form of masks or statues—that is, idols. Without artists there can be no idolatry. The use of masks to portray supernatural beings is prevalent among primitive peoples in many parts of the world. Only Polynesia and Micronesia, in the Pacific, and the Plains and Basin areas, in the United States, are conspicuous in that masking is absent, or nearly so. In the religion of the Plains Indians, deities are of little importance, and ritualism is poorly developed. There is nothing much to mask. In Polynesia, although the pantheon is elaborate and deities are portrayed as statues, as we have noted for the Cook Islands, masking is abjured, for reasons that are obscure.

In North America, the masks of the Northwest Coast attain a richness of variety and form that is rivaled only in parts of Melanesia. Many Northwest Coast masks, by means of hinges and strings, have movable parts that may be manipulated by the actor to heighten the dramatic effect. Some, like the Bella Coola double mask depicted in Fig. 19-11, have an inner and an outer face to portray the dual character (animal and human) of the early mythological progenitors. The most important of the factors that have combined to produce the exotic elaborateness of Northwest Coast masks are (1) a social organization emphasizing hereditary status based in part on descent from mythological

[8] E. R. Leach, "Aesthetics," in E. E. Evans-Pritchard, *The Institutions of Primitive Society*, p. 32.

ancestral lineage founders, (2) elaboration of dance drama depicting the deeds of the mythical heroes, (3) technical mastery of the skills of carving, and (4) a vigorous creative drive to translate ideas and mental imagery into objective representations.

At the eastern end of our continent, Iroquois masks as made and used by the False Face Society of curers are not so rich in variety or so elaborate as those of the Northwest Coast, but they bear the stamp of a grotesquely humorous realism designed to frighten away evil spirits (Fig. 19-12). While the intent of the masks is serious, one cannot help feeling that the artist carves with his tongue in his cheek.

A mask is not necessarily art. Dime-store false faces for Halloween are genuine attempts at representation of something or other, and they surely titillate the spines and hair roots of small boys and girls, but it is unlikely that they ever speed the pulse of an art critic. Some Pueblo Indian masks have artistic qualities. Many do not, for they are nothing more than cylinders that cover the head like an inverted bucket. Although Pueblo masks have various appendages and are painted, little effort is expended to work out notable patterns of line or color. Southwest Indians do little wood carving, and none of their masks is made of wood.[9] Leather (occasionally gourd or wicker) is the material used—a medium that does not lend itself to delicate molding or modeling. Although Pueblo design in pottery has reached a high artistic level, only the crudest of geometric design patterns are transferred to the masks. Thus in spite of the ritual importance of masks in Pueblo society, they have failed to become objects of intensive creative, artistic interest. All the ideological stimuli for artistry in masks are present, but unlike the cultural situation on the Northwest Coast, no suitable technical medium is at hand in the Pueblo cultural tradition; the Pueblo religious craftsman has turned his creative, aesthetic interests elsewhere.

Masking associated with religious belief has generated rich art products in both Africa and

[9] E. C. Parsons, *Pueblo Indian Religion,* Vol. 1, p. 340.

Fig. 19-12 A member of the Iroquois False Face Society in his sacred tobacco patch. Ontario, Canada. (Courtesy of the National Museum of Canada.)

Melanesia, but of the two areas, Melanesia has been the more prolific. Hence we shall briefly discuss its products. In Africa and Melanesia, the worship and veneration of ancestral spirits loom large in virtually all tribal religions (see Chapter 33). In Melanesia, particularly, the masks are representations of ancestors and are used in elaborate memorial rites. On the island of New Ireland, this complex reached its most elaborate expression in the ritual and art of the *malagan,* a system of festivals in memory of the recently deceased.

Tradition decreed so strongly that these ceremonies be performed that the survivors of the deceased would lose caste if they did not conform, and their prestige would be enhanced in proportion to the magnificence of the ceremonies held. This attitude served as a powerful incentive to provide the maximum of food for the feasts and the richest possible carvings.[10] Some of these carvings were intricately worked plaques, but most of them were masks. Colored in red, yellow, blue, and white, they are truly spectacular and impressive (Fig. 19-13). Obviously these masks are the work of professional artists, who are, in fact, well paid for their services, which are secretly performed

[10]Linton and Wingert, *op. cit.*, p. 160.

Fig. 19-13 Head mask. Carved and painted wood. New Ireland, Melanesia. (Courtesy of the American Museum of Natural History.)

within a high-walled enclosure close by the cemetery of the clan that is holding the *malagan*. The sculptors work for nearly a year preparing the boards and masks before they are all finally ready for public display and use. In style, as Wingert has noted, the basic carving, although complex, is well organized, while the painted surface designs are overelaborate, even jittery.

Statuary in religious art   Statuary as a medium of primitive religious art is common in Africa and Melanesia, and also in Polynesia and Central America. African statuary has had considerable influence upon modern European artists. It possesses a living quality eagerly sought after by modernists. It embodies the people's hopes and fears; it terrorizes or delights them as it portrays the nature of the gods on whom they lean or before whom they prostrate themselves.

This is true of African sculpture, as well as Polynesian and Melanesian. The artist is close to his work, and his work is close to the interests and well-being of his people. He is in his society what the modern artist would like to be in ours.

Mass, solidity, and plainness of surface are the impressive features of African sculpture, even though the figures are not usually very large. These qualities are induced partly by the nature of the material in which the artist works, and partly by his own inimitable style. The material is hardwood—mahogany, the aristocrat of timbers, and ironwood—tough, challenging material. No light-minded whittler can work the sculptor's transformation on such a block. The wood is close-grained and invites a high polish with dark lustrous tones. The glistening highlights of the smooth African skin are beautifully reflected in the finished statues. The wedding of subject matter and materials is perfect.

African sculpture is characteristically disproportionate. The head is always too large for the torso; the legs are squat and sturdy. All the work is subject to the limitations of the mass of the block with which the artist works, which is to say that the African woodworker is no joiner. Since he cannot attach projecting pieces to the mass, the arms must be formed close to the body. The legs must be confined within the area of the original block. Such limitations contribute to the feeling of compactness that emerges from the art. Concentration of attention on the head of the statue, lineal elongation of the body, and dwarfing of the lower limbs are matters of stylistic choice in the African tradition.

It is true that to those of us who have been trained in the naturalistic idealism of sculpture in the Greek tradition, African distortions appear at first to be shocking grotesquerie. But, with familiarity, the cubic way of cutting out the surfaces, the rhythm that moves between the parts of the statue, the basic simplicity in the generalization of the human figure, and the exquisite texture of the finish combine to caress the aesthetic sense of the sympathetic observer.

Yet our emotional response is only a dilute aesthetic reaction, hardly comparable to the tremendous emotional significance these statues have for the Africans. The overtones that the mortuary and fetishistic pieces convey to the native can never be sensed by outsiders. Most African statues represent dead ancestors; they are created to house their spirits. The statue, when the spirit has taken up its abode, is in the true sense a fetish.[11] It is not just a work of art to be viewed objectively in a museum. It is a personage, alive with all the pulsating powers of the personality it represents—powers that are superhumanly potent because the personality it represents is no longer mere man but god.

Symbolism in art

A symbol is any phenomenon that stands for something else in the idea system of a culture. It is so closely identified with the symbolized object in meaning that it stimulates like responses.

A general characteristic of symbols is their

[11]See R. H. Lowie, *Primitive Religion,* pp. 268–270.

Fig. 19-14 *Prehistoric, painted mask representing the head of a mule deer. Created between* A.D. *800– 1400 in Florida. (Courtesy of The University Museum, Philadelphia.)*

nondiffuseness. In one form or another, symbols are always overt; they must be seen, heard, felt, or smelled. They condense abstractions into delimited objects. Whereas words are vocal symbols, symbols in art are made up of combinations of line, color, texture, form, and sound that stand for concrete objects or abstractions. They also possess definite aesthetic qualities.

Symbolic art is at the opposite pole from naturalistic representation. Stylization and conventionalization are intermediate forms. In conventionalized art, the process of selection and elimination of detail has gone so far that, although a perceptible similarity to the original object is still preserved, the representation has become more symbolic than naturalistic.

Evolution in art symbolism The genetic relation of symbolism to naturalism in art has long stimulated the interest of anthropologists. In the late nineteenth century, it posed one of the primary problems that were taken up by such writers as Balfour, Haddon, and Holmes.[12] Current anthropological interest is focused upon the sociopsychological functions of symbolism rather than upon its evolution, but the genesis of symbolism remains an important cultural problem.

Meaningless geometric decorative design is rare among primitives; there is almost always some consciousness of symbolization. But the degree of consciousness may be more or less sharp, and the meaning of the symbols more or less standardized, according to the person and the culture.

Thus among the Arapaho, according to an early study by Kroeber,[13] beadwork patterns had the symbolic values shown in Fig. 19-16. Certain patterns had multiple symbolic values, however, that were variously interpreted according to the context and the intent of the beadworker. The simple diamond, listed as a star symbol, can also stand for a navel, an eye, a lake, a person, life, a buffalo wallow, or the interior of a tipi. The personal factor loomed so large in symbolism that conscientious Indians refuse to interpret the ornamentation on another person's article, on the grounds that they do not know the particular artist's intent. Nowadays, however, Indians engaged in commerical trading will make up glib and cryptic interpretations for the white man who insists on knowing the meaning of the designs. It is all a part of the sale.

Associative symbolism can be arrived at from two directions. Geometric forms may be created out of doodling, or the inherent limitations and possibilities of a technique, such as twilling and weaving, may suggest an idea that is associated with the form, just as the inkblots in the Rorschach test remind people of various

Fig. 19-15   Three examples of West African sculpture: left, "The Wheeler." Masked dancers of the Yoruba Gelede Society add modern themes to a traditional art; center, the traditional characteristics of large head and short legs are shown; the paired lumps on the shoulders and chest represent scarifications; right, a mask in ivory, one of the Museum of Primitive Art's most prized possessions. (Left, courtesy of The Museum of Primitive Art; center, Marc and Evelyne Bernheim, from Rapho Guillumette Pictures; right, courtesy of The Museum of Primitive Art.)

[12]H. Balfour, *The Evolution of Decorative Art;* A. C. Haddon, *Art in Evolution;* W. H. Holmes, *Ancient Art of the Province of Chiriqui* (Bureau of American Ethnology, Annual Report 6, 1888), pp. 13–186.
[13]A. L. Kroeber, "Decorative Symbolism of the Arapaho" (*American Anthropologist,* Vol. 3, 1901), pp. 308ff.

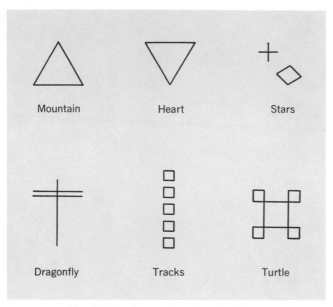

Mountain   Heart   Stars

Dragonfly   Tracks   Turtle

Fig. 19-16   Conventional symbols in Arapaho bead-work designs. (After Kroeber.)

things. Or, on the other hand, the artist may make a naturalistic representation of something. Then, in time, the naturalistic form is transformed into a conventionalized symbol by subsequent artists.

One of the best demonstrations of the second process is that advanced by Holmes in his discussion of Chiriquian pottery designs from pre-Columbian Panama.[14] Among the several design motifs discussed by Holmes, that of the alligator is most arresting. In Fig. 19-17, some of the alligator designs are arranged to show progressive abstraction from stylized representations.

In the lower right is the painted figure of an alligator with upturned snout and tail and dots to represent his scales. Below him is a conventionalized figure of an alligator that is almost unrecognizable, while below it appears a meandering abstraction that would be hard to identify as an alligator symbol if more realistic representations were not available for comparison. At the bottom is a simple curvilinear

[14]Holmes, *op. cit.*, pp. 171–186.

representation of an alligator that is progressively simplified through symbolic abstraction to become a mere curved line and a dot. The "alligatoric" symbol encased in the circular field in the left bottom is apparently abstracted from the sort of alligator picture embraced in the trapezoidal field shown above it. To fit his picture into the field or area to be covered by the picture, the artist has bent the tail of the alligator down while curving the tip inward. The head is turned in to fit into the dip formed by the beast's sagging back. The legs and the double-hooked representation of scales at the back of the neck form three appended units.

Although the complex spiral shown within the circle is a far cry from an alligator, it is most assuredly derived from the idea of the alligator represented above it. It occurs on pottery of a type that is commonly decorated with alligators; it has the same in-turned hook of the tail; it has three semicircular protuberances (no more, no less), just as the alligator has three groups of semicircular legs and neck scales; and the inner loop of the spiral corresponds to the hooked loop of the alligator's nose. What looks like geometric scribbling is a meaningful symbol abstracted from a stylized representation of a real animal form.

Holmes was quite convinced that in the case of Chiriquian forms, a definite evolution from realistic through conventionalized to abstract symbols occurred. Critical objections have been raised to this thesis because it implies a temporal sequence from a typological classification, and Holmes had no proof that the realistic forms were actually earlier in time. Boas and others have pointed out that since in some known instances the evolution of an art style is found to have moved from geometric figures to realistic,[15] there is no justification for assuming priority of naturalistic forms unless there is stratigraphic or actual historical evidence implying such a time sequence.

[15]See F. Boas's study of Eskimo needlecases. Archaic geometric decorative elements are shown to have evolved into animal figures. *Decorative Designs of Alaskan Needlecases* (United States National Museum, Reports, Vol. 39, 1908), pp. 221–344.

While it is true that there is no direct evidence of temporal sequence in the Chiriquian series, the probability that the abstract designs of Chiriquian ware are the derivatives of the realistic designs is certainly much greater than the reverse possibility.

Art and writing

All art is a form of communication. Writing is communication by means of visual symbols substituted for spoken words. All writing is therefore symbolic, and its origins lie in symbolic art and thought.

Conventionalization is often considered to be a process of degeneration of art. This is true only when conventionalization reflects a decline in technique—a simplification of line and form due to slovenliness or sheer lack of skill on the part of the artist. It is not true when the interest of the artist is actually shifted from the *image* of the object portrayed to its *meaning*. To abstract the meaning of an object and to be able to represent it with a simple symbol requires a degree of mental sophistication that is on a high level of performance.

When archaeologists lament the "decline" of Paleolithic art and its "degeneration" to the red ochre paintings on pebbles in the Mesolithic culture of Mas d'Azil, in France,[16] they are wasting their tears. The so-called "degenerate" figures on the painted pebbles are the rudiments of an embryonic system of writing. To lament the invention of writing is to lament one of the greatest intellectual feats of human history—the attainment of the one feature of culture that all anthropologists agree distinguishes civilized culture from primitive.

In the cavern of Cogul, in Portugal, is a painted wall upon which prehistoric man of the

[16]For example, H. F. Cleland, *Our Prehistoric Ancestors*, p. 63: "The art of the Late Paleolithic had completely disintegrated and now consisted merely of crude geometric designs painted on pebbles and cave walls."

Fig. 19-17 Conventionalization and abstraction of alligator designs on Chiriquian pottery. (After Holmes.)

Fig. 19-18   Three degrees of conventionalization in the representation of the stag in the East Spanish art from Cogul.

Fig. 19-19   Probable female and male symbols (?) on painted pebbles from Le Mas d'Azil (right) compared with female and male pictographs from late Upper Paleolithic cave art in East Spain (left). (After Obermaier.)

Capsian culture has left many pictures of cattle and antelope and a picture of a ring of half-clothed females dancing about a phallic male. One of the pictures shows a man confronting a stag (Fig. 19-18). On another part of the wall is a crudely conventionalized picture of a hunter who has just shot a large arrow at a stag. In yet another spot is a very queer figure, which by itself it would be no more intelligible to us than the Chiriquian alligator symbols. We know, however, that the Capsian hunters were very much interested in dead deer, and with the more naturalistic examples before us, we can compare the number of prongs in the forklike projections on this figure with the prongs of the antlers in the naturalistic pictures. That a deer is meant is certain. Furthermore, since the four feet of the object are sticking straight up in the air, we may feel reasonably sure that this is the symbol for a dead deer, presumably a magic hunting symbol to help the deerslayer. A Winnebago Indian has described in detail the working of such magic among his people. A vital fragment of his story was given in Chapter 15.

What took place at Cogul occurred elsewhere on the Iberian Peninsula. Obermaier, in arguing for a genetic relationship between the Azilian painted pebbles and the painted petroglyphs of the Spanish caves and rock shelters, prepared the comparative chart shown in Fig. 19-19. Clearly, the Azilian ∧ symbolizes a squatting female, and the ⋒ is a male. Azilian man had apparently progressed from picture writing to the use of ideographs—drawn or written symbols that stand directly for things or notions instead of the sounds of words in the language of the users. Such is the first step in the evolution and origin of all systems of writing. The scribe is the intellectual offspring of the artist.

A poignant message left by a starving Eskimo effectively illustrates the essential nature of the pictorial ideograph. As seen in Fig. 19-20, it reads: "I went out hunting in my kayak (a man in a boat); on this island I was stranded and pitched my winter tent (the crosshatched triangle); I had nothing (a man with outstretched arms) to eat (a man with hand to mouth)."

On a much more elaborate level, the Chinese system of characters is fundamentally an ideographic picture writing which has become reduced to a set of timesaving brushstrokes and which is in some aspects also phonetic. Its ideographic quality may be readily discerned in the manner of writing such words as "prisoner" or "happiness." In the character for "prisoner," we see a man, 人 , in an enclosure, 囚 . "Happiness" is a woman (wife), 女 , with a son, 女子 . The earlier pictographic derivation of a number of Chinese characters may be seen in Fig. 19-21.

The occurrence in all languages of words that are identically pronounced but have different meanings (*homophones*)[17] makes possible a ready extension of ideographic writing as soon as a people is able to make the mental leap of partially disassociating the picture from the idea and linking it to sounds as such. Thus the Chinese word for "horse," which is "mar," is represented by 馬 . The Chinese term for "mother" used within the intimate confines of the family is sometimes "mama." Phonetically, then, it would be possible for the Chinese to write "mama" as 馬 馬 . This, however, would be ambiguous, for unless the context made it clear, the reader would not be certain whether the symbol represented two horses or one mother. The Chinese get around this difficulty by first writing the symbol for woman, 女 , followed by the homophone symbol for "mar." Thus they have produced a way of writing "mama" that is half ideogram and half phonogram. Because of its way of mixing ideograms and phonograms, Chinese writing is classed as a *transitional system,* a means of written communication which has gone beyond the more primitive forms of pictography but which still falls short of pure phonetic representation.

The ancient Egyptian, Hittite, Cretan, and cuneiform (Sumerian, Babylonian, Assyrian)

Fig. 19-20   Incised Eskimo pictogram on wood.

script systems also developed out of picture writing by use of similar basic principles, although each evolved its own special forms. These and the Chinese plus the Indic and Mayan-Aztec systems are the only definitely known independent basic scripts invented by man. The transformation of art to writing is a supreme human achievement, so difficult that few peoples have done it on their own. Most men have achieved literacy through borrowing.

Our own alphabet had its beginnings in

Fig. 19-21   Pictographic derivation of some seventeenth century Chinese characters. (After Brouner and Fung.)

Sun   Moon   Mountain

Child   Horse   Tree

[17]For example, *saw:* (1) past tense of *to see;* (2) a cutting tool with a serrated edge; (3) to cut with a sawlike tool; (4) to cut as if with a sawlike tool; (5) a sententious saying or proverb.

Egyptian pictography. Its development from early Greek inscriptions is well known and, indeed, testified to by the very word by which we identify it: a compound of the first two words of the Grecian system, the *alpha* and *beta*. Beyond the Grecian alphabet, however, lies the Semitic from which it in turn is clearly derived: Hebrew, *aleph, beth, gimel*. Some Semitic symbols have clear derivation from Egyptian hieroglyphs; many do not. Known archaic Semitic inscriptions are few and far between, far too few to enable paleographers to advance well-founded reconstructions of the full history of the emergence of the alphabet. Although there are indications that parallel attempts at developing alphabetic systems were more or less simultaneously under way among several different Semitic peoples around the second millennium B.C., only one system (that of the Phoenicians) was finally perfected. From this, and this alone, all the extant alphabets of the world have descended. Here was a cultural triumph so difficult to conceive, and so perfect in form and function, that with minor modifications it could be adapted to any and all languages. It has superseded all other alphabetic systems; mankind has never again had either the need or the capacity to repeat it!

Of the Semitic symbols derived from Egyptian hieroglyphic ideograms, the first letter of the alphabet will suffice for illustrative purposes. *Aleph*, in Semitic, means "ox." The Egyptian hieroglyph is ☞ . On the Moabite stone, which presents a Semitic inscription of Mesha, king of Moab, in the ninth century B.C., the symbol is formed with three straight lines, ◁ . In later Greek it was inverted on its horns, and became A. Similar transitions may be seen for *beta, gamma, delta,* and other letters. The Egyptian word sounds for "ox," "house," and so on were ignored by the Semitic scribes; what they succeeded in doing was to make pictorially derived symbols from Egyptian prototypes, which were subsequently associated with the separate consonants that went to make up their speech. The Semites never included vowels in

their script, but wrote each word with only its consonantal sounds. The *aleph* symbol stood for the glottal stop, which is exceedingly important in Semitic speech. The Greeks had no use for the glottal stop, but they were able to represent the vowels of their speech in a way the Semites could not, and they completed the basic modern alphabet with the invention of vowel symbols. They converted the A to represent the first vowel and made other adjustments to take care of the rest.

The capstone was thus put on the transition from art to writing. The communication of generalized states of emotion and ideas through the aesthetic medium had at long last been transmuted to the communication of precise linguistic expression through phonetically representative symbols.

SUMMARY

The essence of art lies in the creation of contemplation of some human activity or product that, because of its form, evokes the emotional sensation called "aesthetic experience." Art serves individual needs and also functions to enhance social identity through symbolic representation of religious ideology and mythology.

Much art is decorative, embellishing an artifact in either a formal or a representative way. Most primitive art departs from naturalistic representation to develop distinctive form in styles. Religious art is always symbolic and charged with meaning that can be sensed only if one has been immersed in the culture in which the art originates. Masks and statues are extensively created as means of representing gods and spirit beings. The material representation is but a small part of the whole, however. It is the entry of the spirit into the statue or mask that gives it a vitality which transcends the object itself. Religious art is more than a form; it is a vehicle for the presence of a supernatural being or force.

Representative art does not necessarily precede symbolic art in the development of an art tradition. But it is evident that writing evolves out of progressive conventionalization of representative art forms, until the units of symbolic representation ultimately stand for sounds rather than for things or ideas as such. Then a phonetic writing system is produced. Conventionalization may be the result of deterioration in artistic technique, but, as a graphic shorthand of a sort, it may very well express a great advance in intellectual achievement.

SELECTED READINGS

Boas, F.: *Primitive Art* (1929). The classic work on the subject.

Breuil, H.: *Four Hundred Centuries of Cave Art* (1950). The most comprehensive summary of paleolithic art.

Buehler, A., T. Barrow, and C. P. Mountford: *The Art of the South Seas, Including Australia and New Zealand* (1962). Many beautiful color plates and numerous line drawings adorn this very competent ethnography of Oceanic art.

Derringer, D.: *The Alphabet* (1948). A detailed, but not too technical, discussion.

Elwin, V.: *The Tribal Art of Middle India* (1951). A descriptive account with good illustrations of the arts, crafts, and bodily ornament of a primitive people.

Herskovits, M. J.: *Backgrounds of African Art* (1945). A useful survey of the major art styles of Africa.

Inverarity, R. B.: *Art of the Northwest Coast Indians* (1950). A profusely and beautifully illustrated book on the distinctive aboriginal art of the Northwest Coast of North America.

Krieger, H. W.: "Design Areas in Oceania" (*United States National Museum, Proceedings*, Vol. 79, 1932), pp. 1–53. A good example of an ethnological study of stylistic distributions.

Kroeber, A. L.: "Art," in J. H. Steward (ed.), *Handbook of South American Indians*, Vol. 5, *The Comparative Ethnology of South American Indians* (1946), pp. 411–492. A comprehensive survey of aboriginal, including prehistoric, art in South American cultures.

Linton, R., and P. S. Wingert: *Arts of the South Seas* (1946). A well-illustrated and stimulating coverage of this subject.

Redfield, R., M. J. Herskovits, and G. F. Ekholm: *Aspects of Primitive Art* (1959). Three lectures presented by three distinguished American anthropologists at the Museum of Primitive Art in New York in 1959.

Smith, M. W. (ed.): *The Artist in Tribal Society* (1961). An anthropological exploration of the roles and functions of the primitive artist by a symposium of experts convened by The Royal Anthropological Institute in London. The verbatim record of the discussions is particularly interesting.

Status
and role

chapter 20

In the previous chapters we have been concerned with the concept of culture in its several manifestations: the evolution of man and culture, race and culture, the subsistence base of society, technology and the material manifestations of culture, and the artistic expressions of culture.

Social structure

We now turn to the organization of society and to that part of anthropology which is known as *social anthropology*, the study of social structure and relationships. By *social structure* we mean the ways in which groups and individuals are organized and related to one another in the functioning entity that is society. The culture of every society includes a figurative "manual" that lays out the major tasks to be performed, the job definitions of key personnel, and specific directions for carrying out the assigned functions. The tasks to be performed (as values) constitute what Malinowski called the *charter of social institutions*. The job definitions may be called *social statuses*. The directives for accomplishing various tasks may be called *roles*.

Institutional charters, social statuses, and social roles may or may not be explicitly spelled out in any given culture. Most of them are not; they are implicit in customary, or normalized, action. Many of them, however, are stated in ritual, lore, proverbs, myth, dogma, and law. Whether norms are unstated and covert or formally verbalized and overtly manifest, they can be searched out, reported on, and analyzed.

This is the task of the social anthropologist and other behavioral scientists.

Social institutions An institution is a network of procedures centered upon certain nuclear interests. Economic institutions, for example, comprise the characteristic behaviors that center upon the production, the allocation and distribution, and the use and consumption of goods. Economic institutions include behavioral networks of food production and the manufacture of artifacts; barter, exchange, sale, preemption, gift, and inheritance; utilization, hoarding, and consumption; and ownership, possession, and usufruct—everything that focuses upon production and utilization of goods and services. Marital institutions focus upon organization of intersexual relations, particularly the stabilization of mating, the nurture and enculturation of the young, household economic activities, the establishment and maintenance of mutual aid between kinship groups, and the legalizing of inheritance. Religious institutions focus upon the definition of the supernatural, the formulation of effective ritual for dealing with the supernatural, and symbolic representation of the social entirety. All institutions within a society overlap and interweave. That is why we have emphasized "focused upon" in stating the central interests or goals of given types of institutions. Institutions are far from being mutually exclusive.

The charters of institutions The charter of an institution consists of "statements" explaining why the institution exists and for what purpose. For example, myths, legends, beliefs, and judgments give sanctity and authority to the choices and commitments a society has made; they state why things are as they are and why they must be as they are, and they state why individuals must commit themselves to the goals as the goals are given.

The personnel of institutions All institutions have personnel. Institutions represent stability and order established by the traditional past; yet they exist only in present action—in the behavior of functioning persons. The groups of people who carry out the roles of any institution constitute its personnel. Institutionally organized groups in preliterate societies are recognized as *kinship groups* (family, extended family, ramage, lineage, clan, phratry, and moiety) or *associations* (age sets, clubs and fraternities, cults, corporations, work groups, guilds, and the state). The personnel of an association consists of *members* and *specialists* (functionaries or officials).

The nature of status

An individual's status is his social position with reference to the other members of his society as determined by a specific attribute, a cluster of attributes, or the generalized summation of all his attributes. Thus, every person has a number of statuses simultaneously. He has, in the most specific and narrow sense, as many statuses as there are recognized characteristics of the individual in his culture. Such characteristics are age, sex, bodily traits, and specific social experiences and affiliations. On the next level of abstraction, he has the more commonly recognized statuses that derive from the posession of certain combinations of traits, for example, the wisdom, courage, kindness, generosity, and even temper that characterize the Plains Indian peace chief. Finally, each person may have the generalized sort of status that is referred to as "social" status. This last sort of status identification calls for gross stereotyping of individuals. It seizes upon a small number of obvious criteria for lumping individual personalities into an undifferentiated class mass. The first sort of status identification, in contrast, calls for knowledge of numerous attributes of the individual and thus leads to a greater concern with the uniqueness of his personality.

Thus, it should be kept in mind that status can be either specific or generalized and that there are varying degrees of generalization.

Status hierarchy: rank The status system of every society involves also a certain amount of

Fig. 20-1 High status cap of fiber with pigtail. Probably from the Soko tribe in the Congo. (Smithsonian Institution.)

Fig. 20-2 Brass miniatures of chief and servants. Dahomey, West Africa. Cast brass figurines with punctate and incised surface etchings representing the chief carried in his hammock by two porters accompanied by man carrying umbrella of state, drummers, cymbalist, story teller, talkman, dancers, and carriers of food. (Smithsonian Institution.)

ranking. But, it should be noted, status and rank are not the same. "Status" is a neutral term, which refers only to position. "Rank" refers to hierarchical status—higher or lower with reference to other statuses. The rank order of a society is its system of status gradation. A high status is one that carries prestige; i.e., the attitudes associated with it are those of deference, reverence, submission, and subordination on the part of those of lower status. Prestige translated into action means power—the capacity to influence or direct the behavior of others. A low status carries little prestige; there is little power capacity associated with it.

The range embraced in a rank order will be wide or narrow depending upon the disparities in power structures formed by the culture. In simple democratic hunting and gathering socieites, such as that of the Eskimos, the range is narrow. In complex, class-organized societies, such as that of the Dahomeans, the range between slave and king is great.

Ascribed and achieved status The statuses that an individual holds are attained in various ways. They may be sought through striving and competitive mastery of the roles linked to the various statuses. Such statuses in the terminology suggested by Linton are called *achieved*.[1] MacIver calls them *functional determinants* of social position.[2] Other statuses devolve upon the individual by virtue of innate biological characteris-

[1] R. Linton, *The Study of Man*, pp. 113–114.
[2] R. M. MacIver, *Society*, pp. 78–79.

tics such as sex, age, and race or by virtue of his preexisting social affinities, such as the statuses of his parents and kinsmen and the involuntary associations into which he is born. These statuses are *ascribed* to the individual by his social system, and there is little he can do to escape them or to alter them. It is important to note that achieved statuses are attained only by first mastering the roles. As Barton has observed of the Kalinga in northern Luzon: "Elevation to rank and power in the community is a gradual process of emergence in which power is attained before the rank is acknowledged by the people."[3] When the role is finally mastered, the status flows from this fact. A master hunter must first master hunting.

In the case of ascribed statuses, on the other hand, the status comes first, and the roles are mastered subsequently. It is even possible to inherit ascribed status without mastery of the roles. There are betimes unkingly kings, ignoble nobles, unladylike ladies.

Ascribed status distinctions based on age, sex, the premarital state, childbearing, and kinship are the universal foundations of human social structure.

Achieved status criteria that are ubiquitous to all societies are those based on technological skill or artisanship (all peoples make tools), supernaturalism (all peoples have magico-religious specialists), the marital state, fecundity, and political leadership.

Nonuniversal ascribed statuses include caste-determined occupations, inherited supernaturalism, inherited possession of wealth, inherited possession of various religious and social perquisites and paraphernalia, and inherited political position (i.e., royalty).

Nonuniversal achieved statuses include those based upon hunting skills, skill in games and dances, bravery and skill in war, skill in head-hunting, storytelling ability, possession or distribution of wealth, bodily mutilation, and membership in various specialized associations. (This list is not exhaustive.)

The functional importance of all these different statuses rests in the fact that they limit and

[3]R. F. Barton, *The Kalinga*, p. 148.

influence the degree and direction of cultural participation and the manner and amount of interaction for individuals and groups. No one person ever manifests all the behavior characteristic of his culture because, for one reason, no one person ever enjoys all the statuses in his society.

The greater the number of achievable statuses in a culture, the greater the opportunity for full participation (potentially, at least) by all members. The more extensive and rigid the ascribed statuses, the more constrained are the individuals in their culturally prescribed roles.

Cultures that emphasize achievable status are marked by internal social mobility, social striving, and (on the whole) competitiveness and individualism. Emphasis is placed upon "fulfillment of self" and assertiveness. The social gain is ideally a greater ultimate efficiency because capable persons are not barred from effective performance in those capacities for which they have adequate aptitudes. Conversely, caste and rigid class systems are socially wasteful because they ascribe roles to people who are not necessarily well suited to their performance, while at the same time they bar potential adepts.

On the other hand, the advantages of social systems that emphasize ascribed statuses lie in reduced strain and anxiety for the participating members of the society. Competitive insecurity is presumably reduced. Frustration born of failure to achieve a sought-after status is avoided.

When ascribed status systems begin to lose their authority, however, and persons in statuses of marked social disability begin to aspire to achievable statuses, their frustration and the anxiety of those in the threatened ascribed positions become acute and difficult to tolerate, in the way that marks interracial relations in some parts of the American population today.

The nature of role

Role is the customary complex of behavior associated with a particular status. "When we ain't fightin'," Willie morosely acknowledges to Joe, "we should ack like sojers."[4] Every man is to some degree a poseur, for life in society is a playing of roles.

The command, "Just be your natural self," does not mean what it says. It really means, "Suppress your conscious awareness of the roles you must enact." A person's behavior is "natural," is free of posing, only when he has become so habituated to all his roles that he does not register awareness of them while performing them. Newborn infants in their first hours have no acquired roles as complements to their statuses. Consequently, no one expects much of them.

Because every person has multiple statuses, he also manifests many different roles. A married professor behaves differently in the intimacy of his family (the father role) from the way he does in the classroom (the professor role). And if he is a volunteer fireman, he behaves quite differently when engaged in "fire-manic" activities, of either a fire-fighting or a social nature. At different times, therefore, different roles come to the fore. Several roles may be operative simultaneously, but the intensity of their effectiveness is variable. If the professor's child visits the class, the professor activates both the role of professor and that of father, but in all propriety the professorial behavior should be strongest.

At times, various roles may be held in abeyance or inactivated. A Pueblo Indian, while cultivating his fields, holds his dancing roles as a member of the Flint society in abeyance. A person's roles could be likened to his wardrobe, from which he selects the costume suitable for each occasion, with many quick changes called for. Roles are therefore latent, except when they are being activated.

Age statuses and roles   Age statuses are recognized in all societies. The universal minimum includes at least three categories: child, adult, and old person, or, respectively, those not yet ripe for full social participation, those who perform the major maintenance activities of the

[4]B. Mauldin, *Up Front*, p. 83.

society, and those who are beyond the stage of active participation and responsibility. Generally, recognized age statuses are more numerous. Thus, the Comanches recognize five ages: baby, preadolescent, unmarried "brave" or girl, grown person, and old man or woman. Each age has its separate, specific appellation. Young children may be highly valued as objects of desire, but they never have prestige merely by virtue of their status as infants. In the exceptional instances in which infants do enjoy high status and prestige, it is always as a consequence of some special factor other than age, as in the case of a princeling by birth or a twin with imputed supernatural qualities (as among the Dahomeans).[5]

Youths and persons of middle age rarely enjoy favored status by virtue of their age, although prowess and wealth may bring prestige status to them. The aged, however, almost universally enjoy statuses of respect, reverence, and privilege because of the attributes that are ascribed to them by virtue of their being old.[6] It is not just being old that brings prestige; it is the accumulated wisdom and lore of the oldsters—the association of ancient custom with ancient people. As has been said of the Haida Indians of Queen Charlotte Island on the Northwest Coast: "They had great respect for the aged, whose advice in most matters has great weight."[7]

In stable societies, accumulated experience is valuable. Elders really do know more than youngsters, and what they know holds good. But in a rapidly changing culture, accumulated knowledge often becomes quickly shopworn. What was valid in the youth of the aged is no longer so. Wisdom based on outdated knowledge is, alas, of little use to him who clutches it as a source of prestige.

In the primitive world, the oldsters are "elders" in politics and government, magicians and priests in supernaturalism, and owners of property in some systems of economic organiza-

[5]M. J. Herskovits, *Dahomey*, Vol. 1, pp. 263, 270–272.
[6]L. Simmons, *The Role of the Aged in Primitive Society*, p. 79.
[7]A. P. Nibback, *The Coast Indians of Southern Alaska and Northern British Columbia* (Board of Regents of the Smithsonian Institution, Annual Report, 1890) p. 240.

tion. These are sources of power. Since such sources are more available to men than to women, old men usually have higher status than old women.[8] The positions of the aged are more secure in the settled horticultural tribes than among hunting and collecting peoples, especially those who live in the arctic and its fringes, where old people are unable to participate in primary productive activities to any extent. The support of the aged is a luxury which many marginal societies find themselves unable to sustain in times of stress. Senilicide is general among the Eskimos. Old people may be blocked up in a snow hut to be abandoned to cold and starvation, or they may be killed by more violent means when they themselves request it.[9] However, of the seventy-one societies tabulated by Simmons, only two (both Eskimo) violently remove the aged; seven abandon or expose them to natural elements to hasten their deaths.[10] This does not mean that in these seven societies, all old people are destroyed when their powers wane. It depends upon individuals and circumstances.

Almost all observers remark that old people are respected in the tribes they have visited. Only the Bushmen of South Africa and the Witotos of South America are said definitely to withhold respect from aged men. Eight of the tribes studied by Simmons deny deference to old women.

The Andaman Islands provide anthropologists with a favorite example of age as a status determinant. Kinship, which is so important in most primitive societies, is here somewhat muted. Rather:

The duties that one person owes to another are determined much less by their relation to one another by consanguinity and marriage, than by their respective ages and social status. . . . There is very little of any special customs relating to conduct towards different kinds of relatives. Corresponding to this we find very few terms to denote relationships and a considerable development of terms which denote age and social status.[11]

[8]Simmons, *op. cit.*, pp. 47–49.
[9]E. A. Hoebel, *The Law of Primitive Man*, pp. 76–79.
[10]Simmons, *op. cit.*, table 6.
[11]A. R. Radcliffe-Brown, *The Andaman Islanders*, p. 81.

Older persons have many food privileges denied to the young. Gradually, and with elaborate ritual, the food tabus are removed for the growing youth, until at full maturity he may enjoy all the delicacies permitted for his sex. Younger persons must defer to the older in all matters.

In Australia, where, as in the Andaman Islands, we find some of our most primitive peoples, seniority has reached its greatest significance—so much so that Australian social organization is dubbed *gerontocracy*, "the rule of elders." The preeminent domination of the Australian local group by old, grizzled men gave birth and impetus to the nineteenth-century notion that the primeval condition of man was that of browbeaten youth frustrated by the hoary patriarch. Australia, however, represents a special elaboration of age status in a way not universally characteristic of the hunters and gatherers (in contrast are the African Bushmen and American Shoshones).

Sexual statuses and roles Sex dichotomy is a biological fact upon which culturally determined statuses are built. But what is biological and what is cultural in sex differences is not established with certainty for all types of activity. True, certain physiological functions are sex-linked. Females produce ova, while males produce sperm. Females have specialized sex organs for the nurture and incubation of fertilized ova; males do not. Females are capable of parturition; males are not. *Homo sapiens* is a bisexual animal in which the basic reproductive roles are biologically fixed. So long as babies are born of women, differential statuses of male and female will be recognized and culturally reflected. The real social revolution will come when perfected biogenetic techniques make possible the fertilization and incubation of the human ovum outside the womb. But that day is not at hand. Every society, therefore, assigns to the male and female different roles. But the patterns of these roles reveal a remarkable flexibility as between different cultures. Each society expects men and women to behave differently;

what men do is one thing, and what women do is another.

In the pueblo of San Ildefonso:

There is a sharp line between men's work and women's work, and in the respective attitudes of the sexes towards their work. Men's work on the whole tends to be cooperative. The ditches are dug by the male community in the spring; the fields are tended as a group enterprise. . . . Among women, on the contrary, work has tended to become competitive; women seldom carry on any of their activities as a group. . . . Theoretically, at least, women play comparatively minor roles. San Ildefonso men do work which elsewhere is frequently the task of women. Their special province is called "outside work." Traditionally they hunt, dress the skins of the animals they kill, cut and sew moccasins for themselves and for the women, weave baskets, and weave and create their own dance costumes. . . . Men till the fields and the gardens, plant and reap, cut and haul firewood. Within the village itself they build the houses, care for the kivas, and clean the plaza before fiestas and dances. . . . Women's work is "inside." They care for the household, grind the grain, cook, and tend their children. They make and fire the pottery, and if there is no man in the family who can decorate it, the women may decorate their own.[12]

Of Lesu, in Melanesia, Powdermaker writes: "It is the sexual division of labour adhered to so rigidly that first strikes the ethnological observer. Men have one kind of work and women another, and a third kind may be done by either one of them jointly."[13] The division of labor is set forth in Table 20–1.

But although each society divides men's work and women's, what is distinctly men's work in one society may be women's work in another. As obvious examples we may note that the weaving of Navaho blankets is women's work, while among the neighboring Hopi, both spinning and weaving are confined to men. In nineteenth-century America, boys were supposed to be able to swim, and girls were not; yet among the Yahgan of Tierra del Fuego, women are the swimmers. Among the Pueblo Indians, most garden work is done by men;

among the Iroquois, hunting and fighting were for men, but tilling was for women only. Among the Maricopa Indians of southern Arizona, pottery making was "wholly a woman's occupation and a year-round task."[14] Weaving was properly men's work. Women harvested and ginned the cotton, which was grown exclusively by the men, and both sexes spun the yarn.

Because of such facts, anthropologists have learned to reject all generalizations such as that women are "naturally" housekeepers or that they are more peaceful or more religious than men. But anthropology has also established that throughout the world, certain kinds of work activities are quite consistently assigned to men and other kinds to women. In three-fourths of all societies, the tasks of food and fuel gathering, grinding seeds and grain, preparing foodstuffs for preservation, weaving, and manufacturing pottery, baskets, and mats are assigned to women. These are all jobs that, except for the gathering of foodstuffs, can be carried on in the immediate vicinity of the hearth and infant. Hunting is men's work in 93 per cent of all societies, fishing in 70 per cent, and herding in 96 per cent.[15] These predominantly male activities demand mobility, stamina, and an intimate knowledge of the tribal terrain.

The anthropological position is that certain sex-linked behaviors are biologically based, although subject to cultural modifications within limits. The roles in any society may be empirically observed and ethnographically recorded.

Aptitudes and status If skill is a joy to any man, it should also be true that skill in any function valued by a society brings prestige and high status to the expert. By and large, anthropological data support this supposition.

Militaristically oriented societies applaud and honor proved valor. Jivaro head-hunters count their glory in the number of shrunken heads they tally in their personal collections. The Icelandic sagas resound the fame of Gun-

[12]W. Whitman, *The Pueblo Indians of San Ildefonso*, pp. 99–100.
[13]H. Powdermaker, *Life in Lesu*, pp. 161, 163.
[14]L. Spier, *Yuman Tribes of the Gila River*, p. 104.
[15]G. P. Murdock, "Comparative Data on the Division of Labor by Sex" (*Social Forces*, Vol. 15, 1937), pp. 551–553; and A. D. Coult and R. W. Habenstein, *Cross Tabulations of Murdock's World Ethnographic Sample.*

Table 20-1   The Division of Labor in Lesu, Melanesia.

masculine	feminine	joint
Clearing ground for new garden and building garden fence Planting trees Getting sago Fishing	Planting taro and yams; weeding; gathering crops and carrying them home Catching crabs on the reef	Catching the sea worm, beta
Hunting wild pig and phalanger Cutting firewood; making the *liga;* bringing the leaves for cooking Preparing pigs, fish, and sago to be cooked Burying bananas in the sand Housebuilding and repairing	Feeding domestic pigs Drawing water Preparing taro and yams to be cooked Sweeping the house and keeping it in order	
Making of masks, canoes, *malanggans,* fishing nets, spears, ornaments	Carrying heavy burdens with the exception of fish and pigs	Making baskets and mats. Taking care of children. Medicine and magic. Making "paint" for the hair

SOURCE: After H. Powdermaker.

nar of the "singing battle ax," mighty slayer of men. The Iroquois rewarded outstanding fighters with the opportunity to recite their deeds of valor before the admiring multitude at the victory dance, and each war leader had a war post upon which he depicted his exploits.

On the Plains, elaborate systems of coup counting were built up in a manner that inspired the merit-badge system of the Boy Scouts. A blow struck against the enemy is a coup in a literal sense. To ride or run into a howling mob of painted adversaries and touch an enemy stood high on the list of war merits. It was more praiseworthy than to kill him, for a dead man is not dangerous. It takes more courage to strike an enemy and run away than to lay him low. This often worked to the advantage of our own troopers in the Indian wars, who, when battle was joined, fought for keeps,

not for fun. Indians who were intent on showing off made better shooting than shooters.

It was also a coup to kill an enemy, but even in this act there were degrees of merit. A kill with a knife, tomahawk, or spear rated much higher than a lethal shot with bow or gun. Scalps were desirable souvenirs of victory, but taking a scalp after the battle was over was no coup at all. Life in a Plains Indian camp was studded with opportunities, ritual and otherwise, for brave men to recite their coups and to receive the plaudits of the people. These men became war leaders.

The pacifistic Pueblos gave special status to warriors who had killed and scalped. But it was not a glorified status. Rather, it was the status of polluted men who had to be purified through ritual initiation into the Warriors' Fraternity. In World War II, the men of one Keresan pueblo in

New Mexico were exhorted on leaving for the service not to touch any dead Germans or Japanese or to pick up any battlefield souvenirs that had belonged to the enemy because there was no one then living who knew how to initiate them into the Warrior's Fraternity. They would remain polluted and dangerous for life if contaminated by the enemy dead.[16]

Proficiency in supernaturalism gives special status to shamans and priests the world over—a status that bears a greater or lesser degree of prestige in almost all cases. The social position of sorcerers is esteemed or hated as the culture legitimatizes or rejects their works. There are good magicians and evil, skillful and incompetent. The test imposed by primitive man is pragmatic; he who makes magic work is always respected (whether honored or feared depends on his use of it); he who flubs his magical undertakings is scorned and debased, neither honored nor feared.

Proficiency in craftsmanship usually brings moderately high status among primitive people, but it tends to rank below military prowess, supernaturalism, political leadership, and wealth manipulation as a prestige generator. Polynesians, among all recorded primitives, gave the most conscious and organized recognition to craftsmanship. The *Tuhunga,* or great adept, of the Tonga tribe in Polynesia was highly revered, whether he was a master of oratory, tribal lore, house building, or canoe manufacture. Only by virtue of much mana (see page 468) was it possible for a man to excel in anything. And all Polynesians were impressed by mana.

Occupations linked to inferior castes in Africa and India bring no kudos to their practitioners, no matter how skilled the craftsman. A Masai blacksmith is doomed for life to despicable subordination, for that is the pariah status his culture ascribes to blacksmiths.

[16]Nevertheless, some of the veterans did return home thus contaminated. In 1948, therefore, the men of this pueblo invited the Opi (Warrior) Fraternity leaders from another Keresan-speaking pueblo to initiate the veterans because they were "acting crazy."

When people of like statuses group together to form a sharply identifiable social cluster within the larger population of their society, we have associations (called *sodalities* by some) or classes.

Wealth and status   There are definite limits to the amount of goods that roving collectors of food are able to carry around with them. It is not possible for such people to accumulate wealth; there are no rich men. The possession of wealth is not for the lower primitives a status determinant of great significance.

The giving away of food and goods is another matter, however. Food claims are communal in nature in almost all primitive societies (see pages 420–421). Prestige and leadership go to hunters who have food to dispense, hides to bestow, arrows to give, and (among Plains Indians) horses to lavish upon favored friends, wayfaring visitors, and indigent neighbors. Plains Indians recognized as families of good standing those whose tipis were well kept and decorated and whose industrious men and women kept their lodges well supplied with victuals, fine robes, and handsome clothes; but above all, they respected those who gave freely of what they possessed. Fluid wealth brought high status in its train. Hoarded wealth brought only contempt. This is what settlers on the Indian frontier could not understand when silent Indians appeared at the cabin door expecting a ready handout.

The potlatch of the Northwest Coast Indians   On the Northwest Coast, the fluidity of wealth is guaranteed by the *potlatch*—an elaborate institution of feasting accompanied by the lavish distribution of presents by the host and his kinsmen to guests of another lineage or tribe. Its primary function is to serve as a demonstration of the family and individual statuses of the hosts. The guests are witnesses to the hosts' claims to certain statuses. Although accumulations of wealth are necessary for potlatching, it is not the wealth that gives status; it is the legitimate possession of honorific prerogatives, which are linked with specific names and titles, which are inheritable, but which may not be used until publicly assumed at a potlatch given for the purpose. To use a name not publicly notarized at a potlatch is a shameful presumption, and to address a person by a name he has inherited but has not validated is an insult to his standing.[17]

Record of a Tsimshian potlatch that took place around 1930 illustrates the old principle with some modern touches. It is the story of the chief of the Gitlan tribe and a member of the Wolf clan. When Gusgai'in, chief of the Gitlan, died, his nephew announced that he would take up his uncle's name at some later date. Before this could be done, he and a Wolf clansman jammed their motorboat between the piles of a bridge, and were left hung up when the tide flowed out from beneath them. This would be enough to cause any good boatman chagrin, but when they were badgered with the remark, "We saw a Wolf hanging up under the bridge," the status of all Wolves was impaired.

A potlatch was necessary to rehabilitate their position, and so they undertook to give a traditional ceremony, the family Feast of the Early Snow, commemorating the exploit of the ancestral chief, Gusgai'in, whose name was now to be assumed by his descendant. This ancestor had passed beneath a glacier in his flight from enemy captors, so with poetic flavor the *pièce de résistance* of the commemorative banquet was to be a native sherbet made of snow mixed with olachen grease, berries, and crabapples. In keeping with the times, however, ice cream was served at this potlatch. Before each person who had taunted the hosts was placed a heaping dish of ice cream, more than he could possibly eat.

Gorging a guest and then making fun of him was a favorite form of ridicule and provided much amusement for the guests. . . . When the feast and hilarity were over [so goes Garfield's account], the chief arose and explained the mythological background for the feast they were giving. He thanked the guests for coming and announced that, in so far as he was able, he would fill the position of his late uncle. Then La'is, the senior Wolf of the Gilutsa'u tribe, arose as the chief's spokesman and said that, as the chief had been publicly addressed as Gusgai'in, the latter was hereby acknowledging the name and assuming the position. . . . Spokesmen for each guest chief affirmed Gusgai'in's right to the name and welcomed the new chief as a brother. They also acknowledged that the bridge incident and other slurs would be forgotten. Much of tribal history was narrated during the speeches and many compliments were paid the host and his lineage.

Gifts of food and handkerchiefs were then distributed among the guests. Dancing ended the potlatch.[18]

The potlatch serves to affirm the status of the host, and the protocol of seating, serving of food, and distribution of gifts does the same for the guests. Invariably the giving is in order of rank. The person with the highest rank is called upon to come up first to receive his allotted share, and so on down the line. The position of each person with respect to every other is rigidly determined by the nature of the validated titular prerogatives he holds.[19] The mere giving of a potlatch does not validate a person's claim to status. The real validation comes when he is called forth to receive his gifts when he is a guest at other potlatches. Only if his hosts call him forward at the moment warranted by the position he has claimed are his claims validated.

Similar practices are prevalent in many parts of Melanesia, where "big men" get to be such through the giving of expensive feasts and the lending out of pigs or other forms of capital goods.[20] To rise through the various degrees of the all-important men's club of the Banks Islanders calls for the payment of heavy initiation

[17]See P. Drucker, "Rank, Wealth, and Kinship in Northwest Coast Society" (*American Anthropologist*, Vol. 41, 1939), pp. 55–61.

[18]V. E. Garfield, "Tsimshian Clan and Society" (*University of Washington Publications in Anthropology*, Vol. 7, No. 3, 1939), pp. 205–206.

[19]Drucker, *op. cit.*, p. 215.

[20]C. D. Forde, *Habitat, Economy, and Society*, pp. 180ff.; M. Mead, "The Arapesh of New Guinea," in *Cooperation and Competition among Primitive Peoples*, pp. 32–35; and especially D. L. Oliver, *A Solomon Island Society*.

fees. None but the richest of men can afford to purchase the higher degrees. Indeed, as Lowie has summarized the data:

It is only the man of wealth who can reach the highest degrees and thus acquire prestige. Yet the aboriginal conception is not that of avariciously hoarding wealth but rather of displaying one's greatness by exhibiting contempt for property. So a man of the loftiest status in the club may still promote his renown by providing the lavish entertainment associated with certain festivals; nay, a suggestion of niggardliness on these occasions would go far to destroy his influence.[21]

Trobriand chieftains gather great stores of yams brought in as subject tribute. But this wealth must be dissipated in public feasts eaten by the populace and chieftains alike.[22]

The stewardship of wealth is not emphasized by primitive apologists. Yet as an anthropological principle, it may be said that the management of wealth rather than its possession brings social recognition among primitive peoples. Social compulsion stimulates altruism, philanthropy, and good works. It has been easier to negate this principle in civilization than in the primitive world.

Kinship and marital statuses and roles Marriage is a universal phenomenon at all levels of cultural development. Premarital, marital, and postmarital statuses are therefore ubiquitous. The roles of husband and wife are of such extreme importance in any society that marriage and the family are subjects requiring special treatment in separate chapters (Chapters 22 and 23).

Kinship, which consists of a network of status and roles, is of such fundamental significance in all societies, especially those we call primitive, that it also will require special chapters (Chapters 24 and 25) for exposition and analysis.

[21]R. H. Lowie, *Primitive Society*, p. 277.
[22]B. Malinowski, *Argonauts of the Western Pacific*, p. 64.

SUMMARY

The concepts of status and role are fundamental to the understanding of all social systems. Statuses are specified positions within the system of social structure. Roles are the characteristic ways of acting that go with specific statuses. Statuses give rise to standardized behavioral expectancies. Social structure consists of sets of statuses and roles organized in institutions: networks of behavior patterns focused upon specific goals and interests. Social behavior is the behavior of persons performing their appropriate roles according to the statuses which have been ascribed to them or which they have achieved by mastery of the roles. Institutional personnel consists of persons who fill the statuses identified with the institution.

Age, sex, marital, and kinship statuses are fundamental and universal in human societies. Achieved, aptitudinally based statuses are also universal, but which aptitudes are valued and built into the status system is a variable factor. The statuses of religious specialist and political leader are universal, but, again, the degree to which they are emphasized and elaborated is highly relative.

SELECTED READINGS

Drucker, P.: "Rank, Wealth, and Kinship in Northwest Coast Society" (*American Anthropologist*, Vol. 41, 1939), pp. 55–65.

Griffin, N. M.: *The Roles of Men and Women in Eskimo Culture* (1930). Treats the division of labor by sexes in a simple culture.

Kuper, H.: *An African Aristocracy: Rank among the Swazi* (1947). Royalty and commoners in a South African tribe.

Mead, M.: *Male and Female* (1949). An insightful and informative cross-cultural study of sexual roles in a changing world.

Simmons, L.: *The Role of the Aged in Primitive Society* (1945). A general survey of the status of old people.

From a gross biological point of view, life may be reduced to a simple formula: to be born, to mature, to reproduce, and to die. However, even the biologist will acknowledge that at least a few other events of significance occur along the way. Man embroiders upon the fundamental pattern.

Nevertheless, birth, maturity, reproduction, and death are the four basic and universal crises in the completed life cycle. In the earthly span of the human organism, every individual who fulfills his biological destiny must pass through each of these peaks in the cycle of life. Therefore, in no human culture are these critical periods wholly ignored. They may, however, be approached and surmounted with varying degrees of intensity. Some peoples are habituated to treat one or another of the life crises in a matter-of-fact manner. Others exhibit much anxiety. In the latter situation, there is considerable cultural emphasis of the crisis situation.

In general, however, since crisis periods are times of critical uncertainty—times when the fate of the individual or the group seems to hang in the balance—men are not inclined supinely to leave the outcome to mere chance or unbridled circumstance. Natural and supernatural forces may be controlled in fact and in belief. Therefore, positive techniques of rational assistance are employed, along with magic and ritual ceremonialism, to frustrate destructive and disruptive supernatural powers or to encourage and invoke positive and helpful forces. Through ritual and ceremony, a bridge is thrown across the yawning chasms of fear and doubt that carries men over transitional states to a safe arrival and a firm footing in the new status awaiting on the other side.

Primitive theories of conception

The life cycle begins with conception. Yet no primitive peoples have a scientifically accurate knowledge of the nature of conception. This is not the result of prudery but of sheer ignorance. After all, even civilized man has acquired a sophisticated knowledge of genetics only in the last hundred years, and there is still a good deal of talk about storks in our society.

However, most primitive peoples can recognize causal sequences with sufficient astuteness to be able to associate the act of sexual intercourse with conception. Some are even acute enough to be able to recognize that the male semen plays a role in the generation of life. Yet the naïve notion that the male plants a seed, which the female nurtures, is the closest primitive man can come to reality.

Explicit notions of miraculous conception abound in the primitive world. In its most common form, the belief is expressed that a child is the reincarnation of an ancestral spirit, who has slipped into the womb of the mother to be regenerated.[1] In Australia, this belief is raised to the status of a dogma so strong that the natives deny any relation between the sex act and conception other than to admit that the womb must first be opened so that ancestral spirits may enter.

The physiology of paternity Earlier anthropologists took this Australoid denial of the physiology of paternity at face value. Modern anthropologists see it as a cultural suppression of recognizable fact, the purpose of which is to sustain the shibboleths of the social system.[2] Ancestor worship and totemism are important themes in Australian culture. The continuity of the totemic group is sustained by means of the doctrine of spiritual reincarnation. To give expression to the fact of physiological paternity would be a subversive undermining of the sacred institutions of Australian social life—it would be definitely un-Australian.

The matrilineal (see page 371) Trobriand Islanders say that the male plays no role in conception. Rather, the spirit of a dead clan ancestor (called *baloma*) enters the womb when the woman is wading in the lagoon. It grows and becomes a child. The nearby Dobu, who believe that semen is voided coconut milk, which, when it enters a woman, causes the blood within her womb to coagulate and form a fetus, say bluntly that the Trobriand Islanders lie. The point is verily a sore one. So many angry words have been exchanged over this moot issue in the past that nowadays when Dobus and Trobriand Islanders meet, they tacitly avoid the touchy subject. Fortune's Dobu companions scolded him for broaching the subject on a visit to the Trobriand Islands.[3] Not without reason is anthropology sometimes called the "study of rude cultures by rude people."

The Dobu notion that babies are formed by

[1]See, for example, B. Malinowski, "Baloma: The Spirits of the Dead in the Trobriand Islands," in *Magic, Science and Religion and Other Essays*, pp. 125–227.
[2]See M. F. Ashley-Montagu, *Coming into Being among the Australian Aborigines.*
[3]R. F. Fortune, *Sorcerers of Dobu*, pp. 238–239.

the coagulation of blood is shared by many primitives sporadically distributed about the globe. They reason from the observed fact of cessation of menstruation during gestation. By inversion, they say that the clotting of the blood to form the baby stops the regular flow.

Pregnancy Life begins with conception, and conception produces pregnancy. No matter how they may envision conception, all primitive peoples recognize pregnancy in empirical physiological terms. There are a number of externally observable biological alterations that occur in mothers of all races. More notable among them are enlargement of the breasts and nipples, exudation of colostrum, cessation of menstruation, abdominal enlargement, and frequently nausea.

From the little that has been written on this subject by anthropologists, most peoples seem to focus on one or two of the symptoms as signs of coming events, although it is probable that they make note of all of them. Cessation of menstruation is the one universally recognized sign. A fair percentage of the tribes are even so alert as to calculate the expected birth at ten lunar months after the last period.

Various Oceanic and African tribes make note of breast changes; the Arunta of Australia, the Pukapuka of Polynesia, and others have been put on record as noting "morning sickness." Others have told field workers that a valuable sign is diminution of appetite and a tendency to become lazy.[4]

Prenatal tabus Pregnancy is the foreshadowing of birth. It is, therefore, in itself a crisis condition, or a preliminary phase of the critical event of giving birth. Most primitive peoples seize upon the gestation period as calling for a cultural relief of their anxieties. Chief among these anxieties are (1) fear that the child will not develop ideally, (2) fear that the fetus will miscarry, and (3) fear that the birth will be difficult. Pregnancy tabus and injunctions are supposed to bring freedom from these fears.

Thus Ray reports for the Sanpoil Indians of Washington that a childbearing woman and her husband may not eat trout, lest the child shake like that lively fish. They may not eat rabbit, lest the child get weak legs. They may not eat "fool hen," lest the child be a moron. More than this, the mother-to-be has to rise before sunrise, stay awake through the day, swim in cold water, walk and run, and (in modern times) ride horseback to strengthen her for the ordeal to come.[5]

It may reassure some modern mothers and induce some husbands to more indulgent understanding to know that queer food preferences in pregnancy are not silly whims. Quite a number of primitive peoples recognize that the pregnant woman has a craving for peculiar foods. Ford notes, however, that there do not seem to be any particular kinds of foods that are craved. The desire is for *variety*. What the basis of this desire may be we do not know.[6]

Childbirth practices

It is a strange thing that most of the anxiety over the crisis of childbirth comes before the event, not during it. Magic, ritual, and tabu dominate the prenatal period; yet when the moment of birth is reached, the obstetrical problems are in normal cases handled with matter-of-fact effectiveness, free of mumbo jumbo. For the most part, birth is strictly a woman's affair. However, a few tribes permit or require the husband to assist or to be present. Generally, however, the expectant mother retires into the house with one or two older female relatives to assist her. Midwife specialists are called upon among some people.

A widely accepted falsehood is that childbirth is easy for primitive women. It has even been anthropologically maintained that just as domestication increases birth difficulties for animals, so increasing domestication through civilization makes birth progressively more difficult for the modern mother. There is little evidence

[4]C. L. Ford, *A Comparative Study of Human Reproduction* (Yale University Publications in Anthropology, No. 32, 1945), p. 44.

[5]V. F. Ray, "The Sanpoil and Nespelem" (*University of Washington Publications in Anthropology*, Vol. 5, 1932), p. 124.
[6]Ford, *op. cit.*, p. 48.

for this neat idea. On the contrary, there is much empirical evidence in the record to prove that primitive women often suffer much agony and difficulty in childbirth; the multifarious magical provisions designed to assure an easy birth are surely ample evidence of the primitive's fear of hard delivery.

Practically all primitives have special emergency medical practices to call into play when birth is unusually difficult. In easy cases, there is little use of magic at the time of birth, but in drawn-out labor, medicine men and women are hastily invoked. The Cheyennes send for a medicine man who has derived power from the otter. Otters make a delightful sport of sliding down mudbanks. This is the way the baby should behave and an otter medicine man can bring it about—so they say.

The couvade A truly quaint custom is the *couvade*. On the birth of the child, the mother gets up and goes about her affairs, while the father goes to bed, apparently to recover from the effects of childbirth. During the period of his confinement, he is subjected to many tabus. This may be variously interpreted as a petulant demand for attention on the part of the male, as a symbolic assertion of the father's identification with the child, or, perhaps, as a form of magical assistance in the establishment of the child in the everyday world. But it is hardly, as some young fathers might think, a consequence of sheer exhaustion. That it is the symbolic assertion of identification of father and child seems to be the likeliest possibility.

As a matter of fact, not many cultures have produced the couvade. The Caribs and various of their South American neighbors are the outstanding couvadists. The Ainus of Japan and also the Chinese of Marco Polo's time should be included, as well as certain tribes of South India. In the northern mountains of the Iberian Peninsula, the couvade was practiced until very recent times.

According to Seed Eater Shoshone informants, they also practiced a real couvade in the old days.[7] When the expectant mother retired to her birth hut, the father went into a retirement hut of his own made for him by his mother. There he stayed isolated for five days, until the umbilical cord dropped from the newborn babe.[8] He observed all the tabus that normally applied to a menstruating women. No meat or soup could be eaten, only cereals. On the day of birth, his mother came to him, and he rubbed himself with sage. If she said, "You have a boy," he took a long walk in the mountains—where the game abide—but he did not hunt. If she said, "You have a daughter," he walked down into the valleys, where the wild seeds grow. Thus he magically associated his child with its future occupation. When the five days were up, he bathed, and then when he killed his first game, he gave it away to the people.

The four widely scattered centers of the couvade (East Asia, the Pyrenees, northeastern South America, and the Plateau area of North America) indicate independent development and elaboration of the father's role in the birth crisis in these areas.

Naming and presentation of the child

The mere fact of birth does not necessarily complete the transition of the child from the status of fetus to that of a member of the community. Many people feel that there must be a formal presentation to the people and the spirits. Many people feel that until this act is completed, mother and child must remain in isolation. The mother is contaminated by her blood and by the dangerous forces of the birth crisis. This is the putative rationalization of primi-

[7] E. A. Hoebel, *Shoshone Field Notes* (unpublished, 1934); also R. H. Lowie, "Notes on Shoshonean Ethnography" (*American Museum of Natural History, Anthropological Papers*, Vol. 20, Part 3, 1924), pp. 265–270.

[8] "A striking instance of numerical imposition is the frequent relationship between the sacred number of a group and the day on which the umbilical cord 'falls off': in Bali, where the mother is in a special state for the first three days after birth, the cord falls off in three days; in Itamul, where the magic number is five, it falls off in five." M. Mead, "On the Implications for Anthropology of the Gesell-Ilg Approach to Maturation" (*American Anthropologist*, Vol. 49, 1947), p. 74.

tives. Practically, of course, it is a good thing for the mother to have a chance to rest.

Postnatal isolation   The Hopi child and mother, although visited by relatives on the day of birth, remain isolated for twenty days. On the twentieth day, mother, father, and child are bathed many times over. Relatives of every clan give the infant at least one name associated with each of their clans. Then as the sun rises, the infant is carried out to be held before the Sun God, who is told all the names of the child.[9]

The Seed Eater Shoshone mother and child were isolated even longer—forty days. The birth hut was built by the woman's mother a long way from the camp. When the baby's umbilical cord dropped off after five days, the hut was moved closer to the camp. All menstrual tabus were followed exactly as by the father, but, in addition, the maternal grandmother prepared each day a bed of grass over hot coals for the mother to lie upon. (Today a hot-water bottle is used.) Throughout the day, the mother worked busily at weaving and other small tasks. Few friends came to visit her. After six weeks, she and the child rejoined the village.

The Omaha Indian child was touchingly introduced to the entire cosmos on the eighth day after birth in a traditional ritual always performed by a priest of a given subclan. On the eighth day, the priest was sent for. When he arrived, he took his place at the door of the tipi in which the child was born. His right hand raised, palm up to the sky, he intoned this beautiful invocation in a loud, ringing voice for all the world to hear:

Ho! Ye Sun, Moon, Stars, all ye that move in the heavens,
    I bid you hear me!
Into your midst has come a new life.
    Consent ye, I implore!
Make its path smooth, that it may reach the brow of the first hill!

Ho! Ye Winds, Clouds, Rain, Mist, all ye that move in the air,
    I bid you hear me!
Into your midst has come a new life.
    Consent ye, I implore!
Make its path smooth, that it may reach the brow of the second hill!

Ho! Ye Hills, Valleys, Rivers, Lakes, Trees, Grasses, all ye of the earth,
    I bid you hear me!
Into your midst has come a new life.
    Consent ye, I implore!
Make its path smooth, that it may reach the brow of the third hill!

Ho! Ye Birds, great and small, that fly in the air,
Ho! Ye Animals, great and small, that dwell in the forest,
Ho! Ye Insects that creep among the grasses and burrow in the ground,
    I bid you hear me!
Into your midst has come a new life.
    Consent ye, I implore!
Make its path smooth, that it may reach the brow of the fourth hill!

Ho! All ye of the Heavens, all ye of the Air, all ye of the Earth,
    I bid you all to hear me!
Into your midst has come a new life.
    Consent ye, consent ye all, I implore!
Make its path smooth—then shall it travel beyond the four hills![10]

Yet even this ritual did not make the child a real member of the tribe, for a baby did not complete its transition until it could walk. Then it went through a "turning of the child ritual," wherein it discarded its baby name and got new moccasins. Baby moccasins always had a hole cut in the sole so that if a messenger from the spirit world came to claim the little infant, the child could answer, "I cannot go on a journey —my moccasins are worn out!" New moccasins without holes were an assurance that the child was prepared for the journey of life and that its journey would be a long one.

[9]A fascinating autobiographical description of the entire birth ritual may be found in L. Simmons (ed.), *Sun Chief,* chap. 1.

[10]A. C. Fletcher and F. LaFlesche, *The Omaha Tribe* (Bureau of American Ethnology, Annual Report 27, 1911), pp. 115–116.

In Africa, the Ashanti entertain similar notions. The child is not ceremonially named and publicly presented until eight days have passed. Then it becomes a genuine human being. Should it die before that time, its little corpse is casually thrown on the garbage heap, for it is believed to have been but the husk of a ghost child whose mother in the spirit world had pawned it off on a living mother for a short period while she went off on some jaunt or other. On returning from her undertaking, she recalled her little spirit baby.

Further to the south in Africa, a Swazi baby, until the third month of life, is described as a "thing." It has no name, it cannot be handled by the men, and if it dies, it may not be publicly mourned. It is recognized as being very weak and vulnerable (infant mortality is tragically high), and the parents perform various rituals to protect it against dangers emanating from animals, humans, and nature herself. In the third month, the infant is shown to the moon and symbolically introduced to the world of nature. It is entered into the category of persons and is given a name, which may be sung to it in its first lullaby.[11]

Not all societies undertake a formal presentation, but most of them, including our own, with its christenings and baptisms, seem to do so. Virtually all societies do isolate mother and child for periods of time varying from a few days to several months.

Naming, incidentally, is a universal human practice. Shakespeare to the contrary, there is much in a name. It symbolizes the individual's personality and often indicates some aspects of his social status. The name is usually bestowed at the end of the seclusion period. If the name is ceremonially bestowed, this is usually done by a near relative; otherwise, the most common practice is for the mother to decide what her child is to be called. Names that are associated with good luck or great deeds tend generally to be preferred. Thus the Menominee discard their original names if they are chronically sick, in the hope that a new name will bring a healthier state of being.

[11]H. Kuper, *The Swazi*, p. 50.

Change of names or acquisition of additional ones often occurs in the course of the individual's lifespan in many primitive societies, as new names are assumed to indicate new statuses.

Puberty rites and transition of status

The second crisis in the life cycle is adolescence or puberty. Puberty, like birth, is a manifestation of a basic alteration of the biological state of the individual. It is the time of maturation of the secondary sexual characteristics and the final growth to functional capacity of the sex organs. Puberty marks the twilight of youth and the dawn of adulthood.

In both boys and girls, puberty is not an abrupt transition, but an accelerated development extending from the eleventh to the sixteenth year. Body hair does not sprout overnight on boys; the lengthening of the vocal cords, with embarrassing sound effects, is not instantaneous; and the relative broadening of the shoulders is a process of adolescent growth as much as the activation of the testicles and the production of fully formed seminal fluid are.

In the case of the female, the majority of puberty changes, including emergence of body hair, broadening of the hips, increase of subcutaneous adipose tissue (especially on the hips and breasts), and development of the sex organs, all occur over a period of months. One function alone, however, first manifests itself at a particular moment. The onset of menstruation quite definitely signals the attainment of puberty for the female.

The cultural definition of puberty The transition from adolescence to adulthood is fundamentally a biological phenomenon. Yet for human beings it represents also a sociological transition. Because social status is culturally defined, adolescence is for most peoples more a cultural than a biological problem. The first fact to note is that some cultures handle adolescence most casually.[12] The second is that some ritualize it for one sex or the other or for both, with most cultures placing heaviest emphasis on adolescence rites for boys. The third factor is that puberty rites do not necessarily synchronize with biological pubescence. They occur when, sociologically, childhood is left behind and adulthood is entered.

Negatively, this principle is admirably demonstrated in the case of the Alorese in the East Indies. For boys, the attainment of adulthood is a long-drawn-out process calling for extensive economic enterprising. Because of this, and since there are no men's clubs and no secret societies, there are no rites of transition, no tribal initiation. Instead, ". . . at about sixteen the boys begin to let their hair grow long. At this time they begin to acquire male dress ornaments: sword, shields, areca basket, wide belt, bow, combs, and head plumes. This is ridiculed by the women, who hoot the men, and scoff at this manifestation of masculine vanity."[13] The boys also file their incisors halfway down and blacken their teeth.

The Polynesians, in general, present an even more decisive manifestation of the principle just enunciated. Gifford says:

The absence of anything that might be called initiation rites that ushered boys into manhood is due to the fact that in Polynesia a boy left the company of women and was accepted into association with men at weaning, when the food tabu that required men to eat apart from women was laid upon him. The Polynesian boy became a man when he began to eat the food of men, not at adolescence.[14]

Thus, although superincision of boys was practiced by most Polynesians outside of New Zealand, the operation was performed at any time

Fig. 21-1 Circumcision ceremony for young boys of the Wagogo tribe, Tanzania. For a period varying from 10 days to 3 weeks, initiates virtually become women. They are attended by women and often dress as girls. Then they are blindfolded and, except in the privacy of the ceremonial huts, they do not see the world again until the masks are removed after the circumcision is actually performed. The masks vary in design. These are of reeds decorated with guinea fowl feathers. (George Rodger, Magnum.)

---

[12] For example, Samoa, ". . . Adolescence represented no period of crisis or stress, but was instead an orderly development of slowly maturing interests and activities. The girls' minds were perplexed by no conflicts, troubled by no philosophical queries, beset by no remote ambitions." M. Mead, *Coming of Age in Samoa*, p. 157.

[13] C. DuBois, "The Alorese," in *The Psychological Frontiers of Society*, p. 139.

[14] E. W. Gifford, *Tongan Society* (Bernice P. Bishop Museum, Bulletin 61, 1929), p. 187.

Fig. 21-2   *The distinctive coiffure of these Hopi girls, photographed in 1879, proclaims their unmarried status. (Smithsonian Office of Anthropology, Bureau of American Ethnology Collection.)*

But the Northern Shoshones and other peoples of the Columbian Plateau made a real crisis of the event for the girl. The pubescent Shoshone girl was isolated just for the period of her flow, but she had to be very busy so that she would not become a lazy woman. "Whatever she does then lasts for life." She could eat no meat and could not scratch herself, except with a special stick. At the end of her first isolation, she was brought new clothes by her mother—women's clothes.

Northern Shoshone attitudes were but a pale attenuation of those of the Carrier Indians to the north of them. As Benedict says: "The fear and horror of a girl's puberty was at its height. Her three or four years of seclusion was called 'the burying alive.' . . . She was herself in danger and she was a source of danger to everybody else."[15]

In such societies as those of Africa and aboriginal Australia, both peoples who place much emphasis on age grading (see Chapter 26), adolescence rites become genuine "tribal initiations." This is especially true where men's secret societies are of great importance. Consequently, boys' initiations are also striking in many parts of eastern Melanesia.

Andaman Island rites   As an example of the more dramatic forms of puberty rites, we may quote from Radcliffe-Brown's account of the Negrito Andaman Islanders. These pygmy people have no secret societies or other associations, but they do place great emphasis upon age status. To be marked and accepted as an adult, each boy and girl must go through specific ceremonies. Beginning early in childhood, both sexes are gradually scarred over their entire bodies with small incisions "to help them grow strong," but the culmination is reached at puberty in the following manner: at the first sign of her menses, the girl is wept over her by her mother and female relatives. Andaman weeping, let us hasten to say, does not express sorrow but rather marks an occasion of importance. The lass then plunges into the ocean for a two-hour bath—an act of ritual cleansing—

from infancy on. It was necessary only that the operation be completed before marriage.

Among the warrior tribes of the Plains and eastern North America, there were no puberty rites per se. But at adolescence young men set out on vision quests to obtain the supernatural power that was so essential to a successful life. However, vision vigils were carried on by adults, too, so it cannot be said that any great emphasis was placed upon puberty by these people. In the same manner, they treated the adolescence of girls most casually. Although all the tribes isolated the menstruating woman, nothing much was made of the first menses, except that the Cheyenne father proudly stood in the door of his tipi shouting the good news to the whole camp and celebrated his daughter's womanhood by a giveaway of a fine horse to some poor oldster.

[15]R. F. Benedict, *Patterns of Culture*, p. 28.

after which she is tastefully decorated with pandanus leaves and clay.

Thus covered with leaves the girl must sit in the hut allotted to her, with her legs doubled up beneath her and her arms folded. . . . The girl sits thus for three days. Early every morning she leaves the hut to bathe for an hour in the sea. At the end of the three days she resumes her life in the village. For a month following she must bathe in the sea every morning at dawn.[16]

When the friends and relatives of a boy decide that he is old enough to have the incisions made on his back, a dance is held throughout the night and the next morning.

The boy kneels down and bends forward until his elbows rest on the ground in front. One of the older men takes a pig-arrow and with the sharpened blade makes a series of cuts on the boy's back. Each cut is horizontal, and they are arranged in three vertical rows, each row consisting of from 20 to 30 cuts. When the cutting is finished the boy sits up, with a fire at his back, until the bleeding stops. During the operation and a few hours following it the boy must remain silent.[17]

Immediately upon completion of the puberty rites, a number of food tabus are imposed upon both sexes. These are gradually removed in a series of formal ceremonies over a period of several years. Neither a boy nor a girl is considered to be a full-fledged adult until all the tabus have been removed.

If the whole ritual cycle is viewed as an entity, as should be done, then we see again that adolescence rites do not represent a fixed biological phenomenon so much as a social event roughly correlated to the biological.

West African rites West African initiatory rites are frequently extremely elaborate and impressive. Of the Kpelle of Liberia, where initiation is into the tribal secret fraternity, the Poro, Gibbs writes:

While a boy is in the Poro bush, he is instructed in tribal lore: farming, house building, crafts, the use of medicines, dancing, warfare, history, the treatment of women, and deportment before chiefs and elders.

Physical ordeals, hazing, and the meting out of harsh punishment not only ensure that he learns well but that he acquires a deeply ingrained willingness to submit to authority because it is authority.

When a Poro initiate enters the bush it is said that he is "eaten" by ŋamu. By the time he comes out, he has acquired a *bi laa* or "bush name," by which he is known thereafter. The uninitiated person has died, and a new person has been born in his place. His new status and rebirth are also evident in the cicatrices on his back and chest, said to be the teeth marks of the Great Masked Figure imprinted in the process of disgorging the initiate at his rebirth. Circumcision is usually arranged individually before the boy becomes an initiate.[18]

To isolate and "kill" the initiate is a widespread practice symbolizing the end of his old status. Without undertaking to be so specific about it, our college fraternities and men's secret societies use hazing to perform the same social function. Hazing the neophyte[19] is a process of degradation that destroys his ego. With his old ego destroyed, he is ready for the formal ritual initiation, from which he emerges a "new man" in the ranks of the exalted. To take another example from Western society, when old-time Army sergeants bully and insult rookies, they are not being merely sadistic, nor are they necessarily working off personal frustrations. Although sergeants may not be aware of any principles of functional anthropology, they do know that recruits have to be made over and put through a quick transition rite. A first and unfortunately necessary act is the destruction of civilian ways and civilian thoughts: "You're in the Army now." Induction means death of the civilian, and the "top kick" is the executioner. Completion of basic training means resurrection in a new status—General Issue.

Torture in the puberty rites of Australian and many African tribes rises to heights of sheer cruelty. Yet beneath it can usually be found a functional rationalization. In Australia, circum-

---

[16]A. R. Radcliffe-Brown, *The Andaman Islanders*, p. 93.
[17]*Ibid.*, p. 95.

[18]J. L. Gibbs, Jr., "The Kpelle of Liberia," in J. L. Gibbs, Jr. (ed.), *Peoples of Africa*, p. 222. Copyright © by Holt, Rinehart and Winston, Inc., publishers. Used by permission.
[19]Note that the very word means "produce anew" (Gr. *neos*, new + *phytos*, grown).

cision and subincision, painful and dangerous surgical operations when crudely performed with stone knives, are but symbolic acts signifying the sexual and social completeness of the males in a type of society that rejects and culturally suppresses the significance of women.

In all cases, transition is the main theme— transition from the limited and undeveloped state of childhood to that of the adult endowed with the wisdom and privileges of a mature person. Thus, death and resurrection are recurrent themes of stepped-up puberty rites: death means the destruction of the childhood personality, and resurrection means that the person is restored to the community in a new status with new roles. The boy who retires to the hidden initiatory school in the bush, secreted from the eyes of all females and preadolescent boys, is "dead." When he returns to the camp of the band, circumcised, subincised, and cicatrized, with a few teeth knocked out and with new knowledge of totemic mythology, he is a new man.

Relation of puberty rites to social types Becoming a man or a woman means finding one's place in the social system. It means accepting ascribed statuses and winning those which may appropriately be achieved. Psychologically, it means internalization of a self-identity that is adequately related to the social system in which one must function. It means anchoring of the self primarily within the kinship group or, alternatively, to social units outside the kinship group. In either case, since every society is larger than the nuclear family (see pages 358–359), it becomes universally necessary to detach the individual to some degree from his family of birth.

The factor of social independence Yehudi Cohen classifies two types of societies: (1) those which train for social independence, i.e., those in which anchorage and identification are in the nuclear family, and (2) those in which children are brought up for sociological interde-

pendence, i.e., anchorage in wider kinship groups such as lineages and clans (see Chapter 24). Statistical correlations based on data from sixty-five societies show that type-2 societies overwhelmingly (36 to 1) use initiation ceremonies as a part of the socialization process. Among the type-1 societies in Cohen's sample, the ratio is only 10 with initiations to 18 without.[20] Societies that train for family identification use other means than initiatory techniques.

Circumcision in relation to other culture traits Whiting and his associates have engaged in an intensive search for the whys and wherefores of circumcision as a part of transition rites. They discovered that the circumcision of boys, particularly when it occurs as a part of initiation rites, is strongly associated with three other cultural phenomena: (1) the custom of having a mother and baby sleep together, while the father sleeps separately; (2) a tabu of a year or longer on resumption of sexual relations between parents after the birth of a child; and (3) virilocal residence (see pages 360–361). The first two customs result in strong mother-son identification, and the third intensifies the ultimate claim of the father's kinsmen to the boy's social allegiance or identification. Hence, the severe hazing at puberty to break the mother-son tie and to transfer the boy into the world of men.[21]

It is an interesting fact of ethnography that circumcision is exclusively restricted to Africa and the Pacific Islands. It is generally absent in Eurasia and absolutely absent in North and South America.[22]

---

[20]The correlations read: $X^2 = 26.44$, $T = .64$, $p < .001$. Y. Cohen, *The Transition from Childhood to Adolescence*, p. 114.
[21]J. W. M. Whiting, R. Kluckhohn, and H. S. Anthony, "The Function of Male Initiation Ceremonies at Puberty," in E. E. Maccoby, T. Newcomb, and E. Hartley (eds.), *Readings in Social Psychology* (1958), pp. 359–370. See also the discussion of Professor Hart's thesis concerning prepubertal and postpubertal education in Chap. 4, p. 60.
[22]This statement refers, of course, to the aboriginal cultures. Whiting offers an involved and intriguing explanatory hypothesis in terms of climate, but it is too removed from our interests here. See J. W. M. Whiting, "Effects of Climate on Certain Cultural Practices," in W. H. Goodenough (ed.), *Explorations in Cultural Anthropology*, pp. 551–544.

Maturity

There are a number of ancillary functions tied up with puberty ceremonialism. Cicatrization and the filing or knocking out of front teeth serve both as decorative elements and status identifications and as tests of the neophyte's ability to endure physical pain.[23] Strict discipline imposed during the rites works to fix the authority of the elders. The instruction in etiquette, mythology, and magic that usually accompanies puberty initiations embraces education and training in a practical sense and enhances ties of individual loyalty to the institutions of the tribal society. Yet under and through it all is the basic fact of transition—a transition that is fundamentally biological but often elaborately cultural.

Adulthood means full participation in the responsibilities and privileges of the society. It means marriage and parenthood and political, religious, economic, and club life. These are spelled out in detail in the remaining chapters.

Death and mortuary rituals

Death has no absolute finality for any primitive people. All of them believe in the immortality of the soul.[24] Yet all men well know that death marks the end of corporeal existence. Belief in the transition from the carnal to a wholly spiritual existence at death comes through faith and imagination, a projection of life from a tangible and material state to an ethereal illusory condition sustained in the dogma of culture. Because the dead are no longer constantly among the living but appear or make their influence felt only indirectly, they are almost always relegated to another state of being in human cosmogony.

Funeral rites serve five basic functions: (1) Participation in mortuary ceremonies, by habitual dramatization of the faith in immortality, prepares the living for the death that awaits

Fig. 21-3 Death. A Haida chieftain of the Northwest Coast of North America lives on in his wooden grave monument. (Courtesy of The American Museum of Natural History.)

them. "The belief in immortality," wrote Malinowski, "lived through ritually . . . makes him cherish more firmly the belief in his own future life. . . . Thus the ritual before death confirms the emotional outlook which a dying man has come to need in his supreme conflict."[25] (2) Funeral rites serve magically to assure the separation of the soul from its body, to guide the deceased through the supreme transition safely and properly. (3) The rites serve to readjust the community after the loss of a member and to regularize the emotional disturbances that result from the upset of affective habits in connection with the deceased. Death usually evokes grief. (4) Where feasting and property giveaways are involved, mortuary rites effect a redistribution of wealth and statuses. (5) Finally, the rites lend color, richness and depth to life through the drama of their performance.

In early prehistoric times, Neandertal man of the Mousterian epoch was the first creature to give evidence of concern over death. He

[23]When Elizabeth M. Thomas acknowledged to a Dodoth that Americans do not pierce the lower lip so as to be able to wear a labret, he said, "That is cowardly."
[24]See Chap. 32 for a discussion of the soul concept.

[25]B. Malinowski, "Culture" (*Encyclopedia of the Social Sciences*, Vol. 4, 1931), p. 641.

*Fig. 21-4 Death. Within the tapestry effigy figure is
a basket containing the sun-dried mummy of a
prehistoric Peruvian buried in the great necropolis
at Pachacamac, near the coast of Central Peru.
(Courtesy of The University Museum, Philadelphia.)*

deliberately buried his deceased fellow tribes-men—a boon to archaeologists and an indication that he had developed imaginative intelligence to the point where the soul concept had become possible. All later men have consistently worked into their cultures some form of disposal of the corpse accompanied by a greater or lesser development of transitional funerary rites.

SUMMARY

At each stage of the journey through life, human beings have made a social issue of the transition crises. Each crisis marks a change in social status. Life is never wholly drab for any group of people. Ritual and ceremony, anticipation and anxiety, and preparation and performance all color and lend zest to the act of living. Each person in turn fulfills his roles and plays his parts. None can escape the beginning and the end. The favored few mature and reproduce as they traverse the whole cycle of birth, adolescence, maturity, and death, and work out their potentialities within the framework permitted by the cultures of the societies within which they are destined to live and die.

SELECTED READINGS

Cohen, Y. A.: *The Transition from Childhood to Adolescence.* (1964). Undertakes to distinguish prepubertal and postpubertal rites of separation of the child from its family and to correlate each type with specific social orientations.

Evans-Pritchard, E. E.: "Heredity and Gestation as the Azande See Them," in *Essays in Social Anthropology* (1963), pp. 117–130. A brief but highly informative descriptive analysis of the beliefs of an important East African people of the Upper Nile.

Ford, C. S.: *A Comparative Study of Human Reproduction* (Yale University Publications in Anthropology, No. 32, 1945). Summarizes primitive natal attitudes and birth practices.

Goody, J.: *Death, Property and the Ancestors* (1962). The most comprehensive analysis available of the death practices and their functional significance in a primitive culture.

Lowie, R. H.: *The Crow Indians* (1935), chap. 3, "From Cradle to Grave." A description of the life cycle in a famous Plains Indian tribe.

Opler, M. E.: *An Apache Life-way* (1942). From conception to death in the culture of the Chiricahua Apaches.

Van Gennep, A.: *The Rites of Passage.* The classic work in this field. It is, however, exceedingly formalistic in its effort to classify different types of transition rites.

Whiting, B. B. (ed.): *Six Cultures: Studies of Child Rearing* (1963). Detailed, comparative studies of the ethnographic background and child-rearing practices of six communities in Africa, India, Okinawa, Mexico, the Philippines, and New England. A rich source.

The prolonged dependence of the human individual on adult nurture, character shaping, and culture transmission, tied in with the peculiarities of relations within the conjugal-natal family, which is a nearly universal form in all human societies, makes untrammeled expression of sexuality socially impossible. Thus, all societies, primitive and civilized, impose rigorous limitations on sexual activities and undertake to steer such sexual activity as is allowed in certain clearly defined directions. There is no such thing as a promiscuous human society. To be human is, in the nature of things, to be subject to sexual inhibition. The amount of inhibition and the forms it takes vary, as does everything else, from culture to culture. Anthropological examination of the cross-cultural record shows that American society imposes and engenders a greater degree of inhibition than is usual, although in recent times it appears to be moving away from this distinctive position.

In the formal regulation of sex, Americans extend a prohibition against all sexual intercourse outside of the monogamous family relationship of husband and wife. The prohibition bans all premarital intercourse and all adultery (sexual relations outside of marriage between two persons, at least one of whom is married).

Murdock's comprehensive survey of kinship institutions among the representative sample of 250 societies in the Yale University Cross Cultural Survey leads him to estimate that, "From available evidence . . . it seems unlikely that a general prohibition of sexual relations outside of marriage occurs in as many as five percent of the peoples of the earth."[1] From this it can be seen that the American position is highly atypical. Nevertheless, it still remains true that all societies impose a number of limitations on sexual activity and attempt to regulate reproduction and mating.

Mating

Mating is *the pairing off of individuals of opposite sex under the influence of the sexual drive*. It is preponderantly a psychophysical phenomenon, basically instinctive in nature. But among human beings it is definitely influenced by various culture patterns that control the forms of its expression. The purpose of this chapter is to describe the nature of the cultural controls of mating.

Mating implies more than mere sexual intercourse; a degree of permanence is involved in the association of the mated pair. However, mating is not to be confused with marriage; intimately related though the two may be, they are not inseparable. As in the case of nonhuman animals, mating can occur on a purely biological plane, without benefit of marriage—the connubial institution. Conversely, marriages can occur without mating.

Marriage is a social institution determined *in toto* by culture. *Marriage is the complex of social norms that define and control the relations of a connubial pair to each other, their kinsmen, their offspring, and society at large.* It defines all the institutional demand rights, duties, immunities, and so on of the pair as husband and wife. It is the institution that shapes the form and activities of the association known as the *family*.

Premarital mating In contrast to our fairly strict usages, a number of primitive societies accept free premarital sexual experimentation without disapproval. Of the Trobriand Islanders it is written, presumably without exaggeration:

Chastity is an unknown virtue among the natives. At an incredibly early age they become initiated into sexual life, and many of the innocent-looking plays of childhood are not so innocuous as they appear. As they grow up, they live in promiscuous free love, which gradually develops into more permanent attachments, one of which ends in marriage.[2]

In the absence of the severe guilt feelings that ordinarily color premarital sex activity among our youthful population, premarital activity may function among primitives to prepare young people for marriage. It can provide an intimate test of the compatibility of mating pairs before they actually enter into marriage, with all its social and economic responsibilities. This is Malinowski's principle of the *social function of premarital sexual activity*.[3] There is little doubt but that the end to which Malinowski calls attention may so be served in some societies, but it seems more likely that societies are apt to permit the free play of the biological drives, outside of the limits of the incest tabu, before marriage because of indifference to the effects of such activity. At any rate, not much emphasis can be placed upon the function of premarital experience as a factor in mate selection in the vast number of primitive societies in which the boy and girl have very little to say about whom they marry. It will be shown later to how small a degree marriage in primitive society is concerned with sexual gratification and personal compatibility on the basis of romantic love. Primitive societies are much more concerned with (1) the biological perpetuation of the group, (2) the perpetuation of the culture and social existence of the group through proper nurture and training of the oncoming generation, and (3), last but not least, the furthering of immediate special interests in prestige, property, and prerogatives of the *extended families* of the pair to be joined in marriage.

This last point is well illustrated in the practices of the Philippine Ifugaos, who permit free premarital sexual activity only for members of those classes in which there is not much stake in property and prestige. Each night, adolescent boys of the lower and middle classes must seek the congenial comfort of the house of a widow,

[1] G. P. Murdock, *Social Structure*, p. 264.

[2] B. Malinowski, *The Argonauts of the Western Pacific*, p. 53.
[3] B. Malinowski, "Culture" (*Encyclopedia of the Social Sciences*, Vol. 4, 1931), p. 630.

which also serves the regular purpose of a dormitory for unmarried adolescent girls, who, by custom, are not permitted to sleep under the family roof. In the deep of the night, the boys try their luck at lovemaking. Much experimentation in different dormitories ultimately leads to a permanent attachment to some one girl—a form of companionate marriage that eventually blossoms into a fully accredited marriage, when the numerous exchange gifts have been made and family rituals of marriage have been observed.

Upper-class Ifugaos, however, behave in quite a different manner, since the parents do not care to run the risk of permitting their children to mate in accordance with mere amatory whim. The society of the Ifugaos rests on a subsistence base of wet-rice culture in paddies that have been carved in rugged mountainsides through the prodigious efforts of untold generations of labor. Possession of rice fields is a precious heritage: the major means to wealth, prestige, and upper-class status—the cherished goal of the Ifugao. Because family status rests heavily on property, marriage is a useful instrument for augmenting the status of the next generation by combining the resources of two families of property. To have a scion find a compatible but propertyless bride in the damsels' dormitory is, for the upper-class Ifugao, an economic calamity. To avert such an eventuality, rich children of the Ifugaos are betrothed in infancy, or even before birth. A contract marriage is arranged by the parents, who guarantee the amount of land and other goods that will be conveyed to the bride and groom. Throughout childhood, the boy and girl take turns living in each other's parents' homes, until they establish a home of their own on marriage, shortly after adolescence.[4]

A similar situation, in which freedom is allowed some young persons but not others, occurs in Samoa and elsewhere in Oceania. Boys and girls of the commoner class are allowed virtually unrestricted sex freedom

[4] R. F. Barton, *Philippine Pagans;* also "Ifugao Law" (*The University of California Publications in American Archaeology and Ethnology*, Vol. 15, 1919), pp. 15–22.

"under the palms," but woe to the royal princess who does not preserve her chastity and is exposed at the public rituals of defloration when the emissaries of another village come to claim her for their royal chief. In the old days, she was killed by her female relatives.

Among the American Indians of the Plains, we again find premarital unchastity the rule (except for the strict Cheyennes), but families of high standing endeavored to inculcate virtuous behavior in their daughters. The girl who retained unimpugned chastity until marriage was greatly respected in public opinion and doubly cherished by her husband. This seeming paradox crops up in many ways in numerous societies, civilized and uncivilized. It certainly manifests a conflict of interests and values. Important elements in the situation include the desire of the individual for biological gratification between the attainment of puberty and marriage, on the one hand, and the sense of enhanced value in exclusive possession, on the other.

The illustrations cited above indicate that economic factors definitely influence the imposition of checks on free premarital sexual activity. This must have played an increasingly important role in the unfolding of human history as societies built up more and more property. The control of mating in order to effect the control of property therefore looms as something of a necessity among civilized peoples in a way that is not the case with the more propertyless primitives. Mating becomes more than the crude expression of biological drives. It also binds and directs the disposition and control of property.

While economic determinism has a sturdy finger in the pie, other factors must also be recognized. Religious belief is pervasive. In the area of sex control, its power cannot be overestimated. The Polynesian princess must lead a carefully guarded life because she is inherently charged with mana and is therefore tabu to ordinary mortals. Inca maidens dedicated to serve the sun in the nunneries of Cuzco were required to remain virgins until they were married off to a worthy dignitary, who was the recipient of royal favor from the demigod, the Great Sun, the ruling Inca. Rome had her vestal virgins. And the military societies of the Cheyenne Indians each had four honorary virgins to perform ritual services in the society ceremonies. An active sexual life is often incompatible with religion.

Shamans are generally devoted to this principle. Unless they are engaged in fertility rites to bring on a crop of babies or corn, they almost universally submit themselves to temporary celibacy when they are about to invoke their mystic powers. The belief is that the female physiology is itself charged with a mystic power of great potency. In this man-dominated world, the unique female power is looked upon as evil and dangerous, dangerous especially to the mystic powers of men. Contamination of a male's supernatural power by the negative power of the female is believed to result from sexual association. When this attitude is exaggerated, it leads to the sexual asceticism of some of the Late Classical cults and early Christianity, an asceticism that survives in the celibacy of the Catholic clergy and the Puritan distrust of sex that is embedded in much of our culture. Such intense elaboration of sex asceticism is only another example of the principle of skewed elaboration of culture. Sociology can adduce few good functional reasons for its existence. Psychiatry and psychology can adduce manifold instances of malfunctioning as a result of it—the psychotic and neurotic quirks of the repressed personality.

Various combinations of one or more of the considerations just mentioned have led a slight majority of contemporary primitive societies to prohibit, or at least to try to check, premarital sexual activity among their young. The Trobriand Island instance represents a minority situation. The primitive societies that do impose a check on adolescent premarital sex experience do so 'for the most part not because they view such activity as inherently evil, but rather because economic and other social interests have priority over sex. Ubiquitously, however,

every society prohibits sexuality between brother and sister at all ages. This is the consequence of the universal prohibition of incest.

The prohibition of incest

Mating with any person who is *culturally defined* as a member of one's kinship group is commonly forbidden. Any such prohibited mating is incestuous. The prohibition of sex relations between culturally identified relatives is therefore known as the *incest tabu.* It automatically follows in the case of forbidden sex relations that marriage between persons subject to this rule is also forbidden.

Incest tabus are universal among all peoples because incest is repugnant to the least as well as to the most civilized. The universality of incest prohibition and the fact that it is concerned with a basic biological act have led to the common view that it is instinctive. Universality, however, is not in itself any evidence of instinct. We might as well say that fire making is an instinct, since all peoples practice it. The weight of the evidence is on the other side. Incest prohibition is not instinctive; rather, it is rooted in a social, not a biological, basis.

Exceptions to the incest tabu Let us observe how this works. *The tabu on the mating of brother and sister occurs everywhere, as does the tabu on mating between parent and child.* The exceptions that bar absolute universality are few and far between, nor do they in any case apply to the entire population of any society. The exceptions to the brother-sister rule are the famous cases of the royalty of Egypt, Hawaii, and the Incas. In these instances, marriage between brother and sister of royal lineage was required in the belief that the supreme royalty was divine and that marriage with mortals was a corruption of the divinity. But alas for ideals! Cleopatra, although she married her twelve-year-old brother, saw to his murder while she mated with Julius Caesar and Mark Antony. Whether because of the example of the Ptolemies or as a result of other historical causes, brother-sister marriage as a means of keeping property within the family was evidently not uncommon in Egypt during the period of Roman rule following the death of Cleopatra.[5]

Another special and very peculiar exception to the brother-sister tabu exists among the Balinese, who suppose that boy and girl twins have been too intimate in their mother's womb. The penalties for incest are severe in Bali, but in the case of baby twins, temporary banishment of the parents and the "erring" twins, followed by a ceremony of purification and atonement, negates the sin. This makes it permissible for the mating in the womb to be completed as a true marriage in later life.[6] Ordinary brother-sister marriages are said to have been permissible among the aboriginal Ainus of Japan, but the evidence for this is merely mythological, and myth is not good historical evidence. It has also been reported that the Lamet tribe of Southeast Asia countenances brother-sister marriage if the pair have been raised in separate households, i.e., are not sociologically members of the same family.[7]

Edmund Leach has recently reported another tribe of Southeast Asia who permit half brothers and sisters to marry under certain circumstances. In calling attention to the Lakher, he writes:

They consider that the child of a properly married man is exclusively his and that his divorced wife has absolutely no rights in the child whatsoever. It follows that if a woman has a son and a daughter by two different husbands the children are deemed unrelated to one another. Therefore they may marry without restraint. In contrast, the son and daughter of one man by two different mothers stand in an incestuous relationship to one another.[8]

The fact that such marriages are permissible shows that when social considerations make it legitimate, there is no horror of sex relations within the family.

[5]R. Middleton, "Brother-Sister and Father-Daughter Marriage in Ancient Greece" (*American Sociological Review*, Vol. 27, 1962), pp. 603–611.
[6]J. Belo, "A Study of a Balinese Family" (*American Anthropologist*, Vol. 38, 1936), p. 30.
[7]K. G. Izikowitz, *Lamet, Hill Peasants in French Indochina*, pp. 134–135.
[8]E. R. Leach, *Rethinking Anthropology*, p. 14.

The effect of kinship terminology on the scope of the incest tabu More remarkable than the exceptions to the narrow rules of incest prohibition are the arbitrary practices of many primitives in the extension of the scope of relationship terms to include persons of diverse genealogical status in an arbitrarily established social status. American Indian boys and girls who have gone to white schools speak of "my sister" and "my Indian sister." What is the distinction? To us, a sister is a girl born of the same parents as oneself. However, Catholics do stretch the term to include nuns, and members of a sorority extend the term to include one another. When the Indian boy of today makes the distinction between "sister" and "Indian sister," he is trying to make clear that the Indian concept of "sister" is somewhat different from the standard American concept. If the speaker is a Seed Eater Shoshone from Idaho, the term "sister" in its native sense means not only "daughter of my own mother" but also all female cousins through both father and mother. Primitives take their relationship terms quite literally; therefore, a girl called "sister" *is* a sister and must be treated as such in all respects. Sex relations and marriage with all "sisters" are therefore automatically tabued.

This broadening of relationship categories has been aptly called *lumping*.[9] It is the usual characteristic of relationship systems that are identified as *classificatory*. Because most primitive systems are classificatory, many individuals are embraced within the incest prohibitions by the simple fiat of a social system that dubs them "father," "mother," "brother," or "sister," when in biological fact they are no such thing. (See pages 383–384 for a more detailed discussion of this phenomenon.)

The terminological distinction in types of cousins The Shoshones and the Hawaiians, for example, lump all cousins in a single sibling (brother and sister) category. Many other peoples indulge in a curious discrimination that intensi-

[9]R. H. Lowie, "Kinship" (*Encyclopedia of the Social Sciences*, Vol. 3, 1931), pp. 568–572.

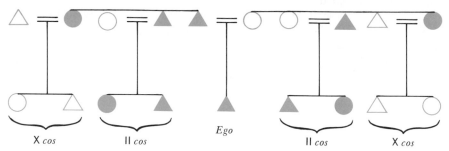

Fig. 22-1 Genealogical separation of cross- and parallel-cousins.

fies the impression of arbitrary disregard of biological reality. A certain type of cousin is classified as brother or sister, but another type of cousin is regarded as not being a kinsman at all. The first type of cousin we call *parallel-cousins* because the parents through whom they are related are of like sex. The other type of cousin we call *cross-cousins,* not because of any temperamental peculiarities, but because the parents through whom they are related are of opposite sex; there is a crossing over from one sex to the other in the genealogy of relationship (Fig. 22-1). In any tribe in which cross-cousins are distinguished from parallel-cousins, cross-cousins are never reckoned as belonging to the same kinship group. In the dogma of the social system, they are not kinsmen. The logic of such a premise produces a biological absurdity, but the biologist protests in vain. To marry a parallel-cousin may be incest, and to marry a parallel-cousin who is a member of one's own clan *is* incest. However, to marry a cross-cousin may be the accepted thing to do; it may even be the required thing to do. Thus, one is forbidden to marry a first cousin of parallel relationship, whereas it is good form to marry a first cousin of cross relationship. Both are equally close in genetic kinship, but the second is no relative at all in culturally *determined* kinship.

The relation of social structure to the incest tabu Anthropologists recognize a well-established law governing the extensions of incest tabus beyond the immediate conjugal family.

The specific identification of the individuals who are brought within the scope of the incest tabu is a function of the forms of kinship organization that prevail in a given society.

One or more types of cousins are tabued in one out of every five cultures.[10] In a notable number of social systems, however, sex relations with cousins who fall outside a person's kinship group are allowed, and marriage with these particular cousins may even be socially encouraged or prescribed. Whether or not a particular kind of relative is tabued depends upon the social structure of the society.

Biological explanations of the incest tabu It has been argued by Westermarck[11] and Morgan,[12] among earlier anthropologists, that primitive man became cognizant of genetic deterioration resulting from close inbreeding. They averred that on this basis, humanity preserved its genetic health by preventing close inbreeding through the establishment of incest prohibitions. This is the popular belief of most people in the United States. The fact is, however, that inbreeding does not necessarily produce physical deterioration. Inbreeding does no more than intensify the phenotypic traits that the inbreeding population possessed at the outset. Recessive traits have a better chance of obtaining somatic realization where inbreeding is marked. If undesirable recessives are in the stock, they may well come to the fore, and deterioration may then result. Nevertheless, it is equally true that inbreeding intensifies the influence of

[10]A. D. Coult and R. W. Habenstein, *Cross Tabulations of Murdock's World Ethnographic Sample,* p. 415.
[11]F. Westermarck, *The History of Human Marriage,* Vol. 2, pp. 218–241.
[12]L. H. Morgan, *Ancient Society,* p. 424.

dominant traits. A stock with desirable dominants becomes stronger. The end result may be good or bad; it all depends on the distribution of traits with respect to dominance and desirability. Among the mountaineers of Kentucky, the inbred populations of some pocketed valleys have been observed to send young men and women of consistently superior mentality to Berea College. The populations of other pocketed valleys in the same area are distinguished for the occurrence of epilepsy. Cleopatra, the last of the Ptolemies and the product of twelve generations of brother-sister marriages, was hardly a specimen of physical degeneration, whatever may be said of her morals.

Functional explanations of the incest tabu If biological factors do not suffice to explain so important a social phenomenon as incest prohibition, it behooves the anthropologist to discover what social factors may be responsible for such rigorous and universal rules. Unfortunately, all explanations of incest prohibitions must forever remain hypotheses, for the insurmountable reason that no observations can be made on any group of people in which there is an absolute absence of rules restricting mating and inbreeding. Nor is it probable that an experimental incestuous society will ever be set up for scientific study. We can therefore do no more than accept as most probable that hypothesis which most reasonably fits the known facts.

There are two types of functional theories in explanation of the incest tabu. One emphasizes principles of social structure and the importance of marital alliances as means of broadening the scope of social integration. The other rests on psychological principles and emphasizes the potentially disruptive effect of sexual competition within the kinship group. The first is usually associated with the name of Sir Edward Tylor; the second received its fullest statement by Malinowski. Both, however, were anticipated by Lord Bolingbroke (1678–1751), who scouted the idea that incest aversion is the expression of an innate moral sense, as was argued by eighteenth-century Scottish moral

philosophers. Bolingbroke baldly stated that far from being instinctive or innate, "the abhorrence of incest, as well as other forms of sexual modesty, is wholly artificial." Rather, he argued, exogamy works "to improve sociability among men, and to extend it as wide as possible, in opposition to that insociability which is so apt to grow up between distinct families and states." Lord Bolingbroke anticipated Malinowski's psychological-functional theory of incest prohibition by holding that an additional effect of the incest tabu and exogamy was to prevent the destruction of the foundations of society. Children who marry their parents, he reasoned, will have less respect for them as the chief magistrates of the family; and what weakens the family weakens the greater commonwealth.[13]

Malinowski's psychological-functional theory of the incest tabu Malinowski posits the proposition that sexual affection is anteceded in the development of the individual by strongly conditioned parental and fraternal affection, based on intimate family associations, which occurs before the maturation of the sex drives. These are the affective emotions that cement the bonds of family and kin and give solidarity to the foundation group of any society—the group of immediate kinsmen. The family is founded in part upon the sexual association of spouses, between whom the sex drive may have legitimate play. But sex is a dangerous element. From its drives arise powerful emotional disturbances of great disruptive potentiality. In preadolescence, the sex drives are unmatured; they are not yet dangerous. On maturation under unrestricted conditions, however, gratification of the sex drives would frequently be sought with those nearest at hand, toward whom one already has affection—the members of one's own household. This would naturally lead to mating between siblings and parents and offspring. The violent emotions engendered by sexual affection would blast and disrupt fam-

[13]For further details, see A. O. Aldridge, "The Meaning of Incest from Hutcheson to Gibbon" (*Ethics*, Vol. 61, 1951), pp. 309–313.

ily unity built upon the earlier established filial-fraternal affections. *A house divided against itself cannot stand; it will become all one thing, or all the other.* Overt sexual rivalry within the functioning kinship group cannot be permitted. The solidarity of the foundation unit of society is protected against its disruptive effects through the universal incest prohibition and its variant extensions.[14] Promiscuity and the family cannot exist side by side; sex relations, except for those of the father and mother, must be barred within it. Thus the preservation of the kinship group, the foundation unit of society, is maintained.

The penalties for incest The punishments, or negative sanctions, for the violation of the incest tabus vary greatly from one society to another, but a definite regional distribution of characteristic reactions is discernible. In Australia, where kinship is a subject of intense interest, most tribes punish incest with death. Plains Indians, on the other hand, do not consider incest either a crime or a sin. They simply look upon it as impossible behavior, so inconceivable that only insane persons indulge in it. Yet the punishment was mild in the few rare cases that have been recorded. A Dakota father of an incestuous brother and sister proclaimed, "Now I am the father of dogs!" Comanche informants cannot remember a single actual case of incest among their people, nor can they stretch their imaginations sufficiently to give a specific statement of what the public reaction would have been had such a case occurred, except to say that the people would have shunned them and called them *keshuant*, crazy.

In ancient Bali, the punishment was symbolic and devastating. The hapless couple were adorned with yokes customarily worn by pigs. They were then made to crawl on all fours to drink from the swill trough of the hogs. After this humiliation, they were banished forever from the village, and their lands were confiscated. No other village would take them in for fear of ill luck and disaster. They were doomed to a fearsome existence alone in the jungle.[15]

The forensic Ashanti of the West African Sudan give vivid reasons for the imposition of the death penalty for incest. According to them, if the sinful crime were to have gone unpunished, ". . . hunters would have ceased to kill the animals in the forest, the crops would have refused to bear fruit, children would have ceased to be born, the *'Samanfo* (spirits of dead ancestors) would have been angered, gods would have been angered, *abusua* (clans) would have ceased to exist, and all would have been chaos (*basa basa*) in the world."[16]

Whether indoctrination of the young is so successful that no specific punishment for incest exists because incest never occurs (as in Comanche society), or whether the punishment is death, in all societies incest or its possibility is viewed with such emotional intensity that we commonly speak of the emotion as "incest horror."

The exogamous effect of the incest tabu Exogamy (Gr. *ex,* outside + *gamos,* marriage) results from the incest prohibitions as they affect marriage. Exogamy may be defined as the *social rule that requires an individual to marry outside a culturally defined group of which he is a member.* The universal conjugal-natal family is always exogamous. Lineages and clans are almost always exogamous. Murdock found that only one in about twenty unilinear societies is nonexogamous in practice.[17] The exogamous unit, it can be readily seen, is always a subdivision of a larger society, for the society must contain multiple groups that intermarry.

Preferential mating

The family is such an integral and important element in social structure that for most societies, culture not only defines whom one may not marry but also goes much further to prescribe certain classes of persons whom one ought to, or must, marry. These limitations constitute the rules of preferential mating. Each type of preferential mating has its own functional reasons for being and must therefore be

[14]B. Malinowski, "Culture," p. 630.
[15]Belo, *op. cit.,* p. 29.

[16]R. S. Rattray, *Ashanti Law and Constitution,* p. 304.
[17]G. P. Murdock, *Social Structure,* p. 48.

explained separately. Furthermore, the operation and effect of any particular type of preferential mating may be different in different cultural contexts. This raises the necessity of special examination of the exact nature of the requirements in each culture if an accurate analysis is to be made. To do this is beyond our powers in an introduction to anthropology, but the main characteristics of preferred marriage forms can be adequately formulated in terms of general principles.

Endogamy Endogamy (Gr. *endo,* within + *gamos,* marriage) is the converse of exogamy. It is the *social rule that requires a person to marry within a culturally defined group of which he is a member.* Endogamy is much less common than exogamy. Unlike exogamy, there is no particular universal type of social group to which the endogamous rule applies. Nevertheless, endogamy is found to some degree in many societies, although the rule is not always explicit and verbalized. It frequently expresses itself as a tendency, without actually being a requirement. It may also apply to any kind of social group. The discussion of incest prohibitions has shown, however, that because of the prevalence of exogamic rules, the application of endogamy to family or clan is most exceptional. Rules of exogamy and endogamy are contradictory and cannot apply simultaneously to the same social group. Endogamous groups must always contain at least two exogamous subgroups within them.

The world's most famous system of endogamy is the caste organization of India, with its two thousand or so castes and subcastes, between which marriage was formally prohibited on the grounds that contact with lower castes is ritually polluting for members of upper castes. The new constitution of India attempts to apply Mahatma Gandhi's principles of democratic equality and brotherhood through the legal abolition of castes and caste rules of endogamy, but as with racial integration in the United States, India still has a long way to go to achieve Gandhi's ideal.[18]

The African Sudan exhibits numerous tribes in which caste endogamy is prevalent. Among the East African Masai, ironworkers form a pariah occupational caste subject to the domination of the warrior caste. Each caste marries from among its own numbers. The neighboring Ruanda (see page 237) are divided into castes made up of the lanky, ruling, pastoral nobility—alien conquerors from the north—the horticultural Hutu, and the lowly Twa hunters. A ruling-caste Tussi may on occasion marry a Hutu woman if his fortunes have sunk so low that he cannot find a mate of his own rank. But neither a Tussi nor a Hutu will stoop to marriage with a Twa.[19] Detailed examination of a number of caste structures in different parts of the world will be found in Chapter 27.

While castes are explicitly endogamous, social classes are prone to exhibit similar tendencies without recourse to explicitly prescribed rules. We are all familar with many subtle manifestations of this. Its roots are in the desire to retain the exclusive and distinctive qualities of self-regarding in-groups. Intermarriage is a leveler and universalizer of culture and race. In-groups who implicitly feel that their values are too dear to leave open to competition raise the barricade of endogamy. Orthodox Jews may not marry Gentiles on pain of banishment from synagogue and family, followed by the performance of mourning rituals for the dead. Stumbling blocks are put in the path of marriage between Catholic and non-Catholic.

Special forms of endogamy that occur among primitives include the village endogamy of the Bella Coola Indians of the Northwest Coast and the spectacular lineage endogamy of the Islamic societies of the Middle East, Pakistan, and India, who practice parallel-cousin marriage.

Parallel-cousin marriage The marriage of a man to his father's brother's daughter is a unique exception to the usual rule of lineage and clan exogamy. It originated among the biblical Semites, who were patrilineal pastoral-

[18]Gallanter, M.: "Law and Caste in Modern India" (*Asian Survey,* 1963), pp. 544–559.

[19]See. R. H. Lowie, *The Origin of the State,* pp. 29–33, for a detailed discussion of Ruanda caste interrelations.

ists; it became firmly fixed among the Arabic Muslims (followers of Islam, the religion founded by Muhammed in the seventh century) and later converts to Islam such as the Muslims of India and Pakistan. As a preferential, and sometimes prescribed, form of marriage, it requires selection of a wife from within the kinship group. Thus in the King James version of the Old Testament (Num. 36:8–9), it is stated: "And every daughter that possesseth an inheritance in any tribe of the children of Israel, shall be wife unto one of the family [patrilineage] of the tribe of her father, that the children of Israel may enjoy every man of the inheritance of his fathers. Neither shall the inheritance remove from one tribe to another tribe."

And so it was that Jacob, when he followed the orders of Isaac, his father, that he not take a wife from among the daughters of Canaan, but rather marry a daughter of his mother's brother, was marrying within his own patrilineage. The fact that Leah and Rachel were cross-cousins (mother's brother's daughters) was incidental and irrelevant. The significant fact can be readily seen if Jacob's and his wives' ancestries are traced back to Terah and his sons, Abraham and Nahor. Abraham is Jacob's father's father, through Isaac. Jacob's wives, Leah and Rachel, are direct patrilineal descendants of Terah through Nahor, Bethuel, and Laban. Jacob married his father's father's brother's son's son's daughters—all members of the same patrilineage derived from Terah (Gen. 11:27).

Among some Arabs, a man has an absolute right to marry his father's brother's daughter; a girl must marry her father's brother's son unless he explicitly waives his preferential rights in favor of another. For this waiver of his right to his parallel-cousin, he can demand and receive a good payment. What is more, if a girl marries another man without her cousin's permission, he may undertake to kill her or her father, his uncle, if the uncle is the one who arranged her illegal marriage. In Pakistan, refusal to assent to such a marriage frequently produces intense conflict between

brothers. Leach is quite right in suggesting that the Islamic legal specification of large rights of inheritance for a daughter runs counter to the patrilineal principle and that parallel-cousin marriage serves to keep her share of the property within the lineage.[20] R. F. Spencer, and Murphy and Kasdan suggest that parallel-cousin marriage is a consequence of a low level of political organization among fighting, pastoral predators, who in the absence of a centralized tribal authority need all their manpower and herds to counter the assaults of competitive local lineages. By marrying within, they intensify the solidarity of the fighting male cadres.[21]

Barth demonstrates that among those Kurds who have developed a feudalistic political structure in addition to the lineage one, parallel-cousin marriage is statistically much less frequent. Where moderately adequate politico-economic institutions of a different type supplement the Arabic lineage structure, parallel-cousin marriage becomes functionally less significant and, in fact, much less frequent in occurrence.[22] Patai's report shows that modernized city Arabs, for whom the lineage increasingly loses its significance, are rapidly reducing the practice of cousin-right to a vestigial custom, as its functional reasons for existence dissolve.

The powerful insistence on parallel-cousin marriage among the Muslims reinforces the principle that the incest tabu is nonbiological in nature. When there are impelling reasons for marriage within the culturally defined kinship group, they may even negate the normal exogamic tendencies.

Cross-cousin marriage Marriage of cross-cousins is by no means a freak occurrence. It is preferred or even required among virtually all

[20]Leach, *op. cit.*, p. 110.
[21]R. F. Spencer, "The Arabian Matriarchate: An Old Controversy" (*Southwestern Journal of Anthropology*, Vol. 8, 1952), pp. 481–490; R. F. Murphy and L. Kasdan, "The Structure of Parallel Cousin Marriage" (*American Anthropologist*, Vol. 61, 1959), pp. 17–29.
[22]F. Barth, "Father's Brother's Daughter Marriage in Kurdistan" (*Southwestern Journal of Anthropology*, Vol. 10, 1954), pp. 164–171.

the tribes of North and Central Australia and a large part of Melanesia. Many people of Asia marry in accordance with the dictates of cross-cousin marriage, as did even those of ancient China. Africans follow the practice (except for the Sudanese). Polynesians, on the other hand, never took to the notion, excepting the natives of Tonga, who have had close contact with the Melanesian Fijis. In aboriginal America, cross-cousin marriage occurs in California and the Great Basin and sporadically among Algonquins of the Northeast.

In Murdock's sample of 565 societies, there are unequivocal reports on cross-cousin marriage for 492 cultures. Of these, 377, or approximately four-fifths, prefer cross-cousin marriage, while one-fifth of the societies prohibit it. Of those who permit marriage to cross-cousins, 313, or 82 per cent, allow marriage of a boy to either his mother's brother's daughter or his father's sister's daughter. They practice bilateral, or symmetrical, cross-cousin marriage. Sixty-four of the cultures in the sample restrict cross-cousin marriage to just one type of cousin. Such preferred marriages are unilateral, or assymmetrical; they are directed toward one side only. Of these, forty-eight cases are matrilateral; i.e., a boy marries his mother's brother's daughter (Fig. 22-2, top). Only sixteen cases are patrilateral; i.e., a boy marries his father's sister's daughter (Fig. 22-2, bottom).

Explanations of cross-cousin marriage Why should cousin marriage, especially cross-cousin marriage, be so frequently preferred? And why should so many peoples prefer the symmetrical to the assymetrical form of cross-cousin marriage? Why are matrilateral cross-cousins preferred as wives three times as often as patrilateral cross-cousins? These questions can be answered only in terms of the specific kinship organization of specific tribes. There are two major theories to account for the phenomenon of cross-cousin marriage. The first is the *Lévi-Strauss theory of marital exchange;* the second is the *Homans-Schneider theory of locus of jural authority.*

THE LÉVI-STRAUSS THEORY The distinguished French anthropologist Claude Lévi-Strauss ar-

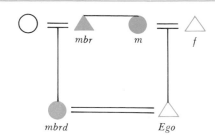

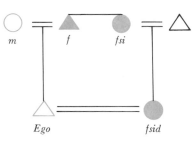

Fig. 22-2 Above, matrilateral cross-cousin marriage in a patrilineal society. A male ego marries his mother's brother's daughter (mbrd), who does not belong to his patrilineage. Below, patrilateral cross-cousin marriage in a matrilineal society. A male ego marries his father's sister's daughter (fsid), who does not belong to his matrilineage.

gues that cross-cousin marriage exists because it promotes social integration through regularization of group interdependence in the exchange of women.[23] He builds on the theory of his predecessor, Emile Durkheim (1858–1917), to the effect that the expansion of human society involves specialization and division of labor; such specialization requires stabilization of interdependence, if the society is not to come apart at the seams. The basic function of exchange and trade is to promote interdependence and social solidarity. Women, holds Lévi-Strauss, are the most highly valued scarce commodity. Therefore, exchange of women is of prime importance in ordering interdependence. In bilateral, or symmetrical, cross-cousin marriage, woman swapping is practiced in all directions; it may tie closely related groups more

[23]C. Lévi-Strauss, *Les structures élémentaires de la parenté.*

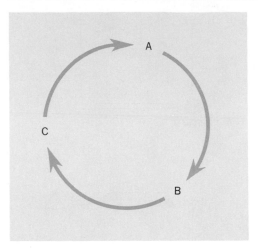

Fig. 22-3   The circulation of women through prescribed matrilateral cross-cousin marriage creates a closed circle of interdependence. Group A gives women to B and receives them from C; B gives to C and receives from A; C gives to A and receives from B. Progeny price, dowry, and giftgiving are means of more direct, complimentary equivalence; so, B receives women from A and gives other items of value to A in exchange.

tightly to one another, but it does not produce a strong integrating principle. Lévi-Strauss demonstrates that matrilateral cross-cousin marriage in a society with matrilineal descent groups results in group A giving its women to group B, which gives its women to group C, which gives its women to group A. The three groups, which constitute a society, are thus bound to one another in a closed circle (Fig. 22-3).[24] This presupposes that matrilateral cross-cousin marriage is prescriptive, or required, rather than merely preferential. Lévi-Strauss argues that matrilateral cross-cousin marriage in matrilineal societies is a "best" way of producing social solidarity.

THE HOMANS-SCHNEIDER THEORY   Since the 1950s, there has been great controversy among specialists in social anthropology over the validity of Lévi-Strauss's theory. The argument is,

however, too technical for consideration in an introductory text. A major alternative theory, however, is based on the fact that mother's-brother's-daughter marriages occur three times as frequently as father's-sister's-daughter marriages and that such marriages show a positive correlation (phi = 0.181) to the existence of patrilineal-descent groups. Homans and Schneider show that in such societies, the father is an authority figure, while the maternal uncle is a kind of older pal, an indulgent sponsor, helper, and adviser to the boy. Providing the boy with a wife (the uncle's daughter) is one expression of this relationship of sentimental identity with the uncle, who is a close kinsman but not a member of the boy's patrilineal kinship group.[25]

Lévi-Strauss's theory is built on the proposition that the needs of social solidarity produce asymmetrical cross-cousin marriage (a structural argument). The theory of Homans and Schneider is built on the proposition that residence, kinship organization, and locus of authority produce psychological effects that may lead to particular types of cross-cousin marriage. The two points of view express the difference between the British-French type of social anthropology and the culture and personality orientation of American anthropology, as they have existed between 1940 and 1965.

Affinal, substitution, or continuation marriage Much more pervasive than the general rules of endogamy are the rules of preferential marriage that bring about exogamous marriages between in-laws, hence called *affinal marriages,* or marriages to relatives through marriage. To identify such marriages as affinal, as is the usual practice of American and English anthropologists, is to emphasize the form of the marriage. The Dutch anthropologists, who have given more weight to the functional aspects of such marriages, call them *substitution* or *continuation marriages,* for their function is to continue the relationship between the two kinship groups of the original marriage partners and to hold

[24]Of course there may be more than three kinship groups in the system.

[25]G. C. Homans and D. M. Schneider, *Marriage, Authority and Final Causes.*

the children of the original marriage within the extended family.

The levirate Marriage of a woman to her brother-in-law, known as the *levirate* (L. *levir*, brother-in-law), is the most popular affinal marriage form among the peoples of the world. Under the simple levirate, the marriage occurs only after the death of the husband, when the widow is inherited by the dead man's brother. In the case of the *junior levirate*, only a younger brother may be the inheritor. This handy practice occurs in all parts of the world among peoples of the most diverse levels of cultural development. The rude Australians made it a rule; the biblical Hebrews approved of it; and the civilized Incas provided for the inheritance of all a man's secondary wives by his younger brother or perhaps by his sons. An Inca first wife never remarried. She was supported by the state, if necessary, with a widow's pension proffered by an effective social-security system.

Whether the young man who finds himself with his brother's widow on his hands likes it or not depends partly on personalities but also on cultural determinants. The Comanche inheritor of a widow was apt to look on this inheritance as a right and a privilege, especially since the widow might not marry another man without that person's obtaining a quitclaim from the heir. And that required a consideration—a horse or two, or perhaps some blankets. In other cases there is no element of choice for the collateral heir. The woman is his, willy-nilly. Her family has a claim on him as much as he has a claim on her. His family also has a voice, as in the case of a Shoshone Indian who in 1933 was forced to divorce the wife of his own choice in order to marry his dead brother's wife. His people wanted to keep the girl in the family, and the laws of Idaho do not permit a man to have two wives.

The purpose of the levirate is not hard to discern. It effects a continuation of the link between the two kinship groups that was established through the original marriage. It is a manifestation of the intergroup character of marriage in that the defunct husband's kin have the privilege and right to prevent the widow from leaving their group. Her obligation is not only to the man she married but also to his kin. Of equal importance, in view of the fact that in primitive society the children usually follow the mother when a home is broken, the children are not lost to the father's group. On the other hand, the claims of the widow's kin upon the group of the defunct husband are maintained in the substitution of a brother. The situation is one of balanced reciprocity.

The sororate As in the levirate, where a living brother takes the place of the dead father in a bereaved household, so in the sororate a sister is substituted for the mother. Therefore, in the sororate a bereaved husband marries his deceased wife's sister. From the woman's angle, a girl marries her dead sister's husband.

The sororate goes hand-in-hand with the levirate; each is the complement of the other. It is observed by virtually every tribe of North America outside of the Pueblo area and is widely distributed throughout the world.

The common mistake of confusing the sororate with *sororal polygyny* should be avoided. Under the true sororate, a man is married to only one sister at a time. Under sororal polygyny, he does not wait for the death of his wife to marry her younger sister; he takes her when she becomes of age.

Extended affinal marriages In a few societies, if a sibling is not directly available within the immediate conjugal-natal family for substitution for a husband or wife and if there is not an available cousin who stands in the brother or sister category, a substitute from an older or younger generation may be taken. This results in such peculiarities as (1) marriage of a man to his wife's brother's daughter, (2) marriage of a woman to her father's sister's husband, and (3) marriage of a woman to her husband's sister's son (see Fig. 22-4). Wife's-brother's-daughter marriage is an extension of the sororate principle to another generation. Such extensions are limited to societies in which the uni-

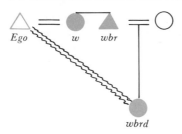

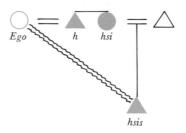

Fig. 22-4   *Left, wife's brother's daughter marriage in a patrilineal system, represents the secondary affinal marriage. Wife and wife's brother's daughter belong to the same lineage. Right, husband's sister's son marriage in a matrilineal system. Husband and husband's sister's son belong to the same lineage.*

lineal principle of descent is strong, and each type of marriage is closely related to the kind of unilinealism that prevails.

Thus, in a patrilineal system, a girl automatically belongs to the same clan as her father's sister (her paternal aunt). She has the same clan identity as her aunt, and her individuality is submerged in the corporate identity. She steps up to represent her unilineal group in the continuation of the marital alliance.

On the other hand, in a matrilineal system, a boy automatically belongs to the same clan as his mother's brother (his maternal uncle). He has the same clan identity as his maternal uncle, and his individuality is submerged in the corporate identity of the maternal kinship group. He steps forward to represent his unilineal group in the continuation of the marital alliance (see Crow Kinship System, pages 388–389).

Marriage with extended affinal relatives is not common; only a small minority of societies find it worth bothering with or necessary to fall back upon. But in a strong unilineal system inclined to generalize the principle of clan identity, such marriages follow logically enough.[26]

Modes of acquiring a wife

We have thus far been concerned with the matter of whom one may or may not marry. The next question is: "How does a man get a wife?"

[26]See L. A. White, "A Problem in Kinship Terminology" (*American Anthropologist,* Vol. 41, 1939), pp. 569–570.

Very few societies leave it to individuals who are to be married to decide for themselves. The near-anarchy of American practice in this respect is most exceptional, although it represents a discernibly increasing trend in many parts of the world, as the acids of "modernity" corrode the old kinship bonds. Most marriages are still either arranged by the families concerned or involve family consent and participation. For this reason, to understand marriage at all, and primitive marriage especially, it is necessary to grasp this basic principle: *marriage constitutes an alliance between two kinship groups in which the couple concerned is merely the most conspicuous link.* Every man learns, sooner or later, that when he marries the "one and only," he marries not only her but all her relatives as well. Brides, of course, have the same experience.

In spite of what aspirant youth may feel about it, marriage is not a concern of the marrying pair alone. Society at large has its stake in the affair and what ensues from it. The families of the principals to a marriage have their very direct interests in its many ramifications.

Thus, of the seven formalized modes of acquiring a wife, only two (marriage by capture and marriage by elopement) do not heavily involve the active participation of the kinship groups of the bride and groom. The seven modes are (1) by progeny price, or bride wealth; (2) by suitor service; (3) by gift exchange; (4) by capture; (5) by inheritance; (6) by elopement; and (7) by adoption.

Progeny price   In the primitive world, the formal exchange of goods of value for the offspring a woman is expected to produce is the normal, or most usual, method of getting a wife. *Progeny price,* was found to prevail in 303 of the 434 tribes that were statistically sampled by the

English anthropologists Hobhouse, Wheeler, and Ginsberg.[27] Murdock's sample reveals the paying of progeny price as occurring in almost half the cultures.[28] It is the common thing in Africa;[29] it is the regular practice among the patrilineal tribes of Indonesia; and it occurs in one form or another in all other parts of the world.

It must not be assumed that the payment of progeny price for a woman means that women are degraded slaves to be sold from the auction block of a marriage mart—a sordid commercial commodity. A commercial element necessarily colors the institution, for, after all, a family with five daughters and one son for whom a bride must be acquired is economically better off than the family with one daughter and five sons to be provided for. But women are not fluid goods in a free market.

Nor does the occurrence of progeny price mean that the position of woman in terms of prestige, privilege, power, and labor is necessarily high or low. It does mean, however, that women as progenitors have value as members of the kinship group. The value of a woman in terms of progeny price is determined by a compound of the social and economic status of the groom's family balanced against that of the bride's family. In some instances, the personal qualities of the bride and groom may also be factors.

The social prestige of a married woman is directly influenced by the amount of the progeny price that has been paid on her account. A twenty-cow wife in East Africa has a definite advantage in any argument with a woman on whose account only ten cows have been given. Among the Yuroks of California, this is so fixed that the social status and wergild of a man are determined absolutely by the progeny price paid for his mother.

Progeny price may be in part compensation

for the loss of the girl by her kinship group, but it is much more an act of compensation to that group for its loss of a legal claim to the children that she will bear. Two facts make this clear. The transference of progeny price is closely correlated with patrilineal-descent systems and residence of the married couple with the groom's kin. Again referring to Murdock's comparative data, we learn that of 217 societies demanding progeny price, all but eighteen are virilocal. Of the eighteen nonvirilocal societies, only six are uxorilocal.[30] Clearly, the loss of the woman's children from the residential seat of her kin is a factor that must be balanced by reciprocal payment of other items of value. But beyond this, there is the circumstance that virilocal residence tends strongly to generate patrilineality. Although the wife does not become a member of her husband's unilineal group, her children do. In patrilineal societies, therefore, each marriage of a woman means that her lineage suffers a loss of all the progeny that may be born through her. For this sacrifice, they expect and receive redress. Patrilineal kinship groups and progeny price show a high phi correlation at 0.412, while matrilineal kinship groups and progeny price show a negative correlation of −0.112.

That it is in exchange for a quitclaim, so to speak, on posterity rather than for the bride herself that the progeny price is demanded may be seen more clearly in the fact that an implicit warranty of the fertility of the bride is part of the transaction. It is therefore a common expectancy among Africans that the bride's family must substitute a younger sister without charge if no issue is forthcoming from the first daughter for whom they have received progeny price. As an alternative, the sum of the progeny price must be refunded. This is often difficult, however, because the capital received in payment for the daughter may already have been invested in the purchase of a wife for a son. Thus, it has been reported (for the Thonga, for instance) that the family may be required to

[27]L. T. Hobhouse, G. C. Wheeler, and M. Ginsberg, *The Material Culture and Social Institutions of the Simpler Peoples.*
[28]In 248 out of 555 cultures. A. D. Coult and R. W. Habenstein, *Cross Tabulations of Murdock's World Ethnographic Sample*, p. 248.
[29]The Native Administration Act of 1927, Union of South Africa, in recognition of the importance of progeny price in native society, expressly forbade any court from setting aside *Lobola* or *bogadi* as "repugnant to natural law." J. Lewin, *Studies in African Native Law*, p. 57.

[30]Coult and Habenstein, *op. cit.*, p. 378. The phi for progeny price/virilocality is 0.391; for progeny price/uxorilocality, it is 0.192, and for avunculocality, 0.055.

surrender their son's wife to their son-in-law in lieu of their barren daughter. These same requirements hold if the married daughter deserts her husband, who has paid for her.

Establishment of jural rights   Linton's report on the Vezo Sakalava of Madagascar shows to what extent progeny price is actually the establishment of a jural, or a legally effective, right to children among these people. In the case of divorce, neither a refund of the cattle paid nor the substitution of another woman is socially permissible. The divorced wife may remarry, but only with her former husband's permission. This will be forthcoming upon agreement by the wife and her new husband-to-be that the first children born to them (up to the limit of three) will be deeded over to the first husband, who is the one who paid the progeny price to her family. The woman nurses and keeps the children until weaning, whereupon they are turned over to her first husband and become his legal heirs without the formality of adoption.[31] All this illustrates another basic principle to be referred to in more detail later on: *among primitives, jural fatherhood is generally of more significance than biological fatherhood.* A nice Sakalava refinement is that although legally a divorced husband may demand a refund, good form does not countenance it. That would be putting material values above human values. Such a man would put cattle above children.

Finally, among the Bavenda of South Africa and other tribes, if the progeny price is paid in installments, the children do not pass to the husband's kinship group until the sum is paid in full.

An interesting twist to progeny price as a means of obtaining offspring is found among the Dahomeans of West Africa. Here a married woman may arrange for a second wife for her husband as a means of providing him with children. These children call their sire's first wife

"father" because she, after all, is the one who paid for them.[32] This may seem to be carrying the principle of sociological fatherhood a bit far, but who can deny that it is logical? In one form or another, this practice is not uncommon among the patrilineal tribes of Africa.

Progeny price as a social institution cannot be comprehended unless it is viewed also in terms of its functional effects in cementing the links in the web of kinship that makes possible the expansion of the scope of society. Social groups are often in opposition to one another, disputing, quarreling, even feuding and fighting. Intermarriage imposes a check on the disruptive tendencies of intergroup conflict. Marriage alone tends to exert a tranquilizing effect in this direction, but it takes more than marriage in and of itself adequately to achieve cohesion. Progeny price involves a number of kinsmen in a network of economic obligations and expectancies. Many more than just the husband, on the one side, and the bride's parents, on the other, are drawn into the activity.

Distribution of marriage cattle among the Nuer   To illustrate the complex and highly ritualized socioeconomic aspects of progeny price, we may turn to the Nuer, a tribe of cattle raisers living on the upper reaches of the White Nile. Here, each marriage ideally calls for the transfer of forty head of cattle. Of these, twenty go to members of the bride's primary composite family, ten to her father's primary composite family, and ten to that of her mother. The distribution is as follows (see Fig. 22-5):

1. *Primary family of the bride:* To the bride's father (*a*), eight head, specified as three cows and their calves and two oxen; to her brother born of another mother (*b*), two cows; to her brother born of the same mother (*c*), two oxen, three cows, and a cow and its calf (seven head); to her mother (*d*), a cow and its calf and a heifer.

2. *Siblings of the bride's father:* To the bride's

---

[31]R. Linton, "The Tanala" (*Field Museum of Natural History, Anthropological Series*, Vol. 22, 1933). For numerous like examples from Africa, see M. D. W. Jeffrys, "Lobola Is Child-price" (*African Studies*, Vol. 10, 1951), pp. 145–184.

[32]M. J. Herskovits, "A Note on 'Woman Marriage' in Dahomey" (*Africa*, Vol. 10, 1937), pp. 335–341. The term "father," incidentally, in its more exact meaning, should be understood as "person who paid the progeny price."

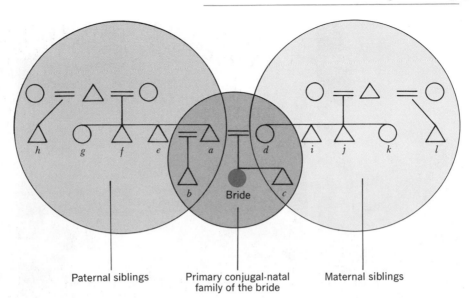

Paternal siblings   Primary conjugal-natal   Maternal siblings
                         family of the bride

Fig. 22-5   Identification of relatives in Nuer progeny price distribution.

father's elder brother by the same mother (*e*), a cow and its calf, a calf, and an ox (four head); to the bride's father's younger brother by the same mother (*f*), a cow and an ox; to the bride's father's sister (*g*), one heifer; to the bride's father's brother by a different mother (*h*), a cow and its calf and an ox.

3. *Siblings of the bride's mother:* To the bride's mother's elder brother by the same mother (*i*), a cow and its calf, a cow, and an ox; to the bride's mother's younger brother by the same mother (*j*), a cow and its calf; to the bride's mother's sister (*k*), one heifer; to a brother of the bride's mother through a different mother (*l*), a cow and its calf and an ox.[33]

In addition to these specific rights to cattle, every patrilineal relative of the bride, even though the relationship be so remote as that of descent from a common ancestor six or seven generations back, may claim a small gift from the groom's kinsmen. Special symbolic gifts of cattle may be called for in the name of ancestral spirits of the bride, of her "father's best friend, of an age classmate of her father, of her father's fireplace, and to the priest who per-

forms magic rituals for enhancement of the bride's fecundity."

All this should make it very clear how much more than just a commercial transaction the transfer of progeny price is.

Suitor service   A cheap, but not easy, way to obtain a wife and rights to her children is to work for them. Jacob put in seven years of labor to win the hand of Rachel, plus seven for Leah, who was not part of his bargain. Among the Siberian Chukchi, Koryak, and Yukaghir tribes, service for the bride is the regular practice; it seems to have replaced progeny price, which was the earlier form for acquisition of a wife.

Scattered tribes in all parts of the world have been found to require service in the bride's household as the price the groom must pay (77 out of 565 cultures).[34] Many of these tribes allow no alternative, but in others, suitor service is simply a substitute for payment of the progeny price, similar to the arrangement by which a vagrant washes dishes to pay for his meal.

The obligation of a son-in-law to work for his

[33] These figures represent the ideal norm among the Eastern Nuer as reported by Evans-Pritchard, "Nuer Bride-wealth" (*Africa*, Vol. 16, 1946), p. 4. In the real culture, they vary by circumstance and district within the tribe. See P. P. Howell, *A Manual of Nuer Law*, pp. 101–124.

[34] Coult and Habenstein, *op. cit.*, p. 424.

Fig. 22-6 *Marriage is an incorporation rite among
the Karamojong, Kenya, in East Africa. The groom
presents at least one animal—a cow, sheep, goat, or
donkey—to each of the bride's close relatives. In
return, he receives their pledge of future support for
himself and the family he is about to found. After the
bartering, the bride is dragged, with mock
protestations, from the hut where she has been hiding
(top left). At the groom's village, the cowives and
sisters-in-law of the bride each present a neckwire to
the bride, then smear her with milk fat (top right).
The bride is hazed by the women, including the girls
of her husband's group (bottom left). She carries a
ridiculously small pot which she must steady on her
head as if she were a clumsy novice who cannot carry
a pot as a proper wife should. To emphasize her low*

wife's parents may be an enduring responsibility. Although the Comanche Indians do not require outright suitor service, a son-in-law is expected to send a good share of the game he slays to the tipi of his mother-in-law. This is why parents want their daughter to marry a good hunter. A son-in-law does not have to do this, but he is a good son-in-law if he does and a poor one if he does not. His reward will be a younger daughter as his second wife. But no meat, no second daughter.

Gift exchange In cultures in which descent is not exclusively vested in any particular line of kinsman (i.e., bilateral descent), there is little likelihood of payment of progeny price (phi = −0.349). Equivalent exchanges of gifts between the families are an alternative possibility.

When gift exchanges are customarily equal, no one comes out ahead. This is the case with the Cheyenne Indians. A boy who has set his heart on a particular girl talks it over with his family. If they think the choice is a good one, after taking into consideration not only the qualities of the girl but also the character of her family, they muster their nicest transferable possessions to place at the disposal of the young swain. These are carefully loaded on a fine horse. They then call upon a respected old woman to lead the horse to the tipi of the girl's elder brother. There she stakes it out for all the camp to see, while she enters the lodge to press the suit of her protégé. The elder brother calls in his cousins for a family conclave. If they decide that the proposal is acceptable, they unload the horse and distribute the gifts among themselves, the brother taking the horse. All

status as the newest female member of her affinal group, the pot is repeatedly knocked from her head with sticks. A mock attack with switches upon the bride and her female attendants by the boys of the groom's village completes the ritualistic wedding pattern (bottom right). (Rada and Neville Dyson-Hudson, Natural History.*)*

then disperse to their separate lodges to rustle up what each will offer as a return gift. Each is expected to bring back in the next day or two something equal in value to what he has received. In the meantime, the bride is made beautiful, and when all is ready, she is mounted on a good horse, the presents are loaded on another, and the old woman is called upon to lead the bride and the gift horse back to the groom's tipi. There she is received by all his family, and her accompanying gifts are distributed among them in accordance with what they gave. So far as economic value goes, they are exactly where they were before.

Perhaps we can understand the social function of such activity better if we reflect on our own elaborate gift exchanges at Christmastime. The amount of energy, trouble, and effort that goes into acquiring and distributing suitable gifts is immense, and the results are frequently discouraging. As often as not, we end up with a collection of items we would just as soon do without. Nevertheless, in the exchange we reaffirm and bind anew the friendships and relationships we value or find desirable.

If may come as a shock to those of us who enter into the elaborate symbolic gift exchanges among friends and kinsmen, institutionalized in our culture, to learn that equivalent exchange of gifts at marriage is actually very rare. Only 12 of 565 cultures employ it. The fact that it is negatively correlated with patrilineal (phi = −0.014) and matrilineal (phi = −0.007) societies reinforces the point that progeny price is compensation for loss of jural rights over the children who are to be forthcoming from a marriage. (Because gift exchange is so infrequent, however, the phi correlations given here have low levels of statistical significance.)

Capture Novelists and romanticists tell of the days when the cave man was supposed to beat his beloved into insensibility with a knobby club and then drag her by her flowing hair to his lair, where she forthwith became his loving wife. This is the wishful notion of the ''get 'em young, treat 'em rough, and tell 'em nothing'' school. When anthropology was young, serious consideration was given to this fantasy as the earliest method of getting a wife. Indeed, marriage by capture was the first premise underlying the theory of social evolution put forth by the Scottish anthropologist J. F. McLennan 100 years ago.[35] Suitors' trials and sham battles at marriage were thought to be symbolic survivals of the scuffles that accompanied the abduction of the feminine prize.

Mock capture is a real and not uncommon practice. When a young Bushman and his bride are to be married, the folk gather from all around to join in the wedding feast. In the midst of the meal, the groom seizes the bride. This is the signal for all her relatives to grab their dibbles and set to beating him. A minor battle royal takes place among the guests while the groom receives his drubbing. If he can keep his hold on the girl, he succeeds in his marriage. If he lets go under the hail of blows, he loses her.[36]

The African Bahima subject the bride to a tug of war between her clan and the groom's, which always wins. When the final pull is given in the groom's favor, the bride is hustled to a cowhide and lifted from the ground by the groom's cohorts, who rush off with her, chased by friends and relatives.[37]

Of course, the hilarious horseplay that climaxes our own weddings and the escape of the bride and groom in a cloud of exhaust smoke (provided a spark plug has not been removed) are cut of the same cloth. If this is not a survival of bride capture, what then is it? Modern anthropology prefers a functional to a pseudo-historical explanation. More properly, it is to be understood as a symbolic expression of latent and repressed hostilities of the two marrying families. True, they are to be allied in marriage, but alliance is possible only where differences exist. Alliance always involves a measure of antagonistic cooperation. Common interests must dominate any alliance, or it will not be

forged. Yet the antagonisms are felt, unconsciously or otherwise. The bride-giving family resents the successful intrusion of the suitor, and they are given the ritual opportunity of letting him know it in a harmless way. In this way, the deep emotions of resentment are drawn off. Likewise, any feeling that the swain is unworthy of the precious daughter may be dispelled by forcing him to prove his worth.

All this is not to contend that marriage by capture does not exist. It does. But we must realize that it could never have been *the* prevailing technique in any supposed stage of human history. Rather, it is a supplementary way of getting a wife. Its advantage is that it is cheap and adventuresome, if risky. On the other hand, its disadvantages, aside from risk, are heavy. Since marriage is an alliance between kinship groups, capturing a wife brings none of the advantages that are to be derived from such an alliance. There are no wife's relatives to back a man up or contribute their share of property. The man who captures his wives will therefore be at a disadvantage, compared with the man who has got his by reciprocal means. His children will not have the advantages and status that his wife's family might bestow, and if his sole wife is from an alien tribe, his children will not be raised in the pure tradition of his own culture.

Plains Indian warriors, like the men of many another primitive tribe, did capture and mate with alien women. Many are the nations who have considered women the legitimate prize of war. However, unless a man is poorly off, he first marries a girl of his own tribe in the regular manner. His captured wives are secondary additions to his household: his concubines and his wife's household drudges. Here, as elsewhere, the position of the captive woman may be closer to that of a slave than of a true wife.

Again and again, we find that the abduction of women is the cause of bitter wars and annihilations. Helen of Troy may be the most famous such *bella causus belli*, but she was neither the first nor the last among her sex.

[35] J. F. McLennan, *Primitive Marriage.*
[36] G. W. Stow, *The Native Races of South Africa,* p. 96.
[37] J. Roscoe, *The Northern Bantu,* Vol. 2, p. 256.

Inheritance   Inheritance of widows through the operation of the levirate and filial inheritance is of course of extreme importance as a form of marriage. However, nothing further need be added here to what we have already said on this subject except to note that the Palvic and Bura tribes of northern Nigeria allow a man to inherit his grandfather's wives.

Filial inheritance Attention has already been called to the Inca practice of permitting a brother or a son to inherit the secondary wives of a dead man. Inheritance of the wives of his father, none of whom were his uterine mother, is also known to have been practiced by the Caribs of South America and by a number of African tribes. Filial inheritance is obviously possible only where there is polygamous marriage. It also serves to keep the women in the family.

Elopement Elopement is a safety valve. It is one of those saving cultural forms whose function is to provide an acceptable byroad for escape from the dictates of formal custom. Marriage, as we have seen, is never left open to the untrammeled choice of the marrying individuals. There are incest and exogamic prohibitions; there are the limitations of preferential mating; and there are the personal prejudices of family members to be considered. On the other hand, there is love. Few people are so given to romantic love as Americans. In our individualistic sentimentalism, we exalt the ideal of marriage based on love—that mysterious psychophysiological reaction. Although many primitive cultures do not allow very much weight to love in marriage (indeed, many seem to ignore it entirely), the fact is that all primitives have their amorous likes and aversions too.

From the evidence, it would appear that elopements take place in every known society. When familial or social disapproval blocks a fervently desired marriage, or when a planned marriage with a distasteful partner is about to be forced on the unwilling one, elopement is a way out. The tribes which require that elders and relatives seek the consent of marriageable youths to the arrangements they plan for them are surely a minority among mankind.

This makes a general human necessity of the path of elopement.

Of course, the existence of a formal rule does not mean that it will always be insisted upon. Cheyenne men hold the legal right to dispose of their sisters as they wish. But as Calf Woman put it, "Kindhearted brothers always found out how their sisters felt about it before they promised them to any man."

It is difficult to formulate a generalization concerning the status of elopement marriages. In the case of the Cheyennes, the elopement would ultimately be recognized as a marriage and be validated by gift exchanges only if the pair ran off before the girl had actually been engaged by her brother to another man. It was a different matter if the promise had already been made. In several Cheyenne cases, brothers committed suicide when their sisters eloped after they had been promised to someone else.[38]

In parts of the Pacific area, the tendency to *cultural orthogenesis* has resulted in elopement becoming the *regular* way of getting married. This is the situation in a number of Australian tribes. According to the reports of Howitt,[39] elopement is the *reductio ad absurdum* of overdeveloped marriage rules among the Kurnai tribe. Broad rules of exogamy combine with narrow rules of localized mating (i.e., the mate must be taken from a specific band) to narrow strictly the field of legitimate choice. Old men dominate the society and have the first choice of young girls. Matters are so carefully controlled that a boy can scarcely find a girl whom he is permitted to marry. Fortunately for the Kurnai, they make "pretend rules" of these principles. Most marriages of young couples are by elopement, and customarily medicine men are expected to help them escape. What then? The righteous citizenry (most of whom married in just this way) are terrible in their anger. A posse of vigilantes sets forth to do social justice. The couple flees to a traditional asylum. If they are overtaken, they are cruelly

[38] K. N. Llewellyn and E. A. Hoebel, *The Cheyenne Way*, chap. 9.
[39] A. W. Howitt, *The Native Tribes of South-east Australia*, pp. 273ff.

wounded and may be killed. Once at the place of asylum, however, they are safe. They stay there until a baby is born. Then they may return home to face a softer music, for they will merely be given a beating and then be accepted as legitimately married.

Adoption In Indonesia and modern Japan, a man may obtain a wife by being adopted into her family.[40] It is a device by which a patrilineally organized family may maintain its line when there are no sons. By legal fiction, the son-in-law thus becomes a "son" in his wife's family, and his children belong to her family and not his. A peculiar aspect of this device is that technically the groom's bride becomes his own "sister." It is necessary that the people close their eyes to this bit of logic, for that, of course, would be incest. Convenience masters logic, and the husband is a "son" of his father-in-law for purposes of reckoning descent.

Pseudo marriage

Forms of pseudo marriage occur occasionally. Among them are the special practices of the Kwakiutl and the Nuer. In the case of the Kwakiutl the inheritance of chiefly prerogatives passes from a titled man to his grandson through his son-in-law, the grandson's father. It is not possible for the titles to pass to succeeding generations through the chief's sons directly. If there are no daughters, such inheritance could be blocked for lack of a son-in-law. Boas writes:

In such a case a man who desires to acquire the use of a crest and the other privileges connected with the name performs a sham marriage with the son of the bearer of the name. The ceremony is performed in the same manner as a real marriage. In case the bearer of the name has no children at all, a sham marriage with a part of his body is performed, with his right or left side, a leg or an arm, and the privileges are conveyed in the same manner as in the case of a real marriage.[41]

[40]B. ter Haar, *Adat Law in Indonesia*, pp. 175–176; J. F. Embree, *The Japanese Nation*, p. 162.
[41]F. Boas, *Social Organization and Secret Societies of the Kwakiutl Indians* (United States National Museum, Report, 1895), p. 359.

The son-in-law acquires the titles and then begets children by a second wife. These children are able to inherit from their jural grandfather.

We have already seen how strong the ties of kinship are among the Nuer, as expressed in progeny-price exchanges. So important is the maintenance of lineage inheritance that the Nuers often rely on what they call *ghost marriage* to give offspring to a male, man or boy, who has died without begetting heirs. For it is necessary to "keep green" the name of a man whose position in the lineage structure is important. In such an instance, one of his "brothers" (from a kinship status that is overstocked or less important) marries a woman on behalf of the dead man or, as they say, "to the name of his brother." This man lives with the woman as in any ordinary conjugal family except that *he* is not married to her. The children that he begets take their place in the lineage as the offspring of their ghost father; they inherit accordingly and receive and give progeny price and wergild in like manner.[42]

The Nuer also have a form of "wife marriage" that differs from that already noted for the Dahomeans. Among the Nuer, a woman who is beyond childbearing age may sometimes use the cattle that belonged to her dead husband to set up a marriage between a man and woman in the name of her husband and herself. The children of such a marriage then belong to her deceased husband and herself, and they inherit accordingly.

In another Nuer variant, an old woman whose lineage is about to die out because she has no living paternal relatives may, if she has the requisite cattle for the progeny price, marry a woman to the name of a dead man of her lineage. Then she invites some unrelated male to have intercourse with the "ghost bride," thus legally establishing a line of heirs.

[42]Compare the ancient Hebrew practice spelled out in the Old Testament: "If brethen dwell together, and one of them die, and have no son, the wife of the dead shall not be married without [the lineage] unto a stranger: her husband's brother shall go in unto her, and take her to him as a wife, and perform the duty of a husband's brother unto her. And it shall be, that the first-born that she beareth shall succeed in the name of his brother that is dead, that his name be not blotted out of Israel" (Deut. 25:5–6).

Pushing the use of fiction to its ultimate, the Nuer give a barren woman the status of a male. After all, has she not demonstrated that she is lacking in the essential attribute of the female? In exceptional cases, then, a wife may be married to her name. That is, a marriage between a man and woman is arranged in which the *man* is the legal substitute for the barren woman in question. The children belong to her name, which means, because she is accorded the status of a male, that they take their patrilineal descent from her, so closing a link in the patrilineal lineage.[43]

Professor Paul Bohannan prefers that these "pseudo marriages" not be viewed as marriages at all, since in some instances no man gets a woman out of it. This is true of the Kwakiutl case and of several of the Nuer practices that emphasize the importance of passing jural and property rights from one generation to another through the production of jural offspring. In these situations, the arrangement is treated as if it were a marriage, and the legal consequences of a marriage flow from it.[44]

Divorce and the dissolution of marriage

In spite of the desire of kinsmen to retain the marriage link, primitive marriages are brittle things. Romance and individual desire may not play so great a role in determining the choice of a first partner as they do with us, but they are permitted more sway in the shifting of mates after marriage. Only a small proportion of marriages among primitives are for life.

Hobhouse, Wheeler, and Ginsberg found in their study that of 271 tribes, only 4 per cent forbid divorce; 24 per cent allow it for specific causes; 72 per cent permit it on the basis of mutual consent based on incompatibility or whim.[45] The sample may not be statistically perfect. Nevertheless, the results just quoted are probably not too far from accurate fact.

Aside from the economic arrangements that may have to be untangled where a high progeny price was paid or a rich dowry given, divorce does not entail such difficulties among the primitives as it does in Western society. The first reason rests in the fact that although religious ritual may enter into the marriage ceremonies, marriage is hardly a religious affair. In addition, the problem of the care and disposition of the children is more easily handled. Ordinarily, they go with the mother. It has already been noted that sociological fatherhood is more significant to primitive man than biological paternity.

There is little evidence on record to indicate that when the primitive mother remarries, the emotional transition for the children is difficult. If the mother does not remarry right away, it is easy for her and her brood to settle among her relatives, for the tribal community is small and she has not been far from her kin at any time. If she is a captive from an alien tribe, she probably remarries without delay. Unmarried adult women are unthinkable to most primitives.

The prevalence of wife stealing is another important unsettling factor. In societies in which sexual competition among the men is a means of attaining social status, no home is truly safe. Eskimos may cooperate economically, but they engage in violent competition for women. To steal another's wife and get away with it proves the abductor a better man than the loser. The risk is great, however, because the husband, if half a man, will attempt to murder the absconder. A would-be wife taker often anticipates this by killing the husband first and marrying the widow afterward.

In the 1920s, Knud Rasmussen visited a village of Musk Ox Eskimos in Canada. He found that every adult male in the community had been involved in a murder centering about wife stealing.[46]

Special practices, such as the licensed wife stealing of the Crow Indians, may also break up the family. This is a phase of competition between two rival military associations, the Foxes and the Knobby Sticks. Each spring one or another of the fraternities is privileged to

[43]Howell, *op. cit.*, pp. 74–75.

[44]See P. Bohannan, *Social Anthropology*, p. 77.

[45]L. T. Hobhouse, G. C. Wheeler, and M. Ginsberg, *The Material Culture and Social Institutions of the Simpler Peoples*, chap. 3.

[46]K. Rasmussen, *Across Arctic America*, p. 250.

capture any wife of a member of the other fraternity, provided she has had premarital sexual relations with the captor. The husband may not resist the abduction or take his wife back. The triumph of the kidnaping fraternity is supreme.

Cheyennes and other Plains tribesmen considered it a great feat ceremonially to throw away wives at a special dance. The Cheyenne warrior tossed a stick among the male spectators, and whoever was struck by it had to marry his wife, if only for a day.

Until recently, anthropologists were of the opinion that men were allowed more leeway than women in the matter of divorce. However, a cross-cultural survey by Murdock invalidates this conclusion. Among forty objectively-selected cultures from all parts of the world, it was impossible in three-fourths of the sample for Murdock to detect any substantial difference in the rights of men and women to terminate an unsatisfactory marriage. Six cultures, it is true, stack the cards in favor of the men. But on the other hand, four cultures allow superior privileges to the women as regards divorce. Insofar as the right to get divorced is concerned, Murdock concludes that "the sterotype of the oppressed aboriginal woman proved to be a complete myth."[47] Matrilineal descent, plus resident in the locality of the wife's kin, strengthens the hand of the woman. Among the highly matrilineal Hopi and Zuñi, where women own the houses, a woman can divorce her husband simply by setting his gear outside the door. Any man who comes home and sees his pile of belongings outside the door knows just what it means. It is time to go home to mother.

The causes of divorce and the grounds for it may be two quite different things. Yet it may be illuminating to close this chapter with a listing of what the Ifugao of Luzon consider grounds for divorce:

1. A bad omen of the bile sac of the sacri-

ficial animal at any one of the four feasts of the marriage ritual

2. A bad omen of the bile sac at any of the three principal rice feasts of either family during the first year after the completion of the marriage rituals

3. Barrenness

4. Continual dying of offspring

5. Permanent sexual disability

6. Unwillingness to perform the sexual act

7. Neglect in time of sickness, "failure to cherish"

8. Insulting language by an in-law

9. Reduction of the area of fields agreed on in the marriage contract

10. Selling of a rice field for insufficient reason and without consent of the other spouse

11. Continued refusal of a father-in-law to deliver the fields called for in the marriage contract when the couple reaches a reasonable age

12. Incurring of unreasonable debts

SUMMARY

The stabilization of sex relations is one of the most basic imperatives in the formation of cultures. Man is endowed with strong sex drives and is not instinctively monogamous. Because infancy is prolonged through so many years among human beings, the successful survival of the group requires that adult males and females organize in cooperative groups to tend and train the dependent young. Marriage is designed to effect this end.

Most primitive social systems do not punish premarital sexual activity, although there are special inhibitions in some instances. The incest tabu, a prohibition of mating among relatives who belong to the socially effective kinship group, is universal. Exogamy is merely the positive aspect of this negative rule. All cultures also include norms of preferential mating. Marriages with in-laws are means of reinforcing the marital alliance between two kinship groups or of continuing it, if a spouse should die; such affinal marriages find expression in the levirate, the sororate, wife's-brother's-

[47]G. P. Murdock, "Family Stability in Non-European Cultures" (*The Annals of the American Academy of Political and Social Science,* Vol. 272, 1948), pp. 195–201.

daughter, and husband's-sister's-son marriages. Cross-cousin preferred marriages unite closely related relatives who are not members of the same kinship group. Father's-brother's-daughter marriages among the Muslims unite members of the same patrilineage in an exceptional effort to maintain the strength of the fighting lineage in a highly segmented type of society and to keep property within the patrilineage.

No human society leaves the search for sexual mates to sheer whim or chance. Each lays down definite rules identifying the forbidden and the preferred mates.

In most societies, marriage is an alliance between kinship groups; alliances are usually formalized by symbolic acts.

The seven major ways of acquiring a wife are (1) by progeny price, or bride wealth; (2) by suitor service; (3) by gift exchange; (4) by capture; (5) by inheritance; (6) by elopement; and (7) by adoption.

Pseudo marriage is a legal fiction whereby lines of property transmission are kept open by providing jural descendants, using one device or another.

Divorce is permitted in almost all human societies. Thus, its existence is a recognition of the fact that although marriage is an arrangement between two groups of kinsmen, it hangs on the ability of spouses to live together as a working team.

SELECTED READINGS

Evans-Pritchard, E. E.: *Kinship and Marriage among the Nuer* (1951). An authoritative study based upon detailed knowledge of a tribe of cattle raisers in the African Sudan.

Lowie, R. H.: *Primitive Society* (1920), chap. 2, "Marriage." Concise and comprehensive.

Murdock, G. P.: *Social Structure* (1949), chaps. 7 and 11, "Determinants of Kinship Terminology" and "Social Law of Sexual Choice." Correlates marriage forms with other aspects of social organization. The last chapter offers a comprehensive theory of selective mating.

Needham, R.: *Structure and Sentiment* (1962). The clash of theories, pro and contra Lévi-Strauss, pushed to the extreme.

Radcliffe-Brown, A. R., and D. Forde (eds.): *African Systems of Kinship and Marriage* (1950). Synoptic analyses of nine African marriage and kinship systems.

Schapera, I.: *Married Life in a South African Tribe* (1950). Old ways and new in the contemporary setting of South Africa.

ter Haar, B.: *Adat Law in Indonesia* (1948), chap. 9, "Marriage Law." Gives a straightforward exposition of basic marriage forms as they occur in Indonesia.

Westermarck, E.: *The History of Human Marriage* (1925). Although the theoretical system of this work has been long outdated, it contains a wealth of very useful descriptive material on marriage practices around the world.

The family

chapter 23

Marriage establishes the family, a group consisting of mated spouses and their offspring. It defines a set of statuses and related roles and expectancies governing the relations of the nuclear group as spouses, parents, offspring, and siblings. It defines their statuses and roles in relation to wider groups of kinsmen and to the wider world of nonkinsmen. Marriage, it will be remembered from the previous chapter, is the institution; the family is the group, or body of personnel, whose actions are directed toward fulfilling the aims of the institution.

Functions of the family

M. J. Levy and L. A. Fallers suggest that the functions of the family may be grouped in four categories: (1) sexual, (2) reproductive, (3) economic, and (4) educational.[1] More explicitly, the functions of the family may be stated as follows: (1) The institutionalization of mating and the channeling of sexual outlets, thus establishing a legal father for a woman's children and a legal mother for a man's children; each acquires a "monopoly" in the sexuality of the other. (2) The nurture and basic enculturation of the young in an atmosphere of intimacy, preparing them to accept the statuses that will come to them as the jural heirs of their established parents and kinsmen. (3) The organization of a complementary division of labor

[1]M. J. Levy and L. A. Fallers, "The Family: Some Comparative Considerations" (*American Anthropologist*, Vol. 61, 1959), pp. 647–651.

between spouses, allocating to each certain rights in the labor of the other and in such goods or property as they may acquire through their individual or joint efforts. (4) The linkage of each spouse and the offspring within the wider network of kinsmen: the establishment of relationships of descent and affinity.[2] These functions are universally performed by the family as a social unit. Other social arrangements may also exist wherein these functions are performed, but they are always ancillary to the family. And above all, they are not universal, whereas the family is (see the discussion of the matrilateral groups, pages 366–367).

In many societies, the sex drive may be legitimately satisfied prior to marriage; in such cases, there would be no reason for the individual to take on the responsibilities of marriage if sex gratification alone were a function of the family.

Care of the infant and childhood generation is the matter of major concern. The rather casual interest of primitive societies in the question of actual biological fatherhood has already been sufficiently emphasized. But that some man or group of men must be tagged with the responsibility of performing the adult male activities necessary to keeping the young ones alive, growing, and learning is universally recognized as of the utmost importance. There must be jural fatherhood to regularize transference of statuses from one generation to the next. In meeting the requirements of infant care and child development, the sex differences of male and female are such that a cooperative division of labor makes for greater efficiency and skill in the work that is to be done. Childbearing obviously must be done by women. Nursing ties women down, while men have greater freedom of movement. Mobility, combined with greater strength, inevitably allows men to become more efficient hunters. Many skills can be performed equally well by either sex, but inasmuch as practice makes perfect, each sex is more likely to develop high skills

if it concentrates on certain tasks and relies on the opposite sex to do likewise with certain others; so the spouses and the children all harvest greater benefits from such an arrangement.

The basic functions of the family may be performed with varying degrees of effectiveness from culture to culture, and the details of the ways in which families within different culture systems carry out these functions produce the remarkably different individual personalities of children and adults, as was indicated in Chapter 4. At this juncture, the most relevant fact is that evidently no substitute can serve the functions of child development as well as the family. Those anthropologists who have paid special attention to the relations of culture to personality formation by means of direct observation of primitive societies agree that anthropological data give universal significance to the conclusions drawn from recent studies of children in institutions. Margaret Mead sums it up:

It has been . . . effectively demonstrated that children do not thrive, in spite of good physical care, if kept as young infants in impersonal institutions, and that separation from the mother—especially at certain periods—has serious deleterious effects on the child. Retardation, failure to learn to talk, apathy, regression, and death all appear as accompaniments to institutionalization when no mother surrogate is provided.[3]

Substitute, or surrogate, mothers may, if the relationship is personal and within the intimate setting of the family circle, provide that direct emotional response with which the human infant must be provided. Nursing involves more than the imbibing of mother's milk. The surrogates may in many instances be direct substitutes for the biological mother or father, as in the operation of the sororate and the levirate, or they may be collateral surrogates, who play the parental roles on a less intensive level. A Navaho child may find himself cared for, and nursed by, a number of clan sisters

[2]See also E. R. Leach, "Polyandry, Inheritance and the Definition of Marriage: With Particular Reference to Sinhalese Customary Law," in *Rethinking Anthropology*, pp. 105ff.

[3]M. Mead, "Some Theoretical Considerations on the Problem of Mother-Child Separation" (*The American Journal of Orthopsychiatry*, Vol. 24, 1954), p. 474.

of his mother, whom he learns to call "mother" under the Navaho system of kinship terminology and who, for their part, call him "son" from the beginning. The family is not necessarily the small, nuclear family, isolated in its separate dwelling unit; it may be this, but it may also exist as a regular cell-like feature of a larger familial structure.

Thus, although the nuclear family occurs in all societies, it is the sole form of familial unit in only about one-fourth of them. In about half of the societies of the world, the nuclear family is encysted within some kind of extended family, a larger kinship group that includes more than a single set of spouses and their children.[4]

The conjugal-natal family

Every individual who is legitimately born and not forthwith orphaned, and who ultimately marries, is a member of a primary and a secondary conjugal-natal family: that of his parents, into which he is born, and that which he founds with his spouse in wedlock. In the first he is an offspring; in the second he is a pro-

[4] G. P. Murdock, *Social Structure,* p. 2.

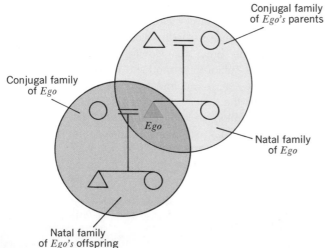

Fig. 23-1 The dual nature of the conjugal-natal family. Each family is a conjugal family for the spouses who establish it and a natal family for the offspring who are born into it.

Conjugal family of *Ego's* parents

Conjugal family of *Ego*

Ego

Natal family of *Ego*

Natal family of *Ego's* offspring

genitor. Viewed from the outside, the two families are alike in terms of form and function. The statuses of the given individual within the two families are very different, however, and his role experiences in each are quite unlike.

The conjugal-natal family is limited both in scope of membership and in duration. It can include no more persons than a mated pair can produce within their time of fecundity, and it cannot endure for more than the lifespan of two generations: the lifespan of the founding spouses and the lifespan of the children who are born into their marriage. Each conjugal-natal family gradually wastes away as death takes its toll, until at last it is no more. The conjugal-natal family is a discontinuous social unit. Each such family is born and destined to die within the span of a century.

This is a consequence of the universal incest tabu, for if parent could marry child and brother could marry sister, a conjugal-natal family could be continued indefinitely through internal replacement as the original members died off. Perpetuity of the conjugal-natal family is forgone, however, in the interests of temporary stability. The individual family sacrifices itself as an entity in the interests of maintenance of the stability of the whole society, for this is of more fundamental importance.

However much we may cherish the conjugal-natal family as a social unit, it is functionally far from ideally suited to the ends it must fulfill. In the first place, the conjugal-natal family is very unstable. There is the constant possibility of divorce, and where divorce is not countenanced, emotional disturbances arising from the incompatibility of the father and mother can easily destroy the affective solidarity that is so important to good family functioning. If a primary purpose of marriage is to fix the biological father of the children with the economic and social responsibility of providing for them, his ability to perform this essential social function is seriously impaired when he divorces the mother. True enough, the consequences of a conjugal-natal family breakup are not so serious in a primitive society, where the mother is securely embedded in the protection of her extended family and where remarriage is easier than is usually the case with us. Nevertheless, the brittleness of the conjugal-natal family is a definite deficiency.

Also, the conjugal-natal family is a temporary association. It begins with the union of the married pairs and ends with the dispersal of the children. Furthermore, upon marriage, a person enters a new conjugal-natal family, and his loyalties are split. From our own experience, we know the tensions that can result from the pull of loyalty to our husbands or wives as against our fathers and mothers. The instability of the conjugal-natal family and its short lifespan also limit its usefulness as a means of inheritance of property and perquisites.

Monogamy and family structure The independent conjugal-natal family is possible only when marriage is monogamous, but monogamy is the sole permitted marital form in only a minority of human societies (1 in 4 societies).[5]

The normal state of affairs is to allow polygamy, especially in the case of men in positions of power and social leadership. Still, it is important to realize that what is permitted in a culture and what prevails in fact may be two different things. Thus, it is usual to refer to societies whose cultures permit multiple marriages as *polygamous;* yet it is unlikely that more than a few marriages in any society will actually be polygamous, since a number of factors limit multiple marriages.

First, there is the relative balance of the sex ratio. Approximately equal numbers of males and females are born. Unless some selective factor operates in favor of one sex and against the other, there will be an approximate equality in the numbers of adult males and females available for marriage. If this is the case, whenever one man has two wives, some other man in the tribe has to do without. There is, of course, the possibility that the short-wived men may band together to share one wife among themselves, but such polyandrous arrangements are very rare.

If it is the current practice for a man to settle in the household of his wife, he obviously cannot live with all his wives simultaneously unless they are sisters. Uxorilocal residence[6] discourages the polygynous form of polygamy. Beyond this, the attitudes of his in-laws will discourage marriage with women from other kinship groups, especially if the society is matrilineal and the wife's relationship group is in a strong position. Marriage is a kinship-group alliance, and a son-in-law whose affinal allegiances are multiple is apt to be less desirable than one whose affinity is to one group alone.

Few precise statistics are available, but all reports indicate that monogamous marriages actually predominate in most societies that permit polygamy. Contrary to the notions of nineteenth-century anthropologists, monogamy most definitely is not the end product of an evolutionary series narrowing down from primitive promiscuity to civilized monogamy. The very primitive Andaman Islanders and the Semangs of the Malay forests limit themselves to one wife apiece, but the Semangs marry again and again in serial monogamy, Hollywood style. Inca commoners were forbidden to marry more than one wife, but a man might receive a concubine as a gift in reward for faithful service to his overlord. The occurrence of prescribed monogamy among the matrilineal, uxorilocal Iroquois in New York and the equally matrilineal, uxorilocal Hopi and Zuñi suggests that in these instances, monogamy is correlated with female-dominated residence and economy. Monogamy prevails among all the Southwest Pueblos, but among the Eastern Pueblos of New Mexico, where female dominance fades out, it is impossible to tell whether this is due to ancient Pueblo custom or whether it has been brought about by the influence of the Catholic Church. Among the Zuñi and Hopi, monogamous marriages are very brittle. Among the Keresan Pueblos, however, the Catholic injunction against divorce is rigidly adhered to. Clandestine relations outside marriage occur among all these people.

Exclusive monogamy is not correlated with any stage of culture. Its absence among pas-

[5]A. D. Coult and R. W. Habenstein, *Cross Tabulations of Murdock's World Ethnographic Sample,* p. 409.

[6]The practice whereby a married couple settles in the locale of the wife's parents.

toral nomads, who are predominantly patrilineal, is nevertheless a notable fact.

Residence A conjugal-natal family almost always has a home. Because of the sentiments that suffuse the family relationship, "home" connotes a good deal more than "house." A long-abandoned dwelling is a house, but it was once also a home. We sing fondly of "home, sweet home," but it is unimaginable, for reasons that are clear enough, that we would ever burst into heart-moving song over "house, sweet house."

The rules of exogamy require that a man and wife always come from separate conjugal-natal families and separate households. Upon marriage, the first question to be settled is: "Where shall we live?" In most societies, this issue is resolved ahead of time and therefore does not call for debate or allow much room for individual preference. The custom of the tribe may be *virilocal* (L. *vir*, male + *locus*, place), according to which the newlywed couple settles in the locality of the husband's primary conjugal-natal family. "Virilocal" is synonymous with "patrilocal," the more traditional term in ethnological usage, which literally means "residence with the father." Inasmuch as it is the locality of the husband's home that is the determining factor, "virilocal" should be the preferred term.

On the other hand, the custom of the tribe may be for the couple to settle in the locality of the wife's parents, in which case it is called *uxorilocal* (L. *uxori*, wife + *locus*, place), which is synonymous with "matrilocal," a term less preferable for the same reasons that apply to "patrilocal."

A few tribes with little fixed property and weak social organization leave it up to the couple to decide whether to settle in the locality of the bride's or the groom's primary conjugal-natal family. This practice is known as *bilocal* residence.

A small number of matrilineally oriented societies expect the couple to settle in the locality of the male's mother's brother. In this situation, we have *avunculocal* (L. *avunculus*, mother's brother + *locus*, place) residence.

Finally, some social systems, such as our own, provide for independent establishment of residence without too much reference to the prior location of the primary conjugal-natal families of the newly married pair. This condition bespeaks *neolocal* residence, which is in effect an absence of restrictive rules of residence.

There are therefore five basic principles of residence: (1) virilocal, (2) uxorilocal, (3) bilocal, (4) avunculocal, and (5) neolocal. In most societies, one rule alone prevails for the married life of a couple, although some may use combinations of two or more. Thus, among the nomadic Plains Indians, a couple's first tipi was usually set up beside that of the bride's parents for a year or so. Then, when the new household was well established, the young couple was likely to camp with the groom's family. Among the Dobuans, a couple alternates residence in each other's village every other year. And in some complex primitive societies, such as Ashanti in Ghana, where the ideal rule is virilocal, there may actually be a good deal of informal variation from case to case.[7]

It should be immediately obvious that the nature of residence patterns strongly affects the internal quality of the family unit and its extensions. If residence is uxorilocal, the woman is in constant daily interaction with *her* parents and sisters. The children of sisters grow up together, and the children of brothers do not. Husbands are "aliens" in a new setting. Sisters are grouped in a continuing solidarity. The opportunity for women to exert a solid front is enhanced, and their position in the direction of social affairs is stronger. With virilocal residence, just the opposite occurs.

Another factor that affects the quality of the family is whether marriages are based on village exogamy or endogamy. If the marriages take place within the local group or village, the differentiating effects of residence rules are much reduced. In spite of virilocality, if

[7]M. Fortes, "Time and Social Structure: An Ashanti Case Study," in M. Fortes (ed.), *Social Structure*, pp. 54–84.

the home of the bride's parents is only 100 yards away, the continuity of her tie to her primary conjugal-natal family is not so seriously strained as it is when she is transported to another village; concomitantly, the influence of the paternal group cannot be so strong.

The composite conjugal-natal family

Within polygamous marriages, we have been drawing a distinction between polygyny and polyandry. _Polygamy_ means multiple marriages; _polygyny_ means multiple women and _polyandry_ means multiple men. Polygyny is therefore that form of family in which a husband has more than one wife at a time. _Bigamy_ is the more special form of polygamy in which the husband limits himself to two wives, or a woman to two husbands. In societies where there may be more than one husband or wife in a family at the same time, the conjugal-natal families are not independent but are, rather, segments of a _composite conjugal-natal_ family. The latter is therefore a family consisting of two or more conjugal-natal family segments.

Polygyny There are a number of social motives underlying polygyny as an institution. If a man has the means to support several wives, he is able to present a richer and better-equipped household to the world. More women can prepare better clothes and food. If women's handicrafts are marketable or suitable for exchange, his household wealth will be increased. When the Blackfoot Indians found a lucrative outlet for tanned hides in the Canadian fur trade, women as tanners became an economic asset, and polygyny grew to an extent unprecedented in the Plains. Bride price went up, and the age of marriage for girls went down, while the age of marriage for men was set back; well-established Blackfoot entrepreneurs cornered the available women, and it took young men a longer time to acquire enough capital to purchase wives.[8]

[8]O. Lewis, _The Effects of White Contact upon Blackfoot Culture, with Special Reference to the Role of the Fur Trade_ (American Ethnological Society, Monograph 6, 1942), pp. 38–40.

Polygyny may also serve as a mechanism for competitive status in the sexual field when to have and to hold several wives against all comers is a dangerous task, as among the Eskimos.[9]

Strange as it may seem to us, it is repeatedly reported that in many tribes the women do not object to their husbands taking on additional wives. This is most apt to be true when additional wives are coworkers or "chore wives," as among the Comanches of the Plains. A secondary wife may be desired because she will perform special functions, as with the African Baganda, among whom a second wife is chosen from the husband's paternal grandmother's clan. This wife is charged with the responsibility of caring for her husband's hair and nail clippings.

On the other hand, instances are on record of primitive women who have shown extreme jealousy when their husbands brought home a new wife. A Cheyenne woman hanged herself because her husband took a Pawnee captive to wife, but her own grandmother remarked, "She was foolish to hang herself over such a little thing."

Most primitives aver that polygyny works out best when a man's several wives are sisters. This is psychologically reasonable, in as much as sisters are more used to one another's ways than unrelated women are; they are subject to the influence of emotional loyalty acquired in childhood as members of the same conjugal-natal family. As representatives of the same marriage group, their nonpersonal interests in the marriage are identical, which is not the case with unrelated women. Sororal polygyny is in effect an anticipation of sororate privileges. A man does not wait for the death of his wife before he marries her younger sister. Instead, as among the Comanches, he has an expectation that if he performs his son-in-law obligations to his wife's parents, they will reward him with his wife's younger sister when she becomes of age.

[9]E. A. Hoebel, "Law-ways of the Primitive Eskimos" (_Journal of Criminal Law and Criminology_, Vol. 31, 1941), pp. 663–683.

Where exchange marriage prevails, the levirate will also work to produce sororal polygyny, for example, when brothers have married sisters and a man inherits his deceased brother's wife.

Various household arrangements are made as adjustments to the requirements of the multiple-wife family. The Angola practice is probably typical of Sudanese African tribes. Hambly tells of an Angola headman with eleven wives, each of whom has a separate hut in his compound. The husband customarily sleeps with each wife four or seven successive nights, as his personal habit may be.[10] Among the Jie, it will be remembered (pages 260–261), each wife in a polygynous unit within a joint-family household has her own fenced-in yard and sleeping hut. If a Comanche had less than four wives, they usually shared the same tipi. More than four wives necessitated at least two tipis for the household.

Within composite families, there is usually a firm hierarchical distinction between the wives. The first-married wife is given a No. 1 position of authority, so that even though she may be displaced by a later wife as a sexual favorite, she still has the gratification of priority in formal status. The Comanches, again, definitely made such distinctions, for secondary wives were "chore wives," who had to do household work under the direction of No. 1. No wonder the busy wives of great chieftains were usually quite willing to have their husbands marry extra housekeepers. It helped lighten their load.

Polyandry   The actual marriage of several men to one woman is as rare as the marriage of several women to one man is common. Tibetans and the Todas of India are the most famous polyandrists. The Toda polyandrous union is usually, but not necessarily, fraternal.[11] Some polygynous marriages also occur, and quite a few monogamous ones. Children are ordinarily betrothed in infancy, and the boy makes

progeny-price payments twice a year all through his childhood. He also has to provide a buffalo to help pay funeral expenses of members of his betrothed's family. Just before puberty, the girl is deflorated by a man from some clan other than her own. Then she is ready for marriage. Right after puberty, she is given a dowry and taken to the home of her husband. Although she may have been betrothed to just one man, it is understood that she is also the wife of all his brothers. Even a boy yet unborn may become her husband, along with his elder brothers, when he becomes of age. All the brothers live together and share their wife without friction and, we are told, without jealousy. When the wife becomes pregnant, one of the brothers goes through a ritual of "presenting the bow." This makes him the jural father of the ensuing child and the next couple of children to be born. There is no concern over whether he may be the biological sire or not. After he has his share of offspring to sponsor, another brother "presents the bow," thus making himself the father of the next group of children, and so on. This disregard of biological paternity in favor of ceremonially established sociological fatherhood is also manifest in a way reminiscent of Sakalava progeny-price privileges mentioned previously (page 346). Occasionally, a Toda woman may leave her legitimate husbands to live with another man without official approval, or she may take a concubitant, who pays her husbands for the privilege; in either case, her subsequent children still belong to the man (her husband) who performed the bow-and-arrow ritual.[12]

Polyandry in the Darjeeling district of India is restricted to the younger brothers of the man who performs the wedding rite with the wife. If the elder brother dies and the common wife has no children, she may break the polyandrous bond by first tying a string to a finger of her No. 1 husband's corpse and binding it to one of her own fingers. Then by severing the string, she symbolically destroys the marriage tie.

Tibetan and Eskimo polyandry have been attributed to the practice of female infanticide.

---

[10]W. D. Hambly, *Source Book for African Anthropology*, pp. 418–419.

[11]Called "adelphic polyandry" in British social anthropology.

[12]W. H. R. Rivers, *The Todas*, pp. 477–480.

While it is true that both peoples practice infanticide, British census figures do not indicate a surplus of adult men in Tibet, and reliable censuses of the primitive Eskimo indicate that women outnumber men in almost all Eskimo communities, in spite of the common destruction of baby girls.

Although rare, polyandry is more common (at least in a modified form) than was thought to be the case a few decades ago. A form of polyandry has been reported from at least two East African tribes, leading us to expect that there are probably other unreported instances. Among the Banyankole and the Bahima, where progeny price is high, a poor man may call on his younger brothers to contribute cattle to his cause.[13] All the brothers who have contributed take turns living with the bride until she becomes pregnant; she then lives with her "husband." Whoever the sire may be, the resultant child is the jural offspring of the elder brother who married the girl.

Property and polyandry Edmund Leach has proposed that fraternal, or adelphic, polyandry is "intimately associated" with inheritance of land through males only, combined with virilocal residence and dowry. In the South Asian cases, a woman who marries patrilocally may surrender her dowry but receive movable goods from the husband in its stead. Brothers jointly pay the dowry, thus obtaining a joint interest in the sexual prerogatives of the husband.[14]

Extensions of brotherhood Leach's hypothesis is appropriate to the South Asian data, but it does not fit the facts for North America. While economic factors may be at the bottom of polyandry in some societies, there appear to be other motivations elsewhere. Both the Shoshones and the Eskimos practice polyandry, and yet neither shows much concern with property considerations. These are bilateral societies in which a man must depend on his brothers

(and cousins) for security and survival. In Shoshone and Comanche kinship terminology, there is no separate word for "brother-in-law" or "sister-in-law." All female sisters and cousins of a wife are addressed by a single term, *kw3h3*. A woman addresses all her husband's brothers and cousins by the term for "husband," *kumaxp*. The polyandrous emphasis is on the mutuality of the bond of brotherhood.

"A man loves his brother; he knows that if his brother dies, no one can replace him; he gives him everything he can," explained That's It. "A brother therefore sends his wife over to him occasionally as a gift. She cannot go of her own free will or meet him secretly, or her real husband will be angry." It was also expected that when a man was on the warpath, his brother could sleep with his wife.[15]

This notion of the sexual equivalence of brothers crops up in the quaint Shoshone and Comanche custom whereby an aggrieved husband courteously addresses an adulterer who has made him a cuckold as "brother." Men who have had sex relations with the same woman are "brothers," even though unrelated, and even while the husband is prosecuting the adulterer for damages.

Comanche young men frequently enter into a relation of institutionalized friendship with a chosen "chum," called *haints*. They usually marry sisters, whom they freely lend to one another as wives. Shoshones and Comanches have to rely on "brothers," real or putative, in war and in law, in love and in play.[16] Their adelphic polyandry expresses the structural-functional significance of "brotherhood" as the keystone of their social life.

That such attitudes are not mere aberrations of the Comanches is fully attested by Murdock's findings to the effect that nearly two-thirds of the societies in the Yale Cross Cultural Survey for which data are available permit postmarital sexual intercourse between a man and his brother's wife (anticipatory levirate) or between a man and his wife's sister (anticipatory sororate).[17]

[13]Roscoe, *The Banyankole*, p. 123; "The Cow Tribe of Enkole in the Uganda Protectorate" (*Journal of the Royal Anthropological Institute of Great Britain and Ireland*, Vol. 37, 1907), p. 105.
[14]Leach, *op. cit.*, pp. 104–113.

[15]E. Wallace and E. A. Hoebel, *The Comanches*, pp. 138–139.
[16]*Ibid.*, p. 132.
[17]Murdock, *op. cit.*, p. 268.

Eskimo polyandry is of the same order as Shoshone, except that the putative brother with whom an Eskimo normally exchanges wives does not usually live in the same village. A traveling Eskimo needs a woman to dry his fur clothes and chew the hides to keep them soft, among the more necessary amenities of arctic living. Most Eskimo men have at least one regular partner in each village, who will make his wife available on a basis of amicable mutuality.

WIFE HOSPITALITY The widespread primitive practice of men sharing their wives with certain other men on specific occasions is closely related to the institution of polyandry. Most commonly, a host deems that proper social form requires him to offer the hospitality of his wife to an overnight guest. An early white trader on the upper Missouri River, Jean Baptiste Trudeau, took note that "So true is this, that husbands, fathers and brothers, are importunate with the white men who visit them, to make free with their wives, daughters and sisters, particularly those who are most youthful and pretty. . . .[18]

Wife hospitality was practiced because when a man accepted the woman for the duration of his stay in the village, he became a putative son-in-law or brother of his benefactor. Such arrangements helped to establish a network of trade in the eighteenth and early nineteenth centuries throughout the upper Plains. French, English, and American traders solidified their business interests with various Indian tribes by becoming "kinsmen" through sexual sharing.

Similar concepts of hospitality have been noted in all parts of the primitive world by countless explorers, travelers, and lay observers, as well as by anthropologists.[19] As an institutionalized practice, wife lending is functionally analogous to *blood brotherhood,* "a pact or alliance formed between two persons by

a ritual act in which each swallows the blood of the other. The pact is one of mutual assistance and is backed by powerful sanctions."[20] The formal exchange of wives is analogous to intimate exchange of "magical" personal essence. At any rate, it should be clear that wife hospitality in societies that emphasize kinship obligations and privileges of brotherhood is not an act of immorality in the context of those societies. It serves as a means of broadening and strengthening social bonds.

Leach's hypothesis and that offered above are not incompatible or contradictory. Each explains special sets of circumstances. Fraternal polyandry in South Asia and that in North America are alike in that a group of brothers share sexual privileges in a wife or wives, while the woman's offspring are jurally the heirs of a specific male. Although the social reasons (structural and functional) for this are quite different in the two cases, the unlike conditions have produced similar results. This is called *convergence:* separate lines of development have led to a single point.

The composite unilineal family

In following the extensions of polyandry beyond the immediate limits of the patrilateral composite conjugal-natal family, we were led into considerations of "brotherhood." Let us now return to an examination of some ways in which the concept of the family may be extended to incorporate a group of closely related conjugal-natal families into a single property holding, residential group. Such units are usually called the *joint family* or the *composite unilineal family.* The essential difference between the composite conjugal-natal family and the composite unilineal family is that the former involves only one spouse with several mates, while the latter involves several brothers (or sisters) living together in a single household, each with his or her own distinct spouse and offspring.

[18]G. H. Smith, "J. B. Trudeau's Remarks on the Indians of the Upper Missouri, 1794—95" (*American Anthropologist*, Vol. 38, 1930), p. 567.

[19]See E. Westermarck, *The History of Human Marriage*, Vol. 1, pp. 224–230, for a more detailed body of references to the custom.

[20]E. E. Evans-Pritchard, "Zande Blood-brotherhood," in *Essays in Social Anthropology*, p. 131.

The Tanala joint family Linton's description of the patrilineal joint family among the Tanala of Madagascar presents a quite typical example. A Tanala joint family begins with a single conjugal family. When the sons grow up and marry, they build new houses for themselves close to their parental home. The father, as head of the joint family, directs all its activities concerning clearing and cultivating the fields for dry-rice culture, caring for the family cattle, and similar tasks. All earnings of the male members are placed in his hands for investment in cattle and for dispersal for progeny price and such little cash needs as the sons may have. As long as his father lives, a man has little chance to accumulate any wealth in his own right. The joint family is a cooperative work group and a corporate unit in dealing with other members of the society.

As long as the founder lives, his male lineal descendants are bound to the joint family, and it is not uncommon for a patriarch to have a dozen or more able-bodied sons or grandsons under his control. Upon his death, the process of fission starts. Although the family continues to live and work together under the leadership of the eldest son, his brothers do not have to put their earnings into the common holding unless they wish to. When he, in turn, is at last succeeded by his eldest son, the joint family begins to break up. The third-generation leader is younger than most of his uncles, who become restive under his leadership. Moreover, it is likely that the group will have grown too large for its land holdings. Then one or more men split off to found a new joint-family household elsewhere.[21] The functional significance of economics for the joint family is shown by Linton's analysis of the breakdown of the joint family resulting from the introduction of wet-rice culture among the neighboring Betsilio tribe.[22]

Balkan and Asian joint families Among gardening and pastoral peoples, the joint family appears universally to be a corporate landowning entity, living in a single dwelling or closely spaced houses that form a household. Archaic Indo-European peoples commonly favored this type of setup, which is known among the peoples of the Balkans as the *zadruga,* such as was visited a few years ago by Louis Adamic.

. . . we were guests in the home of a family counting sixty-eight members. It was one of the few remaining family *zadrugé,* or collectives, in Serbia. We met about forty of the members, including the *stareshina,* or head of the family, a patriarch of seventy and absolute ruler of the group. The enormous household, with a considerable tract of ground and a twenty-room house, was all but self-sufficient economically. Every member above ten had his or her special duty to attend to. Six women and girls, supervised by the *stareshina's* wife, did nothing but cook and bake. Eight other females only spun, weaved, sewed, and embroidered. Five men and boys attended to all the sheep, goats, buffaloes, cattle, and horses. One man was the family shoemaker. And so on. Eleven families lived under the same roof. The husbands were all the *stareshina's* brothers, sons, and grandsons; their wives had married into the *zadruga* from near-by villages.[23]

In India and Pakistan, the patrilineal joint family, called *kumbah* in Pakistan, is still a vital form even in the urban setting. In such large cities as Karachi, a joint family will occupy a single five- or six-story house, with the parents on the lower floor and each son establishing his secondary conjugal-natal family on succeeding floors in order of seniority—the youngest having the most flights to climb. Even fully trained professional men, if conservatively oriented, turn their salaries over to the household father and mother to administer on behalf of the group as a whole.

If the extension of kinship is on matrilineal lines, the joint family will be matriarchically organized, as is the Iroquois joint family, whose dwelling structure is described in Chapter 16.

The Nyar taravad Of the matrilineal type of joint-family household, that of the famous Nyar

---

[21]R. Linton, "The Tanalas of Madagascar," in A. Kardiner, *The Individual and His Society,* pp. 189–192.
[22]*Ibid.,* pp. 282–290.

[23]L. Adamic, *The Native's Return,* p. 215.

caste of Kerala, the Malabar coast of southern India, has long held the interest of anthropologists.

The Nyar are supposed to have been the ruling class of the aboriginal society predating the Hindu influx. Today they form the third-ranking caste of a complex and caste-dominated society. Above them is the royal house, of great wealth and power, which may have emerged long ago from the Nyars themselves. Beneath the royal house (but far above the Nyars in sublimity) is the caste of Nambudiri Brahmans, whose sacred families are patrilineally organized on a strict basis of primogeniture. The Nyars are a closed caste of landowners and professional soldiers, who in contrast to the Brahmans have been strictly matrilineal and uxorilocal. The household, or *taravad*, is a joint organization housed under one roof. The eldest woman is titular head of the household, but the house, lands, and joint property are administered by the eldest brother for the benefit of the group. All the males (brothers, sons, and grandsons) contribute to the maintenance of the *taravad* and draw their support from it. Only the offspring of the women belong to the *taravad* and are maintained within it. The men mate with women of other *taravad* without obligating themselves to any legal duties toward their "wives" or children.

In its extreme forms, marriage by members of the *taravad* is often no more than a ritual bow to Hindu convention. If a ceremony is performed, it may soon be followed by legal divorce, even though the couple continues an enduring relation as mates. For unlike most joint-family practices elsewhere, the Nyar male may not live in the joint-family household of his mate. The couple merely visit together, and out of these visits come the children who people the *taravad* of the mother.

Both men and women may have several mates simultaneously, since mating involves no formal obligations. Younger sons of the Brahman class may enter into sexual alliances with Nyar women, but they still remain outside the *taravad*, and their children remain irrevocably fixed within it.

Under changing economic and social conditions, the Nyar matrilineal joint family has been gradually dissolving, and patrilineal tendencies have become increasingly strong.[24]

The matrilateral group

Some societies emphasize the brother-sister relationship as a means of overcoming the instability of the conjugal-natal family. The result is a social unit that may be called the *matrilateral group*, which consists of a woman, her brother, and her offspring.[25]

Thus among the Dobu of Melanesia, the conjugal-natal family is the household unit; i.e., its members live together. After he marries, a man never enters his sister's house; consequently, the susu, or matrilateral group, has no household base. However, children cannot eat food grown in their father's fields; all fishing gear, including canoes, is used jointly and is inherited only by members of the matrilateral group. Consequently, the susu has an economic base, and the conjugal-natal family does not. Emotional security is found only in the susu, and not in the conjugal-natal family. All Dobus believe that all other Dobus except those of their own susu are their magical enemies. Husband and wife, coming as they do from different susus, are hostile at marriage and all their days thereafter. Each believes the other is trying to destroy him by foul magic. The susu inherits the corpses and skulls of its members. It bestows personal names and social status in relationship terms. Widows, widowers, and the children of a dead person may never enter the village of the deceased spouse or parent, but susu relatives of a dead person may enter the village of the surviving spouse or children.

The differentiation and interrelationship of conjugal-natal family and matrilateral group are also strikingly revealed by the Zuñis of New Mexico, of whom Benedict wrote:

To the women of the household, the grandmother and her sisters, her daughters and their daughters, belong

[24]K. Gough, in D. M. Schneider and K. Gough (eds.), *Matrilineal Kinship*, chapts. 6, 7, and 17.
[25]It has also been called the *consanguineal family* and *susu*.

the house and the corn that is stored in it. No matter what may happen to marriages the women of the household remain with the house for life. They present a solid front. They care for and feed the sacred objects that belong to them. They keep their secrets together. Their husbands are outsiders, and it is their brothers, married now into houses of other clans, who are united with the household in all affairs of the moment. It is they who return for all the retreats when the sacred objects of the house are set out before the altar. It is they, not the women, who learn the word-perfect ritual of their sacred bundle and perpetuate it. A man goes always, for all important occasions, to his mother's house, which, when she dies, becomes his sister's house, and if his marriage breaks up, he returns to the same household.

This blood-relationship group, rooted in the ownership of the house, united in the care of sacred objects, is the important group in Zuñi. It has permanence and important common concerns. But it is not the economically functioning group. Each married son, each married brother, spends his labour upon the corn which fills his wife's storeroom. Only when his mother's or sister's house lacks male labour does he care for the cornfield of his blood-relationship group. The economic group is the household that lives together, the old grandmother and her husband, her daughters and their husbands. These husbands count in the economic group, though in the ceremonial group they are outsiders.[26]

The matrilateral group exists because it offers certain advantages in which the conjugal-natal family is weak. Yet the conjugal-natal family is definitely preferred over the matrilateral group. The conjugal-natal family is universal; the matrilateral group is not.

What is defective or objectionable in the matrilateral group? The answer will be found in the incest tabu. The basis of the matrilateral group is the sibling bond of brotherhood and sisterhood. Yet all societies find it necessary to tabu sex relations between brother and sister, often manifesting extreme anxiety over the consequences of incestuous relationships. The matrilateral group encourages emotional and functional ties between a pair who must never become sexually involved with each other. This is dangerous business, so much so that many societies apparently prefer to make it impos-

sible for such a situation to exist. In Dobu, for example, a man may not enter his sister's house. Another disadvantage of the matrilateral group is that the splitting of loyalty between it and the conjugal-natal family may produce personal and cultural conflicts that are difficult to resolve. Meyer Fortes observed: "Ashanti discuss the subject interminably, stressing especially the inevitability of conflicting loyalties. For a woman the conflict turns on the difficulties of reconciling attachment to her mother with her duty to her husband."[27]

In a social system in which the matrilateral group is an important functioning unit, the woman who has few sisters and many brothers is certainly more apt to be better off than a woman who has several sisters and only one brother, for as Malinowski has written of the Trobrianders, ". . . the more brothers the merrier for each sister, the more sisters the less endowment for them."[28]

SUMMARY

The conjugal-natal family is the elemental, universal kinship group; it relates the complementary roles of paired mates and of adults to their offspring. It is the organization that, in conjunction with marriage, makes a major contribution to the stabilization of sexual activity; it provides the primary means for nurture and training of the young and for transmission of status and property.

An individual is born into a primary conjugal-natal family and, upon marriage, establishes a secondary conjugal-natal family. The quality of the conjugal-natal family is strongly influenced by the residence rules of the culture, which may be virilocal, uxorilocal, avunculocal, bilocal, or neolocal.

Most cultures allow polygamous marriages, which result in composite conjugal-natal families. In any society, however, only a minority of families are ever polygamous. Polygyny is

[26]R. F. Benedict, *Patterns of Culture*, pp. 75–76.

[27]M. Fortes, "Time and Social Structure: An Ashanti Case Study," in M. Fortes (ed.), *Social Structure*, p. 75.
[28]B. Malinowski, *Coral Gardens and Their Magic*, Vol. 1, p. 189.

much more common than polyandry. Wife hospitality is not a manifestation of promiscuity or sexual communism; it reflects a sentiment that brothers, as members of a close-knit kinship group, share rights in common, which may be extended to the sharing of wives. It is therefore a gesture of brotherhood, a symbolic identification of the guest as a member of his host's kinship group.

Unilateral identification of kinship may produce two major types of "families": (1) the composite unilineal family, or joint family, and (2) the matrilateral group. The first is a residence unit; the second may or may not be.

Joint families and matrilateral groups exist as complements to the conjugal family. They may take over some of its functions and activities, but they rarely wholly replace it.

SELECTED READINGS

Belo, J.: "A Study of a Balinese Family" (*American Anthropologist*, Vol. 38, 1936), pp. 12–31. An account based upon firsthand observation.

Fortes, M.: *The Web of Kinship among the Tallensi* (1949), chaps. 6 and 8, "Husband and Wife in the Structure of the Family" and "The Relationship of Parent and Child." An excellent study.

Geertz, H.: *The Javanese Family* (1961). A modern descriptive account of life within the family circle, with an analysis of the family within the kinship structure.

Goody, J. (ed.): *The Developmental Cycle in Domestic Groups* (1958). The product of joint examination by a group of anthropologists of what happens in families and other domestic groups during the natural history of the family group. Covers a variety of societies.

LaBarre, W.: *The Human Animal* (1954). Brilliantly written, this book presents a biosocial theory of the development and essential nature of family relationships.

Mead, M.: *Male and Female* (1949). A provocative and interesting synthesis of the author's field studies and views on family relationships in seven primitive cultures and the United States.

Roberts, J. M.: "Three Navaho Households" (*Papers of the Peabody Museum of American Archaeology and Ethnology, Harvard University*, Vol. 50, No. 3, 1953).

The extension of kinship: kindred, lineage, clan, moiety, and phratry

chapter 24

The conjugal-natal family, as noted in the previous chapter, is always embedded within a series of larger kinship groupings. These may be the kindred, on the one hand, or some form or forms of a unilineally extended kinship group, on the other.

The kindred and the ramage

The family tie does not end with parents and children, for parents have their parents, grandparents, uncles, aunts, and cousins, to whom the bond of kinship extends. In most societies, the cementing effect of these bonds is strong enough to produce a network of special relations between relatives that makes the relationship group distinguishable as an entity within the larger society. This network is the extended family, or *kindred.*

In our own society, where its members are collectively called "kinfolk" or "relatives," it includes that group of near kinsmen who may be expected to be present and participate on important ceremonial occasions, such as weddings, christenings, funerals, Thanksgiving and Christmas dinners. Members of a kindred visit and entertain one another freely, and between them marriage and pecuniary transactions for profit are ordinarily taboo. However much they may disagree or quarrel, they are expected to support one another against criticism or affront from outsiders.[1]

Theoretically, one's kindred includes every person to whom one can trace a genealogical bond. It includes all one's *cognates,* i.e., everyone who can be traced as descended from a specified common ancestor, whether male or female. In point of fact, however, a kindred as a functioning unit never organizes such a heterogeneous crowd. Because cognate relationships ramify in all directions and multiply geometrically, their boundaries are too inclusive. They become so thin at the edges that the definition of relationship is lost in the mists of uncertainty and vagueness. Consequently, some anthropologists have sought for a more specific concept to distinguish the cognate groups which actually do pull together as relatives and which recognize active bonds of identity and obligatory interaction as kinsmen. Goodenough[2] and Murdock suggest that these groups be called *ramages.* One's ramage consists of that segment of all his kindred who have an interest in him as a kinsman. The members of a ramage respond to the obligation of kinsmen to be concerned about one another and to rally 'round at times of crisis: birth, puberty, mar-

riage, potlatches and feasts, the occasion of a lawsuit, illness, and death. The ramage is egocentered. The ramage of a black sheep will be smaller and less enthusiastic in its support than the ramage of his socially responsible, reliable, and winning brother.

The bilateral principle Because we are so accustomed in Western society to reckoning our kinfolk or relatives bilaterally (we are equally "related" to our paternal and maternal families), it is easy to assume that this type of family pattern is universal and/or best. On the contrary, only about one-third of all human societies build their social structures on this foundation. While the bilateral kinship system appears to work satisfactorily in those societies which use it, it does have inherent limitations and disadvantages, which have been summed up by Murdock as follows:

A particular disadvantage of the kindred appears in the instances in which an individual belongs to the kindreds of two other persons and thereby becomes involved in conflicting or incompatible obligations. If they get into serious difficulties with one another, for example, he may be required to avenge the one and yet to defend the other. If they become estranged, both are likely to turn to him for support and to subject him to emotional conflict and strain. The reader can supply numerous examples from the rankling family quarrels in our own society.[3]

The unilineal principle is an adaptive invention designed to overcome these difficulties for societies that rely on kinship groups to perform most of their basic functions. Two-thirds of the societies represented in the World Ethnographic Survey are based on the lineal principle. One-third, including that of the United States, is bilateral (see Table 24-1).

The unilineal principle

A unilineal kinship group is one that is organized through identification with only one line of relatives, through either males or females. If the identification is through males, the system is *patrilineal,* or *agnatic.*

---

[1]G. P. Murdock, *Social Structure,* pp. 56–57.

[2]W. H. Goodenough, "A Problem in Malayo-Polynesian Social Organization" (*American Anthropologist,* Vol. 57, 1955), pp. 71–83.

[3]*Social Structure,* p. 61.

Table 24-1 *Frequency and Percentage Distributions of Types of Descent Systems in 565 Representative Societies*

descent type	number of cultures	percentage
Bilateral	204	36
Patrilineal	248	44
Matrilineal	84	15
Duolineal	28	5
Unclassifiable	1	less than 0.5
Total	565	100

NOTE: Unilineal systems outnumber bilateral systems, but matrilineal and duolineal systems are relatively rare.
SOURCE: D. M. Schneider and K. Gough (eds.), *Matrilineal Kinship*, table 17-1, p. 663.

In a patrilineal system, the children of both sexes belong to the group of their father, which is, in turn, the group of his father's father, his father's father's father, and so on, as far back as genealogies are kept. The children of the man's sons and of the sons' sons, and so on, belong to the same group, as long as the line does not die out or break up.

In a *matrilineal* system, the children of both sexes belong to the group of their mother, which is, in turn, the group of her mother's mother, her mother's mother's mother, and so on, as far back as genealogies are kept. The relationship is *uterine*. The children of the woman's daughters and of the daughters' daughters, and so on, belong to the same group, as long as the line does not die out or break up.

Each unilineal kinship group is a collective body, a corporate entity, that endures through the ages. It may have a definite beginning, but it has the potential of unending endurance—unlike the conjugal-natal family. Unilineal kinship membership is therefore a matter of predetermined social heredity. One does not join a unilineal group, for it is not a voluntary association. One is born into it perforce. The social fiction of adoption may make possible a change in unilineal affiliation, however. Unilineal group membership is discriminating and exclusive. It arbitrarily segments the population of a tribe; it separates genetic relatives from one another. In compensation, it cements the genetic relatives who are included within the unilineal group into a firmer bond of kinship than is possible through bilateral extension of the family.

In a tribe segmented into lineages, sibs, or moieties . . . the individual knows exactly where he stands. . . . If both disputants are members of his own kin group, he is expected to remain neutral and to use his good offices to compose their differences. If neither is a member, the affair is none of his business. If one is a member but the other is not, he is expected to support his sibmate, regardless of the rights in the matter. In short, most conflict situations are simply and automatically resolved.[4]

In ceremony, economic activity, legal fracas and dispute, inheritance, and marriage, as these are related to kinship, the place and roles of members of unilineal groups are clear-cut.

A further consequence of the inclusive-exclusive character of unilineality is the sharp division it makes among cousins. Cross-cousins can never belong to the same unilineal group, although parallel-cousins may. This is what makes cross-cousin marriage possible. The lineal principle is thus really quite a remarkable invention; its functional contributions to social organization are so great that two-thirds of the societies of men make it a fundamental principle upon which to build their cultures (see Table 24-1).

Types of unilineal kinship groups The simplest type of unilineal group is known as the *lineage*. A lineage is an extended unilineal kinship group descended from a known ancestor, or founder, who ordinarily lived not more than five or six generations back. He, in the case of the patrilineage, or she, in the case of the matrilineage, is a real person and not a mythological or legendary figure. On the next level, above the lineage, there is the *clan*. A clan is an enlarged unilineal kinship group that rests on

[4] *Idem.*

the fiction of common descent from a founding ancestor who lived so far in the distant past as to be mythological. When a tribal society is divided into two unilineal halves, each half is called a *moiety* (Fr. *moitié*, half), and the structure is known as *dual division*. Finally, there are *phratries* (Gk. *phratria*, brother): linked groups of clans, where there are more than two such groups in the tribe. (If there were only two, they would be moieties.)

The possible extended unilineal groups are therefore (1) the lineage, (2) the clan, (3) the moiety, and (4) the phratry.

The lineage The lineage is the simplest form of extended unilineal kinship group in that it normally is limited to closely related agnatic (male descent line) or uterine (female descent line) kinsmen and is rarely more than six generations deep. The "begats" of the Old Testament are the genealogies of the agnatic lineages of the pastoral Hebrews.

Lineages may be divided and subdivided into smaller segments. In such cases, they are called *segmentary lineages.* In a common African

form, such as described for the Nuer by Evans-Pritchard,[5] each lineage is divided into two secondary lineages, which bifurcate into four tertiary lineages, which bifurcate into eight quaternary (or minimal lineages). See Fig. 24-1. When a minimal lineage fights with its opposite lineage (e.g., *a* versus *b*), no one else is directly involved, except a local Priest of the Earth, who will evoke a settlement if anyone is killed. But if *a* becomes involved in a fight with lineages of *c* or *d*, then *a* and *b* join as segments of *1* to fight with *2*. If *1* gets into a dispute with *3* or *4*, *2* will join it as a segment of *A* against *B*. But all will join together as a maximal lineage, *I*, against all other maximal lineages. Such intensive lineage activity prevails in segmentary societies with weak central governments.

In general terms, the subdivisions of any lineage segment may quarrel with one another but unite against all other segments on the same level.

Lineages may or may not reside as territorially based units. Localized minimal lineages usually form joint-family households or compounds.

Modern recognition of the lineage as a key structure in many social systems is due largely to the influence of A. R. Radcliffe-Brown and the work done in the field by anthropologists who were trained by him.

[5] E. E. Evans-Pritchard, *The Nuer.*

Fig. 24-1 Bifurcating segmentary lineage relations. A and B are secondary segments of the maximal lineage, I. These in turn are segmented into two tertiary lineages each, which in turn segment into two minimal lineages each.

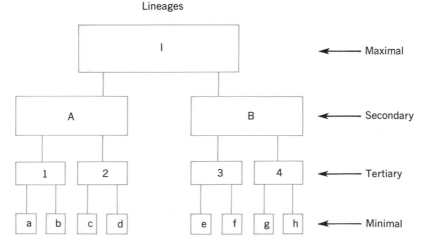

The clan Apart from size, the only essential difference between a lineage and a clan is that the members of a lineage can actually trace out their genealogies of common descent from a known ancestor, while clan members cannot. Nevertheless, if they belong to a given clan, people believe they have common descent, and their behavior is regulated accordingly.

Very often, however, the folklore of the clan includes a myth purporting to give a truthful account of how the clan came to be.

DAHOMEAN CLANS Thus among the patrilineal Dahomeans of West Africa, one clan was founded by the son of a horse "who, bounding from the water in a fury of passion, lay with a woman on the bank of the river." Another clan is said to have descended from the "offspring of a woman and a pig, another from that of a woman and a toad, one from that of a woman and a dog, and the royal family . . . originated from the mating of a female leopard with the King of Adja." Another clan is said to have been created when a peanut was magically transformed into a man, who then mated with a poor woman who lived on roots. Dahomeans believe that the members of the Peanut clan lack the fine, smooth skin of other Dahomeans: "It is rough like the shell of a peanut." Further, the members of the Peanut clan are said to be recognizable on sight.[6] How this can be genetically possible in view of clan exogamy is a little difficult to understand, but ideological stereotypes can dogmatically color perception.

The members of a Dahomean clan have a rather special set of attitudes toward the animal or plant creature who begat their clan founder. All clans revere their clan founder and his descendants, who are their ancestors. All Dahomean clans except one abjure the flesh of the animal species associated with the founder, and many of them bear the name of the founder. All these features give the clans a totemic tinge.

CROW CLANS The usages of the Crow Indians illustrate a different kind of clan-origin legend.

The clan names are taken from certain alleged exploits of the founders, after the manner of a Plains Indian warrior, who bestows names on children that memorialize outstanding events in his life. It would be quite a mistake to jump to the conclusion that members of the Crow "Greasy-inside-of-their-mouths" clan are slippery-tongued, for the name is actually honorific. The clan founder was such a provident hunter that he was always surfeited with rich, fat meat. It is said that his mouth was so coated with fat that when he spat in the campfire, his saliva flared up in the flames. Other Crow clan names memorialize alleged historical incidents or clan characteristics. The Piegan clan was originally called "They-eat-their-own-mucus," which may or may not have been a praiseworthy practice from the Crow point of view, but when these people once abandonded a wounded comrade in battle, they were henceforth dubbed "Piegan," meaning that they acted like the Piegan enemies, which was certainly *not* a complimentary epithet from the Crow point of view.[7]

In all these and similar instances, which could be drawn from a multitude of tribes, the actual origin of the clan is lost in the hoary past; this is not the case with lineages. Lineages may exist with or without clans. Clans may also exist with or without institutionalized lineages within them. Iroquois clans are made up of related groups of maternal lineages; the lineages are localized for the most part in longhouse groupings. Very often lineage heads constitute the clan council, if there is a clan council. In most parts of Indonesia, lineages are the basic functional group, for lineages or subclans form the localized village, while the clans have a more regional character.

The moiety Reciprocity is the basis of all social relationships, for there can be no social relations without interaction. Human beings are so constituted that the isolated person is not a complete man. They are also so constituted that dependence without interdependence

[6]M. J. Herskovits, *An Outline of Dahomean Religious Belief* (American Anthropological Association, Memoir 41, 1933), pp. 24–27.

[7]R. H. Lowie, *The Crow Indians*, pp. 15–16.

is not readily or for long accepted by the giver of services. He who gives would also receive. Through the building of a network of giving and receiving of services, a society expands its potentialities.

The principle of reciprocity is therefore operative in all societies. However, some societies are content to have it remain implicit in their cultures without placing much formal emphasis upon it. Others, such as the Trobriand Islanders and many other Melanesians, go to great lengths to institutionalize reciprocity and focus the spotlight of social awareness upon it.

One of the most effective ways of institutionalizing reciprocity is to organize the society on a moiety basis. Moieties are exogamous with few exceptions; each moiety supplies the other with its marriage partners. Other reciprocal services are invariably linked to the moiety alignments. Moieties thus effectively control certain types of behavior and serve to give concrete form to the reciprocity principle.

In cases where there are only two clans in a tribe, such as the Water and Land groups of the Central Miwok in California, clan and moiety are automatically synonymous. Multiple clans are the more common order, however, and when clans are linked to moieties, the moiety is the larger unit, and the clans are subdivisions of the moieties. Most of the Iroquois tribes have this kind of arrangement. Among the Seneca, to take a typical example, the Bear, Wolf, Turtle, and Beaver clans constitute one moiety, and the Deer, Snipe, Heron, and Hawk constitute the other. Originally, the moieties were exogamous, but in recent centuries they have lost their control over marriage, and only the clans have retained the exogamous rule. Each moiety performs the important mourning rituals on behalf of the other; the moieties compete against each other in the old Indian game of lacrosse, which is as much a ceremonial ritual as it is a sport. On the other hand, they do not enter into the political structure, although clans and lineages do.

Many American tribes possessing moieties associate them with the duality of the cosmos: sky and earth, water and land, winter and summer, red and white (war and peace). This may be seen as merely another way of objectifying the principle of reciprocity in the minds of the people.

The phratry The clans in a phratry system retain their separate identities, but each clan in a phratry feels some sort of special identity to the others within its phratry. Moreover, they may have special obligations to fulfill toward one another.

The Hopi Indians have a large number of matrilineal clans, which are loosely linked into twelve exogamous phratries. The Aztecs, for their part, had four phratries embracing twenty clans among them. The Aztec phratries were important political and religious divisions in the structure of the empire, and they thus played a significant part in the social life of the people.

Nevertheless, it may be said that in general, phratry organization is a relatively rare and functionally insignificant phenomenon. It does not usually control marriage, although Crow Indians think that it is better if members of the same phratry do not intermarry. Still, they have no prohibition against such action. For the most part, the phratry sentiment seems to rest either on a tradition of common origin or on common interests in ceremonial activity.

The universal functions of unilineal groups

Unilineal groups, except for the phratry, have two universal functions: (1) to broaden the base of the security group founded on the kinship bond by providing mutual aid and collective protection and liability in legal action and disputes and (2) to regulate and control marriage.

Mutual aid and security The lineage, clan, or moiety provides a large mutual-aid organization rooted in kinship. Man never stands alone. In seeking a firmer base for personal security than he can find without organization of his efforts and those of his fellow men, he casts about for some valid common interests that will serve to join him in social communion with others. There can be no doubt that the most generalized interest served by the clan is that of fulfilling the desire for security. The family, as we noted earlier, is the primary incubator of personal security. The clan expands this fundamental function of the family while at the same time tightening up the structure by reducing the diffusive effects of bilateral extension.

To meet the needs of security, lineages usually present a solid front to the rest of the world. In his personal interrelations with all persons outside the lineage, every lineage member must ideally be aided, abetted, and protected by all other members. This is the source of feuding in so many societies and the primary defect of so many tribal legal systems.

As a complement of its united protection of individual members, the lineage or clan is frequently collectively liable for the illegal acts of its own members against members of other clans or lineages. Thus, if a man commits murder, vengeance may commonly be taken on any member of the lineage, for even though he is innocent in fact, his person is merged with the persons of all his fellow kinsmen.

The regulation of marriage   The second universal function of the unilineal kinship group is to regulate marriage by means of exogamy. This, if we follow Malinowski's hypothesis, is a self-protective device that ensures solidarity by directing the sexual drive toward persons outside the essential kinship group. We must not, however, overlook the fact that an additional security device is to be found in clan exogamy. Marriage imposes affinal obligations on the spouse's kin and clan. It tends to reduce overt aggression between the maritally allied groups; it also extends the base of support on which a man may depend.

Secondary functions of unilineal groups

In addition to the broad and universal functions mentioned above, clans carry additional responsibilities in the maintenance of culture.

Both the nature of these responsibilities and the means of carrying them out vary from culture to culture. However, in general, these secondary functions cover a broad range of legal, governmental, economic, religious, and symbolic purposes.

Legal functions   The lineage or clan commonly represents its individual members in lawsuits and is, conversely, responsible for their illegal acts. This function is discussed in detail in Chapter 30.

Governmental functions   A function that the clan may or may not take on is that of government or law. The twenty Aztec clan heads, called *speakers*, made up the Aztec tribal council. This group controlled ordinary political decisions, made war and peace, and as a judicial body decided disputes between clans and members of different clans. These same clan speakers sat on the grand national council, whose jurisdiction covered the most important law cases and election of the king. Aztec clans were grouped in four phratries, each of which had a captain-general, who served as a high-ranking military officer and who, in addition to his military post, served on the grand national council.

Many tribes have raised one clan to the position of royalty, and the hereditary chief must come from this clan. In Melanesia, this is true of the Trobriand Islanders; in Africa, the Dahomeans and the Ashanti are two examples among many.

Among the American Indians, the Winnebago of Wisconsin assigned political functions to seven of their twelve clans. The tribal chief was selected from the Thunderbird clan. In addition, this clan performed important functions connected with the preservation of peace (its governmental functions were mainly civil). The Warrior clan, as its name implies, provided war leadership; the village and hunt policemen came from the Bear clan; and the camp crier and aide-de-camp for the chief was always selected from the Buffalo clan. The Wolf, Water-spirit, and Elk clans had less important political assignments. This was true not only of the Winnebago but also of the other highly organized Siouan tribes.[8]

Economic functions Among clan-organized tribes practicing hoe culture, the garden lands are almost inevitably owned or administered by the clans. Each Aztec clan owned its own segment of the land. Assignments for use were made by the clan headman, who kept a record of all holdings. Every family head had the right to a plot of land (unless he had forfeited his clan membership by refusing to marry or carry out his clan obligations, in which case he became a common proletarian laborer). As long as a clansman was in good standing, he could use his land or rent it to a fellow clansman (but not to an outsider). He could allot it to a clan descendant by testamentary disposition, but he could not alienate it (i.e., pass title to an outsider), for ownership of title was vested in the clan. He had what a lawyer would call a *possessory right of usufruct*, but not ownership. This same land-use system by clans prevails throughout Indonesia at this very time; it is also prevalent in Africa.

Clans may own other material goods in common, such as temples, meetinghouses, and sacred and ceremonial objects (see Chapter 28).

Religious and ceremonial functions Clans or lineages may have their own supernatural beings and devices for controlling the supernatural world for their own ends, or they may possess certain ritual paraphernalia and ceremonies that they are expected to use for the well-being of the whole society.

Ancestor-worshiping Africans who have clan organization represent the first situation. The deceased clan ancestors are elevated to the status of clan deities. The clan head is usually the chief priest of the clan and the intermediary between his kinsmen and the ancestral spirits.

Among the Hopi and Zuñi, the all-important

ceremonial organization is inextricably intertwined with the clan system; each clan must perform its part of the ceremonial activities for the benefit of the whole pueblo. Winnebago clans possess sacred bundles of religious paraphernalia that are used in ceremonial activity. These are examples of the second kind of situation.

Totemic functions Finally, clans may have totemic associations involving a feeling of identity with a plant, animal, or other natural object. This bond of emotional identity may extend from a mere feeling of kinship to actual reverence and worship. It may also lead to symbolic representation of the totemic object in clan fetishes.

Double descent[9]

Prior to 1927, anthropologists thought that a society could embrace only one clan system, which had to be either matrilineal or patrilineal. Evidence to the contrary first came to the attention of English-reading anthropologists in R. S. Rattray's studies of the Ashanti, who were shown by this keen student of African tribes to have matrilineal clans called *abusua* and patrilineal groups called *ntoro*. The ntoro principle of inheritance is associated with the semen, and although the ntoro group is not organized, it, like the abusua, regulates marriage and sets certain incest prohibitions. It is totemic and imposes certain food tabus on its members.[10]

A subsequent report by Forde on another African tribe, the Umor, analyzes an even more precise system of dual descent.[11] The Umoran patrilineal, virilocal clan determines house and land affiliation and is called the *kepun*. There are twenty-two of these. At the same time, there are four *yajima* (plural form), which are matrilineal, nonlocalized clans through which

[8]P. Radin, *The Winnebago Tribe* (Bureau of American Ethnology, Annual Report 37, 1923).

[9]Also called *duolineal descent* and *double unilineal descent*.
[10]R. S. Rattray, *Ashanti; Ashanti Law and Constitution.* Dual descent as found in a neighboring people is explicitly examined in detail in a monograph by J. B. Christensen, *Double Descent among the Fanti.*
[11]C. D. Forde, "Kinship in Umor: Double Unilateral Organization in a Semi-Bantu Society" (*American Anthropologist*, Vol. 41, 1939), pp. 523–553.

movable property—principally livestock and currency—is inherited and marriage exchanges (progeny price and dowry) are made. "A man eats in his kepun and inherits in his lejima [singular form]," is the native adage. Murdock has put the phenomenon into focus by showing that double descent has a widely scattered distribution in Africa, India, Australia, Melanesia, and Polynesia.[12]

That it took English-speaking anthropologists so long to discover double descent shows how difficult it is for even carefully trained scientists to formulate conceptions necessary to the perception of new facts when those facts are completely alien to their experience and cultural background.

Lineage and clan in social evolution

In the evolutionary theories of the nineteenth century, a major issue was whether matrilineal or patrilineal clans came first in the evolution of human society. Morgan, followed by Marx and Engels, argued that matrilineal systems took priority in a kind of communistic elysium. Patriliny, according to Marx and Engels, followed after the introduction of paired marriages, whereupon men were no longer content to pass their property collaterally to their sisters' sons. They established patrilineal inheritance, initiated private property in their domesticated herds, introduced slavery, and subordinated women to patriarchal domination. These practices resulted in what Engels called the first great social revolution and "the world-historical defeat of the female sex."[13] Bachofen also argued for the priority of the maternal clan in his work *Das Mutterrecht.* Others, such as McLennan, claimed that the patrilineal clan with patriarchal rule came first. In the Western world, the battle has long since been stilled,[14] but Communist an-

thropologists in Russia still hold faithfully to Engels's interpretation of Morgan.

Of course, there is no way of knowing from direct observation just what prehistoric social organization was like. Archaeological data can tell us what the technological traditions of a given locale were, they can reveal the outlines of settlement patterns, and they can yield exciting treasures of art, as well as the bones of men and animals, but in the absence of historical records, they tell us little of certainty about beliefs, values, marriage practices, kinship, inheritance, economic exchange, mythology, religion, ceremonialism, government, or law.

As for descent groups, bilateral, patrilineal, matrilineal, and double-descent extensions of the kinship group appear on *all* levels of cultural development and in all the major geographic areas of the world.

Among the most primitive or culturally undeveloped tribes . . . the Andamanese pygmies, the Paiute of the Great Basin, and the Yahgan of Tierra del Fuego are bilateral in descent, the Vedda of Ceylon, the Rankokamekra of east-central Brazil, and the Kutchin of northern Canada are matrilineal, and the Witoto of Amazonia, the Gilyak of Siberia, and the Miwok of California are patrilineal, while several native Australian tribes are characterized by double descent. All rules of descent are likewise well represented on the intermediate levels of culture, among agricultural and developed pastoral people. Even among literate peoples with relatively complex civilizations, our sample includes the bilateral Yankees and Syrian Christians, the patrilineal Chinese and Manchus, and the matrilineal Minangkabau Malays of Sumatra and Brahman Nyars of India.[15]

David Aberle has collated some very relevant data in which the societies represented in the World Ethnographic Survey are cross-classified by type (or level) of subsistence techniques and type of descent system.[16] Table 24-2 shows the percentages of bilateral, matrilineal, patrilineal, and duolineal cultures that occur on each level of subsistence technology.

---

[12]G. P. Murdock, "Double Descent" (*American Anthropologist,* Vol. 42, 1940), pp. 555–561. See also J. Goody, "The Classification of Double Descent Systems (*Current Anthropology,* Vol. 2, 1961), pp. 3–26.

[13]F. Engels, *The Origin of the Family, Property and the State in the Light of the Researches of Lewis Henry Morgan,* p. 50.

[14]R. H. Lówie finally laid the issue to rest in his great synthesis of cultural anthropology, *Primitive Society,* published in 1920. See especially chap. 6.

[15]G. P. Murdock, *Social Structure,* p. 186.

[16]D. F. Aberle, "Matrilineal Descent in Cross-cultural Perspective," in D. M. Schneider and K. Gough (eds.), *Matrilineal Kinship,* table 17-4, p. 677.

Table 24-2   *Per Cent of Occurrence of Types of Descent Groups in a Sample of 505 Societies, Classified According to Dominant Type of Subsistence Base*

type of subsistence base	bilateral	patrilineal	matrilineal	duolineal	number of tribes in sample
Plow agriculture	32%	59%	8%	1%	117
Pastoralism	12%	77%	5%	6%	66
Developed agriculture	35%	35%	25%	5%	188
Incipient agriculture	45%	34%	15%	6%	33
Hunting and gathering	61%	19%	13%	7%	101

SOURCE: Data selected and converted to percentages from D. M. Schneider and K. Gough (eds.), *Matrilineal Kinship*, Table 17-4, p. 677.

Descent groups among hunters and gatherers If hunting and gathering are taken as the most primitive food-getting techniques, such as were characteristic of the cultures of the Paleolithic era, we see that a majority (61 per cent) of such societies are bilateral and that there is no significant difference between the number that are patrilineal and the number that are matrilineal (19 and 13 per cent, respectively). Although 39 per cent of contemporary hunting and gathering cultures are unilineal or duolineal, it is not possible to say of any specific prehistoric culture whether it was organized bilaterally or not, except that the odds are 1.5 to 1 that it was.

Descent groups among incipient agriculturalists Prehistoric hunting and foraging cultures marked the inception of the food revolution and the era of incipient agriculture in the Neolithic Age. Among recent practitioners of hunting, fishing, and subsidiary gardening, there is a rise in the proportion of unilineal systems to 55 per cent. Patrilineality shows a marked increase. Thus, there is a slight trend toward lineages and clans, but it remains impossible to say whether any set of prehistoric foragers was unilineal or bilateral in a situation in which the odds are no greater than 5 to 4 in favor of unilineality over bilateralism.

Descent groups among developed agriculturalists On the level of developed agriculturalists, unilineality achieves a clear ascendancy: 65 per cent of the societies in the sample are unilineal, but there is no very great difference between matrilineal and patrilineal frequencies (25 per cent matrilineal, 35 per cent patrilineal). Matrilineal descent as a principle of social organization reaches its highest peak of frequency among developed agriculturalists, but even so, it is less common than either bilaterality or patrilineality. Gardening obviously encourages the formation of uxorilocal residence, for although women rarely hunt, they are the root and seed gatherers and, quite often, the gardeners. This is all work that can be done while tending a baby. Mothers and daughters work together, and men come to live with their wives. Only in such situations are matrilineal and matrilateral socioeconomic interests sufficiently strong to coalesce into matrilineages and matriclans; ". . . matrilocality is a necessary but not a sufficient condition for the development of matrilineal descent groups. . . ."[17] Obviously, a rather unique and quite powerful combination of circumstances is required to overcome the more usual and effective factors that favor bilateral or patrilineal organization.

[17]Aberle, *op. cit.*, p. 659.

Descent groups among pastoralists The intimate relationship between males and livestock is dramatically reflected in the overwhelming patrilineality of pastoralism. Almost four-fifths (77 per cent) of all pastoral cultures are patrilineal.[18] "The cow," as Aberle says, "is the enemy of matriliny, and the friend of patriliny."[19] This is the only safe generalization one could use in reconstructing the kinds of descent groups that were likely to have existed in any prehistoric stage of social evolution. And even this is of slight utility, since pastoralism is characteristic of a relatively minor proportion (12 per cent) of the cultures covered in the World Ethnographic Survey.

Descent groups among plow agriculturalists The hitching of the horse or oxen to the plow is the final step in precivilized evolution of subsistence techniques. It occurred in the Old World Late Neolithic Age. Plow agriculture subordinates the pastoralist's interest in animals to the horticulturalist's concern with farming. This is reflected in a reduction of the degree of frequency of patrilineality among pastoral societies as compared with societies with plow agriculture: from 77 per cent down to 59 per cent. There is a significant rise in bilaterality (12 to 32 per cent) as well as some increase in matrilineality and duolineal organization.

In Western civilization, the shift to bilateralism is a reflection of the influence of urbanization and the invention of the legal instrument of contract, whereby a person is able to stand as a self-determining, individual legal entity, rather than as a unit in the corporate kinship group (see pages 449–450 for further development of this point).

---

[18]This figure, as given in Table 24-2, does not include Aberle's category of "New World pastoralists," which consists of societies that acquired domesticated livestock in post-Columbian times. There are 13 such tribes in the total sample of 565. Most of them are horse-herding hunters who were previously bilateral and who had acquired horses so recently that they did not have sufficient time to readjust their descent groups. Of the thirteen tribes, eleven (85 per cent) are bilateral, and two (15 per cent) are matrilineal. New World pastoralism is such an aberrant phenomenon that we have excluded it from the table.
[19]*Ibid.,* p. 680.

As Fig. 24-2 graphically reveals, most hunters and gatherers are bilateral, and as one "moves up" the evolutionary scale to developed agriculture, bilateralism declines. The patrilineal curve is the obverse to the bilateral. Matrilineality realizes its highest potential among intensive agriculturalists, but at no level does it ever exceed other forms of descent groups. On the highest level of food production (plow agriculture), it all but disappears.

Looking to the future, as the scientific, industrialized technology of Western civilization is introduced all around the world, it is improbable that any unilineal systems of kinship organization will survive into the twenty-second century, except perhaps in a few backward, peasant areas (see Chapter 36).

SUMMARY

The boundaries of kinship are never limited to the conjugal-natal family, for such a family is invariably embedded in a larger web of kinship.

Bilateral extension of kinship produces the kindred and the ramage. When extended beyond three degrees, it embraces so many persons that it becomes unwieldy in size. But even more fatal is the fact that each person must belong to a number of such extended groups, and is faced with the problem of conflicting loyalties. The majority of societies have therefore found it expedient to utilize the unilineal principle for extended kinship reckoning. The unilineal principle has certain inherent advantages. It automatically reduces the number of potential members of the group by including only one-half of a person's relatives. Above all, it clearly establishes kinship identity and lessens the problem of conflicting loyalties.

Types of groups formed on the unilineal principle are the lineage, the clan, the phratry, and the moiety. Whether the matrilineal or patrilineal pattern prevails in a given culture is strongly influenced by the residence customs: uxorilocal, virilocal, avunculocal, neolocal, or bilocal. Residence, in turn, is strongly influ-

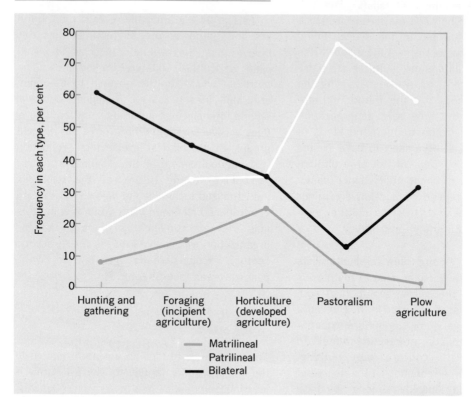

Fig. 24-2   *Inferred evolutionary trends in the occurrence of types of descent groups as revealed by the percentage of frequencies of descent groups in societies classified according to subsistence base. Pastoralism is not to be read as a higher evolutionary form than horticulture.*

enced by the type of dominant subsistence base in a culture. Although among simple hunters and gatherers the bilateral principle of organization is dominant, unilineal groups are found in one-third of human societies on this level. Bilateralism progressively gives way to lineage and clan organization, as culture develops to foraging and intensive gardening. Its lowest frequency is found among the strongly patrilineal pastoralists. Patrilineality is relatively weak among hunters and gatherers; it becomes relatively stronger as cultures develop a horticultural base; it overwhelms all other forms among pastoralists; and it remains the dominant form among the protocivilized prac-

titioners of plow agriculture. Matrilineality exists as a minor form of kinship organization on all levels of cultural development, except the highest, where it completely disappears. Developed agriculture is the subsistence base that is most favorable to the development of matrilineal social systems, but even in this most favorable setting, matrilineages and matriclans are less common than either patrilineal or bilateral units of organization.

The very earliest Paleolithic societies were probably bilateral, since this is the most generalized and the least specialized type of kinship system. The domestication of plants and animals fostered the development of special property interests and unilocal residence patterns in many societies, with the result that lineages and clans apparently came into prominence. Yet, to the extent that one can make inferences about prehistoric social organization from present-day frequency distributions, clan organization could never have wholly displaced bilateralism.

Generalizations concerning prehistoric kinship structures can be formulated only in broad, relatively unspecific terms. They may never be taken as statements of scientific laws; at best, they qualify as suggestive inferences drawn from contemporary primitive societies believed, on the basis of their material cultures, to be analogically similar to prehistoric societies whose material bases are known from archaeological data. Inferences about prehistoric social organization are never verifiable in specific content.

SELECTED READINGS

Bohannan, P.: *Social Anthropology* (1963), Part 2 (pp. 54–142). Approaches the subject of this chapter with a somewhat different methodological emphasis and constitutes a very useful complementary alternative to that which we have presented here.

Fortes, M.: *The Web of Kinship among the Tallensi* (1949), chaps. 1, 5, and 11, "Kinship and the Lineage System," "Parents and Children in the Framework of the Lineage," and "The Web of Extra-clan Kinship." A masterful analysis of the complexities of kinship in an African tribe.

————: "Structure of Unilinear Descent Groups" (*American Anthropologist*, Vol. 55, 1953), pp. 17–44. A most excellent exposition of the application of the unilineal principle in primitive cultures.

Lowie, R. H.: *Primitive Society* (1920), chap. 6, "The Sib." Although this contains some discussions of problems that are no longer live issues in anthropology, the chapter is highly informative.

Murdock, G. P.: *Social Structure* (1949), chaps. 3 and 4, "Consanguineal Kin Groups" and "The Clan."

Radcliffe-Brown, A. R., and M. Fortes (eds.): *African Systems of Kinship and Marriage* (1950). Descriptive analyses of a number of African examples of differing types of kinship organization.

Schneider, D. M., and K. Gough (eds.): *Matrilineal Kinship* (1961). An impressive work in which six anthropologists pool their efforts in ethnological examination of a series of matrilineal societies. Schneider proposes a set of hypothetical characteristics of matrilineal systems, Gough interprets the ethnographic data, and Aberle puts their propositions to the statistical test of cross-cultural validation on a broad scale.

Kinship systems and terminology

chapter 25

Behavior toward relatives is not the same as behavior toward nonrelatives. Rich uncles win special deference. A person always has certain obligations to his kinsmen. The status of a relative is unique, compared with that of the rest of mankind.

As a striking manifestation of this fundamental fact, E. E. Evans-Pritchard observes:

If you wish to live among the Nuer, you must do so on their terms, which means that you must treat them as kinsmen and they will treat you as a kind of kinsman. Rights, privileges and obligations are determined by kinship. Either a man is a kinsman, actually or by fiction, or he is a person to whom you owe no reciprocal obligations and whom you treat as a potential enemy.[1]

Because we live in an industrialized society of great social mobility, in which we depend to a great degree upon our own efforts and those of mutual-aid associations (insurance and benevolent societies), unions, and philanthropic and governmental agencies to provide social security, rather than our relatives, it is hard for most of us to comprehend the importance of kinsmen in simpler societies. In primitive society, most of these responsibilities rest with the kinship group.

The contrast is philosophically stated by an old Pomo Indian of California, who soliloquized:

What is a man? A man is nothing. Without his family he is of less importance than that bug crossing the trail, or less importance than the sputum or exuviale. At least *they* can be used to help poison a man. A

[1]E. E. Evans-Pritchard, *The Nuer*, p. 182.

man must be with his family to amount to anything with us. If he had nobody else to help him, the first trouble he got into he would be killed by his enemies, because there would be no relatives to help him fight the poison of the other group. No woman would marry him. . . . He would be poorer than a new-born child, he would be poorer than a worm. . . . The family is important. If a man has a large family, . . . and upbringing by a family that is known to produce good children, then he is somebody and every family is willing to have him marry a woman of their group. In the White way of doing things the family is not so important. The police and soldiers take care of protecting you, the courts give you justice, the post office carries messages for you, the school teaches you. Everything is taken care of, even your children, if you die; but with us the family must do all of that.

Without the family we are nothing, and in the old days before the White people came, the family was given first consideration by anyone who was about to do anything at all. That is why we got along. . . .

With us the family was everything. Now it is nothing. We are getting like the White people and it is bad for the old people. We had no old people's home like you. The old people were important. They were wise. Your old people must be fools.[2]

The patterns of kinship behavior are only in slight degree biologically determined. Kinship relations consist of the interacting roles that are customarily ascribed to the different statuses of relationship by a people. Every culture includes a set of words, or labels, that symbolize each of its kinship statuses. These labels are called *kinship terms*, and the whole is called the *system of kinship* (or *relationship*) *terminology*.

The classificatory principle

The first important principle to grasp in the study of kinship systems is that *no system provides a separate and distinct term for every possible kind or position of genealogical relationship.* All systems equate, lump, or merge some relatives of different genealogical positions into one single category, which is identified by a specific term. For example, the Comanche Indians equate

father, father's brother, and mother's sister's husband all under one term, *ap'*. Father's brother and mother's sister's husband (both of whom we call "uncle") are genealogically distinct from father, but to the Comanche they are merged or equated under the same identifying term of relationship.

Kinship terms that result from merging are called *classificatory terms*. A kinship term that applies to a particular genealogical status and no other is called *particularizing* or *descriptive*. We, for instance, tend to apply the terms "father" and "mother" only to our actual progenitors when referring to relatives. However, as no system is ever wholly particularizing or classificatory, we also have certain classificatory terms, such as "cousin," "uncle," "aunt," "niece," "nephew," "grandfather," "grandmother," "grandson," and "granddaughter."

Our insistence on particularizing "father" and "mother" is sociologically significant, for it will be noted that in addition to particularizing "father" and "mother," we use the words "son" and "daughter" to mean only our own children and not those of our brothers or sisters.[3] Likewise, we use the terms "brother" and "sister" to refer exclusively to the siblings of our own primary conjugal-natal family. Other relatives of our own generation level we call "cousins." Our terminology thus places strong emphasis upon the exclusiveness of our primary conjugal-natal family; it rigidly distinguishes more remote relatives. This reflects the great social significance of our close relatives in the conjugal-natal family as against the rest of our larger kindred. Lineal relatives are more important to us than collateral ones.

In most primitive societies, as we have noted, extended kinship groups play larger roles than is the case with us. In such societies, merging or lumping of relatives on a collateral basis is therefore much more likely.

Since kinship terms designate social sta-

[2]B. W. Aginsky, "An Indian's Soliloquy" (*The American Journal of Sociology*, Vol. 46, 1940), pp. 43–44.

[3]See A. M. Hocart, "Kinship Systems," in E. A. Hoebel, J. D. Jennings, and E. R. Smith, *Readings in Anthropology*, pp. 189–193, for an explanation of how such terms should be conceived.

tuses, what you must call a person ideally determines how you should behave toward him. Further, all persons who are called by the same kinship term should (and again, ideally) receive the same sort of treatment, since they enjoy ideologically identical statuses in the system of social organization.

Comanche kinship terminology

It will help to get the feel of kinship if we briefly explore the way in which relatives are grouped and identified in a few systems other than our own. To do this, we shall begin with a look at the way the Comanche Indians classify relatives.

Comanche social structure is bilateral and bilocal. Polygynous marriages are permissible. The Comanche kindred is exogamous; no one may marry a relative within three or so degrees of recognized relationship.

In treating any system of kinship terminology, it is necessary to have a starting point in a particular individual. We shall call this person *ego* (L. *ego,* I) and start with ego as a male, for it makes a difference whether a man or woman is speaking.

Ego calls his mother *pia.* But there are also other female relatives called *pia,* namely, his mother's sisters, his mother's female cousins, and his father's brother's wife. *Pia* can thus be seen to mean not "mother" to a Comanche, but more exactly, "female relative of my mother's generation and kindred."

His father he calls *ap'.* But there are also other male relatives called *ap',* namely, his father's brothers, his father's male cousins, and his father's sister's husband. *Ap'* thus does not mean "father" to a Comanche, but "male relative of my father's generation and kindred."

The Comanche calls his mother's brother by a different term, *ara.* Thus, where we merge father's brother and mother's brother together as "uncle," the Comanche merges father and father's brother in one category, while distinguishing mother's brother in another.

The same thing is done with aunts. Mother and mother's sister are both classified as *pia,* but father's sister is distinguished as *paha.* This practice is called *forked merging* or *bifurcate merging.*

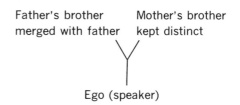

Father's brother merged with father   Mother's brother kept distinct

Ego (speaker)

Members of the agnatic and uterine kindreds are thus kept distinct.

Within his own generation, all relatives are "brother" and "sister" to a Comanche; cousins are not recognized as such. But relative age *is,* so the Comanche distinguishes between *paβi* and *tami,* "older male relative of my own generation" and "younger male relative of my own generation." A *paβi* may be ego's elder brother, father's brother's son, father's sister's son, mother's brother's son, mother's sister's son, and wife's sister's husband (if ego is a male) or husband's sister's husband (if ego is a female). *Tami* applies to all these categories if the person referred to is younger than ego.

A "son" to ego includes not only his own boys but also the male offspring of all his *paβi* and *tami,* the sons of his wife's sisters, and his sister's daughter's husband. All these are called *tua.*

A "daughter" includes his own female offspring and the female offspring of all his *patsi* (elder female relatives of his own generation) and *nami* (younger female relatives of his own generation), his wife's sister's daughters, and his sister's son's wife. All these are called *pedi.*[4]

The kinship terms that have been described here cover the members of ego's primary and secondary conjugal-natal families. Whereas we use exclusive, descriptive terms that isolate the two conjugal-natal families, it may readily be seen that the Comanches merge such indi-

[4]For a full analysis of the Comanche system, see E. A. Hoebel, "Comanche and H3kandika Shoshone Relationship Systems" (*American Anthropologist,* Vol. 41, 1939), pp. 440–457.

viduals within the larger kindred. For them, the kindred is the socially more important group.

All in all, the Comanches recognize thirty-six different kinship categories, each of which has a different kinship term. None of them is identical to the groupings or distinctions drawn by us in our kinship system. *The way in which any society identifies relatives is dependent upon the nature of its kinship groups.* These, in turn, are predominantly determined by the rules of residence and subsistence practices that prevail in the culture.

Principles of kinship identification

In a classic paper, Kroeber identified the following eight principles of kinship distinctions that may be seized upon in shaping a kinship system.[5]

1. Difference in generation levels (father, son; grandparent, grandchild; etc.)

2. Difference in age levels within the same generation (elder and younger brother; father's elder brother; etc.)

3. Difference between lineal and collateral relationship (father, uncle; brother, cousin; etc.)

4. Difference in sex of relatives (brother, sister, uncle, aunt, etc.)

5. Difference in sex of the speaker (males and females may have two separate systems of terms)

[5]A. L. Kroeber, "Classificatory Systems of Relationship" (*Journal of the Royal Anthropological Institute of Great Britain and Ireland,* Vol. 39, 1909), pp. 77–84.

6. Difference of sex of the person through whom the relationship is established (*father's* brother, *mother's* brother; *father's* father, *mother's* father; father's *father's sister's daughter's* daughter, etc.)

7. Difference between genetic relatives and those connected by marriage (sister, mother; husband's mother, etc.)

8. Difference in status or life condition of the person *through whom* the relationship is established (living or dead, single or married, etc.)

Few systems make use of all eight distinctions, but many use the first seven.

If the reader will carefully examine the Comanche terms that we have given, he will be able to identify each of the first seven principles in them. The Anglo-American system, on the other hand, utilizes only four of the eight (1, 3, 4, 7).

Types of kinship systems

It is a remarkable fact that although a very large number of differing kinship systems are theoretically possible, society after society classifies its kinsmen in essentially similar ways, so that the types of kinship systems that actually come into existence are few in number.

The classification (or typing) of kinship

Fig. 25-1   The distinction of collateral and lineal kinsmen.

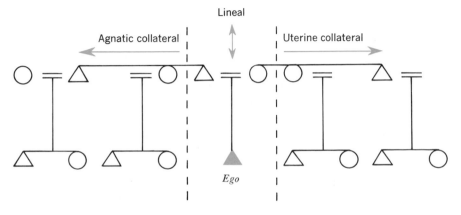

Lineal

Agnatic collateral

Uterine collateral

Ego

systems presents all the usual problems of selection of criteria that were discussed in an earlier chapter (pages 97–99). As is the case with races, fewer or more types result, according to the quality and number of criteria used.[6] The most significant criteria used by anthropologists for general classification of systems of kinship terminologies are of two orders: (1) the degree of merging and bifurcation of lineal and collateral kin in the parental generation and (2) the degree of merging and bifurcation of collateral kin in ego's own generation.[7]

Kinship systems based on classification of parental generation Use of the criterion of classification of lineal and collateral kin on the parental level produces four types of kinship systems: (1) generational, (2) lineal, (3) bifurcate merging, and (4) bifurcate collateral.

Generational systems The emphasis in this type of system is on merging of all relatives on a given generational level. Thus, mother, mother's sister, and father's sister are all lumped under a single kinship term. The same is true of father, father's brother, and mother's brother.

Lineal systems A lineal system emphasizes the distinction between direct ascendant and descendant relatives as separate from collaterals. Therefore, mother is distinguished from

mother's sister and fathers's sister, who are merged, as in English "aunt." The same holds for father and his collaterals, who are merged, as in English "uncle." Lineal systems are also associated with bilateral systems of descent groups.

Bifurcate-merging systems Lineage systems of descent groups tend to produce bifurcate-merging systems of terminology, as will be demonstrated in the analysis of Crow terminology given below. Father's brother is merged with father, while both are distinguished from mother's brother. Put in another way, father and paternal uncle are lumped, and maternal uncle is distinguished. Likewise, mother and maternal aunt are lumped, and paternal aunt is distinguished. Members of the two descent groups are rigorously kept separate from each other.

Bifurcate-collateral systems In this type of system, all collaterals on the parental generation level are bifurcated, or distinguished. Father, father's brother, and mother's brother all are called by separate terms of designation, as are mother, mother's sister, and father's sister. There is no significant correlation between bifurcate-collateral terminology and any particular system of descent groups, nor is there any adequate theory to account for the prevalence of this highly particularizing method of classification.

RELATIVE FREQUENCY OF SYSTEMS BASED ON CLASSIFICATION OF PARENTAL GENERATION Forty-four per cent of the kinship systems in the World Ethnographic Survey are of the bifurcate-merging type. This happens because most descent systems are unilineal and automatically place mother's and father's brothers in different descent groups. Bifurcate-merging terminology reflects this simple fact.

Generational-type kinship systems go with bilateral descent systems and occur in 30 per cent of the cases. Bilateral systems do not separate mother's and father's kin, nor does generational terminology.

---

[6]Leslie White, on noting that ". . . no one . . . has been able to work out and establish a valid theory of the evolution of kinship systems" (*The Evolution of Culture*, p. 135), feels that the trouble is in the way in which kinship is studied rather than in an actual absence of evolution in this area of culture. In other words, concepts stand in the way of recognition of fact. See also E. R. Service, *Primitive Social Organization*, pp. 185–195. Until new techniques and thoughts demonstrate an actual evolution in kinship systems, however, the negative conclusion must stand that kinship systems do not fit any evolutionary scheme.

[7]The first system was formulated by R. H. Lowie and published in the fourteenth edition of the *Encyclopaedia Britannica*, in the article "Relationship Terms." The second system was formalized by G. P. Murdock, *Social Structure*, pp. 223–259.

Table 25-1   Types of Kinship Systems According to Patterns of Classification of Relatives in the Parental and in Ego's Own Generations.

type of descent group	classification of parental generation		classification of ego's own generation	
	type	merging and bifurcation	type	merging and bifurcation
Bilateral	Generational	[Mo = MoSi = FaSi] [Fa = FaBr = MoBr]	Hawaiian	[×Cos = ‖Cos = Sib]
Bilateral	Lineal	Mo ≠ [MoSi = FaSi] Fa ≠ [FaBr = MoBr]	Eskimo	[×Cos = ‖Cos] ≠ Sib
Matrilineal or patrilineal	Bifurcate merging	[Mo = MoSi] ≠ FaSi [Fa = FaBr] ≠ MoBr	Crow, Iroquois, Omaha	×Cos ≠ [‖Cos = Sib]
	Bifurcate collateral	Mo ≠ MoSi ≠ FaSi Fa ≠ FaBr ≠ MoBr	Sudanese	×Cos ≠ ‖Cos ≠ Sib

NOTE: The Hawaiian generational type merges all parents and all cousins; the Eskimo lineal type distinguishes parents and siblings from their collaterals; the three bifurcate-merging systems merge parents with collaterals of like sex and merge parallel-cousins with siblings, while distinguishing cross-cousins; the Sudanese bifurcate-collateral type distinguishes all parental kin and cousins. [=] = merged categories; ≠ = distinguished or bifurcated categories; ×Cos = cross-cousins; ‖Cos = parallel-cousins; Sib = siblings.

Lineal systems, which occur in 17 per cent of the cases, are strongly associated with the occurrence of bilateral descent systems.

Bifurcate-collateral types are fairly rare (9 per cent) and do not correlate with any particular type of descent; they have not been adequately explained.

Kinship systems based on classification of cousins   Use of the criterion of merging and particularizing of siblings, cross-cousins, and parallel-cousins produces more refined results than analysis of the parental generation terminology alone. Therefore, Murdock has developed a typology of kinship systems based upon these criteria.

Murdock's classification sets up six types of kinship systems with respect to distinctions or lack of distinctions made in their terminologies for cousins. They are (1) the Hawaiian, (2) the Eskimo, (3) the Iroquois, (4) the Crow, (5) the Omaha, and (6) the Sudanese. These are actually the same as the generational categories, as can be seen from Table 25-1, except

that the category of bifurcate merging is refined into the Crow, Iroquois, and Omaha types.

The Hawaiian system   This is the same as the generational system. Because of its emphasis on generation equivalence, the Hawaiian system draws no distinction between cousins and siblings, all of whom belong to the same kindreds.

The Eskimo system   The Eskimo system draws no distinctions between cross- and parallel-cousins but does distinguish cousins from siblings. Its emphasis is on the immediate chain of conjugal-natal families. The Eskimo system is familiar to all speakers of the English language, for this is the system used in Anglo-American culture.

The Iroquois system   In the Iroquois system of terminology, siblings and parallel-cousins of the same sex are usually equated under one term, whereas cross-cousins are distinguished by different terms. Iroquois terminology is almost nonexistent among bilaterally organized tribes. It is weakly correlated (phi = 0.135)[8] with matrilineal and duolineal descent groups and appears to be the product of a weak matrilineal, uxorilocal system of social organization.

The Crow system The Crow system is based on a social structure that contains strongly developed matrilineal lineages and/or clans.

In cousin terminology, cross-cousins are distinguished from each other (i.e., there are separate terms for father's sister's son or daughter and mother's brother's son or daughter); these are also distinguished from parallel-cousins and from siblings. But paternal cross-

[8]A. D. Coult and R. W. Habenstein, *Cross Tabulations of Murdock's World Ethnographic Survey*, p. 512.

cousins are merged with father and father's sister, according to sex.

It is in this last lumping of father's sister's daughter with her paternal aunt that the lineage emphasis is made clearest. Hocart has shown us how earlier anthropologists were trapped into false conceptions of kinship by thinking of such classificatory terms as "father" as meaning an extension of fatherhood. Thus, Lowie translated the Crow Indian term *birupxe* as "father." *Birupxe* is the term applied to ego's father, father's brother, and father's sister's son (when ego is a male). Properly understood, it means not "father," but "male of my father's matrilineal lineage or clan." For the same reason, the term used in reference to ego's father's sister means "female of my father's matrilineal lineage or clan." The term for "mother" means "woman married to a male of my own matrilineal lineage or clan." Figure 25-2 diagrams this clearly.

Because father, father's brother, father's sister's son, and father's sister's daughter's son are all lumped together under one term as members of the same matrilineage, ego's mother is called "wife" by all of them. She may marry any one of them in secondary affinal marriage. Therefore, levirate and hus-

Fig. 25-2   Crow-type kinship identifications. Note that the male patrilateral cross-cousin may marry Ego's mother and is called by the same term as father. The female patrilateral cross-cousin is merged with father's sister. Ego may marry his maternal uncle's wife and he calls her by the same term as wife; matrilateral cross-cousins are called by the same term as son and daughter.

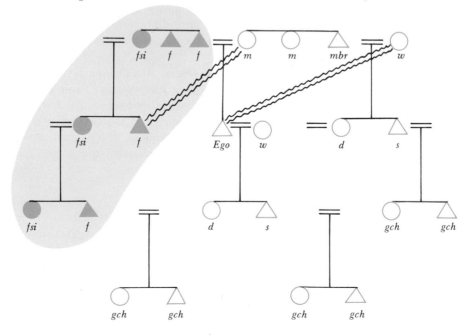

band's-sister's-son marriages are preferential forms in systems of marriage related to strong matrilineal descent systems and Crow terminology. Conversely, a man may marry his mother's brother's wife. The effect of all this on cousin terminology is that patrilateral cross-cousins are called by the same term as that used for father, and matrilateral cross-cousins, as children of the woman ego calls "wife," are designated by the same term as that used for son and daughter. It should be noted, however, that although these secondary affinal marriages are permissible, they are not reported as preferred marriages in all cultures in which Crow-type terminology occurs.

The Omaha system   The Omaha system is the patrilineal obverse of the Crow system. Mother and female matrilateral cross-cousin (mother's brother's daughter) are merged under one term that means "female member of my mother's patrilineage or clan." Father's sister's daughter (patrilateral cross-cousin) is merged with sister's daughter under a term that means "daughter of a female of my father's patrilineage or clan."

The Sudanese system   This type is at the opposite pole from the Hawaiian in that its terms are emphatically particularizing, or descriptive. Consequently, it has separate terms for each type of cousin, for siblings, and for aunts, nieces, uncles, and nephews.

The American kinship system

Our kinship system is of the Eskimo type. We lump all cousins, but we distinguish them from brothers and sisters. In the absence of lineages and clans, we show no lineal emphasis except within the primary and secondary conjugal-natal families. These are sharply set off from the kindred by the exclusive limitation of terms like "father," "mother," "brother," "sister," "son," and "daughter" to those who actually belong to the two conjugal-natal families.[9]

Monogamy is reflected in the fact that the words "father," "mother," "husband," and "wife" can apply to only one person within the kinship system. When these terms are used within the church system, they imply and evoke certain filial responses and behaviors that carry over from the kinship system, but no one makes the mistake of assuming that they imply genetic relationship. We see this also in the panhandler's claim to kinship assistance when he puts the touch with his plaintive, "Brother, can you spare a dime?"

One thing that is genuinely distinctive about our kinship terminology is the abundance of alternative terms used in addition to "mother," "father," "husband," and "wife." For "father" these are "dad," "daddy," "pop," "pa," "old man," "boss," "pater," and "governor." None of these carry the respect connotations, however, of the word "father." Their use varies in accordance with the authority roles acknowledged to the father by his children within the particular family, and they reflect the flexible nature of American family patterns. By and large, the term "daddy," widely used by youngsters, is dropped by boys as they grow up, although it is often retained by daughters for many years. Father-son relations become more restrained and formal, whereas there is much evidence to support the inference that the persistence of the use of the word "daddy" by girls expresses a continuance of preadolescent affectivity between father and daughter.

A parallel series of terms exists for "mother": "mom," "mommy," "mummy," "ma," "mama," "mater," and "old woman." Very similar role qualities are ascribed to these terms as to the alternatives to "father." Both boys and girls tend to shift from use of informal mother terms to the more formal "mother" as they grow up. Boys, in other words, do not keep the familiar term for "mother" the way girls carry on with "daddy."[10]

Affinal relatives are all distinguished by

[9]T. C. Parsons, "The Kinship System of the Contemporary United States" (*American Anthropologist*, Vol. 45, 1943), p. 24.

[10]D. M. Schneider and G. C. Homans, "Kinship Terminology and the American Kinship System" (*American Anthropologist*, Vol. 57, 1955), pp. 1195–1199.

means of the "in-law" suffix. However, we often use a device of teknonymy, the practice of naming an adult after the name of his child, to soften the stiffness of the "in-law" term when addressing our mother-in-law and father-in-law. This is managed by identifying ourselves with our offspring and addressing our spouses' parents as "grandmother" and "grandfather." They are lineal kin to our children, and so by this fictive device we draw them into our lineal family group.

Except for a slight linguistic emphasis given to the patrilineal line through patronymy, the consequences of which are more attitudinal than structural or behavioral, our system is symmetrically multilateral. We treat all ramifications extending out from the immediate lineal line with equal weight (or lack of it). Such distinctions in emphasis as do occur are the result of personal preferences or aversions and proximity of residence, not the consequences of any systematic emphasis.

The lack of structural cohesiveness outside the inner circle of families in lineal descent in our kinship system reflects the weak role kinship groups play in our society. We emphasize the independence of separate conjugal-natal family units. Most of our problems concerning marriage and the family rise directly or indirectly from this fact. Parent-child conflict is generated because children must develop independence to be able to found their own economically independent families with separate households.

Much of the erratic behavior of adolescents, so baffling or amusing to adults, may be traced to the insecurity of the emergent boy or girl, who is in transition from the bonds of his primary family of birth to the expectant secondary conjugal-natal family he or she must soon found. Insecurity in old age is the lot of many parents whose secondary conjugal-natal family has been pared down until only they are left. When one of them dies, the survivor is at sea, with no comfortable base in which to harbor. Old people's homes and old-age security legislation are the palliative social consequences.

Few of the social relations of children are predetermined by kinship status outside the immediate conjugal-natal family. Children are thrown into open competition for social status; some are rewarded with success and prestige, and others find only frustration and insecurity.

Marriage in the United States rests heavily on the bond of love and affection, for there are no absolutely ascribed preferential matings within the kinship group to solve the problem of mating, nor is there much family control of mating, as in Asia or France. These are only some of the upsetting consequences of our open, weak kinship system.

The advantages of this system are those which derive from individual freedom of action in social and economic relations: freedom to choose one's friends within or without the relationship group, freedom to choose one's mate, freedom to find an occupation fairly untrammeled by kinship status, and freedom to live where one wills.

In America today, the individual couple is largely on its own, to stand or fall as a unit according to its ability to surmount the hazards of our loose kinship system and to utilize the freedoms of our mobile and rapidly changing society. The divorce mills grind for those who fail, and questing college students flock to sociology courses in marriage and the family.

SUMMARY

Systems of kinship terminology reflect the forms of kinship grouping in the social organization of any culture. The kinship terms of address or reference are tags or labels symbolic of each relative's status in relation to the speaker of the term. Each status has its customary roles, or norms of behavior, and the behavior of relatives is generally standardized according to status.

No kinship system distinguishes each separate genetic relationship. On the contrary, the tendency is to lump relatives of unlike genetic status into categories of like kinship status. Systems that lump relatives extensively are called *classificatory;* systems that emphasize genetic distinctions are called *descriptive* or *particularizing.*

Kroeber's eight principles of kinship distinctions reveal the possible factors that may be used in developing kinship categories of terminological identification.

Lowie introduced a system for classifying kinship terminologies according to *merging* or *bifurcation* of the parental level of kinsman. This results in a four-class system: *generational, lineal, bifurcate merging,* and *bifurcate collateral.* Murdock's system classifies kinship terminologies according to merging or bifurcation of siblings and cousins. It produces a sixfold set of primary classes, which are identified with the names of the tribe (or area, in the case of the Sudanese) in which the type was first described at length. They are the Hawaiian, Eskimo, Crow, Iroquois, Omaha, and Sudanese.

The Hawaiian type of terminology, which equates all relatives of each generation level, is the most highly classificatory. Hawaiian and Eskimo terminologies are associated with bilateral social structure. At the other end of the pole, Crow and Omaha terminologies are associated with strong matrilineal and patrilineal social structures.

The American kinship system is bilateral, with an Eskimo lineal type of terminology. Beyond the conjugal-natal family, there is only the kindred or the ramage, and this in weak form. Alternative kinship terms, used by Americans, reflect differences in degree of respect and familiarity between relatives on an individual basis, and in this there appear to be psychologically and socially significant differences on a sex basis. Kinship systems are reflected in relationship terminologies. Kinship dominates all relationships in most non-Western societies.

SELECTED READINGS

Bellah, R. N.: *Apache Kinship Systems* (1952). A technical analysis of the structure and function of Southwest Athapascan kinship systems in historical perspective.

Eggan, F.: *Social Organization of the Western Pueblos* (1950). This will not be easy reading for the beginner, but it is one of the finest comparative studies of kinship systems.

———— (ed.): *Social Anthropology of North American Tribes* (2d ed., 1955). Contains highly informative articles on the kinship systems of six American Indian tribes.

Lowie, R. H.: "Kinship," *Encyclopedia of the Social Sciences,* Vol. 3, 1931, pp. 568–572. The elements of kinship systems clearly presented.

Murdock, G. P.: *Social Structure* (1949), chaps. 6 and 7, "Analysis of Kinship" and "Determinants of Kinship Terminology." Requires hard thinking, but analysis of kinship systems is never easy.

Schusky, E. L.: *Manual for Kinship Analysis* (1965). A helpful handbook for identification and analysis of kinship systems.

Clubs
and age groups

chapter 26

The urge to form clubs is not a trait of civilized men exclusively. Most primitives, too, have found the means to make life more intriguing, colorful, and meaningful through club life.

When we analyze clubs from a sociological point of view, we see that structurally they are just one form of association. In the definition of associations, we find it useful to follow the line laid down by MacIver, who distinguishes associations from institutions in that an *association* is defined as a group specifically organized for the pursuit of special interests, while an *institution* is "the set method of procedure," the complex of behavior, characteristic of an association.[1]

[1] R. M. MacIver, *Society*, pp. 12–15.

We shall treat clubs as those associations which are not based on the kinship factor, which have exclusive membership within the larger society, which definitely possess a formal institutional structure, and which engender a discernible feeling of congeniality among the members along with *esprit de corps*, or the "we-feeling."

Further, although it is traditional in anthropology to speak of Australian "secret societies," Plains Indian "military societies," and Pueblo Indian "curing societies," it will help eliminate confusion if we do not use the word "society" in the sense of club or association. It will be legitimate, however, to continue to call men's clubs *fraternities*, which is traditional anthropological usage in those instances in which clubs promote the social fiction of brotherhood among their members.

Finally, associations that include all the men of a given age range are known as *age groups, age grades, age classes,* or *age sets.*

Club life and the sexes

The profusion of women's auxiliaries, bridge clubs, sewing circles, women's clubs, and women's leagues that is to be seen about us today leads some myopic observers to the conclusion that women are the sociable sex. It is doubtful, even within this club-ridden society of ours, that there are more women's clubs than men's or that men spend less time and are less active in club life than women. In the primitive world, however, there is no question but that men are the devotees of club life and women are not. The clubwoman of the modern civilized world is one of the revolutionary developments of recent times. There was nothing like her in earlier human history.

Women in primitive societies rarely participate in club life; sometimes they enter into men's organizations as auxiliaries. When they do have clubs of their own, they are weak counterparts of the vigorous organizations of the men. There are rarely all-embracing tribal associations of women, as there are of men.

Indeed, club life among primitive women is so undeveloped that Schurtz, who at the turn of the century gave anthropology its classic study of men's societies and age grades, advanced the theory that females are innately unsociable. They are inhibited in the formation of clubs, wrote Schurtz, because by instinct their activities and interests concentrate on reproduction, hearth, and home.[2]

This must be dismissed as androcentric prejudice. In its stead, a cultural-functional explanation that is nearer the facts of human experience may be advanced. First, the demands of family nurture tend to isolate women and leave them little time for club activities. American experience of the last few decades shows that given time and the opportunity, women take to club life. Second, primitive women, in addition to having little time for club activities, are in most male-dominated societies definitely discouraged from entering into the club systems set up by men, nor do the men look with favor upon female imitations of their organizations. This is found to be true especially in tribes that link secret men's clubs with religious activities. Revelation of the secrets of ritual and hocus-pocus to women (and uninitiated boys) meant death in Australia and West Africa and even among the matrilineal Pueblos of the Southwest. A woman who accidentally witnessed the secret rites of Central Australian men's groups might possibly still be speared on the spot, as she would have been before the days of Australian governmental police and courts. The men's secret clubs of the Banks Islands and certain other Melanesian tribes terrorize and bully the noninitiates (including all women).

When so much ado is made about the necessity of protecting the sacred secrets from women and when the sanctions imposed upon women who happen to penetrate the secrets are so fatal, is it surprising that women do not expose themselves to such risks by undertaking the formation of clubs along the lines so jealously guarded by the men?

[2]H. Schurtz, *Altersklassen und Männerbunde.*

Tribal secret fraternities

Secret fraternities that include all the adult men of a society are called *tribal fraternities.* The adjective "tribal" serves to distinguish them from the more limited type of associations that are open to only a privileged few.

Tribal fraternities are a direct outgrowth of adolescence transition rites. Puberty rites, as we have seen, serve as bridges over the yawning chasms of anxiety that threaten men when they confront the crises of life. Those who have successfully bridged the chasms by passing through the rites of puberty do not necessarily organize into an association because of this fact. But because passage through puberty gives an exalted status of maturity and because puberty rites for boys and girls are almost always separate, all those men who have been made conscious of their newly achieved status by the rites are apt to crystallize their special status in an organized association. The puberty rite then becomes an initiatory rite. Not only is such an initiatory rite a transitional rite over a life crisis, but it also opens the door into the fraternity of men.

Such rites emphasize the destruction of the preinitiation personality of the neophyte. As Webster long ago noted:

Almost universally initiation rites include a mimic representation of the death and resurrection of the novice. The new life to which he awakes after initiation is one utterly forgetful of the old; a new name, a new language, and new privileges are its natural accompaniments.[3]

A new name and a new language are not in fact always forthcoming, but seclusion from the women and children followed by "rebirth" are regular features of primitive initiatory rites. In tribes where girls are initiated by the women, men and boys are rigidly excluded from their rites. Clearly, the process is one of intensification of sex-linked roles on either side.

The line to be drawn between mere puberty rites and tribal initiation ceremonies is not a sharp one. Whether we decide that a ritual

[3]H. Webster, *Primitive Secret Societies*, p. 38.

falls into one class or the other depends on whether it leads merely to the status of adult or whether it brings adult status *plus* membership in a specific association of adults. Sometimes there is an intermediary borderline condition on which it would be most arbitrary to make a classificatory judgment.

Thus, in the case of the Andaman Islanders' puberty rites, we contemplate solemn and elaborate but nonsecret rituals that effect status shifts for boys and girls. Full-fledged men are distinctly separated from fledgling boys, and they enjoy many perquisites of adult status. They seem to be bound together by the bonds of consciousness of their common privileges and interests. Yet they do not seem to form a men's fraternity.

On the other hand, in the case of the Central Australian tribes, the initiated married men form a domineering, tightly knit group, possessed of much secret lore and enjoying many lordly privileges, all of which indicates without doubt that here we have true tribal associations.

Aside from Central Australia and certain Melanesian groups, the great center for the development of tribal fraternities is Africa, particularly West Africa from Sierra Leone into Nigeria, Cameroon, and the jungle region of the Congo.[4] In Africa, the subjugation and exclusion of women, so noticeable elsewhere, is much attenuated. Although the tribal associations may be for men, they often include women. And what is more notable, women frequently have powerful clubs of their own. In Sierra Leone and Liberia, although some men's associations admit females, no women's clubs admit men. In view of the greater social power and prestige of the men's organizations, when absolute exclusiveness breaks down there is more pressure from the women to penetrate the men's clubs than vice versa.

In West Africa, the *porro* and *bondu* fraternities and sororities of such tribes as the Mendi and Temne of Sierra Leone and the Kpelle of Liberia are most famous. All boys

[4]W. D. Hambly, "Source Book for African Anthropology" (*Field Museum of Natural History, Anthropological Series,* Vol. 26, Part 2, 1937), p. 498.

upon completion of their puberty rites enter the *porro;* the girls find themselves members of the *bondu.* Among the Kpelle, the *porro* is a central integrating and controlling feature of tribal life—family, religious, and political.[5] The chief officer (grand master) of the *porro* wields effective political power and social prestige. Membership in the *porro* is a prerequisite for marriage and for admission to all other clubs and offices. The *porro* is internally graded according to the general social status and ages of the members.

Nontribal secret fraternities

By far the most notorious of the widespread African secret fraternities are the limited and exclusive secret orders of the Leopard, Crocodile, and Snake or of other beasts, reptiles, or birds. Of these, the Leopards are the most feared. *Egbo, Ekkpe,* and *Ngbe* are but variant tribal names for the Leopard order. Human sacrifice and cannibalism give a terroristic aura to the Leopards. Like the Ku Klux Klan, they strike in the dark against their victims, who are selected because they have evoked the ire of the membership or merely because sacrifices are needed for fertility rites. The Leopard men wear leopard-skin cloaks. With wooden dies they make false leopard imprints in the earth to leave the impression that real leopards have seized the victims. With clawlike knives they mutilate and lacerate the flesh of their victims.

The terroristic activities of the Mau Mau among the Kikuyu tribesmen of Kenya in the 1950s was an aberrant development of the pattern of secret fraternities.

Functions of secret fraternities The functions of African secret orders are by no means wholly homicidal. Their bloody activities are only incidental to deeper-lying interests. The associations are mutual-aid organizations that have taken on important social control responsibilities in addition to their magical, religious, and merely social aspects.

[5] J. L. Gibbs, Jr., *Peoples of Africa,* p. 223.

They counterbalance the power of the tribal king and work to keep royal power in check. Unquestionably, they serve at times as the people's solution to the trying problems that result from the need to temper anarchy with monarchy, which in turn must be stopped short of despotism. Within the framework of the tribal constitution, the secret orders are often cited as assisting the king in the application of the sanctions that uphold the tribal laws.[6]

As mutual-aid protective associations, the secret orders of West Africa pay special attention to the interests of their members as against those of the world at large. They collect private debts from delinquent creditors on behalf of their members, and they punish other transgressions against the brotherhood as well. In some sections of Sierra Leone, the overextension of these practices into exploitative terrorism has caused violent public reactions, resulting in the outlawing of such clubs as the Leopard by the tribal chief.

Experience proves that secret orders are dangerous devices for use as instruments of government and social control. With the best of intentions they may serve the public weal, but since the members are not publicly accountable for their acts, there can be no safe check on the inevitable temptation to use their heady power in their own selfish interests. Exclusive secret orders are inherently corruptible and corrupting in any society, be it *Egbo* in Liberia, *tamate* in the Banks Islands, or Ku Klux Klan in the United States.

Secret clubs of a purely congenial, ceremonial, or magico-religious nature are generally exempt from such strictures. Thus, in Dahomey, where the power of the king appears to have become sultanistic in its strength, all secret orders were banned by royal edict. The king brooked no opposition or competition. There was, however, no objection to the banding together of men for mutual aid, as long as it was not done secretly. The Dahomean *gbe*

[6] See Webster, *op. cit.*, pp. 115–120; R. H. Lowie, *The Origin of the State,* pp. 91–94.

Fig. 26-1 Interior of a Men's Club House, Papua, New Guinea, with symbolically painted ceremonial "shields." (Courtesy of the American Museum of Natural History)

was (and is) organized by a group of young men, not necessarily of the same age group. They socialize together, but the basic function of their organizations is to enable each member to make more impressive displays at weddings and funerals by calling upon the resources of all other members not in excess of a stipulated sum.[7] Women may belong to such clubs, or they may have separate clubs of their own. In effect, these secular nonsecret associations are exactly comparable to our own cooperative credit unions.

The various pueblos of the Southwest each have their several secret fraternities whose main functions are to perform masked *kachina* dances impersonating the gods and to perform complex rituals according to calendric cycles. The dances and rituals are performed for the benefit of all the people. Most of the ritual and accompanying liturgy is secret among the

[7]M. J. Herskovits, *Dahomey*, Vol. 1, pp. 250–253.

initiated members, but public dances are also performed. Thus, the village *cacique* (sacred chief) of Sia Pueblo calls upon the Flint fraternity to perform the stick-swallowing dance on behalf of the whole pueblo. The dancers shove sticks down their throats, imitating the poking of planters' dibbles into the ground, and the dance works to ensure a good spring sowing.

The functions of such fraternities in the pueblos are wholly religious, magical, and ceremonial. Only as the high-ranking leaders of all the secret orders form an ecclesiastical council do they enter into the governing of men.

Secret ceremonial associations also play an important role in the lives of the Indians of the Northwest Coast.[8]

Secular associations

Purely secular organizations, given to furthering nonmystic interests and not concerned with terrorizing women and children, have no compulsive need to surround themselves with secrecy.

Such were the military and dancing clubs of the Plains Indians. These associations of warriors were fellowships for conviviality among men, whose warlike flame was sustained and fanned by the stories, the rituals, and the songs and dances of their lodges. Their basic interests were two: warfare and congeniality. Their enjoyment was derived not from roistering but from the quieter glow that builds up in companionate smoking of a pipe, huddled singing about a thumping drum, parading two by two in all their finery upon their best horses, or dancing for all the tribe to see.

Plains Indian military associations Although the Plains Indian men's clubs are commonly called "military societies," they were military only in the sense that the American Legion is military—their members were all fighting men. Rarely did the Plains Indian men's clubs go to war as units. They did not form regular

[8]See F. Boas, *Social Organization and Secret Societies of the Kwakiutl Indians* (United States National Museum, Reports, 1895).

segments of an army, for Plains Indian fighting was too individualistic for that, but they idealized and glorified war and labored to sustain the war ideal among their members.

Their officers were "chosen to die." In battle, they planted their insignia—a crooked spear like a shepherd's crook or a trailing shoulder sash that could be pegged to the ground—in the face of the enemy. They could not retreat from that spot unless a fellow member dashed into the melee to pull up the peg or staff. Nominees for such offices were supposed to be bashful toward acceptance of the honor. Witness what Lowie was told by the Crow Indian Young Jackrabbit:

"All declined to smoke, then they came towards me. Some one asked them, 'Whom are you looking for?' They answered, 'Young Jackrabbit.' I was seated in the rear and tried to hide. They brought the pipe to me, but I refused to accept it. One of the pipe-carriers was my own older brother. He seized me by the hair, struck my chest, and said, 'You are brave, why don't you smoke the pipe?' He wished me to die, that is why he desired me to smoke the pipe. He said, 'You are of the right age to die, you are good-looking, and if you get killed your friends will cry. All your relatives will cut their hair, fast and mourn. Your bravery will be recognized; and your friends will feel gratified.' I took the pipe and began to smoke. They asked me whether I wished to have a straight or a hooked-staff. I chose the hooked-staff. My comrade also smoked the pipe."[9]

Plains Indian men's clubs have been classified into ungraded and graded types. The ungraded, which occurred among the Crow, Cheyenne, Kiowa, Wind River Shoshone, and other tribes, were voluntary associations open to all men without regard to age. A man needed merely a sponsor within the club; he also gave "presents" to the club upon his entry. There was no initiation.

The number of such ungraded clubs varied in different tribes. The Crows, in 1833, had eight. Toward the end of the century, these had been reduced to only two active ones, the Foxes and the Lumpwoods (Knobby Sticks).[10]

The Cheyennes had six clubs: the Fox, Elk, Shield, Bowstring, Dogs, and Northern Crazy Dogs.[11]

Age classes, or age sets The graded associations occurred only among the Mandan, Hidatsa, Arapaho, Gros Ventre, and Blackfoot. Each of these tribes had a system of associations that were graded in a prestige hierarchy from young to old; age qualification was a prerequisite for membership in all cases. Normally, every member of a tribe, if he lived long enough, would pass through all grades. The higher grades naturally had progressively smaller membership, which, combined with the increasing age of the membership, gave greater prestige.

Plains Indian age clubs Movement from one grade to another was by collective purchase of all the rights and paraphernalia of the club just above. Among the Hidatsa, for example, all the adolescent boys banded together and, aided by their families, made a great collection of hides, arrows, parfleches, etc. After indicating to the Kit Foxes, the lowest club, that they wanted to buy, arrangements would be made for ceremonial payment and transfer of the club to the upstarts. In addition, each neophyte chose a ceremonial father, or sponsor, who had to be a member of the neophyte's father's clan, from among the members of the Kit Foxes. To this man he offered gifts and entertainment—including his wife if he had one. The ethics of ceremonial wife lending were mixed, however. The gesture had to be made, but most ceremonial fathers were "afraid" to use the privilege.

Thus, each candidate had to make individual payment to join an age society, but at the same time, it was absolutely necessary that his age group act collectively to acquire the rights to the club. Such clubs were therefore joint incorporeal property transferable only by sale (see pages 423–424). Northern Plains Indian age associations are not pure

[9]R. H. Lowie, *The Crow Indians*, pp. 177–178.
[10]R. H. Lowie, *"Societies of the Crow, Hidatsa, and Mandan Indians"* (*American Museum of Natural History, Anthropological Papers*, Vol. 11, 1913).
[11]K. N. Llewellyn and E. A. Hoebel, *The Cheyenne Way: Conflict and Case Law in Primitive Jurisprudence*, p. 99.

age grades or age classes, i.e., a series of groups each of which is automatically composed of all the persons of a given sex and approximate age. After an incumbent group of Hidatsa Kit Foxes sold their club to the next younger group, they were without any club organization until they succeeded in purchasing the Half-shaved Head club from the group above them, who then had to purchase from the Dogs, who then had to purchase from the Lumpwoods. So it went up the line, until the oldest men entered the Bull club.

The element of age grading in the Plains is a piece of fancy embroidery added by the more sophisticated sedentary gardening tribes of the Upper Missouri Valley to the simpler ungraded complex as seen among the nomadic tribes. From the Mandan and Hidatsa, the pattern spread to the Arapaho, the Gros Ventre, and ultimately the Blackfoot. The breakdown of aboriginal Plains culture came before the complex could spread farther.[12]

There were also women's clubs in the Plains. Women joined in military association festivities on many occasions. Indeed, numerous tribal systems included a few female functionaries within the men's clubs. Each Cheyenne unit had four unmarried virgins who had ritual responsibilities and were called "sisters" by the members. But aside from participation in the men's clubs, women had organizations of their own. Cheyenne women who had quilled thirty buffalo robes with porcupine-quill embroidery could join a club of robe quillers.[13]

African age sets Age grades, or age sets (as they are called by English anthropologists), occur in their most highly developed form in Africa, and according to the World Ethnographic Survey, three-fourths of all societies containing age classes are African.[14]

NANDI AGE SETS The Nandi of Kenya may be taken as an example. There are a number of grades of males in this tribe. The first grade is that of the uninitiated boys. For the scion of a wealthy family, initiation may occur as early as ten years of age, or a youth may be nearly twenty before he is put up by his family for initiation. Initiations, which occur every seven or eight years, are the highlight of tribal life and a rough time for the boys, who, as if circumcision were not enough, are beaten with stinging nettles and stung with hornets. Part of the initiation includes military instruction, for after initiation, the boys become warriors. The initiated group receives name emblems and ornaments. War formerly was their chief concern; they could play at love and enjoy sex, but they were not to be fretted with the responsibilities of marriage and children. After four years of experience, they were ready to "receive the country" from the elder grades. The age set above them, which was retiring from active warrior status, laid aside its warrior clothing, assumed the raiment of elders, and could then marry and settle down to connubial domesticity. This is not of an exclusive sort, however, since in formal custom each married man is expected to extend the hospitality of his home to any visiting classmate. Hospitality to a Nandi means wife lending, a gratuity he will deny to all who are not members of his own age set. As a set advances in age, it ultimately enters the body of statesmen and tribal advisers.[15]

To the south, in the Swaziland Protectorate, the Swazi, a nation related to the better-known Zulus, reveal an age-set system remarkably similar to that just described. In the Swazi system, however, the whole organization is tightly controlled by the national king, who utilizes the classes of fighting age as regiments in a standing army and as work corps in time of peace. Like the Nandi warrior, a Swazi man cannot marry until his set graduates to the grade of elders.[16]

NUER AGE SETS Age sets in Africa have been

---

[12]Lowie worked out a classic age-area distribution study directed toward historical reconstruction of the development of such clubs. See his "Plains Indian Age Societies" (*American Museum of Natural History, Anthropological Papers*, Vol. 11, 1916), pp. 877–984.
[13]G. B. Grinnell, *The Cheyenne Indians*, Vol. 1, pp. 159–169.
[14]A. D. Coult and R. W. Habenstein, *Cross Tabulations of Murdock's World Ethnographic Survey*, p. 27.
[15]A. C. Hollis, *The Nandi*. For an excellent detailed study of three variant systems of East African age sets, see A. H. J. Prins, *East African Age Class Systems*.
[16]H. Kuper, *An African Aristocracy*, pp. 117–136.

made to serve well as devices of social integration and efficiency. They cause greater internal segmentation, it is true, but it is a segmentation that promotes specialization of function along effective lines. It harnesses the energies of youth to the ends of the society and gives to each age group a strong awareness of its own status. In even so widely dispersed and scattered a population as the Nuer in the Nilotic Sudan, who have only the weakest of tribal structures in spite of the fact that they number over 100,000 persons, the age-set system is one order of organization that runs through all the tribes of the nation. Because of a generally undeveloped social and political structure, Nuer age sets are necessarily lacking in the qualities that distinguish their counterparts in Nandi and Swazi. As Evans-Pritchard reports:

The age-sets have no corporate activities and cannot be said to have specific political functions. There are no grades of "warriors" and "elders" concerned with the administration of the country, and the sets are not regiments, for a man fights with the members of his local community, irrespective of age. In the rites of initiation there is no educative or moral training. There is no leadership in the sets.[17]

What then do they do? They fix and emphasize the status of all males toward other males as equals, juniors, and seniors. They are merely weak counterparts of the functionally more significant age sets to the south of them.

NYAKYUSA AGE SETS In sharp contrast to the weakly developed Nuer age sets are those of the Nyakyusa, who live on the northwest shores of Lake Nyasa. Little Nyakyusa boys of six to eleven years of age band together to herd their fathers' cattle, and for several years, they spend their waking hours together on the range. When they reach twelve or so, they leave off herding to take up the hoe in the gardens of their fathers; they then move into a village of older boys, no more to sleep at home. They return to the parental homestead for meals, but only when accompanied by a group of their age-mates. Boys should associate with boys even when visiting their par-

ents. They live as members of a tightly knit juvenile gang, but without the element of gangsterism. They have no need to express hostility to the adult world. Their culture moves them steadily and early into the shouldering of the responsibilities of men through the concerted activities of youth.

When the young men approach the age of twenty-five, one by one they marry. Each brings his wife into the age village of his peers, and what was once Boys' Town is gradually transformed into a family village of husbands and wives and their children. It is unique in that all the men of the village are of an age. Now each youth receives his own fields from his father, and he ceases to return to his parents' house for meals, eating instead under his own roof food prepared by his wife rather than his mother.

In another ten years, when all the villages of a given age level within a district have matured, the formal government of the territory is ritually handed over to them, and they rule the land while their new generation of sons begins anew the process, breaking off to start the formation of their own age villages-to-be.

In Nyasaland, the age set is more than an auxiliary to the kinship group or a segment of village life. While closely linked to his primary conjugal-natal family in many ways, the Nyakyusa boy begins the severance of the primary family strands long before he is ready to start a family of his own, and his age set becomes the core of the social structure of his entire society.[18]

Incidence of age sets The use of age as a basis of status identification is, as was pointed out in Chapter 20, a universal cultural phenomenon. The institutionalization of age groups into definite age sets is, on the contrary, exceedingly rare; it occurs in only 23 out of 547 cultures included in the World Ethnographic Survey, or 4 per cent of the sample. Sixteen of the twenty-three are located in Africa,[19] where

[17]E. E. Evans-Pritchard, "The Nuer of the Southern Sudan," in *African Political Systems*, p. 289.

[18]M. Wilson, *Good Company: A Study of Nyakyusa Age-villages.*
[19]Coult and Habenstein, *loc. cit.*

the frequency of age grading (which even there equals only 15 per cent of the tribes) is clearly a result of diffusion, as it is among the Plains tribes of North America. But the sporadic distribution of age grades around the world is good evidence of its independent invention in the several continental areas.

Eisenstadt's theory of age groupings In a comparative study of age groupings, S. N. Eisenstadt developed the hypothesis that: "Age-homogeneous groups tend to arise in those societies in which the allocation of roles, facilities and rewards is not based on membership in kinship—or otherwise particularistically defined—units and criteria."[20]

This hypothesis is plausible, for it does seem reasonable to suppose that where desirable statuses do not flow from kinship ties, alternatives will be seized upon. Age groups would seem to be easily developed substitutes in view of the universality of age as a biological fact. However, the data of the World Ethnographic Survey raise serious doubts as to the significance of the hypothesis. There are too many societies that allocate roles outside the kinship system and do not develop age grades. Unidentified negative forces neutralize whatever tendency there might logically seem to be at work. Age grades are, it is true, very interesting to contemplate in themselves, but surprisingly they are not of as much significance in human affairs as anthropologists once thought.

SUMMARY

The club-forming impulse finds expression, especially for males, in many societies. The structure of club organization is variable from

[20]S. N. Eisenstadt, *From Generation to Generation,* p. 54.

culture to culture, but everywhere the principle of association works to cut across divisive kinship lines and bind the men together in mutual enterprise and social brotherhood. Except as they become sharply exclusive and selfishly centered around their own interests, they work to integrate the society and lend color and interest to the round of life. They may perform secondary functions of government in such areas as policing, judging, the military, and public works. They may provide for mutual aid and assistance among members. They usually have ceremonial and often religious responsibilities. But above all, they perform a major socialization function for males. They institutionalize adult male statuses and, through their initiation rites, effect and reinforce the transition from boyhood to manhood.

Formal age classes occur most commonly in Africa and only sporadically elsewhere. They are a highly specialized form of nonkinship group organization.

SELECTED READINGS

Eisenstadt, S. N.: *From Generation to Generation* (1956). Particularly interesting in its comparative analysis of youth movements in Germany and Israel in relation to primitive age grading.

Llewellyn, K. N., and E. A. Hoebel: *The Cheyenne Way: Conflict and Case Law in Primitive Jurisprudence* (1941), chap. 5, "The Military Societies." A case study of Cheyenne Indian men's clubs in operation.

Lowie, R. H.: *Primitive Society* (1920), chaps. 10 and 11, "Associations" and "Theory of Associations." An excellent comparative discussion of clubs and age groups in several primitive societies.

Webster, H.: *Primitive Secret Societies* (1908). An old but valuable work.

Wilson, M.: *Good Company: A Study of Nyakyusa Age-villages* (1951). A truly fascinating account of a unique development of the age-grading principle.

Social classes

chapter 27

The Communist doctrine of class antagonism and its accompanying dogma of class struggle pose one of the great challenges of the age to contemporary humanity. A clear understanding of what classes are and how they act in different types of societies is absolutely essential to a rational meeting of the challenge. Are there any societies that are classless? Are classes in primitive societies at war with one another? Are they given to exploitation of other classes? Is slavery a primitive institution or one that is characteristic of certain orders of civilization? These are some of the questions upon which anthropological findings may be brought to bear.

The nature of classes

"The concept of class is concerned with the social differentiation of groups."[1] A clear-cut definition, however, poses the knotty problem of what *kind* of groups. In its broadest sense, a class is any group of people within a population who possess some diagnostic trait in common. All people whose feet take 10B shoes would constitute this sort of class. This is not what is meant by a social class, however.

The working criteria of social class are both objective and subjective. Economic determinists emphasize the objective criteria of relationship to the instruments of production, i.e., ownership or nonownership of land and capital. This is the Marxian choice. Max Weber includes economic criteria in his analysis of class, but

[1] P. Mombert, "Class" (*Encyclopedia of the Social Sciences*, Vol. 3, 1930), p. 531.

he adds also the nature of the external standard of living (which is only indirectly related to the possession of economic means), plus cultural and recreational opportunities. American sociologists, reflecting the more fluid and blurred nature of classes in our society, emphasize the subjective nature of class. There are no social classes, but thinking makes them so. MacIver declares:

We shall then mean by a social class any portion of a community which is marked off from the rest . . . primarily by a sense of social distance. Such a subjective character involves as a rule objective differences, income levels, occupational distinctions and so forth, within the society. But these differences, apart from a recognized order of superiority and inferiority, would not establish cohesive groups. It is the sense of status, sustained by economic, political, or ecclesiastical power and by distinctive modes of life and cultural expressions corresponding to them, which draws class apart from class, gives cohesion to each, and stratifies a whole society.[2]

A social class is therefore *a group within a society, whose members hold a number of distinctive statuses in common and who, through the operation of the roles associated with these statuses, develop an awareness of their like interests as against the unlike traits and interests of other groups.* A social class can exist only with reference to other social classes. A one-class society is necessarily a classless society, Furthermore, if there is no consciousness of class, there can be no dynamics of class action; then the classes will have no functional significance. People must act in terms of class if the class concept is to be functionally significant.

Finally, there are a number of things that a social class is not. It is not organized. Classes are not in themselves associations. But there may be, of course, associations that represent the interests of specific classes, as the AFL-CIO does for certain segments of the industrial workers in the United States or as the National Association of Manufacturers does for a portion of the industrial owners and manufacturers. Yet even in Russia, only a small part of the

[2]R. M. MacIver, *Society,* pp. 78–79.

proletariat is organized within the Communist party and its affiliate associations.

The frequency of classes in primitive society
There is clearly a direct and positive correlation between the degree of complexity of culture and the presence of social classes. For the most part, extremely simple cultures do not provide sufficient differentiation of role and function among their members to produce class identification. Exceptions to this generalization occur primarily in those societies which allow slavery. Eskimos, Andaman Islanders, Australians, Semangs, Veddas, Great Basin Shoshones, Fuegians, and African Bushmen are conspicuously free of social classes. In these societies, there is no possibility of the accumulation of capital goods; all persons have equal access to all natural resources, and none has notable political power over others.

Thus among the 101 cultures on the hunting and gathering level included in the World Ethnographic Survey, only one is listed as having a definite class system among freemen. Twenty-seven, however, keep slaves! Twenty admit of notable distinctions in wealth without the formulation of social classes. But sixty-seven reveal no significant social-class distinctions of any kind (again, among freemen).

At the other end of the developmental scale, of 117 cultures built upon plow agriculture, only nine (8 per cent) had *no* class distinctions, while sixty-eight (58 per cent) had three or more social classes apart from slaves. Intensive gardening societies, of which 189 are listed, show comparable figures of 48 per cent classless and 8 per cent with complex class systems.

Types of class systems

Inasmuch as classes are an expression of attitudes associated with differences in status and role, the characters of class systems exhibit very marked qualitative differences from one type of culture to another. This can be illustrated by examination of a selected sample of societies possessing different types of class systems.

Table 27-1   Percentage Frequencies of Social Differentiation of Freemen (Slavery Excluded) in 565 Cultures of the Major Geographic Areas of the World

geographic areas	per cent of all tribes in each area				
	no distinctions	age sets present	wealth distinction important	complex class system	nobility present
Africa	36	14	10	12	28
Circum-Mediterranean	9	2	18	55	14
Eurasia	19	0	23	35	23
Pacific Islands	49	1	19	5	26
North America	57	3	20	6	14
South America	63	4	8	7	17

NOTE: American Indians are the most egalitarian. Africa emphasizes age sets and nobility. Mediterranean cultures are class-differentiated. Eurasia utilizes all distinctions except age sets.

SOURCE: Data converted to percentages from A. D. Coult and R. W. Habenstein, *Cross Tabulations of Murdock's World Ethnographic Survey, op. cit.*, p. 27.

Plains Indians   Among the Plains Indians, a nascent sense of class was noticeable. Grinnell writes:

Family rank, which existed among the Cheyennes as among other Indians, depended on the estimation in which the family was held by the best people. A good family was one that produced brave men and good sensible women, and that possessed more or less property. A brave and successful man has raised his family from low to very high rank; or a generation of inefficient men might cause a family to retrograde.[3]

But there was no real social gap between good and not-so-good families. The poor, instead of being driven into servitude to the upper crust by means of debt, wage dependence, or clientage, seem rather to have sponged upon the chief, the successful hunter, and the taker of war booty.

Similar ideas exist among the Western Apache, who distinguish sharply between a class of poor people and the rich. "Those who had little or no property, lacked the ability or desire and energy to accumulate it, and had no social prestige were termed poor; the people with opposite traits were called rich." Poverty is pitied, and the wealthy person is ex-

[3]G. B. Grinnell, *The Cheyenne Indians,* Vol. 1, p. 129.

pected to be generous with largess. For this he receives public approval and hangers-on among the poor, who are then called *bidigishi,* "his incompetents or weaklings."[4]

Out of such elemental notions of class differences, the Kiowa Indians of the Plains developed a strong sense of class ranking. Four classes were recognized by name: *onde, ondegupa, kɔɔn,* and *dapom.* The *onde,* who constituted about one-tenth of the population, were those whose family heads were handsome on a horse, wealthy and generous, proud in bearing, courteous in demeanor, and, above all, possessed of an outstanding war record. The *ondegupa* were the able artisans, hunters, herders, and medicine men, who had wealth, were generous, and were noble in character and behavior but who lacked sufficient war credits. They made up one-third of the tribe. The *kɔɔn* were the common stuff, undistinguished in war or other accomplishments. They lived with their more illustrious kinsmen as poor relatives. Half the tribe was of the lower class. The *dapom* were simply *déclassé.* Shiftless and lazy, they filched and stole within the camp. Practically disowned by their own relatives, they were virtual out-

[4]G. Goodwin, *The Social Organization of the Western Apache,* pp. 541–543.

casts. They imposed upon the generosity of the good people; theft was not looked upon or treated as a legal infraction. The *dapom* was not punished or extruded from the group. He was merely scorned and suffered to be borne.[5]

Northwest Coast Indians Class was more marked on the Northwest Coast of North America, where in every tribe a sharp division existed between freemen and slaves—unfortunates captured from other tribes. In the early nineteenth century, slaves constituted from 10 to 30 per cent of the total populations of various Northwest Coast tribes. They were in effect a depressed caste whose function was to produce food for their masters by hunting and fishing and to do the menial work around the village, as well as to paddle the seagoing canoes. Whatever their rank in their own tribe, all slaves were reduced to the level of productive capital in the tribe of their masters. Just as any valuable good, a canoe or copper, could be destroyed at a potlatch, slaves too could be killed to show their masters' unconcern for wealth.

Most authorities have described the body of freemen in Northwest Coast society as consisting of two classes: nobles and commoners. Nobles were those men and their wives who had attained the rank of chieftain through the inheritance of chiefly titles, which they had validated by potlatching. Since most tribes held to primogeniture, the nobility consisted of first-born, while subsequent children or nephews (in matrilineal societies) became commoners. Among the Tsimshian, according to Jenness, even finer distinctions were drawn. Intermarriage among the first-born children of the highest-ranking families of the nobility was reputedly obligatory, so that there was even an endogamous "royalty" within the nobility.[6]

[5] J. Richardson, *Law and Status among the Kiowa Indians* (American Ethnological Society, Monograph 1, 1940); B. Mishkin, *Rank and Warfare among the Plains Indians* (American Ethnological Society, Monograph 3, 1940).
[6] D. Jenness, *The Indians of Canada* (National Museum of Canada, Bulletin 68, Anthropological Series, No. 15, 2d ed., 1934), p. 337.

Drucker, who has studied Northwest Coast culture at firsthand, takes issue with the orthodox view of Northwest Coast social classes. He flatly maintains that there was no class of nobility set off from a class of commoners, much less a threefold or fourfold class system. What actually occurred as he sees it was "that each society consisted not of two or more social classes, but of a complete series of statuses graded relatively, one for each individual of the group."[7] He argues that between high and low there were differences in degree but not in kind.

This particular conflict of interpretations is not resolvable; it merely points up the ambiguity of the concept of class in certain settings. It precisely parallels the situation that existed in the United States, when most Americans argued that we had no social classes at the same time that Warner and his coworkers were assiduously dividing us into Upper upper, Lower upper, Upper middle, Lower middle, Upper lower, and Lower lower (than which there are no lower) classes.[8]

The Aztecs Among the peoples of high culture in Central America and the Andean region of South America, class differentiation was strongly fixed.

The Aztecs, in their meteoric rise and fall, developed from an apparently classless, unsegmented society with a rude material culture, prior to 1300, to a highly organized, sophisticated protocivilization in the fourteenth century. At the time of the arrival of the Spaniards in 1518, they were rapidly evolving a feudal aristocracy at the expense of the earlier clan socialism. The society then consisted of royalty, nobility, common freemen, propertyless proletariat, and slaves.

The core and largest part of the Aztec population was the body of free commoners, members of one or another of twenty localized clans (*calpulli*). Every married man enjoyed the

[7] P. Drucker, "Rank, Wealth, and Kinship in Northwest Coast Society" (*American Anthropologist*, Vol. 41, 1939), p. 57.
[8] W. L. Warner and P. S. Lund, *The Social Life of a Modern Community.*

right to cultivate a plot of clan garden land and to have a flat-roofed, dingy, one-room hut of adobe or clay-plastered wattle. He might become a craftsman, specializing in one of the many productive arts and trades. He had security and continuous employment and an obligation to perform military service. But he was hedged in by a code of sumptuary laws that reserved to the rich and to distinguished warriors and officials the rights of wearing fine cotton, jewelry, and particular hairdos. Presumption above one's rank was summarily and severely punished. The upper classes in Mexico were not harassed by a dizzily whirling style cycle, in which the pacesetters must have a new fashion every two or three years in order to keep ahead of the imitative masses.

Class distinctions cut across kinship groups, for the class of honorary lords was recruited from all clans. They formed a nonhereditary order of merit with various grades conferred by the government as a lifetime reward for outstanding military accomplishment, service in civil office, service to the state as a traveling merchant-spy, or exceptional religiosity. They wore the beautiful and elaborate costumery depicted in Aztec art. They lived in the mansions of Tenochtitlan. They received homage and led a rich life apart from their common fellow clansmen. In theory, the huge parcels of conquered lands that they received as rewards for their services could not be inherited as family estates. All such rewards were to be redistributed to a new worthy after the death of the holder. This was always done, but, by a process not difficult to understand, a system of preference was crystallizing whereby sons of nobles were appointed to their fathers' positions of nobility. Inheritance of rank and landed estates was thus leading rapidly to the freezing of a hereditary aristocracy.

Above the nobles, in luxuriant splendor, stood the royal lineage, from among whose members the *tlacatecutli*, or king, was elected by the great council of lords.

Far below the royalty and nobles was the hapless proletariat. Aliens whose goods and lands had been expropriated by the state and Aztecs who had lost their clan privileges for failure to fulfill clan obligations eked out a meager and sweaty existence as burden-bearing coolies on the streets of the city and roads of the country, or they grubbed for their livelihood upon the estates of the lords. Taxes and feudal services left little to them.

Slavery was the lot of impecunious Aztecs who could not meet their bills, In like manner, criminals who could not make restitution for their thefts became the slaves of the freemen they had victimized. Children were sold into slavery by impoverished parents, and even adults among the proletariat might voluntarily sell themselves into servitude. Many slaves were alien boys and girls taken as tribute from conquered neighbors.

The society of the Aztec Indians was on the road to becoming the same type of pyramidal, exploitative society that existed in the flourishing days of the archaic Mediterranean civilizations. The Aztecs, however, had not hardened the inequalities of their society. Children of slaves were born free (into the proletariat). Slaves could not be killed or abused by their masters; they could even acquire property in their own right (although it is not likely that this opportunity meant much to many slaves); they could not be sold to another master except by self-consent; and if married by master or mistress, they become freemen.[9]

The Natchez Indians   To the north, where the charming city of Natchez, Mississippi, now stands, lived a gardening tribe that gave its own peculiar twist to the Central American concepts of religion and social classes. This was the Natchez tribe, an outstanding member of the great southeastern Muskogean language family.

The Natchez people were devoted worshipers of the sun, and their towns were dominated by small pyramids at either end of a plaza. Upon each mound was a temple or the dwelling of a priest-chief. Each morning the Sun of Suns, exalted ruler, brother of the celestial sun,

[9]G. C. Vaillant, *Aztecs of Mexico.*

Table 27-2   *Marriage and Descent in the Natchez Class System*

wife	*husband*	*offspring*	*wife*	*husband*
Sun	All	Suns →	All	Sun
Noble	husbands	Nobles ↙	wives	Noble
Honored	are	Honored ↙	are	Honored
Stinker	Stinkers	Stinkers ↙	Stinkers	Stinker

greeted his illustrious ancestor before the Sun Temple. In another temple, the perpetual sacred fire of the village was tended.

The people, as was usual in the Southeast Woodlands, were divided into moieties. What was unusual about Natchez moieties was their unequal social positions. Reciprocity in dual organization had become neglected in favor of aristocratic exaltation. The result was a monstrosity in social organization. Interest in aristocracy as a principle had produced a three-fold subdivision of the aristocratic moiety into Suns, Nobles, and Honored People. For the common moiety, there were no such grandilo-quent names. They were all Stinkers. The meager material culture of the Natchez allowed for no such economic ostentation as the Aztec royalty and nobility drew to themselves, but the social superiority of the Natchez Suns and Nobles colored the behavior of all life in the tribe.

A startling Natchez rule was that the aris-tocrats had to marry *outside* the aristocracy; there was no alternative for them but to marry Stinkers. Such a rule is compatible with the principle of moiety exogamy but not in the least with the principle of aristocratic exclusive-ness. Indeed, one critical evaluation of the tra-ditional scheme of Natchez social organiza-tion centered upon the objection that the scheme is impossible as a reality, since in a few generations' time, almost everyone would be an aristocrat. A truly comic-opera situation would result, and the system would be self-

liquidating.[10] This is because in all intermoiety marriages, except that of Honored Person and Stinker, the children were born aristocrats. The population of Stinkers would not be self-replac-ing and would soon be exhausted.

If we look at the descent system in more detail, we find that when aristocratic women married, their children belonged to the same moiety and class as the mother. When aris-tocratic men married, their children were de-based one grade, thus, the children of a Sun male married to a Stinker female became members of the Noble class. When the boys of this group married Stinker women, their chil-dren in turn became members of the Honored class. When Honored men married Stinker women, their offspring dropped out of the aristocracy to become common Stinkers (see Table 27-2). The effect of the system is one in which the children of the highest-ranking class are downgraded gradually instead of in one harsh jump. Here we have a recognition of the fact that a higher nobility must continue to distribute its surplus members back into the ranks of the commoners to prevent undue overcrowding at the top.

The rule of exogamy did not apply to Stinkers. If not espoused to an aristocrat, a Stinker could marry a Stinker, and their chil-dren assumed that status. There was nothing lower than a Stinker.

[10]C. W. M. Hart, "A Reconsideration of the Natchez Social Structure" (*American Anthropologist*, Vol. 45, 1943), pp. 374–386.

Hart's contention that the Natchez social system was inherently self-destructive rests on the assumption of a stable population. Contrary to this, Quimby has effectively brought together historical and archaeological data to demonstrate that the Natchez actually replenished the Stinker moiety by absorption of shattered remnants of neighboring tribes decimated by enemies. Adopted foreigners were always Stinkers.[11] Quimby's excavations in Natchez sites indicate that the Natchez archaeological culture came into its own around 1600.[12] The French smashed the Natchez nation in three wars between 1716 and 1731, annihilating hundreds. Nearly five hundred Natchez captives went as slaves into Santo Domingo, while surviving remnants were sheltered by the Chickasaw and the English colony of South Carolina. It is thus likely that the unique Natchez class system was a social mutation sustainable for a short period by absorption of outside populations but inherently incapable of long enduring. Its social survival value was negative. That it was not an ancient system is indicated by the fact that it did not occur among any other tribes of the Southeast, who were essentially similar in other fundamentals of culture.

Polynesia In Polynesia, native usage tends to run to class distinctions hedged in by much preferential etiquette. All Polynesians recognize a divine nobility, a gentry, a body of commoners, and slaves. Direct descent from a god gives a claim to nobility and innate mana to the class of sacerdotal chiefs. In democratic Samoa, the social and political power of the nobles is limited and subject to personal modification. In Hawaii, Tonga, and Tahiti, on the other hand, the sacredness of royalty before the days of white dominion was such that all the king touched became tabu to lesser men. Commoners were humbled before the royalty

[11]G. I. Quimby, "Natchez Social Structure as an Instrument of Assimilation" (*American Anthropologist*, Vol. 48 1946), pp. 134–136.
[12]G. I. Quimby, "The Natchezan Culture Type" (*American Antiquity*, Vol. 7, 1942), pp. 255–275.

in the few contacts they had with it. Relations approached the feudal in nature. In Tonga, commoners paid in kind for the privilege of using their local chief's land. He in turn passed on some of this wealth to the higher chiefs.

In Samoa, deemphasis of divinity was accompanied by emphasis upon craft skill, so that occupational guilds tended to enjoy the functional role played by royal classes elsewhere in the area.

Melanesia In the western and interior parts of Melanesia inhabited by the more primitive Papuans, social classes as such are practically nonexistent. In the eastern islands, where the Melanesian-speaking people predominate, differentiation into social classes is characteristic, even though there are classless tribes, such as the Dobu. The actual governing of men throughout Melanesia is usually in the hands of a council of village elders, but there is commonly a class of wealthy chiefs who enjoy much social prestige by reason of their economic, ceremonial, and religious, if not political, powers.

Melanesian chiefs are almost always descendants of an immigrant group that has bamboozled the local populace into believing that they have superior magical powers and control valuable rituals that will benefit the community. For this reason, it is considered only right that the chiefly class enjoy exalted sanctity and privileged superiority. The chiefs are also universally regarded by the people and themselves as a class of feast givers and ceremonialists who reflect glory upon their people.

Fiji, on the Melanesian-Polynesian borderline, is typical enough. About ten generations ago, a group of warriors moved into the island of Lau. They may have muscled in with forceful measures, but present tradition says that the local population accepted them as "civilizers" who brought light (*rarama*) to those who were living in darkness (*mbutombuto*).

The primordial clan system of the original people was reworked into a graded hierarchy in which every clan stood in a definite relationship to every other clan. Clans descended from the immigrants formed the chiefly class (*yavasu turanga*), and clans descended from the original indigenous population formed a peasantry, or "land class" (*yavusa vanua*). Through intermarriage, the sibs of the newcomers also have acquired some land, but in this instance there has been no expropriation of the lands belonging to the lower class. Sibs of the land people still own most of the land. They also show more interest in gardening, while they are excelled by the chiefly class in sailing, fish spearing, and craftsmanship.[13]

Africa In Africa, the range of social differentiation is from homogeneous democracy, as exemplified by the Nuer, to heterogeneous conquest states with formal caste systems. We shall take the Kingdom of Ankole in Uganda as an example of East African stratified societies.

The basic caste division in Ankole is between pastoralists, who call themselves *Bahima,* and gardeners, who are known as *Bairu.*[14] The Bahima are Hamitic or Hamiticized Negro cattle people, who came down the grassland corridor between Lake Victoria on the east and the mountain and lake chain on the west. Their original home was probably southern Abyssinia. Racially and culturally, they were and are distinct from the Bantu horticulturalists, who had preceded them in occupation of the country. As they moved southward, the Bahima proved themselves as fighters to be superior to the Bantu-speaking Bairu and capable of effective enlargement of their social groups for politico-military ends. They conquered the Bairu and proceeded successfully to subjugate them, without apparent difficulty, although the Bairu outnumbered them ten to one.

[13]L. Thompson, "The Culture History of the Lau Islands, Fiji" (*American Anthropologist,* Vol. 40, 1938), pp. 185–189.
[14]In Bantu speech, the prefix "Mu" refers to a particular person; "Ba," to the tribe collectively; "Bu," to the tribal territory; and "Lu," to the language. Thus we have Bahima, Muhima, Buhima, and Luhima and also Bairu and Mwiru.

Unbreachable disabilities were imposed upon the Bairu:

1. All Bairu are forbidden to own fecund cattle. It is true that they are sometimes given barren cows or bull calves for services rendered a Muhima, but any Muhima can arbitrarily expropriate any productive cows found in the possession of a Mwiru.

2. While all Bahima males are liable to be called for military service, the Bairu are barred from bearing arms. They are kept militarily ineffective, and the chances of successful revolution are kept at a low level.

3. There can be no intermarriage between Bahima and Bairu. Aside from the customary prohibition of intermarriage, the injunction against Bairu cattle holding is an effective bar. No marriage is valid without progeny price in cattle, and the Bairu can receive no reproductive cows, nor do they have any to give.

4. Bahima men (especially chiefs) can take Bairu girls as concubines, but Bairu men do not have an equivalent privilege with Bahima girls.

5. No Bairu may hold high political office. At best, they may serve as district tax collectors under a Muhima.

6. All Bairu have to work for, and pay tribute to, the Bahima chieftains, who in turn distribute the garden products and derivatives to their fellows. The Bahima have had no desire to kill the goose that lays the golden eggs, and therefore the individual Muhima is barred from abuse of the Bairu, who is privileged to plead before a Bahima chief for compensation when ill-treated or exploited by an unauthorized Muhima.

7. When a Mwiru killed a Mwiru, that was a matter for retaliatory revenge among themselves. But if a Muhima killed a Mwiru, the law denied the right of direct action to the Bairu kinship group. The most they could hope for was to be able to plead with the Bahima king that he obtain compensation on their behalf, and they were lucky if they got anything at all. But if a lowly Mwiru dared to kill a Muhima, the Bahima dispatched him forthwith.

Domination and exploitation in the Banyankole state is direct, unabashed, and efficient. It is an example par excellence of the oft-repeated story of the parasitic mastery of a sedentary people by nomadic herdsmen.

However, the class structure is not the simple dichotomous arrangement we have thus far described. The Banyankole kingdom does not exist in a vacuum, and there are other Bahima kingdoms and tribelets in the area. Although racially self-conscious, the predatory Muhima has not been averse to raiding alien Bahima. To put a stop to this, the kingdom of Ankole undertook the subjugation of various Bahima neighbors, who were then incorporated into the Banyankole tribal society as a separate tribute-paying class, known as *Abatoro*. These can intermarry with their conquerors, and they suffer no serious legal disabilities.

Yet a fourth class is the *Abambari*. Prohibition of intermarriage never prevents miscegenation. Out of the Bahima-Bairu concubine relations come half-caste offspring. Legally, the *Abambari* are classed as Bairu, in the same way that mulattoes are classed as Negroes by most American laws. But the personal interest of a Muhima father often mitigates the strict working of this rule. Those who have no legitimate heirs often raise the son of a concubine to the status of heir. Thus the exclusive separatism of the ruling caste has been self-defeated and, ironically enough, to the greatest degree among the chiefly families and lineages. For it is just in this group that today a definitely larger percentage of dark Bantu Negroid physical types is found than occurs among the ordinary Bahima herdsmen in the more remote rural districts.

Lastly, there are the *Abahuku*, or slaves. Because of the convenience and effectiveness of the system of exploiting the Bairu and the limited economic possibilities in slavery when Bairu tools and gardening methods are used, slavery has never been extensive. The slaves are Bairu taken in raids upon neighboring kingdoms. Ankole Bairu were never enslaved. Slaves are used as menials in the households of the very rich. They neither garden nor tend the herds. They are chattels of their individual masters, and their ears are cut off to keep them from passing as Bairu if they succeed in running away.[15]

Caste

Caste is the result of intensification of the class principle. It is the freezing of social classes by means of endogamy and hereditarily ascribed status. It is thus a device by which a dominant group attempts to perpetuate itself and guarantee unto itself and its descendants a special and favored position in life. In theory, no person can escape his caste, whatever his potentialities and capabilities may be. Kroeber has pointed out that the caste "resembles the clan in being a sub-grouping within the larger political or cultural whole, and in being marriage regulating."[16] However, it differs from the clan in that while clans are exogamous, castes are endogamous. Clans are usually (but not always) of more or less equal social rank, whereas castes are implicitly higher or lower in social status. The very existence of caste is a denial of any concept of social equality. The American dilemma rests in the contradiction between the devotion to the Christian ideal of brotherhood and to the democratic ideal of political equality and fraternity among all men and the occurrence of racial castes, which have resulted from earlier conquests of Negroes and Indians.

[handwritten margin note: — marry outside clan, marry within group]

Slavery in primitive society

Slaves have entered several times into our discussion of class systems. Slavery is one of the most important of human social institutions and at the same time one that has not been adequately studied by anthropologists.

[15]K. Oberg, "The Kingdom of Ankole in Uganda," in E. E. Evans-Pritchard and M. Fortes (eds.), *African Political Systems*, pp. 121–162.

[16]A. L. Kroeber, "Caste" (*Encyclopedia of the Social Sciences*, Vol. 3, 1930), p. 254.

The nature of slavery Contemporary democratic morality in the United States condemns slavery in such strong terms that we recoil from the idea of it in horror. It is now hard for us to conceive of involuntary servitude as an implicit aspect of any society, and yet slavery has been an important part of human cultures for a far longer period of time than that during which civilizations have extirpated it from the social body.

Slavery is not in itself an absolute concept. In operation, it ranges from the complete degradation of a whole class of people by means of dogmatic denial of their humanity (slaves as chattels) to the inclusion of slaves as adopted members of the master's family and kinship group. Slavery, we are safe in saying, is a condition rarely welcomed by the slaves. There are few social advantages in being a slave and usually a good many disadvantages. The lot of the slave depends to a large degree on whether the tribe customarily utilizes its slaves as household servants or as field workers. In the former case, the relation of slave to master is unavoidably intimate, and slaves reap the benefit. If slaves are used as field workers, the master's chief interest becomes one of sheer economic exploitation, and, especially where there are great numbers of slaves, relationships become impersonal and harsh.

Slaves are derived both from within and from without a society. Internal slavery occurs only in the more advanced primitive societies with quasicapitalistic practices of borrowing and lending. A borrower may pledge himself or a son or daughter as security on a loan. Default means servitude. Or, as in the case of the Ashanti of Ghana, a man could pawn his brother's son to raise a sum. The boy then worked for the creditor until the loan was repaid; the labor he performed constituted the interest on the loan. Debt slavery does not produce huge masses of slaves, nor are their positions ordinarily harsh. A second internal source of slaves is the condemnation of criminals to servitude. This, too, is found only in the more highly advanced cultures, since a strongly centralized law system is a necessity.

The great source of slaves, however, is war and the exploitation of war captives, but war may or may not be waged to take captives. Slaves are in the tribe, but not of it. Without citizenship, slaves are outside the realm of jural personality, and their debased status does not contradict the slaveholders' notions of social equality—for themselves, exclusive of the slaves.

Table 27-3   Frequency and Percentage Distributions of Cultures with and without Slavery, According to Level of Subsistence Base

subsistence base	slavery present		slavery absent		total numbers
	number of cultures	*per cent of cultures*	*number of cultures*	*per cent of cultures*	
Plow agriculture	59	53	52	47	111
Pastoral	27	55	22	45	49
Developed agricultural	103	47	115	53	218
Incipient agricultural	6	20	25	80	31
Hunting and gathering	27	27	74	73	101

SOURCE: A. D. Coult and R. W. Habenstein, *Cross Tabulations of Murdock's World Ethnographic Survey,* p. 512.

Table 27-4   Frequency Distribution of Cultures with Slavery, According to Major Geographic Areas

geographic areas	number of cultures by areas	number of cultures with slavery	percentage of occurrence of slavery in each area
Africa	111	77	69
Circum-Mediterranean	73	38	52
Eurasia	78	42	53
Pacific Islands	98	30	30
North America	108	32	29
South America	72	29	30
Total	540	248	

SOURCE: A. D. Coult and R. W. Habenstein, *Cross Tabulations of Murdock's World Ethnographic Survey*, p. 28.

The occurrence of slavery Almost half the cultures of the primitive world incorporate slavery. Even as many as one-fourth of the hunters and gatherers and the peoples practicing incipient agriculture keep slaves (Table 27-3). How far a cry is the grim fact from the ideal belief expressed by a layman: "But nature's children do not enslave each other!"[17] The distribution of slavery has interesting implications for culture history. Table 27-4 shows that it is least common among American Indian and Pacific Island cultures (less than one-third). In Africa to the south of the Sahara, slavery occurs in more than two-thirds (69 per cent) of the cultures. Slavery is a cultural invention that has a distribution clearly influenced to some degree by diffusion from a more or less common source in Africa. The high incidence of pastoralism and developed agriculture might have contributed to the spread of slavery in Africa. Yet the presence of both of these types of subsistence economies in high frequency in Eurasia and the Mediterranean regions did not produce nearly so much slavery in those parts of the world. Future research into the structural-functional aspects

[17]Response of a listener to a lecture on Northwest Coast cultures, given by Professor Erna Gunther (personal communication).

of slavery may provide an answer to the African problem; none is available now.

SUMMARY

Primitive societies are neither classless nor class-ridden. Two-thirds of the societies on the level of hunters and gatherers are classless. On the highest levels of culture and subsistence development, however, classes exist in nine out of ten instances. Complex class systems occur to a large extent only among peoples who subsist as pastoralists or on the basis of plow agriculture. The intensification of class distinctions is a discernible evolutionary phenomenon. The classless primitive elysium of Marx's and Engels's theory is a hypothetical condition that would have to have existed far back in Paleolithic times, so far as one can tell from current facts.

Slavery is a far more common form of social differentiation than the division of freemen into social classes. Its occurrence is partly a function of cultural complexity and of the economic base of social structure. Its geographic distribution, however, indicates that it also exists or is rejected as an "idea." Hence, slavery is "overconcentrated" in Africa and "underrepresented" in others, particularly in North and South America and Oceania, where it failed to flourish as it did in the Old World.

SELECTED READINGS

Fischer, J. L.: "Solutions for the Natchez Paradox" (*Ethnology,* Vol. 3, 1964), pp. 53–65. A technical analysis of alternative explanations, with special attention to mathematical probabilities.

Hutton, J. H.: *Caste in India: Its Nature, Function and Origin* (1946). A general survey.

Kroeber, A. L.: "Caste" (*Encyclopedia of the Social Sciences,* Vol. 3, 1930), pp. 254–256. A brief summary of the phenomenon.

Mishkin, B.: *Rank and Warfare among Plains Indians* (American Ethnological Society, Monograph 3, 1940). The basis of class differentiation among some American Indians.

Oberg, K.: "The Kingdom of Ankole in Uganda," in E. E. Evans-Pritchard and M. Fortes (eds.), *African Political Systems* (1940), pp. 121–164. For greater detail on the system described in this chapter.

Tumin, M. M.: *Caste in a Peasant Society: A Case Study of the Dynamics of Caste* (1952). The workings of a caste system in a Guatemalan community.

The ownership
of goods and ideas

chapter 28

Property is a universal feature of human culture. The land upon which the social group is located and from which it draws its sustenance, the beasts that rove upon it wild, the animals that graze upon it tame, the trees and the crops, the houses that men erect, the clothes they wear, the songs they sing, the dances they execute, the charms they incant, these and many more are objects of property. Men tend to bring within the scope of property whatever they rely upon for the maintenance of life or value for other reasons. So it is that property is as ubiquitous as man, a part of the basic fabric of all society.

The nature of property

Property may be held in various ways: individually (personal property), by groups (joint property), or by the society at large (communal property). It may be fixed and immovable (real estate), or it may be movable. It may be material and concrete, or it may be an idea or a way of acting (incorporeal). It may be transferable by gift, barter, sale, inheritance, or confiscation, or it may be inalienable. It may or may not be protected by law. Many people habitually think of property only as a thing or things, whereas the thing itself is in fact but one element in the reality of property. The genuine nature of property is found in its qualities as a social institution.

Property: a social creation   Property in its full sense is *a web of social relations with respect to the utilization of some object (material or nonmaterial) in which a person or group is tacitly or explicitly recognized to hold quasiexclusive and limiting connections.*

As an illustration, a stone conveniently shaped for use as an ax head lies unnoticed and unused for years on the surface of the ground. It is not property. It is, in legal terminology, a *res nullius:* a nothing. A wandering tribesman finds it, takes it, and uses it as a hand ax. This in itself is mere possession. If the social practices of the possessor's tribe are such that any other person could appropriate this tool at will, it would still be a mere matter of possession. But if the custom is such that his fellow tribesmen recognize that he has a special *right* to possess that piece of rock and that all others have a *duty* to desist from using or taking it, then it is an object of property. The stone has not changed, but the social pattern with respect to it has. It is the special and peculiar set of social relations that have transformed the rock into an object of property. Thus, we have two irreducible aspects of property: (1) the object and (2) the web of social relations that establishes a limiting and defined status relationship between persons and the object.

This limiting relationship is often referred to by lawyers and economists as an *exclusive right of use.* It is exclusive insofar as it excludes nonowners from legitimate use without the express or tacit approval of the owner. However, the right is rarely, if ever, so absolutely exclusive that the owner may utilize the object in any way his whim may dictate. His rights of use are always limited to some extent by the demands of society. After all, society, not the individual, creates and maintains the institution of property. This is not to say that society created the *object.* The point of emphasis is that an object does not become property until the members of the society at large agree to bestow the property attribute upon it by regulating their behavior in a self-limiting manner. This is done because social experience has led to the conclusion that social benefits are derived from granting "exclusive" rights to individuals and groups with respect to certain classes of objects that they have created or acquired. By the same token, men always limit the extent of that exclusiveness in accordance with their conception of the needs of social good. Property—a social creation—is consequently always subject to social limitations, even in the most individualistic societies. Thus it is that as social concepts change from time to time, the specific content of property concepts undergoes alterations. The form and content of property notions are not the expression of immutable instinct or of any imagined laws of nature. Property in the United States today is not what it was in the mid-nineteenth century, nor what it will be at the dawn of the twenty-first.

Yurok property concepts   As an example of the way in which property is constituted, we may briefly analyze canoe ownership among the Yuroks of California—a highly individualistic people. A Yurok boat owner nominally possesses his canoe as private property. It is his. He has a series of demand rights against all other persons not to molest or damage his boat. He has the privilege right to use it upon the public waters. He does not have to sell or give it away. These are all marks of exclusive rights. Yet he is also subject to a series of well-recognized duties that limit his exclusive prerogatives. For one thing, he is obligated to ferry any sojourner over the river when called upon to do so. Failure to perform this duty gives the traveler a demand right for legal damages equal to one dentalium shell. On the other hand, if the owner suffers injury because of the service he has to render, the traveler is subject to damages. Thus, when one canoeman's house burned down while he was in midstream, his passenger had to pay for it.

This is what Cook meant when he said, ". . . ownership . . . is found to consist not only of an indefinite number of rights in the strict sense or claims available against an indefinite number of persons, each of whom is under a corresponding duty, but also a large and indefinite number of privileges, powers and immunities . . . ."[1]

Finally, we should take note of the relation of property to law. In the modern world, it is a fact that a vast proportion of the law of the state is devoted to the definition of the relationships between owners of property. Much of the activity of our courts and police is concerned with maintaining and enforcing these relationships. Government feeds and grows on the complexity of property in a heterogeneous industrial civilization.

But to state that property rights "exist only because government recognizes and protects them"[2] is an expression of an amazingly myopic point of view. Property rights are tacitly and explicitly recognized and upheld by all forms of social sanction, legal and nonlegal alike. And in the case of primitive society, the recognition and support of property institutions are in fact more frequently nonlegal than legal.

[1]W. W. Cook, "Ownership and Possession" (*Encyclopedia of the Social Sciences*, Vol. 11, 1933), p. 521.

[2]R. M. MacIver, "Government and Property" (*Journal of Political and Legal Sociology*, Vol. 4, 1946), p. 5. For an opposite point of view, see A. I. Hallowell, "The Nature and Function of Property as a Social Institution" (*Journal of Legal and Political Sociology*, Vol. 1, 1943), pp. 115–138, especially pp. 130ff. Above all, every student should read the article by W. H. Hamilton and I. Till, "Property" (*Encyclopedia of the Social Sciences*, Vol. 12, 1934), pp. 528–538.

Even when legal in nature, primitive property law falls predominantly within the area of private law, which operates independently of the formal governmental machinery.

Land as property in primitive cultures

Land is a *sine qua non* of human existence. It is therefore the most important single object of property. All societies are territorially based,[3] and most sustenance is drawn from the soil, either directly or indirectly.

Land tenure among food gatherers and hunters Most human societies claim property rights in land as communities. The Australians, African Bushmen, the Veddas of Ceylon, and the Tasmanians recognize clearly discernible natural boundaries as marking off local group territories. Each resents uninvited or surreptitious incursions—usually reacting with recourse to war or to regulated expiatory combat. Recognition of the possessory communal right as a true communal property right is seen in the Australian practice whereby one band sends an emissary to another to ask permission to collect certain foods on the lands of the second community. It is up to the tribal elders to grant or reject the request.

In addition to the obvious economic reasons for tribal exclusiveness in the use of their land, Australian tribes have a vital mystic relation to the land. The land is tied up with their dead ancestors; they cannot migrate from the land because that would break an immutable tie to the ancestors, and neither do they wish to have upsetting strangers poking around their sacred territory.

Special sharing of resources Although Shoshone Indians of the Great Basin identify local groups with their home territories, they freely move into one another's domains under certain conditions.

[3]One notable, possibly the only, exception to this is the case of the Orang Laut, the Malayan sea gypsies of the Java and Flores Seas. These tribes are autonomous units, living a roving existence entirely in boats.

Steward has given an admirable explanation of the situation in terms of ecological factors. The uncertainty and variability of the pine-nut and wild-seed crops are so great that territories exploited by different groups varied greatly from year to year. When there were good crops in any locality, they ripened so fast and fell to the ground so quickly that the people who ordinarily lived in the area could not possibly gather them all. When a good harvest was promised, they therefore spread the news abroad so that people whose crops had failed could come to share their bounty with them. "Under such conditions," claims Steward, "ownership of vegetable food resources would have been a disadvantage to everyone."[4] Nonetheless, the fact is that the Shoshones held a country they called their own—they owned it and shared it among themselves.

An almost identical practice exists in Australia. There certain tribes are dependent upon a fruit known as *bunya-bunya*, which, like pine nuts, is uneven in its yield. A territorial group that anticipates a large yield in a given season sends out messengers carrying invitation sticks to other groups, sometimes as far as 100 miles away, or they may raise smoke signals. The visitors may under no circumstances hunt in the hosts' territory, but they may harvest to their hearts' content for about a month and a half. One observer counted more than twenty tribes, speaking different languages, amicably gathered at a single bunya-bunya harvest.[5]

Among the Eskimos, land is not property in any sense, nor is local group sovereignty applied to territory. Anyone, whatever his local group, may hunt where he pleases; the idea of restricting the pursuit of food is repugnant to all Eskimos (except for some groups in western Alaska, who were influenced by the very property-minded Indians of the Northwest Coast).[6]

[4] J. H. Steward, *Basin Plateau Aboriginal Socio-political Groups* (Bureau of American Ethnology, Bulletin 120, 1938), p. 254.
[5] J. Dawson, *Australian Aborigines*, p. 22.
[6] But even here, Margaret Lantis reports that when Eskimos from the mainland came to hunt on Nunivak Island, it never occurred to the Nunivakers to object to, or apparently even resent, the intrusion, although the supply of game was limited. (Oral communication.)

Eskimo interest is in game per se. Land is ignored and not conceptualized as property, in spite of the fact that each local group is identified by the territory in which it lives.

Such exceptions as these indicate that territorial exclusiveness is by no means universal. However, it is perfectly correct to say that the vast majority of food-gathering and hunting tribes do hold their land in common. Any member of the tribe may hunt where he will; as Neighbors once wrote of the Comanches: "No dispute ever arises between the tribes [bands] with regard to their hunting grounds, the whole being held in common."[7]

Land as joint or individual property On the other hand, a few hunting peoples have developed practices of joint, and even individual, ownership of hunting and fishing areas. Notable among these are the Algonquian tribes of Canada and certain Indians of California and the Northwest Coast. There is a considerable body of analytical material on Algonquian land tenure, beginning with Speck's classic paper, "The Family Hunting Band as the Basis of Algonkian Social Organization,"[8] and summarized and weighed by Cooper in 1939, who wrote:

The [Algonquian] band territory is divided up, into sections or segments . . . each section being claimed by a particular "family." . . . It appears . . . that the title to the land rests more in the individual than in the family as such . . . The right to the hunting ground is a permanent and abiding one. . . .[9]

Beavers and muskrats, which are the chief game, are sedentary. Unlike the roving beasts, they stay close to their homesites. Hence, it is possible for individual owners to conserve and protect the supply of such game on their individual tracts. To set traps on another man's property without invitation leads to violent sanctions—bloodshed or sorcery. A hunter who follows the trail of a large fur bearer, such as

[7] R. S. Neighbors, *History of the Indian Tribes of the United States*, Vol. 2, p. 131.
[8] *American Anthropologist*, Vol. 17, 1915, pp. 289–305.
[9] J. M. Cooper, "Is the Algonquian Family Hunting Ground System Pre-Columbian?" (*American Anthropologist*, Vol. 41, 1939), pp. 66–67.

the fox or bear, into the land of another man may kill the beast, although he usually takes pains to notify the landowner, with whom he usually divides the spoils. Berry picking, fishing, root gathering, and birch-bark collecting are prohibited by some Algonquians but not by others. Among the Têtes de Boule of eastern Canada, studied in the field by Cooper, there is a superfluity of berries, and fish are plentiful. "There is no scarcity, and no need for individual claims on such resources."

The Tungus of Siberia have very similar notions, although hunting areas are owned by families rather than by individuals. A man should not hunt or trap in the territory of another family, although he may follow in wounded game for the kill.

The Kwakiutls of British Columbia partitioned coastal areas of water as private property for fishing purposes. All intruders were driven off. In a similar vein, the California Yuroks exhibited a partial private proprietary right to ocean areas. Kroeber told of a Yurok family that "owned" a portion of the sea off the beach extending about 4 miles in either direction from their house site. Other people could fish there, but they had to surrender the flippers of all sea lions taken within the area.[10]

General principles of land ownership among hunters and gatherers Food gatherers, hunters, and fishers usually hold large land and water areas communally as common property, excluding from exploitation of their "sovereign possession" all aliens except those friends to whom they extend privileges. Exceptions are found in the instance of the Eskimos, who at the one extreme have no exclusive concepts with respect to land, and the Algonquians and West Coast Indians, who permit individual or family holdings of hunting and fishing grounds.

[10]A. L. Kroeber, lecture, *Seminar in Psychological Approaches to Culture* (University of California, spring, 1941). An interesting legal case arising from failure to surrender the flippers is analyzed in E. A. Hoebel, "Fundamental Legal Concepts as Applied in the Study of Primitive Law" (*Yale Law Journal*, Vol. 51, 1942), p. 958. A variant of this case is dramatized in *The Ways of Mankind*, Series I, Record 5, "The Sea Lion Flippers: A Study in Ethics."

Land tenure among pastoralists Among pastoral herders, there is a notorious "carelessness as to land." The Comanches, for instance, who were horse herders and hunters of game, had no concept of land. "Land was a matter of unconcern for them, being held neither individually, jointly nor communally."[11] Buffalo herds could be found anywhere, and pasturage for their horses was unlimited.

Even among people whose grazing resources are limited, the tendency is to treat the pasturage as public domain. Notable exceptions have, nevertheless, been reported for the Tungus reindeer herders of Siberia and the Kazaks (or Kirghiz, as the Russians call them to avoid confusion with the Cossacks) of Central Asia east of the Caspian Sea.

Although the Chukchi and Samoyed, neighbors of the Tungus, do not subdivide their pastures within the tribe, the Tungus treat the pastures as the common property of a group of cooperating and intermarrying clans, from which they exclude other groups and their herds by force, if necessary. In some instances, a territory is divided among clans as such. In recent times, individual families have utilized customary grazing grounds somewhat exclusively and irrespective of clan ties.[12]

Kazak practices are even more distinctive. These excellent horsemen subsist on large flocks of sheep and a few goats and camels. As is so often the case in primitive economy, they vary their life and social organization according to the seasons. It is their custom to summer in the lowlands, where they graze their herds at will in the tribal territory. In April, each household sneaks out of the winter village in an attempt to get to good pasturage before the others. In midsummer, drought so parches the land that constant movement from one grass spot to another is necessary. The families and clans do not lay claims to any piece of the country at this season, for the

[11]E. A. Hoebel, *The Political Organization and Law-ways of the Comanche Indians* (American Anthropological Association, Memoir 54: Contributions from the Laboratory of Anthropology, 4, 1940), p. 118.

[12]C. D. Forde, *Habitat, Economy, and Society*, p. 361.

richness of the herbage varies greatly from year to year. Winter camps are fixed settlements conveniently located near a well-protected pasturage amid the trees in a deep river valley. Each lineage or family group has its winter grazing sites established with natural boundaries or rock piles and stakes.

Land tenure among gardeners Gardening and agriculture set quite different situations from those we have thus far discussed. Since full-fledged gardeners and farmers are more or less intimately bound to the soil, it is hardly surprising that they show greater interest in it.

For the most part, primitive gardeners work their lands individually, by lineages, or by clans, and occasionally by clubs, but the ultimate title to the land commonly rests in the community. This makes it necessary to draw a clear distinction between proprietary title and *usufruct:* the *right-of-use granted by the property owner to someone else.* Usufruct may be for a lifetime; it may even extend through a family for generations, but the ultimate control rests in the owner. Sometimes the distinction between usufruct and ownership is very real; at other times it is more ideological than active.

In a number of monarchistic West African tribes, a sort of feudal system prevails. All land "belongs" to the paramount chief. He assigns it to various chiefs, who in turn allocate it to clans, whose headmen assign individual plots to each gardener. In return, the land-working populace owes fealty to the chiefs and above all to the king. They must do public work, pay taxes, and perform military service. As long as they are loyal and faithful in their duties and as long as they are not involved in serious crime, they may not be ousted from their lands. The privilege of use passes down through the family. However, a man may not transfer or sell his plot outside the family without approval of his clan elders. Often the family will pawn or sell a member into slavery in order to avoid alienation of its hold on the land. Since the services that are called for from landholders are general public duties, they are actually services to the king only in theory. The king's

ownership of all land is therefore largely ideological. The kingship serves as the symbol of community unity, and landed property is phrased in terms to fit the ideal.

Land tenure in Indonesia In Indonesia, among the indigenous rice growers, we find the relationship between communal ownership and individual holding clearly delineated. In the autonomous villages of the independent tribes, all land belongs to the village, which is made up of a core of related clansmen. The solidarity of the group is strong and mystically symbolized in the possession of a common temple and sacred relics. The deceased village ancestors are buried in the soil, which contributes to the group's sacred feeling of intimacy with its land. Any member of the community may reclaim and cultivate from the unused communal land as much ground as he can handle, provided he first informs and obtains the consent of the headman and makes a ritual sacrifice. Then he alone is entitled to cultivate that land as long as he works it and keeps it clear. He has continuing right of usufruct. Among some Indonesians, however, if he neglects to prepare the field at the start of any season, he may be confronted by someone else who wants to take it up. Then he must set to work or let the field go. Generally, however, if he abandons a field, he retains a right of exclusive usufruct until the jungle has reclaimed it. Then it reverts wholly to the community area of disposal. If he has built dikes, it may be that his hold remains unimpeded until all traces of the dikes have disappeared.

He may borrow goods or money on such lands as he holds by pledging the land as security. But he may never "sell" the land, nor can a creditor ever obtain a complete foreclosure. There is no possibility of alienation. Land belongs forever to the community.

Outsiders may acquire use of land from the community area of disposal by arranging for payments to the local headman. The contract is in theory for one year only and must be renewed annually. The importance of inalienability to survival of native life was recognized by the Dutch in the last century when they forbade the selling of land to nonnatives and limited the duration of leaseholds by Europeans and other aliens.

Among the inhabitants of a village, the right of usufruct is inheritable within the family line, but if a line dies out, the land reverts directly to the area of disposal for redistribution by the headman. An interesting aspect of the close social bond between the community and its land is seen in the event of a secret murder of an outsider on community land. If the murderer cannot be found, the community that owns the land must indemnify the victim's kinsmen. After all, he died on their common property, so it is presumed that he was killed by someone in that group.[13]

Ifugao land tenure In the Philippines, the Ifugaos reveal a pattern basically similar to that which has just been generalized for Indonesia at large. The Ifugaos are extreme individualists, however, and have no organized villages. Terraced rice fields belong to families, with usufruct inherited by both males and females as a part of their marriage portions. *Camote,* or sweet potato, fields are hewn from the public domain in the mountainside forests by man and wife together and are owned by them jointly as long as they are cultivated. Soil depletion in *camote* fields is so rapid, however, that such fields are abandoned after several years. Still, the title remains with the clearers of the fields until the second growth of underbrush has reached the thickness that prevailed before clearing.

Abandoned rice fields may be taken up without permission by a person other than the owner for a period equal to the exact number of years they have lain unused. After that, the title of the original owner becomes active once again. This certainly seems to be a sensible safeguard against withdrawal of needed land from production by overlanded gentry.[14]

The rule that a person must work lands recently acquired from the public domain in order to retain title is a general and basic one

among primitive gardeners the world over. It effectively guards against one of man's besetting social evils—land hoarding by a wealthy few and the closing of the doors of opportunity to the land-hungry.

Hopi land tenure How fundamental and widespread the African and Indonesian land-use principles are in the primitive gardening complex can be seen from Titiev's comment on the Hopi Pueblo of Oraibi in Arizona:

The Village chief is the theoretical owner of all his town's lands; these lands are divided among the clans residing in his pueblo; and each individual farms a specified portion of his clan's holdings. In addition, there is a large piece of unassigned land, part of which may be used by any villager with his chief's consent. Under such a system land is never bartered or sold, and only rarely exchanged. Ownership is restricted to the privilege of use, but this right is so carefully recognized that if a man decides to allow some of his fields to lie fallow, no other farmer may use them without the specific permission of the owner.[15]

Grazing land for sheep, goats, cattle, and horses is communally shared. The Hopi practice is characteristic of all the pueblos of New Mexico and Arizona.

General principles of land tenure among gardeners Primitive gardeners assign the right of usufruct to individuals or families. In some instances, title is vested in the clan, but usually ultimate ownership is vested in the community. In parts of Africa, this communism is transformed into a type of feudal monarchy, where the king symbolizes community entity. Unused land is public domain from which enterprising individuals may carve their plots, with or without official approval, depending on tribal practice.

On the whole, primitive peoples overwhelmingly treat their land resources as a communal asset. In this sense, they are preponderantly communistic. Pastoralists are, for the most

---

[13]B. ter Haar, *Adat Law in Indonesia,* p. 88.

[14]R. F. Barton, "Ifugao Law" (*University of California Publications in American Ethnology and Archaeology,* Vol. 15, 1919), pp. 40–44.

[15]M. Titiev, "Old Oraibi" (*Papers of the Peabody Museum of American Archaeology and Ethnology, Harvard University,* Vol. 22, No. 1, 1944), p. 181.

part, land communists because the necessity to rove makes individual ownership impractical. In the case of the hunters and gatherers, there is also little impulse to private ownership of land, since so far as the hunters are concerned, most animals are free-ranging, and it is more advantageous to rove at will when on the chase. When the habits of prized animals make it feasible, such primitives as the Algonquians and Northwest Coast Indians are quite ready to abandon land communism for vested rights. The primeval savage is not by nature a communist. But he responds to ecological and economic determinism.

Theories of social evolution that assume "primitive communism" as the first mile on man's rough road thus have some foundation, as far as use of the basic land resources goes.

Those who take the institutions of private property for granted are prone to point to the widespread communism of primitive man as proof of the "advanced" quality of private-property institutions. Communism, they hold, is representative of a primitive state, and the spread of modern Communism is a reversion to a condition of savagery.

With equal lack of balance, Marxists see the land communism of the primitives as proof that communism is the "natural" and therefore the proper and manifest condition for all human society.

The anthropologist notes that the real estate practices of primitives are not properly to be conceived as a justification for any particular economic forms in modern civilization. They demonstrate merely that men can, and usually do, adjust their social institutions to the special needs of their subsistence technologies and natural resources.

Property rights in game

Food is undoubtedly one of the most basic property interests of omnivorous man. Land may seem important, but that is largely because it is the chief original source of the food supply. We have already seen that some food-

stuffs are in some societies free goods, as is the air we breathe. But elsewhere and oftentimes access to food is limited; the ethics of food use fluctuate. The sense of the necessity of mutual aid and a realization of the inescapable interdependence of men struggle eternally with the self-assertive urges of bare-bones survival (when resources give but slim pickings) and selfish gratification of desires. Selfishness corrupts altruistic ideals; mutual aid tempers the harshest self-interest. Property rights in food are the formal crystallization of each society's struggle to regulate the distribution and use of this essential commodity.

Wild plants and animals on communal lands are communal property, but the slaying of game and the collection of plant stuffs alter the economic condition of these goods, subjecting them to altered property statuses. So it is that while the general principle of collective ownership of free-running game and unharvested plants holds good, we find that in most instances, the expenditure of work in reducing the game and plants into consumable food stocks converts them into private property. All peoples recognize private ownership of food. Yet inasmuch as private ownership never entails absolute exclusiveness and since among hunters and gatherers food is derived from communally owned resources, the communal claim upon privately owned foodstuffs is insistent.

Among the Comanches, anyone coming upon a hunter who had just made a kill could claim the choicest quarter of the animal merely by placing his hand upon it. If four different people happened on the unfortunate hunter, they took everything except the hide. This, custom decreed, he could retain by hanging onto the tail of the beast. Far to the north, Boas recorded the following as typical for the Baffin Land Eskimos: "Who first strikes a walrus receives the tusks and one of the forequarters; the next man, the neck and head; the following, the belly; and each of the next two, one of the hindquarters."[16]

Again, in the practice of the Comanches,

[16] F. Boas, *The Eskimo of Baffinland and Hudson Bay* (American Museum of Natural History, Bulletin No. 15, 1907), p. 116.

any hunter returning to the camp with game was obliged to come in openly and share his spoils with all who came to his lodge for a portion of it. "If a man won't give it away, they camp on him until he does." To frustrate this social lien on the products of their individual efforts, some families camped alone during hard times.

After the communal antelope hunts of the Plains Indians, the meat was equally divided among all participating families, for the whole project was a gigantic cooperative undertaking. In communal bison hunts, after the acquisition of horses, all Plains tribes allowed each man whose marked arrow had killed a bison to keep the meat. But even so, the old and infirm who could not hunt and the wives of luckless hunters received their shares from those who had made a kill, and it was the usual thing to teach a boy to give away all his first kill of any large game animal.

Food sharing Sharing of food, even though the food is privately owned, is the basic virtue of almost all American Indian tribes and of most of the primitive hunters of the world. To be generous with food—that is the ideal. But as Lowie has pointed out, etiquette which demands that all comers be fed from a man's private larder is something quite different from actual communal ownership of a common hoard by all the members of the group.[17] The psychological and social response to private beneficence results in a different order of social prestige ranking from that which is produced by common ownership.

Outright pooling of food occurs less commonly among the hunting and collecting peoples than among the gardeners. In the South Pacific, it is associated with prestige competition between local groups and tribes. Great quantities of produce are offered to the chief to be used in feasting rival tribes. The chief's storehouses among the Maori, for example, were the people's storehouses, for the people identified his needs as their needs. They were regularly fed from the great storehouses, but above all, their great

[17]R. H. Lowie, *Primitive Society,* p. 207.

concern was that the chief should be able to entertain visitors munificently. Should he fail in this, their outraged pride would make them ashamed before the world. Eating was to the Maori the supreme pleasure, and only by the joint efforts of all could it reach the great heights they so cherished.

Communal pooling of certain foods is also characteristic of American Pueblo Indians. Annual rabbit hunts are held every fall, and all men must participate as a religious duty. The dried rabbits are offered to the head priest-chief of the pueblo, who stores them in his house to be used in ceremonial meals and to be doled out by him to the poor and hungry families of his pueblo in time of need.

Individual property rights in game At the opposite extreme, certain Algonquian hunters of North America, such as the Ojibwa, demonstrate the ideological lengths to which rugged individualism in food procured from wild game can go. Says Landes:

The game and fish that a man catches in the winter are his private property. When he returns with them to his lodge . . . he decides what to do with them . . . . When he gives game to his wife . . . he has lost all claim to it. It is never said that he gives game to his wife for her use in making food and clothing for the family; but they phrase it that a man gives game to his wife and therefore the game belongs to her to do with as she pleases. . . . The wife now employs "her" property in the manufacture of food and clothing. She gives the finished product to her husband, immature children, and herself. When these gifts have been given, they become the property of the recipients.[18]

Among many hunting tribes, animals that have a fixed abode, such as a hibernating bear, a bee, or an eagle, are often seized upon as objects of private ownership, even where all other claims to animals are communal. The Nama Hottentot places a few broken twigs before a wild beehive, and a Sia Indian publicly announces the location of bee trees that

[18]R. Landes, "The Ojibwa of Canada," in M. Mead (ed.), *Cooperation and Competition among Primitive Peoples,* pp. 90–91.

he has discovered—not to invite others to find the way to the delicacy, but to warn them off. Eagle nests are privately owned among all the Pueblo Indians, so that eagles born in the nest belong to the owner of it. A Pueblo hunter who finds a bear's den marks it, and the bear is his to take in the spring.

Similarly, wild fruit trees in Indonesia and among many peoples of the South Pacific may be blazed or otherwise marked by an individual so that he alone may harvest the tree's yield. In the Melanesian area, the tree is guarded by a magic charm that brings foul diseases to any violator of the property right of the owner. Ownership of such trees is usually divorced from the land upon which the tree stands. In some places, it is even possible to own a tree that stands on another man's land.

Property rights in livestock

The word "chattel," which means any object of personal ownership, is derived from the Old French word *chatel*. The modern Anglo-American word "cattle" has the same origin. *Chatel* has its ultimate etymology in the Latin word *caput*, meaning "head." *Chatel* in ancient France referred to property of the greatest value, head property. Cattle were so much the chief form of property among our pastoral ancestors that our specialized word for personal property grew from the same root. And the word "pecuniary" (pertaining to money) derives directly from the class of movable property known as *pecunia* in Roman law, where the term was itself derived directly from the Latin word *pecus*, meaning "herd."

This small fragment of word history formulates the universal principle of stock ownership among all primitive peoples. Cattle are chattels. They are privately owned. The one great known exception occurred in that remarkable progenitor of the totalitarian socialist state, the Inca Empire. Among the Incas, private citizens could own up to ten llamas, but the vast majority of the beasts were state property. The wool collected from the state herds was stored in government warehouses, to be distributed annually in equal allotments to each family head.[19]

Grazing land among migratory primitive pastoralists does not economically lend itself to subdivision. Hence, as has been noted, it is usually communally held and used. But livestock comes in individual units to which individuals may readily attach themselves. Undoubtedly, there is a deep emotional impulse underlying this tendency. Domestication begins in a symbiotic relationship between man and animal that is fundamentally personal. It is most clearly seen in the affectionate relation between man and his dog, the first of the domesticated beasts. It runs through all herders in greater or lesser degree. Nuer men, when they have nothing more pressing to do, spend hours in sensuous contemplation of their cattle.[20]

"Some men," said Post Oak Jim, of the Comanche herders of 1850, "loved their horses more than their wives." Favorite horses among most Plains Indians were treated almost as members of the family. Among the Solomon Islanders and many other Melanesians, pigs are the chief objects of value.

In the history of mankind, the domestication of animals has undoubtedly been a great stimulus to the development of private-property institutions. Thus the World Ethnographic Survey shows wealth to be a significant factor in the social differentiation of freemen only among pastoralists (phi = 0.157).[21]

Property rights in garden produce

Ownership of foodstuffs produced by gardening tends generally to be vested in individuals or family households, but the lines are not drawn with universal consistency. Since most garden plots are worked under private usufruct or outright ownership and since most of the

[19] J. H. Rowe, "Inca Culture at the Time of the Spanish Conquest," in J. H. Steward (ed.), *Handbook of South American Indians*, Vol. 2, pp. 219, 267.
[20] E. E. Evans-Pritchard, *The Nuer*.
[21] A. D. Coult and R. W. Habenstein, *Cross Tabulations of Murdock's Ethnographic Survey*, p. 518.

expended effort is individual effort, harvests are commonly individually owned. Polynesian practices in contravention of this usage have already been noted, however. Among the Keresan-speaking Pueblos, just as rabbit hunts are communal duties, so are the planting and cultivating of the cacique's, or chief's, garden. The harvest is stored in the cacique's house for communal use.

Matrilateral practices in Melanesia require that a man raise his crops on his sister's behalf. Since his sister's household is not his own household, he must in effect transfer the yams from his garden to the storehouses of her husband. His storehouses in turn are filled in part by his wife's brother. What a man produces does not necessarily remain his own property.

Property rights in artifacts

Weapons and implements for individual use are ordinarily owned either by their creator or by their user. According to the *principle of individual effort,* proprietary ownership of movables is usually vested in the person who has wrought the object through the expenditure of individual effort. Primitive women ordinarily own the pottery they have modeled. A man owns the spear or ax he has shaped himself. There is to some extent an identity between the artisan and his creation, as though it were an extension of his personality. Most of mankind has recognized this identity and respected it by establishing protective devices in the form of personal-property institutions. Recognition of this aspect of property does not entail forgetfulness that social limitations on the rights of the individual owner are always present.

Incorporeal property

It no longer surprises anthropologists that non-material things of value are objects of property in primitive society.[22] It never would have sur-

prised us at all if it had not been that our grandfather's generation and its predecessors were so smugly self-assured that uncivilized men where of childlike mentality and that Europeans alone were capable of mental abstraction. However, the better to understand the nature of incorporeal property, consider the case of a Plains Indian visionary who has fasted and sought supernatural power. A bear has appeared to him in a dream; it spoke to him and taught him four new songs, and it also instructed him in the preparation of a rawhide shield to be painted with a bear symbol and other devices. The bear in the vision also instructed his tutelary that a shield made in accordance with the instructions would provide immunity in battle if the four songs were sung before an engagement began. The visionary has made a shield as instructed; he has sung the songs; his comrades have heard the words; and he has deliberately exposed himself to the missiles of the enemy, coming through unscathed. The value of the shield and the songs has been publicly demonstrated. The shield, as Lowie has made clear, is a material object that is clearly personal property. But the shield as such, in the culture of the Plains Indians, is of little value. What is of value in conjunction with the shield are the songs and the mystic power that the two engender together. The incorporeal property is the thing of worth. The complex of shield, song, and power may be transferred as a gift to son, nephew, brother, or friend (in at least one Comanche case that the author has recorded, the transfer had to be followed by a vision on the part of the recipient before the mystic power would become operative, however, and this may frequently be the case among other tribes). Or this same complex may be sold in a commercial transaction that has the qualities of a contractual sale. In either case, the recipient may use the complex if he has properly acquired the rights through regularized transfer, but not otherwise. The consequence of unauthorized use of the shield and songs is that the usurper will most certainly be killed by enemy missiles because

[22] *Cf.* See R. H. Lowie, "Incorporeal Property in Primitive Society" (*Yale Law Journal,* Vol. 38, 1928), p. 551; and *Primitive Society,* pp. 235–243. See also E. A. Hoebel, *The Law of Primitive Man,* pp. 60–63.

of the punitive action of the supernatural power. But there is no reason to believe that the true owner may not recover the shield if it is stolen, and with it his enjoyment of the songs.

Certainly we have here a sufficiently large aggregate of rights denoted by ownership so that we may properly speak of them as incorporeal property. Thus, we find again and again that magic rites and charms, songs, dances, and names are the property of persons and groups of persons. Myths and legends may belong to lineages, as among the Indians of the Northwest Coast. These are objects of property in exactly the same sense as are our copyrights, patents, and "goodwill." After all, if a people is capable of creating intangible patterns for behavior, such as magic and songs, it is not a great step into the abstruse to attach protective social rules to these abstractions when and if they become objects of value.

Likewise, the hereditary right to work is a traditional incorporeal property right for certain groups in India, and the available work is distributed accordingly. N. S. Reddy writes of the Madiga caste of leatherworkers in Madras: "The right to work is inherited as any other piece of property, and the quantum of employment that accrues to the individual holder is upheld by the community at large."[23]

SUMMARY

The essential nature of property is to be found in social relations rather than in any inherent attributes of the thing or object that we call *property*. Property, in other words, is not a thing, but a network of social relations that governs the conduct of people with respect to the use and disposition of things. Each member of a society has a status in relation to the property object. The status in turn has an associated role, or customary ways of behaving, which determines each person's rights to use the object, on the one hand, or which forbids or

[23] N. S. Reddy, *Transition in Caste Structure in Andrah Desh with Particular Reference to Depressed Castes*, p. 61.

limits his use of it, on the other. If any object can be used by anybody or everybody, it is not "property" but a free good. If it is thought by the members of a society to be equally accessible (even though only in theory) to all the members of that society, then we have *communal property*. If the statuses of the members of a group, such as a family, lineage, or association, are predominantly similar in relation to the use of an object, then we have *joint property*. If the status of an individual in relation to the object is such that he alone has predominant priority in its use and disposition, then we are confronted with *private property*. Property relations, however, are so complex that such labels must be used with great restraint, for any given manifestation of property may be compounded of qualities of all three orders. Property can properly be analyzed only in terms of the detailed norms of behavior that exist in each culture.

Such analysis does, however, show that certain kinds of objects have a tendency to become communal, joint, or private property, according to the nature of the subsistence culture.

Land is the most basic form of property. Among most primitives, the ultimate title to land is vested in the tribe, although a few hunters, like the Eskimos, have no concept of land as property. Pastoral people, in particular, tend not to bother to establish property claims in land, although they have highly refined individual or lineage property rights in their herds. Gardening tribes vest the right of usufruct in family lines, which in turn assign the land to individuals, or else village headmen assign plots periodically, acting on behalf of the tribal chief, who symbolically is the owner for all the tribe.

Food is usually private property, but its use and distribution may often be subject to complex customs that express a social claim which requires a sharing of food through exchange, tribute to a chief, or hospitality. Tools, weapons, clothing, and ornaments are generally private property.

Primitive peoples are, in general terms, neither more nor less communistic than civilized peoples in ownership of property, except that land is more consistently held in common and landlordship is rare.

SELECTED READINGS

Goody, J.: *Death, Property, and the Ancestors* (1962). Part III (pp. 273–327) is an excellent conceptual analysis of property in primitive and civilized cultures. The entire book is a masterful study of mortuary ceremonies and property transmission and of their functional relation to social structure in two African tribes.

Hallowell, A. I.: "The Nature and Function of Property as a Social Institution" (*Journal of Political and Legal Philosophy*, Vol. I, 1943), pp. 115–138. The most thorough anthropological treatment of the subject.

Herskovits, M. J.: *Economic Anthropology* (1952), Part IV, "Property." An extensive treatment of the subject.

ter Haar, B.: *Adat Law in Indonesia* (1948), chaps. 2 and 10, "Land Rights" and "Inheritance." A comprehensive survey of adat law among the many tribes of this area of Southeast Asia.

Thurnwald, R.: *Economics in Primitive Communities* (1932), chap. 10, "Ownership and Property." A very brief statement of general principles.

Gifts, trade, and inheritance

chapter 29

Gift giving is a human activity of fundamental and universal social significance. It functions as a concrete symbolic representation of mutual interdependence among the members of a society, enhancing social solidarity and effecting a redistribution of economic goods.

The basis of gift giving is the reciprocity underlying all social relations.

Normally, a gift is an outright transfer that alienates the donor's proprietary title. Anglo-American law requires that the donor part not only with the possession but also with the dominion. It holds that a perfect gift is irrevocable. Among primitive peoples, however, there are circumstances in which the gift may be conditional and must be returned if the conditions are not fulfilled. This is, in fact, the origin of the epithet "Indian giver."

A pure gift is a gratuity offered as a free enrichment of the recipient without desire for reciprocity. Only anonymous giving meets this ideal qualification, however. Motives for gift giving are many, and in all instances the donor receives some sort of return, be it no more than the self-gratification of his ego known to himself alone.

Gift exchanges in primitive society

On the lowest level of culture, the Andaman Islanders nicely exemplify primitive behavior in gift exchange. Movables are all privately owned by these people, and yet no one may possess a particular article for long.

When two friends meet who have not seen each other for some time, one of the first things they do is to

exchange presents with one another. Even in the ordinary everyday life of the village there is a constant giving and receiving of presents. A younger man or woman may give some article to an older one without expecting or receiving any return, but between equals a person who gives a present always expects that he will receive something of equal value in exchange. At the meetings that take place between neighboring local groups the exchange of presents is of great importance. . . .

Almost every object that the Andamanese possess is thus constantly changing hands.[1]

Among American Plains Indians, generosity was considered one of the highest virtues; accumulation of property was socially limited. Gifts of horses were constantly being made. Whenever a guest admired an object, his host forthwith made a gift of it. Sooner or later, a return gift was expected, but it did not have to be of equivalent worth. Chiefs, above all other people, were obligated to give, for this is one way of attracting and holding followers (as our own politicians well know). Cheyenne Indians today are reluctant to become chiefs in the old way now that they have become "Americanized." They do not want to have to give away their property. Political leaders among all people are in fact subject to the demands of compulsive giving. Marquesas Island chieftains, according to Linton, used the sexual favors of their wives as a form of gift to attract and hold their henchmen.[2]

Among many primitives, gift giving that builds into gift exchange marks every important crisis period in the individual life cycle or any other change of personal status. Birth, puberty, marriage, death, and entrance into a club or assumption of an office are called to public attention by the bestowal of gifts. The famous potlatches of the Northwest Coast Indians, with all their lavish expenditure of gifts, center around such occasions. Contractual arrangements such as marriage call for immediate two-way exchanges, often extending over months.

Gift exchange of economic significance may border on trade. Yet it may be merely symbolic in nature when the rule of equivalence is strong. The person who views our ceremonial gift exchanges on the occasion of the Christmas festival only in terms of the usableness of the gifts measured against cost and effort naturally thinks the whole business is silly. But he, poor soul, misses the point. Quite true, we all end up with a number of things we neither need nor want. Quite true, it would be more rational to offer gift certificates or even money to one's friends or family so that they could buy what they wanted and needed. But how flat are such gifts! Their donors confuse the social function of gift giving with utility. They forget that the gifts are symbolic of a social bond between giver and receiver. Gifts represent a state of social relations and a set of emotions, not business.

Trade

The essential difference between trade and gift exchange is in their relative functions. In trade, the emphasis is on economic redistribution. In gift exchange, the emphasis is on social relationships. Trade rests on and fosters social interaction, but its main concern is with the distribution of goods. Gift exchange distributes goods, but its main concern is with personal relations.

Within small tribes, there is little trade. Gift exchange suffices for the most part. The level of culture is also a factor of some influence. Simple cultures with little specialization of labor do not call forth much intratribal trade. It is primarily the high cultures with large populations that are capable of considerable specialization of effort among their members. Services and products are then available for exchange and trade.

However, virtually all societies, large and small, engage in intertribal or international trade. Every society has its unique goods or possesses natural resources from which to supply materials not available elsewhere. Salt-water shells find their way hundreds of miles inland in New Guinea and North America. In

[1]A. R. Radcliffe-Brown, *The Andaman Islanders*, pp. 42–43.
[2]R. Linton, in A. Kardiner, *The Individual and His Society*, pp. 152ff.

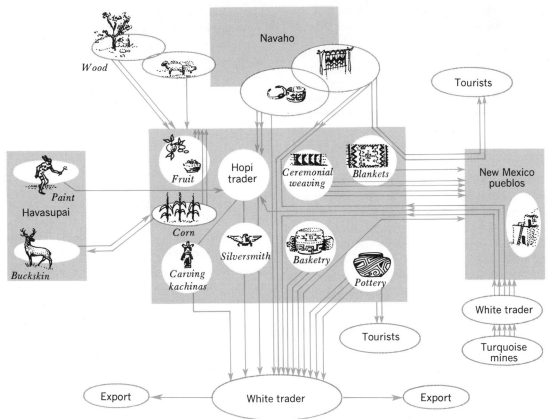

Fig. 29-1 Trade relations of the Hopi Indians. Hopi craftsmen trade finished products to Navahos and Havasupai Indians in exchange for raw materials, paint and blankets. From white traders and New Mexico Pueblos they get industrial products. (From L. Thompson and A. Joseph, The Hopi Way, *p. 23.)*

the Bronze Age, copper from Cyprus followed trade routes all over Europe. Beeswax flint from Grand-Pressigny, France, found wide use over all western Europe in Neolithic times. Melanesian inlanders trade vegetables for fish with the coastal dwellers.

Specialization based on custom rather than limitation of resources induces a good deal of trade. In New Mexico, Sia Indian women make excellent pottery. The pueblo of Jemez, less than 10 miles away, made none for many centuries, although the same clays are avail-

able to both. Jemez exchanged corn for Sia pots in the old days. Hopis trade maize with the nearby Havasupai for buckskins and paint, and maize for wood and wool with the surrounding Navaho (Fig. 29-1). But within the Hopi tribe, only the women of the pueblos on Second Mesa make coiled baskets; those who live on Third Mesa make them of wicker, and painted pottery is produced only on First Mesa.

The Crow Indians of the Plains were capable of growing tobacco. Indeed, they had a ceremonial organization, the Tobacco Society, whose interest centered around the growing of tobacco as a sacred ritual. Nevertheless, the nicotine plant was not grown for use, and common tobacco had to be obtained by trade with other tribes.[3]

In western Melanesia, the Southern Massim own large seagoing canoes, which they do not manufacture themselves, although they could.

[3]R. H. Lowie, *The Crow Indians*, pp. 274ff.

Instead, they obtain them in trade from the tribes of the Northern Massim district.

Within the small group of Trobriand Islands, local specialization is very marked. Two towns alone produce the red shell disks so valued in the *kula* exchange (see below). The people of the island of Kayleula make canoes and trade with the inhabitants of the western D'Entrecasteaux Islands for betel nuts, sago, pottery, and turtle shell.

To the east of the Trobriands, the natives of Woodlark Island produce homogeneous greenstone for tools and the best carved ebony of the area; both products are valued objects of trade.[4]

Dumb barter It shocks many people to discover that businessmen carry on trade with enemy nations. A high command will deliberately spare certain enemy plants because by means of trade through neutrals, it is possible to secure products of those plants. Enemies not infrequently find it advantageous to let economic interests override their antagonisms.

This is the basis of the dumb barter, or silent trade, among certain primitives. The pygmy Semang of Malaya, for example, exchange forest products for goods offered by their enemies, the Sakai. Neither group sees the other party during the transaction. The Semang place their goods in a customary place and retire. When the Sakai find the offering, they appropriate it and replace it with whatever they wish to exchange. Later, the little Semangs come back to pick up the goods before retiring to their jungle fastness. In like manner, the Mountain Vedda of Ceylon trade game for iron arrowheads with the Singhalese smiths. They lay their game in front of the smiths' huts at night, to return the next night to gather the returns.

Herodotus describes how Carthaginian merchants carried on dumb barter with the natives of the northwest coast of Africa. The Carthaginians placed their goods on shore and retired to their ships, sending up a smoke signal. The natives came and replaced the goods with

gold. They got what they deemed necessary, for the natives knew that if the mariners were shortchanged they would not return again.[5] Dumb barter still occurs in parts of Africa.

A modernized version of dumb barter was practiced in the Ozark Mountain country of Arkansas into the 1930s, where "moonshine" corn whiskey could be bought as "stump liquor." As a means of avoiding revenue officers, it was the practice to leave one dollar on a known tree stump. During the night, a gallon of corn whiskey would replace it, to be picked up by the purchaser in the morning. The moonshiner did not have to expose himself to possible arrest.

Markets Open trade is naturally much more convenient, and primitive peoples often develop elaborate machinery for this purpose. In Nigeria, huge market towns of great antiquity are in existence. Native artisans bring their brasswork, pottery, mats, baskets, leatherwork, and foodstuffs many miles to these trading centers. The Kede tribe of northern Nigeria act as river transporters of trade goods, for the Kede are the consummate canoemen of the Niger. They carry kola nuts and palm oil north from Nigeria, bringing back gowns, mats, fish, rice, horses, and potash from the Hausa and Nupe tribes.[6]

In Africa, the marketplace is often under the magical protection of some great native chief, whose supernatural authority evokes the "peace of the market" so that enemy tribes may trade in safety. Chiefs frequently provide police and courts for markets in their districts, as well.

Bohannan points out that African markets in tribal subsistence economies are "peripheral"; that is, the markets are not essential to the economic livelihood of the societies because the number of people who actually derive their living from the markets is small.

[4]B. Malinowski, *Argonauts of the Western Pacific,* chap. 1.

[5]W. D. Hambly, *"Source Book for African Anthropology"* (*Field Museum of Natural History, Anthropological Series,* Vol. 26, Part 2), p. 650.
[6]S. F. Nadel, "The Kede," in E. E. Evans-Pritchard and M. Fortes (eds.), *African Political Systems,* p. 169.

The economic function of African markets is but one part of the whole picture. Markets are public meeting places and communication centers for dispersal of gossip, news, and official pronouncements. Entertainers use markets as fairs are used in the United States—as places where audiences are gathered without effort. And markets, like fairs, are ready-made festivals. "The market day," observes Bohannan, "usually falls off into a beer drink."[7]

The Kula Without doubt, the most elaborate and exciting system of trade yet noted for the primitive world is the *kula* of northwestern Melanesia. Malinowski's thorough description of the kula will stand as a classic of anthropological economics for many years to come. The kula enterprise is a vast complex of trade, magic, ceremonial exchange, overseas travel, and pleasure seeking that involves the enter-

[7]P. Bohannan, *Social Anthropology*, p. 242.

prisers of tribes many miles apart. The framework through which the whole organization is expressed is the exchange of white shell armbands, called *mwali* (Trobriand), and long necklaces of red shell, called *soulava*. Exchange is intertribal and interisland. *Soulava* are always traded in a clockwise direction. *Mwali* go counterclockwise (Fig. 29-2). There is no exception to this rule.

Each of these articles meets on its way articles of the other class, and is constantly being exchanged for them. Every movement of the Kula articles, every detail of the transactions is fixed and regulated by a set of traditional rules and conventions, and some acts of the Kula are accompanied by an elaborate magical ritual and public ceremonies.

On every island and in every village, a more or less limited number of men take part in the Kula—that is to say, receive the goods, hold them for a short time, and then pass them on. . . . Thus no man ever keeps any of the articles for any length of time in his possession. One transaction does not finish the Kula relationship, the rule being "once in the Kula, always in the Kula," and a partnership between two men is a permanent and lifelong affair. . . .

The ceremonial exchange of the two articles is the main, the fundamental aspect of the Kula. But associated with it, and done under its cover, we find a great number of secondary activities and features.

Fig. 29-2   The kula ring of the southwest Pacific. Lines show overseas trade routes. Arrows indicate directions followed by necklaces (soulava) and arm bands (mwali). (Adapted from Malinowski.)

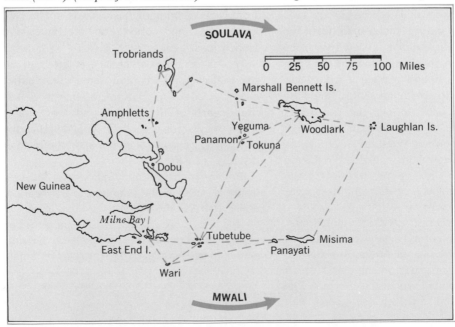

Thus, side by side with the ritual exchange of arm-shells and necklaces, the natives carry on ordinary trade, bartering from one island to another a great number of utilities, often unprocurable in the district to which they are imported, and indispensable there.[8]

Not all trade among primitives is by means of direct barter. Various media of exchange are known in several parts of the world. Shells serve most commonly as a species of money: cowrie shells in the Pacific area and in Africa, and dentalium shells among the Indians of California. Wampum beads were used in exchange among our eastern Indians, and the early Dutch in New York treated them as good cash. Importation of poor counterfeits caused the city council of New Amsterdam in 1650 to pass an ordinance pegging the exchange value of good beads at six white and three black per *stiver*. Poor wampum was pegged at eight and four. Polished stone ax heads and bronze celts were used extensively in late prehistoric times in Europe. Livestock—pigs in the Solomon Islands and cattle in East Africa—are used in such a way that they may properly be called media of exchange.

Iron hoes serve as a medium of exchange in parts of Africa, but the strangest of all primitive moneys is the huge limestone wheels of the Island of Yap in Micronesia.

Inheritance

Inheritance, in the words of G. D. H. Cole, "is the entrance of living persons into the possession of dead persons' property."[9] That is one way of putting it. This, however, leaves much unsaid. In the preceding chapter, property was identified as consisting of (1) an object (material or incorporeal) and (2) a web of social relations that establishes a limiting and defined relationship between persons and that object. This web of relationships consists of the roles or patterns of behavior that are associated with certain statuses, which are in turn related to the object of property. Own-

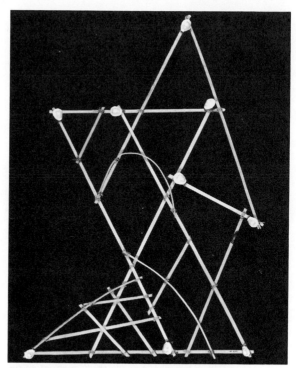

Fig. 29-3 Micronesian navigator's chart made of split bamboo and cowrie shells. The shells represent islands; the curved sticks, currents. (Smithsonian Institution.)

ership, therefore, is a complex of statuses and roles that allow certain persons the socially recognized privilege-right of limited control of the use or disposition of objects. These rights of control, though limited, establish the owners' active and positive relations to the object. Nonowners are under a duty to refrain from use of the object, or they are at least subject to much more restrictive access to its use. In other words, in the property relationship, the status and roles of A with respect to the object are distinct and special as against those of X, Y, or Z.

Analyzed in terms of culture theory, inheritance is not transfer of possession; it is the transference of statuses. And although much inheritance involves transfer after death, many statuses may be transferred *inter vivos*, during life. Nyakyusa sons of chiefs "inherit the coun-

[8] Malinowski, *op, cit.*, pp. 82–83.
[9] G. D. H. Cole, "Inheritance" (*Encyclopedia of the Social Sciences*, Vol. 20, 1935), p. 286.

try''; i.e., they assume the chieftainship, while their fathers still live. Ifugao children inherit the parental rice fields on marriage. But obviously not all transfers of status are what we recognize as inheritance. Cheyenne peace chiefs on the Council of Forty-four were replaced every ten years by selection, not inheritance. The presidency of the United States involves a transfer of status every time we change administration, but the office is noninheritable.

Inheritance, therefore, means a transference of status based upon a preexisting relationship between the predecessor and the successor. The relationship is personal and, usually, traditional.

Radcliffe-Brown, in his survey of patrilineal and matrilineal succession in primitive societies, came very close to realization of this when he concluded: ''In general, though there are a few exceptions, transmission of property follows the same line as transmission of status.''[10] The reason is that transmission of property *is* transmission of status. It follows that if most kinds of status are transmitted down one line or another, property statuses will follow along the same line. Therefore, a close correlation of type of social organization and devolution of property will naturally occur.

Testamentary disposition In instances in which an individual wishes to transfer his property status to another person who is not specifically defined as an heir in custom or law, *testamentary disposition* may be allowed for. This is what we know as ''making a will.'' The power of testamentary disposition probably exists in most primitive societies, although this matter has not been subjected to systematic investigation. In those societies in which it does exist, it does not apply evenly to all forms of property. The disposition of garden plots, for example, is usually subject to strict rules of inheritance not subject to individual meddling. At the same time, a man or

woman may be quite free to alter the normal lines of inheritance of personal property in movables by use of the will. In some instances, the spoken will is inviolable; in others, it may be set aside by the living as contrary to law and custom. What is proper and what is improper at this point may often be as troublesome a question for primitive peoples as it is for us.[11] A case occurring among the Ashanti of Ghana in 1942 is a good example. Inheritance of land among the Ashanti runs down the maternal line; it should go from a man to his brother (who belongs to the same maternal clan) and then to a sister's son, but not to a son of either man, for this person belongs to a different clan.

A man when on his death-bed made a dying declaration giving one of his cocoa-farms to his son, and swore an oath enjoining his brother, who was his successor, to see that the gift was honoured. ''If you do not give it to him,'' said the dying man, ''I shall call you before the ancestors for our case to be judged.''

. . . The man died and his brother succeeded to the property, but refused, with the concurrence of the other members of the family, to give the cocoa-farm to his deceased brother's son. Three months later a fire broke out in the village. The surviving brother fell from a roof while helping to put out one of the fires, and sustained an injury to his leg from which he subsequently died. Before he died, he told his family that he believed his deceased brother was summoning him to the spirit world to answer for his conduct in not honouring his brother's death-bed declaration. The general belief was that his death was due to his failure to carry out his deceased brother's instructions. The next successor to the property duly gave the cocoa-farm to the son to whom it had been left.[12]

In the simplest societies, inheritance is poorly developed. Nomadic hunters and collectors have few goods, and most of these are personal working equipment. Because of the universality of belief in an afterlife, many primitives assume that the deceased want and

[10]A. R. Radcliffe-Brown, ''Patrilineal and Matrilineal Succession'' (*Iowa Law Review*, Vol. 20, 1935), p. 297.

[11]See B. Malinowski, *Crime and Custom in Savage Society*, for examples.
[12]A. K. Busia, *The Position of the Chief in the Modern Political System of Ashanti*, p. 43.

need their goods. The result is, as Radcliffe-Brown has noted:

With us one of the most important aspects of succession is the transmission of property by inheritance. Yet in some of the simplest societies this is a matter of almost no significance at all. In an Australian tribe, for example, a man possesses a few weapons, tools, utensils, and personal ornaments, things of little value or permanence. On his death some of them may be destroyed, others may be distributed among his relatives or friends. But their disposal is of so little importance, unless in relation to ritual, that it is often difficult to find any rules of customary procedure.[13]

The same may be said of the African Bushmen, the Andaman Islanders, the Semangs, the Eskimos, and the Shoshones.

Destruction of property

In the instance of the Comanches:

In the disposal of a deceased's property there is but one rule which stood out with constancy: upon the death of a person all effects of his (or her) personal usage were destroyed. This included clothing, weapons, saddles, tools, paraphernalia, and horses customarily ridden by the deceased. . . . Further, even the tipi in which the dead person, man or woman, lived was totally destroyed; also for a child, but not for a baby. Articles of intimate personal usage were buried with the corpse. Other less important articles were burned. Possessions with medicine powers were either destroyed by throwing them into the river, or by placing them in an unfrequented tree where they could rot.[14]

All Plains Indians had similar rules. Surpluses were variously handled. The Comanches passed the residual estate to the widow, who in turn was obliged to pass some of it on to her husband's friends and relatives, and especially to nonrelatives, who hung around as enthusiastic mourners; they mourned and mourned until they were given sufficient gifts to stop them. Inheritance by nonrelatives was,

in point of fact, characteristic in the Plains area. A family that went the whole way in mourning made itself destitute, until in due time friends and relatives reoutfitted them with gifts.

On the lower levels of culture, it is difficult to generalize inheritance rules with accuracy. Often there is no single rule of inheritance controlling all situations, or any single line of practice under any of the legal rules. Our canny Cheyenne informant, Calf Woman, cautioned: "Some families did differently than others."

Distinctions by sexes

In general, it may be said that husband and wife do not inherit from each other in the primitive world. This is an easily understood consequence of the nature of marriage as an alliance of two kinship groups.[15] What is left by either spouse is more than likely to revert to the family or lineage from which he or she came. Men's goods are inherited by men, and women's by women. Two factors that are present on the primitive level are responsible for these conditions. The first is the absence or undeveloped state of a free market and money economy. Goods cannot be divorced from use with any appreciable degree of ease. They are not readily convertible into fluid capital. Therefore, they must be possessed by a competent user; the sexual division of labor bars inheritance of sex-linked property across sex lines. Second, in all primitive societies a person is more closely tied to his or her kinship group than to the marriage partner. The claims of surviving kinsmen outweigh the claims of the surviving spouse.[16]

Effect of unilineal descent

In the event that a death is followed by a sororal or levirate marriage, the movable property of the deceased spouse stays right in the household of the

[13]Radcliffe-Brown, "Patrilineal and Matrilineal Succession," p. 286.
[14]E. A. Hoebel, *The Political Organization and Law-ways of the Comanche Indians* (American Anthropological Association, Memoir 54: Contributions from the Laboratory of Anthropology, 4, 1940), pp. 120–121.
[15]See R. F. Barton, "Ifugao Law" (*University of California Publications in American Archaeology and Ethnology,* Vol. 15, 1919), p. 26, for the Ifugao exemplification of this rule.
[16]See R. F. Benedict, "Marital Property Rights in Bilateral Society" (*American Anthropologist,* Vol. 38, 1936), pp. 368–373.

surviving spouse, and the landed property remains in the relation to the survivor that it exhibited before the death of the spouse. But this is only because of the coincidence of identity of status between the deceased spouse and the one who replaces her (or him) in the household. The inheritance runs from deceased wife to her sister who replaces her, not from deceased wife to husband to his second wife.

Inheritance of usufruct in land follows fairly clear lines. Among matrilineal gardeners, where women till the soil, inheritance runs from mother to daughters. If the picture is complicated with matrilineal organization coupled with virilocal residence and male gardening (as in the Trobriand Islands), inheritance runs from mother's brother to sister's son. In parts of Melanesia, although land is inherited matrilineally, fruit trees privately owned by males are inherited patrilineally.

Whether matrilineal or patrilineal organization prevails also strongly influences the lines of inheritance of movable and incorporeal property. Patrilineal societies favor filial inheritance. Matrilineal societies favor inheritance from maternal uncle to sister's son. It is quite possible for a tribe to subject some forms of property to the avunculate and other forms to paternal succession. It is not necessary that the inheritance system be absolutely consistent with one principle or the other.

The sexual equivalence of brothers in marriage arrangements is reflected in their equivalence in relation to property. Thus *collateral inheritance,* or inheritance by brothers or sisters from brother or sister in preference to the children, indicates that the members of a fraternity have a solidarity that supersedes that of the conjugal-natal family. Plains Indians applied this rule to the inheritance of horses especially. The generation tie outweighs the filial or avuncular. This may well be reinforced in political inheritance of chiefship, where it is advantageous to avoid letting the mantle of leadership fall on a callow youth.

Incorporeal properties, especially magic formulas and medical powers, must be par-

tially transferred before death if they involve secret knowledge. A man may transfer his charms or songs to son or nephew as a gift, without anticipation of his departure from life. This would be a gift *inter vivos,* not properly a matter of inheritance. Or it may be that the necessary knowledge is taught to the beneficiary without transfer of the right of use until after the death of the donor, which would be a true case of a gift *causa mortis,* a gift made in the prospect of death and properly an aspect of inheritance.

Primogeniture In societies of growing populations given to gardening or agriculture on limited land resources, there is always the problem of dispersal of the family holdings through inheritance by too many heirs. Primogeniture is the solution hit upon by some peoples. All property devolves upon the eldest son, who then has the duty to support the other members of the family in exchange for their labor. "A family must have a strong center," say the Ifugaos. Primogeniture more often applies to inheritance of chiefship and office, however, than to landed property. The mana of the Polynesian chief passes to the first-born son in an unending line. So strong is the primogeniture rule among the Maoris of New Zealand that on occasion a first-born woman may take a man's name and acquire the status of a first-born son.

Primogeniture can be a force in an expansionistic movement. Power and glory are available to second-born sons who sally forth to gain new land, wealth, and rank and who found new lineages by leading a group of colonists to unsettled territory.

The evidence is clear for the Maori, and we may infer that primogeniture was a force in Polynesia that worked to drive younger sons out on overseas expeditions of exploration and colonization.[17]

How much of the brunt of empire building was borne by the younger sons of Britain who were shut out at home by the laws of primo-

[17]B. W. Aginsky and P. H. Buck, "Interacting Forces in the Maori Family" (*American Anthropologist,* Vol. 42, 1940), pp. 195ff.

usefulness stressed over any other factor (beauty).

geniture? In the classical laissez-faire economics of nineteenth-century England, primogeniture was hailed as a double-acting social device: it avoided inefficient division of the family inheritance, and it forced the younger members to fend for themselves, thus enriching society by their efforts. Those primitives who practice primogeniture recognize the first of these benefits, but it is unlikely that the second ever entered their conscious thoughts. Primogeniture is not much favored in the Western world today. Feudalism is gone, and enterprise capitalism is not favorable to primogeniture.

Ultimogeniture There are a few tribes that turn the tables completely about. By means of *ultimogeniture,* the youngest son inherits the greater portion of the family estate. Among certain peoples of India, Asia, and Africa, the elder brothers are set up with herds or households in part by family resources used in progeny price. What is left over at the father's death tends in cases of ultimogeniture to go to the youngest of them all on the grounds that he is the least likely to be well set up in life.

In concluding a discussion of primogeniture and ultimogeniture, a note of caution should be sounded. The vast majority of societies adhere to neither of the set rules.

SUMMARY

As human society rests on reciprocity in social relations, the flow and exchange of goods among peoples are important aspects of life. Exchange exists both within and between societies. Prehistoric finds prove that early in human history, material goods were traded over vast distances. The wide distribution of basic Paleolithic culture traditions in the Old World also shows that with intercourse in goods went intercourse in ideas and ways of doing things.

The giving of gifts is the most elemental and ubiquitous mechanism of exchange there is. Gift exchange symbolizes in concrete form the existence of mutual interdependence between individuals and groups. Its function is both utilitarian and social. Trade differs from gift exchange in its greater degree of concern with utilitarian ends. This reaches its extreme expression in dumb barter between hostile groups of primitives and in the development of the market. The kula of the Trobriand Islanders and their neighbors exemplifies an elaborate institutionalization of trade for both utilitarian and social purposes.

The worth of goods is determined not only by their materialistic usefulness and real scarcity but by their symbolic qualities as well. In any event, value is culturally determined, except for the basic necessities without which existence is impossible.

The devolution of statuses with respect to goods from deceased persons to living survivors is what constitutes the inheritance of property. Communal goods cannot be privately inherited, but all forms of joint and private property may be. In many cultures, however, some types of personal property are buried or destroyed at the death of the owner, for their spiritual essence remains tied to their immortal owners.

The most fundamental and general rule governing primitive inheritance is that a person can inherit only those kinds of goods which he or she may customarily use. Thus, "men's goods" may not be inherited by women, and wives are barred from inheritance of such of their husbands' property. The same rule holds for women's goods.

In matrilineally organized societies, because each man's kinship status is determined by his affiliation with his mother's kinship group, most of his inherited property status must come from male members of that group—his mother's brothers or his own brothers—rather than from his father.

Primogeniture gives precedence to the first-born as a means of preventing dispersal of basic property. Ultimogeniture gives precedence to the last born. Where it holds, it is usually in conjunction with the existence of progeny price.

SELECTED READINGS

Bohannan, P., and G. Dalton: *Markets in Africa* (1962). A modern analysis based on good anthropological accounts of indigenous trading centers.

Bunzel, R.: "The Economics of Organization of Primitive Peoples," in F. Boas et al., *General Anthropology* (1938), chap. 8. A useful general summary.

Firth, R.: *Primitive Polynesian Economy* (1939). A model field study of tribal economic activity.

Herskovits, M. J.: *Economic Anthropology* (1952), Part III, "Exchange and Distribution." Provides an extensive descriptive and theoretical analysis.

Mauss, M.: *The Gift: Forms and Functions of Exchange in Archaic Societies* (1954). A comparative study of the social functions of organized gift exchanges in primitive societies and classical civilizations.

Thurnwald, R.: *Economics in Primitive Communities* (1932), chaps. 5–9, "Barter," "Trade," "The Market," "Purchase," and "Distribution of Goods and Wealth."

Law and
the social order

chapter 30

"If your subject is law, the roads are plain to anthropology . . . . It is perfectly proper to regard and study the law simply as a great anthropological document. . . . The study pursued for such ends becomes science in the strictest sense." Such is the judgment of one of the greatest jurists of the age.[1]

On a much more humble level, a Cheyenne Indian, High Forehead, after ruminating on my search for cases of grievance, dispute, and trouble and what was done about them, reflectively said: "The Indian on the prairie, before there was the White man to put him in the guardhouse, had to have something to keep him from doing wrong." Not only the Indian on the prairie, but every society has to struggle to maintain its social order. Most societies include law within their systems of social control designed to achieve this end: "Anthropologically considered, law is merely one aspect of . . . culture—the aspect which employs the force of organized society to prevent, redress or punish deviations from prescribed norms."[2]

What is law?

Law is obviously a complex of human behavior. The problem is: What kinds of behavior? What sets off legal behavior from that which is non-legal or other than legal? What is it that makes law, law?

[1]O. W. Holmes, Jr., "Law in Science and Science in Law" (*Harvard Law Review*, Vol. 12, 1899), p. 443.
[2]S. P. Simpson and R. Field, "Law and the Social Sciences" (*Virginia Law Review*, Vol. 32, 1946), p. 858.

The significance of courts It is not legislation that creates law. Most primitive law is not legislated, and modern sociological jurisprudence and legal realism, from Holmes down, have made it perfectly clear that much of modern law is not legislated either.[3] English jurisprudence has long since given assent to this point of view, as witnessed by Salmond:

But all law, however made, is recognized and administered by the Courts, and no rules are recognized by the Courts which are not rules of law. It is therefore to the Courts and not to the Legislature that we must go in order to ascertain the true nature of Law.[4]

The now classic formulation of this concept of the nature of law is Justice Cardozo's statement that law is "a principle or rule of conduct so established as to justify a prediction with reasonable certainty that it will be enforced by the courts if its authority is challenged."[5]

This behavioristic concept of law gives the anthropologist a handle he can grasp, but it is still not enough. For if we think of courts in our traditional manner, i.e., as a formal sitting of professional judges, with bailiffs, clerks, and advocates, we must conclude: no courts, no law. This is what bothered Max Radin, who well understood the anthropologist's problem, and perhaps led him to assert:

But there is an infallible test for recognizing whether an imagined course of conduct is lawful or unlawful. This infallible test, in our system, is to submit the question to the judgment of a court. In other systems exactly the same test will be used, but it is often difficult to recognize the court. None the less, although difficult, it can be done in almost every system at any time.[6]

Max Radin is right. But what sort of courts did he have in mind? Some courts are difficult to identify. Anthropologically, they may be regularly constituted tribal courts, such as the tribal council of an American Indian pueblo sitting in judicial capacity or a court of the West African Ashanti, constituted of the chief, his council of elders, and his henchmen.

That type of primitive court is not hard to recognize. Any member of the American Bar Association would readily see it for what it is. But a more obscure type of court may be found in the Cheyenne Indian military fraternity. Consider the case of Wolf Lies Down, whose horse was "borrowed" by a friend in the absence of the owner. When the friend did not return from the warpath with the horse, Wolf Lies Down put the matter before his fraternity, the Elk Soldiers. "Now I want to know what to do," he said. "I want you to tell me the right thing." The fraternity chiefs sent a messenger to bring the friend in from the camp of a remote band. The friend gave an adequate and acceptable explanation of his conduct and offered handsome restitution to the complainant in addition to making him his blood brother. Then said the chiefs: "Now we have settled this thing." But they went on, half as a legislature: "Now we shall make a new rule. There shall be no more borrowing of horses without asking. If any man takes another's goods without asking, we will go over and get them back for him. More than that, if the taker tries to keep them, we will give him a whipping." Can anyone deny that the Elk Soldiers were in effect sitting as a court for the entire tribe? The test is, first, one of responsibility. That they knew. Second, it is one of effective authority. That they achieved. Third, it is one of method. Unhampered by a system of formal precedent that required them to judge according to the past, they recognized that the rule according to which they were settling this case was new, and so they announced it.[7]

Among the Yurok Indians of California, as typical of a less specifically organized people, the court was less definite, but it was neverthe-

---

[3]O. W. Holmes, Jr., "The Path of the Law" (*Harvard Law Review*, Vol. 10, 1897), p. 457.

[4]J. W. Salmond, *Jurisprudence*, p. 49.

[5]B. N. Cardozo, *The Growth of the Law*, p. 52.

[6]Max Radin, "A Restatement of Hohfeld" (*Harvard Law Review*, Vol. 51, 1938), p. 1145.

[7]For a full account of this case, see K. N. Llewellyn and E. A. Hoebel, *The Cheyenne Way: Conflict and Case Law in Primitive Jurisprudence*, p. 127.

less there. An aggrieved Yurok who felt he had a legitimate claim engaged the services of two nonrelatives from a community other than his own. The defendant did likewise. These persons were called *crossers* because they crossed back and forth between the litigants. The litigants did not face each other in the dispute. After hearing all that each side offered in evidence and argument, the crossers rendered a judgment on the facts. If the judgment was for the plaintiff, they rendered a decision for damages according to a well-established scale that was known to all. For their footwork and efforts, each received a piece of shell currency called a *moccasin*. Here again we have a court.[8]

On an even more primitive level, if an aggrieved party or his kinsmen must institute and carry through the prosecution without the intervention of a third party, there will still be a court, if the proceedings follow the lines of recognized and established order. There will be then at least the compulsion of recognized legal procedure, although the ultimate court may be the bar of public opinion. When vigorous public opinion recognizes and accepts the procedure of the plaintiff as correct and the settlement or punishment meted out as sound, and the wrongdoer in consequence accedes to the settlement because he feels he must yield, then the plaintiff and his supporting public opinion constitute a rudimentary sort of court, and the procedure is inescapably legal.

Consider the Eskimo dealing with recidivist homicide. Killing on a single occasion leads merely to feud, inasmuch as the avenger enjoys no recognized privilege of imposing the death penalty on the murderer or his kinsman with immunity against a counterkilling. A feud, of course, represents an absence of law, since blood revenge is more a sociological law than a legal one. But to kill someone on a second occasion makes the culprit a public enemy in the Eskimo view. It then becomes incumbent

upon some public-spirited man of initiative to interview all the adult males of the community to determine whether they agree that he should be executed. If unanimous consent is given, he then undertakes to execute the criminal, and no revenge may be taken on him by the murderer's relatives. Cases show that, in fact, no revenge is taken.[9] A community court has spoken. Such are the kinds of courts Max Radin had in mind.

The legitimate use of physical coercion Although courts in the sense described above exist in most primitive societies, insistence on the concept of courts is not really necessary for the determination of law. The real *sine qua non* of law in any society is the legitimate use of physical coercion. The law has teeth, and teeth that can bite, although they need not be bared, for, as Holmes put it: "The foundation of jurisdiction is physical power, although in civilized times it is not necessary to maintain that power throughout proceedings properly begun."[10] We would merely add to that declaration that it was not necessary to limit the latency of power to civilized times; primitive men often found that it was not necessary to display the power behind the law when the defendant acceded to proceedings carried through properly. Jhering has emphasized the factor of force in law: "Law without force is an empty name." Again, more poetically, we find: "A legal rule without coercion is a fire that does not burn, a light that does not shine."[11] In this we agree.

But force in law has a special meaning. Force means coercion, which in its absolute form is physical compulsion. There are, of course, as many forms of coercion as there are forms of power, and only certain methods and forms are legal. Coercion by gangsters is not legal. Even physical coercion by a parent

[8]See A. L. Kroeber, "Yurok Law" (*Proceedings of the 22d International Congress of Americanists*, 1922), pp. 511ff. A dramatic presentation of a Yurok case-in-action is given in *The Ways of Mankind*, Series I, Record 5, "The Sea Lion Flippers: A Study in Ethics."

[9]For a report of such a case, see F. Boas, *The Central Eskimo* (Bureau of American Ethnology, Annual Report 6, 1888), p. 668.
[10]O. W. Holmes, Jr., *McDonald v. Maybee* (*Supreme Court Reporter*, Vol. 37, 1917), p. 343.
[11]R. von Jhering, *Law as Means to an End*, p. 190.

is not legal if it is extreme in form. The essentials of legal coercion are general acceptance of the application of physical power, in threat or in fact, by a privileged party, for a legitimate cause, in a legitimate way, and at a legitimate time. This distinguishes the sanction of law from other social rules.

The privilege of applying force constitutes the official element in law. In most primitive societies, this privilege is vested in the wronged individual or kinship groups. They must prosecute on their own behalf and exact the proper legal penalty. This is known as *private law.* If a public official is responsible for penalizing a breach of law, it is public, or criminal law. He who is generally or specifically recognized as rightly exerting the element of physical coercion is a fragment of social authority. It is not necessary that he be an official with legal office or a constable's badge. In any primitive society, the so-called "private prosecutor" of a private injury is implicitly a public offical *pro tempore, pro eo solo delicto.* He is not and cannot be acting solely on his own, his family's, or his clan's behalf and still enjoy the approval or tacit support of the disinterested remainder of his society. If the rest of the tribal population supports him in opinion, even though not in overt action, it can mean only that the society feels that the behavior of the defendant was wrong in its broadest implications, i.e., contrary to the standards of the society as a whole. Thus it is in itself an injury to the society, although the group feeling may not be strong enough to generate overt and specific action by the group as a group and on its own initiative. However, the private prosecutor remains the representative of the general social interest as well as of that which is specifically his own. This fundamental fact is ordinarily ignored in discussions of primitive law, and it is in this sense that we may say that the difference between criminal law and private law is a difference in degree rather than in kind, though there can be no doubt that some matters touch the general interest in fact and evoke group feeling much

more vigorously than others in primitive law, e.g., sacrilege, homicidal tendencies, and, frequently, treason.

Regularity in law Regularity is what law in the legal sense has in common with law in the scientific sense. Regularity, it must be warned, does not mean absolute certainty. There can be no true certainty where human beings are involved, and yet there is much regularity, for all society is based on it. In law, the doctrine of precedent is not the unique possession of the Anglo-American common-law jurist. Primitive law also builds on precedents, for new decisions rest on old rules of law or norms of custom. Regularity removes the threat of personal whim and caprice from law. Regularity lends to law its attribute of certainty. The norms of law make prediction of legal outcomes reasonably certain. The characteristics of law are therefore *official authority, the right to apply force* (*legitimate coercion*), and *regularity.* It is these qualities which distinguish law from custom or morals in any culture.

Law defined Thus we may form a working definition of law that fits primitive as well as civilized law in the following terms: *a law is a social norm the infraction of which is sanctioned in threat or in fact by the application of physical force by a party possessing the socially recognized privilege of so acting.*

It is necessary to qualify the element of application of physical force with the phrase "in threat or in fact," since substitutes for physical force, in the form of confiscation of property by means of damages or fines, are often used. But there is always the final resort of physical punishment if the offender balks at confiscation or resists whatever other substitutes the law enforcers apply.

Recognition of the privilege of applying the sanctions prevents revenge reactions by the offender or his kin. Where there is no acceptance of this principle, there is no law. Thus the so-called "law of blood revenge" unrestrained by social limitations is no law at all but is merely a social norm. When the killing of a murderer by his victim's kinsmen leads to a counterkilling, and so on and on, we have the reign of feud, not of law. Feud is internecine warfare. It is a form of anarchy, not order. Such is the present law of nations, which measured against the background of the world society is amazingly similar to private law on the primitive level.

Primitive law is predominantly private law. The concept of community of interests is not easily recognized by men in the more primitive cultures; for them, kinship is more real than society. The family and the clan are often preferred as the security group, as has been seen in an earlier chapter. Thus, offenses are more often seen and treated as injuries primarily to individuals and the kinship group rather than as crimes against the society as an entity.

The cultural background of law

In Chapter 2, it was established that each society is confronted by the imperative of selection in the formation of its culture. Human behavior must be narrowed down from its full range of potential variety to a moderately limited body of norms. Expectancies of probable behavior must be maintained so that people can manage their lives with a high degree of certainty that their own activities will evoke anticipated responses from their fellow men and will have the expected results. Culture sets such patterns. It was also shown that selectivity in the building of cultures is achieved in accordance with a number of basic postulates, existential and normative. Social control is exercised to guide the learning process. Success in adaptation to the norms and expectancies that are set in the culture is rewarded; deviation from the norms and expectancies or failure to adapt is penalized. Law is an aspect of social control. It is one of the major devices used by society to penalize behavior that varies too much from certain selected norms. Legal norms are thus social norms that are reinforced by legal sanctions, as identified above. They are selected in ac-

cordance with their consistency in relation to jural postulates: the cultural assumptions that undergird the legal system.

Substantive law identifies the norms that are to be sanctioned by legal action. In most instances, substantive law undertakes to translate basic cultural postulates into social action by decision as to what particular behavior in a given instance may best be interpreted as conforming to the basic assumptions underlying the culture. Law implements the imperative of selection by saying implicity: "In this society, this is permitted and that is not." *Procedural* or *adjective law* designates who may rightly punish a breach of substantive law; it also lays down the rules for prosecuting a case and fixes the customary penalties to be applied to each type of offense. Law is therefore a major instrument in the shaping and maintenance of cultures.

The functions of law Law performs four fundamental functions essential to the maintenance of society:

1. The definition of relationships between the members of a society, so as to assert which activities are permitted and which are ruled out and to maintain at least minimal integration between the activities of individuals and groups within the society

2. The allocation of authority and the designation of who may exercise physical coercion as a socially recognized privilege-right so that force is controlled and directed toward social goals

3. The disposition of trouble cases as they arise so that social harmony may be reestablished

4. The redefinition of relations between individuals and groups as the conditions of life change[12]

A society may manage these functions with more or less skill; its legal system may function with sure effectiveness, achieving justice and order with a minimum of bungling and harshness, or it may be rigid and brutal, with

[12]E. A. Hoebel, *The Law of Primitive Man,* p. 275.

order imposed by tyranny, and justice a fugitive in the land.

Case law and the settlement of diputes In his search for understanding of primitive legal systems and how they came into being, the anthropologist has benefited greatly from modern jurisprudence, which points up the fact that breach and disputes in conflicts of claims are the most constant source of the law. "Breach," says Seagle, "is the mother of law as necessity is the mother of invention."[13] On the authority of Holmes, we have it that ". . . a law embodies beliefs that have triumphed in the battle of ideas and then translated themselves into action." In the same vein, Pound has written: "The law is an attempt to reconcile, to harmonize, to compromise . . . overlapping or conflicting interests."[14] Law exists to channel behavior so that conflicts of interest do not result in an overt clash. It moves into action when interests do clash. New decisions are ideally so shaped as to determine which interests best accord with the accepted standards of what is good for the society. Of course, it is unfortunately true that tyrants, usurpers, and pettifoggers can and do pervert the ends of law to their own designs without regard to social interests or prevailing standards of what is right.

As a canon of realistic law, we may say that regardless of the law that exists concerning a particular situation, an actual dispute must arise before the principles of the law can be tested; a law that is never broken may exist as nothing more than a custom, for one will never know the full implications of it until it is tested in a legal action.

The role of the claimant is the most important single factor in the development of law in primitive societies. Numerous writers have commented upon the relative absence of legislative enactment by primitive government.

Lowie, who is distinguished among American anthropologists for his unique contributions to the study of legal phenomena, has offered a general statement that is fairly typical of the prevailing opinion: ". . . it should be noted that the legislative function in most primitive communities seems strangely curtailed when compared with that exercised in the more complex civilizations."[15] Salmond parallels this with the statement that ". . . the function of the State in its earlier conception is to *enforce* the law, not to *make* it."[16] Lowie continues: "All the exigencies of normal social intercourse are covered by customary law, and the business of such governmental machinery as exists is rather to exact obedience to traditional usage than to create new precedents."[17]

Now this would be true for wholly static societies, but, as Lowie would have been among the first to acknowledge, no society is wholly static. New exigencies always arise. One permanent thing about human society is its impermanence. Especially when unlike cultures come into contact do new materials, new ways of behaving, and new ideas enter into the cultural picture.

These new elements are not usually adopted simultaneously by all members of the society. The consequence is that when some members get new goods and new ideas, they have new interests for which the old lines of the culture have made no provision. Their use of their new acquisitions comes into conflict with the old standards held by others. New custom and new law must then be generated.

However or by whomever the judgment may be rendered in any dispute, it is the claimant and the defendant who lay the grounds of the claim and counterclaim or denial. If one or the other does it skillfully, soundly, and wisely, the basis of decision is likely to be found in his statement of his claim. No matter how selfish the motivation of a disputant may be,

[13]W. Seagle, *The Quest for Law*, p. 35.
[14]R. Pound, "A Theory of Legal Interests" (*American Sociological Society, Publications*, Vol. 16, 1920), p. 44.

[15]R. H. Lowie, *Primitive Society*, p. 358.
[16]Salmond, *loc. cit.*
[17]Lowie, *op. cit.*, p. 358. (By "customary law" is meant "unwritten law".)

unless he is a fool indeed, he poses his claim against the background of "right" social principles, general rightness, and the well-being of the entire social group. How else can he gain enduring social acceptance of his position? Naturally, also, the more skillfully he argues his case in terms of the consonance of his claim with the well-established principles of social order, the greater the probability that he will shape the law as he wishes it to be determined.[18]

Evidence   Any lawsuit or criminal trial involves at least two questions: "Is the alleged offense an illegal act?" "If so, is the defendant guilty of the offense?" The first is a question of law. The second is a question of fact. If the first can be brought to a negative answer, then there is no need to seek an answer to the second. The case must be dropped.

Assuming that there is a legal rule covering the alleged act, how are the facts then determined? On the lower levels of legal development, the question of evidence is not of great importance. In a small community, not much behavior is secret. As a Shoshone once commented to the author: "They just wait around. Sooner or later the facts will come out." In Comanche trials, the question of guilt or innocence was rarely raised. The usual point of argument was only the extent of damages.

JUDICIAL HEARINGS   In systems in which the administration of law is centralized in the hands of regular judges, the eliciting of evidence may be skillfully conducted. As an example, Max Gluckman's penetrating analysis of the judicial process among the Barotse of Rhodesia, in Africa, reveals in rich detail the institutional structure of the Lozi courts (*kuta*) made up of three sets of councilors: headmen or nonroyal chiefs, royal officers or stewards,

and princes and prince consorts. Because the Lozi have no lawyers, ". . . the whole onus of eliciting and analyzing the evidence falls on the judges." Standards of judicial impartiality are explicitly strong: "A marked feature in all the judgments is the emphasis that the kuta decides by evidence and reasoning, and without favour."[19] Kinship allegiance should not enter:

The key concept here . . . is trial by due process of law (*tatubo kamulao*). The process is based on hearing evidence (*bupaki*) which establishes proof (also *bupaki*) on the facts (*litaba* = also things). Evidence itself is reduced by concepts of relevance (*bupaki bobuswanela*, appropriate or right evidence; *bupaki bobukena*, evidence which enters); of cogency (*bupaki bobutiile*, strong evidence); of credibility (*bupaki bobusepehala*); and of corroboration (*bupaki bobuyemela*). These types of evidence are tested as direct, circumstantial, or hearsay.[20]

When, through direct examination, the judges have elicited evidence sufficient to their needs, they enter a process of explicit formulation of a judgment. One after another, from the most junior judge up, in reversed order of seniority, the members of the kuta render their individual opinions, until the holding of the case is stated in the opinion of the senior chief:

Large parts of the judgments read like sermons, for they are all lectures on the theme "your station and its duties." The standards publicly stated for the parties are the norms involved in their social positions and relationships. . . . The essence of the judicial process is to state these norms to the world and to assess against them the behaviour of the parties in a specific series of situations.[21]

Lozi judges are shrewdly appraised by the people, who express the reputations of individual judges in the following terms:

kutalungusha—to be able to classify affairs;

kunyanyama—to be clever and of prompt decision;

sishongololi—a judge who relates matters lengthily and correctly;

muswanikisi—a judge who has good reasoning power and is able to ask searching questions.

---

[18]Many examples of this process may be found in Llewellyn and Hoebel, *op. cit.,* or in J. Richardson, *Law and Status among the Kiowa Indians* (American Ethnological Society, Monograph 1, 1940). Because Cheyenne and Kiowa societies were undergoing rapid change during the period covered by these studies, the process of judicial lawmaking was more intensified than is the case in more stable cultures.

[19]M. Gluckman, *The Judicial Process among the Barotse of Northern Rhodesia,* pp. 82 and 61.

[20]*Ibid,* p. 316.

[21]*Ibid,* p. 49.

Other words scorn poor reasoning:

kuyungula—to speak on matters without coming to the point;

kunjongoloka—to wander away from the subject when speaking;

kubulela siweko—to talk without understanding;

muyauluki—a judge who speaks without touching on the important points at issue;

siswasiwa—a person who gets entangled in words;

siyambutuki—a talker at random.[22]

Obviously, judges are themselves judged by severe standards of performance. Generally speaking, however, the role of judges is much less significant in primitive legal systems than it is in the more developed legal orders of civilizations. Other devices used by primitive societies include resort to supernatural devices such as divination, conditional curse, and ordeal.

DIVINATION, CONDITIONAL CURSE, ORDEAL, AND OATH   Extortion of confessions by third-degree methods occurs in a few tribes; for example, a Comanche husband could choke his wife or hold her over a fire until she named her lover. But more commonly the primitive man, when he cannot get at the facts by direct means, has recourse to the supernatural.

Divination is the most common device. It is the process of evoking knowledge of some secret or hidden thing by mechanical or manipulative techniques. Thus an Eskimo shaman searches out answers by tying a thong to some reclining object such as a person, a bundle, or even his own foot. After inducing a spirit into the object, he asks it questions to which "yes" or "no" answers may be given. Then he tries to lift the object with the thong. If it is hard to lift, the answer is "no." If it raises easily, the answer is "yes."

Among many North American Indians, the still surface of water that has been put into the abdominal cavity of an animal reveals the image of the culprit. "Just as easy as reading a newspaper," said Post Oak Jim, the Comanche. Trobriand Islanders dig up the newly buried corpse of a dead person to see what signs it may reveal. Maggots mean the lamented one was killed by the chief's sorcerer for having been too successful with women. If the lips are pursed, the same conclusion is indicated. Blotches of color on the skin mean he painted his house too ostentatiously for one of his social station, and so was done in by a jealous chief.

The Azande of Africa feed poison to a chicken, declaring repeatedly: "If this charge be true, let the chicken die. If this charge be false, spare its life." After the first chicken has responded, a second is given the test, but with the invocation reversed ("If the charge be true, let the chicken live; if it be false, let it die"). Thus if the first chicken dies and the second lives, the allegation is confirmed.[23]

Conditional curse enters into trial procedure among almost all peoples. It is the assertion that always includes or implies the clause: "If what I say is not true, *then* may the supernatural destroy me." "You [Sun] saw me. May the one who lies die before winter."[24]

Even our own courts do not rely wholly upon our laws against perjury, since every witness must first swear a conditional curse: "So help me God." ("May God smite me if I lie.") Or is it, since the laws of criminal perjury are more recent than the conditional curse, that the courts do not have full faith in the efficacy of the curse?

Ordeal is peculiarly rare in the New World, which was to the good fortune of the Indians, to say the least. But most of the hideous forms known to medieval Europe were practiced with variations throughout Asia, Indonesia, and Africa. The ordeal by hot iron, with which Ibsen opens his historical play *The Pretenders,* had its counterpart in Ifugao. Various Philippine tribes used the old technique of tying up the two litigants and throwing them in a river. He who rose to the surface first was guilty. Ordeal by poison is popular in Africa. In Ashanti, the defendant in a trial may drink a poison brew. If he vomits, he is inno-

[22] *Ibid.,* p. 277.

[23] E. E. Evans-Pritchard, *Witchcraft, Oracles and Magic among the Azande,* pp. 258–351.

[24] R. H. Lowie, *The Crow Indians,* p. 217.

cent; if he does not vomit, he dies. And that is proof enough for any man.

Oath is merely a formal declaration that the testimony given is true. It may or may not imply the sanction of a supernatural power against falsehood. Often it is accompanied by a ritual act, such as touching the pipe to the lips among Indians, touching an arrow laid across the horns of a buffalo skull, or—as in American courts—placing one's hand upon the Bible.

Representative legal systems

In order better to understand the nature of primitive law systems, it will be useful to sketch several thoroughly studied legal cultures, ranging from very simple and poorly developed types to highly developed ones that employ centralized governmental control. For this purpose we shall use the Eskimo, Comanche, Ifugao, Nuer, and Ashanti.

Eskimo law The Eskimos provide a good example of law on the lowest levels of social organization. The small Eskimo local group rarely numbers more than 100 members. Its organization is based on the bilateral family, beyond which there is nothing. There is no lineage, no clan, no clubs of either men or women, and no government. Each group has its headman: he who is "tacitly, half-unconsciously, recognized as first among equals"; he who is variously called *ihumatak*, "he who thinks (for others)," *anaiyuhok*, "the one to whom all listen," or *pimain*, "he who knows everything best." The headman leads, but he does not govern. He lends direction to his people's activity, but he does not direct. No Eskimo will give an order to another; therefore, the headman exercises no legal or judicial authority.

Many acts that we consider heinous are accepted as necessary by the Eskimos. Thus, certain forms of homicide are socially justified and legally permitted. Infanticide, invalidicide, suicide, and senilicide fall in this category. They are all responses to the basic principle that only those may survive who are able, or potentially able, to contribute to the subsistence economy of the community. Life is precarious in the arctic.

There can be few legal offenses against property among the Eskimos because there is no property in land and free borrowing of goods makes stealing pointless.

Eskimo law grows out of the aggressive status struggle that bedevils the men. The society is wholly democratic, but prestige rivalry among the men is strong. Status can be gained through superior hunting skill and by stealing the wives of other men. The better the reputation of a man, the more likely he is to have his wife stolen. Wife stealing is not done primarily for sexual reasons. An Eskimo can enjoy sex without running the risks involved in home breaking. The motive lies in an attempt to outrank the man whose wife he takes, if he can get away with it.

Wife stealing is not a crime, but most litigation arises from it. The challenge results either in murder or in wager of song, wrestling, or buffeting. Rasmussen found that all the adult males in a Musk Ox Eskimo group had been involved in murder, either as principals or as accessories; ". . . the motive was invariably some quarrel about a woman."[25] The fact that Eskimo husbands will lend their wives does not mean that they are free of jealousy. If a man lends his wife, he enjoys the prestige of a giver of gifts. But if another man assumes sexual rights without permission, that is adultery and an assault on the husband's ego that cannot go unchallenged. Murder must be avenged, sooner or later. And since it is the usual Eskimo custom for the killer to marry his victim's widow and to adopt his children, a man may raise the boy who will slay him when he comes of age.

The alternative to killing an aggressor (and thus becoming involved in feud) is to challenge

[25] K. Rasmussen, *Across Arctic America*, p. 250. The full flavor of the song duel is given in the radio drama, "The Case of the Borrowed Wife: Eskimo," *The Ways of Mankind*, Series II, Record 1).

him to a juridical song contest. In the manner of Provençal troubadours of the thirteenth century, the two litigants scurrilously abuse each other with songs composed for the occasion:

Now I shall split off words—little sharp words
Like the splinters which I hack off with my ax.
A song from ancient times—a breath of the ancestors
A song of longing—for my wife.
An impudent, black-skinned oaf has stolen her,
Has tried to belittle her.
A miserable wretch who loves human flesh.
A cannibal from famine days.[26]

He who receives the most applause wins. Thus is the case settled without reference to the right or wrong of the case. But, what is more important, the dispute is laid to rest.

Recidivist homicide, excessive sorcery (which is *de facto* recidivist homicide), and chronic lying are crimes punishable by death. Such is the nature of rudimentary law in the Eskimo anarchy.[27]

Comanche law Comanche Indian law-ways represent a somewhat higher development on the same general plane as Eskimo law.

The Comanches had chiefs, both civil and military. The band was larger than the Eskimo local group, and the Comanches had considerable property, especially in horses. They shared with the Eskimos a fierce drive toward male dominance and competitive rivalry among males for status by means of wife stealing. To this they also added the road of military glory. The Comanches recognized nine common legal offenses against the individual: adultery, wife absconding, violation of levirate privileges, homicide, killing a favorite horse, sorcery, causing another person to commit suicide (a form of homicide), failure to fulfill a contract, and theft.

Homicide called for the killing of the offender by the aggrieved kin of the dead man.

This was a true legal penalty, for custom prevented the kin of the executed murderer from retaliating.

Adultery and wife stealing were handled variously, but in every case the aggrieved person was forced by public opinion to act. He could, and often did, proceed directly against the erring wife, killing her, cutting off her nose, or otherwise mutilating her hapless body. This was a husband's legal privilege. Or, if he preferred, he could collect damages from the male offender. This would be done by a direct demand. Whether or not he got what he first went after depended on how courageous the defendant was. If the aggrieved husband was not strong or fearless enough, he could call in his friends or kinsmen to prosecute for him. But then "the lawyers got the a' of it," for his helpers kept all the damages for themselves. Or, lacking kin and friends, he could call upon any brave warrior to prosecute for him. Great braves were willing, for prestige reasons, to do this without any material recompense whatever.[28]

Ifugao law The Ifugaos provide yet another interesting example of law on the primitive level of organization. These mountain-dwelling head-hunters of Luzon possess no government worthy of being called such. Over 100,000 tribesmen live scattered throughout the deep valleys that crease their rugged homeland. Although there are clusters of houses in the more favorable spots, the Ifugaos have not even formed true villages, nor do they have a clan organization. The bilateral group of kinsmen is tightly knit, however. In the course of centuries, the Ifugaos have carved the steep walls of their mountains into stupendous rice terraces fed by intricate irrigation systems. Their paddies are privately owned and protected by a complex body of substantive law. Ifugaos are capitalists who have many legal rules controlling credit and debt. In addition,

[26]K. Rasmussen, *Gronlandsagen*, p. 235.
[27]E. A. Hoebel, "Law-ways of the Primitive Eskimos" (*Journal of Criminal Law and Criminology*, Vol. 13, 1941), pp. 663–683, or *The Law of Primitive Man*, chap. 5.

[28]E. A. Hoebel, *The Political Organization and Law-ways of the Comanche Indians* (American Anthropological Association, Memoir 54: Contributions from the Laboratory of Anthropology, 4, 1940), or *The Law of Primitive Man*, pp. 127–142.

disputable at law.

they are litigious in the extreme, for each man is sensitive about his "face" and quick to take offense. Their list of possible legal wrongs is long indeed.

How do they handle a legal case? A man with a grievance or a claim tries first to exact a satisfactory settlement from the opposite party. Failing this, he must go to a *monkalun,* or "go-between," who is a member of the highest social class and who has a reputation as a man of affairs and a number of enemy heads to his credit. The *monkalun* hears his story and accosts the defendant with the charges. The defendant in turn pleads his cause. Meanwhile, both plaintiff and defendant are marshaling their fighting relatives—just in case. The *monkalun* shuttles back and forth between the two parties, wheedling, arguing, threatening, cajoling—attempting to induce them to give ground so that they may meet on terms acceptable to each. Customary law makes the penalties and obligations of both parties quite explicit for every conceivable offense, but first there must be agreement on the exact nature and degree of the offense. Claim must be balanced against counterclaim. Each side weighs the fighting strength and inclination of the other. But at long last, if the patience of the *monkalun* and the litigants endures, a settlement is reached and damages are paid (if it is an assault case), or the debt is satisfied (if it is an economic dispute). But if no settlement satisfactory to each disputant is reached, the *monkalun* finally withdraws from the case. Then the plaintiff or his kinsmen undertake to kill the defendant—or any convenient kinsman of his. Feud is forthcoming. The legal machinery has broken down.[29]

The *monkalun* represents the public interest by his intervention. Yet he is only incipiently a public officer. He makes no decision and enforces no judgment, but he provides the means through his good offices of bringing disputants to a resolution of their conflict. All Ifugao legal offenses are wrongs to be prosecuted by the aggrieved individual. There are no recognized crimes against society at large.[30]

Nuer law The legal system of the Nuer of the African Sudan is similar to that of the Ifugaos in many respects. The Nuer, like the Ifugaos, have no state. Unlike the Ifugaos, they are organized into segmented lineages (see page 372). The lineages represent the legal units that stand in opposition to one another. Evans-Pritchard saw them as a people who have no law because ". . . there is no constituted and impartial authority who decides on the rights and wrongs of a dispute and there is no external power to enforce such a decision were it given."[31]

According to Evans-Pritchard's analysis, feud and the threat of feud are the legal mechanisms by means of which adherence to norms is maintained. Violation of a norm can set off a feud between lineages. But among the Nuer, "A feud cannot be tolerated within a village and it is impossible to maintain one for a long period between nearby villages."[32]

We have already indicated that formal judges are not a necessary attribute of law. The Nuer, like the Ifugaos, employ the services of a mediator, the Priest of the Earth, to settle serious disputes. This is the priest who is especially related to the sanctity of the earth and who is also called the Leopard Skin Chief because he wears a leopard skin as an emblem of his office. Most Nuer offenses are legally settled by direct negotiation between the lineages without intervention of the Priest of the Earth. Bodily injuries give rise to damages paid in cattle according to a definite and detailed scale commensurate with the degree of injury done the victim. Adultery and seduction of unmarried girls are also private wrongs

[29] Ifugao procedure is fully dramatized in "The Case of the Bamboo-sized Pigs: Ifugao," in *The Ways of Mankind,* Series II.

[30] R. F. Barton, "Ifugao Law" (*University of California Publications in American Archaeology and Ethnology,* Vol. 15, 1919); also Hoebel, *The Law of Primitive Man,* chap. 6.

[31] E. E. Evans-Pritchard, "The Nuer of the Southern Sudan," in M. Fortes and E. E. Evans-Pritchard (eds.), *African Political Systems,* pp. 293–294.

[32] E. E. Evans-Pritchard, *The Nuer,* p. 159.

for which compensation in cattle may be demanded and received. There are also suits over the return of progeny price after a divorce has taken place.

The Nuer are a proud and independent people, quick to resort to violence. Failure to pay the customary damages in cattle may bring deadly resort to the spear; then a feud may be launched and the equilibrium of the society seriously disturbed. In spite of their truculence, however, the Nuer value good relations among neighbors and within the tribe. The killing of a Nuer by a Nuer results in the spiritual contamination of the murderer and all his household. The contamination, called *nueer*, brings disease and death unless it is ritually removed by the Priest of the Earth.

A killing, therefore, *may* entail the inconvenience of a feud, and it certainly entails the dangers and costs of *nueer*. A murderer may therefore seek asylum in the homestead of Priest of the Earth. There he is secure against revenge while, the priest arranges the payment of blood money by the killer's lineage to the lineage of his victim. If one or the other lineage holds out unreasonably in agreeing to an acceptable settlement, the priest may threaten to curse them. If the curse is uttered, their cattle will sicken, their crops wither, and their people die—not a happy prospect! The ultimate sanction in Nuer law, therefore, is physical, albeit by supernatural means. When the blood money has finally been paid, the homestead, cattle, and body of the murderer are ritually purified. Social relations between the two kinship groups are thus restored, and life may resume its course.

Ashanti law   Finally, the Ashanti of West Africa may be cited as a primitive people who were well on the road toward civilized law by the middle of the last century. Today they are part of the new nation of Ghana.

The Ashanti were a powerful nation who developed their own constitutional monarchy. Clan feuding was checked, and all private law was brought within the potential jurisdic-

tion of the royal criminal courts. Any private dispute ordinarily settled between the household heads of the two disputants could be thrown into royal hands by the simple device of one of the quarreling persons' swearing an oath on the Great Forbidden Name of a god that the other was guilty of an offense. In rebuttal, his adversary would swear on the same forbidden name that he did not commit the wrong. One or the other was then guilty of a false oath, perjury, which was a capital crime for which the liar lost his head.

Whoever heard the swearing had to arrest the two, for every citizen was the king's agent in such an event. He led them to a log kept for the purpose and chained them to it, after which he trotted off to the king's bailiff with the news. A day was then set for the trial. When hauled before the king and his council of elders, each litigant was called upon to tell his story. The stories were then repeated verbatim by the king's speaker, and each affirmed the accuracy of the repetition. So was the issued joined. Next, one or the other of the prisoners before the bar named a witness, who was brought forth to swear a deadly conditional curse that what he was about to say was the truth of the matter. In this the Ashanti placed implicit faith, for the whole trial hinged on what was now said. On the testimony of the single witness, one party was freed and the other condemned to be beheaded—unless the king in deference to the needs of his treasury allowed the luckless one "to buy his head," i.e., pay a fine.[33]

Aside from this crude but remarkable device for extending the king's peace, there was also a great body of criminal regulations; the violation of any one of these would be punished by death. These ranged from homicide—"only the king may wield the knife"—to carrying a chicken on top of a load. Even suicide was a capital offense, for it constituted a usurpation of the king's exclusive right to kill. The corpse

[33]Ashanti procedure and the techniques of shifting a quarrel from the area of private law to that of criminal law are dramatized in "The Forbidden Name of Wednesday: Ashanti," *The Ways of Mankind*, Series II.

of the suicide was hauled into court, tried, and ostentatiously decapitated. As a more practical gesture, his properties were also confiscated on behalf of the king's treasury.

Ashanti criminal law overreached the mark in much the same way as did the law of eighteenth-century England, with its 200 capital crimes. It is significant as an example of the way in which monarchy becomes the means of expressing the social interest in the maintenance of order by replacement of private law by criminal law. This is a genuine social advance over the chaos of societies that allow feuding.[34]

The trend of the law *seems contradictory but may be true*

It is a seeming paradox, on first thought, that the more civilized a society becomes, the greater is the need for law, and the wider the reach of law becomes. But it is no paradox, if the functions of law are kept in mind. Simple societies have little need of law, and on the earliest levels of human culture there were probably no legal institutions. In such groups as the Shoshones, Eskimos, Andaman Islanders, and African Bushmen, there is little of what we would call law. Almost all relations in the tribe are face-to-face and intimate. The demands imposed by culture are relatively few; child training is direct and comprehensive. Ridicule is keenly felt, for there is no escape in anonymity. Tabu and the fear of supernatural sanctions cover a large area of behavior. Special interests are few, for there is little accumulated wealth. Conflict arises mostly in interpersonal relations. Hence, homicide and adultery are the most common legal focuses. Sorcery as a form of homicide always looms large as an illegal possibility, but among the simpler peoples, sorcery, which uses supernatural techniques, is usually met with supernatural countermeasures rather than with legal action.

[34]This description applied a century ago. R. S. Rattray, *Ashanti Law and Constitution;* A. K. Busia, *The Position of the Chief in the Modern Political System of Ashanti;* Hoebel, *The Law of Primitive Man,* chap. 9.

Among the higher hunters, the pastoralists, and the ruder gardening peoples, the size of the group and the increased complexity of the culture make possible greater divergence of interests between the members of the tribe. Conflict of interests grows, and the need for legal devices for settlement and control of the internal clash of interests begins to be felt. Private law emerges and spreads. It exerts a restraining influence, but, like the clan, it has inherent limitations that prevent it from completely satisfying the need it must meet. As no man is competent to judge his own cause, procedure under private law leads too often not to a just settlement but to internecine fighting. A society that is to advance beyond the limited horizons of lower savagery must master the feudistic tendencies of kinship-group organization. And every society that has survived for us to study has some set procedures for avoiding feud or for bringing it to a halt if once it gets under way.

As the scope of commonality expands, as community of interest reaches out beyond the kindred and clan, beyond the local group and tribe, men gradually create the means to check internecine strife within the bounds of the larger society through the expansion of the scope of law.

Experience in the development of other branches of culture is also accompanied by experience in the manipulation of the social-control phases of culture. Instruments and devices of government are created. To a greater and greater extent, private law is replaced by public law.

From status to contract: Sir Henry Maine Sir Henry Maine, whose work *Ancient Law,* first published in 1861, remains a classic to this day, contrasted the importance of private law in primitive societies and the importance of public law in civilized societies.

If therefore the criterion of a *delict, wrong,* or *tort* be that the person who suffers it, and not the State, is conceived to be wronged, it may be asserted that in the infancy of jurisprudence the citizen depends for protection against violence or fraud not on the Law of Crime but on the Law of Tort.[35]

The state and its agencies corrode away the legal powers of the kinship group. The individual becomes increasingly free to make his own legal commitments independently of his kinship status. The trend was formulated by Maine as follows:

The movement of the progressive societies has hitherto been a movement from *Status to Contract.* . . . The individual is steadily substituted for the Family [kinship group], as the unit of which the civil laws take account. . . . Nor is it difficult to see what is the tie between man and man which replaces by degrees those forms of reciprocity in rights and duties which have their origin in the Family. It is Contract . . . in which all these relations [of persons] arise from the free agreement of individuals.[36]

There are many limitations to Maine's generalization, but it is an evolutionary proposition of great significance. There is good reason to believe that the development of the abstract notion of contract, which was worked out in Roman law, is the great inventive key to modern free society. It parallels the significance of abstract mathematical conceptualization, which is the key to modern science and technology.[37]

World law The next development in law that may be foreseen on the basis of past trends and growing need is the freeing of the individual from the limitations of nationality and, concomitantly, the expansion of the scope of law to embrace a worldwide system framed and administered by a world commonwealth. Ultimately, it will be this or regression. Today, primitive law prevails between nations. By and large, what passes as international law consists of no more than normative rules for the conduct of affairs between nations as they have been enunciated and agreed upon

from time to time by means of treaties, pacts, and covenants. In addition, a body of prevailing custom in international intercourse, recognized by tacit consensus or verbalized in arbitration, World Court awards, and United Nations decisions, provides the other main source of its substance. But this body of social norms for international intercourse is as yet no more than the by-laws of the subgroups we call nations. International law now consists of substantive rules without imperative legal sanctions.

The United Nations today, like the League of Nations of yesterday, because the power of universal coercive, absolute force is withheld from it, cannot make law of the international norms upon which it determines. Whatever the idealist may desire or the nationalist fear, force and the threat of force remain the ultimate powers in the implementation of law between nations, as they do in law within the nation or tribe. But until the use of force and the threat of force as now exercised by nation against nation are brought under the socialized control of a world community, by and for world society, they remain not the sanctions of world law but the instruments of social anarchy and the constant threat to the survival of present civilizations.

The metamorphosis from primitive law to modern law on the plane of international intercourse awaits the emergence of the consciousness of world community by all men. If the fulfillment comes in our time it will be our happy destiny to participate in the greatest event in the legal history of mankind.

SUMMARY

Law is that part of culture which is devoted to the regulation of behavior through the socially approved use, or threat of the use, of physical force. The attributes of law consist of a high degree of regularity (a law is a social norm), the element of officialdom (the enforcers), and the potential of legitimate application of physical coercion. Law has four ma-

---

[35] H. S. Maine, *Ancient Law,* p. 359.
[36] *Ibid.,* pp. 165, 163.
[37] See F. S. C. Northrop and H. H. Livingston (eds.), *Cross Cultural Understanding* (1964), especially chaps. 12, 13, 15, and 16, for further development of this point.

jor functions: (1) to identify acceptable lines of behavior for inclusion in the culture and to penalize contradictory behavior, so as to maintain at least minimal integration between the activities of individuals and groups within the society; (2) to allocate authority and to determine who may legitimately apply force to maintain the legal norms; (3) to settle trouble cases as they arise; and (4) to redefine relationships as the conditions of life change, so as to help keep the culture adaptable.

Among simpler primitive tribes, the responsibility and privilege of enforcing the law rest for the most part with the injured individual and his kinsmen. Such law is called *private law*. Enforcement of private law is possible without recourse to feud because the kinsmen of the wrongdoer recognize the rightness of the plaintiff's case, because they are impelled by public opinion to recognize it, or because they fear the inconvenience or danger that feud may engender. Virtually all known societies have methods for settling disputes by due process of law or for controlling feud once it gets started. Feud represents an absence or breakdown of law.

In very small tribal societies, where most relations are face-to-face, the problem of evidence does not raise many difficulties. When the facts are not known, however, or the claims of the aggrieved party are denied by the defendant, recourse is usually to the supernatural powers by means of divination, conditional curse, or ordeal. In some rare cultures or situations, a simple oath suffices.

Public, or criminal, law is that law in which the responsibility for prosecution and punishment rests with the entire society or its special officials. It tends to gain in importance as societies become more complex. The trend of the law has been one of an increasing shift of responsibility for the maintenance of legal norms away from the individual and his kinship group to the agents of the society as a whole. In like manner, the individual tends to

be allowed greater freedom in contractual determination of his social responsibilities. Concomitantly, there is less dependence upon ascribed kinship statuses in the more highly developed societies.

As society expands, so does the scope of the law, for unless the functions of law are adequately fulfilled, the existence of the society is endangered. The great modern problem of survival and cultural adaptation is the creation of an effective system of world law to meet the functional prerequisities of the new world society.

SELECTED READINGS

Bohannan, P.: *Justice and Judgment among the Tiv* (1957). An inside view of how a "stateless" West African society operates its law.

Gluckman, M.: *The Judicial Process among the Barotse of Northern Rhodesia* (1955). How trouble cases are settled in a South African tribe. Also, *The Ideas in Barotse Jurisprudence* (1965). A brilliant comparative analysis of Barotse legal concepts.

Hoebel, E. A.: *The Law of Primitive Man* (1954). Presents a theory of law and society. Describes and analyzes the legal culture of seven selected primitive societies, followed by a functional interpretation of law in culture.

Llewellyn, K. N., and E. A. Hoebel: *The Cheyenne Way: Conflict and Case Law in Primitive Jurisprudence* (1941). Contains a number of case records of Cheyenne legal disputes and a systematic analysis of the lawways of this remarkable Indian tribe.

Pospisil, L.: *The Kapauku Papuans and Their Law* (1958). Particularly useful for its analysis of what this New Guinea people think their legal norms are and what they actually are according to the outcome of specific cases.

Schapera, I.: *A Handbook of Tswana Law and Custom* (1938). A very competent and thorough treatment of the social system and formal law of an African tribe.

Political organization

chapter 31

Law can exist without government, but there can be no government without law. Yet wherever there is law, there is political organization. Political organization is more than government as such, and it is not synonymous with the state, for the state is a specialized social phenomenon, while political organization is generalized.

The nature of political organization

The only kind of society that could be said to be without political organization would be one consisting of a single bilateral extended family within which there were no organized subdivisions. Sex and age differences would be present, to be sure, and there would be one or two religious specialists. But the society would be organized as a single large family operating under familial controls. All problems would be settled as family problems, and there would be no other divisive groupings within the community. Family and community would be one.

This kind of society is approximated among some of the simpler primitive peoples, such as the Shoshones, but it exists nowhere among men today, nor has it been observed to have existed since written records have been kept.[1]

Political organization comes into being wherever societies are segmented on the basis of kinship, economics, religion, sex, fraternities, or community. Where there are subgroups that are discrete entities within the social entirety, there is political organization—a system of regulation of relations between groups or members of different groups within the society at large and between one society and another.

Our earlier discussion of subsistence techniques and land tenure have indicated the importance of ecological relations, the patterns of adjustments of human populations to the territory in which they live. Because skillful exploitation of the immediate environment is absolutely essential to survival, man, like all other living creatures, develops an intimate relation to his soil and to its plants, to its lakes, rivers, and springs, and to its denizens. In cooperation with his day-to-day fellows, he works it for all that his technology enables him to win from it. The group molds its culture to the offerings of its territory, and although migrations are common, the general pattern is for a people to hold fast to the land they know—and have come to love.

Because the members of a community live together under a common culture, they share their patterns of living and ideas in common to a large extent. Community means commonality, in which diversity exists but unity prevails. Community means that the feeling of oneness—a sense of entity, an *esprit de corps*—

extends to the whole territorial society. It means that the culture sets values that orient behavior in the direction of common as well as individual or subgroup interests. The common interests are what constitute political interests. The community is the polity. Political organization, therefore, is *that part of the culture which functions explicitly to direct the activities of the members of the society toward community goals.*

The functions of political organization Political organization performs the same functions that were specified for law in the last chapter: (1) the definition of behavioral norms for acceptable conduct, (2) the allocation of force and authority, (3) the settlement of disputes, and (4) the redefinition of norms for conduct. Political organization, and especially government, may well go beyond this, however. In addition, (1) it may organize group efforts for public works, such as tribal hunts, tending the chief's gardens, digging and repairing irrigation ditches, and building roads, temples, and pyramids; (2) it may carry ritual and ceremonial responsibility for religious control of the supernatural world and human conduct (see Sacerdotal Chiefs and Kings, below); (3) it may organize and maintain markets and trading networks; and (4) it may, and usually does, carry the responsibility for defense of the home territory and the waging of war against enemy societies.

The state

It is quite possible to analyze political organization without any recourse to the concept of the state whatsoever. Indeed, the failure of political scientists to realize this until quite recently seriously handicapped the development of viable political theory beyond the realm of European types of government.[2] For a long time, thinking in terms of the state did more harm than good because it diverted attention from the broader, institutional as-

[1]"Among all known people—the autonomous, land-owning socio-political group is greater than the bilateral family." J. H. Steward, "The Economic and Social Basis of Primitive Bands," in *Essays in Anthropology in Honor of Alfred Louis Kroeber*, p. 333. A contrary view is advanced, however, by L. Sharp, "People without Politics," in V. Ray (ed.), *Systems of Political Control and Bureaucracy*, pp. 1–8.

[2]G. A. Almond and J. S. Coleman (eds.), *The Politics of Developing Areas.*

pects of political processes as they are woven through the entire weft of social life. Yet the state is so overpoweringly important in modern civilization, and is growing steadily more so, that it cannot be ignored. Anthropologists now distinguish between stateless and state-organized societies.

The idea of a state embodies three elements: (1) a territory, (2) a culturally organized population, and (3) a government.

The state is an institution among other institutions within a given community's culture. It is not the society or the community; it is a complex of behaviors characteristic of the members of the community in one part of their lives—the political. Thus, as Linton observed, the tribe is a social entity marked by a sentiment of community due to common culture; the state is a subentity marked by common political organization—with or without a well-developed government.[3]

Government is to be thought of as an executive instrument of the state. All citizens are members of a state, but only a few of them may be a part of its government. The personnel of government are the specialists and functionaries who perform the state's business. They are the headmen, chiefs, kings, and council members, and their various aides.

Three principles of organization A state may use one of three major units of political organization as the basis for its structure: (1) genealogical, or kinship, units; (2) geographical, or territorial, units; or (3) associational units.

Kinship Primitive societies, as has already been shown in previous chapters, generally rest most heavily on the kinship principle. Lineages, clans, phratries, and moieties may each have their headmen who not only are responsible for the regulation and guidance of affairs within their respective kinship groups but also formally represent their groups vis-à-vis other kinship groups. Collectively, they may form the several levels of councils that act

[3]R. Linton, *The Study of Man*, p. 240.

within or for the tribe in public affairs. How much of the structure and functioning of primitive legal systems is built upon kinship groups has already been made clear.

Territorialism On the other hand, since every community is a distinguishable territorial entity, every state, both primitive and civilized, uses the geographical unit as a basis of organization as well. The smallest such unit is the *household.* The next largest is the *camp* (among nomadic hunters and gatherers) or the *village* (among sedentary peoples). The next largest is the *band,* comprising a number of camps (among the nomads) or the *district,* comprising several villages (among the sedentes). Above these is the *tribe* or *nation,* the largest group with a common language and culture. (Actually, a tribe may incorporate alien groups.)

Tribes may ally on a more or less permanent basis with other tribes to form a *confederacy.* This is usually done on a voluntary basis for mutual defense or aggression, and in confederacy each tribe remains self-determining in political matters to a greater extent than it yields decisive power to the confederacy. The only real difference between an alliance and a confederacy is in the development of more enduring and explicit institutions for determination of questions of mutual concern between the tribes.

When a tribe or confederacy incorporates the victims of its conquest into a permanent state system on a subordinate basis, the political system has expanded to become an *empire.*

All these forms of territorial statehood were achieved by one or another primitive society.

Associations The use of special associations as a principle of state organization is, on the whole, relatively weak in primitive cultures, but nevertheless quite widespread. The heads of the secret religious fraternities form the tribal council in a number of pueblos. The military fraternities of the Plains Indians performed major governmental functions, as do many of the secret societies of Africa and Melanesia. The age sets of other parts of Africa do likewise. In India, castes still operate as units of government, although the modern constitution of India proscribes them.

The constitutional structure of the United States ignores the associational principle, but churches, labor unions, manufacturers' associations, and a host of other special-interest organizations have secondary political functions, of which lobbying is but one form of expression. One need only stroll the streets of Washington, taking note of the many stately headquarters maintained by a host of organizations, to become aware of how true this is.

So far has the kinship principle fallen into desuetude in many modern states, and especially in the United States, that favoritism on behalf of relatives, called *nepotism,* is often forbidden by law.

Types of political organization

As a society emphasizes one or another principle of organization, or a combination of principles, it produces political systems of different types. Some of these are identifiable among primitive cultures as follows.

Stateless systems Stateless systems have no formal government embracing the entire society. Political functions are performed by subgroups and by functionaries whose political jobs are secondary to other interests and responsibilities. There is no person or group with centralized authority applicable to the society as a whole.

Undifferentiated In such cultures as those of the South African Bushmen, the Eskimos and the Shoshones, kinship and political relations are one and the same. Small, local groups live as isolated, self-governing units, subject to no higher political power. Tensions between members of individual families are settled directly without intervention of a headman.

Segmentary lineage This is the uncentralized political system in which lineages rather than villages or bands form the significant units of organization. There is little or no common decision-making for the tribe, nor is there much in the way of broadly integrative ceremony or ritual. The Nuer of the African Sudan are the classic example.[4] The segmentary lineage organization provides the structural framework. Such systems of political organization are very common in East Africa and in Melanesia, where the Kapauku and the Kuma are good examples.[5]

Age sets Under this system, political matters are in the hands of age sets and their officers. The age sets cut across village and district boundaries and form the framework of political integration. By virtue of the relatively limited distribution of age sets, this system is quite rare.

Village council and associations In this type, there are no tribal governments or corporate lineages in government, but authority is vested in village councils and men's fraternities. The Pueblos of the Southwestern United States and such tribes as the Ibo of West Africa are representative.

Village or band with headman Here, the tribe lacks overall government; each band or village, as the case may be, has a headman or chief endowed with mild political authority. Kinship may be important in many aspects of life, but it is not a major factor in political organization. Territorial identity and personal qualities of leadership on the part of a headman are the determining factors. For example: "The headman of a Chiricahua [Apache] local group can be thought of as a natural-born leader, one who earns the confidence and support of his neighbors. His influence is considerable, but it is of an informal nature."[6]

The leader is expected to speak on all important occasions. Among the Yavapai of

[4]E. E. Evans-Pritchard, *The Nuer,* became the model for a number of penetrating studies of this type of organization.
[5]L. Pospisil, *The Kapauku Papuans of New Guinea,* pp. 32–63; M. Reay, *The Kuma.*
[6]M. E. Opler, *An Apache Life-way,* pp. 233–234.

Arizona, the headman was moderate in speech, stopped quarrels, and knew the best camp-sites. People followed him because his person-ality won their confidence. Of the Comanche headmen, That's It sagely observed: "I hardly know how to tell about them; they never had much to do except to hold the band together."[7] That's It put his finger on it. The headman in the primitive world rarely has explicit author-ity; his functions are so subtle that they defy easy description. Yet he is the focal point of the local group.

As Harrasser notes among the Central Aus-tralians, the "chief is at most *prima inter pares* with few exceptions among the Dieri and in West Victoria."[8] Similar evidence comes from the Shoshones and the Eskimos. The Shoshone headman is called *tegwoni*, which in its fullest sense means "good talk thrown out to the people." In western Alaska, the headmen are those who "by their extended acquaintance with the traditions, customs and rites con-nected with the festivals, as well as being possessed of an unusual degree of common sense, are deferred to and act as chief advisers of the community."[9]

The simplest primitive societies are always democracies; rarely are they subject to dicta-torial political leadership.

State systems State systems have chiefs, kings, or councils with authority over certain spheres of social activity covering the entire society.

Chiefdoms Complexity of social life sharpens the need for leadership and the delegation of responsibility. Societies that are developed enough to have a tribal state always possess chiefs. A chief is differentiated from the head-

man merely by degree of authority and social distinction. His position may or may not be inherited. His functions and powers are vari-able among different peoples.

In North America, it was unusual for a chief to have strong power. Great care was taken in many tribes to separate the offices of peace chiefs and war chiefs. Peace chiefs were the civil governors. Usually they were band or clan headmen elevated to the status of mem-bership in the tribal council. They supervised internal tribal relations and had judicial powers over a few classes of crime. Most legal offen-ses, however, remained in the area of private wrongs to be settled by the parties concerned. Sometimes, as in the case of the Cheyennes, Omahas, and Iroquois, the civil chiefs were explicitly chosen for limited tenure. War chiefs were the heads of military fraternities, or a war chief could be any man who had an out-standing war record. Naturally, such war chiefs could make their opinion felt in the tribe, but they had very limited constitutional powers in the operation of the camp in peacetime. The most militaristic American Indians were astute enough to realize that military dictatorship is the greatest of all threats to the democratic way of life.

BANTU CHIEFS The functional significance of chiefs in the Bantu tribes of South Africa may be sensed from Schapera's listing of their activities:

He . . . attends habitually at his council-place . . . where he listens to news, petitions, and complaints, from all over the tribe, and gives orders for what-ever action is required. . . . Legislation has always been a recognized function of the chief . . . he periodically creates a new age-regiment, and thus formally admits youths into the social category of adults . . . he controls the distribution and use of land . . . he also regulates the calendar of agri-cultural and certain other activities . . . organizes large collective hunts . . . mobilizes his people for defense . . . and aggression . . . organizes reli-gious ceremonies upon the due performance of which his tribe's security and prosperity are held to depend . . . [and] to ensure that the rainfall is adequate.[10]

[7]E. A. Hoebel, *The Political Organization and Law-ways of the Comanche Indians* (American Anthropological Association, Memoir 54: Contributions from the Laboratory of Anthro-pology, 4, 1940), p. 18.
[8]A. Harrasser, *Die Rechtsverletzung bei den australischen Einge-borenen* (Beilageheft zur vergleichende Rechtswissenchaft, Vol. 50, 1936).
[9]E. W. Nelson, *The Eskimos about Bering Strait* (Bureau of American Ethnology, Annual Report 18, 1899), p. 304.
[10]I. Schapera, *Government and Politics in Tribal Societies*, pp. 68–75.

Small wonder that Tsonga proverbs say: "A tribe without a chief has lost its reason; it is dead. It is like a woman without a husband," And "In a country without chiefs, the people devour one another."[11]

CEREMONIAL CHIEFS In some systems, the primary responsibilities of chiefs are not necessarily concerned with governing. Yet there is really nothing strange about this, if we consider the Queen of England. Her political functions have atrophied, but her symbolic and ceremonial functions evoke a stir of emotion in British hearts the world over.

In the primitive world, the Trobriand chief enjoys high status and many privileges. Tribute must be paid him, but he utilizes it mostly to put on ceremonial feasts on behalf of his people. He serves more as a mainspring of ceremonial activity than as a political officer. This is true in greater or lesser degree for all Oceania (even in tribes where chiefs stem from conquerors), for as Forde observes:

The origin and development of chieftainship in Melanesia is by no means clear, but everywhere the chiefs claim the same essential rights and powers. They are nearly always real or alleged immigrants who make similar claims to sanctity, superiority and to the control of valuable ritual.

[The chiefs of the Sa'a people on the island of Mala, Solomon Islands, are aliens who] established and maintained their position by arrogance and determination. They are regarded, and regard themselves, as feast givers and the controllers of certain ceremonies. By the splendor of their feasts they enhance the prestige of their district and win the approval of the commoners who make gifts of food for yet more feasts.[12]

Exactly the same could be said of the Indians of the Northwest Coast of North America, with their potlatching chiefs.

Monarchy Kingship results from the development of the hereditary tendency into a hereditary principle. Its main function is to introduce stability into the administration of government. Strong clans make for intratribal strife.

[11] *Ibid.,* p. 105.
[12] C. D. Forde, *Habitat, Economy, and Society,* pp. 183, 182. See also C. S. Ford, "The Role of a Fijian Chief" (*American Sociological Review,* Vol. 3, 1938), pp. 542–550.

The law of blood revenge must be superseded by a stronger law of the whole society. This can conveniently be the king's law and the king's peace. But the power of paramount chieftains is in itself a luscious prize for power-hungry men. With bloody intrigue and with turmoil in their struggles to project themselves into chieftainship, they can rend the peace of the tribe. Clearly defined hereditary succession puts a check on such social abscesses. Yet the oftentimes fatal defect of the hereditary principle is that the heir to succession may have no aptitude for the job. The king may be a feeble weakling or, worse still, a dangerous egomaniac. In the one event, the state may fail to function effectively in times of crisis. In the other, tyranny supplants social justice, and men suffer under corruption.

Kingship is so common among advanced primitive societies that we must conclude that the need for centralized control outweighs the urge for democratic freedom at this level of social development. The resurgence of democracy comes later. But where democracy fails, the need for centralization produces dictatorship or fitful moves for the restoration of monarchy.

The hereditary principle is no thought-out device. It develops quite naturally and without conscious awareness. We can see this among those American Indian tribes who explicitly deny hereditary succession to chieftainship. In spite of the fact that any good man may become a chief, records show again and again that a chief is succeeded by one of his sons or maternal nephews. Chiefship runs in family or lineage lines. This arises from the fact that the training and high example set by the senior relative engender chiefly qualities in the boys. People come to expect leadership from such lines. The boys assume that people will respond to their superior leadership—and they do. Eventually, the tendency may become a prescription.

In Polynesia and Africa, primogeniture often fixes succession upon the eldest son. Yet most tribes maintain functional flexibility by leaving succession open to selection from among the chief's heirs by the royal council or the matriarch (in Ashanti, the Queen Mother; among the Iroquois, the oldest woman in the lineage). This is a sound device except as it leads to palace feuds between the parties of the heirs who rely on the *coup d'état* to circumvent council deliberations. Civil war and temporary anarchy are the usual concomitants of the death of a monarch in many a Bantu kingdom. Indeed, as a precaution against this sort of thing, the death of the king is often kept secret until his successor is chosen and everything is ready for the coronation.

SACERDOTAL CHIEFS AND KINGS   The skeins of religion and politics are composed of separate threads. They are woven into the tapestry that is society, sometimes carefully separated, each forming its own design, and sometimes intertwined, joining church and state in one pattern. The warrior's sword and the magician's wand are different artifacts. A man may wield one or the other, but if he is skilled enough and if his culture permits, he may seize the sword in his right hand and the wand in his left. Then, indeed, he becomes an awesome power to cope with. The essential doctrine of separation of church and state in American democratic tradition is a needful defensive reaction to that power.

Shamans and priests are specialists in controlling the action of the supernatural; headmen, chiefs, and kings are specialists in controlling the actions of men. But the actions of men must be controlled in their relations to the supernatural; the priest always has temporal influence. The politician uses religious means for political purposes when he is able to control religious power; the priest in turn is apt to use political means to attain religious ends when he has the techniques to do so. When either one has specialized his own peculiar techniques to a high degree and religious and political instruments are clearly developed, it sometimes occurs in the primitive world, as it so often does in the modern world, that rivalry and hostility between church and state are sharp. Among primitive men,

however, a working agreement between the two often exists; for example, the Trobriand chief employs his hereditary sorcerer to destroy upstarts,[13] and the Yokuts-Mono chiefs in California connive with medicine men to mulct the guileless public.[14] On the other hand, use of supernatural power for self-advantage through black magic is almost universally treated as a deadly crime if carried too far.

In general, supernaturalism is so ubiquitous in the primitive world that it colors all government to a greater or lesser degree. Political officers almost invariably possess some magic power or religious sanctity. War making, legislation, and judicial procedure inevitably involve religious ritual.

In highly organized gardening societies of sedentary peoples dependent on fixed crops, the chief is usually the high priest of the rain, fertility, and garden cults. As he is the supervisor of politico-legal relations, so is he also responsible for the economic well-being and religious security of his folk. If his society is one of ancestor worshipers, as is usually the case in Africa and Oceania, he is also the ancestral viceroy on earth—his people's highest link to the ancestral spirits. He is himself a direct descendant of the gods and has godhood in him. In Africa, again and again, he symbolizes the tribal soul: a soul that must be hale and vigorous, or else the tribe wanes and dies. Hence, the fate of the king who becomes feeble or ill is believed to be the poison cup or strangulation by his chief councilors.[15] It is no unalloyed privilege to be a ruler. Eminence entails responsibility.

The extreme sacredness of the god-king limits his activites. In Tonga (Polynesia), the *tuithonga* may not walk abroad, for where he places his foot, the earth becomes tabu.

THE TALKING CHIEF   "A White House spokesman announced today. . . ." The device of

[13] B. Malinowski, *Crime and Custom in Savage Society*, pp. 85–86, 92–93.
[14] A. H. Gayton, "Yokuts-Mono Chiefs and Shamans" (*University of California Publications in American Archaeology and Ethnology*, Vol. 24, 1930), pp. 361–420.
[15] See J. G. Frazer, *The Golden Bough*, chap. 24, "The Killing of the Divine King."

presidents is a possession of primitive chiefs and kings the world over. The Ashanti king or the paramount chief of a district rarely speaks in public. To do so is bad etiquette and policy on his part. He has his *okeyame* to serve as his mouthpiece. Most African kings have a court mouthpiece. In Samoa, each chief has his Talking Chief, who recites his chief's genealogy before every meeting of the native "parliament." He speaks his chief's mind in debate. Kwakiutl and other Northwest Coast chieftains have their speakers at potlatches to extol the ancestry and virtues of their masters. Every Plains Indian peace chief had his crier, who announced decisions to the camp at large; his "loudspeaker," the Cheyenne interpreter, High Forehead, always called him.

The reason for these spokesmen is subtle but sound. When chieftains rise above the level of headmen, their power increases. He who wields powers of decision and enforcement must not be too familiar to the multitude. Some good men can maintain influence and fraternity simultaneously, but they are rare. It is a safer and surer technique to let a minion undertake the vulgar task of shouting to the masses.

The council   The one universal instrument of government is the council. No tribe or nation does without it. No man can govern alone, nor is he permitted to. Monarchy, if taken literally, is a misnomer. Every king or chief operates within the network of his advisers and cronies. Some are helplessly enmeshed in it.

In small primitive bands and tribes, the council is a democratic gathering of adult males. In gerontocratic Australia, participation is limited to the elders. Elsewhere, it is mostly open to all males. Among American Indians, decision of the council had to be unanimous; one stubborn holdout could block action. Still there were neat devices for attaining unanimity. Tribal councils commonly consisted of all the band headmen. Among the Aztecs, for a special example, every family sent its headman to a clan council. Each clan council had a clan headman, a war chief, and a speaker.

The speakers of the twenty clans formed the tribal, or national, council, which worked with the king and his executive officer, the Snake Woman (who was not a woman, but a man).

Among the great African monarchies, the king has the superficial appearance of an absolute autocrat. Yet he can rarely act without full approval of the council, and this is not forthcoming until the royal elders have sounded out tribal public opinion. Kings who abuse their power can generally be deposed; in the old days, they could be destroyed.

Monarchy, like every other social relation, rests on reciprocity. If the exalted ruler receives great social privilege, he must give service to the people in return. Some kings and dictators may ignore this precept, but it is difficult for them successfully to ignore for long the principle voiced in the Balinese proverb: "The ruler owes his might to the people."

Nonpolitical associations in government

It is an error to think of government solely in terms of the organs explicitly designed for governmental purposes. All government is pluralistic, and various extrastate organizations play their parts in determining and executing political policy.

The author for some years belonged to a small-town volunteer fire company. It is a closed fraternity, which elects its members by secret vote. It has all the trappings of a lodge: sworn secrecy, uniforms with gold buttons, rituals, dances, and ceremonial feasting. It also puts out fires as the occasion demands. This firemanic fraternity is a private association, a true men's club. Yet it is an official branch of government under the laws of the State of New York. The costs of its fire-fighting equipment and meeting rooms are met by public taxation. It is regulated by public law and is controlled by publicly elected fire commissioners. It remains a club and yet is an organ of government, just as the Plains Indian military fraternities were, the social aspects of which have already been discussed in Chapter 26. Fraternity, feasting, dancing, and social enjoyment were the primary activities of such men's clubs, but they also took on police, judicial, and legislative powers when the need arose.[16] The tribal councils constitutionally possessed all judicial and legislative powers covering criminal activity. However, the council chiefs were peace chiefs not given to coercive action. When coercive restraint or punishment was needed, they were not suited to the task. They were "fathers" to all the tribe, and Indian fathers do not punish their children. What was more natural than that the extragovernmental societies of warriors should take over policing the hunt, the rice harvest, and the great tribal ceremonials of the sun dance? This they did with vigor and dispatch. In later years, as the Plains tribes began to crumble before the onslaught of the white men, the Cheyenne military societies assumed more and more governmental power as crisis piled on crisis. But to no avail; they were overwhelmed.

In Africa, as we have already seen, various secret societies among certain West Sudanese tribes imposed peace, collected debts on behalf of their members, and, in the case of the Egbo society, punished wrongs.

In Melanesia, the numerous men's secret societies also directly and indirectly determine policy and operate as law-enforcing agencies.

Plains Indian military societies were not secret, and as a result their role in government was essentially democratic. It is quite otherwise with the exclusive secret orders of Africa and Melanesia. They are more akin to the Ku Klux Klan and other such cryptic groups, who spring up in our midst to usurp the functions of the state and to corrupt democracy. That these extralegal bodies can sporadically attain a measure of success is testimony to the Hydra-headed nature of government in society.

[16]R. H. Lowie, *Primitive Society*, p. 415; *The Origin of the State*, pp. 94–107; "Property Rights and Coercive Powers of the Plains Indian Military Societies" (*Journal of Legal and Political Sociology*, Vol. 1, 1943), pp. 59–71.

Political organization among the Tswana

A highly developed primitive society weaves genealogical, geographical, and associational units together into a multicelled state system. Professor Schapera's lucid report on the Tswana, an African nation of Northern Rhodesia, provides us with one of the finest examples of how this is done.[17] It forms the basis for this summary.

The Tswana, or Bechuana, constitute an ethnologically identifiable group of tribes. Each tribe is a politically independent unit, although the more newly formed tribes recognize the seniority of the tribes from which they broke off. Tribal populations exceed 100,000.

The integrating focus of the tribe is in the person and office of the chief, who is not only the supreme ruler but also "the visible symbol of its cohesion and solidarity." People may leave the tribe of their birth, and tribal citizenship is expressed by allegiance to a particular chief. Each Tswana tribe has a capital town (ranging in population from 600 to 25,000) and a number of smaller outlying villages.

Within the village or town, the households (which consist of one or more conjugal-natal families) are clustered to form the spatially distinguished family group. Closely related family groups live in a well-defined administrative unit, called a *ward*. All the wards together make up the tribe, except that in two of the larger tribes, the wards are grouped in sections.

A small hamlet may contain no more than one household. A small village may consist of a single family group. A larger village may have only one ward. A village, if large enough, may, however, embrace several family groups and wards. Each of these groups is a kinship-territorial-governmental unit of social structure.

The leader of the household is the husband and father; for the family group, the leader is the senior male descendant of the common paternal grandfather whose name the group

[17]I. Schapera; *A Handbook of Tswana Law and Custom*, pp. 1–34, 53–124.

bears. His position is hereditary and ascribed. He directs the group's activities and keeps the peace within his flock. In important matters, he acts in consultation with a family-group council of all adult males.

The headman of a ward holds his position by right of hereditary descent as the senior son of the preceding headman. He is not appointed by the chief except upon formation of a new ward. He does, however, act as his ward's representative to the chief, and he is responsible for the orderly conduct of his people and the execution of the chief's commands. He collects tribute for the chief and holds judicial authority in minor cases involving two family groups within his jurisdiction. He is also the leader of the men of his ward in their common age set.

A headman must act in consultation with a ward council made up of the senior members of his own family group and the leaders of the other family groups in his ward. If guilty of malfeasance in office, his own council will reprimand him or complain to the chief, who may then try to punish him through the Royal Court. Occasionally, the ward headman convenes all the adult males of the ward in a general folkmoot for review of problems of wide concern. The headman carries many burdens of responsibility for which he receives little material compensation but great prestige and respect—providing he does his job well.

Each village, in turn, has its headman. If the village and ward are one, the ward headman and village headman are one and the same. Should there be two or more wards, the headman of the senior ward is the village head. His duties are similar to those of the ward headman, except that they are town-wide in scope.

In those tribes which have districts, village organization remains the same as that described above, but the district will have as a special representative to the capital the headman of one of its more important indigenous villages (some outlying villages will consist of immigrant aliens).

This brings us to the central tribal government organized around the chief. A chief is chief through primogeniture. *Kgosi ke kgosi ka a tsetswe,* a chief is chief because he is born to it. In succession, the direct line precedes all collateral lines; i.e., the sons of the chief succeed, but his brothers and their sons cannot, although a brother of a dead king may serve as regent during the minority of the heir. If a chief dies with no male issue, the chieftainship passes to the next senior brother of the chief.

Functionally, the Tswana chief "is at once ruler, judge, maker and guardian of the law, repository of wealth, dispenser of gifts, leader in war, priest and magician of the people." He and his family take precedence in all things and receive high honors. Failure to obey his orders or to show him respect is a criminal offense. He is sustained by a royal coterie and with tribute.

In return, much is expected of him. His time is his people's. He must keep himself well-informed of tribal affairs, be accessible to all who have complaints, organize and direct the army, sit as chief justice, preside over the tribal council, perform the major religious rituals, and above all be generous, redistributing most of the tribute that comes to him.

The male relatives of the chief form a nobility, a kind of House of Lords, with whom he must remain in close consultation. To maintain effective democratic control, the chief has an informally constituted body of confidential advisers (a "cabinet") drawn from among the important men of the tribe on whom he feels he can rely; they are usually, but by no means always, paternal relatives.

The government also includes a formal tribal council of all the ward headmen, who meet in secret, executive session whenever convened by the chief.

Affairs of great tribal import, although they are first taken up by the two preceding groups of advisers, cannot become offical policy until they have been discussed and approved in open tribal assembly. To this all the headmen come *and* all adult men who want to make it their business.

Thus, although a chief is chief because he is born to it, the Tswana have an even more fundamental proverb: *Kgosi ke kgosi ka morafe,* a chief is chief by grace of his tribe. The constitution of the state is such that he is subject to representative checks and balances. A self-willed chief does not last long.

There is yet another arm of the Tswana state to be mentioned. All Tswana men are initiated into age sets at puberty. These have important congeniality functions to perform, but they are equally important as units of political organization. An age set cuts right across the local segments of the tribe and counteracts the parochialism that inherently exerts a neutralizing effect on national integration. Each age set (which numbers from fifty to several hundred boys or men, depending on the size of the tribe) is headed by a commander, who is always a member of the royal family. In war, the age sets constitute regiments in the tribal army. The men of a given ward form "companies" within the regiment under the leadership of a son or close relative of their ward headman. In times of peace, the age sets serve as work brigades to perform any public service or job of construction that the chief deems necessary.

Women's age sets also exist and are organized along the same lines as the men's. In the sphere of women's work, they also perform public services, though of a lighter nature.

The Tswana system exemplifies how the state, as a political system in an advanced primitive society, weaves and balances kinship, territorial, and associational groupings into a harmonious whole. It shows how the functional prerequisite of allocation of authority to responsible leaders is checked and balanced with concomitant reliance on organized group consultation, through the provision of councils on each level of administrative structure, with a final check imposed through general assemblies at each level for consideration of all major or crucial decisions. Tswana political organization has the essential elements of monarchy, democracy, oligarchy, theocracy, and gerontocracy. It is each of these and all. It has no need for elective procedures and spares itself a good deal of trouble and uncertainty thereby, for internal social mobility is limited, and in this type of society the hereditary principle works well enough.

SUMMARY

Political organization consists of the network of customs and institutions that regulate relations between groups within a society and between one society and another. The units of political organization may be genealogical, territorial, or associational. The genealogical units, such as the family, kindred, lineage, clan, phratry, moiety, or deme, are usually subdivisions of territorial units. These range in scope from local group, band, village, district, and tribe, up to confederacy, empire, and federation, or commonwealth.

The functions of political organization include definition of norms, allocation of force and authority, settlement of disputes, public works, ceremony and ritual control of the supernatural, economic activities (markets), and war.

Political organization may be stateless, but where government is added in the form of centralized authority for the whole tribe or society and endowed with specific (if even only part-time) functionaries, it becomes a state.

Government, from the most primitive to the most civilized, includes the council in one form or another. Very simple primitive societies vest leadership in headmen rather than chiefs. All adult males participate directly in decision making. Elemental primitive societies are essentially democracies. Chiefship is characteristic of the more developed primitive societies. Kingship exists in those in which chiefship has become hereditary. The chief or king is often the functioning symbol of the collective existence of the society; hence, his activities may be largely ritual and ceremonial. He is both priest or god and political head: the divine king.

The state is always multidimensional; it is made up of diverse elements. Governments can also consist of a variety of agencies that have nongovernmental aspects. Thus kinship groups and associations that exist primarily for other purposes may perform governmental functions and so exist as an integral part of the state system.

SELECTED READINGS

Evans-Pritchard, E. E., and M. Fortes (eds.): *African Political Systems* (1940). A symposium of excellent studies of political structure in a number of African tribes.

Lowie, R. H.: *The Origin of the State* (1927). A stimulating pioneer study of the processes of state development among primitive peoples.

Mair, L.: *Primitive Government* (1964). A general, nontheoretical description of the major types of government in African tribal societies. Contains an informative final chapter entitled "Primitive Government and Modern Times."

Middleton, J., and D. Tait (eds.): *Tribes without Rulers* (1958). The purpose of this book is to present new data on six African stateless tribes that are organized on the basis of unilineal kinship groups.

Rattray, R. S.: *Ashanti Law and Constitution* (1927). A most valuable study of the historical development of the great federated monarchy of the Ashanti of the Gold Coast of Africa.

Schapera, I.: *Government and Politics in Tribal Society* (1956). A comparative study of three South African tribal systems.

Southall, A. W.: *Alur Society* (1956). Subtitled *A Study in the Processes and Types of Domination*, this book analyzes the structure of a primitive political state embracing a multiple number of tribes.

Animism, mana, and the supernatural

chapter 32

Of all the manifestations of man's emotional, intellectual, and social life, none is so elusive of definition as religion. Yet none is more important. For religion, as an aspect of supernaturalism, consists of systems of belief, thought, and action that are deeply imbedded in all cultures. These systems of belief and action work upward and outward throughout the cultural fabric. At some points they thread so finely into the total pattern that it is impossible to say where the religious ends and the mundane begins. Religion presents so many aspects, intertwined with so many phases of culture, and is so variable that it is difficult to delineate it in terms both broad enough to encompass the whole and discriminating enough to isolate it for study.

As is often the case, it is best to clear the ground by a negative statement of what religion is not. We must first peel away the parochial to find the universal core. The view of Fielding's Parson Thwackum in the novel *Tom Jones* is clearly the expression of the kind of attitude that, while it simplifies the problem, would make any anthropological study of religion impossible.

"When I mention religion," dogmatically declared the parson, "I mean the Christian religion; and not only the Christian religion but the Protestant religion; and not only the Protestant religion, but the Church of England."[1]

Religion cannot be defined in terms of any particular religion, nor does it depend on a belief in one god. Many religions are polytheistic. In his study of Ifugao religion in the Philippine Islands, for instance, R. F. Barton had some five-thousand deities identified for him by family priests; yet he felt sure he had by no means exhausted the list.[2] Few religions are strictly monotheistic.[3] Religion does not even depend on a belief in deities. Many religions have not developed concepts of such exalted spiritual beings as may properly be called "gods." They may be essentially *animistic*; i.e., they may center on spirit beings rather than deities. Religion does not depend upon a clearly formulated creed or explicit body of dogma; obviously among primitive peoples, it cannot involve sacred books. Religion does not depend upon the existence of bodies of worshipers organized into churches or cult groups. Many religions are highly individualistic. Nor for the same reason does religion necessarily involve a priesthood, although there are religious specialists and practitioners in every society.

What, then, is the *sine qua non* of religion? What are the essential features that occur everywhere? The belief in supernatural forces, combined with particular ways of behaving in consequence of such belief, is the basis of all religion; supernaturalistic beliefs and the attitudes and conduct related to such beliefs are what constitute religion.

[1]Cited by R. H. Lowie in *Primitive Religion*, p. x.
[2]R. F. Barton, *The Religion of the Ifugaos*.
[3]P. Radin, *Monotheism in Primitive Religion*.

Supernaturalism

The fundamental problem is, then, first to examine the nature of what is meant by *supernaturalism*. It clearly implies a dichotomy of ideas: that which is natural and that which is more than natural or, indeed, superior to the natural. In any thought system, the difference between the two depends upon a people's general philosophy concerning the nature of things, on their basic *existential postulates* and the way these are worked out in their *world view*. (See Chapter 34). What is seen as *natural* and what as *supernatural* is relative to the culture of the moment. In the systems of knowledge of the Western world, many things that were once viewed as supernatural have been moved over into the area of the natural. The Neolithic axes (celts) that eighteenth-century Europeans thought were Jove's thunderbolts or elves' spittle are today recognized as man's handiwork from time gone by—perfectly natural products of human activity. Nothing is inherently supernatural; it depends on how people evaluate and look at things.

Some anthropologists note that many primitive peoples make no distinction between the natural and the supernatural. They hold that this dichotomy is a product of European rationalism and that it is an intellectualistic artifact imposed on primitive cultures by ethnocentric Western thinkers.[4] In part this is true. "Natural" and "supernatural" are analytical concepts for classifying phenomena, and their exact counterparts need not necessarily exist in the language and conceptional systems of all other peoples. The important question is: "Are the concepts as they are generally used in anthropology relevant to the facts as we observe them?" The answer is "yes."

The sacred and the profane The essential difference between the natural and the supernatural lies in the qualitative emotional (affective) attitudes of mind and feeling, or, as put

[4]For example, M. Wax and R. Wax, "The Notion of Magic" (*Current Anthropology*, Vol. 4, 1963), pp. 519–532.

by Professor Lowie, in "a sense of something transcending the expected or natural, a sense of the Extraordinary, Mysterious, or Supernatural."[5] Religious belief is essentially mystical and subjective, whereas naturalistic belief emphasizes objective and rational determination of the facts.

This becomes clearer when put in the terms advanced by the French sociologist-anthropologist Émile Durkheim,[6] who contrasted two polar attitudes: that which looks on certain things as *profane* and on others as *sacred*.

the profane	the sacred
The sphere of the routine, mundane, taken-for granted, workaday world.	The sphere of the unusual, extraordinary, not-to-be-taken-casually, "out-of-this-world."
Attitudes: blasé acceptance on a basis of common familiarity.	Attitudes: awe, sense of mystery, circumspection in dealing with something special.

The terms "profane" and "sacred," so used, have meanings somewhat broader than ordinarily accorded them in common English usage, and care should be taken to keep this constantly in mind. The profane, then, is that which is taken naturally; the sacred, that which is taken supernaturally. The natural works in ways that are accepted as ordinary, as in accord with daily experience. The supernatural works in ways that are looked upon as unusual and special. The emotional connotations are consequently different. They are the product of human mental states.

Religion and magic therefore rest upon a belief in the supernatural, and they are basically matters of ideology and the kinds of feeling that accompany them. They require thought. Animals, although they certainly feel, do not engage in symbolic thought, as we have seen. Man alone symbolizes, and man's ideas about the supernatural are always symbolically expressed. So it is that on the subhuman level there is no religion or magic—no supernaturalism.

Supernaturalism is consequently a product

of the evolutionary development of the human brain. Animals are too unintelligent to produce either religion or magic. Man reflects on the universe of experiences that engulf him, and he comes up with ideas about their nature, their causation, and their consequences. Some are supernaturalistic; some are not. The first religions were probably born way back in the Early Paleolithic, and mystic thinking has controlled much of human life since then down to Aristotle, Plato, and the other Greek founders of modern science. Urban culture contributed to the birth of the Age of Enlightenment and the Age of Reason following the Renaissance in the West, greatly reducing the relative importance of supernaturalism in civilized thinking, as compared with its importance among primitive peoples. Whether naturalism will entirely displace supernaturalism in future cultures cannot be said, although the general trend in the evolution of culture and human thought can certainly be said to be in that direction.

Animism

What are the forms that supernatural ideas take? Basically, they may be broken down into *animism* and *mana*. Animism, (L. *anima*, soul, spirit) as defined by the great nineteenth-century English anthropologist Sir Edward Burnett Tylor, is the belief in spirit beings.[7] We all know them by name: souls, ghosts, goblins, poltergeists, genies, trolls, sprites, elves, pixies, leprechauns, fairies, witches, demons, devils, angels, and gods. Their essential quality is their ethereal embodiment; they are beings without real flesh and blood—nonmaterial, but real enough for those who believe in them.

As spirits, they are not subject to the "laws of nature." They are uninhibited by the limitations of physical matter, by the weaknesses of human flesh. They transcend matter, time, and space. They are supernatural. It is this that makes them wonderful, mysterious.

Tylor's theory   In his remarkable study, Tylor examined many manifestations of animism

[5]Lowie, *op. cit.,* p. xvi.
[6]É. Durkheim, *Elementary Forms of the Religious Life.*
[7]E. B. Tylor, *Primitive Culture,* Vol. I, p. 424.

among primitives, but he was interested in more than just describing its forms. Tylor was essentially an evolutionist. For him the ultimate question was: "How and why did human beings create the concept of spirit beings?" Somewhere along the line in prehistoric times, the human mind peopled the universe with spirits. What led it to do so?

Tylor saw the origin of animism in the phenomena of dreams, of life and of death. Dreams are a form of hallucination, an illusory experience. But that men dream is an empirical fact. In dreams we transcend reality. We soar to great heights of attainment and pleasure; we experience horrible happenings; we relive the past and anticipate the future; we visit places once visited and those where our feet have never yet been; we commune with the dead and departed or with the living who are far distant. Time, space, and limitations of the body do not hinder us—in our dreams.

Yet in sleep or in coma, the body does not leave its resting place. We wake where we lie down to rest—except in the case of the unfortunate somnambulist. The body has not performed the miracles dreamed, but it is hard, even for the sophisticate, not to take dream experiences as real. To the primitive and, indeed, to many civilized men, the dream experience *is* reality.

The soul concept Primitive man reflected and concluded that there were two parts to man: the bodily self of mortal flesh and the spiritual *alter ego*, the soul. The soul concept is the root of animism. It is a universal concept.

The soul is, in itself, quite intangible. In the language of many peoples, the word "soul" is synonymous with "shadow" or "shade." Intangible though it is, it is oftentimes perceptible in the image of the body it normally inhabits.

The soul is the vital force. Its presence animates the body; its departure stills it. It is in the stillness of sleep that the soul goes wandering. Man's restlessness is of the spirit, not the body.

The long sleep that is death comes when the sojourning soul does not return. The body

that is the vessel for the soul has no further function once its soul has abandoned it. Disintegration follows. Illness is due to intrusive corruption of the soul or to soul loss.

This, according to Tylor, is the logic of the soul concept—in part.

Man does not live alone. The beasts of wood and field, the fowl of the air, and the fishes of the waters are also endowed with vitality. So too are the plants. By means of analogical reasoning, primitive man attributes souls to them also, as the cause of their vitality. Yet he does not do this completely by false analogy, for animals appear in dreams, even as man. Thus, in most primitive belief, not only man but all living beings possess souls.

Souls after death become ghosts or free spirits wholly disembodied. They live on in the world of man, within his very community or in a special realm, which the spirits of living men may on occasion visit or from which souls may come to visit the living.

Whether or not the concept of free spirits could arise only from the soul concept, as Tylor thought, or whether early man was imaginatively capable of creating the spirit concept

Fig. 32-1 In an Ainu village on Hokkaido, Japan, a family headman gives a prayer of thanks to the god of fishing for the first salmon of the autumn. (Ruike Y. Ante.)

out of mere nothingness, we shall never know. It is enough that pure spirits inhabit the believing minds of people in all societies and that these imaginary beings are thought to be beyond the laws of nature. They and souls are living elements in all religions.

Nature worship   The attribution of spirit qualities to plants and objects then produced, according to Tylor, what we call *nature worship*. From this came totemism and the creation of species deities, i.e., the deification not of persons (ancestor worship) but of animal creatures and plants. From these practices, Tylor derived the higher polytheism of the later barbarians, with its sky, earth, rain, thunder, lightning, fire, wind, water, sun, and moon gods, as well as gods of agriculture, hunting, birth, war, and death.

"What ethnography has to teach of that great element of the religion of mankind, the worship of well and lake, brook and river, is simply this—that what is poetry to us was philosophy to early man; that to his mind water acted not by laws of force, but by life and will. . . ."[8]

Tylor's notions on the origins of monotheism and the Supreme Deity will be noted in the discussion of High Gods at the close of this chapter.

Of Tylor's anthropological theory of religion, it may be said that it suffers some inadequacies, but in the main we can concur with Lowie's judgment:

His theory is avowedly a psychological interpretation pure and simple, but inasmuch as it not only explains the empirical observations, but operates exclusively with facts like death, dreams and visions, all of which demonstrably exercise a strong influence on the minds of primitive men, it must be conceded to have a high degree or probability. I, for one, certainly have never encountered any rival hypothesis that could be considered a serious competitor.[9]

Like all evolutionary theories that try to formulate the details of nonmaterial culture in

[8]Tylor, *op. cit.*, Vol. II, p. 209.
[9]Lowie, *op. cit.*, p. 108.

prehistoric times, Tylor's theory is speculative and unverifiable. But stripped of its evolutionary ordering of the data, it stands, as Lowie has said, as a valuable general analysis of a considerable part of the religious attitudes and behavior of men. Animism, however, is by no means the whole story. There is also *mana* and the matter of religion as social expression, both of which call for theoretical explanation.

Mana

Supernaturalism does not find its only expression in beliefs in spirit beings; there are also beliefs in the existence of supernatural forces that do not emanate from any kind of being. Such forces are expressed as special attributes of things, much as the force of gravity is related to objects that have mass. Following the suggestion of another early student of primitive religion, R. R. Marett (1866–1943), anthropologists call it *mana*, a word derived from the languages of Melanesia where the concept of mana is strong and clear in native life.

Mana is a force, but not a vitalistic force. It exists as a supernatural attribute of persons and things. Above all, it is the exceptional power to do things that are unusual. Mana is therefore manifest in the unusual, when the unusual is not the work of spirits.

Extraordinary aptitudes of men are explained in terms of mana. The master craftsman in Polynesia excels in his skill because he possesses mana. The learned pundit excels in lore and knowledge because he possesses mana. The mighty warrior excels in the killing of men because he possesses mana. The outstanding healer, the expert canoeman, and any others who stand above their fellow men do so because of personal possession or control of mana. Mana, though it is an impersonal force, can be manifest in and through persons, as well as in stock and stone. The queerly shaped or unusually marked stone may be believed to possess miracle-working power. This is its mana. The canoe that can outdistance all others, the song that heals, the war club that smashes more than a normal quota of skulls, the talisman that in itself brings good luck—all these have power, power that is mana.

The power that is extraordinary is not mundane force. It does not follow the regular laws of ordinary technologies or skills. Like the power of spirits, it transcends the natural. Mana is supernatural.

Religion and magic

Man acts on the basis of his beliefs. Animism and mana are attributes of the subjective aspects of supernaturalism. Religion and magic are concepts based upon the ways in which man behaves in relation to the supernatural forces in which he believes. They constitute two forms of the external objectification of beliefs. The distinction rests on man's assessment of the motivating forces behind the supernatural. Is man subordinate to the caprice and will of the supernatural beings to whom psychological characteristics are attributed? If his answer is "yes," his dealings with these beings, and theirs with him, will be religious in nature. Can man under certain conditions dominate and control the supernatural forces, be they animistic or manaistic? If his answer is "yes," his dealings with the supernatural will be magical in nature.

Prayer and magic are the two basic techniques of dealing with the supernatural. The first is a means of seeking spiritual rapport on a basis of subordination to animistic beings. The second is a technique of gaining external control over supernatural powers, animistic and manaistic. Between these poles, every possible form of interpersonal behavior may find its religious counterpart. As Benedict observed: "There is probably no customary behavior towards one's fellows that is not to be found somewhere as a religious technique."

The only limits on religion are the limits set by imagination and the human physical system. Both allow tremendous scope for variation and elaboration. Hunting is limited by ecology, animal habits, and the physical laws of mechanics in the development of weapons. There are few variants among hunting techniques the world over; not so the varieties of religious experience and practice.

The religious attitude That which distinguishes religion from magic is neither the goodness of one nor the evil of the other, but the state of mind of the believer and his consequent modes of behavior. This is the distinction that was originally pointed out by Sir James G. Frazer.[10] In the religious state of mind, man acknowledges the superiority of the supernatural powers upon whose action his well-being depends. His attitudes are preponderantly those of submission and reverence. The objective behavior put forth is manifestly that of beseeching, petition, and appeasement in prayer, offerings, and sacrifice.

Father have pity on me,
Father have pity on me,
I am crying for thirst,
I am crying for thirst,
All is gone—I have nothing to eat,
All is gone—I have nothing to eat.

Such is the tenor of an Arapaho ghost-dance song, "sung to a plaintive tune, sometimes with tears rolling down the cheeks of the dancers."[11] It epitomizes the religious attitude, as does the Lord's Prayer, with its "Hallowed be thy name" (reverence); "Give us this day our daily bread" (petition); "Thine is the Kingdom, the Power and the Glory, forever" (subordination and awe).

"Oh spirits, here, humble in heart, I stand beseeching you" is the opening plaint of the Winnebago on a vision quest.

The magical attitude The magician, on the other hand, believes that he *controls* supernatural power under certain conditions. He

[10]See J. G. Frazer, *The Golden Bough*, chap. 4. Frazer argued a theoretical priority of magic over religion in prehistoric origins. This is a futile and irrelevant problem for which there are no empirical data upon which to base a conclusion.
[11]Mooney, *The Ghost Dance Religion and the Sioux Outbreak of 1890* (Bureau of American Ethnology, Annual Report 14, 1896), p. 977.

has power over power. He feels confirmed in his belief that if he possesses a tested formula and if he executes the formula perfectly, barring outside interference, he will get the results which that formula is specified to give. The supernatural power has no volition or choice of its own. It must respond. The magician works with a confidence similar to that of the student in the laboratory who knows that if he follows the manual instructions correctly, he will obtain a predictable result. The religious attitude and behavior are devout; the magician works with a kind of arrogance—or, at the least, self-assurance.

Magic often does appear to produce the expected results. It seems to meet the pragmatic test. What works is so. At least, it must work in its initial applications, or the magical formula is usually rejected as false or worthless. When magic works, it does so for two reasons: (1) coincidence—if sufficient time is allowed, the desired event may well come to pass—and (2) psychological suggestion—when magic is directed against persons who suspect or fear that they are its objects, hysteria or compulsion grips them; they sicken and often die. Psychologists call this *somatic compliance* and *thanatomania* (the depression of the will to live to the point of extinction). The records of travelers and anthropologists abound with cases from the primitive world. Clinical records reveal many authentic cases among civilized men. Doctors well know the importance of the psychological state of the patient in crucial illness or injury.

Magic also serves its ends by giving the magician and his clients a needed psychological boost. As Malinowski reiterated, magic begins where mechanical technology ends. A Melanesian knows that magic cannot dig the soil in which he must plant his yams, so he does his own digging. He knows that he must hoe to keep down weeds, so he hoes. But he also knows that, no matter how great his skill, pests, foraging animals, and climate are beyond his technological ability to control. Yet these and unknown factors affect his crop

for better or worse. He desperately needs a good crop. It is the object of his most ardent wish, so he endeavors to control the unknown element by magic or religion, and the confidence they give him quite definitely helps him to outdo himself in achievement of his wished-for goal.[12]

The warrior who believes he has magic invulnerability can surmount fear and leap to heroism far more easily that the man who confronts danger without such support.

Not only does magic actually help the magician to attain his end in reality, but it also fosters the illusion of attainment. When the dogma of magic is strong, the practitioner often thinks the magical result has come to pass when nothing of the sort has occurred at all. Magic has much in common with daydreaming as a form of wish fulfillment.

Thus, magic, in some of its aspects, is similar to science. When the magician proceeds on the mechanistic assumption that the magical formula is a cause that must produce a given effect, his thinking parallels that of the scientist. His method, however, rests on fantasies. But it may be well to remind ourselves that much scientific belief, formerly useful but now discarded, also rested on similar unrealistic belief. It would, perhaps, be more accurate to call magic a technique based upon autistic thinking—imaginative fantasy as means of wish fulfillment.

Finally, it should be noted that magic often appears to work because the primitive magician is a skilled prestidigitator. He simply bamboozles the credulous with skilled stage settings and sleight-of-hand artistry, some of which is really convincing.

It is thus possible analytically to distinguish magic from religion, and the distinction is much more than a mere play on words. The difference between the two methods of approach to the supernatural has tremendous social consequences. Religious emphasis on supernaturalism leads to subordination of men to gods and to the power of cult func-

[12]Malinowski's *Coral Gardens and Their Magic* is an anthropological classic.

tionaries—the shaman and the priest. Religion is much more readily centralized and organized than magic, which is inherently more individualistic. Although organized religions always use a certain amount of magic in their rituals, churches are implicitly antagonistic to magic, since the magical attitude is incompatible with the religious attitude of submission. The conflict endures through the ages.

Because of its elemental kinship to science, magic is more susceptible to displacement by technological advances than religion is, and conversely, religion, with its element of personal dependence, is not so readily displaced by an advance in knowledge as magic is. Modern scientists may still hold to their religious faiths, but all will renounce magic.

The blending of religion and magic Primitive man, however, does not greatly concern himself with the analytical distinction between magic and religion. Rather, he blends them as best he can to attain his ends.

The Plains Indian on his vision quest makes himself pitiable in the eyes of the spirits. If they favor him, they give power along with sundry paraphernalia and the ritual wherewith to invoke power. He acquires his power by means of a religious approach to the spirits. Once he has it, he uses it as a magic instrument of control over them. This is well illustrated in an account of the acquisition, use, and loss of supernatural power that a Bannock Indian headman gave the author in the course of his field work in the Snake River Desert of Idaho in 1933:

"A long time ago the Indians around here learned to play poker. I decided I wanted to be able to win at that game, so I went out to seek *poha* [power].

"I went out into the mountains to a place where I knew there were lots of pack rats. I wore only my breechcloth. I ate no food and drank no water.

"Continuously I prayed to the pack rats, 'Oh, pack rats! Here I stand, a poor, helpless human being. Take pity on me! Wherever you go, you gather everything in. That's the way I

want to be among my people. I want to be able to gather everything in when I play poker.' For three days and nights I fasted and prayed.

"On the fourth night a big pack rat, the grandfather of all the pack rats, appeared before me. 'Human being,' he said, 'I have heard your prayers. I am taking pity on you. I shall give you my power.

"'Now this is what you must do. When morning comes, scrape up the scale that is formed by our urine on the rocks. Make a small buckskin bag to put it in and wear this always around you neck.

"'Now I will teach you four songs. When you want to use my power wash yourself with dry wood ashes to remove all grease and paint.[13] Sing the four songs. Then when you go in to play poker, you will always win. You will be able to gather everything in, even as I do.'"

These things he did, and, according to his testimony, the power worked with great success until he got careless and cut in on a hand of poker right after doing a war dance—without washing off the paint in dry ashes. The effect nearly killed him, and his power was destroyed forever.

In this experience, Running Water, for that was his name, was clearly using the approaches of the religious man. "Oh, pack rats! Here I stand, a poor, helpless human being. Take pity on me!" But he was also to become a magician. With the formula of the songs and the talisman of the urine scale, he automatically gained his ends at will—until he blew up the laboratory by carelessly failing to follow the formula.

Imitative and homeopathic magic Magic, it may also be noted, is often built on two aspects of the psychological principle of association. The first is the assumption that like objects and acts have an affinity for each other. This produces *imitative* or *homeopathic*

[13]Among American Indians, grease is held to counteract supernatural power. Thus, an automobile may not be parked too close to the house of an old-time medicine man on some Indian reservations even today.

Fig. 32-2   A market stand in Dahomey. The vendor's wares—skulls, magic powders, and charms—are used for magic. (Marc and Evelyne Bernheim, Rapho Guillumette Pictures.)

magic, in which the magician puts a hex on an effigy of the person or object on which he would work his desire or in which he ritually re-creates the thing he would affect. Pueblo Indians paint symbolic images of rain-bringing clouds or altar symbols of the cloud image, or they stir up billows of frothy yucca-plant suds in cloudlike masses, magically to induce the life-giving rains to shower their beneficence upon the parched desert gardens.

The second assumption is that things once intimately in contact retain an influence over each other. This produces *contagious magic,* in which a hair, a bit of clothing, or even excrement is filched from the victim, with or upon which the magician works his spell.

Belief in imitative magic often accounts for the hostility of primitive peoples toward having their pictures taken. Who knows what might be done with the image? Belief in contagious magic sometimes makes a people most secretive about defecation. It may be the fear of sorcery rather than a sense of modesty that prompts such reticence.

Sorcery   Sorcery is magic used for antisocial purposes. Magic is in itself amoral, neither good nor bad. It is the uses to which magic is put that determine its moral qualities. Thus, a medicine man or witch doctor, as one who has control over magic, may be thoroughly good in the eyes of his people, or he may be evil, or both. A Shoshone medicine man is called *pohagant,* meaning "one who has power." A sorcerer is called *tidjipohagant,* or "one who uses power evilly."

Sorcery is a form of aggression against fellow beings or their possessions that is not socially approved. Magic may also be used aggressively, but it is not sorcery if its use is socially approved.

Kapauku sorcery The Kapauku of the highlands of West New Guinea exemplify this clearly in their distinction between *kamu* (approved magic) and *kego* (sorcery). According to Pospisil:

From the functional point of view the broad categories of *kamu* can be divided into curative, preventive, counter sorcery, rain-stopping, rain-making, profit-inducing, and war-magic subcategories. The whole variety of these rites may be performed by any Kapauku man or woman. However, there are individuals who have acquired a reputation for being successful in white magical art. The people call these experts *kamu epi me* (lit.: "a man who knows white magic").[14]

Kego tai is the use of magical power to kill another Kapauku. Sorcerers (*kego epi me*) are feared, hated, ostracized, and sometimes executed by the relatives of their supposed victims.

Azande distinctions Among the Azande of Africa, described by Evans-Pritchard, good magic is *wene ngua* and bad magic is *gbigbita*. Vengeance magic (*bagbuduma*) may be legitimately used to kill a person if the poison oracles used by the sorcerer's kin and those used by their chief both say the alleged sorcerer is guilty. *Pe zunga* magic, which may be used when the perpetrator of homicidal sorcery is not known, is also good. "It is regarded as a judge which seeks out the person who is responsible for the death, and as an executioner which slays him." In the words of the Azande, "It decides cases" and "settles cases as judiciously as princes." Even though its

[14] L. Pospisil, *The Kapauku Papuans of West New Guinea,* p. 79.

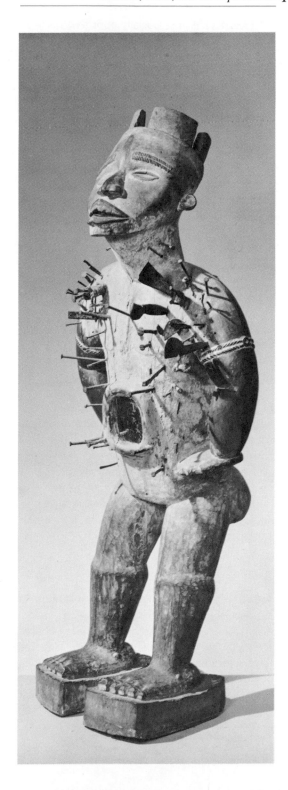

Fig. 32-3   This Bakongo magical figure has a box in its abdomen which is sealed by a mirror that reflects the sun and thus drives off malevolent spirits. The nails are driven into the figure to seal an agreement, to drive out pain at the part of the body where the nail is driven (magic), or to harm an enemy (sorcery). The figure can be used for any of these purposes. (Courtesy of The Brooklyn Museum.)

effect is to kill, it is socially approved because it will work only on behalf of a just cause. If there is no just cause, it will return to kill the person who evoked it. The Zande who wants to kill another without just cause can use a number of forms of *gbigbita* magic, but if he is discovered, he will be executed.[15]

Trobriand usages Among the Trobriand Islanders, chiefs had the power, before the days of Australian administration, to order the execution of social upstarts for being too successful as gardeners, wearing personal ornaments reserved only for chiefs, over-decorating their houses, or boasting and behaving in an unseemly manner in the presence of a chief. Chiefs have not been permitted to execute people for these reasons in recent years, and Malinowski found during his field-work that, instead, they were employing sorcerers to do the job secretly. The magician was a royal executioner in cases of lese majesty and status breaking.

On the whole, however, sorcery is one kind of cultural substitute for centralized legal authority in the settlement of disputes. Beatrice Whiting has indicated a high statistical correlation between the occurrence of sorcery and the absence of judicial methods of settling disputes, and vice versa.[16] In general, sorcery, because it is by nature antisocial, is also usually punished as an illegal act, and excessive sorcery is treated as a crime.[17]

Tabu

Tabu is the inevitable negative element in supernaturalism. Supernatural power is implicitly dangerous. It is like fire or a heavy charge of electricity. When under control and directed toward desirable ends, it is beneficent. When out of control, it may well be disastrous. Man cannot get along without fire, and yet he must

[15]E. E. Evans-Pritchard, *Witchcraft, Oracles and Magic among the Azande*, pp. 388–389.
[16]B. B. Whiting, *Paiute Sorcery*, pp. 86ff.
[17]See E. A. Hoebel, *The Law of Primitive Man*, chap. 10, "Religion, Magic, and Law," pp. 257–274.

fight a constant battle against it. Modern civilization cannot function without electricity, but electricity must be handled with insulated tools and gloves.

Spirits and mana are deemed by most people to be absolutely essential forces in the human conception of the universe. They must be manipulated for human ends, but if improperly approached or used, they can backfire most dangerously. Running Water, the Bannock Indian, was nearly killed by his own pack-rat medicine because he became careless.

Supernatural power, it must be remembered, is above the realm of the ordinary. Because of this, it may not be approached or dealt with casually. It, too, must be handled with rubber gloves. Figuratively, tabus are great "Caution! Handle with Care!" signs. Tabu does not mean *verboten*, in the German sense. Rather, it carries the overtones of the French *défense de toucher*. The sense of awe that Professor Lowie saw as the important component of religion is intimately linked to the psychology that is responsible for the development of tabus.

In content, tabu consists of a series of negative rules, each of which states a form of behavior that will cause a supernatural power to backfire and injure the user. In reality, very few tabued acts are physically or socially dangerous in themselves. This is why rationalistic attempts to explain the Hebraic or Islamic tabus on the eating of pork in terms of hygiene are really beside the point.

Typical of the irrelevance of most tabus was the injunction that went with the war bonnet of the famous Cheyenne chieftain, Roman Nose. His bonnet had the power to give invulnerability in battle. With it Roman Nose rose, unscathed, to fame on the Western Plains. One of the rules of the bonnet was that its wearer must not eat any food taken from a dish with an iron utensil. If he did, a bullet or iron-tipped arrow could pierce him, just as the sharp metal pierced the meat, and the protective power of the hat would be nullified until restored through a long and elaborate ceremony of purification and atonement.

Just before the famous Beecher's Island fight with Colonel Forsyth's men on the Republican River of western Nebraska, in 1868, Roman Nose ate as a guest in the camp of the Sioux Indians. When it was pointed out to him that the wife of his host was using a fork in her cooking, he said, "That breaks my medicine." The battle began before Roman Nose could make atonement, so, like Achilles, he sulked in his tent. But under pressure, like Achilles, he donned his war gear, saying, "My food was lifted with an iron tool. I know that I shall be killed today." Roman Nose was killed by a bullet before he had a chance to strike a single blow in the battle.[18]

Violation of a tabu not only nullifies the positive power of medicine but may also bring disaster as a consequence.

The functions of tabu The first function of tabu, as just indicated, is to sustain the awesomeness of the supernatural by reinforcing attitudes of care and mystery and by punishing attidues of carelessness and profanity in dealing with the supernatural. It helps keep the sacred, sacred.

The second function of tabu is to set off the members of one social group from those of another and to strengthen their sense of solidarity. Just as a traditional hairdo may indicate that the social status of a married woman is different from that of an unmarried girl who has only reached puberty, or as men's hairdos set them apart from women, so adherence to special tabus may help set off the medicine man from the ordinary layman. Thus the Hebraic and Islamic tabus on pork help to identify membership in these religious groups, as did abstinence from meat on Friday by Catholics and as does the Mormon tabu on the use of tobacco and the drinking of coffee, tea, or alcoholic beverages.

Third, tabu is an essential ingredient of social control. In Polynesia, whence comes the word "tabu," high-ranking nobles possess mana because of their direct descent from the

Fig. 32-4 Masked impersonators of supernatural beings standing before the men's tribal fraternity club house of the Urama tribe, Papua, New Guinea. With ritual dance and incantation they tabu the fruit trees which are dedicated to produce food for fraternity ceremonies. (Courtesy of the American Museum of Natural History.)

gods. So potent is their charge of mana that their very persons are surrounded with tabus, as is everything they touch. Sin, in Polynesia as elsewhere, is the violation of a tabu—an act punishable by supernatural sanction.

Not only is tabu applied to the requirements of care in handling supernatural objects, but it also can be, and is, applied to social standards of behavior which are not directly associated with the supernatural but in which, it is held, the supernatural takes an interest.[19] Incest, for example, is commonly

[18]A thrilling account of the whole fight is given in G. B. Grinnell, *The Fighting Cheyennes*, pp. 267–282.

[19]For an excellent example, see A. I. Hallowell, "The Social Function of Anxiety among the Salteaux Indians," in D. Haring (ed.), *Personality and Cultural Milieu* (3d revised edition), pp. 389–403.

subject to supernatural punishment as well as to mundane social sanctions, in most societies.

Folklore and mythology

Folklore and mythology embrace much more than just religion, for they encompass all the oral traditions of a people. Tales are often quite secular and make few supernatural assumptions. Yet most of the spoken traditions of primitive peoples are suffused with animistic beliefs and are thoroughly imbued with supernaturalism. Although some folklore may be separated from religion, religion is never divorced from folklore and myth. The origins of spirit beings, their qualities, and their activities are commonly given literary expression in tales colored with high drama and imaginative appeal.

The questing mind of man has always asked the eternal "Why?" The creative minds of artists have always spun a literary web of answers in words and ideas. The human animal does not submit supinely either to the harsh demands of the physical world or to the ever-pressing demands of his society and its culture-bound limitations of individual freedom. Reasons are demanded. Reasons are given.

Myth in general is more than idle speculation about the origins of things. "It justifies by precedent the existing order and it supplies a retrospective pattern of moral values, of sociological discriminations and burdens and of magical belief. . . . The myth of magic [of religion, or of any other body of customs or single custom] is definitely a warrant of its truth, a pedigree of its filiation, a charter of its claims to validity."[20] Myth believing is more than infantile self-deception; it is also social reassurance—a device of education and learning, of culture maintenance.

Although primitive mythology is rich in variety, it is truly remarkable how stable the solid core of basic myths is, the world over. It would seem that the fundamental myths strike right to the roots of the questions of what man is, how he came to be, why there is life and death, and why there is evil—and good. Once developed by primitive literary philosophers, refined and shaped through generations of telling and retelling, their appeal became so elemental that they spread smoothly and quickly from primitive hearth to primitive hearth, until the whole world was girdled with a pristine web of common stories. So it is that the Scandinavian scholar Olrik speaks the experience of all students of primitive and civilized folklore when he writes: "Everyone who deals with folk-literature has had the experience that when he reads compositions from widely different peoples he has a feeling of recognition, even when the particular group and its world of folktales has thus far been unknown to him."[21] It is for this reason that Sir James Frazer was able to show in a fascinating book, *Folklore in the Old Testament,* the ancient and primitive common heritage of many of the primeval tales of the ancient Hebrew tribe inscribed in the Bible. The Creation, the Flood, the Fall of Man, the Mark of Cain, the Tower of Babel, and many others are part of a worldwide heritage of ancient myth, part religious and part secular.

Folktale, legend, and myth are the timeless handmaidens of religion and magic. They are also the fertile seedbeds from which grew the sacred books of the great religions of later civilizations.

SUMMARY

Religion and magic are two manifestations of supernaturalism. What constitutes the supernatural varies from culture to culture, but in essence it is the quality of the extraordinary in the phenomena of the universe. Religion and magic consist subjectively of belief in the existence of the supernatural and objectively of ways of dealing with it. The distinction be-

[20]B. Malinowski, "Culture" (*Encyclopedia of the Social Sciences,* Vol. 4, 1937), p. 640.

[21]Quoted in S. Thompson, *The Folktale,* p. 456. This book summarizes myth motifs for the Old World. See his *Tales of the North American Indians* for those of this continent.

tween magic and religion is drawn in terms of the attitudes and practices of the believer. The religious person acknowledges his inferiority to spirit beings; the magician believes he has mastered a supernatural force through the possession of a compulsive formula.

According to the theory of Tylor, the belief in the existence of spirit beings (animism) developed as a psychological rationalization of dreams and was applied to the explanation of otherwise not understood occurrences. Mana is, however, supernatural power not embodied in, or derived from, spirit beings.

Supernaturalism permeates primitive cultures and all civilizations. It is unique with human beings, and it is, at the same time, a universal feature of culture.

Tabu is the negative aspect of supernaturalism, which functions to stress the sacredness of the supernatural, reinforce the process of social control, and enhance the sense of group uniqueness and social solidarity.

Folklore and mythology add a literary expression to religious beliefs.

SELECTED READINGS

Evans-Pritchard, E. E.: *Nuer Religion* (1956). A penetrating field study of the concept and role of supernatural forces in a culture that lacks dogma, liturgy, sacraments (in a strict sense), and a developed religious cult and mythology.

Goode, W. J.: *Religion among the Primitives* (1951). This book undertakes to scrutinize the interrelations of religion with other aspects of culture.

Howells, W. H.: *The Heathens* (1948). A lively overview of primitive religious practices.

Hsu, F. L. K.: *Religion, Science and Human Crisis* (1952). A case study of the uses of magic, religion, and scientific medicine in the folk response to a cholera epidemic in a Chinese village.

Lessa, W. A., and E. Z. Vogt: *Reader in Comparative Religion* (1958). A very useful source book of writings on a wide range of religions and on the nature of religion.

Lowie, R. H.: *Primitive Religion* (1924). Brief vignettes of several primitive religions, followed by a critical discussion of a number of anthropological theories of religion.

Norbeck, E.: *Religion in Primitive Society* (1961). A concise and well-balanced general introduction to the subject of religion as a social phenomenon.

Wax, M., and R. Wax: "The Notion of Magic" (*Current Anthropology*, Vol. 4, 1963), pp. 495–518. Reading this article in conjunction with the comments on it (pp. 503–517) demonstrates how difficult it is to come to a common agreement on anthropological concepts in the area of religion and magic.

Shamans, priests, and cults

chapter 33

The subjective element of religion and magic is always given external form. Art, as we have seen in an earlier chapter, often transforms the imagined spirit or god into an object of art that can be seen and felt, perhaps even smelled. Religion and magic are also transmuted into dramatic ritual in the form of ceremonial practices and repeated patterns of word, movement, and sound. Belief is reinforced by the dinning of such patterns into the entire receptor and kinesthetic system of each individual member of society.

Ritual as the symbolic expression of social unity

Ritual is the recurring performance of a standardized set of acts in the belief that the acts are necessary to the maintenance of the *status quo* or to the achievement of specified ends. *Ceremony* is a complex of rituals. All religion involves ritual and ceremony, for the subjectivity of belief becomes more compelling when it is made objective. Thus, although ritual may be developed for many nonreligious occasions, religion is particularly prone to ceremonial elaboration. All tribal religions are *instrumental:* they aim to get things done, to keep the society in tune with the requirements of the supernatural world, and to influence the workings of the supernatural world in a way that furthers the aspirations of the tribal members.

Much religion is, indeed, a matter of individual experience, such as that of the North American Indian who must seek vision in which a spirit bestows the power of medicine (supernatural power) upon him. Yet all religions build on the participation of the public, if only as spectators, in acts that not only affect the workings of extrahuman forces but also express the solidarity of the group and at the same time internalize group loyalty and commitment to unified social purposes. This was the thesis of Émile Durkheim, Malinowski, and the functionalists. For Durkheim, to whom society was the supreme reality, to explain religion on the basis of dreams, as did Tylor, was to explain a reality by recourse to a fantasy.

Durkheim saw ritual participation as the true essence of religion. Man rises above the humdrum monotony of eking out his living and shares in the ecstasy of sacred experience obtainable only through periodic group dances and ceremonies, such as the *corroborees* of the Australian aborigines. Religion, for Durkheim, is an expression of social solidarity and collective beliefs. Man alone is as nothing. He realizes his significance and worth only as a member of a social group. Sacred rituals and beliefs symbolize society. *N'est-ce-pas que le dieu et la société ne font qu'un?*

Durkheim's interpretation of the nature and function of religion may be extreme. Nevertheless, he is right in recognizing that ritual and ceremony translate the intangible into the real and felt, cementing the solidarity of the group.

In every primitive society, all the people participate in some aspects of religious observances. Yet, because every society is internally segmented by sex, age, kinship, and marital groupings, access to religious power and the privileges of religious participation are not equally distributed. In the first place, years of experience and learning are necessary before an individual can know enough about basic religious beliefs to be in a position to master religious activities. Children always participate on a lower level.

Religion and magic are sources of power; they are means of influencing or controlling supernatural power, the greatest of all powers. Authority vested in adults is implicitly necessary to the perpetuation of culture. This is a special

reason for keeping the heart of religious power in the hands of grownups.

The centers of religious power are also almost universally vested in men. Male-dominance tendencies lead men to keep access to the supernatural as a vested interest of their own sex. In more advanced, class-stratified societies, formal religious power is almost inevitably an upper-class monopoly.

Shamans

Within the body of those who qualify for religious power, there are those who achieve an even more intimate access to the supernatural. They become religious specialists. Religion and magic are always so complex and, by their very nature so extraordinary that the layman who is wrapped up in the day-to-day activities of making a living cannot penetrate very far into the realm of the sacred. To do this, a person must spend time away from the basic tasks of food production and must have an unusual personality and special aptitudes and skills. The men who have the time and the skills may become religious functionaries: shamans or priests. The shaman is the more primitive type of specialist. He exists in systems in which religion has not developed a church. *The shaman derives his presumptive power directly from a supernatural source,* either through mystic experience or through his ability to perform rites and his possession of paraphernalia as an individual. *The power of priests is derived from their office in a cult or church.*

Siberian shamanism A center of the most intensive development of shamanism in the primitive world is aboriginal Siberia. The very word "shaman" comes from a native Siberian tongue. Synonyms also meaning "shaman" are "medicine man" (usually applied to American Indians), "witch doctor" (usually applied to shamans of Africa and Melanesia), and *angakok*, in Eskimo.

The Siberian shaman is more definitely set off from his fellow men than his North American counterpart is. For one thing, his personality is more clearly marked. For another, his "call" and training are more definite. Bogoras, the famous Siberianist, wrote of the Chukchi:

For men, the preparatory stage of shamanistic inspiration is in most cases very painful, and extends over a long time. The call comes in an abrupt and obscure manner, leaving the young novice in much uncertainty regarding it. He feels "bashful" and frightened. . . . The young novice, the "newly inspired," loses all interest in the ordinary affairs of life. He ceases to work, takes little food and without relishing it, ceases to talk to people, does not even answer their questions. The greater part of his time he spends in sleep.[1]

Bogoras observed that shamans were as a rule excitable and hysterical. He even opined that not a few of them were "half crazy." Psychiatry was not the vogue in Bogoras's day or he would have attached the label "schizophrenic" to the personality of the Siberian shaman.

Becoming a shaman   The personal experience of a Northern Paiute Indian, who lived in western Nevada, is more or less typical of the way in which an American medicine man received power. As recorded by Willard Park, it runs as follows:

When I was a young man I had dreams in which I doctored people. I did not take those dreams seriously. My uncle was an Indian doctor. He knew what was coming to me. He told me to be careful in talking, not to speak harshly (in order not to offend the supernatural spirits). I did not become a doctor from these dreams. Finally, I decided to go to the cave near Dayton. I was about fifty then. My uncle did not tell me to go there. I just decided to do this myself.

I went into the cave in the evening. As soon as I got inside, I prayed and asked for power to doctor sickness. I said, "My people are sick. I want to save them. I want to keep them well. You can help me make them well. I want you to help me to save them. When they have died give me power to bring them back [return the lost soul]." I said this to the spirit in the cave. It is not a person. It comes along with the darkness. This is a prayer to the night.

Then I tried to go to sleep. It was hard to sleep there. I heard all kinds of noises. I could hear all the animals. There were bears, mountain lions, deer, and other animals. They were all in caves in the mountain. After I went to sleep I could hear people at a doctoring. They were down at the foot of the mountain. I could hear their voices and the songs. Then I heard the patient groan. A doctor was singing and doctoring for him. A woman with a sage-brush shoot in her hand danced. She moved around the fire jumping at every step. Each time she jumped she said, "hə,' hə,' hə'." Then the shaman sprinkled water on the patient with sage-brush. The singing and dancing went on for a long time. Then the singing stopped. The patient had died and the people began to cry.

After a while the rock where I was sleeping began to crack like breaking ice. A man appeared in the crack. He was tall and thin. He had the tail-feather of an eagle in his hand. He said to me, "You are here. You have said the right words. You must do as I tell you. Do that or you will have a hard time. When you doctor, you must follow the instructions that the animals give you. They will tell you how to cure the sickness. I have this feather in my hand. You must get feathers like it. You are also to find the things that go with it. Get dark beads. Put them on the quills of the feathers and tie a strip of buckskin to the quills. Also get a hoof of a deer, and down from the eagle. With these you can go to people to cure them. These are your weapons against sickness. You must get three rolls of tobacco. You can use them to tell your patients what made them sick and then you can cure them. The tobacco will also help you if you are choked with clots of saliva when you suck out the disease. With this you are beginning to be a doctor. You will get your songs when you doctor. The songs are now in a straight line [ready for use]. Bathe in the water at the foot of the cliff and paint yourself with *i • bi* [white paint]."

Then I woke up. It was daylight. I looked around but I could not see anyone. The man was gone and there was no sign of the animals or the people who had been singing and doctoring. Then I did as the spirit had ordered and waited to become a doctor. In about six years I had received enough instructions to begin to cure.[2]

Another more or less typical way of becoming a shaman is described by Barton, concerning female shamans among the Ifugao:

[1]W. Bogoras, "The Chukchee: I, Religion" (*Jesup North Pacific Expedition*, Vol. 7), p. 420.

[2]W. Z. Park, *Shamanism in Western North America*, pp. 27–28.

The priesthood [shamanism] is almost entirely in the hands of women. Entry into it is always in answer to a ''call'' and is, in a sense, compulsory: the woman begins to sleep badly, has many dreams, grows thin, lacks appetite, believes that her soul has married an *anitu*[3] and that she can extricate herself from the condition only by becoming a priestess (*mangaalisig*). Or she may become conscious of the call from getting a stomach upset after she has eaten foods that are taboo to priestesses: eel, dog, certain fish, meat of the cow (but not carabao). She is said to be taught the rituals by the gods themselves, not by the older priestesses. But, of course, she has been watching and hearing these since she was a little girl and wondering whether fate would ever call her to be a priestess when she grew older.[4]

Suggestibility and a greater or lesser degree of emotional instability are essential traits of the shaman who obtains power by mystic experience. He or she must be capable of hallucinations. The person who cannot respond with visions and hallucinations to the pervading cultural suggestion that these form the road to power is out of luck if he would be a shaman. Crashing Thunder, a Winnebago Indian, was one of these. Even when he faked a vision and luck seemed to confirm his power, he knew in his inner self that his power was false. An extrovert whose aggressive personality demanded social prestige and the opportunity to amount to something, he was frustrated by his intellectual hardheadedness. Not finding the social means (supernatural power) to greatness open to him, he took the antisocial road—drunkenness, rowdyism, debauchery, murder, and fraud. Then when peyote at last reached the Winnebagos, the vision-stimulating drug brought visions and power to the tortured man. With power came the reorientation of his personality. He became a pillar of society, a moral leader, and a decent citizen—much to the relief of his fellow tribesmen.[5]

The evidence is clear that as far as becoming a spirit-endowed shaman is concerned, the odds favor those who belong to what we would unkindly call the ''lunatic fringe.'' But the cultures of these people turn their peculiarities to account and make honored medicine men and women of them.

Shamanistic magic The shaman, as inheritor of magical power, is a different matter. True, the magician is the dupe of his own beliefs, but it is possible for him to work with cold calculation. Highly developed magic often involves sheer fraud, skill in prestidigitation, and the creation of optical illusions. Siberian and Eskimo shamans are skilled ventriloquists, using their tambourines so to deflect their voices that the listeners ''after a few minutes . . . begin to lose the power to locate the source of the sound. . . . The song and drum seem to shift from corner to corner, or even to move about without having any definite place at all.''[6]

The Algonquian Indian medicine man holds impressive séances in which the tent rocks and pitches violently upon the arrival of his ''spirit.'' The tent is cleverly constructed to be manipulated mechanically with ropes and thongs.[7]

Pueblo Indian priests put on miracle dramas in which corn grows and ripens overnight and deer and bears materialize before the astounded eyes of uninitiated spectators. Some *kivas* are equipped with the secret tunnels through which the props and actors are brought upon the scene.[8]

However, the deceit practiced by shamans may not always be such crass charlatanism as it at first appears. Eskimo shamans often disclaim their own skill, as did one of the best of them to Peter Freuchen: ''This is nothing for a man like you to look at. I am only a big liar, and even if these idiots are stupid enough

---

[3]Soul of a deceased person.

[4]R. F. Barton, *The Kalingas*, p. 24. The calling of a Yurok girl to shamanhood is portrayed in ''The Reluctant Shaman,'' in *The Ways of Mankind*, Series II.

[5]P. Radin (ed.), *Crashing Thunder*. This book should not be missed by any student of anthropology.

[6]Bogoras, *op. cit.*, p. 430.

[7]F. Densmore, ''An Explanation of a Trick Performed by Indian Jugglers'' (*American Anthropologist*, Vol. 34, 1932), pp. 310–314.

[8]E. A. Hoebel, ''Underground Kiva Passages'' (*American Antiquity*, Vol. 19, 1953), p. 76; and F. H. Hawley, ''Jemez Kiva Magic and Its Relation to Features of Prehistoric Kivas'' (*Southwestern Journal of Anthropology*, Vol. 8, 1952), pp. 147–163.

to believe me, I never expected you to stand for it. I am a foolish old man, and what happens here has nothing to do with the truth."[9] But the effect of his performance on the people in the iglu was ecstasy. People are not averse to being fooled if it gives pleasure. Beyond that, of course, credulous ones are duped without their being the wiser.

It is difficult to draw an accurate balance between the exploitative and the social-service activities of the primitive shamans. It is a false gesture to dismiss them solely as a class of exploiters. Yet it is true that they often turn their position and power to self-advantage. Eskimo shamans can impose almost any tabus they wish on individuals. They can sexually exploit women, married and unmarried, to gratify themselves in the name of spirits. Shamans can use their power particularly to consolidate the position of the elders as against the younger generation. But for this they must pay a price in self-denial of many things, for their work is dangerous in its own terms, and the burden of shamanism is often hard.

Priests

Priesthood is a manifestation of developed religion. It occurs in the more ordered primitive societies whose cultures are rich and complex. On the whole, it calls for an economic base of sufficient richness to support fairly large populations, plus some food and wealth surpluses. It is necessary to be able to organize and sustain permanent cults. The priest may have mana, but his power is less his own than the power resident in the office he holds. Unlike the shaman, he does not acquire his sacredness personally. He is vested in his succession to the *office* of priest. He becomes part of a religious corporation.

There are basically two kinds of priests: (1) the family heads in ancestor-worshiping religions who serve as priestly intermediaries between the kinship group and the deceased ancestors and (2) the priests who serve cult

groups whose interests are directed toward special spirits or deities.

Incipient priesthood is revealed in Gulliver's account of a Jie rainmaking ceremony:

At a ritual assembly, supplications are made by a leader, supported by the chorus of the other men present. The seniormost man present, holding a ritual wand, stands in the open space inside the cluster of seated men; he addresses *Akuj* [the High God] directly, explaining the reason for the assembly and seeking benevolent assistance. Interspersed in the monologue are communal supplications led by the standing man, in which his specific pleas . . . are echoed by the others' chorus. After the seniormost man, other seniors in turn take up the leadership. When a man begins to assume this role with the approval of his more senior associates he has achieved notable seniority [which includes the priestly role].[10]

It should be added that to achieve seniority and priesthood, he must have power from the High God, too.

Although in many primitive cultures there is a recognized division of function between priests and shamans, in the more highly developed cultures in which cults have become strongly organized churches, the priesthood fights an unrelenting war against shamans. Priests work in a rigorously structured hierarchy fixed in a firm set of traditions. Their power comes from, and is vested in, the organization itself. They constitute a religious bureaucracy. Shamans, on the other hand, are arrant individualists. Each is on his own, undisciplined by bureaucratic control; hence, a shaman is always a threat to the order of the organized church. In the view of the priests, they are presumptive pretenders. Joan of Arc was a shaman, for she communed directly with the angels of God. She steadfastly refused to recant and admit delusion, and her martyrdom at the stake was ordained by the functionaries of the church. The struggle between shaman and priest may well be a death struggle.

Priestesses are much less common than female shamans, probably because the orga-

[9]P. Freuchen, *Arctic Adventure*, p. 113.

[10]P. H. Gulliver, "The Jie of Uganda," in J. L. Gibbs, Jr. (ed.), *Peoples of Africa*, p. 188.

nization of associations tends to be correlated almost exclusively with the male sex in primitive societies.

Ancestor worship and cults of the dead

Ancestor worship is by no means a universal form of religious expression, although belief in the spiritual immortality of the dead is. All cultures call for cognizance of ghosts, and all provide some means of dealing with them. The intensity of ghost awareness, however, and the amount of concern over the activity and feelings of ghosts are variable. In North America, the Pueblo Indians pay little attention to ghosts; the Plains Indians fear them, but their ghosts are not too prevalent; and the Navahos and Eskimos are bedeviled by ghost anxiety. They possess definite ghost cults, a body of practices and ritual observances associated with the propitiation or avoidance of ghosts.

Most Plains Indians and the Navahos abandon any house in which a person has died. The ghost haunts the house and disturbs the inhabitants. Navahos, therefore, take a seriously ill patient who is about to die outdoors in order to save the house, or they rush him to the Indian Service Hospital, which is already heavily inhabited by ghosts. The Arizona desert is dotted with hogans abandoned because a death has occurred within. One of the author's Shoshone friends dismantled a log house that he had inherited from his brother, moved it a few hundred feet, and then reassembled it, after mixing up the logs to fool the ghost of his brother, who is now unable to recognize the new house. Ghost fear has long been a hindrance to Indian Service efforts to provide modern housing on some reservations. In the northern Plains, a workable expedient acceptable to the Indians in some places has been the fumigation of the house as an effective antidote to ghosts.

Eskimos believe that ghosts are harmful and relentlessly malicious as long as they remain in the memory of the living. On death, the corpse is not removed from the iglu by way of the door; this would make it too easy

Fig. 33-1 A Congolese female shaman in a state of spirit possession. (Belgian Government Information Center.)

Fig. 33-2 An Alaskan Eskimo shamanistic mask representative of the moon spirit during the half-moon phase. (Courtesy of the University Museum, Philadelphia.)

for the lingering ghost to reenter. Rather, a hole is chopped in the back, later to be refilled after removal of the body. This baffles the ghost. Then, in case the ghost does find the entrance, knives are set in the snow floor of the doorway for three nights after burial. Such booby traps discourage ghosts. Among Eskimos, as with many other people, the name of the dead is tabued, lest it summon the reappearance of the ghost. Later, the name is given to a newborn child, reincarnating the name soul of the deceased ancestor.

Comanches also tabu names of the dead, but when they want to mention a defunct friend named Pork, for example, they call him Bacon. Ghosts are literal-minded, but people can get the idea.

Eskimos, like many other people, bury the dead with grave offerings—the personal equipment and gifts of friends and relatives to serve the ghost in the other world. These are "killed." They are broken to release the animate soul of the object. For it is the spiritual counterpart of the goods that obviously is used in the spirit world.

Plains Indians also sacrificed a warrior's favorite horse on his grave, as did medieval Europeans at times. This is no longer Occidental practice, but the officer's horse led behind the casket-bearing caisson with reversed saddle and upturned stirrups still follows the hero to his grave, only to be spared the final sacrifice.

Grave sacrifices were stepped up to extravagant heights for the royalty of Africa and India. Into the nineteenth century, Hindu wives were immolated on the funeral pyres of their princely husbands. In Dahomey in West Africa, whole corps of wives and retainers were slain to provide an adequate retinue for the deceased king. Shoshone and Comanche tradition has it that in ancient times, wives were killed to accompany their husbands' spirits, but in more recent days, the wives followed the general Plains Indian practice of self-mutilation and abnegation.

Ghost cults usually, but not always, empha-

size the malevolence of ghosts. Manus in Melanesia is an exception. The ghost of the last deceased household head is the preceptor and protector of his family. He punishes their moral derelictions, but above all he is busy thwarting the malignant efforts of other ghosts. All ghosts are malicious toward people not of their own kinship group. The social and economic rivalry that is characteristic of everyday Manus life continues in the afterworld through the jealousy and rivalry of the ghosts. Each family enjoys a brief span of immortal existence while his skull adorns the doorway of his family hut. But the death of an adult male in the household is an indication that the family ghost has not been on the job. He has been negligent enough to permit a rival ghost to kill his descendant. He is no good. Therefore his skull is thrown out and replaced by that of his successor, who then rules as the Honored Ghost of the household, until he, too, fails in his duty.[11]

Ancestor cults Ancestor worship is both an elaboration and an abstraction of the ghost cult. As an elaboration, it is best seen among the Bantu tribes of Africa. Every lineage and clan has its distinct ancestral deities, who are gods to their descendants but who are ignored by the members of other kinship groups. The gods of royal clans, because the heads of such clans must be honored by all the kingdom, are worshiped not only by the royal clan itself but also by all the subjects of the king. In ancestor-worshiping cults of this order, the eldest ranking member of the kinship group is not only its headman but also its priest. He stands nearest to the ancestral gods. He is the intercessor on behalf of his kinsmen. On the gods' behalf, he is the intermediary who is responsible for controlling the acts of his family or clan members. As in modern Japan, he has to keep the ancestral gods informed of the state of affairs within his

[11] R. F. Fortune, *Manus Religion* (Proceedings of the American Philosophical Society, 1935); M. Mead, "The Manus of the Admiralty Islands," in *Cooperation and Competition among Primitive Peoples*, pp. 210–239.

domain. The Mikado has merely to make a ceremonial report at the ancestral shrine, but in Dahomey in West Africa, it was customary to execute a couple of victims to carry the royal message to the ancestors whenever the king had anything of moment to report.

Periodic elaborate feasts and sacrifices on behalf of the ancestral gods are characteristic of the western Sudan. In Dahomey, such ceremonies are held by each clan every year, with litanies, dancing, offerings of food and libations of liquors, and sacrifice of animals. In the annual ceremonies of the royal clan, human victims used to be offered.

Voodoo *Vodun,*[12] among West Indies Negroes, is nothing more than a syncretism of Dahomean ancestral rites and Catholicism.[13] The clan founders of Dahomey are known as *tovodun,* from whom the *vodun* cult is named. Vodun

Fig. 33-3   The Barong dance of Bali, Indonesia. The dance drama of The Witch and the Dragon performed before a Hindu temple. The king has sent his followers to destroy a witch who is devastating the country with disease and death. She magically overpowers them. In a wild state of trance they turn their daggers against their own breasts in utter frustration. Eventually they collapse in a catatonic sleeping trance from which they are released by a priest who sprinkles them with purifying water. (Henri Cartier-Bresson, Magnum.)

rites are fundamentally family rituals with offerings and sacrifices accompanied by chants and dances, in which various gods are impersonated and called upon to visit the ceremony. Dancers representative of specific gods are possessed in turn as each god is called with his drum *salute* (greeting). The trance behavior of the votaries and the ecstasy of the worshipers lend the eerie wildness to the performance that has given vodun its exotic reputation.

Ancestor worship as an abstraction of ghost worship occurs where gods are thought once

[12] *Vodun* is the phonetically correct name for the cult complex popularly called *voodoo.*

[13] See M. J. Herskovits, "African Gods and Catholic Saints in New World Negro Belief" (*American Anthropologist,* Vol. 39, 1937), pp. 635–643; G. E. Simpson, "The Vodun Service in Northern Haiti" (*American Anthropologist,* Vol. 42, 1940), pp. 236–254.

Fig. 33-4   A revered ancestral head from the Sepik River area of Papua, New Guinea. (Courtesy of The Brooklyn Museum.)

to have been human beings but where the more recently deceased are not believed to be potent deities. This may be said to be true of Polynesian and Pueblo Indian religions. Maori chieftains are lineal descendants of gods through primogeniture. Honor is due these gods, but there is no cult of the dead. The masked gods, *kachinas,* of the Pueblos are vaguely thought of as ancestral beings, but dead ancestors are not worshiped as such.

Social conservatism is a characteristic feature of ancestor-worshiping religions. The ancestors as moral preceptors do not favor change from the social practices they knew as men. Since they punish moral lapses with death and illness and their standards are the old ones, the religious sanctions toward conformity are powerful.

Nature worship

Cults deifying various features of nature abound in the primitive world. Among agricultural and gardening peoples, sun, rain, and fertility deities are outstanding. Solstitial rites marked the annual crisis of the sun in the religion of the megalith builders of Neolithic

Europe. Mysterious Stonehenge and Avebury in England and the cromlechs of Carnac in Brittany are aligned to the rising sun at the time of the spring solstice, as is the sun stone in the famous Sun Temple of Mesa Verde National Park, built by prehistoric Pueblo Indians 700 years ago. In ancient Rome, the solstice rites of the Mithraic cult gave way to the Christian Christmas celebration of the birth of Christ as the new light of the world. Each pueblo in the Southwest today has its priestly sunwatcher, who controls the ceremonial cycle with the movements of the sun. Pious people greet the sun with prayer each day.

All the religions in the great Central American culture complex made much of the sun. The Pyramid of the Sun near Mexico City is one of the truly great monuments of all the world. The Natchez of Mississippi and the Incas of Peru built theocratic states around the principle of sun divinity. The Natchez high chief was also high priest, called the Sun, or brother of the Sun. The Inca of Peru was the personification of the divine sun. And until the disaster of 1945 induced the Emperor of Japan to deny it by imperial edict, he was supposed to be a divinity directly descended from the mythical sun goddess Amaterasu.

The sun figured greatly in Plains Indian religion. All tipis opened east, and tribal camp circles likewise. By the nineteenth century, the midsummer sun dance had come to be one of the most spectacular of Plains ceremonials.[14]

Although the sun looms large in the mythologies of the peoples of the Pacific area, it does not assume importance as an actual deity. This is true also of Africa and most of North America. Ancient Europe, the countries of the Mediterranean basin, and India were the great seats of sun worship.

In Africa and Polynesia, although the sun is not glorified, nature worship is not neglected. The entire universe is departmentalized among gods of the skies, earth, waters, trees, and

[14]See G. A. Dorsey, "The Cheyenne, II, The Sun Dance" (*Field Columbian Museum, Publication 103, Anthropological Series,* Vol. 9, No. 2, 1905) for a good description of a typical sun dance with many illustrations. Volume 16 of the *Anthropological Papers of the American Museum of Natural History* contains descriptions of other tribal sun dances.

thunder, with myriads of subdivisions among the specialized deities. On the less-than-god levels, all primitive religions include multitudes of nature spirits associated with particular spots, trees, volcanoes, mountains, rivers, lakes, and rocks.

To primitive man, the whole world lives. Souls, animate things, and whatsoever embodies the soul are spirit beings to be treated with religion or magic—or both.

Fetishism

When a material object is believed to possess mana or to be possessed by a spirit being, and when it is venerated or cherished because of this, it is a fetish. Because of its imputed value, it receives special attention and care, and it is this attribute that leads to our popular phrase "to make a fetish of something." The word is derived from the Latin word *facticius,* meaning "amulet," by way of the Portuguese *feitiço,* after the use of the word by the Portuguese adventurers, who first met with it in their voyages along the west coast of Africa.

Fetishes are symbolic repositories of supernatural power, and they serve the psychological function of objectifying the belief. They are a rallying point for faith, a visual stimulant to belief.

Fetishes may be simple or precious stones, implements, trees, mountains, or often art objects endowed with power. It is commonly recognized that art receives much stimulus from the attempt to express religious belief in concrete form. However, mere art as such is not *ipso facto* fetishistic. As Lowie comments:

> . . . [The representation of a human figure] "is not an effective fetish until it has been through the hands of the medicine-man and received its power from him." What confers upon the object its supernatural potency is solely the mysterious spell sung over it or the substance, wonder-working in its own right like the *ngula* paint, thrust into a ventral cavity. Hence, only a moderate percentage of the human or animal figurines are in reality fetishes. . . . Any object can become a "fetish" if only it has been ritualistically consecrated.[15]

[15]R. H. Lowie, *Primitive Religion,* p. 269.

Fig. 33-5   Mandan Indians in their earthlodge village on the upper Missouri River watching a droughtbreaker make rain. (Courtesy of the American Museum of Natural History.)

The High God concept

The time has passed when informed civilized men could think the primitive mind incapable of conceiving of a Supreme Being or High God. Tylor's greatest error was to infer that the High God concept could be only the end product of a long intellectual evolution, beginning with the soul concept and leading through ghost and ancestor worship to polytheistic nature worship and on to monotheism.[16]

Andrew Lang, (1844–1912), before the turn of this century, proved that Australian, Polynesian, African, and American Indian notions of the High God were not derived from Christian teachings.[17] The indefatigable Austrian anthropologist Wilhelm Schmidt (1868–1954) has confirmed it with his stupendous four-volume work, *Der Ursprung der Gottesidee.*[18]

The essential beliefs of primitive men concerning the High God are that he is the original creator of the world; that the world as he made it was good; that he is not a spirit being

[16]E. B. Tylor, *Primitive Culture.*
[17]A. Lang, *The Making of Religion.*
[18]See W. Schmidt, *The Origin and Growth of Religion,* pp. 167–217, a condensed version of Schmidt's thesis.

(in the usual sense); and that he is nonanthropomorphic and nonnatural, lives in the sky remote from earthly affairs, has retired from active participation in daily events (is otiose), and is on the whole unapproachable and disinterested. Because of this, there is little ritual and cult ceremonial directed in his favor. Temples are not raised to him, no sacrifices are given (except offerings of first fruits), and prayers are offered only infrequently and by few people.

In cosmological lore, his acts of creation are generally only vaguely conceived. Myth tells how he created departmental, executive subdeities charged with the responsibility for filling in the details of creation and running the universe. These are the gods men must appease and pray to. They are the ones who deliver or withhold the goods. Evil in life is due to their perversity or maliciousness. A common counterpart of the High God is a Trickster or Transformer, like Coyote among the Western American Indians, who spoils or modifies the good work of the creator to burden man with death, sin, and travail. The Trickster is the equivalent of the serpent in the Garden of Eden.

Lang felt that the formulation of the High God concept was a consequence of contemplative religious thought. The corruption of this idealism and the creation of the less pure deities he conceived as due to a "myth-making mood" and "the Old Adam" in man—his unsocial desire to obtain advantage over his fellow men. In this the Supreme Being is too ethical to lend a hand; hence, ghosts, spirits, and corruptible gods were formulated in playful and erratic fantasy, which is irrational and debases the gods. Thus, to Lang, when early primitive man was in an elevated mood, he was capable of rational philosophic thought. Yet man also expressed his baser mood of selfish desire to elaborate the pantheisms of the savage world.

Civilized religious reformers have struggled long to suppress the supremacy of the second religious mood, striving to reestablish the Supreme Deity in absolute and undefiled dominance.

The Islamic, Hebrew, and Christian concepts

of God are of this order. But the God concept is still corrupted by petty claims for personal and tribal (national) favor by people who are considered civilized.

Paul Radin (1885–1963) modified Lang's notions in a way worth noting.[19] He abjured the notion of an original purity of the High God later corrupted. Instead, he posited two contrasting types of human mentality, idealist and realist. Idealists are men of intellectual and reflective temperament, men whom anthropological experience has shown to be present in small numbers among all peoples. They philosophize on the conundrum of life and the universe. Their thought seeks a direct, unified, orderly cause in explanation of the universe. The product of their thought is the Supreme Being. As idealists, they are little concerned with crass, material desires. Their god is free from the petty demands of men.

Pospisil's description of Kapauku religious ideology states Radin's case exactly:

Most of the Kapauku people do not ponder the nature of life and the universe around them. They are empiricists who are not inclined to speculate and philosophize. The topics that interest them do not concern the supernatural or metaphysics; indeed, they usually talk about such unphilosophical subjects as contemporary power relations, concrete monetary transactions, love affairs, or news concerning pig feasts and dancing. Philosophizing they leave to the few especially gifted individuals who make it their hobby to try to penetrate the nature of things beyond the barrier imposed by the human senses. Accordingly, the systematic and logically consistent philosophy that is described next is by no means the property of the Kapauku tribe as a whole; it belongs to a few very intelligent individuals from the southern part of the Kamu Valley who have elaborated their views of the universe into a logical systematic whole.[20]

The bulk of men, alas, are materialists. Their bellies, their health, wealth, and social power mean much to them. They develop religion in terms of gods and spirits, who control the means to satisfy these needs. When prayer, appeasement, and magic suffice to win

[19]P. Radin, *Monotheism in Primitive Religion;* see also *Primitive Man as Philosopher.*
[20]L. Pospisil, *The Kapauku Papuans of West New Guinea,* p. 83.

the desired results, all goes well. But hunger, illness, failure, and death stalk the earth, for which the lesser gods and the forces of evil are responsible. Toward them man's emotions are ambivalent. The gods and spirits are both loved and feared. The emotional overtones of religion are mixed indeed. But taken in the main, the anthropologist cannot, on the basis of the facts, concur in the idealistic belief that religion in all its history represents solely man's striving for the highest values of life. Nor is it possible to derive religion from any single mainspring of motivation. Belief in souls, fear of ghosts, fear of fear, worship of ancestors, traffic with hosts of spirits, nature worship, and philosophical reflection all play their parts. Emphasis shifts from culture to culture, but religion is a growth with many roots and many fruits.

SUMMARY

The area of the supernatural tends to have its specialized personnel, just as any highly developed social institution does. Because of the believed power of the supernatural to affect the affairs of men, religious and magical specialists exist everywhere. Shamans, those who have derived special power individually from a supernatural source, are found in all societies. Priests, those whose supernatural authority is by virtue of their position as officers in an organized cult or church, are found in societies whose cultures provide for more elaborate internal institutions.

Religious and magical cults differ in the focus of their predominant interests. They also differ in the detailed characteristics of their spirit beings and in ritual and ceremonial practices. Ancestor worship and cults of the dead are common, but by no means universal, religious forms. Deification or spiritualization of various aspects of nature produces nature worship. Fetishism occurs when a people reveres a material object for its mana or because it is the abode of a spirit being. Cults of a Supreme Being or High God antedate Hebraic monotheism and are indigenous to many primitive cultures.

The quality of any particular religion reflects the basic value system of the society, the nature of its intrafamilial relations, and its economic and political structure. If it is complex enough, as many primitive systems are, it may include varieties of all the major categories of cults that have been mentioned. Certainly, as Émile Durkheim emphasized, magico-religious beliefs and rituals symbolize and reinforce the collective solidarity of the social group.

SELECTED READINGS

Anderson, W. H., and C. Dibble (trs. and eds.): Fray B. Sahagún, *The Florentine Codex: On the Relation of Things in New Spain* (1950). Aztec religious beliefs and practices as recorded in Nahuatl by Aztecs trained by Father Sahagún in the sixteenth century and now translated into English.

Bascom, W. R.: *The Sociological Role of the Yoruba Cult-group* (American Anthropological Association, Memoir 63, 1944). An excellent study of a West African manifestation of religious organization.

Bunzel, R.: *Introduction to Zuni Ceremonialism* (Bureau of American Ethnology, Annual Report 47, 1932). Gives an idea of how pervasive and complex a highly developed primitive religious system can be.

Norbeck, E.: *Religion in Primitive Society* (1961). chaps. 6 and 7, "Unusual Psychological States" and "Religious Practitioners." Provides much interesting detail clearly presented.

Park, W. Z.: *Shamanism in Northwestern North America* (1938). Shamanism among the primitive peoples of the Great Basin area.

Srinivas, M. N.: *Religion and Society among the Coorgs of South India* (1952). A first-rate study of how religion functions in the maintenance of a social system.

Underhill, R.: *Ceremonialism in the Greater Southwest* (American Ethnological Society, Monograph, 1948). Relates shamanism and priestly cults to food-gathering, hunting, and gardening societies.

*Culture
and world view*

chapter 34

The religion of any people expresses a good deal of their view of the world—its nature, its vitality, and the forces that affect it—but it does not express their total view. Nor do custom and usage tell us all the rest of the story. As Kluckhohn has written:

Cultures or group life-ways do not manifest themselves solely in observable customs and artifacts. There is much more to social and cultural phenomena than immediately meets the ear and eye. If the behavioral facts are to be correctly understood, certain presuppositions constituting what might be termed a philosophy or ideology must also be known. The "strain towards consistency" . . . in the folkways and mores of all groups cannot be accounted for unless one postulates a more or less systematic pattern of reaction to experience as a characteristic property of all integrated cultures. . . . Each different way of life makes its own assumptions about the ends and purposes of human existence, about ways by which knowledge may be obtained, about the organization of the pigeonholes in which each sense datum is filed, about what human beings have a right to expect from each other and the gods, about what constitutes fulfillment or frustration. Some of these assumptions are made explicit in the lore of the folk; others are tacit premises which the observer must infer by finding consistent trends in word and deed.[1]

Man faces the bewildering chaos of experience armed with mental artifacts of his own invention with which he organizes the natural phantasmagoria into a manageable and meaningful unity. He thereby assures himself of a reasonable amount of certainty and builds a base of understanding upon which to organize his life in comprehensible terms; absolute chaos is inconceivable, and if this is indeed a disorderly universe, man will impose order on it. He is ". . . endlessly simplifying and generalizing his own view of his environment; he constantly imposes on his environment his own constructions and meanings; these constructions and meanings are characteristic of one culture as opposed to another."[2]

The nature of world view

The view of life and the total environment that an individual holds or that is characteristic of the members of a society is frequently referred to as *Weltanschauung,* or world view. World view carries the suggestion "of the structure of things as man is aware of them,"[3] and it is thus the life scene as people look out upon it. It is the human being's inside view, colored, shaped, and rearranged according to his cultural preconceptions. The planet we live on, a world of physical objects and living things, is by no means the same world to all peoples. Indeed, a simple description of the most basic observable components of this world (the sky, the land, water, trees,) by a member of one culture might prove totally unintelligible to a member of another.[4] Differing conceptions of life purposes and of cosmological factors can be even more highly variable, as we have already seen. Institutions, relationships, arts, and technology vary throughout the world in manifestly observable forms, but underlying them are the basic postulates that orient a people's particular slant on life and the ways in which they organize their culture. Sharply distinctive world views may result, and as three introductory examples, we take those which are succinctly expressed (perhaps somewhat oversimplified) in the contrasting vignettes of the Egyptians and the Greeks by Edith Hamilton and of the Aztecs by Alphonso Caso.

The world view of the Egyptians

In Egypt the center of interest was the dead. . . . Countless numbers of human beings for countless numbers of centuries thought of death as that which was nearest and most familiar to them. It is an extraordinary circumstance which could be made credible by nothing less than the immense mass of Egyptian art centered in the dead. To the Egyptian the enduring world of reality was not the one he walked in the every-day life but the one he should presently go to by the way of death.[5]

---

[1]C. Kluckhohn, "The Philosophy of the Navaho Indians," in F. S. C. Northrop (ed.), *Ideological Differences and World Order*, p. 359.
[2]G. Bateson, quoted in *ibid.*, p. 356.

[3]R. Redfield, *The Primitive World and Its Transformations*, p. 86.
[4]Consider the Sia Indian's conception of the chemiso bush: "I am it and it is me and all my ancestors.
[5]E. Hamilton, *The Greek Way to Western Civilization*, p. 13.

The world view of the Greeks But of the Athenians, Hamilton writes:

To rejoice in life, to find the world beautiful and delightful to live in, was a mark of the Greek spirit which distinguished it from all that had gone before. . . . The joy of life is written upon everything the Greeks left behind. . . . Not in their darkest moments, do they lose their taste for life. It is always a wonder and a delight, the world a place of beauty, and they themselves rejoicing to be alive in it. . . .

The spiritual world was not to them another world from the natural world. It was the same world as that known to the mind. Beauty and rationality were both manifested in it. . . . Reason and feeling were not antagonistic. The truth of poetry and the truth of science were both true.[6]

The world view of the Aztecs Of the Aztecs, seventeen centuries later in an altogether different part of the world, we read in the writings of Alfonso Caso:

Hence the pride of the Aztec, who looked upon himself as a collaborator of the gods, for he knew that his life was dedicated to maintaining cosmic order and struggling against the powers of darkness.

In a sense the universe depended upon him for its continued existence; upon him depended the food for the gods, upon him depended the beneficence of the gifts which they showered upon mankind. Likewise, the light of the sun, the rain that formed in the mountains and watered the corn, the winds that blew through the reeds, bringing clouds or turning into a hurricane, all depended upon him. . . .[7]

In addition to this cosmological ideal, the Aztecs also believed that they had an ethical ideal to attain. The struggle of the sun against the powers of darkness was not only a struggle of the gods, but it was also, above all, the struggle of good against evil. . . .

Opposed to this imperialistic and religious ideal there was always a feeling of pessimism in the depths of the Aztec soul. The Aztecs knew that in the end their leader, the sun, would be defeated . . . and then the powers of evil would prevail . . . and would destroy mankind.

Therefore, this life, for the Aztecs, was only transi-

---

[6]*Ibid.*, pp. 19, 30–31.

[7]In the Aztec world view, man was created by the sacrifice of the gods and in turn was reciprocally bound to sustain them with the magical sustenance of life itself—the blood of human sacrifice.

tory, and a feeling of pessimism and anguish appeared in their vigorous and terrible sculpture and a tinge of profound sadness in their poetry.[8]

The above quotations characterize three civilizations, but what is true of them is true of every society as well; a world view is a significant feature of every culture and is basic to it, even though its philosophic and artistic expression may be more ideological than behavioral, or real. Without comprehension of world views, there is no comprehension of mankind. Therefore, we shall explore the phenomenon more deeply by considering the Navaho, Hopi, Ashanti, and American world views.

The Navaho world view

The Navahos, it will be remembered from the discussion of housing (Chapter 16), are an Athabascan-speaking people who migrated from Canada into the high, arid lands of the southwestern part of the United States some five hundred or more years ago. Originally hunters and foragers, they became gardeners in their new southwestern environment. After the Spanish brought horses, sheep, and goats, they also became pastoralists who were basically gardeners. The cultivation of corn, beans, and squash was learned from the Pueblo Indians, as was much of their mythology and the visual imagery and technique of sand painting. In like manner, the Navaho system of matrilineal clans appears to have been copied from that of the Western Pueblos. But it has already been noted how the Navahos refused to consolidate in settled, compact villages of pueblo structure, preferring to live in scattered settlements of hogan camps. Their social organization is decentralized and quite amorphous. Clan exogamy is rigidly adhered to, but the sanction for incest is an obsessive urge to burn oneself to death—a fate that relatives try to forestall. The punishment is self-imposed. The Navahos hold elaborate ceremonies, known as chants, which are made occasions for social get-togethers, and chanters must learn their

---

[8]A. Caso, *The Aztecs: People of the Sun*, pp. 93–94.

rituals with painstaking care. But chants are performed at the request of individuals or families to cure illness; they are not part of a cult cycle. Singers are individual practitioners, not members of religious fraternities. Clans are not corporate bodies set in segmentary opposition to one another.[9]

An orderly but dangerous universe The basic orientation of the Navaho is individualistic-familistic rather than collectivistic. He views the universe as an orderly but extremely dangerous place that must be treated with the utmost circumspection and caution.

The basis for this view is in the Navaho origin myth, which accounts for the history and character of the Holy People—the supernatural beings who belong to the sacred part of the world, as opposed to the Earth Surface People, who are ordinary human beings, living and dead. The origin myth tells ". . . the People that, from time immemorial, the universe has been a very dangerous place, inhabited by people who were untrustworthy, if not completely evil . . . [who] are forever present to Navaho consciousness as threats to prosperity."[10]

Earth Surface People, except for living relatives, are all potentially dangerous, and even slight contact with nonrelatives may cause serious illness. Anyone may be a witch, but especially those who become too prosperous. Witches are werewolves and ghouls who practice incest and who are the source of the greatest anxiety. But death, too, is horrible in the Navaho view, for ghosts are the witches of the world of the dead; they harass and plague the living with dire portents and unnerving teasing. Even the most forgiving friend may become a malignantly vengeful ghost bent on punishing some slight or neglect. Fear of ghosts makes even adult Navahos loath to face the dark alone.

Eight fundamental Navaho postulates Against this background, Kluckhohn formulated eight

"keystones on which the Navaho view of the world appears to rest":

1. The universe is orderly: all events are caused and interrelated.
   a. Knowledge is power.
   b. The basic quest is for harmony.
   c. Harmony can be restored by orderly procedures.
   d. One price of disorder, in human terms, is illness.
2. The universe tends to be personalized.
   a. Causation is identifiable in personalized terms.
3. The universe is full of dangers.
4. Evil and good are complementary, and both are ever present.
5. Experience is conceived as a continuum differentiated only by sense data.
6. Morality is conceived in traditionalistic and situational terms rather than in terms of abstract absolutes.
7. Human relations are premised upon familistic individualism.
8. Events, not actors or qualities, are primary.[11]

These precepts expand into a world view that has the following major focuses.

THE COMPULSIVE EFFECT OF PRAYER AND RITUAL The universe is mechanistically viewed as an interrelated system of cause and effect. The Holy People may indeed be spirit beings, but they are not free to act capriciously, for they are controlled by laws of their own making. Chant and ceremony are compulsive acts that control results rather than petition for gifts from the gods. Gladys Reichard, in writing of Navaho religion, spoke of prayer as the "compulsive word," which "functions properly because of its completeness and order," and whose "purpose is compulsion by exactness of word."[12] So it is that mastery of an esoteric terminology, along with pragmatically tested, immediately apprehended sense data, gives one power. It is not mystic experience—neither visions nor ascetic self-torture—but *knowledge* (in Navaho terms) that gives power. Power, however, does not mean mastery over nature as Western man seeks it. Rather, the Navaho's

[9]The present tribal council was established under the aegis of the U.S. Office of Indian Affairs in 1923.
[10]C. Kluckhohn and D. Leighton, *The Navaho*, p. 125.

[11]Kluckhohn, *op. cit.*, pp. 359–360.
[12]G. A. Reichard, *Prayer: The Compulsive Word*, p. 10.

basic quest is for harmony. "Individually acquired knowledge can assist in the restoration
of harmony in one person's life, in that of the
community, in that of the universe."[13] Everything in Navaho symbolism, verbal and visual,
is in balanced pairs or quadruplets.

DISHARMONIC FORCES Disharmony, which is
imbalance, means disorder manifest in flood,
catastrophe, and, above all, personal illness.
Every Navaho ceremony is a "cure" sung
over a patient, even though some cures may
also improve the state of the world. Witches
are forever bent upon disturbing the harmony
of things. The Holy People, and all people and
things, witches excepted, are neither inherently
good nor inherently evil. Good and evil are
complementary and ever-present. If things
stay in balance, a man and his family will do
all right, but the universe is full of dangers.
"Navahos," say Kluckhohn and Leighton,
"seem morbid in the variety of threats from
this world and from the world of the supernatural which they fear and name."[14] The
compensatory mechanism of compulsive order-
liness in behavior, art, ritual, and religion is
their positive response. Complementary to for-
malism is the felt need to avoid risks. Excess
of any sort is dangerous. Most acts are not
immoral of themselves, but cause trouble if
performed too intensively. "Stay within safe
limits! Likewise," say the Navahos, "be wary
of nonrelatives." Merely to touch a stranger
can make one sick. The Enemy Way nine-day
chant may be necessary to restore the order
upset by the presence of a stranger. And
where an American in a threatening situation
may cry out, "Don't just stand there! Do something!" the Navaho canon is: "When in a new
and dangerous situation, do nothing!"

In his response to the world as he sees
it, the Navaho is an industrious individualist
who works hard within the framework of the
known. He devotes much time and effort to
combating the disruptive forces that imbalance his world. He strives to be courteous,

polite, and nonaggressive, avoiding trouble
and witches and seeking above all to have
health and strength, to work and to acquire
knowledge, to present a good figure with his
clothes and jewelry, and to provide for his
family—but not to acquire glory or the power
to rule or govern men. There is no place for
dominance over one's fellows in the Navaho
world view.

The Hopi way as a world view

The Hopis are the nearest neighbors of the
Navahos, and they are also the westernmost of
the living Pueblos of the United States today.
They are as typical of the different Pueblos of
the Southwest as any Pueblo can be, although
all Pueblos differ from others in some respects.
A brief examination of the Hopi world view
at this point will be useful because of the
common historico-cultural base from which
both Hopi and Navaho have drawn much of
their ideology and because of the different
orientation and more highly refined conceptual
sophistication of the Hopi system.

The Hopis are intensive gardeners living in
compact, permanently settled villages built of
plastered stone houses set wall-to-wall around
a central ceremonial plaza. Fields and houses
are owned by women; the matrilineage is the
bridge between household and strong matriclans. Kinship and economic life are female-
centered, although men may own sheep. Ceremonial life and political life are male-centered
and are organized around a complex system of
secret religious fraternities.[15]

Laura Thompson summarizes the Hopi
world view in these words:

Here we recognize an organic view of the universe.
The cosmos is formulated as a living whole in which
the subtly balanced relationships of the various parts
to one another and to the multidimensional totality
are similar to those which characterize living organisms. The parts and the whole are believed to
transact for the good of all, according to a single,

[13]Kluckhohn, *op. cit.*, p. 362.
[14]Kluckhohn and Leighton, *op. cit.*, p. 224.

[15]The best general summary of the Hopi social system is
found in F. Eggan, *Social Organization of the Western Pueblos*,
chap. 2, pp. 17–138.

harmonious, immanent law. Man is a psychophysiological whole, differentiated from the rest of nature by his power of volition, which is an integral part of the scheme and is to be used for the commonweal. He cooperates with other men and with his nonhuman partners in fulfilling the law, through kinship and ceremonial groups. And the main mechanisms through which he expresses symbolically the cosmic process are ritual and art, reinforced by concentrated will-prayer.[6]

The intricate balance of parts In more specific terms, this means that the most fundamental Hopi postulate premises the world as a complex, ordered system in which all parts are intimately interdependent on an essentially equivalent footing, each with its role to play in the maintenance of the harmonious working of the whole. Man is on the same footing as all other orders of phenomena—the birds, the beasts, the plants, the insects, the clouds, the mythic beings, the ancestors—all these and many more, each with its ordained function. The world in the Hopi view is tightly integrated and complexly organized, a delicately balanced mechanism.

The human role in the universe Unlike the Navahos, who view the world as dangerous, the Hopis see it as beneficent and predictable —except where human irresponsibility disrupts it. The nonhuman part of the universe is automatically controlled by the "correlativity principle." But man has a measure of willful self-determinism. He has a margin of choice. He may or may not carry out his functions according to the Great Scheme. If he does, the universe continues its orderly unfolding of events—healthily, happily, productively, satisfyingly. If he does not, crops fail, babies die, and famine, pestilence, and disaster sweep over the little community. Chaos and disorder reign.

A Hopi, in the Hopi view, must *want* things to go right. He must want this with all his being, which means that he must work industriously in his fields, at weaving, and at pottery or basket making, and that he must participate

[16]L. Thompson, *Toward a Science of Mankind*, p. 189.

faithfully in all the ceremonies in which he has an assigned part by virtue of his statuses. In addition, he must concentrate all his psychic energy on "willing" or "praying for" (synonymous terms in Hopi) the result. He must think "happy" thoughts. In other words, the Hopi must self-consciously keep himself committed to a positive minding of his role in the universe. Less than this constitutes failure as a human being, and such failure is heresy and treason. There is no room for the indifferent or uncommitted man in the Hopi scheme of things, nor is there room for the individualistic innovator who thinks he can improve on the Great Scheme. Such a person is a dangerous deviationist, even more immediately dangerous than the slovenly slacker. Each in his way is a saboteur of the order, the one because he does not make the effort to will enough, the other because he wills the wrong things. Each is *ka-hopi*, un-Hopi; each runs a great risk not only of being called a "two-heart," a witch who stays alive by taking the lives of relatives, but also of being condemned and killed as a witch by the Kwan secret society. Hopi society is theocratic, collectivistic, and totalitarian.

Hopis fear witches, but differently from the way Navahos do. Navaho anxiety is diffuse, but witchcraft is directed toward individuals, as is ghost malice. Pueblo witchcraft is directed against the whole system. That Hopi witches kill individuals is incidental, for their major motive is to prolong their own lives by killing others, especially relatives.

To the Navaho, knowledge is power. To the Hopi (as to other Pueblo Indians), knowledge is not only power but also an obligation. Knowledge is a requisite to maintaining the balance of the universe; one must strain to know what is expected and needed, and one must will to make it work. But what one is privileged to know is ordained in the pattern. Roles for all persons and things are ideologically blueprinted, and to presume to roles that have not been assigned to one is *ka-hopi*. To know a ceremony for which one is not properly a priest means only that one will misuse it. Possession of unauthorized knowl-edge is feared by men and women throughout the pueblos, for to say of a person, "He knows something," is to say he is a witch.[17]

As an ideological adaptation to a harsh environment in which the Hopis have achieved a highly effective survival capacity, their world view unquestionably represents a high level of consistent integration that permeates their social structure, their art and ritual, and their personalities. Its demands upon the individual are severe, for each man is an Atlas, support-ing the weight of the world upon his shoulders. There is little room for individualism, and there is no tolerance for the wayward. The Hopi socializes—or else. The world view of his soci-ety demands it.

The mechanistic-vitalistic character of Navaho and Hopi world views Although the Hopis and the Navahos posit the existence of spirit beings, and in this sense their world views are colored with animism, both are fundamentally mechanistic in their outlook. The Navahos assume that the acts of Big Holy People, Earth Surface People, and witches may be counteracted by compulsively effective ritual knowledge. The Hopis are even more mecha-nistic in their view of the universe as an intricately meshed set of systems, delicately interrelated in a total order that man must help to maintain by positive willing and correct role performance.

Another type of world view, that in which animistic assumptions are predominant, is, however, perhaps more characteristic of primi-tive cultures. As an example of such an ideo-logical and behavioral outlook, we consider next the Ashanti world view.

[17]Thus Bandalier wrote of the New Mexican Pueblos: "[A cacique, the priest-chief,] can also be removed if the tribe so directs in general council, or if the war captain or the leading shamans so dispose. A degraded cacique seldom, if ever, lives long. There is too much danger in suffering him who is in possession of the most precious arts and knowledge to live while under a cloud. It is the war captain who, officially at least, attends to such executions." A. F. Bandalier, "Final Report" (*Papers of the Archaeological Institute of America*, Vol. 3, 1890), p. 284.

The Ashanti world view

The Ashantis of the Gold Coast of Africa are one of the great tribes of Ghana. When they were conquered by the British in 1874, they had already united in a constitutional mon-archy made up of a number of districts, each under a paramount chief and all bearing alle-giance to the King of Ashanti, the Ashan-tihene. They lived in scattered villages and were ruled from seats of government situated in true towns.

The gods The central theme of the Ashanti world view is ancestoralism, but the ancestors are no more than the most immediate of the numerous spirit beings that people the universe. The Hopi world view, as we have just seen, is predominantly mechanistic, while that of the Navaho is only slightly less so. To the Ashanti, on the other hand, the world is full of spirits, and his world view may be labeled *vitalistic.*

***Onyonkopon,* the Supreme Being** The world is the creation of a high god, *Onyonkopon,* the Supreme Being. Although he originally lived close to men, low in the sky, he removed him-self far beyond their reach because the activi-ties of an old woman annoyed him. He is a person—aloof, remote, and uncensorious; all-powerful, he no longer exercises his power directly. He planned and created the universe, endowing it with a general order, and yet he sets no moral precepts and neither punishes human follies nor rewards human virtues. He is revered and looked upon with awe and ven-eration. Still, there are no priests who serve *Onyonkopon;* there are no rites or rituals of praise, petition, appeasement, or atonement. He gives nothing; he demands nothing. He is the pure unifying principle of the universe—a personified abstraction.

***Abosom,* the executive deities** The administra-tion of the universe is in the hands of the great executive deities (*abosom*), the superin-tending gods of the major departments of nature—the rivers, the lakes, the sea, the clouds, and the earth itself. Beneath these secondary gods are the innumerable lesser spirits that animate trees, animals, and charms; most ubiquitous, however, are the immortal ancestors—veritable busybodies who are concerned that everything be done right and morally. They are the preceptors and censors of all Ashantis, from the humblest slave to the *Ashantihene,* who is their living viceroy in the administration of society.

CALLING THE GODS Unlike the high god, the lesser gods have their priests and shrines. In response to proper offerings and priestly incantations, a god may be induced to take up a temporary abode in one of his shrines— but then again, he may refuse or neglect to come. If he comes, he is beseeched to grant health, wealth, children, or protection from misfortune or witches. He grants or withholds according to his own willful disposition. The Ashanti does not conceive of controlling the gods; he views himself as dependent upon supernatural whim. Should a god respond, he speaks through his priest, either by possessing the priest himself, who then speaks in tongues while an assistant interprets, or by influencing the performance of various divinitory devices manipulated by the priest. Gods and spirits other than the Supreme Deity and ancestors are viewed instrumentally—as means to ends. Their popularity waxes and wanes as they are responsive or unresponsive to human demands.

The gods are treated with respect if they deliver the goods, and with contempt if they fail. . . . The Ashanti, like other Akan tribes, esteem the Supreme Being and the ancestors far above gods and amulets. Attitudes to the latter depend upon their success, and vary from healthy respect to sneering contempt.[18]

The ancestors A basic proposition underlying all Ashanti social structure is that the land belongs to the ancestors and the living enjoy only its use. The ancestral spirits therefore control the subsistence base that is admin-

[18]K. A. Busia, "The Ashanti," in D. Forde (ed.), *African Worlds*, p. 205.

istered on their behalf by the king, who in turn delegates its disposition to district chiefs, who parcel it out to lineage heads, who finally assign it to families.

Blood and maternal descent The next fundamental postulate is that every person inherits his blood from his mother and this is the link from generation to generation. Through blood comes membership in the maternal lineage and clan (*abusua*). From clan membership flow the rights and duties of citizenship in law and in government. Inheritance of property rights, goods, and titles to office derive from clan membership through blood. In dogma, clan membership means common descent from a mythical ancestress, exogamy, and bonds of mutual aid wherever clan members may be found.

Spirit and paternal descent Ashanti postulates undergird a double descent system, however. Everyone receives his spiritual essence (*ntorɔ*) through his father from his father's ancestral patriline. He belongs to an identifiable *ntorɔ* group, which has its own customs, usages, and rituals; from it he inherits his personal *sunsum,* "his ego, his personality, his distinctive character."

The vital soul But from the Creator the Ashanti receives his *kra,* his life force—the bit of animating spirit that returns to the Supreme Being when he dies. The *kra* is the soul, the undying part of him that continues its existence in the abode of ancestors. In short, in the Ashanti view, a man derives his social statuses through his mother's blood, his character through his father's spirit, and his life from the Supreme Being.

Social control through the ancestors The gods, as viewed by the Ashanti, may give or withhold, but they do not punish. The ancestors, in contrast, protect their descendants and punish them if their behavior is reprehensible. Thus it is with reference to the attitudes toward gods that it is often said that the Ashanti world view and religion have no ethical content. The morality imposed by the expectations of the ancestors is, however, strict and severe, for ancestors are not to be offended. Hence: "The Ashanti conception of a good society is one in which harmony is achieved among the living, and between the living and the gods and ancestors."[19]

The responsibility for maintenance of this harmony is vested in the chiefs. Each lineage has its sacred stool. The lineage chief, seated upon the lineage stool (throne) embodying the collective spirit of the ancestors, is the will and voice of the ancestors, concerned with the conduct and well-being of lineage members. On the highest level, the royal stool of the king's lineage is the symbolic representation of all the ancestors of the Ashantis, and, as their intermediary, the Ashantihene governs the nation.

The postulate, "All contraventions of the will of the ancestors are sins," is fundamental to the Ashanti system of social control. Complementary to it is a related postulate: "The ancestors will punish the group as a whole if the group does not itself punish a sinner." From this flows the corollary, "all sins are crimes." All crimes are punishable by death because (postulate): "Men are endowed with conscious will." Therefore, a sinner is one who willfully defies the ancestors, forfeiting thereby his right to enjoy their protection and inclusion in their community of the living. Further: "The ancestors will judge and punish a man in the spirit world if he takes advantage of a miscarriage of justice here."

Great collective ceremonies honoring the ancestors occur every twenty-one days, and once a year all the categories of spirit beings are given simple offerings and asked for their continued help in ceremonies that extend for two weeks.

It can be seen from this description that the operative forces in the Ashanti universe are not mechanical, but wholly personal. As the Ashanti sees his task, it is not to achieve

[19]Busia, *op. cit.*, p. 207.

or maintain compulsive control over a balance of forces or to regenerate a dissipating store of energy. His duties are to remain on good terms with spirit beings, who are admittedly capricious but nonetheless inclined to lend a helping hand to mankind, and to maintain good relations with his fellows because the ancestors demand it.

The American world view

It may seem that the formulation of a descriptive analysis of *a* world view for the people of the United States is too great an undertaking. There are so many and so diverse cultural backgrounds represented in their recent immigrant origins; there is such a wide range in manifest belief, from atheism to devout religiosity; there is such a broad spectrum of interests in terms of occupation, recreation, and learning; and there are such vast differences between life in a tiny crossroads hamlet and life in New York's megalopolis. Yet outsiders generally agree that Americans are, by and large, highly standardized in outlook and manner. Relatively speaking, this is true. American society is marked by a very high degree of consensus and general agreement. There is little of the dogmatic in American ideology—certainly nothing that can be stated so succinctly as a Communist credo, for example. Nonetheless, a distinctive American world view does exist and may be stated in its bolder outlines as the anthropologist sees them. This, then, is how it appears— allowing for subgroup and individual variations, which are screened out in order that the major themes can be brought into clearer focus.

Rationalism and the mechanistic view Historically, the American world view is a derivative of the Judaeo-Christian–Hellenistic traditions as they were blended and modified through the Renaissance, the Reformation, and the Industrial Revolution in Europe. In the American setting, these traditions have taken on their own intensifications and selective qualities.

However much the Judaeo-Christian traditions may survive and influence the American life-way, American thought patterns are rational rather than mystic; the operative conception of the universe is mechanistic. The bedrock proposition upon which the whole world view stands is that the universe is a physical system that operates in a determinate manner according to discoverable scientific laws. Thus, Americans use religion for purposes of social organization, but they rely relatively little upon prayer, ritual, or sacrifice to achieve their ends. Instead, they depend primarily upon basic scientific research and the technical application of the findings of science. Because they view the universe as a mechanism, Americans implicitly believe that man can manipulate it. He need not accept it as it is; he may work on it, and as he gains in knowledge and improves his techniques, he may even redesign it so that it is more to his liking. From this springs the conviction that the conditions of living are improvable: materially, biologically, and socially. Improvement means betterment; betterment means progress. Americans are progressive: neither revolutionary nor conservative, but progressive. Man can himself, in the American view, eliminate hunger and poverty, disease, and social injustice—if he sets himself to the task. This fundamental motivating postulate of contemporary American culture expresses itself in a focal value orientation of "effort-optimism." Because the world view is rational-mechanistic rather than mystic-vitalistic, it leads to action rather than contemplation, to aggressive engagement rather than passive renunciation. Americans "make war" on poverty, "stamp out" disease, "wipe out" illiteracy, and embark on the "conquest" of space, as their forebears "conquered" the wilderness. Such an action orientation makes for emphasis upon technology and science rather than upon philosophy and the arts. It has produced a mechanized agricultural-, industrial-, business-centered civilization rather than an ecclesiastical, scholarly, militaristic, or feudalistic one.

Pragmatic empiricism Concomitantly, the American cultural emphasis is pragmatic-empirical rather than theoretical-dogmatic.

Americans are more concerned with "know-how" and "can-do" than with abstract wisdom or ancient knowledge, even to a considerable degree in science. The test of the validity of the American premise is, in the American view of things, continued expansion of the gross national product, ever-new medical breakthroughs, and continuous expansion of social well-being and opportunity. As long as the standard of living, expressed in wide distribution of consumers' goods, keeps rising, it is felt that things are going well. When the system temporarily collapsed in the Great Depression of the 1930s, Americans panicked and had to be reassured that all they had to fear was fear itself. What unnerved them, however, was not unreasoning fear but the logical anxiety that the most basic premise of the American world view was an unworkable illusion.

Individual-centeredness When the American looks away from the universe and inward toward himself and his society, his focus of view is individual-centered, rather than kin-centered, class-centered, or collectivistically oriented, even though Americans are widely given to group organization. In the religious belief that has permeated much of the morality of the culture, it is premised that a man's moral responsibility rests in his private conscience. In the view of human nature held by Christianity, which is the dominant religion, man is inherently corrupt and sin-ridden by nature, and personal salvation (that is, purification from the moral stain of sin) is possible only in an emotional act of identification with God through Jesus (or his mother, Mary). Americans are therefore generally internally plagued with inner conflict and anxiety. Believing in the improvability of the self as an individual responsibility, and yet also holding (to a certain extent) that man is a sorry being, they accept the proposition that inner psychic conflict is the very essence of human existence. But to control the extreme consequences of such conflict there is less reliance upon religious or philosophic solutions than upon psychiatry and mental hygiene programs.

Pastors are expected to be half counselor and half priest.

Two-thirds of the American population is nominally religious in that it belongs to some church. One-third is sufficiently uninterested in religion as to identify with no church. In contrast to the primitive world view, the function of God, gods, spirits, ghosts, witches, and ancestors in the American world view is more residual than dominant.

Status and social mobility The individual-centeredness of the American world view, combined with its pragmatic action orientation, gives emphasis to status achievement and social mobility. Achievement-in-being is what counts, not an illustrious background. American egalitarianism and its proposition that all men are created equal derives from this combination of qualities. Every American has to prove himself to himself first and to his fellows second—to succeed in manifest ways. He sees himself in a fluid social organization that necessitates fluid status symbols whereby achievement can be tangibly expressed. In a business-based culture, money serves this function. Money is the measure of success; it validates one's efforts, and therefore oneself, by providing the means to purchase such external symbols of success as a college education, a discreetly selected foreign car, or a large house at a good address.

The world view of older, but contemporary, status-structured societies in Europe deprecates the materialism of Americanism. At the same time, a major feature of the revolutionary innovations of the postcolonial world since World War II has been the avid desire of the so-called underdeveloped nations to learn the mechanical-material techniques that have followed from the kind of world view that has had its most intensive development in the United States.[20]

[20]It will undoubtedly have been noted in the foregoing description that, allowing for certain variations in the conception of the individual in relation to the state and in various degrees of coloration, the "world view" of the Russians is not so dissimilar from the American as is commonly thought.

SUMMARY

World view, as stated by Redfield in one of his formulations, is the "insider's total vision and conception of everything," his outlook on life.[21] As a science, anthropology might be content to work with reports on what the anthropologist as an objective observer sees and notes of behavior. Such observations must be so phrased that they are comparable within a scientific frame of analytical reference. Most of the chapters of this book have been presented from this point of view—and it is to be hoped that a good deal about the nature of man and his works has been learned thereby. But none of this tells us what it feels like to be a Navaho, a Hopi, an Ashanti, a Trobriand Islander, a Nuer, or an Ifugao. That calls for the treatment of whole cultures and life-ways as viewed from the inside by the liver of the life-way. Its purpose is to feel and understand the universe not in scientific terms but in the terms, cognitions, and affects of the people concerned, who are not scientists at all. A complete anthropology requires both approaches.

Four world views have been sketched in this chapter. Obviously, the sketches are much too thin to convey how it feels to see the universe as a Hopi does—or as an American does. It is important, though, to sense the basic fact that cultures are not simply ways of doing, or of organizing societies. They also define the nature of the world, of man (existential postulates), and of what is to be sought after and what is to be avoided (normative postulates or values).

The Navaho world view builds on the assumptions that spirit beings established the world as it is and endowed it with order; it is, however, a very dangerous and threatening world, but it may be controlled by compulsive symbolic acts. Individualism is to the fore, and social structure and material culture both reflect this basic fact. Disharmony and imbalance produce personal illness.

The Hopis intensify the concept of an

[21]R. Redfield, *The Little Community*, p. 95.

orderly universe, and although they populate it with spirit beings, they tend to depersonalize it. All elements of the universe are grouped in large categories, which interrelate in an intricately delicate balance that is designed to operate beneficently for the well-being of all. Man, however, is endowed with will, and he is required concentratedly to will the patterned maintenance of the system while he fulfills his ordained roles. Failure on either count disrupts the system and brings on social disaster as well as possible personal sickness. Individuals are consequently under extreme social pressure meticulously to conform to traditional patterns. On the other hand, the effect of ritual acts within the system is so impelling that unauthorized knowledge portends misuse, and the penalty for knowing that which one has no right to know is death.

The Ashantis look out upon an anthropomorphized world of spirits. The order in this world is that sustained by the Supreme Being and the ancestors. The innumerable executive gods are unpredictable and willful; they are propitiated in hopes of obtaining their favors, but eventually they are scorned if they fail too often to respond to human appeals.

The American world view is predominantly rational-mechanistic in its conception of an orderly universe operating according to discoverable scientific laws. The American approach to life is marked by effort-optimism, an activist conviction that the material, biological, and social state of the world is improvable through man's efforts. The social system emphasizes status achievement and individual self-validation through the winning of material tokens of success in which know-how is more important than contemplative wisdom. Individual responsibility, combined with a religious tradition of human sinfulness, contributes to internal anxiety and self-censure. At the same time, the democratic egalitarianism of Americans fits into the notion that every man should have an equal chance to show what he can do. It is a world view which looks forward to an always-changing future and which is concerned with the past largely as a key to what may be.

SELECTED READINGS

Forde, D. (ed.): *African Worlds: Studies in the Cosmological Ideas and Social Values of African Peoples* (1954). Nine studies of the world views of a selected group of African societies. Includes the very famous formalized statement derived from a native systematizer of thought among the Dogon of the French Sudan (pp. 83–110).

Geertz, C.: *The Religion of Java* (1960). The world view of Javanese analyzed in terms of Hindu tradition, Islamic precepts, and indigenous beliefs.

Hamilton, E.: *The Greek Way to Western Civilization* (1930). A sympathetic approach to Greek thought and action by way of Greek literature.

Hoebel, E. A.: *The Cheyennes* (1960). Part I, "Ritual and Tribal Integration," and Part IV, "World View and the Cheyenne Personality," show how the Cheyenne view of the need to husband and renew the limited energy quotient of the universe is culturally expressed.

Leslie, C. M.: *Now We Are Civilized: A Study of the World View of the Zapotec Indians of Mitla, Oaxaca* (1960). A penetrating and gracefully written expression of the world view of a Mexican people in transition from the old to the new.

Radin, P.: *Primitive Man as Philosopher* (1927; rev. ed., 1955). This is the classic work that opened the door to the inside view of primitive thinking. It disposed of the condescending clichés that had previously prevailed about primitive simplemindedness.

Redfield, R.: *The Primitive World and Its Transformations* (1953). Chapter 4, "Primitive World View and Civilization," explores some implications of the concept of world view for modern life.

————: *The Little Community* (1956). Chapter 6, "The Little Community as an Outlook on Life," emphasizes the differences between the outside and inside views of cultures and the problems of investigation of the latter, plus the theoretical significance of world view.

Part 5/ Anthropology today and tomorrow

Anthropology: its growth, methods, and purposes

chapter 35

Anthropology as an organized body of knowl-edge, with a theory and with a corps of spe-cialized thinkers devoting their time and ener-gies to its interests, is now entering its second century, for it may be said to have been born in the decade following 1860. The seeds of anthropology were planted during the Renais-sance in Europe; then followed a long period of germination during the fifteenth and six-teenth centuries. The roots were formed during the seventeenth and eighteenth centuries, as the age of discovery resulted in growing curi-osity, on the part of European political phi-losophers, concerning the meaning of the many strange societies of uncivilized men that explorers and travelers were encountering. Philosophies of history were popular during this period. Then, during the first half of the nineteenth century, something that could be differentiated from philosophies of history began to take shape, until, between 1860 and 1871, anthropology emerged full-flowered as an eagerly cultivated field in its own right.

In 1860 appeared Bastian's first book; in 1861 Maine's *Ancient Law* and Bachofen's *Mutterrecht.* The burst in the first dozen years was phenomenal: Jacob Burckhardt, 1860; Fustel de Coulanges's *Ancient City,* 1864; McLennan's *Primitive Marriage,* 1865; Tylor's *Researches,* 1865; Lubbock's *Origin of Civilization,* 1870; Morgan's *Systems of Consanguinity,* 1871; Tylor's *Primi-tive Culture,* 1871.[1]

By the turn of the twentieth century, great anthropological collections had been estab-

[1]A. L. Kroeber, "The History and Present Orientation of Cultural Anthropology: 1950," in *The Nature of Culture,* p. 144.

lished in the major museums of natural history, chairs of anthropology were being established in various universities, and anthropological societies were flourishing in England, on the Continent, and in the United States. Systematic fieldwork in ethnology and archaeology was well under way. Professional journals devoted to anthropology were firmly established. The nineteenth-century evolutionary edifices of Tylor, Morgan, Frazer, and others were being subjected to serious critical challenge, as the young science showed signs of maturing in methods and thought.

The years between 1900 and 1925 marked the period of Boasian historical reconstructionism in the anthropology of the United States and of diffusion theory and research in Germany and Austria. In France, it was also the period when the foundations of functionalism and the social-structure approaches to anthropology were being laid by Émile Durkheim and his associates. During these decades, ethnographic fieldwork techniques were perfected and modern anthropology reached its first phase of maturity.

From 1930 to 1940, functionalism dominated the scene in both Britain and the United States; anthropology was temporarily destroyed in Germany by the Nazi triumph and except for prehistoric studies, was more or less dormant in France. The old Boasian movement in the United States was being transformed by the infusion of psychological interests, wedded to functionalism. The years following World War II brought a veritable explosion of anthropology around the world, not only in terms of professional developments but also in the areas of university response, public interest, and practical applications of anthropological findings.

This chapter traces the main outlines of the course of this growth and development, not by spelling out each and every happening or by discussing every contributor to anthropology, but by dealing only with movements that have had a major influence on the anthropology we know today. The next and final chapter will undertake to look to the future.

Anthropology in classical thought

Anthropology is one branch of knowledge that does not claim to have its origin among the Greeks. The Greeks, to be sure, were much interested in social organization, especially in political structure, but their thought on the subject was philosophically concerned with ideal systems, and they had little interest in studying actual social and cultural systems or in comparing the ways in which various societies actually dealt with human problems. As noted by John Rowe: "The ancient Greeks for the most part held that the way to understand ourselves is to study ourselves, while what others do is irrelevant."[2] In their exuberant discovery of the potentials of the human mind for intellectual and artistic expression, the Greeks denied that there was anything to be learned from "barbarians," the non-Greeks. All their wisdom notwithstanding, they had not grasped "the essence of the anthropological point of view—that in order to understand ourselves, we need to study others."[3] Herodotus (484–425? B.C.), it is true, is sometimes credited with being the father of anthropology because of his comments on customs of peoples other than the Greeks in the fifth century B.C., but his observations were neither systematic nor firsthand. They seem to be derived mostly from Persian sources, but of these no original documents remain.

Tacitus (*ca.* A.D. 55–120), a Roman historian, five hundred years after Herodotus, wrote a tract on the origin and locality of the Germans that is much referred to as an early ethnography, and indeed it does stand out as a rare, early source of some anthropological significance.

Herodotus and Tacitus notwithstanding, there was no body of literature and no systematic thought or discourse concerned with societies of the outer world; indeed, there was not much interest in such societies. There is little basis for a claim that anthropology had its origins in classical antiquity.

[2] J. H. Rowe, "The Renaissance Foundations of Anthropology" (*American Anthropologist,* Vol. 67, 1965), p. 2.
[3] *Ibid.*

Anthropology in the age of reason

Anthropology is truly a child of the Enlightenment. The Renaissance did not give birth to anthropology per se, but it did establish a comparative point of view. Renaissance man looked to the past rather than to contemporary primitives, but:

The Renaissance scholars . . . treated antiquity as a different world from the one they knew, remote but accessible to all through its literature and monuments. The Renaissance education of their time spread the view that the ancients were both different and worthy of study. Men trained in this tradition were better prepared than any of their predecessors to observe and record cultural differences when the opportunity presented itself.[4]

The opportunity came with the opening of the New World by Columbus's discovery of America and the subsequent exploratory voyages that girdled the globe. For many decades, the journals of explorers and the accounts of the more literate conquistadores—such as Bernal Diaz del Castillo, who fought with Cortez and left vivid pictures of Mexico and the Aztecs as he saw them in 1519, and Cook and Bougainville, who wrote many descriptive passages dealing with peoples of the Pacific—provided fragmentary and episodic accounts of diverse races and customs and set men to further thinking. Such bits and snippets of information did not constitute "anthropology," but they did stir men's minds. The *Jesuit Relations,* which is a vast body of reports from the Jesuit fathers working in North and South America and covers 1-3/4 centuries, from 1610 to 1791, contains much material of ethnographic interest in its seventy-three published volumes. This, too, was cumulative grist for the anthropological mill, but it was not yet anthropology.

Nonetheless, the first true anthropology was done by two Catholic missionaries, the first a Spanish Franciscan, Fray Bernadino de Sahagun (1499–1590), who worked in Mexico between 1529 and 1549, and the second a French Jesuit, Joseph-François Lafitau (1681–

[4] *Ibid.,* p. 12.

1746), who worked at the Jesuit mission of Sault Saint Louis among the Iroquois and the Hurons of western New York.

Sahagun's *General History of Things in New Spain* Tenochtitlan, the capital city of the Aztecs, was destroyed in 1521. Sahagun arrived eight years later to participate in the conversion of the Indians of Mexico. Before long, he was engaged in a full-fledged ethnographic scheme to record the beliefs and customs of the Aztecs in a systematic manner. He trained young Aztecs of the nobility—those who would have become Aztec priests under the old order—to write their native tongue, Nahuatl, in Spanish script. He himself traveled about questioning local informants, who provided answers in the form of hieroglyphic paintings in the old Aztec manner. With the glyphs as the framework of a codex, he pursued his questions with his "research assistants," who carefully wrote out the answers in their native tongue, recording a true "inside view" of Aztec culture.

The Florentine codex The text covers a diverse range of subjects, one after the other: "The Gods"; "The Ceremonies"; "The Origin of the Gods"; "Soothsayers and Omens"; "The Sun, Moon, and the Stars"; "The Binding of the Years"; "Kings and Lords"; "The Merchants"; "The People"; "The Conquest of Mexico." The book on "the people" spells out the ideal role performances for every kinship status and all other recognized statuses in Aztec society, and it describes their polar opposites by detailing the traits of the "bad" performer in each status. Parallel to the Nahuatl text, Sahagun added his own loose, running Spanish translation and commentary. The range and details of material are remarkably rich and fascinatingly objective, a trait which we admire today but which was not well received by Sahagun's superiors at home. Publication of the codex was suppressed; then it was lost or forgotten, at last to be rediscovered after nearly three hundred years. Only between

1947 and 1965 was the translation of the full Nahuatl text undertaken and this unique gift made available to modern anthropology.[5]

In the century following Sahagun, many Spanish chroniclers wrote on the customs and government of the conquered Indian nations. Some of these were official "intelligence" reports, and some were the products of personal scholarship. Of all, the four-volume *Historia del Nuevo Mundo,* written between 1650 and 1660, is judged most useful, being both clear and accurate in content and scientific in its approach.[6] Ethnography was gaining definite substance, but it was still far from becoming a reliable and orderly discipline.

Sahagun's work is straight, descriptive ethnography of a high order but contains no reflective analysis of Aztec customs or society. As a matter of fact, the good priest, who undoubtedly had his eye on the Inquisition, would not have dared to make a dispassionate analysis of Aztec usage even had he been so inclined. For the record, he declared: "My tears fall like hailstones as I think on the multitude of lies by which people here in New Spain were led into error."[7] It was, he said, the work of Satan.

Lafitau's comparative ethnology Father Lafitau wrote a century later, in France, in a different religious and cultural climate. His work is a continuation of Renaissance classical interests carried forward with new information. The very title of his book bespeaks his intent and purpose. Lafitau's two-volume work was published in Paris in 1724 and was called *Moeurs des sauvages amériquaines, comparées aux moeurs des premiers temps* (*Customs of the American Savages, Compared with Customs of Early Times*).

Just as Greece and Rome represented an earlier stage of civilization than eighteenth-century Europe, so too, he reasoned, the cultures of the Hurons and the Iroquois represent an even earlier condition of mankind. Evolutionary theory was taking shape.[8]

Lafitau gave clear expression to three additional principles that have since become basic in anthropology: (1) contemporary primitive cultures throw light on ancient cultures, and vice versa; (2) possible historic relations between cultures cannot be speculatively established but are determinable only on the basis of careful content analysis that demonstrates significant similarity of specific traits; and (3) alien cultures must be evaluated on the basis of the total conditions under which they operate, not in terms of European standards (the principle of cultural relativity).

How far a cry from the cultural snobbery of Greece and the dogmatic intolerance of Sahagun's Spain! Lafitau's mind was cleared for new thinking, and thinking anew he could see facts to which men had previously been blind. So it was that he discovered the Iroquoian form of bifurcate-merging kinship system. His powers of ethnographic observation and description were notable, and the example given by Sol Tax is worthy of reproduction:

Among the Iroquois and the Hurons, all the children of a Cabin [long house] regard their mothers' sisters as their mothers, and their mothers' brothers as their uncles; in the same way they give the name of father to all their fathers' brothers and that of aunt to their fathers' sisters. All of the children on the side of the mother and her sisters and of the father and his brothers they regard as equal to brothers and sisters, but as regards the children of their uncles and aunts—that is to say, of their mothers' brothers and their fathers' sisters—they treat them only on the footing of cousins although they may be as closely related as those whom they

[5]See C. E. Dibble and A. J. O. Anderson, *Florentine Codex: General History of the Things of New Spain* (in thirteen parts).
[6]J. H. Rowe, "Inca Culture at the Time of the Conquest," in J. H. Steward (ed.), *Handbook of South American Indians,* Vol. 2, p. 194. See *ibid.,* pp. 192–197, for a critical evaluation of a number of early sources on Inca culture and history, for example.
[7]Dibble and Anderson, *op. cit.,* Part II, p. 46.
[8]Jacques Bodin (1530–1596), French lawyer, political philosopher, and politician, published the first philosophy of history, replacing the notion of a golden age of the past with the idea of the progressive development of societies from a lower condition in his *Methodus ad facilem historiarum cognitionem* (*A Method for Improvement of Historical Understanding*) (Paris, 1566).

regard as brothers and sisters. In the third generation the grand-uncles and grand-aunts become grandfathers and grandmothers of the children of those whom they call nephews and nieces. This continues always in the descending line according to the same rule.[9]

Robertson's evolutionary ethnology By the middle of the eighteenth century, the idea of a developmental progression of human society had wholly seized the minds of enlightened rationalists in Europe and North America. Voltaire, Montesquieu, Montaigne, and Condorcet, in France; and Hobbes, Hume, and Locke, in England, had all built political philosophies or philosophies of history on the comparative contrast of primitive societies and the current state of sociopolitical development. They used ethnographic data as arguments to buttress their social theories, but they did not contribute to the development of an anthropology except as they further improved the climate of thought that would nourish it.

The first modern, systematic anthropological theorist, as we see him, is not one of these more famous people, but the Scottish historian William Robertson (1721–1793). Robertson's *History of America*, first published in 1777, is not a good ethnography of the American Indians, but it advanced a remarkably rational and surprisingly sophisticated expression of geniune anthropological theory and methodology. He, not Morgan or Tylor, it seems to us, is the first formulator of cultural evolutionism and cultural determinism in systematic terms.

In common with the thought of the Enlightenment, Robertson accepted the comparative evolution of human *society* as the essential fact of primary importance. In explanation of his concern with the American Indians, he wrote:

In order to complete the history of the human mind, and attain to a perfect knowledge of its nature and operations, we must contemplate man in all those various situations wherein he has been placed. We must follow him in his progress through the different stages of society as he gradually advances from the infant state of civil life towards its maturity and decline.[10]

Three stages of evolution In the organization of his material, Robertson used three stages of evolutionary typology: savagery, barbarism, and civilization, in ascendant order. Savages do not have writing, metals, domesticated animals, he noted, thus treating most of the New World tribes under the rubric of savagery.

In tracing the line by which nations proceed towards civilization, the discovery of the useful metals, and the acquisition of dominion over the animal creation, have been marked as steps of capital importance in their progress. In our continent [the Old World], long after men had attained both, society continued in that state which is denominated barbarous. Even with all that command over nature which these confer, many ages elapse, before industry becomes so regular as to render subsistence secure, before the arts which supply the wants and furnish the accommodations of life are brought to any considerable degree of perfection, and before any idea is conceived of various institutions requisite in a well-ordered society.[11]

Archaeological evidence Robertson clearly enunciated the fundamental importance and priority of subsistence technology over other aspects of culture, which modern evolutionists and ecologists are apt to treat as a discovery of Morgan, Tylor, Marx, and White. Nor was his long-range view of human development derived from speculative philosophy. Robertson was acquainted with archaeological fact and explicitly recognized the significance of prehistoric stone artifacts a half century before Boucher de Perthes rocked Europe with his Abbevillian discoveries (see page 157). He gave temporal priority to lithic cultures over bronze and iron cultures three-quarters of a

[9] J. F. Lafitau, *Moeurs des sauvages amériquaines,* Vol. 1 pp. 552–53. Quoted and translated by S. Tax, "From Lafitau to Radcliffe-Brown: A Short History of Social Organization", in F. Eggan (ed.), *Social Anthropology of North American Tribes* (enlarged ed.), pp. 445–446.

[10] W. Robertson, *The History of America,* Vol. 2, p. 262.
[11] *Ibid.,* p. 176.

century before European prehistorians worked out the sequence in detail.

It is a doubtful point, whether the dominion of man over the animal creation, or his acquiring the use of metals, has contributed most to extend his power. The era of this important discovery is unknown, and in our hemisphere very remote. It is only by tradition, or by digging up some rude instruments of our forefathers, that we learn that mankind were originally unacquainted with the use of metals, and endeavored to supply the want of them by employing flints, shells, bones, and other hard substances, for the same purposes which metals serve among polished nations. Nature completes the formation of some metals. Gold, silver, and copper . . . were accordingly the first metals known, and first applied to use. But iron, the most serviceable of all, and to which man is most indebted, is never discovered in its perfect form; its gross and stubborn ore must feel twice the force of fire, and go through two laborious processes, before it becomes fit for use. Man was long acquainted with the other metals, before he acquired the art of fabricating iron, or attained such ingenuity as to perfect an invention, to which he is indebted for those instruments wherewith he subdues the earth, and commands all its inhabitants.[12]

Parallelism Robertson also established the principle of parallelism for use in evolutionary theory:

The character and occupations of the hunter in America must be little different from those of an Asiatic, who depends for subsistence on the chase. A tribe of savages on the banks of the Danube must nearly resemble one upon the plain washed by the Mississippi. Instead then of presuming from this similarity, that there is any affinity between them, we should only conclude, that the disposition and manners of men are formed by their situation, and arise from the state of society in which they live. The moment that begins to vary, the character of a people must change.[13]

In addition, with perfect logical induction, Robertson predicted from known zoological and ethnographic facts the discovery that the Bering Strait had been used to cross from the

Old World to the New, and it was his theory that the American Indians had come from Asia by way of Siberia.

Cultural determinism In explaining behavioral differences among different peoples, Robertson discarded racism, which was the common explanation of cultural differences during his time and which, unfortunately, still is today in many quarters. His statement of enculturation expresses the fundamental postulates of cultural determinism in modern personality and culture theory:

A human being as he comes originally from the hand of nature, is everywhere the same. At his first appearance in the state of infancy, whether it be among the rudest savages, or in the most civilized nations, we can discern no quality which marks any distinction or superiority. The capacity of improvement seems to be the same and the talents he may afterwards acquire, as well as the virtues he may be rendered capable of exercising, depend, in a great measure, upon the state of society in which he is placed. To this state his mind naturally accommodates itself, and from it receives discipline and culture. . . . It is only by attending to this great principle, that we can discover what is the character of man in every different period of his progress.[14]

Finally, he contrasted the world views, personalities, and social institutions of the Aztecs and the Incas in terms of their distinctive "national character,"[15] the very words reintroduced into American anthropology after World War II in relation to such work as that of Benedict on Japan and of Mead and other personality and culture specialists as applied to modern nations.

With William Robertson, Presbyterian minister, principal of the University of Edinburgh, and Historiographer to His Majesty for Scotland, one can say that cultural anthropology was finally born.

Nineteenth-century evolutionists

Archaeology moved ahead more rapidly than ethnology during the first half of the nine-

---

[12]*Ibid.,* Vol. 1, pp. 309–311.
[13]*Ibid.,* Vol. 1, pp. 249–250.

[14]*Ibid.,* Vol. 1, pp. 368–369.
[15]See *Ibid.,* Vol. 2, pp. 206–227.

teenth century. Then, in 1860, ethnology suddenly came to life with a vigor that has never diminished.[16]

The great figures in the creative development of anthropology between 1860 and 1900 were, first and foremost, the evolutionists Sir Edward Tylor, Sir Henry Maine, and Sir James Frazer, in England; Lewis Henry Morgan, in the United States; and Johann Bachofen, in Switzerland. There were numerous lesser figures who played significant roles, but these were the master builders who shaped the growing subject during its early years.[17] Tylor's theory of animism has been discussed briefly in Chapter 32, pages 466 to 468, and the essentials of Morgan's evolutionism have been touched upon in Chapter 6, pages 86–87. Likewise, certain aspects of Darwin's impact on anthropological thinking have been presented in Chapter 8, pages 123–124. However, each deserves to be presented in a fuller contextual setting in this sequential discussion of the history of anthropological development, and we now examine their roles a bit more fully.

Darwin's *Origin of Species*   *The Origin of Species* (1859) is in no sense a work in anthropology, but it should be clear from the discussion in Part II that it has had a profound and ever-increasing influence on anthropology. It established man's natural place in the biological world and strengthened Bodin's proposition that man was not a fallen angel and that primitive societies were not retrograde remnants of an imagined golden age. It confirmed the proposition of the Enlightenment that mankind is struggling upward from a primitive antiquity. *The Origin of Species* established the continuity of all life and demonstrated how

natural selection working upon inheritable variations results in adaptive modifications in life forms, which in turn lead through speciation to radiating evolution. Although Darwin reserved his exploration of man in evolution for a second book, *The Descent of Man* (1871), *The Origin of Species* made it clear that man is the product of biological evolution just as technology, the arts, and society are the products of cultural evolution. Even Robertson had been content to accept the biblical story of Genesis as "infallible certainty," but after Darwin this would never be true again of any anthropologist of major stature. He made it possible for prehistoric studies and zoological analysis to move forward to parallel the development of cultural anthropology. These steps and their results have already been spelled out in Parts II and III and will not be retraced here.

It is amply clear, from all that has already been said, that Darwin *did not* supply the idea for cultural evolution and that he cannot be credited with starting the great anthropological outburst of the decade that followed *The Origin of Species*. Bastian, Morgan, Maine, and Tylor were well along with their works when Darwin's epoch-making study appeared. Morgan and Tylor were clearly building on Robertson (although neither appears to have so acknowledged), and even Darwin, as we have seen (page 86), attributed his inspirational stimulus to Thomas Malthus (1766–1834), who cited Robertson extensively in the three-volume second edition of his *Essay on the Principle of Population* (1803). Nonetheless, Darwin's stimulus clearly quickened the movement to work out in detail just how human societies did evolve. But more important for anthropology in the long run was the establishment by Darwin of man as a subject within the rubric of natural science. It was this fact which gave anthropology such a strong place in the developing museums of natural history and which turned cultural anthropology from a loose philosophy of history into a reasonably tight empirical science.

[16]For a review of the significant ethnographic developments that were occurring in the United States prior to 1860, see A. I. Hallowell, "The Beginnings of Anthropology in America," in F. de Laguna (ed.), *Selected Papers from the American Anthropologist: 1888–1920*, pp. 1–55.

[17]For discussions of some of the secondary figures, see H. R. Hays, *From Ape to Angel: An Informal History of Social Anthropology*, Part I; and T. K. Penniman, *A Hundred Years of Anthropology*, (rev. ed.), chap. 4. We deliberately omit Adolf Bastian as one whose influence seems to have been highly overrated.

Lewis Henry Morgan Morgan and Tylor are the preeminent figures of nineteenth-century cultural evolutionism. Of the two, Morgan made the broader contributions and may be considered first. Anthropologists love to tell and retell Morgan's story: how as a young man he converted his literary society, the Gordian Knot, into the New Confederation of the Iroquois at the inspiration of his friend, the true Iroquois, Ely Parker (later a general in the Union Army and Grand Sachem of the League of the Iroquois), and so became an ethnographer; how he ultimately produced a very professional and enduringly classic monograph on the Iroquois tribe in 1851;[18] how he rediscovered the Iroquois classificatory system of kinship terminology; how he sent comprehensive questionnaires on kinship around the world to get comparative data, which he presented in his monumental *Systems of Consanguinity of the Human Family* (1861), so starting anthropologists on their currently favorite passion—the study of kinship systems and social structure; how, in the meantime, he turned his legal contacts into entrepreneurial capitalism and made a small fortune in railroad building and iron mining, whereupon he gave up law and business to become a full-time ethnologist; how he expanded his explanation of classificatory kinship systems as survivals of earlier stages of social organization so that it became a full-fledged evolutionary account entitled *Ancient Society, or Researches in the Lines of Human Progress from Savagery through Barbarism to Civilization* (1877); and how finally "by a freak of fortune," as Lowie put it, *Ancient Society* attracted the attention of Marx and Engels, who made it a "sacred book" in the dogmatics of Communist thought—a position that it holds to this day (see pages 87–88).[19]

Stages of evolution The central kernel of Morgan's evolutionary thought is presented in the pages referred to above. It will be remembered that he took Robertson's three stages of savagery, barbarism, and civilization and elaborated on them by dividing savagery and barbarism into three substages each (lower, middle, and higher). Morgan than identified specific technological traits as diagnostic for the identification of each successive era:

1. Lower savagery represents the transitional state from ape to man, before fire and speech were used. No populations representing this stage have survived.

2. Middle savagery is marked by the development of speech, control of fire, and hunting and fishing subsistence. The Australian aborigines are presented as contemporary representatives of this stage.

3. Higher savagery is distinguished by the invention and use of the bow and arrow and, in Morgan's scheme, is represented by the Polynesians (an egregious idea, for reasons to be discussed below).

4. Lower barbarism is characterized by the invention and use of pottery and is exemplified by Morgan's own Iroquois.

5. Middle barbarism is marked by the domestication of plants and animals in the Old World and by irrigation and adobe-brick architecture in the New World; the Pueblo Indians and the high cultures of Mexico and Peru, for example, represent this stage.

6. Upper barbarism begins with the use of iron for tools and weapons, as in Homeric Greece.

7. Civilization is achieved when men invent writing. It is divided into ancient and modern substages.

Morgan's *Ancient Society* is essentially an effort to fill out the details of selected aspects of culture for each level. He wrote: "Each of these periods has a distinct culture and exhibits a mode of life more or less special and peculiar to itself."[20]

The evolution of kinship Morgan's major interest was in kinship, and hence his greatest effort was to reconstruct the evolution of kinship organization. In so doing, he seized upon

[18] *The League of the Ho-dé-no-sau-nee or Iroquois.*
[19] See B. J. Stern, *Lewis Henry Morgan: Social Evolutionist;* and Hays, *op. cit.,* chap. 2 and 5.
[20] L. H. Morgan, *Ancient Society,* pp. 12–13.

the most fundamental aspect of primitive culture. Nineteenth-century evolutionary theory has been called "mesological," meaning halfway logical; it worked loosely and without much critical rigor from a number of general assumptions to the establishment of many presumptive details. In kinship, Morgan and others began with the proposition that non-human animals are promiscuous and therefore the earliest transitional protohumans must have been promiscuous. Highly civilized societies (i.e., European) are monogamous and narrowly restrict mating by means of the incest tabu; therefore, since evolution proceeds through gradual modifications, mating went through a series of successive steps during which the range of individuals with whom one may mate or whom one may marry was always narrowing. The evolution of mating is from promiscuity to monogamy; Part III of *Ancient Society*, for example, maps out the road that was presumed to have been followed.

PROMISCUITY   The stage of sexual promiscuity is entirely hypothetical; no known or observed society permits it. The incest tabu is universal.

TABU ON PARENTS AND OFFSPRING   The first limitations on sex occurred, Morgan posited, when mating between parents and offspring was tabued. It was still possible for all the males and females of a given generation to mate at will within the local group. Kinship terminologies were invented at this point, and although this condition of human social organization (which he claimed prevailed on the level of early middle savagery) has not been observed either, Morgan argued that he had found surviving evidence of it in the generational terminology of the Malayans. Because all males and females on the parental levels were presumed to have intermated, he said they were lumped under a single term, distinguished only by a sex prefix. All brothers and sisters and everyone else on one's own generation intermated; hence, there was but one kinship term for them. All offspring could have been sired by any male in one's own generation; hence, everyone in the generation below is called by the same term. Morgan was perfectly aware of the fact that the Hawaiians, whom he used as his type example, however free and easy their sexual practices might have appeared, did not permit uncontrolled intra-generation sexuality. But according to his theory, *they must have* done so in the not-too-remote past, and although their social forms had changed, the kinship terminology was lagging behind as a surviving imprint of the second stage. Hence, the Hawaiians, with their tremendously sophisticated primitive culture, were placed at the next to the bottom rung of the evolutionary ladder. (It does happen that they have no pottery, but that was an art they lost in their overseas migrations to volcanic and coral islands, where ceramic clays are scarce or absent.) Morgan succumbed too easily to the tyranny of his theory.

TABU ON BROTHERS AND SISTERS   To return to Morgan's sequences, the third limitation on promiscuity occurred when ancient man supposedly discovered the eugenic consequences of brother-sister mating and so forbade it. The rule of exogamy was invented. The collective tendency to joint marriage continued to prevail. Now, however, a group of brothers and cousins collectively married and shared a group of wives together. Their own sisters had to marry into an outside band. Bifurcation was thus introduced into descent; i.e., the children of brothers formed one descent group, and the children of their sisters formed another. Descent lines came into existence for the first time, and because children are biologically much more readily identified with their mothers than with their fathers, Morgan claimed that the first clans were matrilineal. Whereas material resources had previously been shared in common by all members of the community in a form of primitive communism, the introduction of the principle of lineal descent substituted joint ownership by matrilineal clans for communal ownership by all. A new kinship terminology replaced the Hawaiian to accord with the new kinship relationships. Bifurcate-merging systems of terminology of the Iroquois type, distinguishing the offspring of brothers and sisters, evolved. All this first took place in the period of lower and middle barbarism.

PAIRING MARRIAGES AND MONOGAMY Late in the period of barbarism, a tendency to *pairing* marriages is said to have occurred. A wife now belonged to a specific man, although he might have several of them. Why pairing was initiated is not explained by Morgan, but once established, man saw it as adaptively superior; hence its spread.

As long as subsistence was predominantly horticultural, the matriclan system could continue. On the other hand, cattle are closely identified with men. Morgan believed pastoralism was a later form, and he could see that it was associated with paternal descent. Since ancient civilizations were patriarchal, earlier lineal systems had to be matrilineal—he thought. (This is a good example of mesological reasoning.) Therefore, with no other evidence, pastoralism and patrilineal clans were assigned a later position on the evolutionary scale. The shift from matriarchal to patriarchal descent occurred because men as stockholders objected to passing their herds to sisters' sons, to whom they felt less sentimentally bound than to their own sons. In the simple communistic dogma of Friedrich Engels, Morgan's popularizer, "Mother right had to be overthrown and overthrown it was," in a revolution by "simple decree"—"one of the most decisive ever experienced by humanity"—a revolution that initiated the "World historical defeat of the female sex."[21] Women became the property of their husbands, as did their children. Patriarchal power was established in the *patria potestas,* as it was known in Rome. Monogamy followed as a means of consolidating property holding by means of limited descent lines. Civilization was born.

Morgan's *Ancient Society* also traces the evolution of property holding and of the state as parallel manifestations of related evolutionary

changes, but there is not sufficient space to follow these through in this book. The nature of nineteenth-century cultural evolutionism should be clear from what has been presented.

Criticism of Morgan's theory On the positive side, Morgan was perfectly right in his basic assumption that culture has evolved out of nothing. He was also on solid ground in accepting the archaeological sequence of hunting and gathering followed by domestication of plants and animals, of preceramic followed by ceramic, of bow and arrow preceeding iron, and of writing coming late in culture history. These are very simple expressions of what we have detailed in a general way in Part II.

Reconstructing the evolution of social organization is a very different matter from tracing general developments in material cutlure, however, and this was Morgan's sole concern. He was an ethnologist rather than an archaeologist. Nor does the cultural evolutionist have the solid evidence to work with that is available to the student of biological evolution. The problem that faces the cultural evolutionist, in contrast to that facing the biological evolutionist, is that the latter has solid datable fossils, while the cultural evolutionist has only the meager vestiges of material culture which the archaeologist provides for him (usually not more than 1 per cent of the total material culture of a group). An organic fossil represents a much greater proportion of the original living entity than archaeological remains do of the once-living intangible culture. Therefore, cultural evolutionists such as Morgan are forced into *inferential reconstructions* of culture patterns and social structures that are to be associated with each evolutionary stage. Their major tool is the weak instrument of analogic inference, and if they try to produce very specific results, it is easy to demolish the product. It is extremely difficult to give detailed substance to a theory of general evolution. Morgan built his system on the concurrent evolution of subsistence technology, kinship, property, and government. Of these, only the first leaves any archaeological evidence of significance—

[21] F. Engels, *The Origin of the Family, Property, and the State in the Light of the Researches of Lewis Henry Morgan,* pp. 49–50.

and our discussions in Part II have indicated the limits of what is known even today. Lafitau established, it is true, the principle that contemporary primitive societies can throw light on prehistoric societies, but "throwing light on" is something less than establishing valid sequential details of evolution of nonmaterial culture.[22]

E. B. Tylor and J. G. Frazer: The evolution of religion Morgan dismissed religion as a subject for evolutionary study, thus showing a degree of circumspection that he did not extend to kinship. He wrote:

The growth of religious ideas is environed with such intrinsic difficulties that it may never receive a perfectly satisfactory exposition. Religion deals so largely with the imaginative and emotional nature, and consequently with such uncertain elements of knowledge, that all primitive religions are to some extent unintelligible.[23]

Morgan has been proved right to doubt the first point: no valid general evolutionary sequence can be established for religious forms. He was wrong on the second point, for all religions can be demonstrably understandable if the principles of cultural relativity are grasped and the basic postulates are perceived upon which strange religions are built.

Morgan notwithstanding, Tylor had published his great two-volume work, which is almost wholly devoted to the evolutionary development of religion and culture, six years previously (1871), and Frazer followed through with his monumental twelve-volume classic on magical and religious developments.[24] The outlines of Tylor's theory of the evolution of religion from the invention of animism and the soul concept, through ghost and ancestor worship, through nature worship, and through these to polytheism and monotheism have been

reviewed in Chapter 32. Frazer's task, as he set it for himself, was to trace the origins of magic and religion. The path he outlined was somewhat different from that presented by Tylor. Frazer identified both religion and magic as means of controlling natural forces, but he assumed that primitive man in the earliest evolution of culture first invented magic, turning to religious belief only after experience taught him the fallibility of magic as a means to ends. His theory was wholly psychological, and he used the device of thinking as he believed primitive men must have thought in the dim, lost ages of the past. (Max Gluckman tells us that Radcliffe-Brown called this the "if-I-were-a-horse" method of evolutionary reconstruction, the method of the farmer whose horse has strayed from the barnyard. Before starting on an aimless search, he scratches his head, chews on a bit of straw, and asks, "Now if I were a horse, where would *I* go?"[25]) Thus, Frazer

for an answer postulated a theory of intellectual development by placing on a time-scale institutions which co-exist [magic, religion, and science]. He worked out the stages on this scale by imagining how he himself would have reasoned had he been there: first, thinking he could control nature by associating like antecedents with like after-events [sympathetic magic]; by thereafter escaping from his keen-witted disillusionment [magic really does not work] into the belief that the powers were there but superior to him [religion]; and yet thereafter escaping from his further disillusionment, this time with religion, to accepting a regularity and an immutability in nature of which man could avail himself, once he bowed to necessity [science].[26]

The evolutionary theory of *The Golden Bough* is an intellectualist dream without a wisp of reality in its form, and yet the book is a golden treasury of ethnographic and classical learning, a fascinating compendium of strange doings and fanciful beliefs, both primitive and classical, written in formally elegant English. It deserves to be read for generations to come, but not for its method or theory.

[22]See R. H. Lowie, *The History of Ethnological Theory*, pp. 54–67; and "Lewis Henry Morgan in Historical Perspective," in *Essays in Anthropology in Honor of Alfred Louis Kroeber*, pp. 169–181, for a fuller critique of Morgan's work.
[23]Morgan, *op. cit.*, p. 5.
[24]E. B. Tylor, *Primitive Culture: Researches into the Development of Mythology, Philosophy, Religion, Language, Art and Custom*; J. G. Frazer, *The Golden Bough: A Study in Magic and Religion*.
[25]M. Gluckman, *Politics, Law, and Ritual in Tribal Society*, p. 2.
[26]*Ibid.*, p. 5.

Henry Maine: From status to contract Maine was a cultural evolutionist who confined his theoretical writings to the subject of the evolution of law. He was a highly specialized legal historian and evolutionary theorist who used not a shred of data from any extant primitive society. His comparative sources were almost entirely limited to Greece and Rome, although he did draw somewhat on his knowledge of the village community in India. Maine's value to anthropology does not lie in his specific series of evolutionary stages in law; this has long since been proved to be without substance and even more chimerical than Morgan's theory.[27]

Ideal types as polar opposites Maine counts today because he established the theoretical use of *ideal types* of societies and institutions as *polar opposites* for purposes of comparative analysis in social science. In *Ancient Law* (1861), he formulated the contrast in terms of primitive and ancient societies in which social relations were dominated by *status*, as opposed to "progressive" societies in which social relations are predominantly determined by *contract*. Status means that a person's kinship indentity predetermines his legal position. Contract means that legal positions arise from free agreement among individuals. The contrast is that between family-centered obligations and identities and those which are individual-centered.

Today, this is the major functional-structural difference between undeveloped and Oriental civilizations and Western, industrialized civilizations. Maine not only drew out the details of the contrasts but also tried to link the two poles in an evolutionary model, even as Morgan had done. He inserted the dimension of time and phrased it in a famous formula: ". . . the movement of the progressive societies has hitherto been a movement from *Status to Contract*."[28] Maine also contrasted the dominance

[27]See R. Redfield, "Maine's *Ancient Law* in the Light of Primitive Societies" (*Western Political Quarterly*, Vol. 3, 1950), pp. 574–589.
[28]H. S. Maine, *Ancient Law*, p. 165.

of private law in primitive societies with that of criminal law in civilized societies. Maine's very important functional analysis of the use of legal fictions and equity to achieve change without structural destruction cannot be examined here. For students of sociology, we should note that Ferdinand Tönnies's contrast of *Gemeinschaft vs. Gesellschaft* stems from Maine, as does Emile Durkheim's contrast of communities bound by "mechanical" solidarity and those bound by "organic" solidarity. Robert Redfield's "folk-urban continuum" is directly in the methodological tradition of Maine's model of polar opposites linked by an intermediate gradation of transitional types. Maine survives because he first fashioned some of the basic tools of the modern social scientist.

Twentieth-century developments

At the turn of the century an important event for anthropology was an upswell of dissatisfaction with the substantive hollowness, however fascinating, of the schemes of the cultural evolutionists. This was to be the century of scientific thinking, and science is as impatient with meta-anthropology as it is with metaphysics. The reaction came first in the work of Franz Boas (1858–1942) and his followers.

Frank Boas: Historical reconstruction The Boasian reaction to speculative evolution has been touched on to some extent in Chapter 6 (see page 88). Its great achievement is that it ushered in the era of modern, empirical anthropology by terminating the three-hundred-year philosophy-of-history phase of speculative evolutionism, and initiated the effort to develop reliable and objective methods of observation and recording in ethnography, physical anthropology, archaeology, and linguistics. It was Boas who introduced the practice of recording the statements of primitive informants in their own languages. To make this possible, he devised the American system of phonetic recording and set the pattern for all American graduate programs in anthropology that require intensive linguistic training of advanced students. He also laid the foundation for all American Indian language studies and for the present "modern" techniques of teaching foreign languages (emphasizing use of vernacular conversation rather than memorization of word lists and grammatical rules). He insisted on detailed reporting of ethnographic observations derived from field research. He developed statistical techniques for handling growth and development data in physical anthropology.

Boas was born a year before *The Origin of Species* was published. He was trained in physics and mathematics. His bent was for natural science, but his interest was the study of human beings; he measured their bodies with exactitude and strove to record their beliefs, myths, and ceremonies as they themselves stated them. He strove for the inside view. Kroeber said, and with truth: "It is perhaps Boas' fundamental contribution to science and civilization: to treat human data with rigorous scientific method on a scale unattempted before."[29]

Boas's aim in the period from 1890 to 1910 was to convert anthropology from the deductive speculativeness of the evolutionists to the inductive exactitude of natural science. This he did with marked success. We do not say that he made a science of anthropology; we say that he converted anthropologists in the United States to the orientation of the scientist in tackling the problems of anthropology.

Controlled comparison and areal analysis Boas's stance was by no means wholly negative. He maintained that universal laws of culture were to be found, but he insisted that they be extracted from painstakingly gathered facts, not from the philosopher's closet. He abhorred premature generalization—which in his time meant almost all generalization. Boas introduced the methods of both *controlled comparison* and *areal analysis* of the development of cultural forms through distribution of traits within a culture area.

TSIMSHIAN MYTHOLOGY The development and application of these combined methods were presented by Boas in 1916, when his study of Tsimshian mythology was published.[30] A full body of Tsimshian myths is given in this work, and the myths are then classified and analyzed to lay bare the component motifs of which each is built up. Next, the distribution of each myth is plotted for the entire Northwest Coast culture area (here is the idea of controlled comparison: the environment is generally homogeneous, and the cultures likewise). The components of each myth throughout the Northwest Coast are also analyzed and plotted. From these data, the steps in the development and elaboration of the myths are reconstructed and the lines of diffusion of the components are plotted. The specific evolution of myths within the Northwest Coast environment was thus worked out with as much exactitude as is humanly possible. What is more, Boas took special pains to show how myths that have intercontinental distribution were changed by the Kwakiutl Indians to reflect Kwakiutl culture. He did not talk in terms of evolutionary adaptation, but he did demonstrate meticulously with fact how specific cultural forms were adapted to the total environment—physical, cultural, and social. Swanton did a parallel study of the distribution of clans within the Northwest Coast area.

NORTHWEST COAST ART Boas also analyzed Northwest Coast art, which, like all other aspects of culture, he viewed functionally in its full cultural context:

This art style can be fully understood only as an integral part of the structure of Northwest coast culture. The fundamental idea underlying the thoughts, feelings, and activities of these tribes is the value of rank which gives title to the use of privileges, most of which find expression in artistic activities or in the use of art forms.[31]

The aims of Boasian methodology Boas's major objection to evolutionist methodology, to be

[29]A. L. Kroeber, "Preface," in W. Goldschmidt (ed.), *The Anthropology of Franz Boas* (American Anthropological Association Memoir 89, 1959), p. vi.

[30]F. Boas, *Tsimshian Mythology.*
[31]F. Boas, *Primitive Art,* p. 280.

more emphatically reiterated by Malinowski and Radcliffe-Brown, was that it tore traits out of context and built with gross disregard for cultures as meaningful wholes.

Myth, art, material culture, ceremonial organization, and social organization—all these were to be studied in depth, in context, within a culture area; distributions were to be plotted to determine which manifestations of a trait were universal within the area, which were special, and where the cultures of greatest complexity lay. *Then* one could say something about the developmental (historical) cultural processes for that area and the conditions it represented. He would go no further. When this had been done for a number of areas, it would be time enough to compare the results between areas to see whether higher levels of generalization with empirical validity were possible. Boas was not a young man in a hurry, and he made short shrift of those who were.

Boas's associates and followers in the first quarter of this century expanded the research in a program of their own. From his center in the anthropological division of the American Museum of Natural History in New York, Clark Wissler (1870–1947) sent out expedition after expedition to round out the ethnographic data on Plains Indian military clubs and the sun dance. Lowie put the results on military societies through the analytical mill, while Leslie Spier did the same for the sun dance.[32]

These manifestations of the Boasian method are usually treated as though they were concerned solely with the reconstruction of historical fragments of cultures. It is often overlooked that the concern was not with chronology so much as with the dynamics of cultural process: how was the sun dance received and restated to fit the ends and purposes, the particular outlooks, and the cultural forms of each society—and what did they have in common?[33] Again, let it be stated, the aim was to specify the details of cultural adaptation, not in terms of a universal general formula, but in terms of variegated diversity of real cultures in specific environmental settings.

To sum up in Boas's own words:

In short then, the method which we try to develop is based on a study of dynamic changes in society that may be observed at the present time. We refrain from the attempt to solve the fundamental problem of the general development of civilization until we have been able to unravel the processes that are going on under our eyes.

. . . if we look for laws, the laws relate to the effects of physiological, psychological, and social conditions, not to sequences of cultural achievement.[34]

Functionalism and social structure In Germany and Austria, an anthropological theory of diffusion of cultures on a broad scale developed as a second alternative to evolutionary anthropology. Under the leadership of Father Wilhelm Schmidt, it flourished for several decades (from 1910 to 1940) but had little influence on the general development of anthropological theory or method; it disappeared with World War II (at least for the time being).[35] Discussion of the *Kulturkreislehre* (culture complex theory) will be waived, as will be that of the British diffusionist writers Elliot Smith and W. J. Perry, who set forth highly speculative diffusionist schemes that were quite devoid of method.

In England, the major reaction to evolutionism came in the form of a total rejection of culture history as a subject for anthropological study; in its stead, Bronislaw Malinowski (1884–1942) and A. R. Radcliffe-Brown (1881–1955) built a new approach to anthropology that emphasized cultures as social systems.

[32] R. H. Lowie, "Plains Indian Age Societies: Historical Summary" (*American Museum of Natural History, Anthropological Papers*, Vol. 11, 1916), pp. 877–984; L. Spier, "The Sun Dance of the Plains Indian" (*American Museum of Natural History, Anthropological Papers*, Vol. 16, Part 1, 1921).

[33] J. W. Bennett, "The Development of Ethnological Theories as Illustrated by Studies of the Plains Indian Sun Dance" (*American Anthropologist*, Vol. 46, 1944), pp. 162–181.

[34] F. Boas, "The Methods of Ethnology" (*American Anthropologist*, Vol. 22, 1920), pp. 316, 328.

[35] See C. Kluckhohn, "Some Reflections on the Method and Theory of the Kulturkreislehre" (*American Anthropologist*, Vol. 38, 1936), pp. 157–196.

Negatively, they took the position that, at worst, historical and cultural evolutionary studies are a futility: there are few verifiable facts to work with, and hence there are no chronological data from prehistory other than archaeological data for a science of anthropology to use. At best, they argued, historical reconstruction is a strategic waste of anthropological time—much richer results may be harvested by focusing on living societies that can be observed in action. Why strain so hard with even such a method as Boas's when it produces what Kroeber called "comparative sterility" because "It does not tell, and does not try to tell, why things happen in society as such."[36]

It is far better, they insisted, to see how societies work as complete systems; one will learn much more about what culture does and what it is used for from verifiable observation. In this they were correct; the payoff from functional research *is* much richer than that derived from the historical reconstructions of the heyday of Boasianism.

Durkheim's basic contribution   The forerunner of the functionalism of Malinowski and Radcliffe-Brown, and the intellectual ancestor of later British social anthropology, in particular, was the French social scientist Émile Durkheim (1858–1917). Durkheim and Boas were contemporaries, and both gave a new direction to anthropology at the turn of the century. Boas's influence was more direct during the first third of this century; Durkheim's was longer delayed, but since 1930 his influence has grown progressively.

Durkheim was professionally more a sociologist than an anthropologist. Like Boas, he emphasized the importance of rigorous method and empirical reality in building a scientific base for the understanding of society. Unlike Boas, he did not himself participate in, or contribute to, the development of ethnographic field studies. Nonetheless, he welcomed anthro-

pological contributions to his highly influential journal, *Année sociologique* (1898 to 1914). His one avowedly anthropological book, *The Elementary Forms of Religious Life*, was less successful than his analysis of social interdependence in his *Division of Labor* and his development of the idea of the entity of society in relation to collective identity, particularly in his study *Suicide.*

Durkheim insisted that the facts of society must be explained in terms of society and not by reference to psychology or biology. Religion for Durkheim is a social, rather than a psychological, phenomenon expressive of social interests. In the study of religion, the prime objective is to seek its origins not in dreams or anxiety but in what it does for society. The function of a social institution, he held, is the relation between it and the needs of the social organism, the society as an entity. The very concept of "functional prerequisites for societal maintenance," which was presented at the beginning of this book (pages 30–31), derives from Durkheim's notion of needs of the social organism. The idea of social function could be developed in differing ways, however, and this was done by Malinowski, Radcliffe-Brown, and their followers.

Malinowski's theory and method   Malinowski's great contribution was the pattern he set for ethnological field research. A citizen of Polish Austria, he was "interned" when, at the outbreak of World War I, he was permitted to spend the duration of the war among the Trobriand Islanders. Although he was trained as a mathematician in Poland, people and anthropology were his natural passion, and it was people living life that entranced him. This is what he looked for; this is what he reported. He, it will be remembered, was the first anthropologist to insist that what people *do* (no matter how seemingly trivial or irrelevant) is what must fill the ethnographer's notebook. What *they say they do* is important to record, to be sure, but it must not be taken

[36]A. L. Kroeber, "Review of R. H. Lowie, *Primitive Society*" (*American Anthropologist*, Vol. 22, 1920), p. 380.

as representing their culture in fact. Evidence is what the field worker can see; informants are to recite myths and roles but not to generalize customs, except as this expresses attitudes.

Beyond observing and reporting, Malinowski's credo was "the theoretical assumption that the total field of data under the observation of the field-worker must somehow fit together and make sense."[37]

There are no such things as survivals, he argued. Every aspect of culture is functionally significant in its matrix. The task of the social anthropologist is to dissect the culture with sufficient skill to reveal its workings: "The real mental effort, the really uphill work is not so much 'to get facts' as to elicit the relevance of these facts and systematize them into an organic whole."[38]

THREE MANIFESTATIONS OF FUNCTION To go further than we did in the brief introduction to functionalism in Chapter 2, it should be stated here that Malinowski's theory and method dealt with function as the organizing principle operating on three levels: (1) the effect of a custom or institution on other customs or institutions within the culture, (2) the goal-achievement effects of a practice as goals are defined by the members of a society, and (3) the part played by a custom or institution in promoting social cohesion (solidarity) and the continuance of a given way of life in a given environment (the functional prerequisites of societal maintenance set forth in Chapter 2).[39] Whether an anthropologist correctly identifies the functions of culture traits and institutions is a subtle problem of validation. There is no foolproof methodology in functionalism, but it is frequently possible to demonstrate the interacting effects of the various aspects of the culture. Societies became living, pulsating, dynamic entities under the Malinowskian method of fieldwork and analysis. With history out the window,

what was lost in the time dimension was gained in an understanding of the social physiology of living societies. The superb quality of field studies done by Malinowski-trained students in England and the United States is testimony to the marked advance made in anthropological methods under his stimulus. Malinowski found a way to give illuminating answers to people who want to know "why."[40]

Radcliffe-Brown and structuralism Radcliffe-Brown's organic analogy of functionalism was presented on page 25. It should be reread at this point. Radcliffe-Brown and subsequent British social anthropologists, such as E. E. Evans-Pritchard, Meyer Fortes, Max Gluckman, and Raymond Firth, moved on from functionalism to concern with social structure, which has been the chief focus of British—and a number of American—social anthropologists since 1940. Functionalism was not rejected; rather, it was absorbed and became an implicit aspect of almost all British, French, and American cultural anthropology. In the opening paragraphs of Chapter 20, we defined social structure as "the ways in which groups and individuals are organized and related to one another in the functioning entity that is a society" (page 308). (Chapters 20 to 31 are concerned with social structure.) From 1935 to the present, several dozen first-rate structural studies of social systems in all parts of the world have emerged from prolonged and sophisticated field studies.

Three negative features that distinguish the British studies in social structure are (1) they have continued the antihistorical bias of Malinowski and Radcliffe-Brown,[41] (2) they have

---

[37]E. R. Leach, "The Epistemological Background to Malinowski's Empiricism," in R. Firth (ed.), *Man and Culture: An Evaluation of the Work of Bronislaw Malinowski*, p. 120.

[38]B. Malinowski, *Coral Gardens and Their Magic*, Vol. 1, p. 322.

[39]Malinowski's functional theory of the incest tabu, discussed in Chap. 22, pp. 37–38, exemplifies this principle.

[40]Malinowski built a theoretical system of the relation of culture to the satisfaction of human organic needs, but as Gluckman points out, the biogenic endowments of mankind are sufficiently similar so that they cannot be a significant factor in accounting for varying social organizations. See M. Gluckman, *Politics, Law, and Ritual in Tribal Society*, pp. 29–30.

[41]Evans-Pritchard has, however, urged his colleagues to accept the fact that the basic assumptions on which structuralist studies rest are capable of validation only in conjunction with historical perspective. See his *Anthropology and History* (1961).

dogmatically followed Durkheim in refusing to utilize psychological theories or concepts in explanation of specific social forms in any given culture, and (3) they have treated their data in terms of only a limited comparative frame of reference (usually African).[42]

Ethnohistorical studies In the United States, documented history has been wedded to anthropology in a small number of studies of American tribes in a way that more accurately represents the historical nature of structural forms. The prototype was Felix Keesing's work on the Menominee, who migrated from Michigan to central Wisconsin in the eighteenth century and whose social system is fully understandable only in the light of the historical forces that were at work on the colonial frontier. Oscar Lewis's study, *The Effect of the Fur Trade on Blackfoot Culture,* is another model modern ethnohistorical study, in contrast to historical reconstructionism. In the Americas, every "primitive" culture that any anthropologist has studied had been profoundly influenced and modified in some respects by the presence of traders and by colonial wars by the time the anthropologist arrived on the scene (this must be true of all parts of the world). It is impossible to ignore history and achieve a fully effective understanding of such cultures. Contemporary anthropologists are now fully aware of this, and they are less prone to ignore the historical dimension; nonetheless, for anthropologists, history is not studied for its own sake but rather for the light it may throw on the processes of cultural adaptation and present forms.

A purely practical development has also contributed to the intensification of historical interests among American anthropologists since 1947. The decision of the Congress of the United States in 1946 to establish a special Commission of Indian Claims to hear and

adjudicate all tribal claims for compensation for lands that were preempted without or contrary to treaty agreement, or that were ceded to the United States without fair and adequate compensation, has drawn a number of American anthropologists into ethnohistorical research as expert witness on behalf of the government or the suing tribes. Much more than mere history is involved. In the Ute Indian claim case, which involves most of the land in Utah and eastern Nevada, the anthropologist for the Utes provided over one thousand historical documents for use in evidence. The crucial issue to be determined, however, is the empirical-conceptual one: "Did the Utes, prior to the coming of the white man, have an indigenous concept of land as property within the meaning of the law?" The answer to that one is worth 25 to 100 million dollars to the United States government or to the Utes. Historical anthropology is more than a scholar's pastime.

Culture and personality research The development of general theory in the study of the interaction of culture upon personality development and the feedback effect of personality types upon cultural institutions has been covered in Chapter 4. The nature of the work by Malinowski, Mead, Benedict, DuBois, Kardiner and Linton, and Whiting and Child, among many others, need not be restated here. Historically, it is interesting to note that while the linguist Edward Sapir personally provided much stimulus to the psychoanalytic interest in the *individual* in primitive societies on the part of Benedict and others, it was as Boas-trained anthropologists that Benedict and Mead gave culture and personality studies the impetus and theoretical start that made them the major interest of American cultural anthropologists from 1930 to 1950.

The great excitement created in the 1930s by the relating of personality psychology to the problems of anthropology has now calmed down, but so long as anthropology does not forsake the study of *man* for the study of dehu-

---

[42] J. Goody has set a new example of the extensive use of comparative data and alternative theoretical approaches in *Death, Property and the Ancestors* (1962), his excellent study of the rituals of death as functional vehicles for transmission of statuses, especially those relating to property, in two tribes of West Africa.

manized culturology or social structure as things *sui generis,* so long will culture and personality research continue to yield rich rewards in terms of interest and useful applications, both in psychotherapy and in cultural-development programs.

Cross-cultural correlational methods A major research resource for anthropology was created when G. P. Murdock initiated the Yale Cross Cultural Survey in 1937. The survey was designed as a classified respository of ethnographic fact. The data were indexed in such a way that anyone wishing to find what had been reported on almost any feature of culture could immediately select the cards bearing the index key for the subject of his interest. Each card contained a verbatim reproduction of what was written on the subject in a given book or article. The cultures included in the survey represented all the geographic areas of the world and all levels of development. The files served from the outset as a convenient reference source so far as the tribes covered by the survey were concerned. The value of the Yale Cross Cultural Survey was such that it was subsequently made an interuniversity project in the form of the Human Relations Area Files.

By their very nature, the files invite statistical testing of anthropological hypotheses. It is usually relatively easy to determine whether a particular culture trait is present or absent in a given culture. If this determination is made with reference to a trait in all the cultures, the relative frequency of the trait can be quickly determined. This then makes possible the substitution of a more exact expression of frequency than "rarely," "commonly," or "usually," which have so long been characteristic of anthropological generalizations.

In any science, relationships count for more than mere frequencies, and this is where statistical coefficients of correlations may be helpful. Does matrilineal organization correlate with horticulture or not? Does virilocal residence correlate with patrilineal descent? With progeny price? With pastoralism? The cultural

anthropologist for years had contented himself with relying on as wide a memory retention of ethnographic fact as possible, on the basis of which he could formulate tentative hypotheses of relationships. When a hypothesis was put forward, other anthropologists would comb their memories to see whether they could think of contradictory cases, especially from the tribes they had specialized in. If there were not too many serious exceptions, the hypothesis would stand, accepted for the time being, at least. This is the *method of disproof by the crucial instance,* still the favorite methodological test of most anthropologists. Obviously, it has its weaknesses. How many facts from how many cultures can even the best-read ethnologist keep in his head?

Murdock's statistical study of social structure In 1941, Murdock built up a checklist of significant facts on family, kinship, kin and local groups, and sexual behavior. The data from eighty-five tribes in the Human Relations Area Files were registered on the lists as indicating presence (+) or absence (−) of a given trait. Similar data lists were made for 165 additional societies not included in the files. Thus Murdock had data sheets on 250 cultures. By counting each occurrence or absence of a trait as a positive or negative unit, he was able to produce quantified four-cell tables for a large number of paired traits, on the basis of which coefficients of correlation could be calculated. For example, bilocal residence paired with generational-type kinship terminology in the classification of mother, father's sister, and mother's sister under one relationship term produced the following frequencies:

	bilocal residence	
	absent (−)	present (+)
present (+) *generation-type terms for m, fsi, msi*	9	33
absent (−)	11	187

Application of Yule's coefficient of association formula (the one used by Murdock) produces a Q (correlation) of + .65 with a .0010 chi-square (X^2) level of confidence in statistical significance.[43]

The correlation for five other groups of generational kinship terms in association with bilocal residence ranged between +.64 and +.75. Thus, the theorem that *bilocal residence tends to be associated with kinship terminology of the generational type* is validated. It changes from an hypothesis or theorem to a rule.

Many standard hypotheses have been tested by Murdock and others by this method. Some have been strongly validated, and some strongly unsubstantiated; on many, the statistical results are inconclusive. Whiting and Child's extension of the method, with modified techniques, to child training and personality was discussed in Chapter 4, pages 65 to 67. In spite of very severe methodological limitations,[44] the Murdock-Whiting method of cross-cultural testing of anthropological hypotheses is gaining ground rapidly and will continue to grow in importance for some time to come.

Murdock's World Ethnographic Sample A sample must reliably represent the whole if its statistical results are not to be dangerously misleading. To test the reliability of the sample used in his book on social structure, Murdock subsequently recalculated correlations on all the major propositions tested in the work. On his rerun, he used two new samples of cultures: one "wholly unselected" and another that contained exactly equal numbers of cultures from each major area of the world. The statistical results differed sufficiently in each test so that he judged it necessary to select a larger sample that would represent culture types and areas. The product is the World Ethnographic Sample of 585 cultures coded according to subsistence, types of community, kinship organization, marriage, kinship terminologies, residence, social classes, and political integration as classified by Murdock himself.[45] IBM

punch cards and all possible cross-correlations from the data are now tabulated in the handbook by Coult and Habenstein, which has been drawn upon a number of times in our discussions of social structure throughout this text. Additional data continue to be added yearly by Murdock in *The World Ethnographic Atlas*, which appears in installments in *Ethnography*, the professional periodical edited by Murdock.

The statistical method of testing cross-cultural correlations is not intended to be an exclusive method of anthropological research, and it is not expected that it will displace unquantified research. But insofar as it can surmount the technical difficulties of achieving valid codification of subtly variable cultural factors, it bids fair to increase its usefulness to anthropology.

Archaeology, physical anthropology, and applied anthropology The significant trends and discoveries in twentieth-century archaeology and physical anthropology have, we believe, been implicitly presented in Parts II and III. The Great Depression of the 1930s stimulated concern with the application of anthropology to the solution of national problems in the United States. The British colonial service was independently drawing upon anthropological assistance in the administration of its African colonies. Since World War II, the race to modernize the tribal societies of the erstwhile colonial dependencies, now new nations, has given new urgency to the practical application of anthropological theory and knowledge. Some aspects of this pressing task are touched upon in the next chapter, as we consider the passing of the primitive world and what it portends for anthropology—and for man.

SUMMARY

Classical Greece and Rome failed to develop any anthropological ideas because, believing there was nothing to be learned from barbar-

[43]G. P. Murdock, *Social Structure*, p. 152.

[44]For example, see the critical problems raised by E. Norbeck, D. E. Walker, and M. Cohen, "The Interpretation of Data: Puberty Rites" (*American Anthropologist*, Vol. 64, 1962), pp. 463–485.

[45]G. P. Murdock, "World Ethnographic Sample" (*American Anthropologist*, Vol. 59, 1957), pp. 664–687.

ians, they were incapable of a comparative approach to human institutions.

Anthropology as an identifiable subject is a child of the Age of Reason, when thinkers of the Enlightenment began to form an evolutionary philosophy of history to account for the newly discovered primitive peoples revealed by the voyages of discovery. Comparative ideas had already been born in the Renaissance, however, as Europeans contemplated the ancient classical world. Fray Sahagun's account of the Aztecs, coming early in the sixteenth century, is the first systematic ethnography of a non-European people. Early in the eighteenth century, Lafitau, the French Jesuit, published the first comparative ethnology—a study of American Indian cultures compared with those of Greece and Rome. William Robertson's *History of America* formulated a number of basic principles of evolutionary anthropology and laid the foundations for the evolutionary systems that would mark the birth of anthropology as a full-fledged field, beginning in 1860.

Nineteenth-century evolutionism is best characterized in the work of L. H. Morgan, who attempted to correlate successive steps in the limitation of sexual relations from promiscuity to monogamy with stages of technological evolution. Kinship systems, social organization, and ownership of property were also inferred in progressive steps related to forms of marriage. The method was mesological, and the resulting evolutionary scheme collapsed when twentieth-century anthropologists proved that there is no demonstrable evolutionary sequence in types of kinship systems.

Tylor and Frazer formulated analogous schemes of evolutionary sequences for spirit beings, from animism to monotheism (Tylor), and for magic, religion, and scientific thought (Frazer). Maine treated the evolution of law as a progressive shift from primitive status-dominated cultures to civilized cultures, which he characterized as basing personal relations on individual contract. The two types of society resulting from such cultures were treated as polar opposites.

In the twentieth century, the American rejection of cultural evolutionism was initiated by Franz Boas, who emphasized the gathering of empirical data in the field and the methodological procedure of trait analysis of specific institutions within a culture area as a means of limited historical reconstruction.

In England, Malinowski and Brown rejected all historical goals for anthropology. Instead, they substituted the study of whole cultures as integrated systems as the type of anthropological research that they claimed would give the most rewarding results. Field studies should overlook nothing in the way of behavior or attitudes because every custom and act is functionally significant. The object of research is to discover the functions as a means of learning how societies hold together and achieve their purposes. Radcliffe-Brown moved from a concern with function to an emphasis on social structure, the organization of interpersonal relations within a social system. Structural theory and research have been characteristic of British social anthropology since 1940, and are also a major feature of contemporary French and American cultural anthropology today.

The use of historical records as a means of following the development of so-called aboriginal cultures has been a significant trend in the United States since 1935. Ethnohistory, as distinct from cultural evolution, is not concerned with reconstruction of unrecorded prehistoric developmental processes.

Culture and personality research became the major American release from the limiting and relatively unproductive method of Boasian historical reconstruction. From 1930 to 1950, it overshadowed all other interests in the United States. It continues as a fruitful and growing area of anthropology, but since 1960 it has been pursued with less extravagant enthusiasm.

Cross-cultural correlational studies have been gaining a steadily increasing foothold in American anthropology since the establishment of the Yale Cross Cultural Survey (now the Human Relations Area Files) and Murdock's use of coefficients of correlation to test a number of long-standing anthropological hypotheses. Murdock's World Ethnographic Sample and the continuing *Ethnographic Atlas* are providing a wide range of coded data for computer calculation of cultural correlations. This still new area of cultural anthropology is expected to continue to gain in strength in the years immediately ahead.

The theoretical and factual developments in prehistoric archaeology and physical anthropology may be reviewed by reference to Chapters 7 to 13. Applied anthropology is a new area of activity that is touched upon in the next chapter.

SELECTED READINGS

Hallowell, A. I.: "The Beginnings of Anthropology in America," in F. de Laguna (ed.), *Selected Papers from the American Anthropologist: 1888–1920* (1960), pp. 1–103. A comprehensive account of the events that led to the establishment of anthropology as a science in the United States.

Hays, H. R.: *From Ape to Angel: An Informal History of Social Anthropology* (1958). The style is breezy (it reminds one of *Time* magazine), and theory is superficially treated, but it certainly tells a lot about anthropologists and the intellectual temper of their times.

Heine-Geldern, R.: "One Hundred Years of Ethnological Theory in the German-speaking Countries: Some Milestones" (*Current Anthropology*, Vol. 5, 1964), pp. 407–429. Should be read to round out the history, which as we have given it concentrates on developments in English-speaking countries.

Kardiner, A., and E. Preble: *They Studied Man* (1961). Essays on Darwin, Herbert Spencer, Tylor, Frazer, Durkheim, Boas, Malinowski, Kroeber, Benedict, and Freud. More limited in coverage than Hays, but equally interesting and much more penetrating.

Lowie, R. H.: *The History of Ethnological Theory* (1937). Should be used to fill in on the English and Austrian diffusionist schools.

Lienhardt, G.: *Social Anthropology* (1965). An historical summary of developments since 1860, written for the layman.

Penniman, T. K.: *A Hundred Years of Anthropology* (rev. ed., 1952). Rather weak in its handling of ethnology, this book is chiefly valuable for its treatment of the development of archaeology and physical anthropology.

Tax, S.: "From Lafitau to Radcliffe-Brown: A Short History of Social Organization," in F. Eggan (ed.), *Social Anthropology of North American Tribes* (enlarged ed., 1955), pp. 445–481. For the most part, traces the development of kinship studies.

Beyond civilization

chapter 36

In this introductory textbook on anthropology, we have outlined broadly the present state of knowledge concerning the origin of man and the archaeological framework of cultural evolution from its earliest beginnings into the dawn of civilization. We have portrayed the diversity of human adjustment to the problems of living by examining a wide range of human institutions as they have been manifest in primitive societies. We have presented the major concepts and modes of anthropological thinking in the hope of showing, at least to some degree, what it is to think and work as an anthropologist does. We have also attempted to convey an understanding of how anthropology has arrived at its present position as both a science and a humanistic discipline.

Anthropology, along with all the sciences, is rapidly moving into the expanding frontiers of knowledge. While its achievements to date are considerable, anthropologists are keenly aware of how much more there is to learn about human relations and human organization. They are equally aware of the extent to which their skills and the adaptability of their science will be challenged. Anthropology does teach us a great deal about the organization and processes of human cultures, but anthropologists have only lately turned intensive attention to the organization of contemporary civilized culture, having left this task largely to sociologists and other social scientists in the past. The kinds of societies that anthropology has studied for the greater part of its existence—primitive, preliterate societies—will not long be with us. The transformation of primitive societies was begun when the first scribes, sitting in urban temple halls, impressed their cuneiform notes in tablets of clay. It has taken approximately five thousand years for the transformation to be carried all around the world, and by the middle of the twenty-first century, no primitive peoples will remain.[1] For fifty years more, anthropologists will be able to do *post facto* studies of primitive cultures, questioning knowledgeable old people about the past, in the same way that the present generation of American anthropologists has been able to interview living American Indians and learn so much about their cultures long after the old life-ways have gone. Archaeologists and physical anthropologists will never run out of subject matter. But will cultural anthropologists? Not as long as there are living men! Less variety will exist among the societies of the future, but the opportunities and the need for continuing development of anthropological insights will steadily increase. For anthropology is the study of man and his works. Where man is, there will always be an enduring field for the cultural anthropologist. The growth, amalgamation, and transformation of mankind's cultural and social systems will challenge anthropology to continue developing as *the* holistic and integrating biosocial science.

Tribal life dominated during the million or more years of the Pleistocene period. Civilization, the culture of the literate city dweller and the farmer, was the great triumph of human achievement during the past six millennia. Now civilization is giving way to a new kind and level of culture that may be called "post-civilization," as Kenneth Boulding suggests, or perhaps "sururbanization," as we would suggest. The task for anthropology is not only to complete the story of man's prehistoric past and to reveal the nature of all known and knowable social systems of yesterday and today but also to clarify the transformations that so confuse our times and to help build a decent and rational life way for all mankind.

The transformation of the primitive world

The process that is now overtaking civilization has recurred repeatedly in the world of primitive man as civilization overtook it. It involves crises in what Redfield called "the moral order" within cultures.[2]

The moral order The moral order is what generates the sense of social commitment in a people—the emotional sense of being a significant part of a community of human beings to whom one has obligations and duties and from whom one receives support, emotionally and socially. The moral order consists of shared understandings about individual and collective goals and their meanings. It becomes manifest as patterns of kinship, neighborhood, club, and work groups, and of recreational, artistic, religious, and community roles in social contexts in which the roles are performed with an accompanying sentiment of "rightness" and gratification. Obviously, the moral order may be closely related to the world view.

The moral order of primitive societies The cultures of most preliterate societies have been governed by moral orders. Few primitive men have doubted the validity of their social systems. Their moral orders sustain them from their early period of enculturation until death. Most primitive cultures are what Edward Sapir called "harmonious, or genuine," cultures:

The genuine culture is not of necessity either high or low; it is merely inherently harmonious, balanced, self-satisfactory. It is the expression of a richly varied and yet somehow unified and consistent attitude toward life, an attitude which sees the significance of any one element of civilization in its relation to all others. . . . The major activities of the individual must directly satisfy his own creative and emotional impulses, must always be something more than

[1] This statement assumes, of course, that no general atomic holocaust will destroy all present civilizations, in which case surviving populations would temporarily, at least, revert to a barbaric level of subsistence and social organization.

[2] R. Redfield, *The Primitive World and Its Transformations*, pp. 20–25.

means to an end. . . . A culture that does not build itself out of the central interests and desires of its bearers, that works from general ends to the individual is an external culture. . . . The genuine culture is internal, it works from the individual to ends.[3]

Through selective adaptation in which symbolic integration and close, personal relations are effectively developed, long-enduring cultures have always possessed effective and "genuine" (in Sapir's sense) moral orders.

We may follow Redfield further in his characterization of primitive societies as possessing certain general characteristics: (1) the community is usually quite small; (2) kinship relations and close, personal bonds extend throughout the community (Maine's condition of status); (3) economic and social interests are homogeneous, and there are few specialists; (4) attitudes and behavior are dominated by religious-mystical assumptions as to the nature of man and the outer world; and (5) suspicion of outsiders (non-kinsmen) commonly leads to a chronic state of warfare with some other groups.

As we know full well by now, the qualitative expression of these traits varies among primitive cultures, but they characterize all small, primitive societies held together by the moral bond.

The technical order A complement to the moral order within cultures is what Redfield called the *Technical order:*

The bonds that co-ordinate the activities of men in the technical order do not rest on convictions as to the good life; they are not characterized by a foundation in human sentiments; they can exist even without the knowledge of those bound together that they are bound together. The technical order is that order which results from mutual usefulness, from deliberate coercion, or from the mere utilization of the same means. In the technical order men are bound by things, or are themselves things.[4]

[3]E. Sapir, "Culture, Genuine and Spurious" (*American Journal of Sociology*, Vol. 29, 1924), p. 410. Of course Sapir uses the words "genuine" and "spurious" in specific senses. All cultures are genuine in the sense that they exist.
[4]Redfield, *op. cit.*, p. 21.

Civilization and the technical order The rise of cities has repeatedly shattered the moral orders of the people who have been drawn into them. A city is rarely, if ever, the product of a local population that has stayed put and "just growed." As far back as the time of Çatal Hüyük, trade was the lifeblood of the city, although it relied, too, on the food products of the surrounding country. All cities incorporate strangers, and in the initial phases of a city's life, the separate little moral orders, according to which the strangers have previously been organized in tribal life ways, dissolve. New urban civilizations are held together mainly by reliance on technical order. Regulations, prescripts, and edicts set the formal patterns to be observed. Magisterial and priestly exactments drive or exhort men to obey. Religious spectaculars and civil carnivals are designed by the priests and rulers to substitute as symbolic integrators for the old tribal rituals. Soldiers, jailers, and executioners coerce the recalcitrants into the behavior that they feel insufficiently commited to adopt for themselves. The dungeon and the prison are inventions of early civilizations.

The moral order becomes managed by an elite, or functional class, and in which the reflection and systematization accomplished by the literati have added a new dimension to the ethical and intellectual life. The moral order now has a public phase connected with deliberate policy. . . . Religion is now, in short, a way of making citizens.[5]

Civilization, the city way of life, is always marked by a new kind of social bonding. At the outset, the moral order of each urban culture in civilization is managed in contrast to the self-maintaining moral order of primitive societies. For the great civilizations of the past, such orders sufficed for long periods of time. Eventually, they declined in effectiveness as disintegrating forces dissolved their influence. Urban populations of antiquity acquired *proletarii*, which in Rome meant the lowest class of the city, who were regarded as contributing nothing to the state but children. Some urban

[5]*Ibid.*, p. 65.

populations became caught in a welter of conflicting beliefs that tended to nullify one another's influence. The reform religions of Christianity, Islam, and Buddhism each arose to provide foundations for new moral orders upon which new civilizations could be built.

In antiquity, the urban revolution churned up the old tribal world into a condition that was, apparently, both frightening and exhilarating. The Egyptians and the Aztecs, as we have seen, built on fear; the Greeks, on exhilaration. Medieval civilization in Europe was reconstituted on a feudalistic-Christian moral order, and ultimately on an industrial-Christian moral system that has proved to be tremendously effective down to the twentieth century.

ANOMY AND CIVILIZATION Anomy[6] occurs when drastic change causes moral orders to lose their bonding and motivating effect, or when segments of the population are left behind—alienated because no satisfying place exists for them in the changing social structure. The resulting anomy is marked by

. . . the retreat of the individual into his own ego, the skeptical rejection of all social bonds. . . . It signifies the state of mind of one who has been pulled up from his moral roots, who no longer has any standards but only disconnected urges, who no longer has any sense of continuity, of folk, of obligations.[7]

Anomy is the disease of the disintegrating or reconstituting civilization—or of the shattered primitive society. Apathy and demoralization characterize most American Indian populations that have not become extinct or been absorbed into the civilization that has rolled over them. A major task of applied anthropology today is to assist national planners and international development agencies in finding ways to promote modernization without causing the paralyzing disruption of ongoing moral orders before new and effective orders can replace them. This requires, in the first place, a genuine

understanding of the moral orders by which people who are to be "modernized" now live. Even in city slums, the anthropological approach provides the understanding, in ways that otherwise seem to be overlooked. The work of Oscar Lewis in Mexico City, San Juan, Puerto Rico, and New York City is the prototype of what anthropology can offer to this end.

In Lewis's words:

One of the major obstacles to more rapid and significant progress in the current war against poverty is the great gulf that exists between the values and way of life of the very poor and those of the middle-class personnel—teachers, social workers, health workers, and others—who bear the major responsibility in carrying out these programs. We know a great deal about the statistics and economics of poverty, but we are only beginning to understand the psychology and inner life of some of the very poor. In the case of the Puerto Ricans, many of whom have come from rural areas or urban slums, the obstacles to understanding are even greater because of the barrier of language and the differences between cultures. And while Puerto Ricans have been one of the most surveyed and studied groups, most of the studies have been of a questionnaire type and have told us too little about the intimate details of their lives and the conditions which have formed their character.[8]

Peasant society

During the eighteenth and nineteenth centuries, extinction was the fate of many tribes. In the twentieth and twenty-first centuries, except in the case of such marginal peoples as the African Bushmen, incorporation into postcivilizations, rather than extinction, will undoubtedly be achieved by most tribal groups. As populations, either they will be sucked into the industrial-sururban complex, or they may retain a measure of group identity for awhile through a transformation from a tribal to a peasant existence.

A peasant society is a subsociety of a large stratified society which is either pre-industrial or only partly

[6]The French spelling, *anomie*, is also used by some American sociologists under the influence of Émile Durkheim, but the English word has been well-established for at least four hundred years.
[7]R. I. MacIver, *The Ramparts We Guard*, p. 77.
[8]O. Lewis, "Mother and Son in a Puerto Rican Slum; Part I: Felicita" (*Harper's Magazine*, December, 1965), p. 72.

industrialized. It is further characterized by most or all of the following traits: rural residence; familial agriculture on self-owned small land holdings or other simple rural occupations providing a modest or subsistence livelihood; the family as the centrally important social unit; low social status; economic interdependence in varying degree with urban centers; simple culture; and attachment to the soil, the local community and tradition.[9]

Peasant societies are the little communities of the primitive world transformed into culturally marginal units of civilizations. They occupy a developmental position between tribal society and industrial urban society, sharing in some degree, as Norbeck says, characteristics of both.

In Europe, peasant societies are fast disappearing. To a lesser extent, this is true of Russia also. In Asia, Africa, and Middle and South America, detribalization moves on apace. Urbanization is spreading, and tribesmen are becoming peasants. From now to the end of the twentieth century, fieldwork in peasant communities will become an increasingly significant concern of social anthropologists. Pockets of peasant cultures may survive in marginal areas for several centuries to come, engaging the continuing attention of anthropologists. In the meantime, however, the need for more anthropologists to study the many remaining tribal groups before it is too late becomes more pressing every year.

At the same time, the presently growing concern of anthropologists with the study of complex cultures will continue to increase, rapidly moving to the forefront. For today we are witnessing not only the passing of the primitive world but also the dissolution of civilization itself—"civilization" meaning the culture of cities.

Sururbanization: the next stage

Civilization in American and Western Europe is already giving way to *sururbanization*. Kenneth E.

Boulding has written of this stage as "postcivilization,"[10] but, as he rightly emphasizes, the stage we are entering will be less a continuation of the culture of cities than a revolutionized way of life in which not only rural life as a distinctive subculture within societies disappears, but the city itself, the hallmark of civilization, ceases to have any meaning. Temporally, the new cultural era will follow after civilization, but qualitatively it will be something beyond and above civilization. Therefore, the new era may well be called *sururbanization*.

The mechanistic world view of modern Western civilization has resulted in a scientific technology that has raised the efficiency of food production and the means of consumption to a new order of magnitude. In precivilized societies, all ablebodied adults, even kings, were engaged in food production. In early civilizations, probably not more than 10, or at most 20, per cent of a population could be freed from food production to serve as administrators, artisans, and soldiers. In the United States today, not more than 10 per cent of the population is directly engaged in agriculture. In twenty-five years, it will be 3 per cent or less. The farmer is nearly as extinct as the dodo; the city dweller soon will be. From antiquity into the middle of the twentieth century, cities were entities with their own characters, inhabited by urbanites who were conscious of their identities as Parisians, Londoners, New Yorkers. Now the city is but a residual core within a vast sprawling settlement pattern that extends for miles beyond suburbia into exurbia. The Atlantic seaboard of the United States has become one continuous dwelling, factory, and commercial complex from Washington, D.C., to Portland, Maine. At midcentury, the expanded urban complex was called *megalopolis*. Soon, however, the human environment of dwellers in the most advanced countries will be much more than a "monster city." The environment of the future is becoming noncity and noncountry. A

---

[9] E. Norbeck, "Peasant Society," in J. Gould and W. L. Kolb (eds.), *A Dictionary of the Social Sciences*, p. 491.

[10] K. E. Boulding, "The Death of the City: A Frightened Look at Post-civilization" (1961, mimeographed); also, *The Meaning of the 20th Century: The Great Transition.*

new level of societal organization is in its early formative stages. Many of the old institutions of civilization are in the process of breakdown.

The wild disturbances that shake the cities of the world today are more than just expressions of racial discontent and juvenile criminality. They are outbursts of free-floating anger by those who feel left behind and who are uncertain of their place in an automating society. Their numbers will increase in the decades ahead, and times will remain unsettled for some generations to come, as men work out the new, as yet unimagined social system for sururbanization and a viable moral order to keep men at peace with it and with themselves.

Anthropology and the future

Anthropology's great contribution is to the understanding of mankind by man. It has its task cut out for it. How great it would have been had there been anthropologists present to record and analyze the urban revolution as civilization was being born! How infinitely richer and more certain our understanding of the human enterprise would be, had that been possible. Today we are more fortunate; we can observe, record, interpret—and help guide—the greatest cultural revolution of all time, the dawn of the Atomic Era of Sururbanization.

SELECTED READINGS

Barnett, H. G.: *Anthropology in Administration* (1956). Professor Barnett, for two years (1951 to 1953) staff anthropologist in the administration of the United States Trust Territory of the Pacific Islands, discusses how anthropology can best be applied in helping tribal groups adjust to the modern world.

Boulding, K. E.: *The Meaning of the 20th Century: The Great Transition* (1965). One of the most imaginative contemporary social thinkers examines the barriers that are to be surmounted in reaching the new society of the era that is just opening. A brief and stimulating book that looks beyond civilization into the culture of the twenty-first century.

Erasmus, C. J.: *Man Takes Control: Cultural Development and American Aid* (1961). An engrossing and informative discussion of what produces (and hinders) the motivating power of cultures, exemplified by a detailed case study of a development program in a peasant area of northwestern Mexico.

Mead, M. (ed.): *Cultural Patterns and Technical Change* (1955). This manual, prepared by the World Federation for Mental Health, is addressed to the question: "How can technical change be introduced with such regard for the culture pattern that human values are preserved?"

Redfield, R.: *The Primitive World and Its Transformations* (1953). Primitive, peasant, and urban life ways are reviewed to provide an overview of how urbanization has transformed man from the primitive to the civilized state.

Thompson, L: *Toward a Unified Science of Man* (1961). Dr. Thompson advocates attention to applied anthropology as the proving ground for anthropological theory and for social science skill in predicting the results of differing plans of action. The author makes tough problems seem easier to solve than they actually are, but the book is a clarion call to scientific social action.

The behavioral changes that marked the transition from dryopithecine anthropoids to hominids were accompanied by many skeletal modifications. In evaluating a fossil genus, various skeletal features may be compared with those of fossil or living apes, on the one hand, and with those of man, on the other. Narcissistic though it may seem, the measure of evolutionary advance among the anthropoids is the degree of their similarity to modern man, *Homo sapiens.* Therefore, although for the purposes of this introductory text a knowledge of all the bones of the human body and of their characteristics and points for measurement is not required, it is necessary to be familiar with certain of them and with a few anthropometric indexes.[1]

The adult human skeleton normally consists of 206 bones and thirty-two teeth. These bones are related to one another in such ways that they form a number of coordinated units, or parts, such as the skull, spinal column, chest (thorax), arms, hands, pelvis, legs, and feet. These, in turn, may be viewed as grouped in three larger assemblages, which are of more or less distinctive, yet interrelated, significance from the evolutionary point of view: (1) the head, (2) the arms and thorax, and (3) the legs and pelvis. The chest and arms underwent major changes in Oligocene and Miocene times, when the early primates were adapting to brachiation in the trees. These changes are dominant in the platyrrhines and cercopithecoids today. The next set of major changes took place in the pelvis and legs during Late Pliocene and Early Pleistocene times and effected upright posture. These changes are evident in incipient form in the pongoids and strong in man. Skull changes followed pelvic and leg changes in response to upright posture and growth in brain size. Most distinctive characteristics of the skull of the genus *Homo* were acquired during the latter part of the Pleistocene, and they are the dominant characteristics of man.

[1]For fuller details, see M. A. Ashley-Montagu, *An Introduction to Physical Anthropology,* or E. A. Hooton, *Up from the Ape* (rev. ed.), Part VI.

Appendix I

Fundamental reference points of the human skeleton

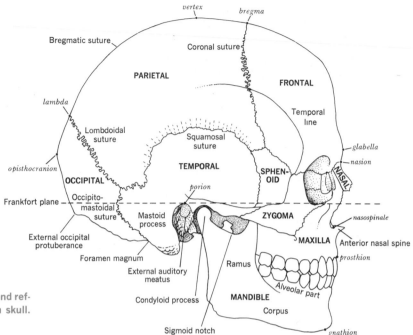

Fig. A-1   Significant parts and reference points of the human skull.

The skull

The skull (Fig. A-1), which is made up of twenty-nine bones, has two parts,—the *cranium*, and the *mandible*, or lower jaw. The cranium consists of the *calvarium* (braincase) and the face (including the jaw). The face consists of two *maxillas* (upper jaws), one on each side; two zygomas (cheek-bones), also one on each side; the teeth; the nose; and lesser parts.

In man, the calvarium is smooth and globular for the most part. The frontal bone is high and spacious. The two *parietals* form the side roofs of the calvarium joined by the *bregmatic suture* (not seen in Fig. A-1). In adult chimpanzees and gorillas, a sharp ridge, or *sagittal crest*, rises along the suture and serves as an anchor for the heavy temporal muscles that support the jaw. The *occipital bone* forms the lower rear and base of the skull and has an opening through which the spinal cord passes. This is called the *foramen magnum*, or great window. The position of the *foramen magnum* indicates the orientation of the spinal column. In upright (orthograde) man, it is well under the skull and parallel to the

Frankfurt horizontal. In apes, it is more to the rear and tilted at an angle to the horizontal. In pronograde (horizontal), four-footed animals, it is far back on the calvarium and strongly tilted. In adult apes, especially males, a marked transverse ridge, the *occipital crest,* runs at right angles to the sagittal crest.

The two temporal bones form the sidewalls of the calvarium. Each is distinguished by a hollow protuberance near the occiput, the *mastoid process,* which is much more marked in man than in other primates; it is associated with upright posture and serves as an anchor point for some of the neck muscles. In front of the mastoid process is the ear opening, or *auditory meatus,* and in front of that is a shallow transverse groove, the *glenoid cavity,* into which the rocker joint of the lower jaw fits. In the lower, forward part of the skull is the *sphenoid* bone, which might be considered the keystone to the whole structure. It articulates with every other bone in the braincase as well as with several facial bones.

The face in man is much reduced in size, relative to the calvarium, compared with that of all other primates. The snout has disappeared, the maxillas are pulled back under the frontal margin, and the dental arch has shortened and broadened to form a V shape in contrast to the long U shape of ape dental arches. The teeth are crowded closely together, and there is no large gap (*diastema*) between the canines and incisors, such as occurs in other primates to accommodate the overlap of their tusklike canines.

The modern human jaw has a short, relatively light mandible with a protruding chin. Other hominoids have relatively heavier, longer jaws with recessive chins. The *ramus,* or vertical part of the jaw, is narrow and light in man and usually has a deeper *sigmoid* notch than does that of apes. At the head of the *condyloid process* is the rocker joint, the *condyle,* which articulates with the glenoid cavity of the calvarium.

Anthropometric points on the skull For statistical comparison of skulls, a number of measurements are taken of the distances between two anatomical landmarks. These may then be combined into ratios (relation of one measurement to another) and angles. The most commonly used points, indicated on Fig. A-1, are as follows:

Bregma: the meeting point of the coronal and sagittal sutures, where the parietal and frontal bones all meet

Basion: the median point on the anterior margin of the *foramen magnum*

Glabella: the most prominent point in the median line between the two browridges above the root of the nose

Gnathion: the lowest median point on the lower border of the mandible

Gonion: the lowest exterior point of the angle between the tooth-bearing section of the mandible and the ascending ramus

Lambda: the meeting point of the lambdoidal and saggital sutures, where the parietal and occipital bones all meet

Nasion: the upper end of the internasal suture, where the nasal and frontal bones all meet

Opisthion: the rearmost point on the saggital line of the skull when on the Frankfurt horizontal

Porion: the uppermost point of the upper margin of the ear hole

Prosthion: the lowest point of the intermaxillary suture, between the two central incisors

Vertex: the highest median point of the skull when on the Frankfurt horizontal

Zygion: the most laterally projecting point of the cheekbones

For purposes of orientation, skulls are usually pictured on the *Frankfurt horizontal*. This is a line passing through the *orion* and *porion* and oriented to the horizontal.

Fig. A-2 Significant parts and reference points of the human pelvis.

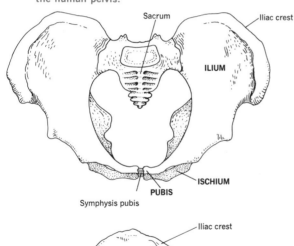

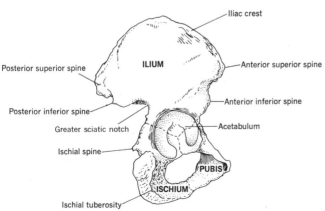

The pelvis

Commonly known as the hip, the pelvis (Fig. A-2) consists of a set of winglike bones (the ilia) attached to the sides of a central set of dorsal vertebrae (the sacrum). Each ilium joins with a ventral and dorsal strut (the *pubis* and *ischium*) to form an arch meeting at the *pubic symphysis*. A deep, round fossa, the *acetabulum*, is located on the outside of each half of the pelvis to receive the head of the thighbone (femur).

The pelvis joins the *axial skeleton* to the *lower appendicular* skeleton at the head of the *sacrum*, the keystone bone. Its shape is critically responsive to habitual posture and also to reproductive functions (see pages 136–137).

The femur

Although every one of the 206 bones that make up the human skeleton is of potential diagnostic significance in the study of fossil man, the femur is the only bone, besides those of the pelvis, to which particular attention need be drawn now (see Fig. A-3). The femur, like the pelvis, quickly reflects adaptive changes in posture; it also fossilizes with relative ease. The *head* of the femur is a ball joint that fits into the acetabulum of the pelvis. The degree of development of the *gluteal tuberosity* to which the gluteal maximus attaches indicates something of the relative development of this muscle, which is so important to the attainment of balance in upright posture. The *linea aspera*, a slight ridge running down the dorsal length of the *shaft*, performs reinforcing functions and serves as an anchor for muscle attachment. Its presence on the femur is a human feature.

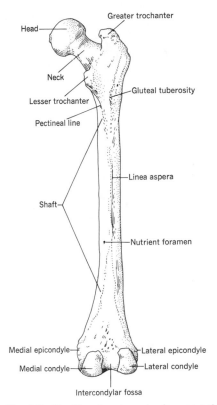

Fig. A-3 Significant parts and reference points of the human femur.

Bibliography

Aarne, A.: *Die Tiere auf der Wanderschaft* (Folklore Fellows Communications, No. 11, 1913).

Aberle, D. F.: "The Psychological Analysis of a Hopi Life-history" (*Comparative Psychological Monographs*, Vol. 211, No. 107, 1951).

Adamic, L.: *The Native's Return: An American Immigrant Visits Jugoslavia and Discovers His Old Country* (New York, 1934).

Aginsky, B. W.: "An Indian's Soliloquy" (*The American Journal of Sociology*, Vol. 46, 1940), pp. 43–44.

———— and P. H. Buck: "Interacting Forces in the Maori Family" (*American Anthropologist*, Vol. 42, 1940), pp. 195–210.

Aitken, M. J.: *Physics and Archaeology* (New York, 1961).

Aldridge, A. O.: "The Meaning of Incest from Hutcheson to Gibbon" (*Ethics*, Vol. 61, 1951), pp. 309–313.

Allison, A. C.: "Aspects of Polymorphism in Man" (*Cold Spring Harbor Symposium on Quantitative Biology*, Vol. 20, 1955), pp. 239–255.

Almond, G. A., and J. S. Coleman: *The Politics of Developing Areas* (Princeton, N.J., 1960).

Amsden, C.: "The Loom and Its Prototypes" (*American Anthropologist*, Vol. 34, 1932), pp. 216–315.

————: *Navaho Weaving* (Albuquerque, N.Mex., 1949).

Anderson, A. J. O., and C. E. Dibble (trs. and eds.): Fray B. de Sahagún, *Florentine Codex: General History of the Things of New Spain* (10 vols., Santa Fe, N.Mex., 1950–1966).

Ardrey, R.: *African Genesis: A Personal Investigation into the Animal Origins and Nature of Man* (New York, 1963).

Ashley-Montagu, M. F.: *Coming into Being among the Australian Aborigines* (New York, 1938).

————: "On the Origin of the Domestication of the Dog" (*Science*, Vol. 96, 1942), pp. 111–112.

————: *Man's Most Dangerous Myth: The Fallacy of Race* (2d ed., New York, 1945).

Atkinson, J. J.: *Primal Law* (London, 1903).

Ayoub, M. R.: "Parallel Cousin Marriage and Endogamy: A Study in Sociometry" (*Southwestern Journal of Anthropology*, Vol. 15, 1959), pp. 266–290.

Bachofen, J. K.: *Das Mutterrecht: eine Untersuchung über die Gynaikokratie der alten Welt nach iherer religiösen und rechtlichen Natur* (Stuttgart, 1861).

Bacon, E.: "A Preliminary Attempt to Determine the Culture Areas of Asia" (*Southwestern Journal of Anthropology*, Vol. 2, 1946), pp. 117–132.

Balfour, H.: *The Evolution of Decorative Art* (London, 1893).

Bandalier, A. F.: "Final Report" (*Papers of the Archaeological Institute of America*, Vol. 3, 1890), p. 284.

Barnett, H. G.: "The Nature of the Potlatch" (*American Anthropologist*, Vol. 40, 1938), pp. 349–358.

————: "Culture Processes" (*American Anthropologist*, Vol. 42, 1940), pp. 21–48.

————: "Applied Anthropology in 1860" (*Applied Anthropology*, Vol. 1, 1942), pp. 19–32.

————: *Innovation: The Basis of Cultural Change* (New York, 1953).

————: *Anthropology in Administration* (Evanston, Ill., 1956).

Barnouw, V.: *Culture and Personality* (Homewood, Ill., 1963).

Barrett, S. A.: "Pomo Indian Basketry" (*University of California Publications in American Archaeology and Ethnology*, Vol. 7, 1908).

Barth, F.: "Father's Brother's Daughter Marriage in Kurdistan" (*Southwestern Journal of Anthropology*, Vol. 10, 1954), pp. 164–171.

Barton, R. F.: "Ifugao Law" (*University of California Publications in American Archaeology and Ethnology*, Vol. 15, 1919).

————: "Ifugao Economics" (*University of California Publications in American Archaeology and Ethnology*, Vol. 15, No. 5, 1922).

————: *The Half-way Sun: Life among the Headhunters of the Philippines* (New York, 1930).

————: *Philippine Pagans: The Autobiographies of Three Ifugaos* (London, 1938).

————: *The Religion of the Ifugaos* (American Anthropological Association Memoir 65, 1946).

————: *The Kalinga: Their Institutions and Custom Law* (Chicago, 1949).

Bascom, W.: *The Sociological Role of the Yoruba Cult-Group* (American Anthropological Association Memoir 63, 1944).

Bauman, H.: "The Division of Work According to Sex in African Hoe Culture" (*Africa,* Vol. 1, 1928), pp. 289–318.

Beaglehole, E.: *Property: A Study in Social Psychology* (London, 1931).

————: "Character Structure: Its Role in the Analysis of Interpersonal Relations" (*Psychiatry,* Vol. 7, 1944), pp. 144–162.

Beals, R., P. Carrasco, and T. McCorkle: *Houses and House Use of the Sierra Tarascans* (Washington, D.C., 1944).

Beattie, J.: *Other Cultures: Aims, Methods and Achievements in Social Anthropology* (Glencoe, Ill., 1964).

Bellah, R. N.: *Apache Kinship Systems* (Cambridge, Mass., 1952).

Belo, J.: "A Study of a Balinese Family" (*American Anthropologist,* Vol. 38, 1936), pp. 12–31.

Bender, M. A., and E. H. Y. Chen: "The Chromosomes of Primates," in J. Buettner-Janusch (ed.), *Evolutionary and Genetic Biology of Primates* (2 vols., New York, 1963), chap. 7.

Benedict, R. F.: *The Concept of the Guardian Spirit in North America* (American Anthropological Association Memoir 29, 1923).

————: "The Science of Custom: The Bearing of Anthropology on Contemporary Thought," in V. F. Calverton (ed.), *The Making of Man: An Outline of Anthropology* (New York, 1931), pp. 805–817.

————: "Marital Property Rights in Bilateral Society" (*American Anthropologist,* Vol. 38, 1936), pp. 368–373.

————: *Patterns of Culture* (New York, 1934).

————: "Religion," in F. Boas (ed.), *General Anthropology* (New York, 1938), chap. 14.

————: *Race: Science and Politics* (New York, 1940).

Bennett, J. W.: "The Development of Ethnological Theories as Illustrated by Studies of the Plains Indian Sun Dance" (*American Anthropologist,* Vol. 46, 1944), pp. 162–181.

———— and M. M. Tumin: *Social Life, Structure and Function: An Introductory General Sociology* (New York, 1948), pp. 45–59.

Bennett, W. C., and R. M. Zingg: *The Tarahumara: An Indian Tribe of Northern Mexico* (Chicago, 1935).

Blackwood, B.: *Both Sides of Buka Passage* (Oxford, 1935).

Boas, F.: *The Central Eskimo* (Bureau of American Ethnology, Annual Report 6, 1888), pp. 399–669.

————: *Social Organization and Secret Societies of the Kwakiutl Indians* (United States National Museum, Annual Report, 1895).

————: "Decorative Designs of Alaskan Needlecases" (*United States National Museum, Annual Reports,* Vol. 39, 1908), pp. 221–344.

————: *Tsimshian Mythology* (Bureau of American Ethnology, Annual Report 31, 1916), pp. 393–558.

————: *Primitive Art* (Oslo, 1929).

————: "Anthropology" (*Encyclopedia of the Social Sciences,* Vol. 2, 1930), pp. 73–100.

————: *Anthropology and Modern Life* (rev. ed., New York, 1932).

———— (ed.): *General Anthropology* (New York, 1938).

Bogoras, W.: "The Chukchee: I, Religion" (*Jesup North Pacific Expedition,* Vol. 7, 1904–1909).

Bohannan, P.: *Justice and Judgment among the Tiv* (London, 1957).

———— and G. Dalton: *Markets in Africa* (Evanston, Ill., 1962).

————: *Social Anthropology* (New York, 1963).

Boulding, K. E.: "The Death of the City: A Frightened Look at Post-civilization" (1961, mimeographed).

————: *The Meaning of the 20th Century: The Great Transition* (New York, 1965).

Bourlière, F.: "Patterns of Social Groupings among Primates," in S. L. Washburn (ed.), *Social Life of Early Man* (Chicago, 1962), pp. 1–10.

Boyd, W. C.: *Genetics and the Races of Man: An Introduction to Modern Physical Anthropology* (Boston, 1950).

————: "The Contributions of Genetics to Anthropology," in A. L. Kroeber (ed.), *Anthropology Today: An Encyclopedic Inventory* (Chicago, 1953), pp. 488–506.

Brace, C. L.: "The Fate of the 'Classic' Neandertals: A Consideration of Hominid Catastrophism" (*Current Anthropology,* Vol. 5, No. 1, 1964), pp. 3–46.

———— and M. F. A. Montagu: *Man's Evolution: An Introduction to Physical Anthropology* (New York, 1965).

Braidwood, R. J.: "Jericho and Its Setting in Near Eastern Prehistory" (*Antiquity,* Vol. 31, 1957), pp. 73–80.

————: *Prehistoric Men* (3d ed., Chicago, 1957).

———— and G. R. Willey (eds.): *Courses toward Urban Life:*

Archaeological Consideration of Some Cultural Alternatives (Viking Fund Publications in Anthropology, No. 32, 1962).

Bram, J.: *An Analysis of Inca Militarism* (American Ethnological Society Monograph 4, 1941).

Breuil, H.: *Four Hundred Centuries of Cave Art* (New York, 1950).

Brew, J. O.: "The Metal Ages: Copper, Bronze and Iron," in H. L. Shapiro (ed.), *Man, Culture, and Society* (New York, 1956), chap. 5.

Briffault, R.: *The Mothers: The Matriarchal Theory of Social Origins* (3 vols., New York, 1927).

Brinton, D. G.: *Religions of Primitive People* (New York, 1897).

Brouner, W. B., and Y. M. Fung: *Chinese Made Easy* (Leiden, 1935).

Brown, H.: "The Age of the Solar System" (*Scientific American*, April, 1957; S.A. Reprint No. 102).

Buck, P. H.: *Vikings of the Sunrise* (New York, 1938).

Buehler, A., T. Barrow, and C. P. Mountford: *The Art of the South Seas, Including Australia and New Zealand* (New York, 1962).

Buettner-Janusch, J. (ed.): "The Relatives of Man: Modern Studies on the Relation of the Evolution of Non-human Primates to Human Evolution" (*Annals of the New York Academy of Science*, Vol. 102(2), 1962), pp. 181–514.

———: *Evolutionary and Genetic Biology of Primates* (2 vols., New York, 1963).

Bunzel, R.: "The Pueblo Potter" (*Columbia University Contributions to Anthropology*, Vol. 8, 1929).

———: *Introduction to Zuni Ceremonialism* (Bureau of American Ethnology, Annual Report 47, 1932).

Burgess, E. W.: "Introduction," in E. F. Frazier, *The Negro Family in the United States* (Chicago, 1939).

Busia, A. K.: *The Position of the Chief in the Modern Political System of Ashanti: A Study of the Influence of Contemporary Social Changes on Ashanti Political Institutions* (Oxford, 1951).

Calverton, V. F. (ed.): *The Making of Man: An Outline of Anthropology* (New York, 1931).

Campbell, B.: "Quantitative Taxonomy and Human Evolution," in S. L. Washburn (ed.), *Classification and Human Evolution* (Viking Fund Publications in Anthropology, No. 37, 1963), pp. 50–70.

Caneiro, R. L.: "Slash and Burn Cultivation among the Kiukuru and Its Implications for Cultural Development in the Amazon Basin," in *The Evolution of Horti-cultural Systems in Native South America: Causes and Consequences—A Symposium* (Anthropologica Supplement No. 2, Caracas, 1961), pp. 47–67.

Cardozo, B. N.: *The Growth of the Law* (New Haven, Conn., 1924).

Carpenter, C. R.: "A Field Study of the Behavior and Social Relations of the Howling Monkeys (*Aloutta palliata*)" (*Comparative Psychological Monographs*, Vol. 10, 1934), pp. 1–168.

———: "Societies of Monkeys and Apes" (*Biological Symposia*, Vol. 8, 1942), pp. 177–204.

Carrol, J. B.: *Language, Thought, and Reality: Selected Writings of Benjamin Lee Whorf* (New York, 1955).

Carter, G. F.: "Origins of American Indian Agriculture" (*American Anthropologist*, Vol. 48, 1946), pp. 1–21.

Caso, A.: *The Aztecs: People of the Sun* (Norman, Okla., 1958).

Childe, V. G.: *The Dawn of European Civilization* (New York, 1925).

———: *New Light on the Most Ancient East* (London, 1935).

———: *What Happened in History* (London, 1942).

———: *Man Makes Himself* (rev. ed., New York, 1951).

Christensen, J. B.: *Double Descent among the Fanti* (Behavior Science Monographs, New Haven, Conn., 1954).

Clark, G., and S. Piggott: *Prehistoric Societies* (New York, 1965).

Clark, J. G. D.: *Prehistoric Europe: The Economic Base* (New York, 1952).

———: *World·Prehistory: An Outline* (Cambridge, England, 1961).

Clarke, J. D.: "Africa South of the Sahara," in R. J. Braidwood and G. R. Willey (eds.), *Courses toward Urban Life: Archaeological Considerations of Some Cultural Alternatives* (Chicago, 1962), pp. 1–33.

Cohen, Y. A.: *The Transition from Childhood to Adolescence* (Chicago, 1964).

Cole, G. D. H.: "Inheritance" (*Encyclopedia of the Social Sciences*, Vol. 8, 1932), pp. 35–43.

Cole, S.: *The Prehistory of East Africa* (New York, 1963).

Comte, A.: *Positive Philosophy* (translated from the French by H. Martineau, London, 1893).

Cook, W. W.: "Ownership and Possession" (*Encyclopedia of the Social Sciences*, Vol. 11, 1953), pp. 521–525.

Coon, C. S.: *The Races of Europe* (New York, 1936).

——: *The Story of Man: From the First Human to Primitive Culture and Beyond* (New York, 1955).

——: *The Origin of Races* (New York, 1963).

——, S. M. Garn, and J. B. Birdsell: *Races: A Study of Race Formation in Man* (Springfield, Ill., 1950).

Cooper, J. M.: "Mental Disease Situations in Certain Cultures" (*Journal of Abnormal and Social Psychology*, Vol. 29, 1934), pp. 10–17.

——: "Is the Algonquian Family Hunting Ground System Pre-Columbian?" (*American Anthropologist*, Vol. 41, 1939), pp. 66–90.

——: "The Patagonian and Pampean Hunters," in J. H. Steward (ed.), *Handbook of South American Indians* (6 vols., Washington, D.C., 1946–1950), Vol. 1, pp. 127–168.

——: "The Yahgan," in J. H. Steward (ed.), *Handbook of South American Indians* (6 vols., Washington, D.C., 1946–1950), Vol. 1, pp. 81–107.

Cottrell, W. F.: *Energy and Society: The Relation between Energy, Social Change, and Economic Development* (New York, 1955).

Count, E. W.: *This Is Race* (New York, 1950).

Curtis, E. S.: *The Kwakiutl* (New York, 1919).

Dalton, G.: "Traditional Production in Primitive African Economies" (*The Quarterly Journal of Economics*, August, 1962), pp. 360–378.

Dart, R. A.: "The Predatory Implemental Technique of Australopithecus (*American Journal of Physical Anthropology*, Vol. 7, 1949), pp. 1–16.

——: *The Osteodontokeratic Culture of Australopithecus prometheus* (Transvaal Museum Memoir 10, 1957).

Darwin, C.: *The Origin of Species by Means of Natural Selection: Or, The Preservation of Favored Races in the Struggle for Life* (Macmillan ed., New York, 1927).

Davidson, D. S.: "Knotless Netting in America and Oceania" (*American Anthropologist*, Vol. 37, 1935), pp. 117–134.

Dawson, J.: *Australian Aborigines* (Melbourne, 1881).

de Jong, J. P. B.: "Lévi-Strauss's Theory of Kinship and Marriage" (*Mededelingen van het Rijksmuseum voor Volkenkunde, Leiden*, No. 10, 1952).

de Montaigne, M: *Selected Essays* (translated by D. M. Frame, New York, 1943).

de Morgan, J.: *Feudalism in Persia: Its Origin, Development and Present Condition* (Washington, D.C., 1914).

Densmore, F.: "An Explanation of a Trick Performed by Indian Jugglers" (*American Anthropologist*, Vol. 34, 1932), pp. 310–314.

Derringer, D.: *The Alphabet* (New York, 1948).

de Schlippe, P.: *Shifting Cultivation in Africa: The Zande System of Agriculture* (London, 1956).

Deutsch, M., and B. Brown: "Social Influences in Negro-White Intelligence Differences" (*The Journal of Social Issues*, Vol. 20, 1964), pp. 24–35.

Dibble, C. E., and A. J. O. Anderson (trs. and eds.): Fray B. de Sahagún, *Florentine Codex: General History of the Things of New Spain* (10 vols., Santa Fe, N.Mex., 1950–1966).

Dobzhansky, T.: *Genetics and the Origin of Species* (3d ed., New York, 1951).

——: *Mankind Evolving: The Evolution of the Human Species* (New Haven, Conn., 1962).

——: "Evolution: Organic and Superorganic" (*The Rockefeller Institute Review*, Vol. 1, No. 2, 1963), pp. 1–9.

Dollard, J.: *Criteria for the Life History, with Analyses of Six Notable Documents* (New Haven, Conn., 1935).

Domenech, E.: *Seven Years' Residence in the Great Deserts of North America* (2 vols., London, 1860).

Dorsey, G. A.: "The Cheyenne: II, The Sun Dance" (*Field Columbian Museum, Publication 103, Anthropological Series*, Vol. 9, No. 2, 1905).

—— and J. R. Murie: "Notes on Skidi Pawnee Society" (*Field Museum of Natural History, Anthropological Series*, Vol. 27, 1940).

Drucker, P.: "Rank, Wealth, and Kinship in Northwest Coast Society" (*American Anthropologist*, Vol. 41, 1939), pp. 55–65; reprinted in E. A. Hoebel, J. D. Jennings, and E. R. Smith, *Readings in Anthropology* (New York, 1955), pp. 214–221.

DuBois, C.: *The People of Alor* (Minneapolis, 1944).

——: "The Alorese," in A. Kardiner (ed.), *The Psychological Frontiers of Society* (New York, 1945), pp. 101–145.

Dumarest, N.: "Notes on Cochiti, New Mexico" (*American Anthropological Association, Memoirs*, Vol. 6, No. 3, 1919).

Dunn, L. C.: *Heredity and Evolution in Human Populations* (Cambridge, Mass., 1960).

—— and T. Dobzhansky: *Heredity, Race, and Society* (rev. ed., New York, 1951).

Durkheim, E.: *Elementary Forms of the Religious Life* (London, 1914).

Eggan, F.: *Social Organization of the Western Pueblos* (Chicago, 1950).

———: "Social Anthropology and Controlled Comparison" (*American Anthropologist*, Vol. 56, 1954), pp. 743–763.

——— (ed.): *Social Anthropology of North American Tribes* (2d ed., Chicago, 1955).

Eiseley, L.: "In the Beginning Was the Artifact" (*Saturday Review*, Dec. 7, 1963).

Eisenstadt, S. N.: *From Generation to Generation* (Glencoe, Ill., 1956).

Elwin, V.: *The Tribal Art of Middle India* (Oxford, 1951).

Embree, J. F.: *The Japanese Nation: A Social Survey* (New York, 1945).

Engels, F.: *The Origin of the Family, Property, and the State in the Light of the Researches of Lewis Henry Morgan* (London, 1885).

Erasmus, C. J.: "Patolli, Pachisi, and the Limitation of Possibilities" (*Southwestern Journal of Anthropology*, Vol. 6, 1950), pp. 369–381.

Evans, B.: *The Natural History of Nonsense* (New York, 1946).

Evans-Pritchard, E. E.: *Witchcraft, Oracles and Magic among the Azande* (Oxford, 1937).

———: *The Nuer: A Description of the Modes of Livelihood and Political Institutions of a Nilotic People* (Oxford, 1940).

———: "The Nuer of the Southern Sudan," in E. E. Evans-Pritchard and M. Fortes (eds.), *African Political Systems* (Oxford, 1940).

———: "Nuer Bridewealth" (*Africa*, Vol. 16, 1946), pp. 1ff.

———: *Kinship and Marriage among the Nuer* (Oxford, 1951).

———: *Social Anthropology* (Oxford, 1951).

———: *Nuer Religion* (Oxford, 1956).

———: *Anthropology and History* (Manchester, 1961).

———: *Essays in Social Anthropology* (Glencoe, Ill., 1963).

———: "Heredity and Gestation as the Azande See Them," in *Essays in Social Anthropology* (Glencoe, Ill., 1963).

——— and M. Fortes (eds.): *African Political Systems* (Oxford, 1940).

Fallers, L. A.: *Bantu Bureaucracy: A Study of Integration and Conflict in the Political Institutions of an East African People* (London, 1956).

Fenton, W. N.: "Locality as a Basic Factor in the Development of Iroquois Social Structure," in *Symposium on Local Diversity in Iroquois Culture* (Bureau of American Ethnology Bulletin 149, 1951).

Firth, R.: *Primitive Polynesian Economy* (London, 1939).

——— (ed.): *Man and Culture: An Evaluation of the Work of Bronislaw Malinowski* (London, 1957).

——— *We, the Tikopia, A Sociological Study of Kinship in Primitive Polynesia* (London, 1936).

Fischer, J. L.: "Solutions for the Natchez Paradox" (*Ethnology*, Vol. 3, 1964), pp. 53–65.

Flint, R. F.: *Glacial Geology and the Pleistocene Epoch* (New York, 1947).

Ford, C. S.: "The Role of a Fijian Chief" (*American Sociological Review*, Vol. 3, 1938), pp. 542–550.

———: *A Comparative Study of Human Reproduction* (Yale University Publications in Anthropology, No. 32, 1945).

Forde, C. D.: *Habitat, Economy, and Society: A Geographical Introduction to Ethnology* (2d ed., New York, 1937).

———: "Kinship in Umor: Double Unilateral Organization in a Semi-Bantu Society" (*American Anthropologist*, Vol. 41, 1939), pp. 523–553.

——— (ed.): *African Worlds: Studies in the Cosmological Ideas and Social Values of African Peoples* (London, 1954).

Fortes, M.: *The Dynamics of Clanship among the Tallensi* (Oxford, 1945).

——— (ed.): *Social Structure: Studies Presented to A. R. Radcliffe-Brown* (Oxford, 1949).

———: *The Web of Kinship among the Tallensi* (Cambridge, Engl., 1949).

———: "Structure of Unilinear Descent Groups" (*American Anthropologist*, Vol. 55, 1953), pp. 17–34.

Fortune, R. F.: *Sorcerers of Dobu: The Social Anthropology of the Dobu Islanders of the Western Pacific* (New York, 1932).

———: *Manus Religion* (Proceedings of the American Philosophical Society, 1935).

Foster, G. M.: "Peasant Society and the Image of the Limited Good" (*American Anthropologist*, Vol. 67, 1965), pp. 293–315.

Frank, J.: "Lawlessness" (*Encyclopedia of the Social Sciences*, Vol. 9, 1933), pp. 277–279.

Franklin, B.: *The Interests of Great Britain Considered* (Boston, 1760).

Frazer, J. G.: *Totemism and Exogamy* (4 vols., London, 1910).

———: *The Golden Bough: A Study in Magic and Religion* (1 vol., abridged ed., New York, 1941).

Frazier, E. F.: *The Negro Family in the United States* (Chicago, 1939).

Freuchen, P.: *Arctic Adventure: My Life in the Frozen North* (New York, 1935).

Freud, S.: *Totem and Taboo* (reprinted in *The Basic Writings of Sigmund Freud*, New York, 1938).

Garfield, V. E.: "Tsimshian Clan and Society" (*University of Washington Publications in Anthropology*, Vol. 7, No. 3, 1939).

Garn, M. S.: *Human Races* (Springfield, Ill., 1961).

Garrett, H. E.: "Negro-White Differences in Mental Ability in the United States" (*The Scientific Monthly*, Vol. 65, 1947), pp. 329–333.

Garth, T. E.: *Race Psychology: A Study of Racial Mental Differences* (New York, 1931).

Gayton, A. H.: "Yokuts-Mono Chiefs and Shamans" (*University of California Publications in American Archaeology and Ethnology*, Vol. 24, 1930).

Geertz, C.: *The Religion of Java* (Glencoe, Ill., 1959).

Geertz, H.: *The Javanese Family: A Study in Kinship and Socialization* (Glencoe, Ill., 1961).

Gibbs, J. L., Jr. (ed.): *Peoples of Africa* (New York, 1965).

Gifford, E. W.: *Tongan Society* (Bernice P. Bishop Museum Bulletin 61, 1929).

Gillin, J. L., and J. P. Gillin: *An Introduction to Sociology* (New York, 1942).

Gillin, J. P.: "The Barama River Caribs of British Guiana" (*Papers of the Peabody Museum of American Archaeology and Ethnology, Harvard University*, Vol. 14, 1936).

————: "Custom and the Range of Human Response" (*Character and Personality*, Vol. 13, 1944), pp. 101–134; reprinted in E. A. Hoebel, J. D. Jennings, and E. R. Smith, *Readings in Anthropology* (New York, 1955), pp. 87–99.

Gladwin, T., and S. B. Sarason: *Truk: Man in Paradise* (Viking Fund Publications in Anthropology, No. 23, 1953).

Gluckman, M.: "How the Bemba Make Their Living: An Appreciation of Richard's 'Land, Labour, and Diet in Northern Rhodesia' " (*Rhodes-Livingstone Institute Journal*, June, 1945), pp. 55–67; reprinted in E. A. Hoebel, J. D. Jennings, and E. R. Smith, *Readings in Anthropology* (New York, 1955), pp. 130–140.

————: *The Judicial Process among the Barotse of Northern Rhodesia* (Manchester and Glencoe, Ill., 1954 and 1955).

————: *The Ideas of Barotse Jurisprudence* (New Haven, Conn., 1965).

————: *Politics, Law, and Ritual in Tribal Society* (Chicago, 1965).

Goldenweiser, A.: *Anthropology* (New York, 1937).

Goldfrank, E. S.: "Socialization, Personality, and the Structure of Pueblo Society (with Particular Reference to Hopi and Zuñi)" (*American Anthropologist*, Vol. 47, 1945), pp. 516–539.

Golding, W.: *The Inheritors* (London and New York, 1955 and 1962).

Goodall, J.: "Tool Using and Aimed Throwing in a Community of Free-living Chimpanzees" (*Nature*, No. 201, 1964), pp. 1264–1266.

Goode, W. J.: *Religion among the Primitives* (Glencoe, Ill., 1951).

Goodenough, W. H.: "A Problem in Malayo-Polynesian Social Organization" (*American Anthropologist*, Vol. 57, 1955), pp. 71–83.

Goodman, M.: "Man's Place in the Phylogeny of Primates as Reflected in Serum Proteins," in S. L. Washburn (ed.), *Classification and Human Evolution* (Chicago, 1963).

Goodwin, G.: *The Social Organization of the Western Apache* (Chicago, 1942).

Goody, J. (ed.): *The Development Cycle in Domestic Groups* (Cambridge, Mass., 1958).

————: "The Classification of Double Descent Systems" (*Current Anthropology*, Vol. 2, 1961), pp. 3–26.

————: *Death, Property and the Ancestors: A Study of the Mortuary Customs of the Lodagaa of West Africa* (Stanford, Calif., 1962).

Gorer, G.: *The American People: A Study in National Character* (New York, 1947).

Gough, E. K.: "Changing Kinship Usages in the Setting of Political and Economic Change among the Nyars of Malabar" (*Journal of the Royal Anthropological Institute of Great Britain and Ireland*, Vol. 82, 1952), pp. 71–87.

Greenberg, J. H.: "Historical Linguistics and Unwritten Languages," in A. L. Kroeber (ed.), *Anthropology Today: An Encyclopedic Inventory* (New York, 1953), pp. 265–286.

Greenman, E. F.: "Material Culture and the Organism" (*American Anthropologist*, Vol. 47, 1945), pp. 211–231.

Griffin, N. M.: *The Roles of Men and Women in Eskimo Culture* (Chicago, 1930).

Grinnell, G. B.: *The Fighting Cheyennes* (New York, 1915).

————: *The Cheyenne Indians: Their History and Ways of Life* (2 vols., New Haven, Conn., 1928).

Gudschinsky, S. H.: "The ABC's of Lexicostatistics (Glottochronology)," in D. Hymes (ed.), *Language in Culture and Society: A Reader in Linguistics and Anthropology* (New York; Evanston, Ill.; and London, 1964), pp. 612–623.

Gulliver, P. H.: "The Jie of Uganda," in J. L. Gibbs, Jr. (ed.), *Peoples of Africa* (New York, 1965), pp. 157–196.

Haddon, A. C.: *Evolution in Art* (London, 1895).

Haines, F.: "The Northward Spread of Horses among the Plains Indians" (*American Anthropologist,* Vol. 40, 1938), pp. 429–437.

——: "Where Did the Plains Indians Get Their Horses?" (*American Anthropologist,* Vol. 40, 1938), pp. 112–117.

Hall, E. T.: *The Silent Language* (New York, 1959).

Hall, G. S.: *Adolescence: Its Psychology and Its Relations to Physiology, Anthropology, Sociology, Sex, Crime, Religion and Education* (2 vols., New York, 1904).

Hallowell, A. I.: "Culture and Mental Disorders" (*Journal of Abnormal and Social Psychology,* Vol. 29, 1934), pp. 1–9.

——: "The Nature and Function of Property as a Social Institution" (*Journal of Political and Legal Sociology,* Vol. 1, 1943), pp. 115–138.

——: "Psychological Leads for Ethnological Field Workers," in D. G. Haring (ed.), *Personal Character and Cultural Milieu* (3d rev. ed., Syracuse, N.Y., 1956), pp. 341–389.

——: "The Beginnings of Anthropology in America," in F. De Laguna (ed.), *Selected Papers from the American Anthropologist: 1888–1920* (Evanston, Ill., 1960), pp. 1–90.

Hambly, W. D.: *The History of Tattooing and Its Significance* (London, 1925).

——: "Source Book for African Anthropology" (*Field Museum of Natural History, Anthropological Series,* Vol. 26, Part 2, 1937).

Hamilton, E.: *The Greek Way to Western Civilization* (New York, 1948 ed.).

Hamilton, W. H., and I. Till: "Property" (*Encyclopedia of the Social Sciences,* Vol. 12, 1934), pp. 528–538.

Hammond, P. B.: *Cultural and Social Anthropology: Selected Readings* (New York, 1964).

——: *Physical Anthropology and Archaeology: Selected Readings* (New York, 1964).

Haring, D. G. (ed.): *Personal Character and Cultural Milieu* (3d rev. ed., Syracuse, N.Y., 1956).

Harrasser, A.: *Die Rechtsverletzung bei den australischer Eingeborenen* (Beilegeheft zur vergleichende Rechtswissenschaft, Vol. 50, 1936).

Hart, C. W. M.: "A Reconsideration of Natchez Social Structure" (*American Anthropologist,* Vol. 45, 1943), pp. 374–386.

——: "Contrasts between Prepubertal and Postpubertal Education," in G. D. Spindler (ed.), *Education and Anthropology* (Stanford, Calif., 1956), pp. 127–145.

—— and A. R. Pilling: *The Tiwi of North Australia* (New York, 1960).

Haury, E. N.: "The Greater American Southwest," in R. J. Braidwood and G. R. Willey (eds.), *Courses toward Urban Life: Archaeological Consideration of Some Cultural Alternatives* (Chicago, 1962), pp. 106–131.

Hawley, F. M.: "Pueblo Social Organization as a Lead to Pueblo History" (*American Anthropologist,* Vol. 39, 1937), pp. 504–522.

Hay, C., et al. (eds.): *The Maya and Their Neighbors* (New York, 1940).

Hays, H. R.: *From Ape to Angel: An Informal History of Social Anthropology* (New York, 1958).

Heine-Geldern, R.: "One Hundred Years of Ethnological Theory in the German-speaking Countries: Some Milestones" (*Current Anthropology,* Vol. 5, 1964), pp. 407–429.

Henry, J.: *Culture against Man* (New York, 1963).

Herskovits, M. J.: "A Preliminary Consideration of Culture Areas of Africa" (*American Anthropologist,* Vol. 26, 1924), pp. 50–63.

——: "African Gods and Catholic Saints in New World Negro Belief" (*American Anthropologist,* Vol. 39, 1937), pp. 635–643.

——: "A Note on 'Woman Marriage' in Dahomey" (*Africa,* Vol. 10, 1937), pp. 335–341.

——: *Acculturation: The Study of Culture Contacts* (New York, 1938).

——: *Dahomey: An Ancient West African Kingdom* (2 vols., New York, 1938).

——: *Backgrounds of African Art* (Denver, Colo., 1945).

——: *Economic Anthropology* (New York, 1952).

—— and F. S. Herskovits: *An Outline of Dahomean Religious Belief* (American Anthropological Association Memoir 41, 1933).

Hibben, F. C.: "Corn" (*The Atlantic,* Vol. 175, 1945), p. 121.

Hill, W. W.: *The Agricultural and Hunting Methods of the Navaho Indians* (Yale University Publications in Anthropology, No. 18, 1938).

Hobhouse, L. H., G. C. Wheeler, and M. Ginsberg: *The Material Culture and Social Institutions of the Simpler Peoples* (London, 1930).

Hocart, A. M.: "Kinship Systems," in *The Life-giving Myth, and Other Essays* (n.d.); reprinted in E. A. Hoebel, J. D. Jennings, and E. R. Smith, *Readings in Anthropology* (New York, 1955), pp. 189–193.

Hockett, C. F., and R. Ascher: "The Human Revolution" (*Current Anthropology*, Vol. 5, No. 4, 1964), pp. 135–168.

Hoebel, E. A.: "The Sun Dance of the H3kandika Shoshone" (*American Anthropologist*, Vol. 37, 1935), pp. 570–581.

————: "Comanche and H3kandika Shoshone Relationship Systems" (*American Anthropologist*, Vol. 41, 1939), pp. 440–457.

————: *The Political Organization and Law-ways of the Comanche Indians* (American Anthropological Association Memoir 54: Contributions from the Laboratory of Anthropology, 4, 1940).

————: "The Asiatic Origin of a Myth of the Northwest Coast" (*Journal of American Folklore*, Vol. 54, 1941), pp. 1–12.

————: "The Comanche Sun Dance and Messianic Outbreak of 1873" (*American Anthropologist*, Vol. 43, 1941), pp. 301–303.

————: "Fundamental Legal Concepts as Applied in the Study of Primitive Law" (*Yale Law Journal*, Vol. 51, 1942), pp. 951–963.

————: "Anent Blood Relationship" (*Science*, Vol. 103, 1946), pp. 600–602.

————: "Law and Anthropology" (*Virginia Law Review*, Vol. 32, 1946), pp. 836–854.

————: "Eskimo Infanticide and Polyandry" (*The Scientific Monthly*, Vol. 64, 1947), p. 535.

————: "Underground Kiva Passages" (*American Antiquity*, Vol. 19, 1953), p. 76.

————: *The Law of Primitive Man: A Study in Comparative Legal Dynamics* (Cambridge, Mass., 1954).

————: *The Cheyennes: Indians of the Great Plains* (New York, 1960).

————: "William Robertson: An Eighteenth Century Anthropologist-Historian" (*American Anthropologist*, Vol. 62, 1960), pp. 648–655.

————, J. D. Jennings, and E. R. Smith: *Readings in Anthropology* (New York, 1955).

Hogbin, H. I.: *Law and Order in Polynesia: A Study of Primitive Legal Institutions* (New York, 1934).

Hole, F., and R. F. Heizer: *An Introduction to Prehistoric Archaeology* (New York, 1965).

Hollis, A. C.: *The Nandi* (Oxford, 1909).

Holmes, O. W., Jr.: *The Common Law* (Boston, 1881).

————: "The Path of the Law" (*Harvard Law Review*, Vol. 10, 1897).

————: "Law in Science and Science in Law" (*Harvard Law Review*, Vol. 12, 1899), pp. 443–463.

————: *McDonald v. Maybee* (*Supreme Court Reporter*, Vol. 37, 1917), p. 343.

Holmes, W. H.: *Ancient Art of the Province of Chiriqui* (Bureau of American Ethnology, Annual Report 6, 1888).

Holmes-Pollock Letters: *The Correspondence of Mr. Justice Holmes and Sir Frederick Pollock: 1874–1932* (2 vols., Cambridge, Mass., 1942).

Homans, G. C., and D. M. Schneider: *Marriage, Authority, and Final Causes: A Study of Unilateral Cross-cousin Marriage* (Glencoe, Ill., 1955).

Hooton, E. A.: *The American Criminal* (Cambridge, Mass., 1938).

————: "The Wages of Biological Sin" (*The Atlantic*, Vol. 164, 1939), pp. 435–445.

————: *Man's Poor Relations* (New York, 1942).

————: *Up from the Ape* (rev. ed., New York, 1947).

Hostetler, J. A.: *The Amish* (Baltimore, Md., 1964).

Howell, F. C.: "The Place of Neandertal Man in Human Evolution" (*American Journal of Physical Anthropology*, Vol. 9, 1951), pp. 379ff.

————: "Pleistocene Glacial Ecology and the Evolution of 'Classical Neandertal' Man" (*Southwestern Journal of Anthropology*, Vol. 8, 1952), pp. 377–460.

————: "The Evolutionary Significance of Variation and Varieties of 'Neanderthal' Man" (*The Quarterly Review of Biology*, Vol. 32, No. 4, 1957), pp. 330–347; reprinted in M. H. Fried (ed.), *Readings in Anthropology*, Vol. 1, pp. 64–83 (New York, 1959).

————: "Potassium-Argon Dating at Olduvai Gorge" (*Current Anthropology*, Vol. 3, No. 3, 1962), pp. 306–308.

———— and F. Bourlière (eds.): *African Ecology and Human Evolution* (Chicago, 1963).

Howell, P. P.: *A Manual of Nuer Law* (Oxford, 1954).

Howells, W. W.: "Fossil Man and the Origin of Races" (*American Anthropologist*, Vol. 44, 1942), pp. 182–193.

————: *Mankind So Far* (Garden City, N.J., 1944).

————: *The Heathens* (Garden City, N.J., 1948).

————: *Back of History* (Garden City, N.J., 1954).

———— : *Mankind in the Making* (New York, 1959).

Howitt, A. W.: *The Native Tribes of South-east Australia* (New York, 1904).

Hrdlička, A.: *The Neandertal Phase of Man* (Smithsonian Institution, Annual Report, 1928), pp. 593–623.

Hsu, F. L. K.: *Religion, Science and Human Crisis* (London, 1952).

Hulse, F. S.: *The Human Species* (New York, 1963).

Hutton, J. H.: *Caste in India: Its Nature, Function, and Origin* (London, 1946).

Huxley, J. S.: *Evolution in Action* (London, 1953).

Huxley, T. H.: *Evidence as to Man's Place in Nature* (London, 1863).

Inverarity, R. B.: *Art of the Northwest Coast Indians* (Berkeley, Calif., 1950).

Izikowitz, K. G.: *Lamet: Hill Peasants in French Indochina* (Goteborg, 1951).

Jacobs, M.: *Pattern in Cultural Anthropology* (Homewood, Ill., 1964).

Jeffrey, M. D. W.: "Lobola Is Child-price" (*African Studies*, Vol. 10, 1951), pp. 1–40.

Jenks, A.: *Wild Rice Culture of the Upper Great Lakes Region* (Bureau of American Ethnology, Annual Report 19, 1898).

Jenness, D.: *The Indians of Canada* (National Museum of Canada Bulletin 68, Anthropological Series, No. 15, 2d ed., 1934).

Jennings, J. D., and E. Norbeck (eds.): *Prehistoric Man in the New World* (Chicago, 1964).

Jhering, R. von: *Law as Means to an End* (translated from the German, New York, 1924).

Jochelson, W.: "Past and Present Subterranean Dwellings of the Tribes of North Eastern Asia and North Western America" (*Proceedings of the 15th International Congress of Americanists*, Quebec, 1907).

Junod, A. H.: *The Life of a South African Tribe* (2 vols., London, 1913).

Kardiner, A. (ed.): *The Individual and His Society* (New York, 1939).

——— (ed.): *The Psychological Frontiers of Society* (New York, 1945).

——— and E. Preble: *They Studied Man* (New York, 1961).

Keesing, F. M.: "Some Notes on Bontoc Social Organization" (*American Anthropologist*, Vol. 51, 1949), pp. 578–600; reprinted in E. A. Hoebel, J. D. Jennings, and E. R. Smith, *Readings in Anthropology* (New York, 1955), pp. 173–189.

Kennedy, R.: "Bark Cloth in Indonesia" (*Journal of the Polynesian Society*, No. 172, 1934).

———: *Islands and Peoples of the Indies* (Smithsonian Institution War Background Studies, No. 14, 1943).

Kenyon, K.: *Digging up Jericho* (London and New York, 1957).

Klineberg, O. H.: "Mental Tests" (*Encyclopedia of the Social Sciences*, Vol. 10, 1933), pp. 323–328.

———: *Race Differences* (New York, 1935).

———: "A Science of National Character" (*Journal of Social Psychology*, S.P.S.S.I. Bulletin 19, 1944), pp. 147–162.

———: "Negro-White Differences in Intelligence Test Performance: A New Look at an Old Problem" (*American Psychologist*, Vol. 18, 1963), pp. 198–203.

Klinger, H. P., et. al.: "The Chromosomes of the Hominoidea," in S. L. Washburn (ed.), *Classification and Human Evolution* (Chicago, 1963).

Kluckhohn, C.: "Some Reflections on the Method and Theory of the Kulturkreislehre" (*American Anthropologist*, Vol. 38, 1936), pp. 157–196.

———: "The Place of Theory in Anthropological Science" (*The Philosophy of Science*, Vol. 6, 1939).

———: "The Influence of Psychiatry on Anthropology in America during the Past One Hundred Years," in J. K. Hall et al. (eds.), *One Hundred Years of American Psychiatry* (New York, 1944).

———: *Mirror for Man: The Relation of Anthropology to Modern Life* (New York, 1949).

———: "Philosophy of the Navaho Indians," in F. S. C. Northrop (ed.), *Ideological Differences and World Order* (New Haven, Conn., 1949), chap. 17.

——— and W. H. Kelley: "The Concept of Culture," in R. Linton (ed.), *The Science of Man in the World Crisis* (New York, 1947), pp. 78–102.

——— and D. Leighton: *The Navaho* (Cambridge, Mass., 1948).

——— and O. H. Mowrer: " 'Culture and Personality': A Conceptual Scheme" (*American Anthropologist*, Vol. 46, 1944), pp. 1–29.

Knopf, A.: "Measuring Geologic Time" (*The Scientific Monthly*, November, 1957), pp. 225–236.

Köhler, W.: *The Mentality of Apes* (New York, 1925).

Kortland, A.: "Chimpanzees in the Wild" (*Scientific American*, Vol. 206, 1962), pp. 128–134.

Krieger, A. D.: "Early Man in the New World," in J. D. Jennings and E. Norbeck (eds.), *Prehistoric Man in the New World* (Chicago, 1964), pp. 23–84.

Krieger, H. W.: "Design Areas in Oceania" (*United States National Museum Proceedings*, Vol. 79, 1932), pp. 1–53.

Kroeber, A. L.: "Decorative Symbolism of the Arapaho" (*American Anthropologist*, Vol. 3, 1901), pp. 308ff.

———: "Classificatory Systems of Relationship" (*Journal of the Royal Anthropological Institute of Great Britain and Ireland*, Vol. 39, 1909), pp. 77–84.

———: "The Superorganic" (*American Anthropologist*, Vol. 19, 1917), pp. 163–213.

———: "Review of R. H. Lowie, *Primitive Society*" (*American Anthropologist*, Vol. 22, 1920), pp. 377–381.

———: "Yurok Law" (*Proceedings of the 22d International Congress of Americanists*, 1922), pp. 511ff.

———: "Caste" (*Encyclopedia of the Social Sciences*, Vol. 3, 1930), pp. 254–256.

———: "Cultural and Natural Areas of Native North America" (*University of California Publications in American Archaeology and Ethnology*, Vol. 39, 1939).

———: "Stepdaughter Marriage" (*American Anthropologist*, Vol. 42, 1940), pp. 562–570.

———: "Stimulus Diffusion" (*American Anthropologist*, Vol. 42, 1940), pp. 1–20.

———: "Culture Element Distributions: XV, Salt, Dogs, Tobacco" (*Anthropological Records*, Vol. 6, No. 1, 1941), pp. 1–20.

———: "Art," in J. H. Steward (ed.), *Handbook of South American Indians* (6 vols., Washington, D.C., 1946–1950), Vol. 5, pp. 411–492.

——— (ed.): *Anthropology Today: An Encyclopedic Inventory* (Chicago, 1953).

———: "Preface," in W. Goldshmidt (ed.), *The Anthropology of Franz Boas* (American Anthropological Association Memoir 89, 1959), pp. v–vii.

——— and C. Kluckhohn: *Culture: A Critical Review of Concepts and Definitions* (Anthropological Papers, Peabody Museum, No. 47, 1952).

Kuper, H.: *An African Aristocracy: Rank among the Swazi* (Oxford, 1947).

———: *The Swazi: A South African Kingdom* (New York, 1963).

Kwang-chih Chang: "New Evidence on Fossil Man in China" (*Science*, Vol. 136, No. 3518, 1962), pp. 749–760.

LaBarre, W.: *The Peyote Cult* (Yale University Publications in Anthropology, No. 19, 1938).

———: "Potato Taxonomy among the Aymara Indians of Bolivia" (*Acta Americana*, Vol. 5, 1947), pp. 83–102.

———: *The Human Animal* (Chicago, 1954).

LaFarge, O.: *The Changing Indian* (Norman, Okla., 1942).

Lafitau, J. F.: *Moeurs des sauvages amériquains comparées aux moeurs des premiers temps* (Paris, 1724).

Lambert, B.: "Ambilineal Desent Groups in the Northern Gilbert Islands" (*American Anthropologist*, Vol. 68, 1966), pp. 641–664.

Landes, R.: "The Ojibway of Canada," in M. Mead (ed.), *Cooperation and Competition among Primitive Peoples* (New York, 1937), pp. 87–126.

Lang, A.: *Myth, Ritual, and Religion* (London, 1887).

———: *The Making of Religion* (London, 1898).

———: *Social Origins* (London, 1903).

Lantis, M.: "The Alaskan Whale Cult and Its Affinities" (*American Anthropologist*, Vol. 40, 1938), pp. 438–464.

Leach, E. R.: *Rethinking Anthropology* (London School of Economics, Monographs on Social Anthropology, No. 22, 1961).

———: "The Epistemological Background to Malinowski's Empiricism," in R. Firth (ed.), *Man and Culture: An Evaluation of the Work of Bronislaw Malinowski* (London, 1957), pp. 119–137.

Leakey, L. S. B.: *Olduvai Gorge: A Report on the Evolution of the Hand-axe Culture in Beds I–IV, with Chapters on the Geology and Fauna by the Late Prof. Hans Reck and Dr. A. T. Hopwood* (Cambridge, England, 1951).

———: "A New Lower Pliocene Fossil Primate from Kenya" (*Annals and Magazine of Natural History*, Vol. 14, 1961), pp. 689–696.

———: "East African Hominoidea and the Classification within the Super-family," in S. L. Washburn (ed.), *Classification and Human Evolution* (Chicago, 1963), pp. 32–49.

Lee, D. D.: "Being and Value in a Primitive Culture" (*The Journal of Philosophy*, Vol. 46, 1939), pp. 401–415.

Lee, O.: "Social Values and the Philosophy of Law" (*Virginia Law Review*, Vol. 32, 1946), pp. 802–817.

Le Gros Clark, W. E.: "Hominid Characteristics of the Australopithecine Dentition" (*Journal of the Royal Anthropological Institute of Great Britain and Ireland*, Vol. 80, 1952), pp. 37–54; reprinted in *Yearbook of Physical Anthropology, 1951* (New York, 1952), pp. 163–187.

———: *History of the Primates: An Introduction to the Study of Fossil Man* (4th ed., London, 1954).

———: *The Fossil Evidence for Human Evolution: An Introduction to the Study of Paleoanthropology* (Chicago, 1955).

——— and L. S. B. Leakey: "The Miocene Hominidae of East Africa" (*British Museum Fossil Mammals of Africa*, No. 1, 1951).

Leslie, C. M.: *Now We Are Civilized: A Study of the World View of the Zapotec Indians of Mitla, Oaxaca* (Detroit, Mich., 1960).

Lessa, W. A.: *An Appraisal of Constitutional Typologies* (American Anthropological Association Memoir 62, 1945).

——— and E. Z. Vogt: *Reader in Comparative Religion: An Anthropological Approach* (2d ed., Evanston, Ill., 1958).

Lesser, A.: "Levirate and Fraternal Polyandry among the Pawnees" (*Man*, Vol. 30, No. 77, 1930), pp. 98–101.

Lévi-Strauss, C.: *Les Structures Élémentaires de la Parenté* (Paris, 1948).

Levy, M. J., and L. A. Fallers: "The Family: Some Comparative Considerations" (*American Anthropologist*, Vol. 61, 1959), pp. 647–651.

Lewin, J.: *Studies in African Native Law* (Cape Town and Philadelphia, 1947).

Lewis, M., and W. Clark: *History of the Expedition of Captains Lewis and Clark: 1804-05-06* (Hosmer ed., 2 vols., Chicago, 1902).

Lewis, O.: *The Effects of White Contact upon Blackfoot Culture, with Special Reference to the Fur Trade* (American Ethnological Society Monograph 6, 1942).

———: "Comparisons in Cultural Anthropology," in W. L. Thomas (ed.), *Yearbook of Anthropology–1955* (New York, 1955).

———: *The Children of Sanchez* (New York, 1961).

———: "Mother and Son in a Puerto Rican Slum; Part 1; Felicita" (*Harper's Magazine*, December, 1965), p. 72.

Lienhardt, G.: *Social Anthropology* (Oxford, 1965).

Life, Editors of: *The Epic of Man* (New York, 1961).

Lindzey, G.: *Projective Techniques and Cross-cultural Research* (New York, 1963).

Linton, R.: "Culture Areas in Madagascar" (*American Anthropologist*, Vol. 30, 1928), pp. 363–390.

———: "The Tanala: A Hill Tribe of Madagascar" (*Field Museum of Natural History, Anthropological Series*, Vol. 22, 1933).

———: *The Study of Man* (New York, 1936).

———: "The Marquesas," in A. Kardiner (ed.), *The Individual and His Society* (New York, 1937).

———: "The Tanala," in A. Kardiner (ed.), *The Individual and His Society* (New York, 1939).

——— (ed.): *Acculturation in Seven American Indian Tribes* (New York, 1940).

———: *The Cultural Background of Personality* (New York, 1945).

——— (ed.): *The Science of Man in the World Crisis* (New York, 1945).

———: *The Tree of Culture* (New York, 1955).

——— and P. S. Wingert: *Arts of the South Seas* (New York, 1946).

Llewellyn, K. N., and E. A. Hoebel: *The Cheyenne Way: Conflict and Case Law in Primitive Jurisprudence* (Norman, Okla., 1941).

Loeb, E. M.: "Javanese Word Formation, High and Low" (*Journal of the American Oriental Society*, Vol. 64, 1944), pp. 113–126.

——— and J. O. M. Broek: "Social Organization and the Long House in Southeast Asia" (*American Anthropologist*, Vol. 49, 1947), pp. 414–425.

Lowie, R. H.: "The Northern Shoshone" (*American Museum of Natural History, Anthropological Papers*, Vol. 11, Part 2, 1909).

———: "Societies of the Crow, Hidatsa, and Mandan Indians" (*American Museum of Natural History, Anthropological Papers*, Vol. 11, 1913).

———: "Plains Indian Age Societies: Historical Summary" (*American Museum of Natural History, Anthropological Papers*, Vol. 11, 1916), pp. 877–984.

———: *Primitive Society* (New York, 1920).

———: "Notes on Shoshonean Ethnography" (*American Museum of Natural History, Anthropological Papers*, Vol. 20, Part 3, 1924).

———: *Primitive Religion* (New York, 1924).

———: *The Origin of the State* (New York, 1927).

———: "Incorporeal Property in Primitive Society" (*Yale Law Journal*, Vol. 38, 1928), pp. 551–563.

———: "Kinship" (*Encyclopedia of the Social Sciences*, Vol. 3, 1931), pp. 568–572.

———: *The Crow Indians* (New York, 1935).

———: "Lewis Henry Morgan in Historical Perspective," in *Essays in Anthropology in Honor of Alfred Louis Kroeber* (Berkeley, Calif., 1936), pp. 169–181.

———: *The History of Ethnological Theory* (New York, 1937).

———: *An Introduction to Cultural Anthropology* (rev. ed., New York, 1940).

———: "Property Rights and Coercive Powers of the Plains Indian Military Societies" (*Journal of Legal and Political Sociology*, Vol. 1, 1943), pp. 59–71.

———: "Evolution in Cultural Anthropology: A Reply to Leslie White" (*American Anthropologist*, Vol. 48, 1946), pp. 229–230.

McCown, T. D., and A. Keith: *The Stone Age of Mt. Carmel* (2 vols., Oxford, 1939).

MacIver, R. M.: *Society: Its Structure and Changes* (New York, 1931).

———: "Government and Property" (*Journal of Political and Legal Sociology*, Vol. 4, 1946), pp. 5–18.

———: *The Web of Government* (New York, 1947).

———: *The Ramparts We Guard* (New York, 1950).

McLennan, J. F.: *Primitive Marriage* (Edinburgh, 1865).

———: *The Patriarchal Theory* (London, 1885).

Maine, H. S.: *Ancient Law: Its Connection with the Early History of Society, and Its Relation to Modern Ideas* (3d American ed., New York, 1879).

Mair, L.: *Primitive Government* (Baltimore, Md., 1964).

Malinowski, B.: *Argonauts of the Western Pacific: An Account of Native Enterprise and Adventure in the Archipelagos of Melanesian New Guinea* (London, 1922).

———: *Crime and Custom in Savage Society* (New York, 1926).

———: *The Father in Primitive Psychology* (New York, 1927).

———: *Sex and Repression in Savage Society* (New York, 1927).

———: "Culture" (*Encyclopedia of the Social Sciences*, Vol. 4, 1931), pp. 621–646.

———: "Preface," in R. Firth, *We, the Tikopia* (London, 1936).

———: *Coral Gardens and Their Magic* (2 vols., New York, 1938).

———: *Magic, Science and Religion and Other Essays* (Glencoe, Ill., 1948).

Malthus, T. R.: *An Essay on the Principle of Population: or, A View of Its Past and Present Effects on Human Happiness; with an Inquiry into Our Prospects Respecting the Future Removal or Mitigation of the Evils Which It Occasions* (London, 1798).

Mandelbaum, D. G., G. W. Lasker, and E. M. Albert: *The Teaching of Anthropology* (Berkeley and Los Angeles, Calif., 1963).

Mangelsdorf, P. C., and R. G. Reeves: "The Origin of Maize: Present Status of the Problem" (*American Anthropologist*, Vol. 47, 1945), pp. 235–243.

Marrett, R. R.: *The Threshold of Religion* (2d ed., London, 1914).

Mason, O. T.: *Aboriginal American Basketry* (United States National Museum, Annual Report, 1904), pp. 171–548.

Mauldin, B.: *Up Front* (New York, 1945).

Mauss, M.: *The Gift: Forms and Functions of Exchange in Archaic Societies* (translated by I. Cunnison, London, 1954).

Mead, M.: *Coming of Age in Samoa: A Psychological Study of Primitive Youth for Western Civilization* (New York, 1928).

———: *Growing up in New Guinea: A Comparative Study of Primitive Education* (New York, 1930).

———: *Sex and Temperament in Three Primitive Societies* (New York, 1935).

——— (ed.): *Cooperation and Competition among Primitive Peoples* (New York, 1937).

———: *And Keep Your Powder Dry* (New York, 1942).

———: "On the Implications for Anthropology of the Gesell-Ilg Approach to Maturation" (*American Anthropologist*, Vol. 49, 1947), pp. 69–77.

———: *Male and Female: A Study of the Sexes in the Changing World* (New York, 1949).

———: "National Character," in A. L. Kroeber (ed.), *Anthropology Today: An Encyclopedic Inventory* (Chicago, 1953), pp. 642–667.

———: "Some Theoretical Considerations on the Problem of Mother-Child Separation" (*American Journal of Orthopsychiatry*, Vol. 24, 1954), pp. 471–483.

———(ed.): *Culture Patterns and Technical Change* (New York, 1955).

——— and M. Wolfenstein (eds.): *Childhood in Contemporary Cultures* (Chicago, 1955).

Meek, C. K.: *The Northern Tribes of Nigeria* (2 vols., Oxford, 1925).

Melaart, J.: "A Neolithic City in Turkey" (*Scientific American*, Vol. 210, No. 4, 1964), pp. 94–105.

Menninger, W. C.: "Psychiatry Today" (*The Atlantic*, Vol. 181, 1948), pp. 65ff.

Metraux, A.: "The Botocudo," in J. H. Steward (ed.), *Handbook of South American Indians* (6 vols., Washington, D.C., 1946–1950), Vol. 1, pp. 531–540.

———: "The Tupinamba," in J. H. Steward (ed.), *Handbook of South American Indians* (6 vols., Washington, D.C., 1946–1950), Vol. 3, pp. 95–133.

———: "Warfare, Cannibalism, and Human Trophies," in J. H. Steward (ed.), *Handbook of South American Indians* (6 vols., Washington, D.C., 1946–1950), Vol. 5, pp. 383–409.

Middleton, J., and D. Tait: *Tribes without Rulers: Studies in African Segmentary Systems* (London, 1958).

Middleton, R.: "Brother-Sister and Father-Daughter Marriage in Ancient Greece" (*American Sociological Review*, Vol. 27, 1962), pp. 603–611.

Miller, N., and J. Dollard: *Social Learning and Imitation* (New Haven, Conn., 1941).

Millikan, R. A.: "Science and the World Tomorrow" (*Scientific Monthly*, Vol. 49, 1939), pp. 212–240.

Mirov, N. T.: "Notes on the Domestication of the Reindeer" (*American Anthropologist*, Vol. 47, 1945), pp. 393–408.

Mishkin, B.: *Rank and Warfare among the Plains Indians* (American Ethnological Society Monograph 3, 1940).

Mombert, P.: "Class" (*Encyclopedia of the Social Sciences*, Vol. 3, 1930), pp. 531–536.

Mooney, J.: *The Ghost Dance Religion and the Sioux Outbreak of 1890* (Bureau of American Ethnology, Annual Report 14, 1896).

Morant, G. M.: "The Form of the Swanscombe Skull" (*Journal of the Royal Anthropological Institute of Great Britain and Ireland*, Vol. 68, 1938), pp. 67–97.

Morgan, L. H.: *Ancient Society, or Researches in the Lines of Human Progress from Savagery, through Barbarism to Civilization* (New York, 1877).

———: "Houses and House Life of the American Aborigines" (*Contributions to American Ethnology*, Vol. 4, 1881).

———: *The League of the Ho-dé-no-sau-nee or Iroquois* (2 vols., New Haven, Conn., 1954).

Morley, S. G.: *The Ancient Maya* (Stanford, Calif., 1946).

Movius, H. L.: "Early Man and Pleistocene Stratigraphy in Southern and Eastern Asia" (*Papers of the Peabody Museum of American Archaeology and Ethnology, Harvard University*, Vol. 19, 1944).

———: "Old World Prehistory: Paleolithic," in A. L. Kroeber (ed.), *Anthropology Today: An Encyclopedic Inventory* (Chicago, 1953), pp. 163–192.

Murdock, G. P.: "The Science of Culture" (*American Anthropologist*, Vol. 34, 1932), pp. 200–215.

———: *Our Primitive Contemporaries* (New York, 1934).

———: "Comparative Data on the Division of Labor by Sex" (*Social Forces*, Vol. 15, 1937), pp. 551–553.

———: "Double Descent" (*American Anthropologist*, Vol. 42, 1940), pp. 555–561.

———: "Bifurcate Merging: A Test of Five Theories" (*American Anthropologist*, Vol. 49, 1947), pp. 56–68.

———: *Social Structure* (New York, 1949).

———: "Family Stability in Non-European Cultures" (*Annals of the American Academy of Political and Social Sciences*, Vol. 272, 1950), pp. 195–201.

——— (ed.): *Social Structure in Southeast Asia* (Viking Fund Publications in Anthropology, No. 29, 1960).

Murphy, R. F., and L. Kasdan: "The Structure of Parallel Cousin Marriage" (*American Anthropologist*, Vol. 61, 1959), pp. 17–29.

Myrdal, G. S.: *An American Dilemma: The Negro Problem and Modern Democracy* (2 vols., New York, 1944).

Nadel, S. F.: "The Kede: A Riverian State in Northern Nigeria," in E. E. Evans-Pritchard and M. Fortes (eds.), *African Political Systems* (Oxford, 1940), pp. 166–195.

Napier, J., and N. A. Barnicot (eds.): *The Primates* (Symposia of the Zoological Society of London, No. 10, 1963).

Needham, R.: *Structure and Sentiment* (Chicago, 1962).

Nelson, E. W.: *The Eskimos about Bering Straits* (Bureau of American Ethnology, Annual Report 18, 1899).

Niblack, A. P.: *The Coast Indians of Southern Alaska and Northern British Columbia* (Board of Regents of the Smithsonian Institution, Annual Report, 1890).

Norbeck, E.: *Religion in Primitive Society* (New York, 1961).

———: "Peasant Society," in J. Gould and W. L. Kolb (eds.), *A Dictionary of the Social Sciences* (Glencoe, Ill., 1964).

Northrop, F. S. C. (ed.): *Ideological Differences and World Order* (New Haven, Conn., 1949).

Oakley, K. P.: "Swanscombe Man" (*Proceedings of the Geologists' Association*, Vol. 63, 1952), pp. 271–300; reprinted in *Yearbook of Physical Anthropology*, 1953 (New York, 1954), pp. 40–70.

———: *Man, the Tool Maker* (Chicago, 1957).

———: "On Man's Use of Fire, with Comments on Tool-making and Hunting," in S. L. Washburn (ed.), *Social Life of Early Man* (Chicago, 1961).

———: *Frameworks for Dating Fossil Man* (Chicago, 1964).

——— and H. M. Muir-Wood: *The Succession of Life through Geologic Time* (2nd ed., London, 1952).

Oberg, K.: "The Kingdom of Ankole in Uganda," in E. E. Evans-Pritchard and M. Fortes (eds.), *African Political Systems* (Oxford, 1940), pp. 121–162.

Olearius: *The Description of the Journey in Muscovia* (Moscow, 1906).

Oliver, D. L.: *A Solomon Island Society: Kinship and Leadership among the Siuai of Bougainville* (Cambridge, Mass., 1953).

O'Neale, L. M.: "Weaving," in J. H. Steward (ed.), *Handbook of South American Indians* (6 vols., Washington, D.C., 1946-1950), Vol. 5, pp. 97–138.

Opler, M. E.: *An Apache Life-way: The Economic, Social, and Religious Institutions of the Chiricahua* (Chicago, 1942).

———: "On the Method of Writing Anthropological Monographs" (*American Anthropologist*, Vol. 45, 1943), pp. 329–332.

———: "Themes as Dynamic Forces in Culture" (*The American Journal of Sociology*, Vol. 51, 1945), pp. 198–206.

Opler, M. K.: "The Integration of the Sun Dance in Ute Religion" (*American Anthropologist*, Vol. 43, 1941), pp. 550–572.

———: *Culture, Psychiatry and Human Values: The Methods and Values of a Social Psychiatry* (Springfield, Ill., 1956).

Oppenheimer, F.: *The State* (translated from the German by Gitterman, New York, 1922).

Park, W. Z.: "Paviotso Polyandry" (*American Anthropologist*, Vol. 39, 1937), pp. 366–368.

———: *Shamanism in Western North America: A Study in Cultural Relationships* (Evanston and Chicago, Ill., 1938).

Parsons, E. C.: *American Indian Life* (New York, 1923).

———: *Pueblo Indian Religion* (2 vols., Chicago, 1937).

Patai, R.: "Cousin-right in Middle Eastern Marriage" (*Southwestern Journal of Anthropology*, Vol. 11, 1955), pp. 371–390.

Paul, B. D.: "Teaching Anthropology in Schools of Public Health," in D. G. Mandelbaum, G. W. Lasker, and E. M. Albert, *The Teaching of Anthropology* (Berkeley and Los Angeles, Calif., 1963), pp. 503–512.

Penniman, T. K.: *One Hundred Years of Anthropology* (Cambridge, Mass., 1936).

Perrot, J.: "Palestine-Syria-Cilicia," in R. J. Braidwood and G. R. Willey (eds.), *Courses toward Urban Life: Archaeological Considerations of Some Cultural Alternatives* (Chicago, 1962), pp. 147–164.

Pettitt, G. A.: "Primitive Education in North America" (*University of California Publications in American Archaeology and Ethnology*, Vol. 43, No. 1, 1946).

Porteus, S. D.: *The Psychology of a Primitive People: A Study of the Australian Aborigine* (New York, 1931).

Pospisil, L.: *The Kapauku Papuans of West New Guinea* (New York, 1963).

Pound, R.: "A Theory of Legal Interests" (*American Sociological Society, Publications,* Vol. 16, 1920).

Powdermaker, H.: *Life in Lesu: The Study of a Melanesian Society in New Ireland* (London, 1933).

Prins, A. H. J.: *East African Age Class Systems: An Inquiry into the Social Order of Galla, Kipsigis and Kikuyu* (Groningen and Djakarta, 1953).

Provinse, J. H.: "Cooperative Ricefield Cultivation among the Siang Dyaks of Central Borneo" (*American Anthropologist*, Vol. 37, 1939), pp. 77–102.

Quimby, G. I.: "The Natchezan Culture Type" (*American Antiquity*, Vol. 7, 1942), pp. 255–275.

———: "Natchez Social Structure as an Instrument of Assimilation" (*American Anthropologist*, Vol. 48, 1946), pp. 134–136.

Radcliffe-Brown, A. R.: *The Andaman Islanders* (Cambridge, Engl., 1922).

———: "The Social Organization of Australian Tribes" (*Oceania*, Vol. 1, Nos. 1–4, 1930–1931); reprinted as Oceania Monographs, No. 1, Melbourne, 1931.

———: "On the Concept of Functionalism in the Social Sciences" (*American Anthropologist*, Vol. 37, 1935), pp. 394–402.

———: "Patrilineal and Matrilineal Succession" (*Iowa Law Review*, Vol. 20, 1935), pp. 286–298.

——— and M. Fortes (eds.): *African Systems of Kinship and Marriage* (Oxford, 1950).

Radin, M.: "A Restatement of Hohfeld" (*Harvard Law Review*, Vol. 51, 1938), pp. 1141ff.

Radin, P.: *The Winnebago Tribe* (Bureau of American Ethnology, Annual Report 37, 1923).

——— (ed.): *Crashing Thunder: The Autobiography of an American Indian* (New York, 1926).

———: *Monotheism in Primitive Religion* (New York, 1927).

———: *Primitive Man as Philosopher* (New York, 1927).

———: "The Mind of Primitive Man" (*New Republic*, Vol. 98, 1939), p. 303.

Rasmussen, K.: *Grønlandsagen* (Berlin, 1922).

———: *Across Arctic America* (New York, 1927).

Rattray, R. S.: *Ashanti* (Oxford, 1923).

———: *Ashanti Law and Constitution* (Oxford, 1927).

Ratzel, F.: *Anthropogeographie* (2 vols., Stuttgart, 1882).

Ray, V. F.: "The Sanpoil and Nespelem: Salishan Peoples of Northeastern Washington" (*University of Washington Publications in Anthropology*, Vol. 5, 1932).

Reay, M.: *The Kuma: Freedom and Conformity in the New Guinea Highlands* (Melbourne, 1959).

Reddy, N. S.: *Transition in Caste Structure in Andrah Presh with Particular Reference to Depressed Castes* (Lucknow, 1952).

Redfield, R.: *The Folk Culture of Yucatan* (Chicago, 1942).

———: "Maine's Ancient Law in the Light of Primitive Societies" (*Western Political Quarterly*, Vol. 3, 1950), pp. 574–589.

———: *The Primitive World and Its Transformations* (Ithaca, N.Y., 1953).

———: *The Little Community and Peasant Society and Culture* (Chicago, 1960).

———: *The Social Uses of Social Science: The Papers of Robert Redfield* (2 vols.; edited by M. P. Redfield, Chicago, 1963).

———, M. J. Herskovits, and G. F. Ekholm: *Aspects of Primitive Art* (New York, 1959).

Reichard, G. A.: "Social Life," in F. Boas (ed.), *General Anthropology* (New York, 1938).

———: *Prayer: The Compulsive Word* (American Ethnological Society Monograph 7, 1944).

Richards, A. I.: *Land, Labour, and Diet in Northern Rhodesia* (Oxford, 1950).

Richardson, J.: *Law and Status among the Kiowa Indians* (American Ethnological Society Monograph 1, 1940).

Rivers, W. H. R.: *The Todas* (London, 1906).

———: *Kinship and Social Organization* (London, 1914).

Roberts, J. M.: "Three Navaho Households" (*Papers of the Peabody Museum of American Archaeology and Ethnology, Harvard University*, Vol. 50, No. 3, 1953).

Robertson, W.: *The History of America* (2 vols., first American ed., Philadelphia, 1812).

Robinson, J. T.: *The Dentition of Australopithecus* (Transvaal Museum Memoirs, No. 9, 1956).

———: "The Australopithecines and Their Bearing on the Origin of Man and of Stone Tool-making" (*South African Journal of Science*, Vol. 57, 1961), pp. 3–13.

———: "Adaptive Radiation in the Australopithecines and the Origin of Man," in F. C. Howell and F. Bourlière (eds.), *African Ecology and Human Evolution* (Chicago, 1963), pp. 385–416.

Romer, A. S.: *The Vertebrate Story* (4th ed., Chicago, 1959).

Roscoe, J.: "The Bahima" (*Journal of the Royal Anthropological Institute of Great Britain and Ireland*, Vol. 37, 1907), pp. 93–118.

———: "The Cow Tribe of Enkole in the Uganda Protectorate" (*Journal of the Royal Anthropological Institute of Great Britain and Ireland*, Vol. 37, 1907).

———: *The Northern Bantu: An Account of Some Central African Tribes of the Uganda Protectorate* (2 vols., Cambridge, Engl., 1915).

———: *The Banyankole* (London, 1923).

Rowe, J. H.: "Inca Culture at the Time of the Spanish Conquest," in J. H. Steward (ed.), *Handbook of South American Indians* (6 vols., Washington, D.C., 1946–1950), Vol. 2, pp. 183–330.

———: "The Renaissance Foundations of Anthropology" (*American Anthropologist*, Vol. 67, 1965), pp. 1–20.

Sahlins, M. D., and E. R. Service (eds.): *Evolution and Culture* (Ann Arbor, Mich., 1960).

Salmond, J. W.: *Jurisprudence* (7th ed., New York, 1924).

Sapir, E.: "Culture, Genuine and Spurious" (*American Journal of Sociology*, Vol. 29, 1924), pp. 401–429.

Sauer, C.: "American Agricultural Origins: A Consideration of Nature and Culture," in *Essays in Anthropology in Honor of Alfred Louis Kroeber* (Berkeley, Calif., 1936), pp. 279–298.

Sayce, R. U.: *Primitive Arts and Crafts: An Introduction to the Study of Material Culture* (Cambridge, Engl., 1933).

Schaller, G. B.: *The Mountain Gorilla: Ecology and Behavior* (Chicago, 1963).

———: *The Year of the Gorilla* (Chicago, 1964).

Schapera, I.: *A Handbook of Tswana Law and Custom: Compiled for the Bechuanaland Protectorate Administration* (Oxford, 1938).

———: *Government and Politics in Tribal Societies* (London, 1956).

———: *Married Life in a South African Tribe* (London, 1950).

Schmidt, W.: *The Origin and Growth of Religion* (translated from the German by H. J. Rose, New York, 1935).

———: "The Position of Women with Regard to Property in Primitive Society" (*American Anthropologist*, Vol. 37, 1935), pp. 244–256.

Schneider, D. M., and K. Gough (eds.): *Matrilineal Kinship* (Berkeley and Los Angeles, Calif., 1961).

Schneider, D. M., and G. C. Homans: "Kinship Terminology and the American Kinship System" (*American Anthropologist*, Vol. 57, 1955), pp. 1194–1208.

Schoolcraft, R. H. (ed.): *History of the Indian Tribes of the United States* (Philadelphia, 1860).

Schurtz, H.: *Altersklassen und Männerbunde* (Berlin, 1902).

Schwabedissen, H.: "Northern Continental Europe," in R. J. Braidwood and G. R. Willey (eds.), *Courses toward Urban Life: Archaeological Considerations of Some Cultural Alternatives* (Chicago, 1962), pp. 254–266.

Seagle, W.: *The Quest for Law* (New York, 1941).

Service, E. R.: *Primitive Social Organization: An Evolutionary Perspective* (New York, 1962).

Seward, G. H.: *Sex and the Social Order* (New York, 1946).

Shapiro, H. L.: *Race Mixture* (Paris, 1953).

Sharp, L.: "People without Politics," in V. Ray (ed.), *Systems of Political Control and Bureaucracy* (Seattle, Wash., 1958).

Sheldon, W. H., and S. S. Stevens: *The Varieties of Temperament: A Psychology of Constitutional Differences* (New York, 1942).

——— and W. B. Tucker: *The Varieties of Human Physique* (New York, 1940).

Simmons, L. (ed.): *Sun Chief: The Autobiography of a Hopi Indian* (New Haven, Conn., 1942).

———: *The Role of the Aged in Primitive Society* (New Haven, Conn., 1945).

Simpson, G. E.: "The Vodun Service in Northern Haiti" (*American Anthropologist,* Vol. 42, 1940), pp. 236–254.

——— and J. M. Yinger: *Racial and Cultural Minorities: An Analysis of Prejudice and Discrimination* (rev. ed., New York, 1958).

Simpson, G. G.: *The Meaning of Evolution* (Oxford, 1950).

———: *Principles of Animal Taxonomy* (New York, 1961).

———: "The Meaning of Taxonomic Statements," in S. L. Washburn (ed.), *Classification and Human Evolution* (Chicago, 1963), pp. 1–31.

Singer, S., E. J. Holmyard, and A. R. Hall (eds.): *A History of Technology* (3 vols., Oxford, 1954).

Skira, A., and G. Bataille: *Prehistoric Painting: Lascaux or the Birth of Art* (Switzerland, n.d.).

Smith, G. H.: "J. B. Trudeau's Remarks on the Indians of the Upper Missouri, 1794–95" (*American Anthropologist,* Vol. 38, 1936), pp. 565–568.

Smith, M. W.: "The War Complex of the Plains Indians" (*American Philosophical Society, Proceedings,* Vol. 28, 1937), pp. 425–464.

——— (ed.): *The Artist in Tribal Society: Proceedings of a Symposium Held at the Royal Anthropological Institute* (New York, 1961).

Smith, P. E. L.: "The Solutrean Culture" (*Scientific American,* Vol. 211, No. 2, 1964), pp. 86–94.

Smyth, H. D.: *Atomic Energy for Military Purposes: The Official Report on the Development of the Atomic Bomb under the Auspices of the United States Government, 1940–1945* (Princeton, N.J., 1946).

Solecki, R. S.: "Prehistory in Shanidar Valley, Northern Iraq" (*Science,* Vol. 139, No. 3551, 1963), pp. 179–193.

Southall, A. W.: *Alur Society* (Cambridge, Engl., 1956).

Southwick, C. H. (ed.): *Primate Social Behavior: An Enduring Problem—Selected Readings* (Princeton, N.J., 1963).

Speck, F. H.: "The Family Hunting Band as the Basis of Algonkian Social Organization" (*American Anthropologist,* Vol. 17, 1915), pp. 289–305.

Spencer, H.: *The Principles of Sociology* (3 vols., London, 1887–1896).

Spencer, R. F.: "Language," in J. Gould and W. L. Kolb (eds.), *Dictionary of the Social Sciences* (Glencoe, Ill., 1964), p. 377.

———: "The Arabian Matriarchate: An Old Controversy" (*Southwestern Journal of Anthropology,* Vol. 8, 1952), pp. 478–502.

Spier, L.: "The Sun Dance of the Plains Indian" (*American Museum of Natural History, Anthropological Papers,* Vol. 16, Part 7, 1921).

———: "Havasupai Ethnology" (*American Museum of Natural History, Anthropological Papers,* Vol. 29, 1928).

———: "Plains Indian Parfleche Designs" (*University of Washington Publications in Anthropology,* Vol. 4, No. 3, 1931).

———: *Yuman Tribes of the Gila River* (Chicago, 1933).

——— and E. Sapir: "Wishram Ethnography" (*University of Washington Publications in Anthropology,* Vol. 3, No. 3, 1930).

Spindler, G. D.: *The Transmission of American Culture* (Cambridge, Mass., 1959).

Spuhler, J. N. (ed.): *The Evolution of Man's Capacity for Culture* (Detroit, Mich., 1959).

Srinivas, M. N.: *Religion and Society among the Coorgs of South India* (Oxford, 1952).

Steggerda, M. G.: "Physical Measurements on Negro, Navajo, and White Girls of College Age" (*American Journal of Physical Anthropology,* Vol. 26, 1940), pp. 417–431.

Steward, J. H.: "The Economic and Social Basis of Primitive Bands," in *Essays in Anthropology in Honor of*

Alfred Louis Kroeber (Berkeley, Calif., 1936), pp. 331–350.

———: "Shoshone Polyandry" (*American Anthropologist*, Vol. 38, 1936), pp. 561–564.

———: "Ecological Aspects of Southwestern Society" (*Anthropos*, Vol. 32, 1937), pp. 82–104.

———: *Basin-plateau Aboriginal Socio-political Groups* (Bureau of American Ethnology Bulletin 120, 1938).

——— (ed.): *Handbook of South American Indians* (6 vols., Washington, D.C., 1946–1950).

———: "Cultural Causality and Law: A Trial Formulation of the Development of Early Civilization" (*American Anthropologist*, Vol. 51, 1949), pp. 1–27: reprinted in E. A. Hoebel, J. D. Jennings, and E. R. Smith, *Readings in Anthropology*, (New York, 1955), pp. 322–340.

———: "Evolution and Process," in A. L. Kroeber (ed.), *Anthropology Today: An Encyclopedic Inventory* (Chicago, 1953), pp. 313–326.

———: *Theory of Culture Change: The Methodology of Multilineal Evolution* (Urbana, Ill., 1955).

Stewart, O. C.: "Fire as the First Great Force Employed by Man," in W. L. Thomas (ed.), *Man's Role in Changing the Face of the Earth* (Chicago, 1956).

Stirling, M. W.: *Historical and Ethnographical Materials on the Jivaro Indians* (Bureau of American Ethnology Bulletin 117, 1938).

Stoll, N. R., et. al.: *International Code of Zoological Nomenclature* (London, 1961).

Stow, G. W.: *The Native Races of South Africa: A History of the Intrusion of the Hottentots and Bantu into the Hunting Grounds of the Bushman* (London, 1905).

Sumner, W. G.: *Folkways: A Study of the Sociological Importance of Usages, Manners, Customs, Mores and Morals* (Boston, 1913).

Swanton, J. R.: "The Social Organization of American Tribes" (*American Anthropologist*, Vol. 7, 1905), pp. 663–673.

Tax, S.: "From Lafitau to Radcliffe-Brown: A Short History of the Study of Social Organization," in F. Eggan (ed.), *Social Anthropology of North American Tribes* (2d ed., Chicago, 1955), pp. 445–481.

———: "Some Problems of Social Organization," in F. Eggan (ed.), *Social Anthropology of North American Tribes* (2d ed., Chicago, 1955), pp. 2–32.

———, L. L. Eiseley, I. Rouse, and C. F. Voegelin: *An Appraisal of Anthropology Today* (Chicago, 1953).

ter Haar, B: *Adat Law in Indonesia* (translated from the Dutch and edited with an introduction by E. A. Hoebel and A. A. Schiller, New York, 1948).

Thomas, E. M.: "The Herdsman" (*The New Yorker*, May 1, 8, 15, and 22, 1965).

Thomas, W. I.: *Primitive Behavior* (New York, 1937).

Thompson, D. F.: "The Joking Relationship and Organized Obscenity in North Queensland" (*American Anthropologist*, Vol. 37, 1935), pp. 460–490.

Thompson, J. E. S.: *The Civilization of the Mayas* (Field Museum of Natural History, Anthropology Leaflet 25, 4th ed., 1942).

———: "A Survey of the Northern Maya Area" (*American Antiquity*, Vol. 2, 1945), pp. 2–24.

Thompson, L.: "The Culture History of the Lau Islands, Fiji" (*American Anthropologist*, Vol. 40, 1938), pp. 181–197.

———: *Toward a Science of Mankind* (New York, 1961).

——— and A. Joseph: *The Hopi Way* (Lawrence, 1944).

Thompson, S.: *Tales of the North American Indians* (Cambridge, Mass., 1929).

———: *The Folktale* (New York, 1946).

Thurnwald, R.: *Banaro Society* (American Anthropological Association Memoir 3, No. 4, 1924).

———: *Economics in Primitive Communities* (Oxford, 1932).

Tilney, F.: *The Brain from Ape to Man* (2 vols., New York, 1928).

Titiev, M.: "The Influence of Common Residence on the Unilateral Classification of Kindred" (*American Anthropologist*, Vol. 45, 1943), pp. 511–530.

———: "Old Oraibi: A Study of the Hopi Indians of the Third Mesa" (*Peabody Museum of American Archaeology and Ethnology, Harvard University*, Vol. 22, No. 1, 1944).

Tobias, P. V.: "The Kanam Jaw" (*Nature*, Vol. 184, No. 4714, 1960), pp. 946–947.

Trowell, M., and K. P. Wachsman: *Tribal Crafts in Uganda* (Oxford, 1953).

Tumin, M. M.: *Caste in a Peasant Society: A Case Study of the Dynamics of Caste* (Princeton, N.J., 1952).

Tylor, E. B.: *Researches into the Early History of Mankind* (2 vols., London, 1871).

———: *Primitive Culture: Researches into the Development of Mythology, Philosophy, Religion, Language, Art and Custom* (2 vols., New York, 1874).

———: "On the Game of Patolli in Ancient America and Its Probable Asiatic Origin" (*Journal of the Royal Anthropological Institute of Great Britain and Ireland*, Vol. 8, 1879), pp. 116–129.

————: *Anthropology: An Introduction into the Study of Man and Civilization* (London, 1881).

————: "On a Method of Investigating the Development of Institutions; Applied to the Laws of Marriage and Descent" (*Journal of the Royal Anthropological Institute of Great Britain and Ireland,* Vol. 18, 1889), pp. 245–272.

————: "American Lot Games as Evidence of Asiatic Intercourse before the Time of Columbus" (*Internationales Archiv für Ethnographie,* Vol. 9, supplement, 1896), pp. 55–67.

Tyrell, J. B. (ed.): *David Thompson's Narrative of His Explorations in Western America, 1784–1812* (Toronto, 1916).

Underhill, R.: *Ceremonialism in the Greater Southwest* (American Ethnological Society Monograph 13, 1948).

UNESCO: *The Race Concept* (Paris, 1952).

————: *African Worlds: Studies in the Cosmological Ideas and Social Values of African Peoples* (Oxford, 1954).

Vaillant, G. C.: *Aztecs of Mexico: Origin, Rise and Fall of the Aztec Nation* (New York, 1941).

Vallois, H.: "Néanderthal-Néandertal" (*L'Anthropologie,* Vol. 55, 1952), pp. 557–558.

van Gennep, A.: *The Rites of Passage* (translated from the French by M. B. Vizedom and G. L. Chafee, Chicago, 1960).

Vavilov, N.: *Studies on the Origin of Cultivated Plants* (Bulletin of Applied Botany and Plant Breeding, Leningrad, 1926).

Vercors: *You Shall Know Them* (Boston, 1953).

von Frisch, K.: "Dialects in the Language of the Bees" (*Scientific American,* August, 1962), pp. 3–7.

Waitz, F. T.: *Anthropologie der Naturvölker* (6 vols., Leipzig, 1859–1871).

Wallace, E., and E. A. Hoebel: *The Comanches: Lords of the South Plains* (Norman, Okla., 1952).

Waln, N.: *The House of Exile* (Boston, 1933).

Warner, W. L.: "Murngin Warfare" (*Oceania,* Vol. 1, 1940).

———— and P. S. Lund: *The Social Life of a Modern Community* (New Haven, Conn., 1941).

Washburn, S. L.: "The New Physical Anthropology" (Transactions of the New York Academy of Sciences, Series II, Vol. 13, 1951), pp. 298–304.

———— (ed.): *Social Life of Early Man* (Chicago, 1961).

———— (ed.): *Classification and Human Evolution* (Chicago, 1963).

Waterbok, H. T.: "The Lower Rhine," in R. J. Braid-wood and G. R. Willey (eds.), *Courses toward Urban Life: Archaeological Consideration of Some Cultural Alternatives* (Viking Fund Publications in Anthropology, No. 32, 1962), pp. 227–253.

Wax, M., and R. Wax: "The Notion of Magic" (*Current Anthropology,* Vol. 4, 1963), pp. 519–533.

Webster, H.: *Primitive Secret Societies: A Study in Early Politics and Religion* (New York, 1908).

Weidenreich, F.: "Some Problems Dealing with Ancient Man" (*American Anthropologist,* Vol. 42, 1940), pp. 375–383.

————: "The Skull of Sinanthropus pekinensis: A Comparative Study on a Primitive Hominid Skull" (*Paleontologia Sinica,* n.s., D, No. 10, 1943), pp. 1–484.

————: "Morphology of Solo Man" (*American Museum of Natural History, Anthropological Papers,* Vol. 43, Part 1, 1951), pp. 205–290.

Weltfish, G.: "Prehistoric North American Basketry Techniques and Modern Distributions" (*American Anthropologist,* Vol. 32, 1930), pp. 454–495.

West, R.: *Conscience and Society: A Study of the Psychological Prerequisites of Law and Order* (New York, 1945).

Westermarck, E.: *The History of Human Marriage* (3 vols., London, 1925).

White, L. A.: "A Problem in Kinship Terminology" (*American Anthropologist,* Vol. 41, 1939), pp. 569–570.

————: "Energy and the Evolution of Culture" (*American Anthropologist,* Vol. 45, 1943), pp. 354–355.

————: "The Symbol: The Origin and Basis of Human Behavior" (*Etc.: A Review of General Semantics,* Vol. 1, 1944), pp. 229–237.

————: " 'Diffusion vs. Evolution': An Anti-evolutionist Fallacy" (*American Anthropologist,* Vol. 47, 1945), pp. 339–355.

————: "The Expansion of the Scope of Science" (*Journal of the Washington Academy of Sciences,* Vol. 37, 1947), pp. 181–210.

————: *The Evolution of Culture* (New York, 1959).

Whiting, B. B.: *Paiute Sorcery* (Viking Fund Publications in Anthropology, No. 15, 1950).

———— (ed.): *Six Cultures: Studies of Child Rearing* (New York and London, 1963).

Whiting, J. W. M.: "Effects of Climate on Certain Cultural Practices," in W. H. Goodenough (ed.), *Explorations in Cultural Anthropology: Essays in Honor of George Peter Murdock* (New York, 1964), pp. 511–544.

———— and I. L. Child: *Child Training and Personality: A Cross-cultural Study* (New Haven, Conn., 1953).

———, R. Kluckhohn, and A. S. Anthony: "The Function of Male Initiation Ceremonies at Puberty," in E. E. Maccoby, T. Newcomb, and E. Hartley (eds.), *Readings in Social Psychology* (New York, 1958), pp. 359–370.

Whitman, W.: *The Pueblo Indians of San Ildefonso* (New York, 1947).

Whorf, B. L.: *Language, Thought, and Reality* (Cambridge, Mass., 1956).

Willey, G. R.: "Archeological Theories and Interpretations," in A. L. Kroeber (ed.), *Anthropology Today: An Encyclopedic Inventory* (Chicago, 1953), pp. 361–385.

Wilson, G. R.: "The Hidatsa Earthlodge" (*American Museum of Natural History Anthropological Papers*, Vol. 33, 1934).

Wilson, M.: *Good Company: A Study of Nyakyusa Age-villages* (London, 1951).

Wissler, C.: "The Influence of the Horse in the Development of Plains Culture" (*American Anthropologist*, Vol. 16, 1914), pp. 1–25; reprinted in E. A. Hoebel, J. D. Jennings, and E. R. Smith, *Readings in Anthropology* (New York, 1955), pp. 155–173.

———: *The American Indian* (3d ed., New York, 1938).

Wolf, E.: "Closed Corporate Peasant Communities in Mesoamerica and Central Java" (*Southwestern Journal of Anthropology*, Vol. 13, 1957), pp. 1–18.

Wundt, W.: *Völkerpsychologie* (10 vols., Leipzig, 1910–1920).

Yerkes, R. M.: "Psychological Examining in the U.S. Army" (*National Academy of Sciences, Memoirs*, Vol. 15, 1921).

——— and A. W. Yerkes: *The Great Apes: A Study of Anthropoid Life* (New Haven, Conn., 1929).

Zeuner, F. E.: *Dating the Past* (3d ed., London, 1952).

———: *A History of Domesticated Animals* (New York and Evanston, Ill., 1963).

Zuckerman, S.: *The Social Life of Monkeys and Apes* (London, 1932).

———: "Taxonomy and Human Evolution" (*Biological Review*, Vol. 25, 1950), pp. 435–478; reprinted in *Yearbook of Physical Anthropology, 1950* (New York, 1951), pp. 221–271.

Glossary

ab·u′sua The matrilineal clan in Ashanti society.

ac·cul″tur·a′tion The process of interaction between two societies in which the culture of the society in the subordinate position is drastically modified to conform to the culture of the dominant society.

A·cheu′li·an A culture of the Lower Paleolithic Age.

a·do′be An unfired, sun-dried clay brick.

af·fi′nal Related by marriage.

age class, age grade, age set An organized association that includes all the members of a tribe who are of a given age and sex.

ag′nate A kinsman related in the male line of descent, i.e., patrilineally.

a·lign′ment A series of standing stones (menhirs) arranged in rows.

al·lele′ One of a pair of genes which give rise to contrasting Mendelian characters and which have identical loci on homologous chromosomes.

al″lo·pat′ric Taking place in, or biologically relating to, different territories.

alter ego The soul, spirit, ghost, or other self of a person.

al·ter′na·tive A behavior pattern in which two or more permissible response norms occur for a given stimulus situation.

am′i·tate The complex of special behavior patterns governing relations between a child and its father's sister.

a·mok′ (to run amok) A form of psychotic behavior prevalent among Malayan peoples. It is characterized by inattention followed by a violent outbreak, often directed toward homicidal assault.

An″a·sa′zi The prehistoric and contemporary culture of the Pueblo Indians of the Southwest.

an″dro·cen′tric Centered about the male.

an″dro·crat′ic Ruled by males.

an′ga·kok″ An Eskimo shaman.

an′i·mat·ism The attribution of life to inanimate objects.

an′i·mism The belief in the existence of spiritual beings. (Tylor's minimum definition of religion.)

an″thro·po·ge·og′ra·phy The study of the effect of geographical factors upon man and society.

an′thro·poid Having the characteristics of the highest family (that of man and the tailless apes) within the primate order.

an″thro·pom′e·try The division of physical anthropology concerned with the measurement of man's bodily characteristics.

an″thro·po·morph′ism The attribution of human form to any object.

an″thro·poph′a·gy Cannibalism.

Ap″ol·lo′ni·an A configuration of culture that emphasizes restraint, moderation, and "middle-of-the-road" behavior in human conduct.

ar′ti·fact Any material object that has been "worked" or has been used as a tool. Also, an imaginary concept used in logical analysis.

as·so″ci·a′tion A social group specifically organized for the pursuit of special interests.

at′latl The Aztec name for a dart or spear thrower.

Au″ri·gna′cian The second culture of the Upper Paleolithic Age in Europe; 28,000 to 22,000 B.C.

aus·tra″lo·pith′e·cine One of any of the varieties of fossil hominoids closely related to *Australopithecus*.

Aus·tra″lo·pi·the′cus af″ri·can′us A genus of

fossil hominoid first found at Taungs, South Africa; Lower Pleistocene age.

Aus·tra''lo·pi·the'cus ro·bus'tus A heavy-bodied genus of fossil hominoid found in Africa; Lower Pleistocene age.

a·void'ance The inhibition of social interaction, especially between affinal relatives.

a·vun'cu·late The complex of special relations between a mother's brother and his sister's child.

A·yan'thi·an A Lower Paleolithic pebble-tool culture from Burma.

A·zil'i·an A culture that is transitional between the Upper Paleolithic and Neolithic Ages in Western Europe; usually associated with the Tardenoisian.

band A territorially based social group that is less inclusive than the tribe.

bar'ba·rism A classification of cultures possessing gardening, agriculture, or domesticated herds but devoid of written language.

bar'row The English term for a burial mound.

bar'ter, dumb Exchange of goods between hostile people without face-to-face contact and without the use of middlemen.

Bas'ket Mak'er A prehistoric culture (or the people who produced it) widely spread throughout the southwestern parts of the United States and antecedent to the Pueblo cultures.

bast The fibrous inner bark of certain trees.

ber·dache' (ber·dash') An American Indian transvestite who assumes the social roles ascribed to women.

bi''fur·ca'tion Separation into two branches or sections.

bi·lat'er·al de·scent' The system of kinship structure in which an individual belongs equally to the kindred of both parents.

blas'tu·la A mass of cells, usually in the shape of a hollow sphere, resulting from the cleavage within an egg.

bo'lo A weapon made of several stones, each encased in a leather pouch at the end of a string, and with the free ends of the strings joined together.

Bon'du The women's tribal secret society among the tribes of Sierra Leone and Liberia in West Africa.

brach''i·a'tion Use of the hands; in a special sense, movement through the trees by swinging from the branches.

brach''y·ce·phal'ic Roundheaded; having a cephalic index of 81 or more.

broth'er e·quiv'a·lence The classifying of brothers within a single kinship status.

bull'-roar''er A flat board that, when whirled at the end of a string, makes a whirring noise.

bu'rin An Upper Paleolithic flint blade, one end of which has a sharp-pointed, chisel edge.

ca·cique' The Carib word for "chief": often used for the sacerdotal head of a Pueblo Indian tribe or any Central or South American tribe.

cal·var'i·um The skullcap, or upper portion of the cranium.

ca'nine fos'sa The pair of small openings in the facial bones just below the eye sockets; the passage for the facial nerves.

car'bon 14 A radioactive isotope that provides the basis for a method of archaeological dating.

car'i·nate Having the form of a beak.

caste An endogamous social group, usually linked with a specific occupation.

Cau·ca'sian race The so-called "white" or European race.

celt A polished stone ax head.

ce·phal'ic in'dex A metric expression of the ratio between head breadth and head length.

$$C.I. = \frac{HB}{HL} \times 100$$

cer'vi·cal Pertaining to the neck or cervix.

chal·ced'o·ny A white, waxy "flint."

Chal''co·lith'ic Age The Copper Age.

Châ''tel·per·ro'ni·an blade An Upper Paleolithic flint blade with a curved cutting edge. The back edge is blunted by the removal of small flakes. Characteristic of the Châtelperronian culture, 32,000 to 28,500 B.C.

Chel′le·an The Lower Paleolithic "hand-ax" culture.

chert An impure form of flint.

chief, peace A chief whose functions are concerned largely with the direction of civil affairs.

chief, talking In many societies the chief does not publicly address the people. A "speaker," or talking chief, does this for him.

cic″a·tri·za′tion Scar tissue produced by making incisions in the skin. Often done in patterns for ornamentation.

cire′per·due′ *See* lost-wax method.

cist An individual, slab-lined grave.

civ″i·li·za′tion A classification of cultures possessing gardening, agriculture, or domesticated herds, and a written language.

Clac·to′ni·an flake A large Lower Paleolithic chopping flake.

clan A unilineal kinship group that maintains the fiction of common genetic descent from a remote ancestor, usually legendary or mythological.

coc′cyx The hidden tail in man, formed of the last several vertebrae at the end of the spinal column.

con·cu′bi·tant A male who has the status of marriageability to a person without necessarily being married to that person.

con·di′tion·al curse A ritual declaration that if the facts are not as stated, or if certain conditions come to pass, ill fortune may strike the person cursed.

con·fig″u·ra′tion of cul′ture The distinctive and characteristic quality of a culture that derives from the special relationship of its parts to one another.

con·ver′gence A process of cultural dynamics in which two or more cultures contain similar institutions or behavior patterns independently arrived at, i.e., without historical connection.

cos′mic time All time prior to the formation of the earth.

coup An attested deed of valor among the Plains Indians.

coup counting The social practice of publicly reciting coups.

coup de poing A flint hand ax characteristic of the Chellean, Acheulian, and Mousterian cultures.

cou·vade′ The practice whereby a husband retires to bed upon the birth of his offspring and acts as though he had just gone through childbirth.

cra′ni·al ca·pac′i·ty The interior volume of the cranium measured in cubic centimeters.

cra′ni·um That portion of the skull which encloses the brain.

Cro-Mag′non man A variety of *Homo sapiens* dominant in Western Europe during the last half of the fourth glaciation.

crom′lech A circular arrangement of standing stones.

cross-cous′ins Cousins whose related parents are siblings of unlike sex. Offspring of a person's mother's brother or father's sister.

cult An organized system or a group, characterized by performance of supernatural rituals and ceremonies and possessing an underlying body of dogmatic belief.

cul′tur·al or″tho·gen′e·sis The relative overdevelopment of one aspect of a culture.

cul′ture The integrated sum total of learned behavior traits characteristic of the members of a society.

culture area A geographical territory within which the cultures tend to be similar in some significant aspects.

culture complex An integrated system of culture traits organized about some nuclear interest.

culture construct A selective and descriptive formulation of the modal or normal behavior characteristic of the members of a society.

culture, ideal A verbalized formulation of normative patterns for behavior as stated by the members of a given society.

culture pattern A normative form of behavior laid down by the consensus of the members of a society.

culture trait or **element** A reputedly irreducible unit of learned behavior pattern or material product thereof.

Cy″pro·lith′ic Pertaining to the Copper Age.

dead′fall″ A type of trap so constructed that a weighted lever, rock, or ceiling drops on the victim when released by a trigger.

deme (1) An endogamous community consisting of a single kindred. (2) A territorial political unit in Attica after the reorganization by Cleisthenes in 509 B.C.

di″a·ste′ma A gap between two teeth.

dib′ble A pointed digging stick.

dif·fu′sion A process in cultural dynamics wherein culture elements or complexes spread from one society to another.

di·mor′phism, sexual A difference in bodily characteristics of the two sexes.

Di″o·nys′i·an A categorical label attached to cultures that emphasize sensate experience.

DNA Deoxyribonucleic acid, the molecular structure of which constitutes the hereditary determinants in genes.

dol″i·cho·ce·phal′ic Long- or narrow-headed; having a cephalic index of less than 75.9.

dol′men A structure formed of three or more slabs of rock set on edge and covered with a flat slab; hence called *table rock*.

dou′ble de·scent′ The existence of a maternal and a paternal descent system side by side within the same culture.

drive A state of neurophysiological tension that motivates an organism toward action.

drive, acquired or **secondary** A learned drive.

drive, basic A drive that is innate in the organism, the satisfaction of which is ultimately necessary to survival of the organism or the species.

Dry″o·pi·the′cus A genus of Miocene fossil ape from which man and the great anthropoids evolved.

dys″tel·e·ol′o·gy *See* vestigial remains.

earth lodge A house built wholly or partially of sod or made of a framework covered with dirt.

e·col′o·gy The study of the relationships between organisms and their total environments.

Eg′bo A secret fraternity identified with the leopard in certain West African tribes.

e′go (1) In kinship analysis, the person who is used as the reference point for identification of kinship relations and terms. (2) In psychoanalysis, the individual's concept of himself.

e″go·ma′ni·ac A person whose self-centeredness reaches psychotic proportions.

Ek′pe *See* Egbo.

e·lec″tro·pho·re′sis The movement of colloidal particles in an electrically charged fluid.

E″le·men·tar′·ge·dank·en Elementary ideas. Cultural concepts that, according to Adolf Bastian, are universal because they are psychic responses to universal human experiences.

em″bry·ol′o·gy The study of the embryo and its development.

en·cul·tu·ra′tion The process by which the individual learns and assimilates the patterns of a culture.

en″do·cra′ni·um The inner surface of the cranium, or braincase.

en·dog′a·my The rule that requires a person to marry within a given social group of which he is a member.

E′o·cene The first period of the Cenozoic era.

e′o·lith A Dawn Stone Age artifact; a stone implement so crudely made that its shape is more fortuitously than purposefully determined.

ep″i·can′thic fold An overlap of the upper eyelid.

Er″te·bolle′ A local manifestation of Early Neolithic culture in Denmark.

eth·nog′ra·phy The division of anthropology devoted to the descriptive recording of cultures.

eth·nol'o·gy   The division of anthropology devoted to the analysis and systematic interpretation of cultural data.

ev''o·lu'tion, biological or organic   The continuous modification of Mendelian populations through modifications in genetic composition.

evolution, cultural   Modification of culture patterns in a given direction through persistent social change. *General evolution* purports to express modifications characteristic of all cultures at specific stages in their development. *Multilineal evolution* purports to express modifications characteristic only of like cultures. *Specific evolution* purports to express changes characteristic of specific cultures.

evolution, divergent or radiating   The process of evolutionary development that results in several lines of progressive modification from an original common form.

evolution, unilinear   The evolution of social forms in a universal and ordered sequence: a theoretical process.

ex·og'a·my   Marriage outside a specific social group of which a person is a member, as required by custom or law.

fam'i·ly   A bilateral kinship group.

family, conjugal-natal   A social group consisting of spouses and their offspring.

family, consanguine   *See* susu.

family, extended   A social group consisting of near relatives in addition to the mated pair and their offspring.

fa'ther·hood, sociological   The institution whereby the adult male who is the husband of a child's mother stands in the functional relationship of father to the child, regardless of his biological relationship.

felt'ing   A cloth-making technique in which the fibers are matted together, not spun and woven.

fe'mur   The thighbone.

fet'ish   An object that is revered because it is believed to house a supernatural power.

fib'u·la   (1) The long bone that, with the tibia (shinbone), makes up the lower part of the leg. (2) A Bronze or Iron Age safety pin.

fo·ra'·men mag'num   The "great window." The hole in the base of the skull through which the spinal cord leaves the cranium.

fo·ra'men men·tal'is   The openings in the lower jaw through which nerves and blood vessels pass to serve the lower portion of the face.

fos'sil   An organic object that has been transformed into stone or has left an imprint in stone.

fra·ter'ni·ty   (1) An association of men. A men's society. (2) The children of a woman. *See* sibling.

func'tion·al·ism   A theoretical and methodological approach to anthropology that emphasizes concern with the part each unit within a culture plays in the total existence of the culture.

ga·mete'   A sex cell.

gas'tru·la   A stage in embryonic development in which the embryo consists of an outer layer of cells, enclosing a cavity and having an opening at one end.

gene   The minimum part of a chromosome that (1) functions to control a single chemical synthesis in a cell, (2) alters just one trait of a cell when its own molecular structure changes (mutates), or (3) "crosses over" to the other chromosome in the pair in a reproductive cell.

gen''er·a'tion e·quiv'a·lence   The classifying of relatives of different genetic relation, but within the same generation level, within a single kinship status.

ge'·no·type   An organic specimen in which both the genes that determine a specific trait are dominant or recessive. The somatic characteristic therefore directly reflects the gene combination.

gens   A patrilineal clan.

ge''o·log'ic time   All time since the formation of the earth.

ger''on·toc'ra·cy   A society dominated by the old men.

ge''ron·to·mor'phism   The tendency to dominance of adult male characteristics in body build.

glot'tal stop   A phoneme produced by closing the glottis.

God, High   The supreme deity in a polytheistic system.

gra·vette' blade   An Upper Paleolithic straight-edged pointed flint blade, the back edge of which has been blunted by the removal of small flakes. Characteristic of the Gravettian culture, 22,000 to 18,000 B.C.

G-string   A string or band of material worn between the legs and fastened around the waist.

half-life   The amount of time required for a radioactive substance to lose one-half of its radioactivity.

head'man   A leader of a kinship or territorial unit who is not endowed with specific and determinative authority; less than a chief.

Hei'del·berg jaw   A fossil mandible found in first interglacial deposits at Mauer, near Heidelberg, Germany; *Homo erectus heidelbergensis.*

het''er·o·zy'gous   Having a dominant and recessive pair of alleles at a chromosome locus.

hi'er·o·glyph''   A highly conventionalized symbol developed from pictorial representation and used as an element in certain archaic writing systems.

ho'gan   The Navaho dwelling.

Ho'ho·kam   Pertaining to a prehistoric culture localized in the desert areas of central Arizona.

hom'i·nid   (1) A primate who belongs to the order of Hominidae, or human beings. (2) Having the characteristics of a human being.

hom'i·noid   Like a human being, but not fully qualifying as such.

Ho'mo e·rec'tus e·rec'tus   A lower Pleistocene fossil species of man found in Java and Africa. Formerly called *Pithecanthropus erectus.*

Ho'mo e·rec'tus pe''ki·nen'sis   A Middle Pleistocene fossil species of man found in China. Formerly called *Sinanthropus pekinensis.*

Ho'mo e·rec'tus mau''ri·tan'i·cus   A Middle Pleistocene fossil variety of man found in North Africa.

Ho'mo e·rec'tus rho·de''si·a·nen'sis   An Upper Pleistocene fossil variety of man found in Rhodesia.

Ho'mo e·rec'tus so''lo·en'sis   An Upper Pleistocene fossil variety of man found in Java.

Ho'mo ha·bi'lis   A fossil hominid found in Bed I at Olduvai Gorge. It may be either an advanced form of australopithecine or the earliest known member of the genus *Homo.*

Ho'mo sa'pi·ens sa'pi·ens   Modern man. The sole existing species of the genus *Homo.*

Ho'mo sa'pi·ens stein''hei·men'sis   The Middle Pleistocene fossil precursor of modern man (*Homo sapiens sapiens*), found in Europe and represented by the Steinheim, Swanscombe, and Fontechevade fossils.

ho·mo·zy'gous   Having two identical genes at the same locus on a chromosome.

hy·per'ga·my   Marriage upward from a lower social class or caste into a higher one.

id   The Freudian term embracing all the innate, unmodified biological impulses of the human being.

id'e·o·graph''   A drawn, carved, or painted symbol which stands directly for an object or idea and which is nonphonetic in the language of its user.

id''i·o·syn'cra·sy   An aspect of behavior uniquely characteristic of an individual.

in'cest   Sexual contact between persons who are members of the same culturally defined kinship group.

in·fan''ti·cide   The killing of infants.

in''sti·tu'tion, social   A complex of behavior patterns organized about some dominant nuclear interest.

in''va·lid'i·cide   The killing of invalids.

in·ven'tion, independent   *See* parallelism.

Ja'va man   A Lower Pleistocene fossil man found in Java; *Homo erectus erectus* (formerly called *Pithecanthropus erectus*).

jok'ing re·la'tion·ship''   An institutionalized pattern of privileged familiarity or joking between persons of specific social statuses.

K-A dat'ing The long-range method of archaeological dating by measuring the degree of disintegration of potassium 40 into argon 40 that has occurred in geological materials.

ka·chi'na The gods in certain Pueblo cultures, who are represented in ceremonials by masked dancers.

Ka·nam' man *Homo kanamensis.* A purported species of modern man represented by a fossilized symphysis found in Kenya, East Africa.

kay·la'si Adultery among the Trobriand Islanders.

kin'dred A local group that is constituted of bilateral relatives.

kin'ship, classificatory The lumping, merging, or equating of relatives of differing genetic relationship into one and the same kinship status.

kinship system The customary complex of statuses and roles governing the behavior of relatives.

kinship terminology The set of names applied to the various statuses in a kinship system.

kitch'en mid'den A refuse heap.

ki'va A semisubterranean ceremonial chamber, usually round, in the Southwest Indian pueblos.

ku'la ring The system of intertribal ceremonial exchange of shell armbands and necklaces in southwestern Melanesia.

Kul·tur'kreis A conception of large culture complexes that, in the theory of the culture historical school (*Kulturkreislehre*) of ethnology, diffuse en bloc over large areas of the globe.

la'bret A plug worn through an incision in the lip.

lau'rel-leaf point A flint blade shaped like a laurel leaf and characteristic of the Solutrean culture.

law A social norm sanctioned by the application of physical coercion, in threat or in fact, by a person or group possessing the recognized privilege-right of so doing.

law, adjective The part of the law that governs legal procedure and the application of legal sanctions.

law, private Law that is normally enforced by the wronged party rather than by a public officer.

law, public Criminal law; that which is enforced by a public officer.

law, substantive The norms that define illegal activity.

le·ji'ma The nonlocalized maternal clan in Umor society.

le'mur A primitive type of primate that first emerged in the Eocene period.

lep're·chaun The fairy cobbler of Irish folk belief, usually in the form of a little old man.

Le·val·loi'si·an A Lower Paleolithic culture characterized by a flint flake tool with a prepared striking platform.

lev'i·rate Brother-in-law marriage. The marriage of a woman to her deceased husband's brother.

levirate, anticipatory The practice in which a husband extends limited sexual privileges with his wife to his younger brother.

li·bi'do The Freudian term for the id energies.

lig'a A pile of heated stones used for baking taro in New Ireland.

lin'e·a as'pe·ra The longitudinal ridge on the posterior surface of the femur.

lin'e·age A unilineal kinship group that traces descent from a known common ancestor, who lived not more than five or six generations back.

lo'bo·la Progeny price among the Bantu-speaking tribes of South Africa.

loess Deposits of rock dust carried by wind from glacial moraines and outwash deposits.

lost-wax meth'od A process of casting metal objects in molds shaped about a wax form, which is then melted out.

Mag''da·le'ni·an The final culture of the Upper Paleolithic Age in Europe.

mag'ic The control of supernatural forces by means of compulsive formulas.

magic, contagious A form of sympathetic magic. It operates on the principle that things once in contact with each other can exert a continuing influence upon each other.

magic, imitative A form of sympathetic magic. It operates on the principle that like influences like.

magic, sympathetic Magic that operates on the principle of homeopathic association, i.e., that one object can exert an influence upon others that have an identity with it.

Mag″le·mo′si·an A local manifestation of the Mesolithic Age in the Great Swamp of the Baltic Coast.

ma″ka·ra′ta A formal, regulated combat among the Murngin of Australia.

ma′la·gan A complex of memorial festivals in New Ireland, Melanesia.

ma′na Supernatural power that does not occur in the form of a spirit being.

man′i·oc A tropical plant of the genus *Manihot,* whose roots yield a nutritious starch; also called *cassava.*

ma′no A grinding stone that is held in the hand.

mar′riage The social institution that regulates the special relations of a mated pair to each other, their offspring, their kinsmen, and society at large.

marriage, affinal Marriage to a spouse's relative. In-law marriage.

marriage, cross-cousin, asymmetrical A preferred marriage form that is restricted to one type of cross-cousin only. Marriage of a man to his mother's brother's daughter is permitted, while marriage to his father's sister's daughter is prohibited, or vice versa.

marriage, cross-cousin, symmetrical Marriage in which either type of cross-cousin is permissible or preferred as a spouse.

marriage, extended affinal Marriage to an affinal relative of a higher or lower generation. Marriage based upon an extension of the levirate or sororate principles.

mas′ta·ba An Egyptian subterranean burial chamber that is prototypic of the pyramids.

ma·tai′ The titular head of a Samoan household.

ma′tri·arch″ate A society distinguished by uxorilocal residence and matrilineal descent.

ma″tri·lat′er·al Pertaining to descent that is reckoned through one's mother's brother.

ma″tri·lin′e·al Of or pertaining to descent through the mother; descended through the mother.

ma″tri·lo′cal *See* uxorilocal.

mean, arithmetical The average. That point in the range of variability of a phenomenon at which exactly equal quantities fall on either side.

me′di·an The midpoint. That point in the range of variability of a phenomenon which falls exactly at the middle of the two extremes.

meg′a·lith A large stone used as a marker, altar, or monument.

meg″a·lith′ic com′plex A cultural system centering about large stone monuments.

mei·o′sis The process of reduction division in which the number of chromosomes in a gamete is reduced by half so that the doubling effect of fertilization is compensated for.

Mel″a·ne′sia The island area of the Southwest Pacific inhabited by dark-skinned natives.

Men·de′li·an pop″u·la′tion An intrabreeding group of organisms.

men′hir An elongated standing stone raised as a monument or altar.

merg′ing (in kinship systems). *See* kinship, classificatory.

mes″o·ce·phal′ic Medium-headed; having a cephalic index of 76 to 80.9.

Mes″o·lith′ic The Middle Stone Age; characterized by intensive seed gathering and foraging.

mes″o·log′i·cal Semilogical or quasilogical; applied to the method of reasoning used by the nineteenth-century lineal evolutionists, who by inference reasoned that beginning with assumed starting points, the successive stages of each form of social institution or material invention could be described.

me·ta′te A flat or grooved grinding stone that functions as a mortar.

mi′cro · lith   A minute stone artifact made from fine flint flakes.

Mi″cro · ne′si · a   Small islands. The island area of the West Central Pacific.

mil′pa   The Maya Indian method of gardening, involving the slash and burn technique of clearing garden plots in the forest.

Mi′o · cene   The middle, or third, period of the Cenozoic era.

mis″ce · ge · na′tion   Interbreeding between two Mendelian populations.

Mith · ra′ic cult   The religious system devoted to the worship of Mithras, the Persian god of light, upholder of the truth and the foe of evil.

mi · to′sis   A form of cell division and reproduction during which chromosomes are duplicated.

mode   The high point. That point in the range of variability of a phenomenon which occurs with the greatest frequency.

Mo″gol · lon′-Mim′bres   A prehistoric Pueblo culture localized in the mountainous area of southeastern Arizona and southwestern New Mexico.

moi′e · ty   Half. The social unit based upon kinship that occurs when the tribe is divided into two recognized units.

mo · nog′a · my   Marriage of one man to one woman.

mon′o · lith   A structure consisting of a single stone.

mon′o · the · ism   The worship of one god.

moraine   The debris of earth and rocks deposited along the edges of a glacier.

mor′pheme   A minimal unit of language that has meaning.

mor · phol′o · gy   The study of the form and structure of an organism or social manifestation.

Mous · te′ri · an   The culture associated with Neandertal man during the third interglacial and fourth glacial epochs in Europe.

mul′ler   A grinding stone held in the hand and rubbed over a metate.

mu · ta′tion   An abrupt modification of the genetic composition of an organism.

na′sal in′dex   The relation between the breadth and height of the nasal orifice. $\text{N.I.} = \dfrac{\text{N.B.}}{\text{N.H.}} \times 100$

na′si · on   The intersection of the internasal suture with the frontal bone of the skull.

Ne · an′der · tal man   An extinct fossil variety of man dominant in Europe from the second interglacial epoch to the climax of the fourth glacial; *Homo sapiens neandertalensis.*

Ne · gri′to   The "little Negro," or Pygmy, race.

Ne′groid   Characteristic of Negroes.

Ne″o · an · throp′ic man   A "modern" or *sapiens* type of man.

Ne″o · lith′ic   The New Stone Age.

neu · ro′sis   A mild form of behavior disorder.

Ngbe   *See* Egbo.

Ni · lot′ic   Pertaining to or designating a people who live in the Nile Basin.

no · bil′i · ty   A class or caste with hereditary status of high prestige and ceremonial or political power.

nor′ma · tive   Relating to or inducing conformity to a norm.

no′to · chord   A rod of cells that forms the beginning of the backbone in vertebrate animals.

nto′ro   The patrilineal clan in Ashanti society.

oath   A formal declaration that the facts are as stated. (Not to be confused with conditional curse.)

oc′ci · put   The bone that forms the rear and lower segment of the cranium.

Oed′i · pus com′plex   A psychological state of a male characterized by sexual desire for the mother and antagonism toward the father.

o · ke · ya′me   The talking chief in Ashanti society.

O″ld · u · wan cul′ture   A Villefranchian and Early Pleistocene pebble-tool culture.

ol′i·gar″chy A state whose government is controlled by a small group within the larger society.

on·tog′e·ny The natural history of an individual, beginning with the fertilized egg.

or·deal′ A ritual method of verification of testimony in which the litigants are subjected to a physical test designed to injure or kill the falsifier.

Pa″le·o·lith′ic The Old Stone Age.

Pa″le·o·sim′i·a A genus of Miocene fossil ape ancestral to the orangutan.

Pa″le·o·zo′ic The third era of geological time.

pal″y·nol′o·gy The branch of science concerned with the study of pollen and spores. Prehistoric climatic conditions can be determined by counting the different kinds of pollen in soil samples.

pa·py′rus The Egyptian paper made from the pith of *Cyperus papyrus,* an Egyptian sedge.

par′al·lel-cous′ins Cousins whose related parents are of like sex. The offspring of a person's mother's sister or father's brother.

par′al·lel·ism The development of similar cultural forms through identical steps without historical interaction or contact.

Par″a·pi·the′cus A genus of fossil primate found in Oligocene deposits and believed to be ancestral to man, the apes, and monkeys.

par′fleche An oblong rawhide box made by Plains Indians.

pas′to·ral·ism A culture marked by a subsistence technique centered about the herding and husbandry of domesticated animals.

pa″ter·fa·mil′i·as The authoritarian father in the Roman family.

pa·tol′li The Aztec form of pachisi, a game played with dice.

pa′tri·arch″ate A society dominated by the father as head of the kinship group, characterized by patrilineal descent and virilocal residence.

pat″ri·lin′e·al Pertaining to descent through the father. Children belong to the kinship group of their father.

pat″ri·lo′cal *See* virilocal.

pa·tron′y·my The custom of giving children the name of their father's kinship group.

Pe′kin man A Middle Pleistocene fossil man; *Homo erectus pekinensis* (formerly called *Sinanthropus pekinensis*).

per·cus′sion flak′ing The technique of shaping flint artifacts by removing flakes with blows of a hammerstone.

per″son·al′i·ty The sum total of behavior traits, overt and covert, characteristic of a person.

personality, basic structure The constellation of behavior traits and attitudes established in the members of a given society by their childhood reactions to the methods of child training characteristic of their culture.

personality, ideal type The construct of the personality configuration most highly emphasized in a culture.

personality, modal The personality configuration most commonly manifested by the members of a society or group.

pet′ro·glyph A symbol incised in rock.

pe·yo′te A variety of cactus (*Lophophora williamsii*) ingested by Indians (notably Plains Indians) to stimulate visions as a form of religious experience.

phae″o·mel′a·nin Black skin pigment that reduces sunburning.

phe′no·type The physically apparent expression of heredity.

pho′neme The smallest sound unit used in a language.

phra′try A social unit consisting of two or more linked clans between which exists a special bond of unity as against clans joined in other phratries within the society.

phy·log′e·ny The natural history of a species or variety.

phys′i·cal an″thro·pol′o·gy The branch of anthropology concerned with the bodily characteristics of mankind.

pic′to·graph A simple picture, or series of pictures, intended to describe a situation or record an event.

pile dwelling A house raised from the ground or built over water on piling.

pit dwelling An earth lodge built over an excavated pit.

Pleis'to·cene The fifth period of the Cenozoic era. The glacial age during which man rose to dominance among life forms.

Pli'o·cene The fourth period of the Cenozoic era; a warm period during which early human types became differentiated from apes.

Pli''o·pi·the'cus A genus of Pliocene fossil ape that is directly ancestral to the gibbon.

plu'vi·al A Pleistocene wet epoch outside the areas of glaciation.

pol'y·an''dry The marriage of a woman to two or more men simultaneously.

polyandry, attenuated The marriage relationship in which a married brother extends limited sexual privileges with his wife to his unmarried younger brothers. Also called *anticipatory levirate.*

polyandry, fraternal A polyandrous marriage in which the husbands are brothers.

po·lyg'a·my Any multiple marriage.

pol''y·gen'e·sis The evolutionary hypothesis which assumes that the several genera of prehistoric man have evolved from different species of Pliocene apes.

po·lyg'y·ny The marriage of a man to two or more women simultaneously.

pol''y·mor'phism The occurrence of a trait in variable forms in a Mendelian population.

Pol''y·ne'si·a Many islands. The area of the Central Pacific that falls within a triangle formed with Hawaii, Easter Island, and New Zealand as the apexes.

pol'y·the·ism Worship of many gods. A system of religion recognizing multiple gods.

pop''u·la'tion ge·net'ics The study of gene frequencies and changes in Mendelian populations.

Por'ro The men's secret fraternity in Sierra Leone and Liberia, West Africa.

pot'latch The Northwest Coast Indian institution of ceremonial feasting accompanied by lavish distribution of gifts.

pref''er·en'ti·al mar'riage A form of marriage that is enjoined or preferred between two persons of specifically defined statuses.

pres'sure flak'ing The technique of shaping flint artifacts by removing fine flakes by means of steady pressure applied with a hard stick or bone.

priest A religious functionary whose supernatural authority is bestowed upon him by a cult or organized church, in contrast to the shaman, who derives his power directly from supernatural sources.

pri'mate An order within the mammalian class.

prim'i·tive Pertaining to a culture or an aspect of a culture that is not characterized by the inclusion of a written language; also pertaining to an individual whose culture includes no written language. Therefore, nonliterate or preliterate.

pri''mo·gen'i·ture Inheritance by the first-born son or child.

priv'i·leged fa·mil''i·ar'i·ty A culturally permissive relation of free joking between individuals of certain statuses.

Pro·con'sul A Miocene hominoid from East Africa.

prog'e·ny price The wealth transferred by the kin of a groom to the kin of his bride in compensation for their release of claim to the children that are produced in the marriage; also known as *bride price* and *bride wealth.*

prog'na·thous Having a projecting jaw.

prom''is·cu'i·ty The absence of any social restraints limiting or regulating sexual behavior.

prop'er·ty The special and socially sanctioned relation of a person or group to the utilization of some object.

property, communal Property that is owned by the entire community.

property, incorporeal Property that involves a nonmaterial object.

property, joint Property that is owned by a group smaller than the entire community.

Pro''pli·o·pi·the'cus A genus of fossil ape found in Oligocene deposits of Egypt. It is a prototype of the gibbon.

pro'tein A class of organic compounds composed of a number of amino (NH_2) acids.

Prot''er·o·zo'ic The second era of geological time.

psy''cho·cul'tu·ral-or·gan'ic The level of natural phenomena that are not preset (instinctive) in the organism. Also called *superorganic.*

psy·cho'sis An extreme form of behavior disorder marked by relatively fixed patterns of maladaptive attitudes and responses.

pueb'lo A village constructed of clay bricks (adobe) or stones, characteristic of the Indians of the southwestern United States and northern Mexico.

Pyg'my *See* Negrito.

py'rite A mineral, such as flint, used for striking fire.

quern A grinding stone.

race A human population that is sufficiently inbred to reveal a distinctive genetic composition manifest in a distinctive combination of physical traits.

race, geographical A human population that has inhabited a land mass or an island chain sufficiently long to have developed its own distinctive genetic composition, as contrasted to that of other continental populations.

race, local A distinctive Mendelian population located within a continental land mass or island chain.

race, microgeographic An extremely isolated, tightly inbreeding small Mendelian population.

rac'ism A doctrine that assumes the inherent superiority of one or another race over others.

ram'age A bilaterally extended kinship group, identified with reference to a specific person.

rel'a·tives, affinal Persons related through marriage.

relatives, genetic Biologically related persons.

re·li'gion A belief in supernatural beings and the attendant ways of behaving in consequence of such a belief.

Rhod·de'sian man *Homo erectus rhodesianensis.*
An Upper Pleistocene fossil found at Broken Hill in Rhodesia, South Africa.

rite de pas·sage' *See* transition rites.

rite, fertility A ritual complex designed to promote genetic reproduction.

role The customary complex of behavior associated with a particular status.

sac''er·do'tal Of a priestly nature.

sa'crum The wedge-shaped bone formed by the joining of the vertebrae that form the posterior segment of the pelvis.

sanc'tion Any social reaction operating to induce conformity to a normative standard of behavior.

sanction, legal A coercive penalty involving the use of physical force in threat or in fact, attached to the violation of a social norm, when the application of the sanction is considered legitimate according to the prevailing standards of the culture.

sa·rong' A loose girdlelike skirt originally made of bark cloth and worn by Polynesian women.

sav'age·ry A state of cultural development marked by the absence of gardening or agriculture and written language.

scar''i·fi·ca'tion The process of mutilation of the body through the artificial raising of scar tissue. *See* cicatrization.

schiz''o·phre'ni·a A behavior disorder marked by a replacement of the learned behavior systems with desocialized behavior dominated by private fantasy.

se·nil'i·cide The killing of the aged.

sha'man A religious specialist who has received his power directly from supernatural sources; synonymous with *medicine man, witch doctor, angakok* (Eskimo).

sib A unilateral kinship group; synonymous with *clan.*

sib'ling Brother or sister; a member of a sib or clan.

si'lent trade *See* barter, dumb.

sim'i·an Apelike.

Sin·an'thro·pus pe''ki·nen'sis   See *Homo erectus pekinensis.*

Skhūl man   A highly variable type of fossil man found in Palestine. It reveals both Neandertaloid and *Homo sapiens sapiens* characteristics.

slav'er·y   The institution whereby persons are subjected to involuntary servitude, are denied the right of freedom of movement or action, and must place their productive efforts at the disposal of the master.

so'cial dis'tance   A term covering the relative "spatial positions" of two statuses; generally used to emphasize limitations on social intercourse.

so'cial struc'ture   The ways in which groups and individuals are organized and relate to one another.

so·ci'e·ty   An aggregation of human beings (a population) living as a distinct entity and possessing a distinct culture.

society, military   An association of warriors.

society, secret   A fraternity or association whose membership and activities are shrouded in secrecy. A tribal secret society embraces all adult males in its membership.

So'lo man   An Upper Paleolithic human fossil type found on the Solo River, Java; *Homo erectus soloensis.*

So·lu'tre·an   A culture of the Upper Paleolithic Age in Europe; characterized by the laurel-leaf point.

sor'cer·y   The use of supernatural power as an aggressive instrument to further the interests of the sorcerer. *Magic* is a more neutral term.

so·ro'ral po·lyg'y·ny   The simultaneous marriage of two or more sisters to one husband.

so·ro'rate   The practice whereby a younger sister marries the widowed husband of her deceased elder sister.

sou·la'va   The red shell necklaces exchanged in the Melanesian kula.

spe''ci·a'tion   The genetic divergence of a species to produce two new populations that are no longer capable of gene exchange (interbreeding) with each other.

sta'di·a   The minor advances of ice sheets interspersed with interstadia within a glacial epoch.

state   The association within a society that undertakes to direct and organize social policy on behalf of and in the name of the entire society.

sta'tus   The social position of an individual with reference to the other members of his society.

ste''a·to·py'gi·a   Large accumulations of fat in the buttocks.

Stein'heim man   A type of fossil man found in Middle Pleistocene deposits at Steinheim, Germany; *Homo sapiens steinheimensis.*

stim'u·lus dif·fu'sion   The process of cultural dynamics in which one people receive the idea of a cultural invention from another but give a new and unique form to the idea.

stra·tig'ra·phy   Analysis of geological deposits in terms of discernible layers. Derivative time sequences are inferred from the relative positions of the strata or layers.

sub''in·ci'sion   A surgical operation in which the urethra of the male sex organ is slit open; a mutilation performed as a part of the male puberty rites in certain Australian tribes.

suit'or ser'vice   A substitute for, or equivalent of, progeny price, in which the potential groom works for his intended bride's kin.

su''per·or·gan'ic   Pertaining to the phenomena, known as *cultural,* that occur on a level over and above the organic; i.e., they are not preset in the organic structure.

su''pra·or'bit·al ridge   A bone ridge above the orbits, or eye sockets.

sur·viv'al   In evolutionary methodology, a culture trait that is purported to have lost its original function. A conceptual equivalent to vestigial remains in biological evolution.

su'su   The kinship group formed of a woman, her children, and her brothers.

su·va·so'va   Breach of exogamy among the Trobriand Islanders.

Swans'combe man   A fossil hominid found in

Middle Pleistocene deposits in southern England; classified as *Homo sapiens steinheimensis.*

sym·pat'ric Pertaining to living forms that inhabit a common territory.

sym'phy·sis The point at which two bones grow together.

syn'cre·tism The fusion of two distinct systems of belief and practice.

ta·bu' Prohibition of an act, violation of which is punishable by supernatural sanctions.

ta'pa Polynesian bark cloth.

tar'a·vad The joint family household consisting of the members of a matrilineage among the Nyar caste in Karella on the Malabar Coast of India.

Tar''de·noi'sian A prehistoric culture of France representing the Mesolithic Age and characterized by microlithic flints.

ta'ro A staple food plant of the Pacific area.

Taungs ape man See *Australopithecus africanus.*

tau''ro·dont'ism An enlargement of the pulp cavity and fusion of the roots in molar and premolar teeth.

tax·on'o·my The systematic classification of things according to scientific principles.

tek·non'y·my The practice of addressing an adult after the name of its child.

tel'e·o·lith'' A purposefully shaped stone.

tell In the Middle East, a mound built up by prolonged human occupation of a site.

than''a·to·ma'ni·a The depression of the will to exist to the point of death.

thau'ma·tur''gy Magic.

the·oc'ra·cy A social order controlled by religious specialists.

till A glacial deposit of unstratified rock and earth.

ti'pi A conical skin tent.

tort An offense that is legally punishable by the wronged individual or as a consequence of legal action instituted by him.

to'tem An object, often an animal or plant, held in special regard by an individual or social group.

to'tem·ism The institutional complex centering about a totem.

to·vo·dun' The deified ancestors in Dahomean religion.

tran·chet' A flaked core-biface stone artifact shaped rather like a modern ax head.

trans·hu'mance A mixed food-producing economy involving nomadism and gardening according to the season of the year.

tran·si'tion rites Ritual complexes associated with important changes in personal status, such as birth, adolescence, marriage, and death.

trans·ves'tite An individual who effects a transfer of sex roles, such as occurs when a male takes on the status and roles of a female, or vice versa.

trau'ma A bodily or psychologic injury, or its effect.

trav'er·tine A porous limestone; also called *tufa.*

tra·vois' A carrying device that has two poles, like the tongues of a buggy, hitched to a draft animal. The free ends of the travois drag along the ground.

tribe A social group speaking a distinctive language or dialect and possessing a distinctive culture that marks it off from other tribes. It is not necessarily organized politically.

Trick'ster A character in mythology who alters the order of things by tricking men or animals into choices or circumstances that they do not expect or desire.

Tri'nil man *Homo erectus erectus.*

troll A supernatural giant or dwarf in old Scandinavian belief.

tu'mu·lus A mound of earth covering a dolmen or burial chamber.

ul''ti·mo·gen'i·ture Inheritance by the youngest son or daughter.

u''ni·lin'e·al Pertaining to descent through one parent only.

u''ni·lo'cal Relating to or designating the practice whereby a married couple regularly settles with, or close to, the parents of one of the spouses. *See* uxorilocal; virilocal.

u″ni·ver′sal A behavior pattern characteristic of all the members of a society.

u′su·fruct The right to use an object of property without possessing title of ownership.

ux·or″i·lo′cal Pertaining to the practice whereby a married couple settles in the domicile of the wife's family; synonymous with *matrilocal residence.*

varve A band of clay deposited annually in a glacial outwash.

ves·tig′i·al re·mains′ Organs whose physiological functions have been lost (as far as can be determined).

Vil·le·fran′chi·an The early part of the Pleistocene, prior to the first glaciation, in which modern genera of animals appear for the first time.

vir″i·lo′cal Pertaining to the practice whereby a married couple settles in the domicile of the husband's family; synonymous with *patrilocal residence.*

vo·dun′ A system of religious belief and practice developed by Caribbean Negroes and combining elements of Catholicism and African, particularly Dahomean, religions. Magic is only a minor element in the entire complex. It is called *voodoo* in the American vernacular.

wam′pum Elongated beads drilled out of clamshells, used by Indians of the northeast woodlands.

warp The parallel-lying foundation threads of a fabric.

weft The threads woven at right angles through the parallel-lying foundation threads, or warp; also called the *woof,* or *filler.*

wer′gild The money payment made by the kin of a murderer to the kin of a murdered man.

wick′i·up″ A beehive-shaped grass hut.

wife lend′ing The custom whereby a husband extends to a household guest the sexual favors of his wife as a symbolic gesture of brotherhood.

wig′wam A domed bark hut of the Algonquian Indians of the northeast woodlands.

wil′low-leaf point A long, slender flint blade characteristic of the Solutrean culture.

win′di·go A type of culturally induced insanity among the Ojibwa and other Algonquian Indians; involves cannibalism.

woof *See* weft.

wrong, private An offense against an individual that is customarily punished by legal action instituted by the injured person or his kinsmen. Private wrongs make up the body of private law.

wrong, public An offense against the social entity punished by the legal action of the group at large or by its official representatives.

wur′ley A lean-to shelter built by Australian aborigines.

ye·pun′ The virilocal, patrilineal clan in Umor society.

yuc′ca A plant belonging to the lily family and possessing long fibrous leaves. The sap of its roots produces suds in water.

Zin·jan′·thro·pus boi′sie A form of *Australopithecus robustus* found in Bed I at Olduvai Gorge.

zy·go′ma The cheekbone.

zy′gote A fertilized egg (female sex cell).

Index

Aarne, A., 77
Abbevillian tradition, (*see* Chellean tradition)
Aberle, D. F., 69, 377–379, 381
Acheulean tradition, 143, 157–158, 164–165
Adamic, L., 365
Adaptation, racial, 214–216
Adolescence, 390
  in Samoa, 5
  (*See also* Puberty)
Adoption, 352
Africa, art, 298–302
  bodily ornamentation, 283–284
  Khartoum, 185
  markets, 429–430
  tribes, Ankole, 408–409
    Anuak, 244
    Ashanti, 324, 338, 376, 442, 448–449,
      496–498
    Azande, 444, 473–474
    Bahima, 350, 408–410
    Bairu, 408–410
    Bakongo, 473
    Bankuntshu, 284
    Bantu, 38, 456–457, 484–485
    Bavenda, 346
    Benin, 275
    Bushman, 220, 254
    Dahomey, 310, 346, 373, 395–396, 485
    Dodoth, 249
    Egypt, 491
    Ghana, 308
    Hottentot, 220
    Jie, 249, 260–261, 482
    Karamajong, 347–348
    Makere, 287
    Nandi, 398
    Nuer, 346–347, 352–353, 372, 382, 399,
      447–448
    Nyakusa, 399
    Ruanda, 214, 237, 339
    Swazi, 324, 398–399
    Tswana, 59, 460–462
    Umor, 376
  (*See also Australopithecus;* Olduvai Gorge)

African race, 220
Age classes, 397–400, 455
  African, 398–399
  in government, 461
Age groups, 326
Aginsky, B. W., 383, 434
Agriculture, 238, 244–248, 378–379, 418–419,
  514
  Neolithic, 188
  (*See also* Plants)
Ainu, 467
Aitken, M. J., 132
Albert, A. M., 15
Aldridge, A. O., 337
Algonquian, 416
  language, 48–49
Allen's rule, 214–215
Alor, 325
  basic personality structure, 63–65
Alphabet, Cherokee, 82
  origins of, 305–306
Alpine race, 218
Amahuaca, child training, 56–57
Amerakaeri, 278
American, Colored, 217
American race, 219
Amsden, C., 274, 276
Anasazi, 356–357
Ancestor worship, 483–386, 497
  (*See also* Cults; Religion)
Andaman Islands, 313, 426–427
Anderson, W. H., 489, 508
Animals, domestication of, Neolithic, 193–195
  (*See also* Cattle; Horse; Pig)
Animism, 466–468
  (*See also* Religion)
Ankole, 408–409
Anomy, 529
Anthony, H. S., 328
Anthropology, 3–15
  applied, 525, 531
  distinctive qualities of, 406
  fieldwork, 4–5, 519–520
  future of, 526–527

Anthropology, history of, 505–525
  physical, 7–8, 523
  social, 8
  social sciences, relation to, 11–14
Ants, social behavior of, 19
Anuak, 244
Apache, 403
  language, 34–35
Apes, 100, 101, 103, 108, 109
  culture capacity, 112
  inventions by, 73
Apollonian configuration, 61
  (*See also* Benedict, R. F.)
Arab, 340
Arambourg, C., 147, 156
Arapaho, 78, 300–302, 469
Arapesh, 56
Arawak, 266
Archaeology, 9–10, 509–510
Ardrey, R., 138, 146
Art, 287–307, 517
  Paleolithic, 177–181, 282, 303–304
Artifacts, 263–276
  Neolithic, 189, 195
  property in, 423
Arunta, 254
Ascher, R., 35, 51
Ashanti, 324, 338, 376, 432
  law, 448–449
  world view, 496–498
Asia, fossil man in (*see Homo erectus*)
  tribes of, Ainu, 467
    Alor, 63–65, 325
    Andaman Islands, 313, 426–427
    Chinese, 38–39, 41, 46, 248, 280–281,
      305
    Chukchi, 480
    India, 339, 409
    Japan, 24, 72, 212, 285, 352
    Kazak, 417
    Kurd, 340
    Nyar, 364–365
    Pakistan, 365
    Semang, 429
    Toda, 362
    Tungus, 417
Asian race, 219
Associations, 317, 318
  (*See also* Age groups; Clubs)
Asylum, legal, 352
Athabascan, language, 34, 49

Augustine, Saint, 3
Aurignacian tradition, 175
Australian aborigines, 313, 320
  art, 289
  intelligence of, 227
  race, 220–221
Australian tribes, Arunta, 254
  Kurnai, 351
  Tiwi, 75
Australopithecus, africanus, 130, 134–146, 162
  prometheus (see Australopithecus, africanus)
  robustus, 134, 138–150, 162
Authority, 439–440
Azande, 444, 473–474

Baboon, 108, 138
Bachofen, J. K., 87, 377, 505
Baer, K. E. von, 104
  Baer's rule, 104
Bahima, 350
Bairu, 408–410
Bakongo, 473
Balfour, H., 300
Bali, 60, 335, 338, 485
Bandalier, A. F., 496
Bankuntshu, 284
Bannock, 471
Bantu, chiefs, 456–457
  language, 38
  religion, 484–485
Banyankole (*see* Ankole)
Barbarism, 89
Barnett, H. G., 72–73, 74, 80, 81, 83, 531
Barnouw, V., 61, 69
Barrett, S. A., 269
Barrow, T., 307
Barter, dumb, 429
Barth, F., 340
Barton, R. F., 247, 311, 333, 419, 434, 447,
  465, 481
Bascom, W. R., 489
Basket Maker culture, 257–258, 269
Baskets, 267–269
Bastian, A., 505
Bat Cave, New Mexico, 200
Bateson, G., 491
Bavenda, 346
Beaglehole, E., 62
Beals, R., 262
Bees, dance of, 19
Behavior, instinctive, 19

Behavior, learned, 18–19, 34
Bellah, R. N., 391
Belo, J., 335, 338, 368
Benedict, R. F., 23–24, 32, 61–62, 67, 69,
    224, 326, 366–367, 434, 469, 521
Benin, West Africa, 275
Bennett, J. W., 30, 518
Bennett, W. C., 243
Bergmann's rule, 214–215
Bible, 340, 352, 476
Biegert, J., 110, 111
Bifurcation, in kinship, 386
Birdsell, J. B., 216, 223
Bison, hunting of, 239
Black Duck, culture, 155–156
Blackfoot, 361
Blackwood, B., 276
Blood, chromosome patterns, 103
    precipitant tests, 103
    protein patterns, chart, 103–104
Blood groups, race, 211–212
Blowgun, 240
Boas, F., 25, 76, 77, 88, 291, 293, 302, 307,
    352, 396, 420, 439, 506, 516–519
Bodin, J., 508
Bogoras, W., 480–481
Bohannan, P., 14, 353, 381, 430, 436, 451
Bolingbroke, Lord, 337
Botocudo, 278
Boulding, K. E., 527, 530–531
Boule-Strauss hypothesis, 127*n*.
Bourke, J. G., 36
Bow, 240, 266
Boyde, W. C., 213, 223
Brace, C. L., 141, 164, 170, 173, 182, 208
Braidwood, R. J., 175, 184, 190, 192–193
Brain, primate, *Australopithecus*, 134, 139–140,
    149
        Homo, erectus, 148–149, 152–153
            habilis, 144
            sapiens, 135, 149
        intelligence, relation to, 135, 149
        Proconsul africanus, 128
        size, 102–103, 135, 149, 226
Brassempouy, Venus of, 181, 282
Breuil, H., 182, 307
Brew, J. O., 203
Bride price (*see* Progeny price)
Brinton, D. G., 87
Broek, J. O. M., 260, 262
Bronze Age, 91, 184, 199–200
Broom, R., 134, 137–138

Brotherhood, extension of, 363–364
Brown, B., 229
Brown, H., 118
Buck, P. H., 434
Buehler, A., 307
Bunzel, R., 271, 276, 436, 489
Burckhardt, J., 505
Burkitt, M. C., 182
Burrows, E. G., 287
Bushman, African, 220, 254
Busia, A. K., 432, 449, 497–498

Cameron, N., 67
Campbell, B., 156, 171, 173
Campbell, D. T., 5, 14
Cardozo, B. N., 438
Carneiro, R., 247–248
Carrasco, P. 262
Carroll, J. B., 51
Carter, G. F., 200
Caso, A., 492
Caste, 409
Castillo, B. D. del, 507
Çatal Hüyük, 188–191
Catarrhines, 108–110
Cattle, 248–249
    in Nuer progeny price, 346–347
Ceremony (*see* Ritual)
Chang, Kwang-Chi, 151
Change, social, 527–531
Chatelperronian tradition, 175
Chattel, 422
Chellean tradition, 140, 143, 157–158, 165
Cherokee, 82–83
Cheyenne, 75, 78, 81, 91, 403
    language, 48
    law, 438
    religion, 474–475, 478
    sundance, 78–80
    tipi, 73–74
Chief, 407, 427, 431–432, 445, 456–457,
    461–462, 474–475, 498
    (*See also* Monarchy; Political organization)
Chilcat blanket, 273
Child, I. L., 65–67, 70, 523
Child training, 357
    Alorese, 63–65
    Amahuaca, 56–57
    and personality, 55–60
    Whiting-Child theory of, 65–67

Childbirth, 321–322
Childe, V. G., 90, 92, 203
Chimpanzee, 101–103, 108–109, 127
  behavior in wild, 111–112
  food habits, 112
  learning by, 19–20
China, 248
  Choukoutien, 9, 151–155
  clothing, 280–281
  fossil men, 151–155
  language, 38–39, 41, 46
  writing, 305
Chiriqui, 302–303
Christensen, J. B., 376
Chukchi, 480
Cicatrization, 284–285
Circumcision, 285, 328–329
Cities, 528–529
  Çatal Hüyük, 188–199
  Mesopotamian, 196–199
Civilization, characteristics of, 198–199
  dawn of, 183–203, 526–531
  defined, 89
Clactonian tradition, 165
Claims, Indian versus United States, 521
Clans, 91, 373
  (*See also* Lineal descent)
Clark, G., 174, 182, 195, 203
Clark, W., 243, 256
Clark, W. G. LeG., 102, 106–107, 128, 132, 136, 159
Clarke, J. D., 184
Class, social, 401–409
Classification, criteria for, 100
  defined, 112–113
  problems of, 97–98
  social, 401–402
Cleland, H. F., 303
Climate (*see* Ecology)
Cloth, bark, 273–274
Clothing, 277–282
Clubs, 392–397, 454–455,
  in government, 459–460
  in religion, 475
  women's, 393
Codex, Florentine, 507–508
Cogul, cavern of, 303–304
Cohen, M., 524
Cohen, Y. A., 328, 330
Cole, G. D. H., 431
Cole, S., 144, 146, 159, 180

Comanche, 29, 231, 250, 343, 363, 383–385, 422, 433
  headman, 456
  law, 446
Communication, among bees, 19
  cross-cultural, 41–42
  (*See also* Art; Language; Symbolism; Writing)
Communism, 512
Comparative method, 4, 517–518
  in linguistics, 47–50
Conception, 320–321
Conflict, 442–443
  (*See also* Law)
Constitution, bodily, influence on personality, 52–54
Contract, 449–450, 516
Cook, W. W., 415
Cook Islands, art of, 294–295
Coon, C. S., 92, 131, 137, 146, 159, 172, 182, 208, 214, 216, 223
Cooper, J. M., 280–281, 416–417
Copper, 275
Cosmetics, 283–284
Cottrell, W. F., 91–92
Coulanges, F. de, 505
Coult, A. D., 238–239, 314, 336, 345, 347, 349, 359, 388, 398–400, 402–403, 410–411, 422
Council, 455, 459, 461–462
  (*See also* Political organization)
Count, E. W., 232
Courts, 438–439, 443
Cousins, classification of, 335–336, 339–343, 387–389
Couvade, 322
Crashing Thunder, 240, 481
Cross-cultural correlation, 522–523
  (*See also* Aberle; Coult; Habenstein; Murdock; Schneider; Whiting)
Crow, 79–80, 353–354, 397
  clans, 373
  kinship system, 388–389
Cues, 34
Culture, alternatives in, 27
  capacity to create, 16–18
  changing, 71–72, 80–87, 527–531
  components of, 26
  configuration of, 61–62
  definition of, 32, 71
  diffusion of, 5–6, 72–83
  evolution of, 17, 83–92
  functional nature of, 18–19, 25–26

Culture, genuine and spurious, 527–528
    ideal, 29–30, 32
    integration of, 21–22
    and language, 33–50
    and law, 441
    and personality, 52–70, 521–522
    proto-, 19–21
    and race, 224–232
    real, 29–32
    relativity of, 24–25
    selection in, 27, 78–83
    and societal maintenance, 30–31
    universals in, 27
    (*See also* Function; Functionalism)
Culture area, 517–518
Culture complex, 26, 27, 83
Culture construct, 28–29
Culture element, 26, 27
Culture traits, 32
    diffusion of, 74–83
Cults, 483–487
Curing, 480–481, 492–494
Curse, conditional, 444
Curtis, E. S., 188
Curve, frequency, 27
Cycle, life, 319–330

Dahomey, 310, 346, 373, 395–396, 485
Dalton, G., 12, 436
Dance, Balinese, 60, 485
Dani, 80
Dart, R. A., 134–138, 140, 146
Darwin, C., 86, 123, 511
Dating of remains, 116–119
    Olduvai Gorge, 141
Davidson, D. S., 267
Dawson, J., 416
Death, 329–330
Dendrochronology, 118–119
Densmore, F., 481
Dentition (*see* Teeth)
Derringer, D., 307
Descent, lineal, 341–342, 344, 370–373, 424,
    497–498
    (*See also* Kinship)
Desert culture (North America), 187–188
Deutsch, M., 229
DeVore, I., 111, 113
Dibble, C., 489, 508
Diffusion, 71–84, 518
    defined, 74

Diffusion, dynamics of, 77
    selective factors in, 78–83
    stimulus, 83
Dionysian configuration, 61
Discovery, nature of, 72, 83
Disease, primitive theories of, 66
    (*See also* Curing)
Divination, 444
Divorce, 352–354
Dobu, 320–321, 366
Dobzhansky, T., 104, 132, 140, 171, 173, 222,
    223
Dodoth, 249
Dollard, J., 54
Domenech, E., 241
Dorsey, G. A., 486
Dreams, 467
Drills, 264–265
Drives, basic (biological), 57–58
Drucker, P., 317–318, 404
Dual division (moiety), 373–374
DuBois, C., 61, 63–64, 325
Dubois, E., 98, 147–150
Dunn, L. C., 132, 223
Durkheim, E., 341, 465, 479, 489, 516, 519,
    529
Dyak, 244–245
Dyk, W., 67

Easter Island, 265
Ecology, cultural, 236, 496
    and race, 214–215
    relation to pastoralism, 248–249
    (*See also* Environment)
Economics, 375, 426–435
    relation to anthropology, 14
    (*See also* Gift giving; Property; Subsistence)
Education, primitive, 58–60
    (*See also* Child training)
Eggan, F., 5, 391, 494
Egypt, 491
Einstein, A., 92
Eiseley, L., 82
Eisenstadt, S. N., 400
Ekholm, G. F., 307
Elopement, 351–352
Elwin, V., 286, 307
Embryonic development, 104–105
Enculturation, 58–60
    (*See also* Child training; Education)

Endogamy, 339–340
Engels, F., 87–88, 377, 512–514
English language, 35–37, 39, 40
Environment, effect on natural selection, 124
    physical, personality and, 54
    (*See also* Ecology)
Erasmus, C. J., 531
Eskimo, 216, 416
    art, 266, 304–305
    cannibalism, 155
    clothing, 280–281
    kinship system, 387
    language, 35
    law, 439, 445–446
    religion, 481, 483–484
    wife lending, 364
    wife stealing, 353
Ethnography, 8
Ethnohistory, 521
Ethnology, 8
Europe, German language, 41–42
    Greece, 492, 506
    Rome, 335
European race, 218
Evans, B., 19
Evans-Pritchard, E. E., 15, 330, 346–347, 355,
        364, 370, 382, 399, 422, 443, 447, 455,
        473–474, 477, 520
Evolution, of art, 299–303
    biological, 17, 99–100, 115–132, 511
    cultural, 16–18, 85–93, 377–380, 509–516
        energy theory of, 91–92
        general, 90–92
        of law, 449–450
        lineal, 86–87
        multilineal, 90–92
        of religion, 466–468
        specific, 89–92
Exchange, marriage, 341–349
Exogamy (*see* Incest; Mating)
Eye, primate, 102–103
Eynam, 185

Face, primate, 102
Fallers, L. A., 356
Family, 356–368
Fayum, Egypt, fossil deposits at, 127
Felting, 274
Fenton, W. N., 260

Fetishism, 487
Feud, 448
Field, R., 437
Field work (*see* Anthropology)
Fiji, 407–408
Fire, use in Paleolithic Age, 151–159, 164, 168
Firth, R., 436, 520
Fischer, J. L., 412
Fishing, 239, 266–267
Flannery, K. V., 203
Fletcher, A. C., 259, 282, 323
Folklore, 476
    (*See also* Mythology)
Fontechevade skull, 164
Ford, C. S., 321, 330, 457
Forde, C. D., 248, 250, 314, 376, 417, 457,
        501
Fortes, M., 262, 360, 367–368, 381, 520
Fortune, R. F., 320, 484
Fossil man, 133–182
Frankfort, H., 196, 203
Franklin, B., 86
Fraternities, secret, 394–396
Frazer, J. G., 76, 87, 458, 469, 476, 515
Frequency distribution curve, 26–27
Freuchen, P., 482
Freud, S., 60
Frisch, K. von, 19
Function, 74
    of art, 288
    of bride capture, 350
    of circumcision, 328
    of family, 356–358
    of incest tabu, 337–338
    of law, 441–442
    of levirate, 343
    of political organization, 453
    of premarital mating, 332
    of rituals, 319–320, 324–328
    status, 311
    of unilineal groups, 374–376
Functionalism, 25–26, 92, 518–520
Funeral practices, 329–330, 433, 483–484

Gallanter, M., 339
Gardening (*see* Agriculture)
Garfield, V. E., 317
Garn, S. M., 208, 213, 216–217, 223
Garrett, H. E., 228
Garrod, D., 170

Garth, T. E., 227
Gayton, A. H., 458
Geertz, C., 501
Geertz, H., 368
Gene, 120–126
Generalization, levels of, 11
Genetic drift, 123, 125–126
Genetics, 119–126
  and race, 209–213
Gennep, A. van, 330
Geologic eras, 116
German language, 41–42
Gesture, 33
Ghana, 308
Ghosts, 483–485
Gibbon, 100–103, 108–111
Gibbs, J. L., Jr., 81, 327, 395
Gifford, E. W., 325
Gift giving, 316–318, 349, 426–427
Gillin, J. P., 15, 22
Ginsberg, M., 345, 353
Gladwin, T., 69
Gleason, H. A., 51
Gloger's rule, 214–215
Glottochronology, 49
Gluckman, M., 443, 451, 515, 520
God, High, 482, 487–489, 496
Gods, 492, 496–497
Golding, W., 17
Goodall, J., 111–113
Goode, W. J., 477
Goodenough, W. H., 370
Goodman, M., 104
Goodwin, G., 403
Goody, J., 330, 368, 377, 425, 521
Gorilla, 100–101, 103, 108–109
  behavior in wild, 111–112
Gough, K., 366, 371, 378, 381
Gould, J., 33
Government, 375, 454
  (*See also* Political organization)
Gravettian tradition, 176–178, 282
Greece, 492, 506
Greenberg, J. H., 47
Greenman, E. F., 73–74, 84
Griffin, N. M., 318
Grimm, J., and fairy tales, 76–78
Grimm's law, 48
Grinnell, G. B., 73–75, 398, 403, 475
Gudschinsky, S. H., 49
Gulliver, P. H., 249, 260–261, 482

Haar, B. ter, 352, 355, 419, 425
Habenstein, R. W., 238–239, 314, 336, 345,
  347, 349, 359, 388, 398–400, 402–403,
  410–411, 422
Haddon, A. C., 87, 300
Haekel, E. von, 104
Haida, 293, 329
Haines, F., 75
Hair, arrangement of, 81, 282–283
Hall, A. R., 84, 276
Hall, E. T., 34, 51
Hall, G. S., 5
Hall, R. A. Jr., 51
Hallowell, A. I., 58, 67, 415, 425, 475, 511,
  525
Hambly, W. D., 248, 286, 362, 394, 429
Hamilton, E., 491, 501
Hamilton, W. H., 415
Hand, primate, 102–103, 110, 111
Handicrafts, 263–276
Haring, D., 58, 69
Harpoon, 177
Harrasser, A., 456
Hart, C. W. M., 60, 75, 328, 406–407
Haury, E. W., 188
Hawaii, kinship system in, 75, 335–336, 387
Hawley, F., 481
Hays, H. R., 511, 525
Headgear, 281
Head-hunting, Maori, 284
Health, public, relation to anthropology, 14
Hebrews, 340, 352
Heine-Geldern, R., 525
Heizer, R. F., 15, 118, 132
Helbeck, H., 203
Henry, J., 15
Herodotus, 506
Hersey, J., 22
Herskovits, M. J., 307, 312, 346, 373, 396,
  425, 436, 485
Hibben, F. C., 74
Hidatsa, 397–398
Hill, W. W., 250, 258
History, 11–12, 521
  of anthropology, 505–525
  reconstruction of, 516–517
Hobbhouse, L. H., 345, 353
Hocart, A. M., 383
Hockett, C. F., 35, 51
Hodgen, M. T., 84

Hoebel, E. A., 23, 29, 77, 79, 90, 243, 313, 322, 351, 361, 363, 384, 397, 400, 417, 423, 434, 438, 441, 443, 446–447, 449, 451, 456, 474, 481, 501
Hole, F., 15, 118, 132
Hollis, A. C., 398
Holmes, O. W., Jr., 287, 437–438, 442
Holmes, W. H., 300, 302–303
Holmyard, E. J., 84, 276
Homans, G. C., 341–342, 389
Homicide, 445–446, 448
Hominid, 100–103
Hominoid, 100–102
Homo erectus, erectus, 98, 130, 147–159, 162
  mauritanicus, 147, 155–159, 162
  pekinensis, 147–155, 158–159, 163
  rhodesianensis, 163, 170–171
  soloensis, 163, 170–171
Homo habilis, 142–147, 159
Homo sapiens, 130, 133, 160–173
  neandertalensis, 163, 165–170, 173
  sapiens, 163, 171–173
  steinheimensis, 161–164, 167
Homosexuality, 67–68
Hooton, E. A., 53, 113, 140–141, 254
Hopi, 323, 326, 419, 428
  language, 44–45
  world view, 494–495
Horace, 115
Horse, 248–250
  Plains Indian, 75
Hostetler, J. A., 23
Hottentot, 220
Houses, 196, 251–262, 483
Howe, B., 193
Howell, F. C., 141, 168, 170–171
Howell, P. P., 347, 353
Howells, W. W., 151, 156, 168, 477
Howitt, A. W., 351–352
Hsu, F. L. K., 14, 477
Hulse, F. S. 213, 223
Human Relations Area Files, 65–66, 522
Hunting, 240–243, 314, 420–422
  and gathering, 238–240, 378, 417–422
Huron, 508–509
Hutton, J. H., 412
Huxley, J. S., 275
Hybridization, 124
Hylobatid (*see* Gibbon)
Hymes, D., 49

Iatmul, 56–57
Ifugao, 246, 332–333, 354, 419, 446–447, 481
  law, 446–447
  religion, 481
Inbreeding, 336–337
  (*See also* Mendelian population; Race)
Inca, 272–273, 275
Incest, 29, 334–338, 513
India, 339, 409
  races, 218–219
Indo-European language, 44, 48–49
Indonesia, 274, 352, 418–419
  Alor, 63–65, 325
  Bali, 60, 335, 338, 485
  Dyak, 244–245
  Ifugao, 246, 332–333, 354, 419, 446–447, 481
  Java, 43, 145–146
  Kalinga, 311
  Punan, 285
  Sakalava, 346
  Tanala, 365
Infanticide, 445
Inheritance, 431–435
  of wives, 350–351
Initiation (*see* Clubs; Ritual)
Instinct, 19
Institution, social, 27, 309, 454
Intelligence, and race, 226–230
Invention, 71–83
  by apes, 73
  defined, 72
  independent, 74, 76
Inverarity, R. B., 307
Iron Age, 91, 184, 199–200
Iroquois, 508–509
  kinship system, 387–388
  longhouse, 259–260
  masks, 297
  moieties, 374
Islam, 339
Izikowitz, K. G., 335

Japan, 352
  culture change, 72
Japanese, behavior of, 24
  stature of, 212
  tattooing, 285
Jarmo, 192–193
Java, fossil finds, 145–146
  language, 43

Java man (*see Homo erectus erectus*)
Jefferson, T., 47
Jeffrys, M. D. W., 346
Jenness, D., 404
Jennings, J. D., 137, 187
Jericho, 191–192
Jhering, R. von, 439
Jie, 249, 260–261, 482
Jivaro, 259–260
Jochelson, W., 256
Judge, 443–444

Kalihari Desert, 133–134
Kalinga, 311
Kapauku, 473, 488
Karamajong, 347–348
Kardiner, A., 61–63, 69, 365, 525
Karimshahir, 184
Kasdan, L., 340
Kawamura, S., 20
Kazak, 417
Keesing, F. M., 521
Keith, A., 170
Kelley, W. H., 32
Kennedy, R., 274
Kenyon, K., 191, 203
Keresan language, 47
Khartoum, 185
Kindred, 369–370
King, R. C., 120, 122
Kinship, affinal, 343–344, 497
  bilateral, 370
  extension of unilineal, 369–381, 433–434,
    484–485
  and government, 454
  and law, 449
  terminology, 382–391
Kiowa, social classes, 403–404
Kiukura, 247
Kiva, 257
Klineberg, O. H., 62, 227–230
Kluckhohn, C., 6, 15, 22–23, 32, 55, 69, 88,
  328, 491–494, 518
Knopf, A., 118
Koenigswald, G. H. R. von, 145, 148, 150
Kohler, W., 73
Kolb, W. L., 33
Kortlandt, A., 112
Krieger, A. D., 187
Krieger, H. W., 307

Kroeber, A. L., 6, 8, 32, 37, 83–84, 91, 236,
  300–302, 307, 385, 391, 409, 412, 417,
  439, 505, 517, 519
Kula ring, 430–431
Kuper, H., 318, 324, 398
Kurds, 340
Kurnai, 351
Kwakiutl, 80, 352
  personality of, 61

LaBarre, W., 368
Labor, division of, 197, 314
Lafitau, J. F., 4, 86–87, 507, 509
La Flesche, F., 259, 282, 323
Land tenure, 415–420
Landes, R., 421
Lang, A., 87, 487
Language, and culture, 33–50
  definition of, 33
  diachronic study of, 37, 47–50
  origins of, 34–35, 46–48
  structure of, 36–47
  synchronic study of, 37–47
  written, 37
  (*See also* Linguistics)
Languages, Algonquian, 48–49
  Apache, 34–35
  Athabascan, 34, 49
  Bantu, 38
  Cheyenne, 48
  Chinese, 38–41, 46
  English, 35–39
  German, 41–42
  Hopi, 44–45
  Indo-European, 44, 48–49
  Javanese, 43
  Keresan, 42
  Latin, 41
  Navaho, 34, 39
  Pueblo Indians, 42
  Shawnee, 45–46
  Spanish, 38
  Tagalog, 38
  Turkish, 40
Lantis, M., 241, 416
Lartet, E., 127
Lasker, G. W., 15
Latin, 41
Laufer, B., 88

Law, 437–451, 461
  relation to anthropology, 14
Leach, E., 295–296, 335, 340, 357, 363–364, 520
Leakey, L. S. B., 128, 131, 142–146, 156–159, 165
Lee, D., 23
Lee, O., 23
Legislation, 442
Lehmann, W. P., 51
Leighton, D., 493
Lemur, 100–101, 106–107
Leslie, C. M., 501
Lessa, W. A., 477
Lesu, 314–315
Levallois tradition, 158, 165–166, 168–169
Lévi-Strauss, C., 341–342
Levirate, 343
Levy, M. J., 356
Lewin, J., 345
Lewis, M., 243, 256
Lewis, O., 5, 15, 361, 521, 529
Lexicostatistics, 49–50
Libby, W. F., 118
Lienhardt, G., 525
Life cycle, 319–330
Lindzey, G., 70
Linguistics, definition of, 9
  glottochronology, 49
  historical, 37, 47–50
  lexicostatistics, 49–50
  morphology, 39–41
  phonology, 37–38
  psycholinguistics, 42
  semantics, 41–42
  structural, 36–47
  syntax, 40–41
  (*See also* Language)
Linnaeus, 99
Linton, R., 29, 61, 74, 92, 247, 294, 298, 307, 310, 346, 365, 427, 454
Livingstone, F. B., 208
Llewellyn, K. N., 351, 397, 400, 438, 443
Loeb, E. M., 260, 262
Loom, 273–274
Lowie, R. H., 88, 90, 93, 243, 248, 299, 318, 322, 330, 335, 339, 355, 373, 377, 381, 386, 391, 395, 397–398, 400, 421, 423, 442–444, 460, 463, 465–468, 477, 487, 512, 515, 525
Lund, P. S., 404

McCorkle, T., 262
McCown, T., 170
MacIver, R. M., 90, 310, 392, 402, 415, 529
McLennan, J. F., 87, 350, 377, 505
MacNeish, R. S., 200, 202–203
Magdalenian tradition, 177–178
Magic, 469–474, 481–482, 515
Maidu, 269
Maine, H. S., 449–450, 505, 516
Makere, 283
Malinowski, B., 26, 29, 53, 60–61, 248, 250, 308, 318, 320, 329, 332, 337–338, 367, 429–432, 458, 470, 476, 519–520
Malthus, T. R., 86, 511
Man, 468–469
  fossil, 133–182
Mandelbaum, D. G., 15
Manioc, 247, 248
Manus, 484
Maori, 265, 284
Markets, 429–430
Marett, R. R., 11, 468
Marriage, 331–355, 375
  (*See also* Divorce; Elopement; Levirate; Progeny price; Soroate)
Marston, A. T., 161
Marx, K., 87, 377, 512–514
Marxism, 87–88
Masks, 296–298, 475, 483
Mason, O. T., 269, 276
Masserman, S. J. H., 22
Mating, 332–334, 339–344
Matrilateral group, 366–367
Mauldin, B., 312
Mauss, M., 436
Maya, 82, 245–246
Mead, M., 5, 56–57, 60–62, 68, 70, 317–318, 322, 325, 357, 368, 484, 521, 531
Mediation, 446–447
Mediterranean race, 218
Meganthropus paleojavanicus (*see Australopithecus robustus*)
Meiosis, 120, 123
Melanesia, 297–298, 317–318, 407–408, 423, 457
  Arapesh, 56
  Dobu, 320–321, 366
  Iatmul, 56–57
  Kapauku, 473, 488
  Lesu, 314–315
  Manus, 484
  Mundugumor, 57

Melanesia, Trobriand Islands, 29, 53, 60, 320, 332, 430–431, 441, 474
Mellaart, J., 188–189
Mendel, G., 119–120
Mendelian inheritance, 120–122
Mendelian population, 123
Menninger, W. C., 67
Mesolithic age, 184–187, 256
  American, 187–188
  art of, 303–304
  Khartoum, 185
Metallurgy, 274–275
Method, comparative, 4, 517–518
    in linguistics, 47–50
  scientific, 10–11
Metraux, A., 278
Microlith, 184
Micronesia, 270, 292–294
Middleton, R., 335
Midland man, 181
Migration and genetic drift, 125–126
Miller, N., 54
Milpa, 244–246
Mishkin, B., 404, 412
Mitosis, 119–120, 123
Mochica, 292
Modjokerto, Java, fossil skulls, 145
Mogollon-Mimbres culture, 256
Moiety, 373–374
Mombert, P., 401
Monarchy, 448–449, 457–458
Money, 431
Monkey, 100–101, 103, 106–108
  Japanese, learning by, 20–21
Monogamy, 359, 514
Montagu, M. F. A., 141, 164, 248, 320
Mooney, J., 469
Moral order, 527–528
Morant, G. M., 164
Morgan, L. H., 86–88, 90, 92, 252–253, 258, 336, 337, 505, 512–515
Morgan, T. H., 121–122
Morley, S. G., 246
Morpheme, 39–40
Morphology, 102–105
Mount Carmel, 184
Mountford, C. P., 307
Mousterian tradition, 158, 168–169
Movius, H. L., Jr., 165, 181–182
Mowrer, O. H., 55
Mundugumor, 57
Murdock, G. P., 61, 65, 238, 254, 259, 262,

314, 331–332, 338, 341, 345, 354–355, 358, 363, 370, 377, 381, 386–389, 391, 522–523
Murphy, R. F., 340
Mutation, biological, 122–124
Myrdal, G., 232
Mythology, 76–78, 154, 476, 488, 493, 517–518
  diffusion of, 76–78

Nadel, S. F., 49
Naming, 322
Nandi, 398
Napier, J., 144, 146
Natchez, 405–407
National character, 62
Natufian tradition, 184–189
Nature worship, 486–487
Navaho, 59, 81, 236–237, 483
  incest, 67
  language, 34, 39
  stature of, 211
  weaving, 273
  world view, 492–494
Neandertal man (*see Homo sapiens neandertalensis*)
Needham, R., 355
Negro, African (*see* African race)
  American (*see* American, Colored)
Neighbors, R. S., 416
Nelson, E. W., 456
Neolithic Age, 91, 184
  pottery, 270
New Guinea, 91
  (*See also* Melanesia)
Nibback, A. P., 312
Nobility, 405–407
Norbeck, E., 477, 489, 523, 530
Norm, social, 26–27
North America, tribes, Algonquian, 48–49, 416
  Anasazi, 356–357
  Apache, 35–35, 403
  Arapaho, 78, 300–302, 469
  Athabascan, 34, 49
  Aztec, 230–231, 376, 404–405, 492, 507–508
  Bannock, 471
  Basket Maker, 257–258, 269
  Blackfoot, 361
  Cherokee, 82–83
  Cheyenne, 48, 73–75, 78–81, 91, 403,

Cheyenne, 438, 474–475, 478
Chiriqui, 302–303
Comanche, 29, 231, 250, 343, 363, 383–385, 422, 433, 446, 456
Crow, 79–80, 353–354, 373, 388–389, 397
Desert Culture, 187–188
Eskimo, 35, 155, 216, 266, 280–281, 304–305, 353, 364, 416, 439, 445–446, 483–484
Haida, 293, 329
Hidatsa, 397–398
Hopi, 44–45, 323–326, 419, 428, 494–495
Huron, 508–509
Iroquois, 279, 259–250, 297, 374, 387–388, 508–509
Kiowa, 403–404
Kwakiutl, 61, 80, 352
Maidu, 269
Maya, 82, 245–246
Natchez, 405–407
Navaho, 34, 39, 59, 67, 81, 236–237, 273, 483, 492–494
Ojibwa, 67
Omaha, 282, 323, 389
Paiute, 480
Pomo, 382–383
San Ildefonso, 314
Sanpoil, 321
Shawnee, 45–46
Shoshone, 78, 231, 240–243, 322–323, 326, 415–416
Tarahumara, 243
Tlingit, 81, 292
Tsimshian, 80, 517–518
Ute, 78
Winnebago, 155, 240, 375, 481
Yurok, 294, 414–415, 438–439
Zapotec, 29
Zuñi, 61, 366–367
(*See also* Northwest Coast Indians; Plains Indians; Pueblo Indians; Southeast Indians)
United States, 282, 389–390, 445, 498–500
Northrop, F. S. C., 23
Northwest Coast Indians 517–518
  art, 290–296
  cannibalism, 80
  classes, 404
  mythology, 77
  potlatch, 316–317

Northwest Coast Indians, weaving, 273
  (*See also* Haida; Kwakiutl; Tlingit; Tsimshian)
Nuer, 346–347, 352–353, 372, 382, 399
  law, 447–448
Nyakusa, 399
Nyar, 364–365

Oakley, K. P., 159, 164, 175
Oath, 445
Oberg, K., 409, 412
Obermaier, H., 304
Oedipus complex, in Trobriand Islands, 60
Ojibwa, 67
Oldowan culture, 142
Olduvai Gorge, 141–146, 156–159, 165
Olearius, 256
Oligopithecus, 130
Oliver, D. L., 317
Omaha, 282, 323
  kinship system, 389
O'Neale, L., 273, 294
Ontogeny, 103–105
Opler, M. E., 330, 455
Opler, M. K., 70, 79
Orangutan, 100–101, 103, 108–111
Ordeal, 444–445
Oreopithecus, 127, 129–130
Organism, functional analogy, 25–26
Ornaments, Bronze Age, 187
  bodily, 272–286
Osborn, H. F., 98

Pachisi, 76
Paiute, 480
Pakistan, 365
Paleolithic Age, Lower, 147–159
  Upper, 174–182
  (*See also under* Acheulean; Aurignacian; Chellean; Clactonian; Gravettian; Levalloisian; Magdelenian; Mousterian; Solutrean)
Paleontology, 7, 119
Palynology, 118
Pan (*see* Chimpanzee)
Parallelism, 87, 510
Paranthropus (*see* Australopithecus robustus)
Parapithecus, 127, 130
Park, W. Z., 480, 489
Parker, E., 512
Parsons, E. C., 297

Parsons, T. C., 389
Pastoralism, 247–279, 379–380, 514
  land tenure in, 417–418
Patagonians, 279, 281
Patai, R., 340
Patjitan, Java, prehistoric cultures, 150–151
Paul, B. P., 15
Pavlov, I., 21
Peasant society, 529–530
Pekin man (*see Homo erectus pekinensis*)
Pelvis, *Australopithecus africanus,* 136–137
  hominoid, 110
Penniman, T. K., 511, 525
Perrot, J., 185
Perry, W. J., 518
Personality, abnormal, 67–68
  basic structure, 62–63
  and bodily constitution, 52–54
  and child training, 55–60
  and culture, 52–70, 521–522
  determinants of, 52–55
  ideal type, 61–62
Perthes, B. de, 157
Peyote cult, 81
Phenomena, natural levels of, 17–18
Phenotypes, 122–124
Phenylthiocarbamide (PTC), 213
Phonology, 37–38
Phratry, 374
Pig, Neolithic, 194
Pilling, A. R., 75
Pithecanthropus (see Homo erectus erectus)
Plains Indians, 315, 326, 333, 338
  age classes, 397–398
  art, 300–304
  classes, 403–404
  clothing, 279
  gift giving, 427, 433
  homosexuality, 68
  housing, 258–259
  religion, 483–548
  vision quest, 423
Plants, domestication of, Neolithic, 193
  New World, 200–202
Plesiadapis, 130
Plesianthropus (see Australopithecus africanus)
Pliopithecus, 127, 130
Political organization, 452–463
  (*See also* Chief; Government; Headman; Law)
Political science, relation to anthropology, 14
Polyandry, 362–364
Polygyny, 361–362

Polynesia, 270–272, 274, 284, 316, 325
  Cook Islands, 294–295
  Easter Island, 265
  Fiji, 407–408
  Hawaii, 75, 335–336, 387
  Maori, 265, 284
  Samoa, 5
Pomo, 382–383
Pongid, 100, 127
Pongo (see Orangutan)
Pope, A., 97
Population, defined, 99
Porro, 327, 394–395
Porteus, S. D., 227
Pospisil, L., 451, 455, 473, 488
Postulates, cultural, 23, 493
  Ashanti, 497–498
  (*See also* World view)
Posture, *Australopithecus,* 136–317, 140
  primate, 102, 108, 110
    Homo, erectus erectus, 148–150
      erectus pekinensis, 153
      sapiens sapiens, 103
Potlatch, 316–317
Pottery, 269–271
  Chiriquian, 302–309
Pound, R., 442
Poverty, culture of, 529
Powdermaker, H., 314–315
Prayer, 469, 493–494
Preble, E., 525
Pregnancy, 321
Priest, 447–448, 482–483
Primate, behavior, 111–112
  characteristics of morphology, 102–106,
    112, 225
  classification of, 97–109
  fossil, 126–131
  nests, 253–254
Primitive, characteristics, 527–528
  defined, 89
Primogeniture, 434–435
Prine, A. H. J., 398
Proconsul africanus, 127–130
Progeny price, 344–347
Property, 376, 413–425
  and polyandry, 363
Propliopithecus, 127, 129–130
Prosimia, 100–101, 103, 106–107, 126
Provinse, J. H., 245
Psychiatry, 67

Psychoanalysis and personality theory, 62, 65
Psychocultural-organic phenomena, 17–18
Psychology, relation to anthropology, 13–14
PTC (Phenylthiocarbamide), 213
Puberty rites, 59, 324–328
  (*See also* Adolescence; Associations)
Pueblo Indians, 236–237, 315, 396
    houses, 81, 252, 256–258
    language, 34, 42
    masks, 297
    religion, 481
    sex status, 314
    weaving, 273
Punan, 285
Pygmy, 81, 153

Quimby, G. I., 407

Race, 206–223
    and behavior, 54
    and culture capacity, 224–232
    defined, 208
    and language, 43
Radcliffe-Brown, A. R., 8, 25–26, 313, 326–
    327, 355, 381, 427, 432, 434, 515, 519–
    520
Radin, M., 438–439
Radin, P., 155, 240, 376, 465, 481, 488, 501
Radioactivity, 117–118
Rainey, F., 188
Ramage, 369–370
Ramapithecus, 130–131
Rank (*see* Status)
Rasmussen, K., 155, 353, 445–446
Rationalism, 498–499
Rattray, R. S., 338, 376, 449, 463
Ray, V. F., 321
Reay, M., 455
Recapitulation, theory of, 103–105
Reciprocity in social relations, 373–374
  (*See also* Gift exchange)
Reddy, N. S., 424
Redfield, R., 90, 92, 245, 307, 491, 500–501,
    516–528, 531
Reichard, G., 493
Religion, 334, 376, 461–489, 528
    Alor, 65
    American, 498–500
    and art, 294–299
    evolution of, 515

Religion, and government, 447–448, 458
    Neolithic, 189
    (*See also* Cults; Magic; Shaman; Super-
      naturalism; World view)
Renaissance, 507
Reproduction, cellular, 119–123
    sexual, 102
Residence, 360–361
Revolution, urban, 196–199
Rice, cultivation of, 243, 246–247
Richards, A. I., 250
Richardson, J., 404, 443
Rights, jural, 346
Ritual, 469–473, 478–479, 482–487, 493–494
Rivers, W. H. R., 362
Robe, 279–280
Roberts, J. M., 368
Robertson W., 86, 224, 509–510
Robinson, J. T., 128, 139–140, 144, 146
Role, social, 308–330
Rome, 335
Roscoe, J., 350, 363
Rowe, J. H., 275, 422, 506–508
Ruanda, 214, 237, 339
Rutherford, E., 117

Sacrifice, 484, 492
Sahagun, B., 489, 507–508
Sahlins, M., 89, 91, 93
Sakalava, 346
Salmond, J. W., 438–442
Samoa, 5
San Ildefonso, 314
Sanctions, 66, 338, 439, 497–498
Sangoan tradition, 180
Sanpoil, 321
Sapir, E., 21, 44, 527–528
Sapir-Whorf hypothesis, 44–46
Sauer, C., 243
Savagery, 89
Sayce, R. U., 276
Scarification, 285
Schaller, G. B., 112–113
Schapera, I., 59, 355, 451, 456, 460, 463
Schlippe, P. de, 250
Schmidt, W., 487, 518
Schneider, D. M., 341–342, 371, 378, 381, 389
Schurtz, H., 393
Schusky, E. L., 391
Schwabedissen, W., 186
Science, social, 5, 11–15
Sciences, hierarchy of, 17–18

Scientific method, 10–11
Sculpture, African, 298–302
  Neolithic, 192
  (*See also* Art)
Seagle, W., 442
Selection, natural, 119, 123
Semang, 429
Sequoya, 82–83
Service, E. R., 89–91, 93, 386
Sewall Wright effect, 125
Sex, regulation of, 332–341
Sexes, status of, 313–314, 433
Shakers, 31
Shaman, 334, 479–482
Shanidar Cave, 184
Shapiro, H. L., 208, 223
Sharp, L., 453
Shawnee language, 45–46
Sheldon, W. H., 53
Shipibo, 75
Shoes, 281–282
Shoshone, 78, 231, 240–243, 279, 322–323, 326, 415–416
Shrew, tree, 100–101, 106–107
Sickle-cell anemia, 124
Simian, 106–112
Simmons, L., 70, 312–313, 318, 323
Simons, E., 128
Simpson, G. E., 232, 485
Simpson, G. G., 98–99, 113, 129, 132
Simpson, S. P., 437
Singer, S., 84, 276
Skeleton, primate, 102, 110
    fossil man, 136–137, 153
    Homo sapiens, neandertalensis, 168
     sapiens, 173
Skull, characteristics of, *Australopithecus*
    africanus, 135
    hominid, 110
    Homo erectus, erectus, 148–149
     pekinensis, 151–152
Slavery, 405, 409–411
Smilodectes, 130
Smith, G. E., 518
Smith, G. H., 364
Smith, M. W., 307
Smyth, H. D., 92
Society, functional prerequisites of, 30–31
Sociology, relation to anthropology, 12–13
Solo man (*see Homo erectus, soloensis*)
Solutrean tradition, 177
Sorcery, 472–474, 495–496
Sororate, 343

Soul, concept of, 467–468, 497
South America, tribes, Amahuaca, 56–57
  Amerakaeri, 278
  Arawak, 266
  Inca, 272–273, 275
  Jivaro, 259–260
  Kiukuru, 247
  Mochica, 292
  Patagonians, 279, 281
  Shipobo, 75
  Tehuelche, 279–281
  Yahgan, 279–280
Southall, A. W., 463
Southeast Indians, 280
Southwick, C. H., 20
Spanish language, 38
Speciation, 126
Speck, F. H., 416
Speech (*see* Language)
Spencer, H., 86, 92
Spencer, R. F., 33, 340
Spier, L., 78, 290, 314, 518
Spindler, G. D., 60
Spuhler, J. N., 32
Srinivas, M. N., 489
State, 453–454
Status, social, 282, 308–330, 345, 500, 516
Stern, B. J., 512
Stevens, S. S., 53
Steward, J. H., 90, 93, 200, 236, 242–243, 250, 258, 262, 416, 453
Stewart, O. C., 236
Stirling, M. W., 259
Stone, grinding, 184, 193
Stow, G. W., 350
Strandskov, H. H., 212
Stratigraphy, 115
Strauss, W. L., Jr., 129
Stroll, N. R., 98
Structure, social, 308, 336, 520–521
  (*See also* Kinship; Law; Political organization; Religion)
Subincision, 285
Subsistence, 234–250, 416–423
  Mesolithic, 187–188
  of monkeys, 20–21
  Neolithic, 187–188
  (*See also* Agriculture; Hunting and gathering; Pastoralism)
Sudanese, kinship system, 389
Suitor service, 347–349
Sumer, 196–198

Sumner, W. G., 279
Sun dance, Plains Indian, 78–80
Supernaturalism, 465–474
Sururbanization, 527, 530–531
Swadesh, M., 50
Swanscombe skull, 161–164
Swanton, J. R., 280
Swazi, 324, 398–399
Swedes, physical characteristics of, 210
Symbolism, in art, 299–306
    and culture, 21–22
    in writing, 303–306
Syntax, 40–41

Tabu, 474–475, 513–514
    functions of, 475
    (*See also* Incest)
Tacitus, 506
Tagalog, 38
Tailoring, 280–281
Tanala, 365
Tarahumara, 243
Taravad, 365–366
Tarsier, 100–101, 106–107
Tasmania, aboriginals of, 279
Tattooing, 284
Tax, S., 144, 146, 508–509, 525
Taxonony, principles of, 98–101, 113
Technical order, 528–529
Teeth, primate, 101–102, 110
    Australopithecus, africanus, 136, 145
        robustus, 139–141, 146
    Dryopithecus Y-pattern, 127–128
    filing of, 286
    Homo erectus, erectus, 148–149
        pekinensis, 152–153
Tehuacán, Mexico, 201–202
Tehuelche, 279–281
Teknonymy, 390
Tell Halaf, 195
Thomas, E. M., 249
Thomas, W. L., 236
Thompson, J. E. S., 245–246
Thompson, L., 408, 494–495, 531
Thompson, S., 476
Thurnwald, R., 425–436
Till, I., 415
Time, geologic, 115–116
Titiev, M., 258, 419
Tiwi, 75

Tlingit, 81, 292
Tobacco, diffusion of, 77
Tobias, P. V., 114–146
Toda, 362
Tonnies, F., 516
Toolmaking, by early man, 138, 140, 142–
    146, 150–151
Totemism, 376
Trade, 427–431
    Neolithic, 189
Transhumance, 249–250
Trinil man (*see Homo erectus erectus*)
Trobriand Islands, 29, 53, 60, 320, 332, 430–
    431, 444, 474
Trowell, M., 276
Trudeau, J. B., 364
Tsimshian, 80, 517–518
Tswana, 59, 460–462
Tucker, W. B., 53
Tumin, M. M., 30, 412
Tungus, 417
Turkish language, 40
Turnbull, C. M., 81
Tylor, E. B., 76, 87, 90, 92, 264, 337, 466–
    468, 487, 505, 515

Ubaid, Sumeria, 196
Ultimogeniture, 435
Umor, 376
Underhill, R., 489
UNESCO, statement on race, 230
United Nations, 450
United States, constitution of, 455
    culture, 282
    kinship, 389–390
    world view, 498–500
Ute, 78

Vaillant, G. C., 405
Vallois, H., 164
Venus, of Brassempouy, 181–282
    of Willendorf, 179–180, 282
Village, as unit of government, 455–456, 460–
    461
Villefranchian, 167
Vision quest, 423, 480–481
Vogt, E., 477
Voodoo, 485–486

Wachsman, K. P., 276
Wagogo, 325
Waitz, F. T., 279
Walker, D. E., 523
Wallace, A., 123
Wallace, E., 79, 363
Waln, N., 262
Wartenstein Symposium, 173
Washburn, S. L., 98, 104, 110–111, 113, 129,
    136, 138, 159, 162
Waterbok, H. T., 186
Wax, M., 465
Wax, R., 465
Wealth, Alorese, 63
    and status, 316–318
Weaving, 271–274
Webster, H., 394–395, 400
Weidenreich, F. von, 150–151, 171
Weisz, P. B., 120–122
Weltfish, G., 269
Wenner-Gren Foundation, 98
Westermarck, E., 87, 336, 355, 364
Whale cult, Alaskan, 241
Wheel, potter's, 270
Wheeler, G. C., 345, 353
White, L. A., 19, 32, 90–91, 93, 344, 386
Whiting, B. B., 330, 474
Whiting, J. W. M., 54, 61, 65–67, 70, 328, 523
Whitman, W., 314
Whorf, B. L., 44
Wife lending, 364, 445
Wife stealing, 353
Willendorf, Venus of, 179–180, 282
Willey, G. R., 184

Wills, 432–433
Wilson, G. R., 259
Wilson, Maurice, 107
Wilson, Monica, 399–400
Windscreens, 254
Wingert, P. S., 294, 298, 307
Winnebago, 155, 240, 375, 481
Wissler, C., 75, 280–281, 286, 518
Wolfenstein, M., 70
Women, clubs for, 393
    (*See also* Sex; Status, social)
World view, 23, 490–501, 527
Writing, 36, 82–83
    development of, 196–197, 303–306
Wundt, W., 252–253

Yahgan, 279–280
Yale Cross Cultural Survey, 522
Yinger, J. M., 232
Yurok, 414–415
    art, 294
    law, 438–439

Zadruga, 365
Zande (*see* Azande)
Zapotec, 291
Zeuner, F. E., 194, 203
Zingg, R. M., 243
Zinjanthropus, 142–143
Zuñi, 366–367
    personality, 61

CULTURE AREAS:

I. North Africa
    A. Mediterranean Coast
    B. Egypt
II. Sahara
III. Sudan
    A. Western Sudan
    B. Eastern Sudan
IV. Guinea Coast
V. East Horn

VI. Cattle Area
    A. Eastern Cattle Area
    B. Western Cattle Area
VII. Congo
VIII. Khoisan
    A. Bushman
    B. Hottentot
IX. Madagascar

TRIBAL GROUPS:

1. Dogon
2. Wolof
3. Mano
4. Hausa
5. Kpelle
6. Tallensi
7. Nupe
8. Ashanti
9. Dahomeans (Fon)
10. Yoruba
11. Ibo (incl. Ibibio)
12. Tiv
13. Azande (Zande)
14. Pygmy Tribes—Twa (Batwa)
15. Herero
16. Bushman
17. Hottentot (incl. Nama, Bergdama)
18. Lozi (Barotse)

19. Ba-Ila (Ila)
20. Zulu
21. Tswana
22. Swazi
23. Bemba (Babemba)
24. Nyakyusa
25. Chaga (Tschagga)
26. Ankole (Banyankole, incl. Bahima and Bairu)
27. Sukuma
28. Watussi (Tussi)
29. Nyoro (Banyoro or Bakitara)
30. Alur
31. Masai
32. Nuer
33. Dinka
34. Tanala-Betsileo
35. Sakalava

Scale at equator

500   0   500

Miles

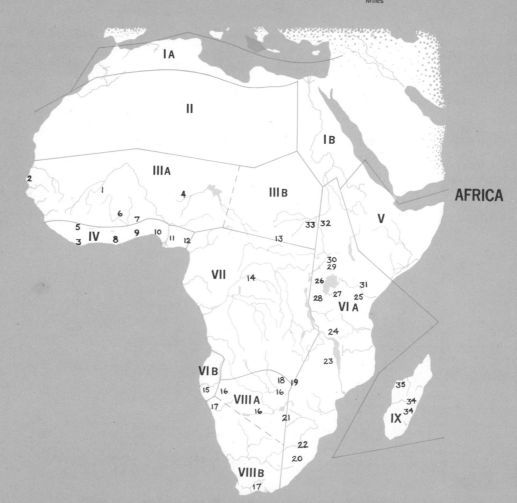

AFRICA